KU-581-769

THE DISTRIBUTION OF BRYOPHYTES IN IRELAND

Edited and published with funding from National Parks and Wildlife (part of The Department of the Environment, Heritage and Local Government, Republic of Ireland) and Environment and Heritage Service (part of Department of Environment Northern Ireland).

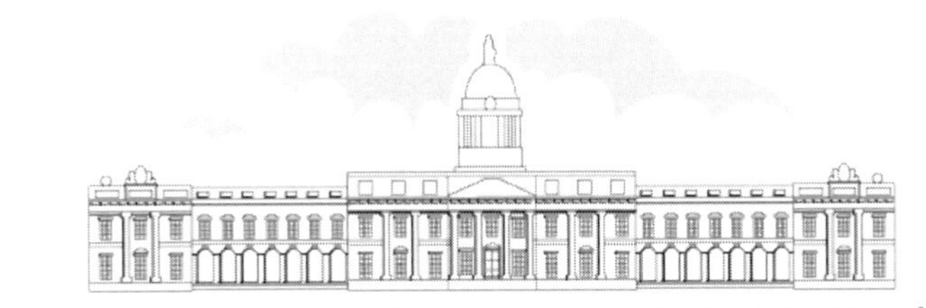

THE DISTRIBUTION OF BRYOPHYTES IN IRELAND

AN ANNOTATED REVIEW OF THE OCCURRENCE OF LIVERWORTS AND MOSSES IN THE IRISH VICE-COUNTIES, BASED MAINLY ON THE RECORDS OF THE BRITISH BRYOLOGICAL SOCIETY

Compiled by D.T. Holyoak

BROADLEAF BOOKS

2003

Published in 2003 by

Broadleaf Books, Roy & Hilary Perry, 35 Cardiff Road, Dinas Powys,
Vale of Glamorgan, CF64 4DH, U.K.

With the support of National Parks and Wildlife (part of The Department of the Environment, Heritage and Local Government, Republic of Ireland) and Environment and Heritage Service (part of Department of Environment Northern Ireland).

Design, typesetting and preparation of accompanying CD-ROM by Wheal Seton Press, Dr Colin French, 12 Seton Gardens, Weeth Road, Camborne, Cornwall TR14 7JS, U.K.

Printed and bound by CA Print & Stationers Ltd, Unit E7, Formal Industrial Park, Treswithian, Camborne, Cornwall TR14 0RT.

The Distribution of Bryophyes in Ireland: An annotated Review of the occurrence of Liverworts and Mosses in the Irish vice-counties, based mainly on the records of the British Bryological Society /
Compiled by DT Holyoak

ISBN: 0-9545285-0-6 hardback

CONTENTS

PREFACE		1
ACKNOWLEDGEMENTS		2
INTRODUCTION		3
A BRIEF HISTORY OF BRYOLOGY IN IRELAND		6
Summary list of BBS Excursions in Ireland and the resulting publications		13
BIBLIOGRAPHICAL NOTES ON PUBLICATIONS OF THE MEC AND BBS		14
LIVERWORTS	(MARCHANTIOPSIDA)	17
HORNWORTS	(ANTHOCEROTOPSIDA)	149
MOSSES:	(SPHAGNOPSIDA)	153
	(ANDREAEOPSIDA)	183
	(BRYOPSIDA)	189
APPENDIX. SYMBOLS AND ABBREVIATIONS		513
REFERENCES		517
Map 1. Vice Counties of Ireland		538
The Vice Counties of Ireland		539
INDEX		541
Instructions for use of CD ROM		back end page

PREFACE

The need for an index of vice-county records of Irish bryophytes is apparent to all who have attempted to trace the source of a record. The records appear in reports spanning more than a hundred years, they are summarised in several *Census Catalogues*, and corrections have been issued at intervals. Throughout this period there have been taxonomic changes, often resulting in one species being split into several, but also resulting in species or varieties being merged. Other than the bare lists in the *Census Catalogues*, no overall index of the records or corrections has appeared. Consequently there are instances where 'new' records have been published twice, where older records have been overlooked, and occasionally where corrections have been overlooked. Duplication of 'new' records does little harm in itself, but may prove hazardous when a voucher is subsequently found to be misidentified leading to deletion of the record since it might not have been the original (or only) record!

Taxonomic changes have often resulted in the same name having different meanings at different times. Where a species is split into two or more species the older records can only be referred to an aggregate species, unless voucher specimens have been reidentified according to the new taxonomic concepts. In other cases the recognition of finely split varieties that troubled earlier generations of bryologists has been abandoned and modern workers can 'lump' the older records into fewer, more inclusive, taxa. The present review of Irish vice-county records of bryophytes since 1896 attempts to clarify the status of as many as possible of the older records in groups where the taxonomy has changed. Reference is made to specimens known to have been reidentified, but others that have not been reassessed are merely listed as belonging to aggregate species or ill-defined groups of species.

Assembly of the published records is intended to be a first step in improving understanding of the distribution of bryophytes in Ireland and the basis for each of the vice-county records. A very large amount of work remains to trace the voucher specimens, a large majority of which survive in public herbaria, mainly in Great Britain (especially the BBSUK and NMW herbaria) and Ireland (especially in the BEL and DBN herbaria). Identification then needs to be checked or revised for a small minority of species where the old material was often misidentified.

Another large task is to collect and verify voucher specimens for a large number of records of mainly common species that have not been checked for very many years, if ever. This need arises because the early *Census Catalogues* (Macvicar 1905, CH Waddell and HW Lett in Barker *et al.* 1907) and the important early lists by McArdle (1904) and Lett (1915) included numerous vice-county records from much older publications and unpublished lists. Even the thorough and detailed moss listings by Lett (1915) omitted locality details for 86 of the commoner mosses 'for the sake of saving space'. Vice-county numbers for many of these plants have been copied in successive editions of the *Census Catalogues*. Absence of the brackets denoting old records for most of them in Blockeel & Long (1998) is commonly on no better basis than the existence of an unchecked field record obtained mainly during the mapping for the *Atlas of the Bryophytes of Britain and Ireland* (Hill *et al.* 1991-1994). Lack of critically checked specimens supporting updates for many of these records does not seem a serious deficiency with common and almost unmistakeable species such as *Calliergonella cuspidata* or *Scleropodium purum*, but there are others among them that are much less common and far from unmistakeable (e.g. *Cephalozia hibernica, Bryum intermedium*).

Besides fieldwork to fill gaps in representation of voucher specimens of common species, there is much more exciting exploration still to be done to reveal the full extent of the rich Irish bryoflora. Fieldwork in the past few years has continued to add new species to the Irish list, both rare native plants (e.g. *Cynodontium jenneri, Ephemerum spinulosum, Meesia uliginosa, Paludella squarrosa, Physcomitrium sphaericum, Weissia brachycarpa* var. *brachycarpa*) and aliens that may have become established recently (*Calomnion complanatum, Heteroscyphus fissistipus, Leptotheca gaudichaudi, Lophocolea bispinosa, L. semiteres*). Several species have been refound which had been unreported for so many years that they were feared extinct (e.g. *Bryum torquescens, B. uliginosum, Cephaloziella turneri, Ephemerum cohaerens*) and the ranges within Ireland have been greatly increased for some rare species through discovery of additional localities (e.g. *Bryum warneum, Cephaloziella integerrima, Marsupella adusta, Myurella julacea*). Much more remains to be found, even in the areas regarded as comparatively well worked for bryophytes.

Ireland has one of the richest bryofloras in Europe and a wealth of Atlantic bryophytes that is shared only with western Scotland. It is no exaggeration to claim that Ireland's bryophytes are among the most important elements of the island's flora, since about 51% of European liverworts occur (compared to less than 10% of European flowering plants) and the moss flora is almost as rich. Development, land-use changes and climatic changes increasingly threaten these rich floras and necessitate careful stocktaking of potentially threatened bryophyte populations and conservation of those shown to be most vulnerable. It is hoped that the inventory of records published here will play a part in making detailed information on bryophytes in Ireland more readily available and hence in contributing to their effective conservation.

ACKNOWLEDGEMENTS

This synthesis is largely a compilation of the work of others and its eventual publication owes much to generous assistance from several other bryologists. Thanks are due to the many bryologists who have contributed records from Ireland over two centuries and ensured that they have been adequately documented. Particular thanks are due to the British Bryological Society's Recorders for Hepatics and Mosses who over the years have checked large numbers of voucher specimens from Ireland and ensured that data on them has been published in annual reports. The Council of the British Bryological Society kindly agreed to publication of this synthesis.

Thanks for advice and information in preparing the present work are due to Tom Blockeel, Tomas Hallingbäck, David Long, Neil Lockhart, Jean Paton, Roy Perry and Donal Synnott. Tim Blackstock and Gordon Rothero kindly made Recorder's Reports on records from 2002 available ahead of publication in *Bulletin of the British Bryological Society* and answered various queries. Donal Synnott has kindly made available a copy of his extensive typescript list of Irish liverwort records (Synnott MS, 1977), which was valuable in checking for omitted records and erroneous details. Nick Stewart made detailed data available that he assembled on rare bryophytes in Ireland. Roy Perry was generous with his time in answering numerous queries and proof-reading. Professor Mark Seaward kindly sorted relevant photographs from the BBS archive and made these available for publication. Paul Hackney of the Ulster Museum and Paddy Reilly of the Dublin Naturalists' Field Club also helped in attempts to locate old photographs and Gordon Rothero kindly provided a more recent photo. Muiris de Butléir generously made available a digital copy of a gazetteer of place names in Ireland that saved much time in checking locality names. Jean and Pat Paton allowed me to use their map of Irish vice-counties. Geraldine Holyoak patiently and carefully inputted over ten thousand records to computer disk. Colin French (Wheal Seton Press) prepared this book and the accompanying CD for publication and made the arrangements for it to be printed by CA Print and Stationers Ltd of Redruth.

The funding to ensure editing and publication of this work was generously provided by National Parks and Wildlife (part of The Department of the Environment, Heritage and Local Government, Republic of Ireland) and Environment and Heritage Service (part of Department of Environment Northern Ireland). The active involvement of Neil Lockhart (NPW) and Richard Weyl (EHS) was crucial in securing the funding and their assistance is gratefully acknowledged.

INTRODUCTION

The distribution of bryophytes in Ireland is constantly changing. Development and agricultural intensification continue to destroy bryophyte habitats, some introduced species are spreading, and some native species may be responding to recent climatic changes. In order to provide a sound basis of knowledge for bryophyte conservation in Ireland, it is therefore important to distinguish not only reliable from unreliable records, but also the very old records from modern ones, and to document the known extinctions.

Throughout the past century the *Census Catalogues* (*CC*) maintained by the British Bryological Society (BBS) have provided the record of bryophyte distribution not only for Britain but also for the vice-counties of Ireland. The records are regarded as authoritative because all those made for the modern *CC* are based on voucher specimens checked by successive BBS Recorders of Hepatics or Recorders of Mosses and almost all of the voucher specimens they studied have been kept in public herbaria. The present list aims to provide fuller details of the records of each moss and liverwort species (plus recognised subspecies and varieties) from each of the vice-counties of Ireland, based largely on the data from these BBS records.

Lists of new vice-county records of Irish bryophytes have been published annually alongside those from Britain for 105 years, starting with the *Moss Exchange Club Report* of 1897 and continuing through publications of the BBS after it was formed in 1923. Because of this long history of recording, the origins of many of the vice-county records of Irish bryophytes are hard to trace, partly because of the need to look in anything up to 105 different annual reports that have never been indexed, but also because taxonomic treatment and identification criteria have changed for very many species over the past century. Thus, for ease of reference and to ensure a clearly defined base-line for future studies, the present list assembles all of the published records and cites each of them in full, along with the many subsequent corrections. It also reports the locations of a few of the voucher specimens that are currently lodged in public herbaria and points out certain records which seem poorly founded according to modern criteria.

Although the first *Moss Exchange Club Report* is taken as a starting point for the present lists, there were few new vice-county records published in the early years. The reviews of records in the first *CC* (1905, 1907) are therefore used to provide most of the oldest records given here. Although these oldest *CC* gave only bare lists of vice county numbers from which each species had been recorded, more detailed publications from around the same time give details of most of the records and their sources. Thus the earliest *CC* for liverworts (Macvicar 1905) followed soon after Lett's (1902) review of '*all the species of hepatics hitherto found in the British Islands*' and McArdle's (1904) more detailed Irish distributional list (in which records were not assigned to vice-counties). It is stated (Macvicar 1905: 4) that in compiling the *CC* 'The Rev. C.H. Waddell has had in charge the distribution of Hepatics in Ireland, and has sent the following note:– "The principal sources are McArdle's List of Irish Hepatics and Lett's Hepatics of the British Islands. Mr. McArdle has made out a list of records for the common species. Several records which referred only to counties could not be used, as they were not localised ..." '. The first moss *CC* (with Ireland covered by CH Waddell and HW Lett in Barker *et al.* 1907) was followed eight years later by the extensive and detailed lists by Lett (1915). Together these authoritative publications from 1904-1915 therefore provide a firm foundation on which to place later bryophyte records, so that the present work merely cites them as sources to be referred to for details of the older records. However, more recent corrections to some of the old records are reported in detail here.

The *CC* prepared by Warburg (1963a) and Paton (1965b) bracketed records for vice-counties where a taxon had not been recorded 'for a long time (usually since 1900)'. The next *CC* by Corley & Hill (1981) used brackets to 'signify vice-counties from which a species has not been seen for fifty years' but noted that this rule was ignored when it was believed that a locality had not been revisited and there was no reason to suppose that the bryophyte concerned had disappeared. The latest *CC* by Blockeel & Long (1998: 25) used records in brackets to signify 'vice-counties from which a species has not been seen since the beginning of 1950', but added that 'In a few instances, brackets have also been added where a post-1950 record exists but the locality in question is known to have been destroyed. However such brackets have not been used for any record made since 1980.' Since about 1980 the annual Recorders' Reports have listed updated as well as new vice-county records. In practice, the data held at the Biological Records Centre (Monks Wood, U.K.) were used to judge whether a post-1950 record exists, despite the fact that many if not a majority of the records involved would have been based on field recording unchecked by microscopy and without any voucher specimen having been retained.

In order to reduce the considerable potential for confusion over which old records have and which have not been reliably updated by new finds (or by refinding the old site) and over known extinctions, the lists of Irish records given here are intended to present:

(1) The earliest record from each vice-county based on reliable literature or a correctly determined specimen with adequate data (fossil or subfossil records are generally ignored, although these are mentioned for a few very rare species);

(2) If different, the first record to be accepted by a BBS Recorder;

(3) Any additional records published contemporaneously with (1) or (2), (e.g. where two collectors sent in the same 'new' record in same year), or potentially confusing duplicate records published in later years;

(4) Where (1) or (2) are pre-1950 records, the latest of the post-1949 records that has been accepted by a BBS Recorder;

(5) All published corrections relevant to (1) - (4);

(6) For a very few rare species, if all populations in a vice-county are believed to have become extinct, e.g. through extensive drainage, then details are given of the reasons for this belief and the source of information.

The taxonomy, nomenclature, sequence and numbering of taxa are based on Blockeel & Long (1998). A few revisions of taxonomy and nomenclature (but not the sequence or numbering of taxa) have been made (based e.g. on Grolle & Long 2000); all such changes are accompanied by an explanation and a reference to the taxonomic literature on which they are based. All names used in *CC*, annual recorder's reports and other primary sources used in compiling the present list are given here (in alphabetical sequence) as synonyms. Any different names adopted in Smith (1978, 1990a), Daniels & Eddy (1990), Hill *et al.* (1991-1994) or Paton (1999) are also listed as synonyms, as are a few other names that have been used in the recent literature.

All records are listed for forms now treated as synonyms, including many varieties that are no longer recognised (especially in *Sphagnum*), since only a complete listing will ensure that records are not overlooked. An attempt has been made to assign all of the old records of often long-forgotten varieties to taxa currently recognised, but this is impossible in some groups without reidentification of the voucher specimens. In order to give a complete listing of the vice-county records, those for certain taxonomically hopeless cases where records cannot be accurately reassigned are collected together under generalised headings (e.g. old records of *Fissidens viridulus* aggregate, unassignable records of *Sphagnum* spp.)

Each entry consists of the following information (where it is known) given in the following sequence:

Vice county number (bracketed if pre-1950)

year:

habitat,

altitude (alt., as metres [m] or feet [ft] above sea-level),

place name,

hectad (ten-kilometre square of Irish grid),

collector,

collection number (if one exists),

name of person confirming (conf.) or determining (det.) specimen (if different to collector) or name of person sending information to BBS recorder ('comm.'; if different to collector),

herbarium [Hb.]where specimen lodged (using abbreviations such as DBN which are listed in Appendix, following *Index Herbariorum*: Holmgren & Keuken 1974),

reference to publication of record (usually in BBS Recorders' Reports: see References),

other notes (if any).

The number of the vice-county is given at the start of each record that is accepted as the basis of the listing of that vice-county in the *CC* (usually but not always the first record), the number *always* being given in parentheses if the record involved is from before 1950, e.g. H(27). The number of the vice-county is also given at the start of each record that updates an entry in the *CC* post-1949 (usually but not always the first published record after 1949), e.g. H27. Rejected and problematical records are listed in square brackets [ ].

The information presented for each record is essentially that given in the original publication. Annotations such as 'new to Ireland' are not reproduced here as that fact will be evident from study of the lists given. More or less lengthy and detailed discussions of the characters of specimens that appeared in some of the older literature are also not reproduced, although their existence is indicated by the comment '(with notes)'.

Obvious errors in localities are noted with a comment, e.g. 'Blackhead [*sic* = Black Head]'. In all cases it is the English language form of the name that is intended and correct usage for the names of centres of population and the main physical features aims to follow the *Gazetteer of Ireland* (anon. 1989). Corrections to a few other names have been noted where they differ from those on the published 1:50,000 Discovery Series maps published by the Ordnance Survey of Ireland or Ordnance Survey of Northern Ireland. The *Gazetteer* should be consulted for the equivalent place names in the Irish language.

Minor typographical slips in names of persons are corrected without comment when there seems no doubt who was intended. Older Recorder's Reports listed collectors, etc. only by their initials (e.g. HWL) and later ones give only surnames (e.g. Lett). These have been expanded so far as possible to give surname plus initials (e.g. HW Lett), but the original printed form is noted when uncertainty may exist.

Locations of voucher specimens in herbaria (code such as DBN, see Appendix) are given where they were noted in the original publication and in a few other instances where they are accurately known (especially with important records, such as the only Irish record). Allowance has usually been made for the knowledge that several important private herbaria have now been incorporated into public collections, notably those of AC Crundwell (now at E), JW and RD Fitzgerald (now at NMW, but H36 material in BEL) and JA Paton (now at E). Older references to BM might include material that is in the BBSUK herbarium, now housed in NMW. An extensive search of all the main herbaria is desirable in future to locate as many as possible of the voucher specimens from Ireland.

As noted above, the latest *CC* (Blockeel & Long 1998) used data held at the Biological Records Centre (Monks Wood, U.K.) to judge whether a post-1950 record exists. Much of this data was accumulated during fieldwork for the *Atlas of the Bryophytes of Britain and Ireland* (Hill *et al.* 1991-1994) and a majority of the records involved would have been based on field recording unchecked by microscopy and without any voucher specimen having been retained. The symbol † is used to identify the numerous entries in the latest *CC* that appear to lack brackets for this reason. A former BBS Recorder of Mosses who was much involved in field recording, AC Crundwell (in Hill *et al.* 1992: 9), guessed that if the full truth were known about the records, then 'perhaps one in thirty would have to be deleted as erroneous'. Many of the *CC* records updated only on the strength of BRC data originate from published sources prior to McArdle (1904) or Lett (1915), so that it is nowadays unclear that specimens have been checked for a century or more, if they ever were. It would therefore seem worthwhile for the BBS Recorders to check new specimens to replace these essentially unchecked records marked † in order to bring them into line with the high standard of verification maintained for other records. The additional work involved in checking these would not be great since most records are of well known and easily identifed species.

In order to increase the usefulness of this publication as a working checklist of Irish bryophytes, it also presents a brief history of bryology in Ireland, with details of all the BBS Excursions held there, and an extensive bibliography of the more important modern literature on bryophytes in Ireland.

A BRIEF HISTORY OF BRYOLOGY IN IRELAND

The earliest botanist who describes any bryophytes found in Ireland is the Rev. John Ray (b. 1627, d. 1703) of Black Notley, in Essex. His *Synopsis Methodica Stirpium Britannicarum* (London 1690; 3rd ed., 1724) mentions and describes eight mosses from Ireland, of which only one has a locality specified. Most, if not all, of these were collected by William Sherard of Oxford during a visit he paid to Co. Down.

Caleb Threlkeld (b. 1676, d. 1738) and Walter Harris (active 1744) provided other early descriptions of a few bryophyte species in Ireland, but as elsewhere in Europe, real progress had to await the adoption of binomial nomenclature, then the development of microscopes during the nineteenth century. The first book devoted to Irish bryophytes was Dawson Turner's *Muscologiae Hibernicae Spicilegium* of 1804, with fine coloured illustrations. This rare book has recently been reprinted as a Facsimile edition by Presses universitaires de Namur, Belgium (1998). Many of the most significant bryophytes described from Ireland by Dawson Turner were sent to him by Ellen Hutchins of Ballylickey near Bantry, a remarkable but unassuming botanist who is commemorated in the names of *Jubula hutchinsiae* and *Ulota hutchinsiae*. The recent publication of selected letters between Ellen Hutchins and Dawson Turner (edited by Mitchell 1999) provides interesting information on Miss Hutchins, the most important of the early bryologists in Ireland.

Lett (1915: 67-79) should be consulted for a detailed account of the great progress made in the study of bryophytes in Ireland through the nineteenth century, which is not repeated here since the main purpose of the present work is to review in detail the records made since 1896. Prominent among the nineteenth-century bryologists whose work is reviewed by Lett were Dr Thomas Taylor (d. 1848) who contributed the section on Musci to part II of Mackay's *Flora Hibernica* (1836), Dr David Moore (b. 1807, d. 1879) who made many bryophyte records during years of work for the Ordnance Survey and ended his career as Director of the Botanic Garden at Glasnevin, and Samuel Alexander Stewart (b. 1826, d. 1910) of Belfast, who prepared the detailed account of bryophytes for *A Flora of the North-East of Ireland* (Stewart & Corry 1888), but scores of other botanists made significant contributions. Bryophyte records from David Orr (d. 1892), assistant to Dr Moore in Glasnevin Gardens, unfortunately include much that is unreliable and this led Lett (1915: 74) to comment that 'Much doubt exists as to some of Orr's discoveries, which prevents reliance being placed upon his work unless it is corroborated by other botanists'.

In late 1895 and early 1896 the Rev. CH Waddell of Saintfield Vicarage, Co. Down proposed by advertisement that a Moss Exchange Club (MEC) should be formed, in letters to *Science Gossip*, *Journal of Botany* and the *Irish Naturalist*. The MEC thus owes its origins to a worker in Ireland, although the already successful Botanical Exchange Club for exchange of vascular plant specimens doubtless provided a model for the Rev. Waddell. 'A short account of the Moss Exchange Club and the British Bryological Society' by Eleonora Armitage (1944; 2nd ed., 1956) gives a useful account of salient points in the subsequent history of the MEC and earlier years of the BBS that has been used in preparing the notes that follow.

Twenty three MEC members were enrolled in 1896, after which the membership rose gradually to 45 then fell again until the functions of the Club were taken over by the British Bryological Society (BBS) when it was formed in 1923. More than 3000 packets (specimens) were distributed to the members in some years (with tens to hundreds from Ireland) and a system of referees was established to check determinations. An annual *Report* and *Census Catalogues* were published (bibliographical notes on the MEC publications are given in a later section). Bryologists from the north of Ireland contributed prominently to the MEC, with four Irish members among the founders: Mr J Hunter (of Londonderry), Rev. HW Lett (Loughbrickland, Co. Down) and Mr JB Parker (Culmore, Co. Londonderry) in addition to Rev. Waddell (of Saintfield, Co. Down, later of Grey Abbey, Co. Down). In later years they were joined by Mr JD Houston (of Kilrea Co. Derry, then Lurgan, Co. Armagh, finally of Elphin, Co. Roscommon) but JB Parker left Ireland to live in Sheffield. Miss Armitage was the sole lady member throughout the history of the MEC.

In 1901 a 'Beginner's Section' was formed that became The Moss Exchange Club Section II. Many of the members of Section II soon outgrew their status as 'beginners' but conflicting personalities kept the two sections of the MEC separate. Section II therefore continued to function as an independent exchange Club for many years until it effectively merged with Section I to create the BBS in 1923. Section II issued its own Reports (see below for bibliographical notes) from 1903 onwards. There were 30 members by 1903 (none in Ireland), the total having risen to 48 by 1921. Like the senior section, the exchange in Section II distributed thousands of packets of bryophytes annually for many years, sometimes with a hundred or two from Ireland. Activity was somewhat reduced during the 1914-1918 war, but 1400 packets were circulated even in 1916. As in Section I, the material was checked by a panel of expert referees. In the later years there were several active contributors in Ireland, especially Mr James Glover (of Kirkcubbin, Co. Down; see Megaw 1925 for obituary), Mr JD Houston (of Lurgan, Co. Armagh, later Elphin, Co. Roscommon) and Mr WN Tetley (of Portora, Enniskillen). It is remarkable that JD Houston was a member of both Sections I and II of the MEC.

A system of vice-counties in Great Britain was devised by HC Watson (1852) and used to record the distribution of British vascular plants in *Topographical Botany* (Watson 1883). An adaptation of the scheme for publication of Irish botanical records was proposed by CC Babington (1859) and modified by RL Praeger for his influential *Irish Topographical Botany* (1901). There was some delay before bryologists fully adopted vice-counties for Irish records, in that *A list of Irish Hepaticae* (McArdle 1904) continued usage of 12 Botanical Districts in Ireland (following the tradition maintained in the 2nd edition of *Cybele Hibernica* by Colgan & Scully 1898). However, the *MEC Report* for 1898 gives a 'New County Record' for *Mnium cuspidatum* in Co. Down (anon. 1899: 17), the *Report* for 1900 gives vice-county numbers for some of the British records, and the earliest *Census Catalogues* issued by the MEC (Hepatics: Macvicar 1905; Mosses: Barker *et al.* 1907) used only vice-counties for Britain and Ireland. It was noteworthy that the 1908 *MEC Report* contained 'new V.C. records' (p.

270) and in the *Report* for the following year HH Knight stated that 'new county records are indicated by placing an asterisk to the V.C. number', a practice maintained until about 1938, after which the new vice-county records were listed separately. The important *Census Report on the Mosses of Ireland* (Lett 1915) presented data by vice-counties.

Cosslett Herbert Waddell (b. 1858, d. 1919; Plate 4A) and Henry William Lett (b. 1836, d. 1920; Plate 4B) were both clergymen of the Church of Ireland and both were among the most active and influential of bryologists in Ireland during the early years of the 20th century. The various parishes in Counties Armagh and Down in which they officiated were within 20 miles of their respective birthplaces, Magheralin and Hillsborough. Waddell's first appointment, a curacy at Lurgan, was in 1880, a time when Lett was rector of Ardmore, only four miles away. Fitzgerald & Fitzgerald (1961) give an account of several Waddell MSS housed at BFT, including the manuscript notebooks of the MEC for 1897-1901. Lett reported on the mosses and liverworts of Clare Island, Co. Mayo as part of an extraordinarily complete investigation of the flora and fauna of the island undertaken from 1901-1911 (Lett 1912). Synnott (1978) gives an account of Lett's main herbarium in DBN; Parnell (1982) reports additional material at TCD.

William Rutledge Megaw (b. 1885, d. 1953; Plate 4C) was born at Carrowdore, Co. Down, son of a Presbyterian minister (Chase 1954). He was ordained in Trinity Church, Ahoghill in 1910 where he ministered until 1919, when he became minister of Newtownbreda where he remained up to his retirement in 1950, after which he went to live at Portstewart. Megaw was local secretary for the BBS meeting at Belfast in 1928 and remained for many years the leading bryologist in the north-east of Ireland. He published a series of lists of significant bryophyte records (Megaw 1926a, 1926b, 1929b, 1929c, 1930, 1936, 1937), a fuller review of new records (Megaw 1929a) and compiled the authoritative account of bryophytes in the 2nd edition of the *Flora of the North East of Ireland* (Megaw 1938). His herbarium is at BFT.

The first field meeting of the BBS to be held in Ireland was based in Belfast from 25th August to 1st September 1928 (Plate 1). Excursions were made to the Giant's Causeway and Portrush, Colin Mountain, Fair Head and Glenarrif, all in Co. Antrim. One day was spent in Co. Down on Slieve Donard. A further excursion was undertaken by some members to Co. Sligo, when Ben Bulben was visited and to part of Co. Leitrim (Duncan 1928, 1929a, Armitage 1956: 11). Numerous interesting and new records were obtained, among the best of the novelties being *Timmia norvegica* new to Ireland from Gleniff in Co. Sligo.

The second BBS field meeting in Ireland was held from 10th to 17th August 1935 at Muckross, Killarney, Co. Kerry (Watson 1936, 1937, Armitage 1956: 17); 25 members attended (some of them are shown in Plate 2), and after the meeting 15 members and friends went on to Dingle, Slea Head and Brandon Mountain. It is recorded that 'Help was rendered by Irish friends, Messrs. Bradshaw, Cronin and Lloyd Praeger in the excursions' and that the 'rare flowering plants were also sought after' (Armitage 1956: 17).

The BBS was evidently much impressed by Irish bryophytes, since a third field meeting was arranged soon after the second, from 19th to 26th June 1937, based at Bundoran in Co. Donegal. About 20 members and friends attended (see Plate 3) and excursions were made into Co. Leitrim and Co. Sligo to explore the bryological riches of the Dartry Mountains in Glenade and Gleniff. Thirteen members went on to Achill Island (Co. Mayo) for a second week (Armitage 1938, 1956: 18-19). After 1937 there was a long wait before the next BBS meeting in Ireland (1951), with not only the Second World War intervening, but also a large decline in bryological activity in Britain and Ireland through the 1940s.

At a time when there was little bryological activity in Britain, Miss JS Thomson (Plate 4D) was associated from 1944 until the early 1950s with a steady flow of new records obtained by The Moss Group, Dublin Naturalists' Field Club from widely scattered localities in Ireland. An article in the *INJ* (by The Moss Group, DNFC 1951) lists Miss Thomson of 28 Lower Baggot Street, Dublin as

Secretary and notes that 'though never having more than five members, [it] has done a great deal of work in filling up gaps in the Irish Moss Census'. Indeed, the article reports 223 new vice-county records for species and an additional 21 for varieties obtained 1945-50, all of them verified by BBS referees.

The 1951 BBS Meeting was held in Co. Kerry, the first week based at Glenbeigh, the second week based at Waterville (RD Fitzgerald 1952a, Richards 1952, RD Fitzgerald & JW Fitzgerald 1952, Wallace 1952; Plate 4E). Nearly 30 members attended and the new finds included at least five species new to Ireland that are still regarded as valid taxa (*Eremonotus myriocarpus, Kurzia sylvatica, Didymodon nicholsonii, Fissidens curvatus, Isopterygiopsis muelleriana*). EC Wallace's (1952) account of the meeting notes that Mr and Mrs Fitzgerald 'were of the party and contributed greatly to the success of the meeting in using their car (as did other members with cars) for local transport'. AC Crundwell (1952) spent an additional week on the Dingle Peninsula and published an account in the *INJ* of the bryophytes he found.

From 1947 to 1977 Mrs AL Kathleen King of Mount Merrion, Dublin made a collection of about 4000 well documented bryophyte specimens that is now housed at DBN (Scannell 1977). Over many years Mrs King was methodical in working previously unexplored and often rather unexciting lowland localities, including State Forest plantations and Bord na Mona bogs. Although numerous new vice-county records were obtained (e.g. King 1950, 1953a, 1953b, 1954b, 1956a, 1966a, 1966b, 1967a, 1967b, 1970), there were few rarities, except that her finds of *Meesia triquetra* (at a flush in an area of peat workings in Co. Mayo, sadly drained long ago: King 1958b, King & Scannell 1960) and *Ptilidium pulcherrimum* (on Scots Pine in a forestry plantation in Co. Louth: King 1954a) provided spectacular additions to the known Irish flora. A small parcel of bryophytes collected in October 1966 by Mr N. Chuter 'while on holiday in Donegal and the West' was passed to Mrs King and yielded *Nardia geoscyphus* new to Ireland from Kinnagoe Bay in East Donegal.

From 1948 to 1958 (with a brief resumption in 1971) AP Fanning collected bryophytes mainly in Co. Kerry and Co. Offaly. Among his finds were new localities for *Fissidens curvatus* and *Petalophyllum ralfsii*, while his material of *Brachythecium mildeanum*, *Rhynchostegium lusitanicum* and *Sematophyllum micans* appears to have been correctly identified by the collector (Synnott 1984, with notes on his herbarium which is now at DBN).

During 1950 to 1969 knowledge of bryophytes mainly in the northern half of Ireland was greatly enriched by the work of RD (Bob) Fitzgerald and Mrs JW (Jean) Fitzgerald (Plates 5A, 5B; for obituaries see Perry 1990, 1991a, Kertland 1991). Both spent their early years in Belfast, where they were married in 1940. They published numerous papers and notes reporting new records (e.g. JW Fitzgerald 1950, 1951, 1958, 1960, 1962, 1969, Fitzgerald & Fitzgerald 1960a, 1966a, 1966b, 1967, 1968a, 1968b, 1969, RD Fitzgerald 1950, 1952b, 1952c, 1952d) and a detailed bryophyte flora for Co. Tyrone (Fitzgerald & Fitzgerald 1960b). Numerous species were added to the Irish list by them, including *Calypogeia suecica, Cephalozia macrostachya, Discelium nudum, Eurhynchium pulchellum, Lejeunea mandonii, Lophozia opacifolia, Pohlia proligera* s.s., *Seligeria calycina* and *Southbya tophacea*. Another important contribution involving Mrs Fitzgerald was the extensive revision of specimens of *Sphagnum* from the north-east of Ireland (vice-counties H38-40: Lobley & Fitzgerald 1970). Their very large collection of Irish bryophytes is mainly in NMW, but with the vouchers for H36 in BEL.

In September 1952 EW Jones (1954) 'spent a short and pleasant holiday collecting bryophytes in NE Ireland, principally in the county of Antrim' but with short visits also to Co. Londonderry and Co. Down. New vice-county records were obtained for several mosses and liverworts.

The BBS meeting for 1957 was held in Co. Galway and northern Co. Clare (Lobley 1958, Parker 1958). About 15 members attended the meeting, which was organised by RE Parker (Plate 6B). Three members 'most fortunately had cars, which solved the great difficulty of transport' (Lobley 1958: 286). Many new vice-county records were obtained, including *Bryum salinum* new to Ireland.

Immediately after the meeting AC Crundwell (1959) spent a week based at Belcoo, obtaining numerous new records from H30 and H33.

Publication of 'An outline of the bryophytes of County Laois (Queen's County)' by Cridland (1958) provided the first modern county bryoflora for any county in the Republic of Ireland.

Fieldwork in Ireland by DA Ratcliffe in Sept. 1961 resulted in the discovery of *Plagiochila carringtonii* in Co. Mayo and a detailed account of the habitat of *Adelanthus lindenbergianus* on Achill Island in the same county (Ratcliffe 1962).

Miss EM Lobley (Plate 6A) also reported observations from holiday visits to Ireland (mainly the north) in 1952, 1953, 1961 and 1962, which were reported in a series of papers and notes in the *INJ* (Lobley 1954, 1955, 1962, 1963). In addition, she attended the 1957 BBS Meeting in Co. Galway and wrote the detailed account of it in the *INJ* (Lobley 1958) and contributed substantially to a revision of sphagna from the north-east of Ireland (Lobley & Fitzgerald 1970).

The 1962 BBS meeting was based at Dunfanaghy, Co. Donegal (Wallace 1963) for a fortnight in early September; eleven members attended, three of them accompanied by their wives. Numerous new vice-county records were made, among the most notable finds being *Adelanthus lindenbergianus* on Errigal and Muckish Mountains by EF Warburg and others, and *Bryum marratii* found on the coast near Dunfanaghy by AC Crundwell 'on before-breakfast forays'. Immediately before this meeting EF Warburg (see Plates 4E, 6B) spent a fortnight on Achill Island, Co. Mayo, resulting in several additions to the known flora of this well studied island and a published list (Warburg 1963c).

A Roy Perry (Plate 6D) began bryological work as a student at Oxford, encouraged by Dr Warburg. He accompanied the Fitzgeralds on some of their visits to Ireland (e.g. in 1963 when *Herbertus aduncus* was rediscovered at Fair Head in Co. Antrim: Fitzgerald & Perry 1964) and also searched independently in later years, during holidays from his post in charge of the Cryptogamic Herbarium at NMW. Work was carried out for several field seasons on a projected bryophyte flora for Connemara and the Burren, but through lack of funding that was reduced to a chapter in the *Flora of Connemara and the Burren* by DA Webb and MJP Scannell (Perry 1983). His numerous new vice-county records include that of *Leiocolea gillmanii* new to Ireland from Achill Island (H27).

The 1966 BBS meeting was based at Clonmel, Co. Tipperary (Synnott 1967a, 1967c). Two liverworts were discovered new to Ireland (*Cephaloziella integerrima* and *Fossombronia incurva*) and one moss, *Fissidens celticus*, which was found at three localities (Little 1967).

Much bryological fieldwork in Ireland was carried out during the 1960s and 1970s by Donal M Synnott (Plate 7B), resulting in a stream of new vice-county records. He also published critical reviews of all the records from Counties Meath, Westmeath and Louth (Synnott 1964, 1967b, 1982) and contributed many important revisions of specimens in DBN for the *CC*. During the 1970s he prepared a distributional checklist of the liverworts of Ireland (Synnott MS, 1977), providing details of the earliest vice-county record for all but the commonest species. Unfortunately this work was never published, but he has kindly made a copy available during the present work, for which it has proved valuable in checking for missing records and erroneous details.

A visit to Ireland by HJB Birks, HH Birks and DA Ratcliffe in autumn 1967 produced numerous significant records including *Geocalyx graveolens* new to Ireland in Co. Kerry (HH Birks, HJB Birks & Ratcliffe 1969) and a short paper on the mountain plants of Slieve League in Co. Donegal (HJB Birks, HH Birks & Ratcliffe 1969).

In 1968 extensive phytosociological studies were carried out in central Ireland by WV Rubers, J Klein and P Hessel from Utrecht, The Netherlands, which included some bryophyte collecting in the area between Roosky and Athlone and along the Shannon and Lough Ree (specimens at U). An interesting account of bryophyte habitats was published (Rubers 1975) and several interesting bryophyte records were made, most notably of *Bryum uliginosum* in Co. Roscommon.

In May and June 1968 and May 1969 Mrs Jean A Paton (Plate 6C) visited Ireland to study liverworts with grant in aid from the Royal Society. Among the most notable of numerous new records were four liverwort species new to Ireland found in 1968 (*Riccardia incurvata*, *Fossombronia husnotii*, *Marsupella adusta* and *Cephalozia pleniceps*: Paton 1969b) and four more found in 1969, *Gymnomitrion corallioides* (although an old Irish record of this species was also reported), *Jungermannia subelliptica* and *Scapania gymnostomophila* (all on Bulbin Mountain, Co. Donegal: Paton 1971b) and *Leiocolea heterocolpos* in Co. Antrim (Paton 1972b).

From 1969 into the early 1970s bombings and other sectarian 'troubles' in Northern Ireland led to a large decline in the number of visitors to all parts of Ireland on holiday from Britain, and a consequent decline in the number of records of bryophytes. BBS meetings in Ireland thus remained poorly attended for many years, but a determined effort was made to continue with an Irish meeting every fourth or fifth year and DM Synnott was steadfast in helping with the arrangements. The need to obtain Irish records for the ten-kilometre square mapping scheme added an increased sense of purpose to the fieldwork.

The 1970 BBS meeting was based at Sligo, with field excursions in Co. Sligo, Co. Leitrim and less extensively in east Co. Mayo and Co. Cavan (Appleyard 1971). The number attending was low, averaging six at any one time. New vice-county records were made of 29 liverworts and 34 mosses, amongst which were new Irish records from the Ben Bulben range of *Timmia austriaca* (Wallace 1972) and *Bryum elegans* (found by JA Paton).

The 1975 BBS meeting was based at Arklow, Co. Wicklow for two weeks (Synnott 1976a, 1976c). Although only six people attended, scores of new vice-county records were obtained, mainly from Co. Wicklow but with some from Co. Carlow.

Bryophytes were collected and recorded by P. Whelan (1978) during visits to Hare Island, Co. Cork in July and August 1975, resulting in new records for H3 of *Homalothecium lutescens* and *Hypnum lacunosum*.

The BBS meeting in 1979 spent the first week based at Limerick (with excursions into Co. Clare, Co. Limerick and Co. Tipperary) and the second week at Glengarriff in Co. Cork, with excursions also into Co. Kerry (Crundwell 1980; Plate 7A). Over 150 new vice-county records were made, including *Atrichum tenellum*, *Bryum tenuisetum* and *Pohlia lescuriana* all new to Ireland. Following the BBS meeting, N Kirby, ND Lockhart and DM Synnott visited Gleniff in Co. Sligo and recorded notes on the bryophytes (Kirby *et al.* 1980).

A series of national habitat inventories and river catchment surveys by the Forest and Wildlife Service (now National Parks and Wildlife) in the Republic of Ireland between the late 1970s and the mid 1990s produced many new vice-county records. Research into the ecology of raised bogs, in particular, gave rise to a better understanding of the distribution of several scarce species, e.g. *Sphagnum pulchrum* (Douglas 1987), and turned up *Tetraplodon angustatus* (found by ND Lockhart) and *Sphagnum subsecundum* (found by C Douglas, H Grogan and JR Cross) new to Ireland.

The 1983 BBS meeting was held in Co. Kerry, the base for the first week being at Killorglin (Kelly 1984a, Lockhart 1984), the base for the second week being at Kenmare (Rothero 1984). It was noted that 15 people attended the second week, when the total number of species seen was 343, with 9 confirmed new vice-county records. DG Long (Plate 7B) found *Fissidens rivularis* new to Ireland during the second week of the BBS Meeting (Long 1984a) and also published a list of the sparse bryoflora on the very exposed island of Skellig Michael (Long 1984b).

J White (1985) published an account of the Gearagh Woodland in Co. Cork including a list of bryophytes (p. 393) mainly found by ND Lockhart that included several new records for H3.

The 1987 BBS meeting was held in Co. Mayo, the first week on Achill Island, the second week based at Westport (Rothero 1988, Rothero & Synnott 1988). About 21 people attended, of whom 10 remained until the end of the second week. The group had an international flavour with bryologists from Alaska, Canada, Germany and the Netherlands added to a strong British contingent. Numerous new vice-county records were obtained, including *Scapania curta* and *Leiocolea gillmanii* new to Ireland on the previously 'well-worked' Achill Island and *Ptilium crista-castrensis* new to Ireland on Mweelrea.

The BBS meeting in 1990 was based in the north of Ireland, the first week in Co. Antrim and Co. Londonderry (Lewis 1991), the second week in Co. Donegal (Blockeel 1991a). The meeting was not well attended, with just six members present during the first week in Northern Ireland of whom only one was from the British mainland (P Martin), although two others arrived for the second week. Nevertheless, the party made several significant discoveries, including *Grimmia atrata* new to Ireland from a mist-shrouded ridge near Lough Feeane.

In 1990 *Glasra*, the journal of the National Botanic Gardens, Glasnevin, Dublin, published three papers that together form a bryophyte flora of Achill Island (Co. Mayo) (Long 1990b, Smith 1990b, Synnott 1990a) along with an account of the bryophytes of Lambay Island (Co. Dublin) (Synnott 1990b).

Persistent research on the floristic composition of calcareous mires by ND Lockhart (1987, 1988, 1989a, 1989b, 1991, 1999) produced a series of important bryophyte records, including finds of *Tomentypnum nitens* at new localities, then of *Leiocolea rutheana* and *Paludella squarrosa* which were both new to Ireland.

Much of the bryological fieldwork in Ireland from the 1960s up to 1990 was devoted to collecting distributional data for *The Atlas of the Bryophytes of Britain and Ireland* (Hill *et al.* 1991-1994). This work followed the lead of vascular plant recording in adopting 10-kilometre grid squares rather than vice-counties as the units for recording distributional information. Whereas mapping for the *Atlas of the British Flora* (Perring & Walters 1962) used an extension of the Ordnance Survey National Grid of Great Britain for Ireland because no gridded maps were available, the bryophyte *Atlas* was able to use the Ordnance Survey/Suirbhéireacht Ordonáis National Grid in Ireland that was available on new maps. Coverage for bryophytes at the scale of ten-kilometre squares was nevertheless poor in Ireland, 'handicapped by the extreme shortage of resident bryologists'. Although 'Some recording has been undertaken by visitors, ... they naturally tend to gravitate towards the species-rich western seaboard. Consequently Kerry, Galway and Sligo are well recorded. Elsewhere well worked areas include Fermanagh, Meath, Tyrone and Wicklow' (Hill *et al.* 1991: 31).

Overall, it might be estimated that only about 10% of the approximately 1000 ten-kilometre squares (hectads) in Ireland were thoroughly covered for bryophytes by the early 1990s and the situation is little better in 2003, but the coverage at the level of the 40 vice-counties is much more complete. Recording of Irish bryophytes at the scale of vice-counties can therefore be regarded as more appropriate than recording by hectads given the generally low levels of study of bryophytes that have existed in Ireland, resulting from a great scarcity of resident bryologists and relative infrequency of extensive survey work by visitors. Fortunately the BBS has not only maintained the system of vice-county recording inherited from the MEC throughout the heady days of hectad recording in Britain and Ireland, but has tended to improve it through insistence that the Recorders check adequate voucher material, and through segregation of old from modern records.

Two days of fieldwork during a visit to Co. Fermanagh in February 1993 by the European Committee for the Conservation of Bryophytes generated several notable records, including *Orthodontium gracile* in the Lough Navar Forest new to Ireland (Hodgetts & Hallingbäck 1994).

A series of visits to Foynes Island and the adjacent mainland, Co. Limerick resulted in a published bryophyte list (Wiltshire 1995) with four mosses as new vice-county records, including *Tortula atrovirens* and *Weissia rutilans*.

The BBS field meeting in 1994 spent the first week in The Burren, Co. Clare (Whitehouse 1995; Plate 8) and the second week based at Clifden (Blockeel 1995a). Clare Island (Co. Mayo) was also visited (Plate 7B). About 12 bryologists attended the first week and 17 the second, which was a joint meeting with the Nordic Bryological Society. Some of the areas visited in Co. Clare and Co. Galway (and also Clare Island) were already well known bryologically, so they produced few new vice-county records, but a visit to the Slieve Aughty Mountains in SE Galway was more productive. As on several previous meetings in Ireland, much of the preparatory work and organisation was carried out by DM Synnott.

A short visit to Lough Navar Forest in Co. Fermanagh by RD Porley in 7-11 June 1999 was unsuccessful in refinding *Orthodontium gracile* at its only Irish station, but he obtained eight new vice-county records including *Mnium thomsonii* and a remarkable inland record of *Geocalyx graveolens* (Porley 2001).

The 1999 BBS meeting was based at Dungarvan for the first week and New Ross for the second week (Fox *et al.* 2001). A total of 15 people participated in at least part of the meeting. The excursions for the first week were mainly in Co. Waterford, with an incursion into East Cork, those for the second week largely in Co. Wexford. Highlights during the first week included *Barbilophozia atlantica, Fissidens rivularis* and *Telaranea nematodes* new to Co. Waterford. In the second week some bryologically rather unpromising country was surveyed, which nevertheless produced numerous new vice-county records. AR Perry and PE Stanley visited Co. Kerry and found the adventives *Calomnion complanatum* and *Leptotheca gaudichaudi* on the trunks of tree ferns, presumably introduced from Australia with the ferns.

During 1998-2002 prolonged field studies were carried out to assess the status of rare bryophytes throughout Ireland in order to work towards a thorough and well researched *Red Data Book of Irish Bryophytes*. This work was commissioned by National Parks and Wildlife in the Republic of Ireland and Environment and Heritage Service in Northern Ireland. These ongoing studies are intended mainly to refind and document known populations of the rarer species, but a proportion of the time is devoted to seeking previously unrecorded populations. A total of over 300 days of fieldwork by DT Holyoak produced several hundreds of new vice-county records, including new records for Ireland of *Meesia uliginosa* in Co. Donegal, *Ephemerum spinulosum* and *Splachnum sphaericum* in Co. Antrim, *Lophocolea semiteres* in Co. Down and *L. bispinosa* in Co. Tyrone. NG Hodgetts worked for shorter periods in Co. Roscommon and Co. Donegal, again producing many new records that included *Cynodontium jenneri* new to Ireland from the latter county.

Summary list of BBS Excursions in Ireland and the resulting publications

1928: Belfast (excursions in Co. Antrim, Co. Down; a further excursion taken by some members visited Co. Sligo and Co. Leitrim) (Duncan 1928, 1929a, Armitage 1956: 11).

1935: Muckross, Killarney, Co. Kerry (Watson 1936, 1937, Armitage 1956: 17).

1937: Bundoran, Co. Donegal (with excursions into Co. Leitrim, Co. Sligo and Co. Fermanagh); later Achill Island, Co. Mayo (Armitage 1938, 1956: 18-19).

1951: Co. Kerry; first week based at Glenbeigh; second week based at Waterville (RD Fitzgerald 1952a, Richards 1952, RD Fitzgerald & JW Fitzgerald 1952, Wallace 1952).

1957: Co. Galway and northern Co. Clare (Lobley 1958, Parker 1958).

1962: Dunfanaghy, Co. Donegal (Wallace 1963).

1966: Clonmel, Co. Tipperary (Synnott 1967a, 1967c).

1970: Sligo (with work in Co. Sligo, Co. Leitrim and less extensively in eastern Co. Mayo and Co. Cavan) (Appleyard 1971).

1975: Arklow, Co. Wicklow (Synnott 1976a, 1976c).

1979: First week: Limerick; second week: Glengarriff, Co. Cork (Crundwell 1980).

1983: First week: Killorglin, Co. Kerry (Kelly 1984a, Lockhart 1984); second week: Kenmare, Co. Kerry (Rothero 1984).

1987: First week: Achill Island, Co. Mayo (Synnott 1988); second week: Westport, Co. Mayo (Rothero 1988, Rothero & Synnott 1988).

1990: First week: Co. Antrim and Co. Londonderry (Lewis 1991); second week: Co. Donegal (Blockeel 1991a).

1994: First week, The Burren, Co. Clare (Whitehouse 1995); second week, Clifden, Co. Galway, with visit to Clare Island, Co. Mayo (Blockeel 1995a).

1999: Dungarvan, Co. Waterford and New Ross, Co. Wexford (Fox *et al.* 2001).

BIBLIOGRAPHICAL NOTES ON PUBLICATIONS OF THE MEC AND BBS

The Moss Exchange Club issued *Reports* from its formation in 1896 up to 1922, when the BBS was formed and took over its functions. The *Reports* for 1896-1898 were issued together in 1899 and those for 1899 and 1900 were issued together in 1900, after which they appeared annually and always within the same year as that indicated in their title. The 1st to 15th reports (1896-1910) had consecutive pagination and are generally bound as *MEC Reports* vol. **1**; likewise the 16th-27th reports (1911-1922) had consecutive pagination and are generally bound as *MEC Reports* vol. **2**. The precise titles of the early reports varied from year to year, as noted in the References, before settling down as e.g. *Moss Exchange Club. The nineteenth Annual Report. March, 1914.* Despite the early variations in title all the *Reports* were quite clearly intended to be a serial publication with continuous pagination, as indicated in the References.

MEC Reports from before 1908 give a single 'List of mosses and hepatics' that is listed in the References as a single publication. From 1908 onwards 'Mosses' and 'Hepatics' appear under separate headings, from 1917 onwards 'Sphagna' gained their own heading apart from 'True Mosses', and a further heading for 'Pleurocarpi' was introduced in 1918. Since each of these anonymous sections may have been compiled by different authors they have been treated as separate publications in the References.

Section II of the MEC published reports annually covering all of the years 1903 to 1922 (when the BBS took over its functions). The Reports of the Secretary and Distributer within each of these published reports are dated in the early months (usually January to May, sometimes as late as July) of the year following that covered by the report. Hence it is apparent that publication will also have occurred in the year following that covered by the report. The *MEC Section II Reports* all had separate pagination. Lists of specimens included in the distribution were published in the *Report for 1910* and subsequently, with 'Mosses' and 'Hepatics' appearing under separate headings. Since each of these anonymous sections may have been compiled by different (or several) authors they have been treated as separate publications in the References.

The British Bryological Society Report was issued annually from 1923 until 1946, except for several years during the 1939-1945 war. The first five *Reports* (published 1923-1927) comprised volume **1** parts 1-5 and had continuous pagination. A similar practice was continued with later reports, so that vol. **2** comprised parts 1-5 (published 1928-1932); vol. **3** parts 1-5 were published 1933-1937, and vol.

4 parts 1-5 were published 1938-1946, all with continuous pagination (no *Reports* being issued in 1941-1943 or 1945).

A potentially confusing but unannounced change of style in the title and content of the *Reports* occurred during 1926-1927. Thus, during 1923-1926 (vol. **1** parts 1-4) the information given in each report was from the year preceding that of its title, so e.g. the '*Report for 1924*' was published and issued in 1924 yet despite its title covered the Meetings, Distribution, etc. for 1923. This was changed from vol. **2** part 1 onwards (this part being erroneously labelled as part 6 on title page), which was '*Report for 1927*' but published and issued in 1928 and covered Meetings, Distribution, etc. for 1927 as implied by the title. The transition occurred in vol. **1** part 5 which was headed '*Report for 1926-7*', covering Meetings, Distribution, etc. for 1926, but was published and issued in 1927.

Authorship of 'Reports on plants sent in by members' is not stated in the *MEC Reports* or *BBS Reports*, or in the lists of new vice-county records in most *BBS Reports* or *Transactions of the BBS* up to and including 1949 (vol. **1** pp. 212-222), except that all three reports published in 1944 bore their respective author's initials and Hepaticae in 1949 were largely attributed to E.W.J.[ones]. For each section of the reports up to 1950 ('Sphagna, True Mosses, Hepatics') it is therefore mainly unclear whether the Recorder, the Distributor, the individual Referees, the 'Referee in Chief', or the author of the previous *Census Catalogue* should be regarded as author(s). Indeed, a combined effort must often have been involved and it is presumably for this reason that the contributions remained unattributed. This review of the records therefore cites all the reports from 1898-1949 (except those published in 1944 and for Hepaticae in 1949) as anonymous (abbreviated as 'anon.').

Dates of publication of *Transactions of the British Bryological Society* (volumes **1-6**) and *Journal of Bryology* (volumes **7-16**) are given in a useful note by Perry (1991b).

The *Census Catalogues* (*CC*) have provided convenient checklists of the bryophytes of Britain and Ireland for many years, with the distribution of each species (or subspecies, or variety) in all vice-counties listed using the vice-county numbers.

CC for liverworts were issued as follows:

Macvicar (1905) [1st edition, MEC]

Ingham (1913) 2nd edition, MEC

Wilson (1930) 3rd edition, BBS (Supplement by Wilson 1935)

Paton (1965b) 4th edition, BBS

CC for mosses were issued as follows:

Barker *et al.* (1907) [1st edition, MEC]

Duncan (1926) 2nd edition, BBS (Supplement by Duncan 1929b, BBS)

(2nd Supplement by Duncan 1935, BBS)

Warburg (1963a) 3rd edition, BBS

All three editions of the moss *CC* included *Sphagnum*, but separate publications for this genus were also issued as follows:

Sherrin (1937) [1st edition, BBS]

Sherrin, revised by Thompson (1946) [2nd edition, BBS]

In recent decades the separate *CC* have been replaced by a single publication covering all groups of bryophytes (co-authored for the BBS by successive Recorders of Hepatics and Recorders of Mosses):

Corley & Hill (1981)

Blockeel & Long (1998)

In the past few decades the BBS recorders have been meticulous in publishing details of additions and deletions to the *CC* in the annual Recorders' Reports, so that the content of each recent *CC* can mainly be predicted (and checked) from work already published. However, before about 1960 very few of the deletions made from the *CC* were explained in any published account, and in the early years records frequently come and go from successive *CC* without any explanation. Most records that were omitted in the early years were doubtless excluded for good reasons, but in the absence of any published explanation it is sometimes unclear whether particular records were excluded or merely overlooked. The present work places old published records in square brackets as doubtful when subsequent *CC* seem clear in excluding them, but some long lost but correct records are doubtless among them.

LIVERWORTS
(MARCHANTIOPSIDA)

1/1 ***Haplomitrium hookeri*** (Sm.) Nees

H(1) listed by Macvicar (1905: 10).
H1 1983: peaty detritus amongst stones on lake shore, E bank of Coomacullen L., nr Coomasaharn, DG Long (Corley 1984: 23).
H2 1983: with *Pellia* on wet shady soil by lake, S end of L. Garagarry, Mangerton Mt., DG Long (Corley 1984: 23).
H3 1968: heathy flush on cliffs, Garinish Point, W of Allihies, JA Paton (Paton 1969a: 867).
H16 1969: gravelly lay-by 3 miles E of Lettercrafroe L., AR Perry & HJ Perry (Paton 1970: 188).
H20 1975: W margin of Upper Lake, Vale of Glendalough, JA Paton & AR Perry (BBS exc.) (Paton 1976: 17).
H(21) listed by Macvicar (1905: 10). H(21) listed by Blockeel & Long (1998: 29).
H27 1968: gravelly layby, Killary Harbour, SW of Aasleagh, JA Paton (Paton 1969a: 867).
H28 1970: roadside quarry nr Masshill, JA Paton (BBS exc.) (Paton 1971a: 369, Appleyard 1971: 389).
H30 1969: floor of old quarry, Blackrocks Cross, Cuilcagh Mts, SW of Swanlinbar, JA Paton (Paton 1970: 188).
H34 1969: S margin of L. Inn, W of Moville, Inishowen, JA Paton (Paton 1970: 188).
H35 1969: peaty soil on cliffs above Skelpoonagh Bay, Glencolumbkille, N of Carrick, JA Paton (Paton 1970: 188).

2/1 ***Mastigophora woodsii*** (Hook.) Nees

H(1) listed by Macvicar (1905: 19).
†H1 listed by Blockeel & Long (1998: 29).
H(2) listed by Macvicar (1905: 19).
†H2 listed by Blockeel & Long (1998: 29).
H16 1957: with *Pleurozia purpurea*, *Plagiochila spinulosa*, *Herberta* etc., among rocks at 1550 ft [alt.], N side of Ben Baun, Twelve Pins, AC Crundwell (BBS exc.) (Castell 1958: 468).
H(27) listed by Macvicar (1905: 19).
†H27 listed by Blockeel & Long (1998: 29).

3/1 ***Herbertus aduncus*** (Dicks.) Gray **subsp. *hutchinsiae*** (Gottsche) R.M. Schust.
(syn. *Herberta hutchinsiae* (Gottsche) A. Evans)

H(1) listed by Macvicar (1905: 19).
†H1 listed by Blockeel & Long (1998: 29).
H(2) listed by Macvicar (1905: 19).
†H2 listed by Blockeel & Long (1998: 29).
[H(3) listed by Macvicar (1905: 19). H3 record deleted, it was error in Record Book (Castell 1953: 302)].
H3 1953: Coomroe corrie, alt. 1400 ft [alt.], nr Gongane [*sic* = Gougane] Barra, ALK King (Castell 1954: 475).
H6 1961: shaded ledges of N-facing cliffs at 2000 ft [alt.], Coumshingaun, Comeragh Mts, DA Ratcliffe (Paton 1962: 362).
H(7) 1943: Lough Muskry, AW Stelfox, per JS Thomson (Wilson 1944: 221). Stelfox (1965) noted that he collected the material 'but the credit for the record and discovery of the plant must be given entirely to Miss Thomson'.
H(7) listed by Macvicar (1905: 19).
†H7 listed by Blockeel & Long (1998: 29).
H(16) listed by Macvicar (1905: 19).
†H16 listed by Blockeel & Long (1998: 29).
[H(20) listed by Macvicar (1905: 19)].
[H27 record deleted, because it was error in Record Book (Castell 1953: 302)].
[H(27) listed by Macvicar (1905: 19)].
H(27) 1919: Slieve More, Achill [I.], WN Tetley (BBSUK) (Castell 1953: 302).
†H27 listed by Blockeel & Long (1998: 29).
H28 1965: cliffs at 1500 ft alt., Gleniff, JW Fitzgerald & EM Lobley (Paton 1966: 181).
[H(29) listed by Macvicar (1905: 19)].
H(29) 1875: Glenade, D Moore (DBN), comm. JW Fitzgerald (Castell 1959: 629).
†H29 listed by Blockeel & Long (1998: 29).
H33 1950: peat over Yoredale Sandstone, Rocky Ledge, with *Bazzania tricrenata* and *Scapania gracilis*, Cuileagh [*sic* = Cuilcagh], alt. *ca* 2100 ft [alt.], J Taylor (Castell 1951: 495).
H(34) 1938: damp rock ledge, Bulbin [Mountain], JPM Brenan (anon. 1949a: 214).
†H34 listed by Blockeel & Long (1998: 29).
H(35) listed by Macvicar (1905: 19).
†H35 listed by Blockeel & Long (1998: 29).
[H(39) listed by Macvicar (1905: 19)].

H39 1952: basalt rocks, Sallagh Braes, EW Jones, 'found in this locality some years ago by WR Megaw, determined by DA Jones and recorded in *Flora of N.E. Ireland as H. adunca*', comm. EW Jones (Castell 1953: 302).
[H(40) listed by Macvicar (1905: 19)].

4/1 ***Blepharostoma trichophyllum*** (L.) Dumort.

H(1) listed by Macvicar (1905: 19).
†H1 listed by Blockeel & Long (1998: 29).
H(2) listed by Macvicar (1905: 19).
†H2 listed by Blockeel & Long (1998: 29).
H(3) listed by Macvicar (1905: 19).
†H3 listed by Blockeel & Long (1998: 29).
H(6) listed by Macvicar (1905: 19).
†H6 listed by Blockeel & Long (1998: 29).
H(16) listed by Macvicar (1905: 19). H(16) listed by Blockeel & Long (1998: 29).
H(20) listed by Macvicar (1905: 19). H(20) listed by Blockeel & Long (1998: 29).
H(27) listed by Macvicar (1905: 19).
†H27 listed by Blockeel & Long (1998: 29).
H(28) 1928: Gleniff, Ben Bulben (BBS exc.) (Duncan 1928: 118).
†H28 listed by Blockeel & Long (1998: 29).
H(29) 1914: Truskmore, WN Tetley (BBSUK) (Castell 1954: 475).
1937: Glenade, no collector named (BBS exc.) (Armitage 1938: 13).
1937: Glenade, W Watson (anon. 1938e: 44).
1937: Glenade, WW (Castell 1954: 475).
†H29 listed by Blockeel & Long (1998: 29).
H(31) listed by Macvicar (1905: 19). H(31) listed by Blockeel & Long (1998: 29).
H(33) 1914: Boho Caves, Gortgall, WN Tetley (BBSUK) (Castell 1954: 475).
1918: Whealt, WN Tetley (Castell 1954: 475).
H33 2000: on vertical side of boulder *ca* 1.0 m above summer level of river in open deciduous woodland, by Cladagh River below Marble Arch, H13, DT Holyoak 00-89 (BBSUK) (Blackstock 2001: 34).
H34 1962: in moss on basic rocks, Bulbin Mountain N of Buncrana, EC Wallace (BBS exc.) (Paton 1963: 489).
H35 1962: damp rocks, Carnboy nr Bunbeg, The Rosses, EM Lobley (BBS exc.) (Paton 1963: 489).
H(38) listed by Macvicar (1905: 19). H(38) listed by Blockeel & Long (1998: 29).
H(39) listed by Macvicar (1905: 19).
†H39 listed by Blockeel & Long (1998: 29).
H40 1966: on rocks nr the water's edge, Cushcapple R., Banagher Glen nr Dungiven, JW Fitzgerald (Paton 1967c: 396).

5/1 ***Trichocolea tomentella*** (Ehrh.) Dumort.

H(1) listed by Macvicar (1905: 19).
†H1 listed by Blockeel & Long (1998: 29).
H(2) listed by Macvicar (1905: 19).
†H2 listed by Blockeel & Long (1998: 29).
H3 1975: on tufts of moss near small stream, Ounmanway, N Kirby (Paton 1976: 17).
H(4) 1851: Ballinhassig Glen, I Carroll (BEL) (Paton 1967c: 396).
H4 1966: on damp ground in wood nr Bellcourt House, MFV Corley & JS Parker (Paton 1967c: 396).
H(5) 1850: Knochananig, nr Fermoy, T Chandlee (DBN) (Castell 1959: 629).
†H5 listed by Blockeel & Long (1998: 29).
H6 1952: dripping rocks in glen, by R. Owenashad, above Lismore, ALK King & MPH Kertland, comm. ALK King (Castell 1953: 302).
†H8 listed by Blockeel & Long (1998: 29).
H9 1976: Glencurran valley nr Castletown, N Kirby (Paton 1977a: 12).
H10 1952: in heavy shade by waterfall in wooded gorge, Silvermines, AD Banwell, PJ Wanstall & EV Watson (Castell 1952: 95).
H(13) *ca* 1867: Cloghrennane Wood 4 miles SW of Carlow, herb. R Clayton-Browne (DBN) (Paton 1968: 621).
H(14) listed by Blockeel & Long (1998: 29).
H16 1957: flush in oakwoods, Ballynahinch, RE Parker (Castell 1958: 468).
H(18) listed by Macvicar (1905: 19). H(18) listed by Blockeel & Long (1998: 29).
H(20) listed by Macvicar (1905: 19). H(20) listed by Blockeel & Long (1998: 29).
H26 1982: on stones in stream, Barnalyra Wood, N of Kilkelly, DM Synnott (DBN) (Long 1999a: 93).
H(27) listed by Macvicar (1905: 19).
†H27 listed by Blockeel & Long (1998: 29).
H28 1965: hummock in calcareous flush at 250 ft alt., N of Glencar Lough, SE of Tormore, EF Warburg & AR Perry (Paton 1966: 182).
H(29) 1928: wooded glen, NE end of Glencar

Lough (BBS exc.) (Duncan 1928: 118).
†H29 listed by Blockeel & Long (1998: 29).
H(30) 1912: Dowra (Cavan side), WN Tetley (BBSUK) (Castell 1953: 302).
†H30 listed by Blockeel & Long (1998: 29).
H(33) 1905: damp banks, Correl Glen, D McArdle (*Irish Nat.* **16**, 237, 1907), comm. JW Fitzgerald (Castell 1952: 95).
†H33 listed by Blockeel & Long (1998: 29).
H(34) listed by Macvicar (1905: 19). H(34) listed by Blockeel & Long (1998: 29).
H(35) listed by Macvicar (1905: 19).
†H35 listed by Blockeel & Long (1998: 29).
H(36) listed by Macvicar (1905: 19).
†H36 listed by Blockeel & Long (1998: 29).
H(38) listed by Macvicar (1905: 19). H(38) listed by Blockeel & Long (1998: 29).
H(39) listed by Macvicar (1905: 19).
†H39 listed by Blockeel & Long (1998: 29).
H(40) listed by Macvicar (1905: 19).
†H40 listed by Blockeel & Long (1998: 29).

6/1 ***Telaranea nematodes*** (Gottsche ex Austin) M.Howe
(syn. *Telaranea sejuncta* auct. non. (Ångstr.) S.W.Arnell)

H1 1935: growing in scattered stems among mosses collected at Waterville, F Verdoorn det. H Buch (Buch 1938, Richards 1938a, anon. 1939c: 111).
[H(2) record (1936: Derrycunihy Wood nr Killarney, PW Richards: Richards 1938a, 1938b, anon. 1939c: 111) should be deleted because the locality is in H1 (see Kelly 1984b) as originally given, not in H2 as given by Castell (1952: 95)].
†H2 listed by Blockeel & Long (1998: 30), but source of record needs checking as it may be from Derrycunihy Wood [in H1].
H3 1955: shaded peat under *Rhododendron*, Dunboy Wood, H Milne-Redhead (Castell 1957: 325).
H6 1999: on humus under *Rhododendron* in N-facing woodland, *ca* 80 m alt., by junction of Glenakeefe River and Owennashad River, Lismore, S01, TL Blockeel 28/194 (Blackstock 2000: 40).
H16 1957: peaty bank in oakwoods, Kylemore, PW Richards, comm. JW Fitzgerald (Paton 1963: 489).
H27 1962: rotting wood and bank under dense *Rhododendron* nr Sraheens Lough, Achill I., EF Warburg (Paton 1963: 489).
H35 2002: small patches on humic soil of rocky deciduous woodland on slope (recently cleared of *Rhododendron*), *ca* 80 m alt., NE of Glenveagh Castle, C02, DT Holyoak 02-720 (Blackstock 2003: 39).

7/1 ***Kurzia pauciflora*** (Dicks.) Grolle
(syn. *Lepidozia setacea* auct. non (G. Weber) Mitt., *L. setacea* var. *sertularioides* Carrington)

H(1) listed by Macvicar (1905: 18).
†H1 listed by Blockeel & Long (1998: 30).
H(2) listed by Macvicar (1905: 18).
†H2 listed by Blockeel & Long (1998: 30).
H(3) listed by Macvicar (1905: 18).
†H3 listed by Blockeel & Long (1998: 30).
H(5) 1851: Glenbower Wood, I Carroll (BEL) (Paton 1967c: 396).
H(6) listed by Macvicar (1905: 18).
†H6 listed by Blockeel & Long (1998: 30).
H(7) listed by Macvicar (1905: 18).
†H7 listed by Blockeel & Long (1998: 30).
H(9) listed by Macvicar (1905: 18).
†H9 listed by Blockeel & Long (1998: 30).
H10 1951: peat bog, alt. *ca* 1300 ft [alt.], Silvermines Mountain, AD Banwell, EV Watson & PJ Wanstall (Castell 1952: 95).
H11 1954: growing through *Sphagnum plumulosum* on Mt Brandon, alt. 1250 ft, ALK King (Castell 1955: 581).
H12 1975: bog by stream, S slope of Black Rock Mt., JA Paton (BBS exc.) (Paton 1976: 18).
H13 1969: peat in bog at St Mullins nr Graiguenemanagh, JW Fitzgerald (Paton 1971a: 369).
H(14) listed by Macvicar (1905: 18).
†H14 listed by Blockeel & Long (1998: 30).
H15 1961: raised bog nr Aughrim, 3 miles SW of Ballinasloe, EM Lobley (Paton 1962: 362).
H16 1953: Craiggamore, nr Roundstone, EC Wallace (Castell 1955: 581).
H(17) listed by Macvicar (1905: 18).
†H17 listed by Blockeel & Long (1998: 30).
H(18) listed by Macvicar (1905: 18).
†H18 listed by Blockeel & Long (1998: 30).
H19 1969: raised bog at Derryvullagh nr Athy, JW Fitzgerald (Paton 1971a: 369).
H(20) listed by Macvicar (1905: 18).

†H20 listed by Blockeel & Long (1998: 30).
H(21) listed by Macvicar (1905: 18).
H21 listed by Blockeel & Long (1998: 30).
H22 1952: Clonycavan Bog, nr Ballivor, ALK King (Castell 1953: 302).
H23 1952: growing through *Sphagnum*, Derries Bog, Athlone, ALK King (Castell 1953: 302).
H24 1966: in *Sphagnum*, Cloontirm Bog nr Longford, ALK King (Paton 1967c: 396).
H25 1952: Carrigynachten Bog, nr Athlone, ALK King (Castell 1953: 302).
H26 1986: among mosses on raised bog, Flughany, C Douglas & H Grogan (Corley 1987: 20).
H(27) listed by Macvicar (1905: 18).
†H27 listed by Blockeel & Long (1998: 30).
H(28) listed by Macvicar (1905: 18).
†H28 listed by Blockeel & Long (1998: 30).
H29 1963: peat in roadside bog, Flughanagh, 3 miles SE of Dromahair, AR Perry & JW Fitzgerald (Paton 1964: 719).
H30 1957: peaty bank, SW side of Tiltinbane, AC Crundwell (Castell 1958: 468).
H(31) listed by Macvicar (1905: 18). H(31) listed by Blockeel & Long (1998: 30).
H33 1905: peaty banks, Correl Glen, D McArdle (*Irish Nat.* **16**, 237, 1907), comm. JW Fitzgerald (Castell 1952: 95).
H34 1962: peaty overhung bank by Barnes Lough, EF Warburg (BBS exc.) (Paton 1963: 489).
H(35) listed by Macvicar (1905: 18).
†H35 listed by Blockeel & Long (1998: 30).
H36 1954: on peat, Fairywater South Bog, nr Drumquin, MS Morrison, comm. JW Fitzgerald (Castell 1955: 581).
H(38) listed by Macvicar (1905: 18). H(38) listed by Blockeel & Long (1998: 30).
H(39) listed by Macvicar (1905: 18).
†H39 listed by Blockeel & Long (1998: 30).

7/2 ***Kurzia sylvatica*** (A.Evans) Grolle
(syn. *Lepidozia sylvatica* A.Evans)

H1 1951: Blackstones Bridge, EW Jones (Castell 1952: 95).
H2 1966: with *L. trichoclados*, wooded bank nr Queen's Cottage, Killarney, JA Paton (Paton 1971a: 370).
H4 1966: peaty bank on moor, Boggeragh Mts, MFV Corley (Corley 1979: 23).
H8 1966: on peat, Slievereagh, nr Ballylanders, MFV Corley (Corley 1979: 23).
H15 1994: peaty bank on heathland above Boleyneendorish River, Slieve Aughty, M50, JA Paton 7628 (Long 1995b: 39).
H16 1970: peaty bank under rhododendrons, E of Kylemore Castle, Letterfrack, JA Paton (Paton 1971a: 370).
H20 1975: with *L. trichoclados* on boggy slope nr Ballycayle, Glencree R., JA Paton (BBS exc.) (Paton 1976: 18).
H26 1987: moorland S of lane W from Partry to Cloon River, JA Paton (Long 1988: 32).
H27 1970: sandy ravine bank, S slope Ben Gorm, N of Killary Harbour, JA Paton (Paton 1971a: 370).
H28 1970: peaty slope, W valley of Bricklieve Mts, JA Paton (BBS exc.) (Paton 1971a: 370, Appleyard 1971: 389).
H33 1959: on moss-covered sandstone boulders nr river, Correll Glen, JW Fitzgerald (Paton 1961: 156).
H34 1969: bog N of Gorey, S of Culdaff, Inishowen, JA Paton (Paton 1971a: 370).
H35 1990: on vertical rock face in oak woodland, 60 m alt., Ballyarr Wood, *ca* 5 km E of Kilmacrenan, C12, TL Blockeel 19/515 (Long 1991: 39).

7/3 ***Kurzia trichoclados*** (Müll.Frib.) Grolle
(syn. *Lepidozia trichoclados* Müll.Frib.)

H(1) listed by Macvicar (1905: 18).
†H1 listed by Blockeel & Long (1998: 30).
H(2) listed by Macvicar (1905: 18).
†H2 listed by Blockeel & Long (1998: 30).
H3 1967: peaty banks, Gougane Barra, JW Fitzgerald (Paton 1968: 621).
H4 1966: on peat cutting at 1200 ft alt., Seefin, and moor, Musheramore, Boggeragh Mts, MFV Corley & JS Parker (Paton 1967c: 396).
H6 1966: peaty bank above Sgilloge Loughs, Comeragh Mts, JA Paton (BBS exc.) (Paton 1967c: 396).
H7 1966: heathy banks nr Bay L Knockmealdown Mts, JA Paton & ER Little (BBS exc.) (Paton 1967c: 396).
[H8 1966: on peat, Slievereagh Ballylanders, MFV Corley & JS P (Paton 1967c: 396). H8 deleted b specimen is *K. sylvatica* (Corley 23)].
[H(9) listed by Macvicar (1905: 18). H because no identifiable speci (Corley 1981: 18)].

H10 1979: peaty bank, S slope of Keeper Hill, JA Paton (Corley 1980a: 27).
H12 1975: peaty banks S of Cloroge, Mt Leinster, JA Paton (BBS exc.) (Paton 1976: 18).
H13 1969: block scree below Caher Roe's Den, Blackstairs Mt., JW Fitzgerald (Paton 1970: 188).
H(16) listed by Macvicar (1905: 18).
†H16 listed by Blockeel & Long (1998: 30).
H(20) listed by Macvicar (1905: 18).
†H20 listed by Blockeel & Long (1998: 30).
[H(21) listed by Macvicar (1905: 18). H21 deleted because no identifiable specimen found (Corley 1981: 18)].
[H23 1952: side of bog-hole, nr NE end of L. Owel, JS Thomson, conf. EW Jones ['Inflorescence not seen'] (Castell 1954: 475). H23 deleted because no identifiable specimen found (Corley 1981: 18)].
H25 1965: peat banks, moorland at 700 ft alt., Kilronan Mt. nr Ballyfarnan, JW Fitzgerald & EM Lobley (Paton 1966: 182).
H26 1965: on peat banks W of L. Talt, [The] Ox Mts, JW Fitzgerald (Paton 1966: 182).
H(27) listed by Macvicar (1905: 18).
†H27 listed by Blockeel & Long (1998: 30).
[H(28) listed by Macvicar (1905: 18). H28 deleted because no identifiable specimen found (Corley 1981: 18)].
H29 1963: peaty bank, bog E of Sriff Cottage nr Dromahair, JW Fitzgerald & AR Perry (Paton 1964: 718).
[H(30) 1916: Tents Mt., WN Tetley (BBSUK), conf. (with notes) EW Jones, but 'no inflorescence seen' (Castell 1953: 302)].
listed by Blockeel & Long (1998: 30).
1907: Correll Glen, WN Tetley (BBSUK), conf. (with notes) EW Jones, 'no inflorescence seen' (Castell 302)].
Bar of Whealt, WN Tetley (*Report Section II*, for 1914, p. 20) 953: 302).
ockeel & Long (1998: 30).
scree at 900 ft alt., Gap of iles N of Buncrana, RD n 1963: 489).
crevice, Lough Agher W Fitzgerald (Castell
swelling cushions,

Lough Bradan, JW Fitzgerald (Castell 1953: 302).
H39 1964: peat banks at 1500 ft alt., Slievenanee, JW Fitzgerald (Paton 1965a: 857).
H40 1968: peaty banks, bog at Lisdillon, 4 miles SE of Londonderry, JW Fitzgerald & HH Birks (Paton 1969a: 868).

8/1 ***Lepidozia reptans*** (L.) Dumort.

H(1) listed by Macvicar (1905: 18).
†H1 listed by Blockeel & Long (1998: 30).
H(2) listed by Macvicar (1905: 18).
†H2 listed by Blockeel & Long (1998: 30).
H(3) listed by Macvicar (1905: 18).
†H3 listed by Blockeel & Long (1998: 30).
H4 2002: on soil on woodland bank, 40 m alt., Curraghbinny Wood, *ca* 6 km E of Carrigaline, W76, TL Blockeel 31/379 (Blackstock 2003: 39).
H5 1956: wood nr Tourig, Youghal, EC Wallace (Castell 1957: 325).
H6 1953: on ground in woods, Lismore Castle, ALK King (Castell 1954: 475).
H(7) listed by Macvicar (1905: 18).
†H7 listed by Blockeel & Long (1998: 30).
H(8) listed by Macvicar (1905: 18).
†H8 listed by Blockeel & Long (1998: 30).
H(9) listed by Macvicar (1905: 18).
†H9 listed by Blockeel & Long (1998: 30).
H10 1967: old stumps, Knockfine, Keeper Hill, JW Fitzgerald (Paton 1968: 621).
H(12) listed by Macvicar (1905: 18).
†H12 listed by Blockeel & Long (1998: 30).
H(13) listed by Macvicar (1905: 18).
†H13 listed by Blockeel & Long (1998: 30).
H14 1955: stump of tree, Abbeyleix, JS Thomson (Castell 1956: 149).
H(15) listed by Macvicar (1905: 18).
†H15 listed by Blockeel & Long (1998: 30).
H16 1957: with *Bazzania trilobata*, oakwoods, Ballynahinch, RE Parker (Castell 1958: 468).
1957: Tullywee Bridge, nr Kylemore, J Appleyard (Castell 1958: 468).
H17 1968: raised bog at Addergoule N[orth], R. Suck nr Ballinasloe, HJB Birks (Paton 1969a: 868).
H(18) listed by Macvicar (1905: 18).
†H18 listed by Blockeel & Long (1998: 30).
[H(19) listed by Macvicar (1905: 18). H19 deleted because no record or voucher traced, comm. MM Yeo (Long 1990a: 27)].

[H(20) listed by Macvicar (1905: 18). H20 deleted because no record traced, comm. MM Yeo, replaced by next two records (Long 1990a: 27-28)].
H20 1879: Lough Bray, D Moore (DBN), comm. DM Synnott (Long 1990a: 28). 1955: Glen of The Downs, ALK King (DBN), comm. DM Synnott (Long 1990a: 28).
[H(21) listed by Macvicar (1905: 18)].
H21 1959: Slievenabawnoge, ALK King (DBN) (Long 1999b: 26).
H(22) listed by Macvicar (1905: 18).
†H22 listed by Blockeel & Long (1998: 30).
H(23) listed by Macvicar (1905: 18).
†H23 listed by Blockeel & Long (1998: 30).
H(24) 1932: Farragh nr Longford, E Bond (DBN), comm. ALK King (Paton 1964: 718).
†H24 listed by Blockeel & Long (1998: 30).
H25 1960: on rotting stumps in woods at Rockingham, Boyle, ALK King (Paton 1961: 156).
H(26) listed by Macvicar (1905: 18).
†H26 listed by Blockeel & Long (1998: 30).
H(27) listed by Macvicar (1905: 18).
†H27 listed by Blockeel & Long (1998: 30).
H(28) listed by Macvicar (1905: 18).
†H28 listed by Blockeel & Long (1998: 30).
H(29) listed by Macvicar (1905: 18).
†H29 listed by Blockeel & Long (1998: 30).
H(30) listed by Macvicar (1905: 18).
†H30 listed by Blockeel & Long (1998: 30).
H(31) listed by Macvicar (1905: 18).
†H31 listed by Blockeel & Long (1998: 30).
†H33 listed by Blockeel & Long (1998: 30).
H34 1962: in scree, Gap of Mamore 6 miles N of Buncrana, RD Fitzgerald (Paton 1963: 489).
H(35) listed by Macvicar (1905: 18).
†H35 listed by Blockeel & Long (1998: 30).
H(36) listed by Macvicar (1905: 18).
†H36 listed by Blockeel & Long (1998: 30).
H37 1964: base of old oak stump, wood at Derrylee, E of Verner's Bridge, JW Fitzgerald & MPH Kertland (Paton 1965a: 857).
H(38) listed by Macvicar (1905: 18).
†H38 listed by Blockeel & Long (1998: 30).
H(39) listed by Macvicar (1905: 18).
†H39 listed by Blockeel & Long (1998: 30).
H(40) listed by Macvicar (1905: 18).
†H40 listed by Blockeel & Long (1998: 30).

8/2 ***Lepidozia pearsonii*** Spruce

H(1) listed by Macvicar (1905: 18).
†H1 listed by Blockeel & Long (1998: 30).
H2 1967: among rocks above L. Glannafreaghaun, The Paps, JW Fitzgerald (Paton 1968: 621).
H3 1979: peaty bank in valley SW of Gouganebarra L., Shehy Mts, JA Paton (Corley 1980a: 27).
H7 1983: mossy turf among sandstone blocks on exposed ridge, O'Loughnan's Castle, Galty Mts, DG Long (Corley 1984: 25).
H16 1994: in hanging mat of bryophytes on damp steep rock face with *Plagiothecium undulatum* etc., 250 m alt., low coire of Benchoona, Lough Fee, L76, GP Rothero 94/044 (Long 1995b: 39).
H20 1975: amongst *Calluna* on rocky slope above L. Ouler, Tonelagee, JA Paton & AR Perry (BBS exc.) (Paton 1976: 17).
H(27) listed by Macvicar (1905: 18).
†H27 listed by Blockeel & Long (1998: 30).
H28 1970: on the way to King's Mt., JA Paton (BBS exc.) (Paton 1971a: 369, Appleyard 1971: 389).
H29 1965: among damp limestone rocks, Peakadaw, Glenade, EM Lobley & JW Fitzgerald (Paton 1966: 182).
H30 1965: clefts at top of Cuilcagh, 2000 ft alt., JW Fitzgerald & EM Lobley (Paton 1966: 182).
H33 1959: with *Hymenophyllum tunbridgense* and *H. wilsoni*, *Bazzania tricrenata* and *Lepidozia pinnata*, shaded crevice in lower rocks at 900 ft [alt.], Cuilcagh, JW Fitzgerald (Castell 1960: 767).
H34 1962: among *Calluna* and other bryophytes, Croaghconnellagh, Tawnawully Mts, EM Lobley, J Appleyard & EC Wallace (BBS exc.) (Paton 1963: 489).
H35 1962: among *Bazzania tricrenata* under *Calluna*, N-facing slope *ca* 1500 ft alt., Muckish Mt., RE Longton (BBS exc.) (Paton 1963: 489).
H39 1952: amongst old *Calluna,* mixed with *Breutelia*, *Rhytidiadelphus loreus*, *Dicranum majus*, *Pleurozium schreberi*, etc., on top of rocks in sheltered hollows of scree of basalt blocks, locally abundant, The Undercliff, Fair Head,

EW Jones (Castell 1953: 302).

8/3 ***Lepidozia cupressina*** (Sw.) Lindenb. (syn. *Lepidozia pinnata* (Hook.) Dumort.)

H(1) listed by Macvicar (1905: 18).
†H1 listed by Blockeel & Long (1998: 30).
H(2) listed by Macvicar (1905: 18).
†H2 listed by Blockeel & Long (1998: 30).
H(3) listed by Macvicar (1905: 18).
†H3 listed by Blockeel & Long (1998: 30).
[H(4) deleted because the locality (1908: Glenbower Wood, S Carroll Bennis (DBN), comm. ALK King, Paton 1964: 718) is in H5, comm. MM Yeo (Long 1990a: 28)].
H(5) 1908: Glenbower Wood, S Carroll Bennis (DBN), comm. ALK King (Paton 1964: 718), originally listed for H4 but transferred to H5 comm. MM Yeo (Long 1990a: 28, Long 1991: 39).
†H5 listed by Blockeel & Long (1998: 30).
H6 1961: amongst large blocks on slope below Coumshingaun, Comeragh Mts, DA Ratcliffe (Paton 1962: 362).
H(8) listed by Macvicar (1905: 18). H(8) listed by Blockeel & Long (1998: 30).
H12 1969: block scree *ca* 1400 ft alt. below Caher Roe's Den, Blackstairs Mt., JW Fitzgerald (Paton 1970: 188).
H(16) listed by Macvicar (1905: 18).
†H16 listed by Blockeel & Long (1998: 30).
[H(20) listed by Macvicar (1905: 18)].
H20 1966: growing through *Scapania* in rock cleft, Raven's Glen, Glencree, ALK King (DBN) (Long 1999b: 26).
[H(21) listed by Macvicar (1905: 18)].
H21 1954: 1200 ft [alt.], Glasavullaun, Glenasmole, AW Stelfox (DBN) (Long 1999b: 26).
H25 2002: shaded rock crevices in NE-facing crags, Kilronan Mountain, Arigna, G91, NG Hodgetts 4157 (Blackstock 2003: 39).
H26 1965: ledge of cliffs S of Glendaduff, [The] Ox Mts, JW Fitzgerald (Paton 1966: 182).
H(27) listed by Macvicar (1905: 18).
†H27 listed by Blockeel & Long (1998: 30).
H28 1966: on rocks and trees, Slish Wood, F Rose (Paton 1967c: 396).
H(29) listed by Macvicar (1905: 18).
†H29 listed by Blockeel & Long (1998: 30).
†H30 listed by Blockeel & Long (1998: 30).
†H33 listed by Blockeel & Long (1998: 30).
H(34) listed by Macvicar (1905: 18).
†H34 listed by Blockeel & Long (1998: 30).
H(35) listed by Macvicar (1905: 18).
†H35 listed by Blockeel & Long (1998: 30).
H36 1956: among limestone rocks, above Lough Lee, at 900 ft [alt.], Castlederg, JW Fitzgerald & MPH Kertland (Castell 1957: 325).
H39 1951: damp basalt boulders, shaded by heather, undercliff, alt. 250 ft, Fair Head, JW Fitzgerald (Castell 1952: 95).
H40 1959: shaded boulders in wood, Altnaheglish, nr Dungiven, JW Fitzgerald (Castell 1960: 767).

9/1 ***Bazzania trilobata*** (L.) Gray (syn. *Bazzania trilobata* var. *minor* Nees)

H(1) listed by Macvicar (1905: 18).
†H1 listed by Blockeel & Long (1998: 31).
H(2) listed by Macvicar (1905: 18).
†H2 listed by Blockeel & Long (1998: 31).
H(3) listed by Macvicar (1905: 18).
†H3 listed by Blockeel & Long (1998: 31).
H(5) 1850: nr Fermoy, T Chandlee (DBN) (Castell 1959: 629).
H6 1999: gorge, Owennashad River, S00, DH Wrench (Blackstock 2001: 34).
H12 1969: rock scree *ca* 1400 ft alt. below Caher Roe's Den, Blackstairs Mt., JW Fitzgerald (Paton 1970: 188).
H(13) listed by Macvicar (1905: 18). H(13) listed by Blockeel & Long (1998: 31).
H(16) listed by Macvicar (1905: 18).
†H16 listed by Blockeel & Long (1998: 31).
H(20) listed by Macvicar (1905: 18). H(20) listed by Blockeel & Long (1998: 31).
H(21) listed by Macvicar (1905: 18). H(21) listed by Blockeel & Long (1998: 31).
H25 2002: NE-facing rock outcrop, *ca* 200 m alt., Kilronan Mountain, G91, NG Hodgetts 4144 (Blackstock 2003: 40).
H(27) listed by Macvicar (1905: 18).
†H27 listed by Blockeel & Long (1998: 31).
H(28) listed by Macvicar (1905: 18).
†H28 listed by Blockeel & Long (1998: 31).
[H(29) listed by Macvicar (1905: 18)].
H29 1965: among boulders beside L. Mahanagh E of Drumkeeran, JW Fitzgerald & EM Lobley (Paton 1966: 182).
H30 1965: among scree below cliffs nr Englishman's House, 3 miles S of

Glenfarne, JW Fitzgerald (Paton 1966: 182).
†H33 listed by Blockeel & Long (1998: 31).
H34 1968: among rocks, Kindrohid nr Clonmany, Inishowen, JW Fitzgerald (Paton 1969a: 868).
H(35) listed by Macvicar (1905: 18).
†H35 listed by Blockeel & Long (1998: 31).
H37 1967: Bessbrook, Richardson, comm. JW Fitzgerald (Paton 1968: 621).
H(38) listed by Macvicar (1905: 18).
†H38 listed by Blockeel & Long (1998: 31).
H(39) listed by Macvicar (1905: 18).
†H39 listed by Blockeel & Long (1998: 31).
H(40) listed by Macvicar (1905: 18). H(40) listed by Blockeel & Long (1998: 31).

9/2 ***Bazzania tricrenata*** (Wahlenb.) Lindb. (syn. *Bazzania triangularis* (Lindb.) Pearson, *B. tricrenata* var. *triangularis* (Lindb.) Schleich.)

H(1) listed by Macvicar (1905: 18).
†H1 listed by Blockeel & Long (1998: 31).
H(2) listed by Macvicar (1905: 18).
†H2 listed by Blockeel & Long (1998: 31).
H3 1956: Hill Banks, Moulin, H Milne-Redhead (Castell 1957: 325).
H4 1967: rocks at 1400 ft alt., Musherabeg, JW Fitzgerald (Paton 1968: 621).
H(6) listed by Macvicar (1905: 18).
†H6 listed by Blockeel & Long (1998: 31).
H(7) 1943: in *Herberta hutchinsiae*, at 1700-2000 ft [alt.], Lough Musky, AW Stelfox, comm. JS Thomson (Castell 1958: 467).
†H7 listed by Blockeel & Long (1998: 31).
†H16 listed by Blockeel & Long (1998: 31).
H(20) 1932: cliffs above Lough Ouler at 2200 ft [alt.], AW Stelfox & M Buchanan (DBN), comm. JW Fitzgerald (Castell 1959: 629).
†H20 listed by Blockeel & Long (1998: 31).
H(27) listed by Macvicar (1905: 18).
†H27 listed by Blockeel & Long (1998: 31).
H(28) listed by Macvicar (1905: 18). H(28) listed by Blockeel & Long (1998: 31).
[H(29) listed by Macvicar (1905: 18)].
H(29) 1937: Glenade, no collector named (BBS exc.) (Armitage 1938: 13).
1937: rocks, Glenade, JB Duncan & EM Lobley, comm. EM Lobley, det. (with notes) by FE Milsom & WE Nicholson (anon. 1938c: 36).
†H29 listed by Blockeel & Long (1998: 31).
H30 1957: among boulders, SW side of Tiltinbane, AC Crundwell (Castell 1958: 467).
H33 1959: boulder scree, 1800 ft [alt.], Cuilcagh, JW Fitzgerald (DBN) (Long 1999b: 26).
H34 1962: among scree at 900 ft alt., Gap of Mamore 6 miles N of Buncrana, RD Fitzgerald (Paton 1963: 489).
H35 1950: Lough Salt, JW Fitzgerald (Castell 1951: 494).
H36 1958: damp turfy bank at 1350 ft [alt.], Mullagh Carn nr Gortin, JW Fitzgerald (Castell 1959: 629).
H39 1963: on basaltic rocks nr sea, Fair Head Undercliff, AR Perry & JW Fitzgerald (Paton 1964: 718).
H40 1957: among boulders at 1900 ft [alt.], N side of Dart Mt., Sperrin Mts, JW Fitzgerald (Castell 1959: 629).

9/3 ***Bazzania pearsonii*** Steph.

H1 1951: wet mossy slope, Coomasaharn nr Glenbeigh, leg. & det. EF Warburg (Castell 1952: 94).
H(2) listed by Macvicar (1905: 18).
†H2 listed by Blockeel & Long (1998: 31).
H16 1957: with *Herberta hutchinsiae* at 1800 ft [alt.], N side of Muckanaght, AC Crundwell (BBS exc.) (Castell 1958: 468).
H(27) 1911: Slievemore, Mayo, JB Duncan; also [collected] by DA Jones (anon. 1912b: 59).
†H27 listed by Blockeel & Long (1998: 31).
H35 1955: rocky ground on shady mountainside, Muckish Mt., UK Duncan (Castell 1956: 149).

10/1 ***Calypogeia fissa*** (L.) Raddi (syn. *Kantia trichomanis* auct. pro parte)

H1 1951: above L. Coomeeneragh, RE Parker, comm. JW Fitzgerald (Castell 1952: 94).
[H2 record (1951: peat and rotten wood, Derrycunihy, JW Fitzgerald: Castell 1952: 94) should be deleted because the locality is in H1 (see Kelly 1984b)].
H(3) 1933: Schull, DB Bradshaw (*Report BBS* **3**, 145) (Castell 1953: 301).
†H3 listed by Blockeel & Long (1998: 31).
H4 1966: on sandy bank in wood by Rathmore House nr Summercave [*sic* =

Summercove?], MFV Corley & JS Parker (Paton 1967c: 397).
†H5 listed by Blockeel & Long (1998: 31).
H6 1966: woodland bank above R. Nier nr Shanballyanne, JA Paton (BBS exc.) (Paton 1967c: 397).
H(7) 1902: Galtymore Mt., D McArdle (DBN), comm. ALK King (Paton 1964: 718).
†H7 listed by Blockeel & Long (1998: 31).
H8 1966: Knockeefin, Nicker, J Appleyard *et al.* (BBS exc.) (Paton 1967c: 397).
H9 1959: amongst *Sphagnum*, wet blanket bog, Knockaunsmountain, W of Slieve Elva, MCF Proctor (Paton 1964: 718).
H10 1951: earth bank on hillside, alt. 600 ft, above Silvermines, AD Banwell, EV Watson [erroneously printed as EFW; corrected by Castell 1953: 304] & PJ Wanstall (Castell 1952: 94).
H11 1955: shaded bank, Woodstock Woods, Inistioge, ALK King (Castell 1956: 149).
H12 1954: side of ditch, road to Curragh Wood, Inch, JS Thomson (Castell 1955: 581).
H13 1979: bog at Crannagh, foot of Mt Leinster, JW Fitzgerald (Paton 1970: 188).
H14 1955: side of ditch, Abbeyleix demesne, JS Thomson (Castell 1956: 149).
H15 1957: on bank in wood, Chevy Chase, nr Gort, AC Crundwell (BBS exc.) (Castell 1958: 467).
H16 1957: woodland ride, Ballynahinch, AC Crundwell (BBS exc.) (Castell 1958: 467).
H17 1965: on peat and on debris on blanket bog beside T.40 road between Cregg R. and R. Clare, AJE Smith (Paton 1966: 182).
H18 1957: among mosses, Annagharvey Bog, nr Tullamore, JS Thomson (Castell 1958: 467).
H19 1950: amongst *Sphagnum*, Ballymount Bog, nr Calverstown, JS Thomson (Castell 1951: 494).
H20 1955: on heavily shaded bank, Glen o' the Downs, ALK King (Paton 1963: 488).
H(21) 1892: bank nr Baily Lighthouse, Howth, D McArdle (DBN), comm. ALK King (Paton 1964: 718).
†H21 listed by Blockeel & Long (1998: 31).
H22 1952: growing in *Sphagnum*, Clonycavan Bog nr Ballivor, ALK King (Paton 1963: 488).
H23 1961: bog N of Castlepollard, EM Lobley (Paton 1963: 488).
H24 1955: cut away surface, Edera Bog nr Ballymahon, [TA] Barry, comm. ALK King (Paton 1963: 488).
H25 1952: Carrigynachten Bog nr Athlone, ALK King (Paton 1963: 488).
†H26 listed by Blockeel & Long (1998: 31).
†H27 listed by Blockeel & Long (1998: 31).
H28 1963: peaty banks, top of Lugnagall, JW Fitzgerald & AR Perry (Paton 1964: 718).
H(29) 1928: wooded glen, NE end of Glencar Lough (BBS exc.) (Duncan 1928: 118).
†H29 listed by Blockeel & Long (1998: 31).
H30 1969: stream bank, NE slope of Slievenakilla, Cuilcagh Mts, JA Paton (Paton 1970: 188).
H31 1955: side of bog-hole, Coole Bog, SW of Ardee, ALK King (Castell 1956: 149).
H32 1961: Killyneill nr Monaghan, JW Fitzgerald (Paton 1963: 488).
H33 1959: bare earth bank, Correll Glen, JW Fitzgerald (Castell 1960: 767).
H34 1962: Croaghconnellagh, Tawnawully Mts, J Appleyard (BBS exc.) (Paton 1963: 488).
H35 1962: peat bank, moorland N of Muckish Mountain, *ca* 600 ft alt., RE Longton (BBS exc.) (Paton 1963: 488-489).
H36 1952: submerged in pool, *Sphagnum* bog, Lough Bradan, JW Fitzgerald (Castell 1953: 301).
†H37 listed by Blockeel & Long (1998: 31).
H38 1950: sandstone, Scrabo quarry, JW Fitzgerald, conf. W Welch (Castell 1951: 494).
H39 1950: Crow Glen, JW Fitzgerald (Castell 1951: 494).
H40 1961: on moss-covered bank in wood, Banagher Glen nr Dungiven, JW Fitzgerald (Paton 1963: 489).

No attempt has been made to incorporate old records of *Kantia trichomanis* and *K. sprengelii* from Macvicar (1905: 18) because the genus was poorly understood in Ireland and Britain at that time and the records will probably include *Calypogeia fissa* and *C. muelleriana*. The voucher specimens involved need to be re-identified.

10/2 ***Calypogeia muelleriana*** (Schiffn.) Müll. Frib.
(syn. *Calypogeia muellerana* auct.)

†H1 listed by Blockeel & Long (1998: 31).
†H2 listed by Blockeel & Long (1998: 31).
H3 1968: peaty bank on coast SW of Dog's Point, Kenmare R., JA Paton (Paton 1969a: 868).
H4 1966: on peat cutting, Seefin, Boggeragh Mts, MFV Corley & JS Parker (Paton 1967c: 396).
H5 1966: woodland floor, Jeffry's Wood nr Kilworth, JG Duckett *et al.* (BBS exc.) (Paton 1967c: 396).
†H6 listed by Blockeel & Long (1998: 31).
H(7) 1902: Galtymore Mt., D McArdle (DBN), comm. ALK King (Paton 1964: 718).
†H7 listed by Blockeel & Long (1998: 31).
H8 1966: peaty bank on moor, Slievereagh nr Ballylanders, MFV Corley & JS Parker (Paton 1967c: 396).
H9 1968: peaty bank nr Shandangan L., NE of Corofin, JA Paton (Paton 1969a: 868).
H10 1967: soil and peaty banks in wooded valley, Clare Glen, nr Newport, HH Birks, HJB Birks & DA Ratcliffe (Paton 1968: 621).
H11 1966: bog, Derryfadda W of Johnstown, J Appleyard *et al.* (BBS exc.) (Paton 1967c: 396).
H12 1975: peaty stream bank, Croghan Mt., JA Paton (BBS exc.) (Paton 1976: 18). 33-40.
H13 1969: among block scree below Caher Roe's Den, Blackstairs Mt., JW Fitzgerald (Paton 1971a: 370).
H14 1955: on shaded root in Abbeyleix Demesne, JS Thomson, comm. ALK King (Paton 1967c: 396).
H16 1961: bog nr Toombeola nr Roundstone, EM Lobley (Paton 1963: 488).
H(17) 1896: Clonbrock, D McArdle (DBN), comm. ALK King (Paton 1964: 718).
H18 1965: in bog at Letter crossroads, Slieve Blooms, ALK King (Paton 1966: 182).
H(19) listed by Blockeel & Long (1998: 31).
†H20 listed by Blockeel & Long (1998: 31).
H(21) 1894: Ballykill, Howth, D McArdle (DBN), comm. ALK King (Paton 1964: 718).
†H21 listed by Blockeel & Long (1998: 31).
†H22 listed by Blockeel & Long (1998: 31).
†H23 listed by Blockeel & Long (1998: 31).
H24 1965: side of ditch at edge of raised bog, S of Roosky, JW Fitzgerald & EM Lobley (Paton 1966: 182).
†H25 listed by Blockeel & Long (1998: 31).
H26 1957: on W slope of [The] Ox Mts, ALK King (Paton 1966: 182).
1965: on peat S of Glendaduff, [The] Ox Mts, JW Fitzgerald (Paton 1966: 182).
†H27 listed by Blockeel & Long (1998: 31).
H28 1963: hole in wet peat at 1200 ft alt., Lugnagall, Glencar, AR Perry & JW Fitzgerald (Paton 1964: 718).
H(29) 1904: Glencar, D McArdle (DBN), comm. ALK King (Paton 1964: 718).
†H29 listed by Blockeel & Long (1998: 31).
H30 1965: on peat at 1800 ft alt., S side of Cuilcagh, JW Fitzgerald & EM Lobley (Paton 1966: 182).
H31 1963: Carlingford Mt., DM Synnott (Paton 1964: 718).
H(32) listed by Blockeel & Long (1998: 31).
†H33 listed by Blockeel & Long (1998: 31).
H34 1962: peaty overhung bank by Barnes Lough, EF Warburg (BBS exc.) (Paton 1963: 488).
1962: hollow under rocks, Croaghconnellagh, EF Warburg (BBS exc.) (Paton 1963: 488).
H35 1962: peaty bank, 550 ft alt., N side of Muckish Mountain, AC Crundwell (BBS exc.) (Paton 1963: 488).
†H36 listed by Blockeel & Long (1998: 31).
H37 1970: peaty bank by road, Armaghbrague nr Newtownhamilton, MFV Corley (Paton 1971a: 370).
H38 1962: on cut-out bog Capel Bridge, Florida, JW Fitzgerald (Paton 1963: 488).
†H39 listed by Blockeel & Long (1998: 31).
H40 1950: Ballyronan, JW Fitzgerald (Paton 1963: 488).

10/3 ***Calypogeia azurea*** Stotler & Crotz
(syn. *Calypogeia trichomanis* auct. pro parte, non (L.) Corda)

H2 1973: bog on summit of ridge N of Horse's Glen, Mangerton, EC Mhic Daeid (Paton 1974b: 162).
H3 1979: humus-rich, wet dripping rocks in Glengarriff Wood, HMH van Melick (Corley 1981: 18).

H6 1968: shaded marsh nr Castle Dodard, Knockmealdown Mts, N of Lishmore, JA Paton (Paton 1969a: 868).

H7 1966: bog W of Longfordpass Bridge, Urlingford, J Appleyard (BBS exc.) (Paton 1967c: 397).

[H(12) 1913: Great Saltee I., HW Lett (*Irish Nat.* **22**, 194, 1913), comm. JW Fitzgerald (Castell 1952: 94). Not accepted for H12 in *CC* by Paton (1965b: 29)].

H16 1970: nr summit of Muckanaght, The Twelve Pins, JA Paton (Paton 1971a: 370).

H20 1975: flushed slope above L. Ouler, Tonelagee, DM Synnott (BBS exc.) (Paton 1976: 18).

[H24 1955: with *Sphagnum plumulosum* on cut-away surface, Edera Bog, nr Ballymahon, TA Barry, comm. ALK King (Castell 1956: 149). Not accepted for H24 in *CC* by Paton (1965b: 29)].

[H25 1952: Carrigynachten Bog, nr Athlone, ALK King, conf. (but 'poor') EC Wallace (Castell 1953: 301). Not accepted for H25 in *CC* by Paton (1965b: 29)].

H27 1970: nr summit of Mweelrea, N of Killary Harbour, JA Paton 1971a: 370).

[H(32) 1947: growing with *Dicranella cerviculata*, bank of bog-hole, Black I., Lake Muckno, Castleblaney, JS Thomson (Castell 1955: 581). H32 not accepted for *CC* by Paton (1965b: 29)].

[H(33) 1913: bog behind Lisgoole, WN Tetley (BBSUK) (Castell 1954: 475). Following entry implies this record was subsequently regarded as unacceptable for *CC*].

H33 1960: on moist sandstone rocks, scarp N of Lough Navar, JW Fitzgerald (Paton 1961: 155).

H34 1967: marshy ground, Gap of Mamore, N of Buncrana, JW Fitzgerald (Paton 1968: 621).

H35 1962: vertical peat under *Calluna*, *ca* 1300 ft alt., NE slope of Slieve Snaght nr Dunlewy, RE Longton (BBS exc.) (Paton 1963: 488).

[H36 1951: peat, Lough Bradan nr Castlederg, JW Fitzgerald (Castell 1952: 94). This record apparently not accepted for *CC* by Paton (1965b: 29)].

H36 1958: plentiful, side of peat drain at 1200 ft [alt.], Mullaghcarbatagh, Sperrin Mts, JW Fitzgerald (Castell 1959: 629).

H40 1958: creeping over bryophytes in wet drip among rocks at 1750 ft [alt.], Dart Mt., Sperrin Mts, JW Fitzgerald (Castell 1959: 629).

10/4 ***Calypogeia neesiana*** (C.Massal. & Carestia) Müll.Frib.

[H2 record (1968: rotting log in Derrycunihy Wood, Killarney, JA Paton: Paton 1969a: 868) should be deleted because the locality is in H1 (see Kelly 1984b)].

H7 1966: under *Calluna*, heathy slope nr Bay L., Knockmealdown Mts, GCG Argent & JA Paton (BBS exc.) (Paton 1967c: 396).

H10 1979: peaty bank, S slope of Keeper Hill, JA Paton (Corley 1980a: 27).

H13 1969: peat among rocks *ca* 2100 ft alt. above Caher Roe's Den, Blackstairs Mt., JW Fitzgerald (Paton 1970: 188).

H15 1994: peaty bank on heathland above Boleyneendorish River, Slieve Aughty, M50, JA Paton 7629 (Long 1995b: 39).

H16 1970: bog W of Derrylea L., E of Clifden, JA Paton (Paton 1971a: 370).

H20 1975: peat on steep rocky slope above L. Bray Upper, Kippure, JA Paton (BBS exc.) (Paton 1976: 18).

H22 1978: dry peat bank by the road through birch-invaded cut-over bog, 1 mile due E of Castlerickard Ho.[use], Longwood, DM Synnott (Corley 1980a: 27).

H23 1979: rotten stump in woodland, peninsula at SE end of L. Derravaragh, DM Synnott (Corley 1980a: 27).

H26 1987: moorland S of lane W from Partry to Cloon River, JA Paton (Long 1988: 32).

H27 1987: peat on boulder, SW side of Lough Nakeeroge (east), NE of Croaghaun, Achill I., JA Paton (Long 1988: 32).

H28 1963: on peat overlying limestone, Carrowkeel nr Lough Arrow, JW Fitzgerald & AR Perry (Paton 1964: 718, Fitzgerald & Fitzgerald 1966a).

H29 1970: N-facing cliffs or hill slopes of Glenfarne, nr Belcoo, JA Paton (BBS exc.) (Paton 1971a: 370, Appleyard 1971: 389).

H30 1965: on peat among block scree, Englishman's House, 3 miles S of Glenfarne, JW Fitzgerald (Paton 1966:

182).

H33 1968: fallen branches and ground in birch shrubwood, Bunnahoon L. *ca* 8½ miles NE of Enniskillen, WV Rubers, P Hessel & J Klein (Paton 1970: 188).

H34 1969: bog N of Gorey, S of Culdaff, Inishowen, JA Paton (Paton 1970: 188).

H35 1969: peaty bank in valley, S slope of Muckish Mt., JA Paton (Paton 1970: 188).

H40 1968: old peat cutting in blanket bog, Lisdillon, 4 miles S of Londonderry, HH Birks & JW Fitzgerald (Paton 1969a: 868).

10/5 ***Calypogeia integristipula*** Steph.
(syn. *Calypogeia neesiana* var. *meylanii* (H.Buch) R.M.Schust.)

[H(1) or H(2) 1905: Horses Glen, Mangerton, DA Jones, SJ Owen & JB Duncan, comm. UK Duncan (Paton 1962: 361-362). H1 deleted because record (from Horses Glen, Mangerton) is in H2 (Paton 1977a: 12)].

H(2) record from Horses Glen, Mangerton transferred from H1 to H2 (Paton 1977a: 12).

[H(33) 1913: with *Lepidozia trichoclados*, Correll Glen, WN Tetley (BBSUK), det. EW Jones (Castell 1953: 301), as *C. neesiana*. Record probably referable to *C. integristipula*].

H33 1961: with *Lepidozia sylvatica* on shaded sandstone rocks, Reyfad, S of Knockmore Cliff, JW Fitzgerald (Paton 1962: 361-362).

H39 1969: shaded sandstone rocks, cliffs on W side of Murlough Bay, E of Ballycastle, JA Paton (Paton 1970: 188).

10/6 ***Calypogeia sphagnicola*** (Arnell & J. Perss.) Warnst. & Loeske

H3 1979: on *Sphagnum papillosum*, Loughs 1 mile NE of Rossnacaragh, Muntervary, DM Synnott (Corley 1980a: 27).

H6 1966: on *Sphagnum* beside stream below Coumshingaun L., Comeragh Mts, JA Paton (BBS exc.) (Paton 1967c: 397).

H7 1966: on *Leucobryum* in bog W of Longfordpass Bridge, Urlingford, JA Paton & ERB Little (BBS exc.) (Paton 1967c: 397).

H9 1979: on *Sphagnum*, bog W of Derrymore Ho.[use], N of Kilkishen, DM Synnott (Corley 1980a: 27).

[H10 1954: growing through *Sphagnum*, Littleton Bog, MJP Scannell, comm. ALK King (Paton 1962: 362). H10 deleted because locality on which record was based is in H7, comm. ALK King (Paton 1968: 621)].

H11 1966: creeping over *Sphagnum*, bog at Derryfadda W of Johnstown, JW Fitzgerald (BBS exc.) (Paton 1967c: 397).

†H14 listed by Blockeel & Long (1998: 31).

H16 1970: among *Sphagnum* in bog, Errisbeg, Roundstone, MFV Corley (Paton 1971a: 370).

H17 1968: in *Sphagnum imbricatum,* raised bog at Addergoule N[orth], R. Suck nr Ballinasloe, HJB Birks (Paton 1970: 868).

H19 1969: among *Sphagnum*, Derryvullagh Bog nr Athy, JW Fitzgerald (Paton 1970: 188).

H22 1965: on *Sphagnum* on cut-away bog S of Summerhill, ALK King (Paton 1966: 182).

H23 1965: growing through *Sphagnum imbricatum*, Lisclogher Bog, ALK King (Paton 1966: 182).

H24 1966: in *Sphagnum magellanicum*, Cloontirm Bog nr Longford, ALK King (Paton 1967c: 397).

H25 2002: creeping amongst *Sphagnum* in raised bog, *ca* 40 m alt., Carrickynaghtan Bog, S of Athlone, N03, NG Hodgetts 4052 (Blackstock 2003: 40).

H27 1968: on *Sphagnum* in bog nr Bulls Mouth, Achill I., JA Paton (Paton 1971a: 370).

H28 1970: bog, W valley of Bricklieve Mts, JA Paton (BBS exc.) (Paton 1971a: 370, Appleyard 1971: 389).

H29 1963: growing over *Sphagnum*, bog at Flughanagh 3 miles SE of Dromahair, JW Fitzgerald & AR Perry (Paton 1964: 718).

H32 1961: creeping over *Sphagnum*, Killyneill, nr Monaghan, JW Fitzgerald (Paton 1962: 362).

H33 1960: creeping over *Sphagnum*, Derrens East nr Florence Court, JW Fitzgerald (Paton 1961: 155-156).

H34 1968: in *Leucobryum glaucum*, bog at Gorey nr Culdaff, Inishowen, JW

Fitzgerald & HH Birks (Paton 1969a: 868).

H35 1969: on *Sphagnum* in bog nr Corveen, N of Derrybeg, Gweedore, JA Paton (Paton 1971a: 370).

H36 1959: creeping over *Sphagnum*, Mullanatoomog Bog, nr Drumquin, JW Fitzgerald (Castell 1960: 767).

H37 1964: bog in townland of Derryadd, E of Lough Gullion, JW Fitzgerald (Paton 1965a: 856).

10/7 ***Calypogeia suecica*** (Arnell & J.Perss.) Müll.Frib.

H1 1967: rotting tree trunk, O'Sullivan's Cascade, JW Fitzgerald (Paton 1968: 621, Fitzgerald & Fitzgerald 1968b).

H33 1959: on bare exposed peat burnt over in 1958, Aghohoorin, nr Boho, JW Fitzgerald (Paton 1962: 362, Fitzgerald 1962).

H36 1957: rotting coniferous wood with *Aneura palmata*, *Sphenolobus exsectiformis,Cephalozia catenulata, C. media, Scapania umbrosa* and *Lophozia incisa*, Sheskinawaddy, JW Fitzgerald (Castell 1958: 467, Fitzgerald 1960).

10/8 ***Calypogeia arguta*** Nees & Mont.
(syn. *Kantia arguta* (Nees & Mont.) Lindb.)

H(1) listed by Macvicar (1905: 18).

†H1 listed by Blockeel & Long (1998: 32).

H(2) listed by Macvicar (1905: 18).

†H2 listed by Blockeel & Long (1998: 32).

H3 1953: bank in Valley Desmond, nr Gougane Barra, ALK King (Castell 1954: 475).

H4 1966: on shady bank nr Rylane Cross, Boggeragh Mts, MFV Corley & JS Parker (Paton 1967c: 397).

H5 1966: on earthy bank by lane, valley of R. Douglas N of Kilworth, ERB Little (BBS exc.) (Paton 1967c: 397).

H(6) listed by Macvicar (1905: 18).

†H6 listed by Blockeel & Long (1998: 32).

H(7) listed by Macvicar (1905: 18).

†H7 listed by Blockeel & Long (1998: 32).

H8 1966: on bank at edge of wood E of Tarbert [*sic* = Tarbet], MFV Corley & JS Parker (Paton 1967c: 397).

H(9) listed by Macvicar (1905: 18).

†H9 listed by Blockeel & Long (1998: 32).

H10 1951: earth bank on hillside, alt. 600 ft, above Silvermines, AD Banwell, EV Watson & PJ Wanstall (Castell 1952: 94).

H11 1955: on ground, Woodstock Woods, Inistioge, ALK King (Castell 1956: 149).

H(12) listed by Macvicar (1905: 18).

†H12 listed by Blockeel & Long (1998: 32).

H(13) listed by Macvicar (1905: 18).

†H13 listed by Blockeel & Long (1998: 32).

H(14) listed by Macvicar (1905: 18).

†H14 listed by Blockeel & Long (1998: 32).

H15 1957: mixed with *C. fissa*, on bank in wood, Chevy Chase, nr Gort, AC Crundwell (BBS exc.) (Castell 1958: 467).

H(16) listed by Macvicar (1905: 18).

†H16 listed by Blockeel & Long (1998: 32).

H(18) listed by Macvicar (1905: 18). H(18) listed by Blockeel & Long (1998: 32).

H19 1958: shaded bank under trees, Elverstown, ALK King (Castell 1959: 629).

H(20) listed by Macvicar (1905: 18).

†H20 listed by Blockeel & Long (1998: 32).

H(21) listed by Macvicar (1905: 18).

†H21 listed by Blockeel & Long (1998: 32).

H23 1957: shaded bank in lane, Culleenmore, nr Mullingar, ALK King (Castell 1958: 467).

H24 1965: banks of ditches, Cornhill nr Drumlish, JW Fitzgerald & EM Lobley (Paton 1966: 182).

H(25) 1897: Mote Park, Prof. Johnson (DBN), comm. JW Fitzgerald (Castell 1959: 629).

†H25 listed by Blockeel & Long (1998: 32).

H26 1965: peaty side of drain W of L. Talt, [The] Ox Mts, JW Fitzgerald (Paton 1966: 182).

H(27) listed by Macvicar (1905: 18).

†H27 listed by Blockeel & Long (1998: 32).

H(28) listed by Macvicar (1905: 18).

H28 1965: bank of track in Slish Wood, Lough Gill, JW Fitzgerald & EM Lobley (Paton 1966: 182).

H(29) 1928: wooded glen, NE end of Glencar Lough (BBS exc.) (Duncan 1928: 118).

†H29 listed by Blockeel & Long (1998: 32).

H30 1955: damp ground by Lough Ramor, State Forest, Virginia, ALK King (Castell 1956: 149).

H(31) 1883: with *Solenostoma*, by stream, Anglesey Mt., CH Waddell (DBN),

comm. ALK King (Paton 1964: 718).
H31 1967: side of ditch in woodland, Blackhall, Termonfeckin, DM Synnott (DBN) (Long 1999b: 26).
H32 1961: on earthy bank in wood, Castleshane, nr Monaghan, JW Fitzgerald (Paton 1962: 362).
H(33) 1905: damp clay banks among rocks, Poulaphuca, D McArdle (*Irish Nat.* **16**, 237, 1907), comm. JW Fitzgerald (Castell 1952: 94).
†H33 listed by Blockeel & Long (1998: 32).
H34 1962: rock crevice, E side of Bulbin [Mt.], EF Warburg (BBS exc.) (Paton 1963: 489).
H(35) listed by Macvicar (1905: 18).
†H35 listed by Blockeel & Long (1998: 32).
H36 1951: sandy bank of stream in beech wood, alt. 340 ft, Drum Manor, Stewartstown, JW Fitzgerald (Castell 1952: 94).
H37 1952: on peaty ground beside ditch, alt. 70 ft, Lough Gullion, JW Fitzgerald, MPH Kertland & EM Lobley (Castell 1955: 581).
H(38) listed by Macvicar (1905: 18).
†H38 listed by Blockeel & Long (1998: 32).
H(39) 1928: stream at Derriaghy (BBS exc.) (Duncan 1928: 116).
†H39 listed by Blockeel & Long (1998: 32).
H40 1964: on earth bank, Legananam Pot, nr Dungiven, JW Fitzgerald (Paton 1965a: 856).

11/1 ***Adelanthus decipiens*** (Hook.) Mitt.

H(1) listed by Macvicar (1905: 17).
†H1 listed by Blockeel & Long (1998: 32).
H(2) listed by Macvicar (1905: 17).
†H2 listed by Blockeel & Long (1998: 32).
H(3) listed by Macvicar (1905: 17).
†H3 listed by Blockeel & Long (1998: 32).
H6 1961: on rock in cascading stream below Coumshingaun, Comeragh Mts, DA Ratcliffe (Paton 1962: 361).
H(7) listed by Blockeel & Long (1998: 32).
H16 1961: on quartzite outcrop at 1700 ft on N slope of Bengower, Twelve Bens, Connemara, DA Ratcliffe (Paton 1962: 361).
H25 2002: shaded rock crevices in NE-facing crags, *ca* 150 m alt., Kilronan Mountain, Arigna, G91, NG Hodgetts 4156 (Blackstock 2003: 40).
H(27) listed by Macvicar (1905: 17).
†H27 listed by Blockeel & Long (1998: 32).
H(28) listed by Macvicar (1905: 17).
†H28 listed by Blockeel & Long (1998: 32).
H(29) listed by Macvicar (1905: 17).
†H29 listed by Blockeel & Long (1998: 32).
[H(30) listed by Macvicar (1905: 17)].
H33 1960: on mossy boulders in oak wood, Garvary Wood nr Belleek, JW Fitzgerald (Paton 1961: 155).
H34 1968: rock crevices, Kindrohid nr Clonmany, Inishowen, JW Fitzgerald (Paton 1969a: 874).
H(35) listed by Macvicar (1905: 17).
†H35 listed by Blockeel & Long (1998: 32).
H(39) listed by Macvicar (1905: 17). H(39) listed by Blockeel & Long (1998: 32).
H40 1959: vertical face of mossy boulder nr river, Banagher Glen, nr Dungiven, JW Fitzgerald (Castell 1960: 766).

11/2 ***Adelanthus lindenbergianus*** (Lehm.) Mitt.
(syn. *Adelanthus dugortiensis* Douin & Lett, *A. unciformis* (Hook.f. & Tayl.) Mitt.)

H16 1961: with bryophytes under *Calluna* on N slopes at 1700-2200 ft [alt.], locally abundant on Bengower and Benbreen, Twelve Bens, Connemara, DA Ratcliffe (Paton 1962: 361).
H(27) listed by Macvicar (1905: 17).
†H27 listed by Blockeel & Long (1998: 32).
H35 1962: among *Calluna* between boulders just N of summit of Muckish Mt., *ca* 2100 ft alt., EF Warburg, J Appleyard, AC Crundwell & RE Longton (BBS exc.) (Paton 1963: 488).

12/1 ***Cephalozia bicuspidata*** (L.) Dumort.
(syn. *Cephalozia bicuspidata* subsp. *lammersiana* (Huebener) R.M.Schust., *C.bicuspidata* var. *lammersiana* (Huebener) Breidl.)

H(1) listed by Macvicar (1905: 16).
†H1 listed by Blockeel & Long (1998: 32).
H(2) listed by Macvicar (1905: 16).
†H2 listed by Blockeel & Long (1998: 32).
H(3) listed by Macvicar (1905: 16).
†H3 listed by Blockeel & Long (1998: 32).
H4 1966: earthy bank in wood by R. Bandon, S of Innishannon, MFV Corley & JS Parker (Paton 1967c: 401).
†H5 listed by Blockeel & Long (1998: 32).

H(6) listed by Macvicar (1905: 16).
†H6 listed by Blockeel & Long (1998: 32).
H(7) listed by Macvicar (1905: 16).
†H7 listed by Blockeel & Long (1998: 32).
H8 1966: on peaty ground in plantation, Paradise Hill, Galtee Mts, MFV Corley & JS Parker (Paton 1967c: 401), as var. *lammersiana*.
H(9) listed by Macvicar (1905: 16).
†H9 listed by Blockeel & Long (1998: 32).
H10 1979: rather wet heath on Keeper Hill, HMH van Melick (Corley 1981: 20), as var. *lammersiana*.
H11 1966: bare peat in bog, Derryfadda, W of Johnstown, JG Duckett *et al.* (BBS exc.) (Paton 1967c: 401).
1966: bog at Derryfadda, W of Johnstown, JW Fitzgerald *et al.* (BBS exc.) (Paton 1967c: 401), as var. *lammersiana*.
H(12) listed by Macvicar (1905: 16).
†H12 listed by Blockeel & Long (1998: 32).
H(13) listed by Macvicar (1905: 16).
†H13 listed by Blockeel & Long (1998: 32).
H(14) listed by Macvicar (1905: 16).
†H14 listed by Blockeel & Long (1998: 32).
H(15) listed by Macvicar (1905: 16).
†H15 listed by Blockeel & Long (1998: 32).
H(16) listed by Macvicar (1905: 16).
†H16 listed by Blockeel & Long (1998: 32).
H(17) listed by Macvicar (1905: 16). H(17) listed by Blockeel & Long (1998: 32).
H(18) listed by Macvicar (1905: 16). H(18) listed by Blockeel & Long (1998: 32).
H(19) listed by Macvicar (1905: 16).
[H19 var. *bicuspidata* deleted because no record traced, comm. MM Yeo, replaced by following record (Long 1990a: 27)].
H(19) 1949: in bog hole on Ballymount Bog nr Calverstown, JS Thomson, comm. ALK King (Paton 1966: 186), as var. *lammersiana*.
H19 1957: growing in *Campylopus*, Cupidstown Hill, ALK King (DBN), comm. DM Synnott (Long 1990a: 27), as var. *bicuspidata*.
H(20) listed by Macvicar (1905: 16).
†H20 listed by Blockeel & Long (1998: 32).
H(21) listed by Macvicar (1905: 16).
†H21 listed by Blockeel & Long (1998: 32).
[H(22) listed by Macvicar (1905: 16). H22 deleted because probable voucher (1956: Rossan Bog, ALK King, DBN) is *C. connivens* (Long 1990a: 27)].
H(23) listed by Macvicar (1905: 16).
†H23 listed by Blockeel & Long (1998: 32).
H24 1965: damp hillside, Corn Hill nr Drumlish, EM Lobley & JW Fitzgerald (Paton 1966: 186).
H25 1952: Carrigynachten Bog, nr Athlone, right bank of R. Shannon, ALK King (Castell 1953: 301).
H(26) listed by Macvicar (1905: 16).
H26 1970: bank by track, Glendaduff, NE of Foxford, MFV Corley (Paton 1971a: 372), as var. *lammersiana*.
H(27) listed by Macvicar (1905: 16).
†H27 listed by Blockeel & Long (1998: 32).
H(28) listed by Macvicar (1905: 16).
†H28 listed by Blockeel & Long (1998: 32).
H(29) listed by Macvicar (1905: 16).
†H29 listed by Blockeel & Long (1998: 32).
H(30) listed by Macvicar (1905: 16).
†H30 listed by Blockeel & Long (1998: 32).
H(31) listed by Macvicar (1905: 16).
†H31 listed by Blockeel & Long (1998: 32).
H32 1961: creeping over *Sphagnum*, Killyneill, nr Monaghan, JW Fitzgerald (Paton 1962: 360).
H33 1969: cutover bog W of Carricknagower L., SE of Belleek, JA Paton (Paton 1970: 192), as var. *lammersiana*.
H(34) listed by Macvicar (1905: 16).
†H34 listed by Blockeel & Long (1998: 32).
H(35) listed by Macvicar (1905: 16).
†H35 listed by Blockeel & Long (1998: 32).
H36 1951: with *C. connivens*, among moss in peat bog, Lough Bradan, nr Castlederg, JW Fitzgerald (Castell 1952: 93).
H(37) listed by Macvicar (1905: 16).
†H37 listed by Blockeel & Long (1998: 32).
†H38 listed by Blockeel & Long (1998: 32).
[H39 var. *lammersiana:* deleted because no localised record or voucher traced, comm. MM Yeo, (Long 1990a: 27)].
H(39) listed by Macvicar (1905: 16).
†H39 listed by Blockeel & Long (1998: 32).
H40 1964: rocks by stream nr top of Glenshane Pass, JW Fitzgerald (Paton 1965a: 855).

12/3 ***Cephalozia catenulata*** (Huebener) Lindb.

H(1) listed by Macvicar (1905: 16).
†H1 listed by Blockeel & Long (1998: 32).
H(2) listed by Macvicar (1905: 16).
†H2 listed by Blockeel & Long (1998: 32).
H(3) listed by Macvicar (1905: 16).
†H3 listed by Blockeel & Long (1998: 32).

H(7) listed by Macvicar (1905: 16).
†H7 listed by Blockeel & Long (1998: 32).
H(9) listed by Macvicar (1905: 16). H(9) listed by Blockeel & Long (1998: 32).
H(13) listed by Macvicar (1905: 16).
†H13 listed by Blockeel & Long (1998: 32).
H(16) listed by Macvicar (1905: 16).
†H16 listed by Blockeel & Long (1998: 32).
H(17) listed by Macvicar (1905: 16). H(17) listed by Blockeel & Long (1998: 32).
H(18) listed by Macvicar (1905: 16). H(18) listed by Blockeel & Long (1998: 32).
H(20) listed by Macvicar (1905: 16).
†H20 listed by Blockeel & Long (1998: 32).
H(21) listed by Macvicar (1905: 16). H(21) listed by Blockeel & Long (1998: 32).
H25 2002: amongst *Sphagnum* in raised bog, with *Kurzia pauciflora* and *Riccardia palmata*, *ca* 80 m alt., Cloonchambers Bog, M68, NG Hodgetts 4120 (Blackstock 2003: 40).
H(27) listed by Macvicar (1905: 16).
†H27 listed by Blockeel & Long (1998: 32).
H28 1963: peaty ground at 1200 ft alt., Lugnagall, Glencar, AR Perry & JW Fitzgerald (Paton 1964: 716).
[H(29) listed by Macvicar (1905: 16). H29 deleted because previous record based on material gathered in H28, comm. AR Perry (Paton 1965a: 855)].
H29 1963: peat on top of hill above Glencar waterfall, AR Perry & JW Fitzgerald (Paton 1965a: 855).
H(30) listed by Macvicar (1905: 16).
†H30 listed by Blockeel & Long (1998: 32).
H31 1967: rotten stump in woodland, Monasterboice, DM Synnott (Paton 1968: 625).
H33 1959: dry exposed peat among rocks, Aghahoorin, nr Boho, JW Fitzgerald (Castell 1960: 766).
H34 1967: peat among scree, Gap of Mamore, N of Buncrana, JW Fitzgerald (Paton 1968: 625).
H(35) listed by Macvicar (1905: 16).
†H35 listed by Blockeel & Long (1998: 32).
H36 1952: peaty crevices in sandstone rocks, Lough Bradan, JW Fitzgerald (Castell 1953: 301).
H(38) listed by Macvicar (1905: 16). H(38) listed by Blockeel & Long (1998: 32).
[H(39) listed by Macvicar (1905: 16)].
H39 1952: on peat, Loughan Bay, nr Cushendun, JW Fitzgerald (Paton 1962: 361).

12/4a *Cephalozia macrostachya* Kaal. **var. *macrostachya***

H1 1968: on *Sphagnum*, bog near River Inny, W of Waterville, V55, JA Paton 7484 (BBSUK, E) (Long 1993b: 46, redet. Paton *et al.* 1996: 338).
[H7 deleted because the voucher (see below for details) belongs to var. *spiniflora* (Paton *et al.* 1996: 339, Long 1997: 40)].
[H20 deleted because the voucher belongs to var. *spiniflora* (Paton 1976: 20, Paton *et al.* 1996: 339, Long 1997: 40)].
H25 1967: with *Lepidozia setacea* in *Sphagnun subsecundum* var. *auriculatum*, in Derreenargan Bog, ALK King (BBSUK), det. & comm. TH Blackstock (Long 1996: 43, Paton *et al.* 1996: 338).
[H34 deleted because the voucher belongs to var. *spiniflora* (Paton *et al.* 1996: 339, Long 1997: 40)].
H35 1969: *Sphag*num in bog, nr Corveen, N of Derrybeg, Gweedore, 05/09, JA Paton 5348(a) (E) (Paton 1970: 192, Paton *et al.* 1996: 338).
H37 1964: on *Leucobryum* in bog, at Derrylee, E of Verners Bridge, 15/0010, JW Fitzgerald & MPH Kertland (BBSUK), det. & comm. TH Blackstock (Paton *et al.* 1996: 338).

12/4b *Cephalozia macrostachya* var. *spiniflora* (Schiffn.) Müll.Frib.

H7 1966: peat in bog, S of Longfordpass Bridge, Urlingford, S26, JA Paton 7485 (BBSUK, E) (Long 1993b: 46 as var. *macrostachya*; redet. Paton *et al.* 1996: 339, Long 1997: 40).
H20 1975: cut-over bog, Rathduffmore, 1½ miles N of Knockananna, 31/0182, JA Paton (BBS exc.) s.n. & 5346 (BBSUK, E) (Paton 1976: 20, Paton *et al.* 1996: 339, Long 1997: 40).
H34 1968: bog, N of Gorey, near Culdaff, Inishowen, 06/70, JW Fitzgerald & HH Birks (BBSUK) (Fitzgerald 1969, Paton 1969a: 873, Paton *et al.* 1996: 339, Long 1997: 40).
1969: bog, N of Gorey, near Culdaff, Inishowen, 06/70, JA Paton 5347 (E) (Paton *et al.* 1996: 339, Long 1997: 40).
H35 1969: *Sphagnum* in bog near Corveen, N of Derrybeg, Gweedore, 05/09, JA Paton

s.n. & 5348(b) (BBSUK, E) (Paton 1970: 192, Paton *et al.* 1996: 339, Long 1997: 40).

12/5 ***Cephalozia leucantha*** Spruce

H1 1951: decaying wood and peat, Finglas River, Waterville, JW Fitzgerald, det. EW Jones (Castell 1952: 93).
[H(2) listed by Macvicar (1905: 16). H2 deleted because locality on which record was probably based (Mt Eagle) is in H1, comm. DM Synnott (Paton 1977a: 14)].
H3 1968: on rotten wood, base of NE slope of Lackawee, Slieve Miskish Mts, JA Paton (Paton 1969a: 873).
H9 1959: amongst *Sphagnum* in wet blanket bog, Knockaunsmountain W of Slieve Elva, MCF Proctor (Paton 1964: 716).
H(12) 1913: Great Saltee I., HW Lett (*Irish Nat.* **22**, 194, 1913), comm. JW Fitzgerald (Castell 1952: 93).
[H(16) listed by Macvicar (1905: 16). H16 deleted because no localised record traced (Paton 1967b, 1968: 625)].
H16 1968: rotting stump by shore of L. Corrib, 1 mile NE of Maumwee L., AR Perry (Paton 1969a: 873).
H20 1975: boggy slope nr Ballycayle, Glencree R., JA Paton (BBS exc.) (Paton1976: 20).
H25 1965: on peat, bog at 700 ft alt., Kilronan Mt. nr Ballyfarnan, JW Fitzgerald & EM Lobley (Paton 1966: 186).
H26 1987: moorland S of lane W from Partry to Cloon River, JA Paton (Long 1988: 32).
H(27) listed by Macvicar (1905: 16).
†H27 listed by Blockeel & Long (1998: 32).
H28 1970: on a boggy slope, Cormac Keagh's Hole, N side of Benbulbin [*sic* = Ben Bulben], JA Paton (BBS exc.) (Paton 1971a: 372, Appleyard 1971: 390).
H(29) 1918: edge of bog hole, Dartry Hills, WN Tetley (BBSUK) (Castell 1954: 474).
†H29 listed by Blockeel & Long (1998: 32).
H30 1970: among boulder scree, below Englishman's House, Glenfarne, nr Belcoo, JA Paton (BBS exc.) (Paton 1971a: 372, Appleyard 1971: 389-390).
H33 1969: cutover bog W of Carricknagower L., SE of Belleek, JA Paton (Paton 1970:191).
H34 1962: peaty overhung bank by Barnes Lough, EF Warburg (BBS exc.) (Paton 1963: 487).
H(35) 1902: Gartan Woods, D McArdle (DBN) (Paton 1965a: 855).
†H35 listed by Blockeel & Long (1998: 32).
H36 1957: bare peat in exposed position, Craigballyharky, nr Cookstown, JW Fitzgerald (Castell 1959: 628).
H40 1969: rotting log in gorge, Eagle Hill, W of Downhill, JA Paton (Paton 1970: 192).

12/6 ***Cephalozia lunulifolia*** (Dumort.) Dumort.
(syn. *Cephalozia lunulaefolia* auct., *C. media* Lindb., *C. pallida* Pearson)

H(1) listed by Macvicar (1905: 16).
H1 1935: on the ground by side of path among Rhododendrons near Old Weir Bridge, Killarney, DA Jones, det. Prof. Schiffner (Jones 1936a, 1936b, anon. 1937b: 369; reported as *C. affinis* Lindb., but the material was probably dioicous and therefore unlikely to represent that problematical autoicous taxon, cf. Paton 1999: 111).
H(2) listed by Macvicar (1905: 16).
†H2 listed by Blockeel & Long (1998: 33).
H3 1967: rotting wood, Glenarriff Woods, JW Fitzgerald (Paton 1968: 625).
H4 2002: on humus in oak woodland, 10 m alt., E bank of River Brandon, *ca* 3 km SE of Inishannon, W55, TL Blockeel 31/374 (Blackstock 2003: 40).
H5 1956: hillside wood, nr Park House, Tourig House, Youghal, EC Wallace (Castell 1957: 325).
H(6) listed by Macvicar (1905: 16).
†H6 listed by Blockeel & Long (1998: 33).
H(7) listed by Macvicar (1905: 16).
†H7 listed by Blockeel & Long (1998: 33).
H8 1979: rotting stump in wood S of Clare R., Clare Glens, S of Newport, JA Paton (Corley 1980a: 30).
H9 1979: on *Sphagnum*, bog W of Derrymore House, N of Kilkishen, JA Paton & AC Crundwell (Corley 1980a: 30).
H10 1979: rotten log in wood above Clare R., Clare Glens, S of Newport, JA Paton (Corley 1980a: 30).
H11 1966: rotting stumps in wood, Castle

Dysart nr Thomastown, JW Fitzgerald *et al.* (BBS exc.) (Paton 1967c: 401).

H13 1969: among block scree below Caher Roe's Den, Blackstairs Mt., JW Fitzgerald (Paton 1971a: 372).

H15 1962: amongst *Sphagnum*, raised bog nr Woodford, AJE Smith (Paton 1963: 487).

H(16) listed by Macvicar (1905: 16).

†H16 listed by Blockeel & Long (1998: 33).

H(18) listed by Macvicar (1905: 16). H(18) listed by Blockeel & Long (1998: 33).

H(20) listed by Macvicar (1905: 16) as *C. pallida*.

H(20) 1912-1914: decayed wood, frequent, Glen of the Downs, Allen, Gunn & D McArdle (in D McArdle, *Irish Nat.* **26**, 73, 1917), comm. JW Fitzgerald (Castell 1952: 93).

†H20 listed by Blockeel & Long (1998: 33).

H(21) listed by Macvicar (1905: 16). H(21) listed by Blockeel & Long (1998: 33).

H21 2001: on rhododendron log in shelter of N-facing crag, *ca* 90 m alt., Muck Rock, Howth Peninsula, O23, TL Blockeel 30/252 (Blackstock: 2002: 39).

H26 1965: on rotting *Luzula* stems, cliffs S of Glendaduff, [The] Ox Mts, JW Fitzgerald (Paton 1966: 186).

H(27) listed by Macvicar (1905: 16).

†H27 listed by Blockeel & Long (1998: 33).

H(28) 1904: Collooney, D McArdle (DBN), comm. ALK King (Paton 1964: 716).

†H28 listed by Blockeel & Long (1998: 33).

H29 1970: N-facing cliffs or hill slopes of Glenfarne, nr Belcoo, JA Paton (BBS exc.) (Paton 1971a: 372, Appleyard 1971: 389).

H30 1916: Tents Mountain, WN Tetley (Long 1990a: 27).

H33 1959: shaded peaty banks, Correll Glen, JW Fitzgerald (Castell 1960: 766).

H34 1968: on peat under *Calluna*, Kindrohid nr Clonmany, Inishowen, JW Fitzgerald (Paton 1969a: 873).

H(35) listed by Macvicar (1905: 16). H(35) listed by Blockeel & Long (1998: 33).

H36 1959: rotting tree trunks, Drumlea Wood, nr Gortin, JW Fitzgerald (Castell 1960: 766).

H(37) listed by Macvicar (1905: 16).

†H37 listed by Blockeel & Long (1998: 33).

H(38) listed by Macvicar (1905: 16).

†H38 listed by Blockeel & Long (1998: 33).

H39 1969: shaded sandstone rocks, cliffs on W side of Murlough Bay, E of Ballycastle, JA Paton 1970: 192).

H40 1959: mossy boulders, Banagher Glen, nr Dungiven, JW Fitzgerald (Castell 1960: 766).

12/7 ***Cephalozia pleniceps*** (Austin) Lindb.

H1 1968: on *Sphagnum plumulosum*, damp rocky bank, Reenearagh, S of Waterville, JA Paton (Paton 1969a: 873, 1969b).

H20 1975: boggy slope nr Ballycayle, Glencree R., JA Paton (BBS exc.) (Paton 1976: 20).

H23 1970: bog S of Doonis L., N of Glassan, JA Paton (Paton 1971a: 372).

H25 2002: among *Sphagnum* in area of pool systems in raised bog, *ca* 90 m alt., Carrowbehy/Caher Bog, M58, NG Hodgetts 4128 (Blackstock 2003: 40).

H26 1987: moorland S of lane W from Partry to Cloon River, JA Paton (Long 1988: 32).

H27 1987: in wet boggy ground near Keel Harbour, Achill I., TL Blockeel & JA Paton (Long 1988: 32).

H35 1969: bog in valley S of Rinnafaghla Pt, Rosguill, JA Paton (Paton 1970: 192).

H39 1969: bog nr Falgarrive, E of Bushmills, JA Paton (Paton 1970: 192).

12/8 ***Cephalozia loitlesbergeri*** Schiffn.

H9 1979: among *Sphagnum*, NE of Lough Cullaunyheeda, nr Derrymore House, HMH van Melick (Corley 1981: 20).

H16 1968: bog nr Tullywee Bridge, Recess, JA Paton (Paton 1969a: 873).

H22 1965: in *Sphagnum* on cut-away bog S of Summerhill, ALK King (Paton 1966: 186).

H24 1986: on peat on raised bog, Mt Jessop, N17, C Douglas & H Grogan, det. TH Blackstock (Long 1994: 34).

[H25 1966: amongst *Sphagnum* in Derreenargan Bog, ALK King (Paton 1968: 625). H25 deleted because voucher is *C. macrostachya* var. *macrostachya*, det. & comm. TH Blackstock (Long 1996: 43).]

H35 1962: on *Sphagnum magellanicum*, Poisoned Glen nr Dunlewy, MPH Kertland, comm. JW Fitzgerald (Paton 1969a: 873).

[H37 1964: on *Leucobryum*, bog at Derrylee E of Verner's Bridge, JW Fitzgerald & MPH Kertland (Paton 1965a: 855, Fitzgerald & Fitzgerald 1966a). H37 deleted because voucher is *C. macrostachya* var. *macrostachya*, det. & comm. TH Blackstock (Long 1996: 43).]

12/9 *Cephalozia connivens* (Dicks.) Lindb.

H(1) listed by Macvicar (1905: 16).
†H1 listed by Blockeel & Long (1998: 33).
H(2) listed by Macvicar (1905: 16).
†H2 listed by Blockeel & Long (1998: 33).
†H3 listed by Blockeel & Long (1998: 33).
H6 1966: wet heathy slope W of the Punchbowl, Comeragh Mts, JA Paton (BBS exc.) (Paton 1967c: 401).
H(7) listed by Macvicar (1905: 16).
†H7 listed by Blockeel & Long (1998: 33).
†H8 listed by Blockeel & Long (1998: 33).
H9 1959: damp peat on derelict raised bog nr Rinroe Bridge, 3 miles ENE of Corrofin, MCF Proctor (Paton 1967c: 401).
H10 1965: in *Sphagnum* and *Aulacomnium* in bog nr L. Nahinch, ALK King (Paton 1966: 186).
H11 1966: bare peat at Derryfadda, W of Johnstown, JG Duckett *et al.* (BBS exc.) (Paton 1967c: 401).
H12 1975: bog by stream, S slope of Black Rock Mt., JA Paton (BBS exc.) (Paton 1976: 20).
H13 1969: peat in bog at Crannagh, foot of Mt Leinster, JW Fitzgerald (Paton 1970: 192).
H14 1955: side of bog cutting, Abbeyleix, JS Thomson (Castell 1956: 148).
H15 1957: peaty bank W of Lough Cutra, nr Gort, AC Crundwell (BBS exc.) (Castell 1958: 466).
H(16) listed by Macvicar (1905: 16).
†H16 listed by Blockeel & Long (1998: 33).
H(17) listed by Macvicar (1905: 16).
†H17 listed by Blockeel & Long (1998: 33).
[H(18) listed by Macvicar (1905: 16)].
H18 1952: Rahan Bog, ALK King (DBN) (Long 1999b: 26).
H(19) 1949: peat, Ballymore Bog, Calverstown, with *Leptoscyphus anomalus* and *Cephalozia bicuspidata*, JS Thomson (Castell 1951: 494).
†H19 listed by Blockeel & Long (1998: 33).
H(20) listed by Macvicar (1905: 16).
†H20 listed by Blockeel & Long (1998: 33).
H(21) listed by Macvicar (1905: 16). H(21) listed by Blockeel & Long (1998: 33).
H22 1965: in *Sphagnum* on cut-away bog S of Summerhill, ALK King (Paton 1966: 186).
H23 1952: growing through *Sphagnum*, Derries Bog, Athlone, ALK King (Castell 1953: 301).
H24 1957: Newtownforbes [*sic* = Newtown Forbes] bog, MPH Kertland & ALK King, comm. ALK King (Castell 1958: 466).
H25 1960: rotting stump in Rockingham Woods, Boyle, ALK King (Paton 1961: 154).
H(27) listed by Macvicar (1905: 16).
†H27 listed by Blockeel & Long (1998: 33).
H(28) listed by Macvicar (1905: 16).
†H28 listed by Blockeel & Long (1998: 33).
H29 1963: with *Riccardia latifrons*, bog at Flughanagh, 3 miles SE of Dromahair, JW Fitzgerald & AR Perry (Paton 1964: 716).
H31 1966: cut-over bog, Ardee, DM Synnott (Paton 1967c: 401).
H(33) 1917: Carricknagower, WN Tetley (BBSUK) (Castell 1954: 474).
†H33 listed by Blockeel & Long (1998: 33).
H34 1968: bog at Gorey nr Culdaff, Inishowen, JW Fitzgerald & HH Birks (Paton 1969a: 873).
H(35) listed by Macvicar (1905: 16).
†H35 listed by Blockeel & Long (1998: 33).
H36 1951: with *Lepidozia* sp., peat bog, Lough Bradan nr Castlederg, JW Fitzgerald (Castell 1952: 93).
H(37) listed by Macvicar (1905: 16).
†H37 listed by Blockeel & Long (1998: 33).
H(38) listed by Macvicar (1905: 16). H(38) listed by Blockeel & Long (1998: 33).
H(39) listed by Macvicar (1905: 16).
†H39 listed by Blockeel & Long (1998: 33).
H(40) listed by Macvicar (1905: 16).
†H40 listed by Blockeel & Long (1998: 33).

12/10 *Cephalozia hibernica* Spruce ex Pearson

H(1) listed by Macvicar (1905: 16).
†H1 listed by Blockeel & Long (1998: 33).
H(2) listed by Macvicar (1905: 16).
†H2 listed by Blockeel & Long (1998: 33).
H16 1968: emergent root of rhododendron in deep shade, thicket in wood E of Kylemore Castle, AR Perry (Paton

1969a: 873).

H27 1987: on peat in deep shade of Rhododendron thicket by Sraheens Lough, ENE of Achill Sound, Achill I., AR Perry & BM Murray (Long 1988: 32).

[H(40) listed by Macvicar (1905: 16). H40 record discounted because no specimen traced to support Lett & Waddell's record from Downhill (Paton 1977a: 14)].

13/1 ***Nowellia curvifolia*** (Dicks.) Mitt.
(syn. *Cephalozia curvifolia* (Dicks.) Dumort.)

H(1) listed by Macvicar (1905: 16).
†H1 listed by Blockeel & Long (1998: 33).
H(2) listed by Macvicar (1905: 16).
†H2 listed by Blockeel & Long (1998: 33).
H(3) listed by Macvicar (1905: 16).
†H3 listed by Blockeel & Long (1998: 33).
H5 1956: on old logs, wood above Park House, by Tourig river, nr Youghal, EC Wallace (Castell 1957: 325).
H6 1999: on rotting logs in oak woodland, *ca* 90 m alt., Owennashad River, just N of Drumber Bridge, Lismore, S00, TL Blockeel 28/209 (Blackstock 2000: 41).
H(7) listed by Macvicar (1905: 16).
†H7 listed by Blockeel & Long (1998: 33).
H9 1959: amongst other mosses in blanket bog on NW slope of Slieve Elva, between Lisdoonvarna and Black Head, MCF Proctor & RB Ivimey-Cook (Paton 1963: 487).
H11 1966: on rotten log in wood, Inistioge, J Appleyard *et al.* (BBS exc.) (Paton 1967c: 402).
H15 1957: fallen tree trunk, Chevy Chase Woods, Owendalulleegh, nr Gort, EM Lobley (Castell 1958: 466).
H(16) listed by Macvicar (1905: 16).
†H16 listed by Blockeel & Long (1998: 33).
H17 1968: bare peat in cuttings, raised bog at Addergoule N[orth], R. Suck nr Ballinasloe, HJB Birks (Paton 1969a: 873).
H18 1992: on rotting xylem of dead stump in mature *Quercus robur* woodland, near boat-house, Charleville estate, Tullamore, N32, DL Kelly (Long 1993b: 46).
H(20) listed by Macvicar (1905: 16).
†H20 listed by Blockeel & Long (1998: 33).
H(21) listed by Macvicar (1905: 16). H(21) listed by Blockeel & Long (1998: 33).
H23 1986: leaning rotting tree trunk in damp mixed woodland, Clonhugh Woodland, nr L. Owel, DL Kelly & S Iremonger (Corley 1987: 20).
H25 1985: decorticate log, secondary woodland on cut-over peat, extension of St John's Wood, nr Blackbrink Bay, W shore of L. Ree, DL Kelly & G O'Donovan (Corley 1986: 18).
H26 1957: below L. Talt, W slope of [The] Ox Mts, ALK King (Castell 1958: 466).
H(27) listed by Macvicar (1905: 16).
H(27) 1937: Dugort, no collector named (BBS exc.) (Armitage 1938: 13).
†H27 listed by Blockeel & Long (1998: 33).
H28 1965: rotting stump, Slish Wood, L. Gill, JW Fitzgerald & EM Lobley (Paton 1966: 186).
H(29) listed by Macvicar (1905: 16).
†H29 listed by Blockeel & Long (1998: 33).
H30 1965: on peat in bog W of Carricknacrannoge Lough nr Dowra, JW Fitzgerald & EM Lobley (Paton 1966: 186).
H31 1968: rotten pine trunk, wet woodland, Darver Castle 4 miles SE of Louth village, DM Synnott (Paton 1969a: 873).
†H33 listed by Blockeel & Long (1998: 33).
H(34) listed by Macvicar (1905: 16).
†H34 listed by Blockeel & Long (1998: 33).
H(35) listed by Macvicar (1905: 16).
†H35 listed by Blockeel & Long (1998: 33).
H36 1957: rotting wood, Baronscourt, JW Fitzgerald (Castell 1958: 628).
H(38) listed by Macvicar (1905: 16).
†H38 listed by Blockeel & Long (1998: 33).
H(39) listed by Blockeel & Long (1998: 33).
H39 1999: on damp decorticated wood of rotting stump in mixed deciduous/ coniferous woodland, Glenariff, D21, DT Holyoak 99-814B (BBSUK) (Blackstock 2000: 41).
H(40) listed by Macvicar (1905: 16).
†H40 listed by Blockeel & Long (1998: 33).

14/1 ***Cladopodiella fluitans*** (Nees) H.Buch
(syn. *Cephalozia fluitans* (Nees) Spruce)

H1 1961: among *Sphagnum* in bog nr Lough Currane, Waterville, EM Lobley (Paton 1962: 361).
H(2) listed by Macvicar (1905: 16).
†H2 listed by Blockeel & Long (1998: 33).

H(16) listed by Macvicar (1905: 16).
†H16 listed by Blockeel & Long (1998: 33).
H18 1978: margin of hollow, Mongan Bog, Clonmacnoise, M Schouten (Corley 1987: 20).
H(20) listed by Macvicar (1905: 16). H(20) listed by Blockeel & Long (1998: 33).
H(21) listed by Macvicar (1905: 16). H(21) listed by Blockeel & Long (1998: 33).
H(23) listed by Macvicar (1905: 16). H(23) listed by Blockeel & Long (1998: 33).
H24 1968: submerged among *Sphagnum*, raised bog 1 mile SW of Cloondara, WV Rubers, P Hessell & J Klein (Paton 1970: 192).
H25 1981: centre of raised bog, Cloonshannagh, S of Roosky, DM Synnott (Corley 1982: 22).
H26 1965: in wet peaty flush S of Glendaduff, [The] Ox Mts, JW Fitzgerald (Paton 1966: 186).
H(27) listed by Macvicar (1905: 16).
†H27 listed by Blockeel & Long (1998: 33).
H33 1990: Croagh Lusty, Tullywania, G96, R Weyl (Blackstock: 2002: 39).
H35 1966: blanket bog hollows, L. Nacung, F Rose (Paton 1967c: 402).
H36 1988: deep pools in raised bog, Monegal Bog, H28, R Weyl, comm. DT Holyoak (BBSUK) (Blackstock 2001: 34).
H(37) listed by Macvicar (1905: 16). H(37) listed by Blockeel & Long (1998: 33).
H(38) listed by Macvicar (1905: 16). H(38) listed by Blockeel & Long (1998: 33).
H(39) listed by Macvicar (1905: 16). H(39) listed by Blockeel & Long (1998: 33).
H39 1988: bog pool, Garron Plateau, D21, R Weyl, comm. DT Holyoak (BBSUK) (Blackstock 2001: 34).

14/2 ***Cladopodiella francisci*** (Hook.) Jörg. (syn. *Cephalozia francisci* (Hook.) Dumort.)

[H(1) listed by Macvicar (1905: 16). H1 deleted because no record traced, comm. MM Yeo, replaced by next record (Long 1990a: 27)].
H1 1983: clay bank by track, Roads, W of Kells, DM Synnott (DBN) (Long 1990a: 27).
H(3) listed by Macvicar (1905: 16). H(3) listed by Blockeel & Long (1998: 33).
[H(6) listed by Macvicar (1905: 16). H6 deleted because this species not present in gathering (DBN) on which record was probably based (Paton 1977a: 14)].
H(21) listed by Macvicar (1905: 16). H(21) listed by Blockeel & Long (1998: 33).
H(27) listed by Macvicar (1905: 16). H(27) listed by Blockeel & Long (1998: 33).
H29 1963: peaty bank, bog E of Sriff Cottage nr Dromahair, JW Fitzgerald & AR Perry (Paton 1964: 716).
[H(35) listed by Macvicar (1905: 16). H35 deleted because this species not present in gathering (DBN) on which record was probably based (Paton 1977a: 14)].
H35 2001: peaty bank nr stream at *Carum verticillatum* site, *ca* 100 m alt., NW of Edergole Bridge, nr Lough Eske, G98, NG Hodgetts 3892 (Blackstock 2003: 40).
H(38) listed by Macvicar (1905: 16). H(38) listed by Blockeel & Long (1998: 33).
H38 2002: on vertical peaty bank above small stream in moorland nr reservoir edge, *ca* 200 m alt., nr N end of Silent Valley Reservoir, J32, DT Holyoak 02-980 (Blackstock 2003: 40).
H(39) listed by Macvicar (1905: 16). H(39) listed by Blockeel & Long (1998: 33).

16/1 ***Hygrobiella laxifolia*** (Hook.) Spruce

H(1) listed by Macvicar (1905: 17).
†H1 listed by Blockeel & Long (1998: 34).
H(2) listed by Macvicar (1905: 17).
†H2 listed by Blockeel & Long (1998: 34).
H(3) listed by Macvicar (1905: 17).
†H3 listed by Blockeel & Long (1998: 34).
H4 1967: rocks by stream, Mushera, JW Fitzgerald (Paton 1968: 621).
H6 1966: stones in stream E of the Punchbowl, Comeragh Mts, JA Paton & ERB Little (BBS exc.) (Paton 1967c: 396).
H7 1966: wet rocks, slopes above L. Curra, Galtee Mts, JA Paton & ERB Little (BBS exc.) (Paton 1967c: 396).
H(16) listed by Macvicar (1905: 17).
†H16 listed by Blockeel & Long (1998: 34).
†H20 listed by Blockeel & Long (1998: 34).
H(21) listed by Macvicar (1905: 17). H(21) listed by Blockeel & Long (1998: 34).
H27 1970: stone in stream, S slope of Ben Gorm, N of Killary Harbour, JA Paton (Paton 1971a: 369).
H28 1970: soft basic rock outcrop facing NE, *ca* 1100 ft alt., S end of corrie on E side

of Benbulbin [*sic* = Ben Bulben], AR Perry & HJ Perry (BBS exc.) (Paton 1974b: 162).

H(33) 1914: Cuilcagh, WN Tetley (BBSUK) (Castell 1953: 301).

H34 1962: damp shaded rock, Bulbin [Mt.], J Appleyard (BBS exc.) (Paton 1963: 488).

H35 1969: shaded rocks beside stream in valley, Fintragh Bay, W of Killybegs, JA Paton (Paton 1970: 188).

H36 1958: wet rocks below flood level, at 700 ft [alt.], Glenlark, 4 miles E of Gortin, JW Fitzgerald (Castell 1959: 629).

H38 2002: on thin soil in crevice of rocks nr river, part shaded by deciduous trees, *ca* 50 m alt., by Shimna River in Tollymore Forest Park, J33, DT Holyoak 02-930 (Blackstock 2003: 40).

H(39) 1928: Glenariff (BBS exc.) (Duncan 1928: 117).

H(39) listed by Blockeel & Long (1998: 34).

H40 1959: rocks beside stream below flood level, Glendra R., Banagher Glen, nr Dungiven, JW Fitzgerald (Castell 1960: 766).

17/1 ***Odontoschisma sphagni*** (Dicks.) Dumort.

H(1) listed by Macvicar (1905: 17).

†H1 listed by Blockeel & Long (1998: 34).

H(2) listed by Macvicar (1905: 17).

†H2 listed by Blockeel & Long (1998: 34).

H(3) listed by Macvicar (1905: 17).

†H3 listed by Blockeel & Long (1998: 34).

H4 1966: among *Sphagnum* at 1200 ft alt., Seefin, Boggeragh Mts, MFV Corley & JS Parker (Paton 1967c: 402).

H5 1967: on *Sphagnum* in bog, Lyrenamon, NW of Carrignavar, JW Fitzgerald (Paton 1968: 626).

H6 1999: on *Sphagnum* in relict bog, Monaneea Lake, *ca* 7 km N of Ardmore, X28, TL Blockeel 28/221 (Blackstock 2001: 34).

H(7) listed by Macvicar (1905: 17).

†H7 listed by Blockeel & Long (1998: 34).

H8 1959: raised bog, Castleconnell, ALK King (Castell 1969: 766).

H(9) listed by Macvicar (1905: 17).

†H9 listed by Blockeel & Long (1998: 34).

H10 1959: bog W of Newport, ALK King (Castell 1960: 766).

1959: bog W of Newport, ALK King (DBN) (Long 1999b: 26).

H11 1966: on peat, bog at Derryfadda, W of Johnstown, ERB Little (BBS exc.) (Paton 1967c: 402).

H(12) listed by Macvicar (1905: 17).

†H12 listed by Blockeel & Long (1998: 34).

H(13) listed by Macvicar (1905: 17).

†H13 listed by Blockeel & Long (1998: 34).

H(14) listed by Macvicar (1905: 17).

†H14 listed by Blockeel & Long (1998: 34).

H(15) listed by Macvicar (1905: 17).

†H15 listed by Blockeel & Long (1998: 34).

H(16) listed by Macvicar (1905: 17).

†H16 listed by Blockeel & Long (1998: 34).

H17 1957: raised bog between mouths of R. Clare and R. Cregg, EM Lobley (BBS exc.) (Castell 1958: 467).

H(18) listed by Macvicar (1905: 17).

†H18 listed by Blockeel & Long (1998: 34).

H(19) listed by Macvicar (1905: 17).

†H19 listed by Blockeel & Long (1998: 34).

H(20) listed by Macvicar (1905: 17).

†H20 listed by Blockeel & Long (1998: 34).

[H(21) listed by Macvicar (1905: 17). H21 deleted because no record or voucher traced, comm. MM Yeo (Long 1990a: 27)].

H(22) listed by Macvicar (1905: 17).

†H22 listed by Blockeel & Long (1998: 34).

H(23) listed by Macvicar (1905: 17).

†H23 listed by Blockeel & Long (1998: 34).

H24 1955: Derryad Bog, nr Killashee, TA Barry, comm. ALK King (Castell 1956: 149).

†H25 listed by Blockeel & Long (1998: 34).

H(26) listed by Macvicar (1905: 17).

†H26 listed by Blockeel & Long (1998: 34).

H(27) listed by Macvicar (1905: 17).

†H27 listed by Blockeel & Long (1998: 34).

H(28) listed by Macvicar (1905: 17).

†H28 listed by Blockeel & Long (1998: 34).

H(29) listed by Macvicar (1905: 17).

†H29 listed by Blockeel & Long (1998: 34).

H(30) listed by Macvicar (1905: 17).

†H30 listed by Blockeel & Long (1998: 34).

[H(31) listed by Macvicar (1905: 17). H31 deleted because no record or voucher traced, comm. MM Yeo (Long 1990a: 27)].

H(32) 1900: Scottstown Bog, CH Waddell (DBN), comm. JW Fitzgerald (Castell 1959: 629).

H(33) 1916: bog, Derrygonnelly, WN Tetley (BBSUK) (Castell 1954: 475).

†H33 listed by Blockeel & Long (1998: 34).
H(34) listed by Macvicar (1905: 17).
†H34 listed by Blockeel & Long (1998: 34).
H(35) listed by Macvicar (1905: 17).
†H35 listed by Blockeel & Long (1998: 34).
H36 1951: among *Sphagnum*, Lough Bradan nr Castlederg, JW Fitzgerald (Castell 1952: 94).
H(37) listed by Macvicar (1905: 17).
†H37 listed by Blockeel & Long (1998: 34).
H(38) listed by Macvicar (1905: 17).
†H38 listed by Blockeel & Long (1998: 34).
H(39) listed by Macvicar (1905: 17).
†H39 listed by Blockeel & Long (1998: 34).
†H40 listed by Blockeel & Long (1998: 34).

17/2 ***Odontoschisma denudatum*** (Mart.) Dumort.

H(1) listed by Macvicar (1905: 17).
†H1 listed by Blockeel & Long (1998: 34).
H(2) 1935: Eagle's Nest, no collector named (BBS exc.) (Watson 1936: 265, anon. 1937b: 369).
†H2 listed by Blockeel & Long (1998: 34).
H3 1967: peat track in bog, Gougane Barra, JW Fitzgerald (Paton 1968: 626).
H7 1966: bog between Seefin and Knockeenatoung, Galtee Mts, EM Lobley & RJ Murphy (BBS exc.) (Paton 1967c: 402).
H9 1959: peaty ground on Slieve Elva, MCF Proctor (Paton 1964: 717).
H10 1979: old, rather dry heath under shade, Keeper Hill, HMH van Melick (Corley 1981: 20).
H11 1966: bare peat, raised bog, Derryfadda, W of Johnstown, JG Duckett (BBS exc.) (Paton 1967c: 402).
H13 1969: bare peat, bog at St Mullins nr Graiguenamanagh, JW Fitzgerald (Paton 1970: 192).
H14 1956: moorland above Johnsborough, Slieve Bloom Mts, AA Cridland (Castell 1958: 467).
H16 1957: peaty bankside above Loch Fee, EM Lobley (BBS exc.) (Castell 1958: 467).
H17 1957: bog S of Clare, J Appleyard (Castell 1958: 467).
H18 1955: side of drain, Cloncreen Bog, ALK King (Castell 1956: 149).
H19 1955: bare peat among *Calluna*, bog, Baronstown East, nr Newbridge, ALK King (Castell 1956: 149).
H(21) listed by Macvicar (1905: 17). H(21) listed by Blockeel & Long (1998: 34).
H22 1978: bare peat, Dalystown Bog, SW of Trim, DM Synnott (Corley 1979: 25).
H23 1970: bog S of Doonis L., N of Glassan JA Paton (Paton 1971a: 372).
H24 1955: drained edge on bog-top, Edera Bog, nr Ballymahon, TA Barry, comm. ALK King (Castell 1956: 149).
H25 1965: wet peat on moor *ca* 700 ft alt., Kilronan nr Ballyfarnan, EM Lobley & JW Fitzgerald (Paton 1966: 187).
H26 1965: on peat hummocks in bog W of L. Talt, [The] Ox Mts, JW Fitzgerald (Paton 1966: 187).
H(27) listed by Macvicar (1905: 17).
†H27 listed by Blockeel & Long (1998: 34).
H28 1959: on peat among limestone debris, top of Lugnagall, JW Fitzgerald & AR Perry (Paton 1964: 717-718).
H29 1963: dry peaty bank, bog E of Sriff Cottage, nr Dromahair, MD Fitzgerald & AR Perry (Paton 1964: 717-718).
H30 1965: on peat bog W of Carricknacrannoge Lough nr Dowra, JW Fitzgerald (Paton 1966: 186).
H31 1968: with *Nowellia* on rotten pine log, wet woodland, Darver Castle 4 miles SE of Louth Village, DM Synnott (Paton 1969a: 873).
H33 1959: peat drying out, Garvany Bog, nr Belleek, JW Fitzgerald (Castell 1960: 766).
H(34) listed by Macvicar (1905: 17).
†H34 listed by Blockeel & Long (1998: 34).
H35 1962: bog by R. Devlin nr Dunlewy, EM Lobley & MPH Kertland (Paton 1964: 717-718).
H36 1952: Lough Bradan, JW Fitzgerald (Castell 1953: 301).
H37 1964: raised bog S of Derrycrow, NW of Lough Gullion, JW Fitzgerald (Paton 1966: 856).
[H(38) listed by Macvicar (1905: 17). H38 deleted because no localised record or voucher traced, comm. MM Yeo (Long 1990a: 27)].
H40 1968: peat bog, Benbradagh, HH Birks & JW Fitzgerald (Paton 1969a: 873).

17/3 ***Odontoschisma elongatum*** (Lindb.) A. Evans

H3 1979: moist soil on rocky ground above the shore, S of League Point, Sheep's

Head Peninsula, JA Paton (Corley 1980a: 31).

H16 1968: amongst *O. sphagni* and *Campylopus brevipilus* in bog near Tullywee Bridge, E of Recess, JA Paton (Corley 1978: 14).

H27 1987: mixed with *Saccogyna viticulosa*, Trawmore Sand SE of Keel, Achill I., HMH van Melick 871327, Hb. van Melick (Long 1989: 22).

18/1 ***Cephaloziella spinigera*** (Lindb.) Warnst.
(syn. *Cephaloziella subdentata* Warnst.)

H1 1968: on *Sphagnum plumulosum*, damp rocky bank, Reenearagh, S of Waterville, JA Paton (Paton 1969a: 872).

H9 1979: on *Sphagnum*, bog W of Derrymore House, N of Kilkishen, JA Paton & AC Crundwell (Corley 1980a: 30).

H20 1975: on *Sphagnum*, cutover bog, Rathduffmore, 1½ miles N of Knockananna, JA Paton (Corley 1986: 18).

H23 1986: among sphagnum on raised bog, Ballinderry, H Grogan & C Douglas (Corley 1987: 19).

H(27) listed by Blockeel & Long (1998: 34).

[H29 1963: amongst fen vegetation in roadside bog, Flughanagh 3 miles SE of Dromahair, AR Perry & JW Fitzgerald (Paton 1964: 717). H29 deleted because specimen is indeterminable, comm. JA Paton (Corley 1985: 21)].

H29 1980: amongst *Sphagnum capillifolium* and *Mylia anomala*, Clooncoe Wood, L. Rinn, N19, N Lockhart, comm. DT Holyoak (BBSUK) (Blackstock 2001: 34).

[H34 1969: *Sphagnum* hummock in bog N of Gorey, S of Culdaff, Inishowen, JA Paton (Paton 1970: 191). H34 deleted because voucher mislaid, comm. JA Paton (Corley 1985: 21)].

[H35 1969: *Sphagnum* hummock in bog in valley S of Rinnafaghla Pt, Rosguill, JA Paton (Paton 1970: 191). H35 deleted because voucher mislaid, comm. JA Paton (Corley 1985: 21)].

H35 1969: bog in valley S of Rinnafaghla Point, Rosguill, JA Paton, NMW, conf. JA Paton (Long 1995b: 39).

18/2 ***Cephaloziella elachista*** (J.B.Jack ex Gottsche & Rabenh.) Schiffn.

[H12 listed in error (Castell 1952: 94) in place of 12, corrected by Castell (1953: 304)].

[H(20) listed by Macvicar (1905: 17). H20 deleted because no specimen traced, comm. JA Paton (Corley 1985: 21)].

H(21) listed by Macvicar (1905: 17). H(21) listed by Blockeel & Long (1998: 34).

H23 1986: among sphagnum in wet area of raised bog, Tully Cross, C Douglas & H Grogan (Corley 1987: 19).

18/3 ***Cephaloziella rubella*** (Nees) Warnst.

H9 1979: bog W of Derrymore House, S of Tulla, AC Crundwell, Hb. AC Crundwell (Corley 1983: 48).

H20 1975: on *Sphagnum*, cutover bog, Rathduffmore, 1½ miles N of Knockananna, JA Paton, Hb. JA Paton (Corley 1983: 48-49).

H23 1970: peat cutting, bog S of Doonis Lough, 6 miles N of Glassan, JA Paton, Hb. JA Paton (Corley 1983: 49).

H34 1968: dry exposed peat, Dunree Head, Inishowen, JW Fitzgerald (Paton 1969a: 872).

H37 1964: on dry peat, raised bog S of Derrycrow, NW of Lough Gullion, JW Fitzgerald (Paton 1965a: 855).

H39 1952: Colin Mt., Belfast, EW Jones & JW Fitzgerald, comm. EW Jones (Castell 1953: 301).

18/4 ***Cephaloziella hampeana*** (Nees) Schiffn.

H1 1951: bank nr Caherdaniel, AC Crundwell (Castell 1952: 94).
1951: Ross-Behy, EW Jones (Castell 1952: 94).

[H2 record (1951: Derrycunihy Woods, AC Crundwell: Castell 1952: 94) should be deleted because the locality is in H1 (see Kelly 1984b)].

H3 1979: dead *Molinia* tussock, N slope of Foilastookeen, Shehy Mts, JA Paton (Corley 1980a: 30).

H4 1967: wet rocks, Shournagh R., nr Blarney, JW Fitzgerald (Paton 1968: 625).

H5 1966: gravelly earth by river, Araglin, J Appleyard (BBS exc.) (Paton 1967c:

401).

H6 1966: boulders beside stream below Coumshingaun L., Comeragh Mts, JA Paton (BBS exc.) (Paton 1967c: 401).

H7 1966: heathy bank above L. Curra, Galtee Mts, JA Paton (BBS exc.) (Paton 1967c: 401).

H8 1966: on cattle track, Knockseefin, Pallas Green, JW Fitzgerald *et al.* (BBS exc.) (Paton 1967c: 401).

H9 1959: thin soil over Carboniferous limestone S of Mullagh More, nr Corrofin, MCF Proctor (Paton 1965a: 855).

H10 1979: amongst *Leucobryum*, S slope of Keeper Hill, JA Paton (Corley 1980a: 30).

H11 1966: on *Aulacomnium*, bog at Derryfadda, W of Johnstown, JW Fitzgerald (BBS exc.) (Paton 1967c: 401).

H12 1969: over moss on stones in marshy field, Pallas Bridge nr Wicklow Gap, JW Fitzgerald (Paton 1970: 192).

H13 1954: growing through mosses on bank by towpath, left bank of R. Barrow above Graiguenamanagh, ALK King (Paton 1964: 717).

H16 1969: soil on roadside 2 miles E of Lettercrafroe L., AR Perry & HJ Perry (Paton 1970: 192).

H(18) 1892: Bog of Allen, Geashill, HW Lett (DBN) (Paton 1977a: 14).

H20 1958: growing through mosses on wall of Drumgoff Bridge, Glenmalure, ALK King (Paton 1964: 717).

H22 1965: on side of drain at edge of cut-away bog S of Summerhill, ALK King (Paton 1966: 186).

H23 1970: moorland nr Butler's Bridge S of Mullingar, JA Paton (Paton 1971a: 372).

H24 1966: in *Campylopus*, Corn Hill, ALK King (Paton 1967c: 401).

H25 1965: on boulders, Kilronan nr Ballyfarnan, EM Lobley & JW Fitzgerald (Paton 1966: 186).

H27 1962: wet part of bog in the Harbour, Keel, Achill I., EF Warburg (Paton 1963: 487).

H28 1962: among *Sphagnum* in bog below limestone rocks, Gleniff, Dartry Mts, EM Lobley (BBS exc.) (Paton 1963: 487).

H29 1963: growing over *Sphagnum*, bog at Flughanagh 3 miles SE of Dromahair, JW Fitzgerald & AR Perry (Paton 1964: 717).

H30 1969: floor of old quarry, Blackrocks Cross, Cuilcagh Mts, SW of Swanlinbar, JA Paton (Paton 1970: 192).

H33 1959: creeping over *Sphagnum*, Immeroo Bog, nr Tempo, JW Fitzgerald (Castell 1960: 766).

H34 1969: *Sphagnum* hummock nr The Well, Gap of Mamore, N of Buncrana, JA Paton (Paton 1970: 192).

H35 1962: on *Frullania* on horizontal rock nr Mullaghderg Lough, The Rosses, EF Warburg, J Appleyard & RE Longton (BBS exc.) (Paton 1963: 487).

H36 1951: wet peaty moor beside river, ... , Lough Bradan, JW Fitzgerald, conf. (with notes) by EW Jones (Castell 1952: 94).

H37 1964: bog in townland of Derryadd, E of Lough Gullion, JW Fitzgerald (Paton 1965a: 855).

H38 1964: earth-topped wall, Glassdrummond nr Annalong, JW Fitzgerald & MPH Kertland (Paton 1965a: 855).

H(39) 1928: Colin Mountain (BBS exc.) (Duncan 1928: 113-114, 116).
1928: Glenariff (BBS exc.) (Duncan 1928: 117).

†H39 listed by Blockeel & Long (1998: 35).

H(40) 1928: Portrush, FE Milsom, comm. G Halliday (Paton 1963: 487).

†H40 listed by Blockeel & Long (1998: 35).

18/6 ***Cephaloziella divaricata*** (Sm.) Schiffn. (syn. *Cephaloziella byssacea* auct. non (Roth) Warnst., *C. starkei* (Funck ex Nees) Schiffn. nom. illeg., *C. starkei* var. *scabra* (M.Howe) L.Clark & Frye, *C. starkii* auct.)

H(1) listed by Macvicar (1905: 17). H(1) listed by Blockeel & Long (1998: 35).

H(2) listed by Macvicar (1905: 17).

†H2 listed by Blockeel & Long (1998: 35).

H(3) listed by Macvicar (1905: 17).

†H3 listed by Blockeel & Long (1998: 35).

H4 1967: waste ground by roadside, Carrigthomas, nr Macroom, JW Fitzgerald (Paton 1968: 625).

H(6) 1933: Poolvona, E Armitage (anon. 1934c: 145).

†H6 listed by Blockeel & Long (1998: 35).

H7 1966: amongst *Cephalozia* on damp peat

in bog, Longfordpass South, Urlingford, JA Paton (BBS exc.) (Paton 1967c: 401).
H8 1979: gravelly quarry, N side of Sugar Hill, S of Knockanimpaha, JA Paton (Corley 1980a: 30).
H(9) listed by Macvicar (1905: 17).
†H9 listed by Blockeel & Long (1998: 35).
H10 1979: peat S slope of Keeper Hill, JA Paton (Corley 1980a: 30).
H(12) 1913: Great Saltee I., HW Lett (*Irish Nat.* **22**, 20, 1914), comm. JW Fitzgerald (Castell 1952: 94).
†H12 listed by Blockeel & Long (1998: 35).
H13 1969: peat in bog at St Mullins nr Graiguenamanagh, JW Fitzgerald (Paton 1970: 192).
H16 1957: growing over *Bryum capillare*, Tullywee Bridge, nr Kylemore, J Appleyard (Castell 1958: 466).
1969: shaded siliceous rock outcrop, Farravaun, Glann, Ou[gh]terard, AR Perry & HJ Perry (Paton 1970: 192), as *C. starkei* var. *scabra*.
H(20) no date: Seven Churches, D Moore (DBN), comm. ALK King (Paton 1964: 717).
†H20 listed by Blockeel & Long (1998: 35).
H(21) listed by Macvicar (1905: 17).
†H21 listed by Blockeel & Long (1998: 35).
H22 1970: moorland W of An Uaimh, JA Paton (Paton 1971a: 372).
H23 1970: bog S of Doonis L., N of Glassan, JA Paton (Paton 1971a: 372).
H27 1970: on hepatics on sheltered rocks in ravine, Devil's Mother, N of Killary Harbour, JA Paton (Paton 1971a: 172).
H28 1970: on the way to King's Mt., J Appleyard (BBS exc.) (Paton 1971a: 372, Appleyard 1971: 389).
H29 1963: dry peat above Glencar waterfall, Glencar, JW Fitzgerald & AR Perry (Paton 1964: 717).
H30 1956: wet woodland path, Virginia, JS Thomson (Castell 1957: 325).
[H(31) listed by Macvicar (1905: 17)].
H33 1959: bank of disused sandpit, Brocagh, nr Lack, JW Fitzgerald (Castell 1960: 766).
H34 1969: stream above Meedanmore, N of Malin, JA Paton (Paton 1970: 192).
[H(35) listed by Macvicar (1905: 17)].
H35 1969: peaty bank nr lough N of Carrigan Head, SW of Carrick, JA Paton (Paton 1970: 192).
H36 1953: peat-bog nr Sandholes, MPH Kertland & EM Lobley, comm. EM Lobley (Castell 1956: 148).
H(37) listed by Macvicar (1905: 17).
†H37 listed by Blockeel & Long (1998: 35).
[H(38) listed by Macvicar (1905: 17)].
H(38) 1928: Slieve Donard (BBS exc.) (Duncan 1928: 114, 117).
†H38 listed by Blockeel & Long (1998: 35).
[H(39) listed by Macvicar (1905: 17)].
H(39) 1928: sandhills, Portrush (BBS exc.) (Duncan 1928: 116).
1928: Fair Head (BBS exc.) (Duncan 1928: 116).
1928: Colin Top or Colin Glen (BBS exc.) (Duncan 1928: 116).
†H39 listed by Blockeel & Long (1998: 35).
H40 1964: in scree at 1100 ft alt., Benbradagh, JW Fitzgerald (Paton 1965a: 855).
1965: in scree at 1100 ft alt., Benbradagh, JW Fitzgerald (Paton 1966: 186).

Old records listed as *Cephaloziella bifida* (Schreb.) Schiffn. by Macvicar (1905: 17) may belong partly to this species but the voucher specimens need to be reidentified.

18/7 ***Cephaloziella stellulifera*** (Taylor ex Spruce) Schiffn.

H1 1983: friable copper-bearing rocks on steep slope, gully above Coomnacronia L., SW of Glenbeigh, JA Paton (Corley 1984: 25).
H(2) 1925: Muckross Demesne, WE Nicholson (CGE) (Paton 1968: 625).
†H2 listed by Blockeel & Long (1998: 35).
H3 1968: heathy ground and tracks about old copper mines above Allihies, JA Paton (Paton 1969a: 873).
H6 1966: crevices in wall on cliffs W of Bunmahon, JA Paton (BBS exc.) (Paton 1967c: 401).
H9 1968: anthill on peaty bank near Shandangan L., NE of Corrofin, JA Paton (Corley 1983: 49).
H20 1975: soil in derelict building, old lead works below L. Nahanagan NW of Laragh, JA Paton (BBS exc.) (Paton 1976: 19).
H(27) listed by Blockeel & Long (1998: 35).
H34 1969: sandy peat on track, coast nr

Balloor, Doagh Isle, W of Malin, JA Paton (Paton 1970: 192).

H35 1969: damp lay-by, Mullan, NE of Creeslough, JA Paton (Corley 1983: 49).

18/8 ***Cephaloziella massalongi*** (Spruce) Müll.Frib.
(syn. *Cephaloziella massalongoi* auct.)

H3 1955: on rock and detritus in shaded entrance to disused workings, Allihies Copper Mines, H Milne-Redhead (Castell 1957: 325). H3 listed (Paton 1984: 4-5, Corley 1985: 21).

H6 1966: cave nr high water mark, old copper mines on cliffs E of Bunmahon, RD Fitzgerald & DM Synnott (BBS exc.) (Paton 1967c: 401). H6 listed (Paton 1984: 4-5, Corley 1985: 21).

18/11 ***Cephaloziella turneri*** (Hook.) Müll. Frib.
(syn. *Prionolobus turneri* (Hook.) Schiffn.)

H(2) listed by Macvicar (1905: 17). H(2) listed by Blockeel & Long (1998: 35).

H(3) listed by Macvicar (1905: 17). H(3) listed by Blockeel & Long (1998: 35).

H(20) 1912-1914: ditch bank at 700 ft [alt.], very rare, Glen of the Downs, Allen, Gunn & D McArdle, (in D McArdle, *Irish Nat*. **26**, 73, 1917), comm. JW Fitzgerald (Castell 1952: 94).

H35 2002: with mosses on soil in crevice of low rocks on hillslope shaded by young deciduous woodland, *ca* 35 m, just N of Duntally Bridge, SE of Creeslough, C03, DT Holyoak 02-679 (BBSUK, DBN) (Blackstock 2003: 40).

18/12 ***Cephaloziella integerrima*** (Lindb.) Warnst.

H6 1966: roadside bank E of Coumshingaun L., Comeragh Mts, J Appleyard & JG Duckett (BBS exc.) (Paton 1967c: 401).

H34 2002: on unshaded thin soil among quartzite cobbles in disturbed area of grassland nr buildings, alt. *ca* 50 m, Dunree Head, C23, DT Holyoak 02-786 (BBSUK, DBN) (Blackstock 2003: 40).

19/1 ***Anthelia julacea*** (L.) Dumort.
(syn. *Anthelia julacea* var. *gracilis* Hook.)

H(1) listed by Macvicar (1905: 19).

†H1 listed by Blockeel & Long (1998: 36).

H(2) listed by Macvicar (1905: 19).

†H2 listed by Blockeel & Long (1998: 36).

H3 1979: bank of mountain stream, Mt. W of Gougaun [= Gougane] Barra, N Lockhart (Corley 1980a: 27).

H6 1966: wet rocks on cliffs above Sgilloge Loughs, Comeragh Mts, JA Paton *et al.* (BBS exc.) (Paton 1967c: 396).

H(7) 1902: Lough Muskry, Galtee Mts, HW Lett (DBN), comm. JW Fitzgerald (Castell 1959: 629).

H13 1975: rocks in stream, The Black Banks, Mt Leinster, JA Paton & AR Perry (BBS exc.) (Paton 1976: 17).

H(16) listed by Macvicar (1905: 19).

†H16 listed by Blockeel & Long (1998: 36).

H(20) listed by Macvicar (1905: 19).

†H20 listed by Blockeel & Long (1998: 36).

†H27 listed by Blockeel & Long (1998: 36).

H28 1970: steep acid outcrops of Knockalongy, above L. Minnaun, [The] Ox Mts, DM Synnott (BBS exc.) (Paton 1971a: 369, Appleyard 1971: 387).

H(34) listed by Macvicar (1905: 19).

†H34 listed by Blockeel & Long (1998: 36).

H(35) listed by Macvicar (1905: 19).

†H35 listed by Blockeel & Long (1998: 36).

H(38) listed by Macvicar (1905: 19).

†H38 listed by Blockeel & Long (1998: 36).

H(40) listed by Macvicar (1905: 19). H(40) listed by Blockeel & Long (1998: 36).

19/2 ***Anthelia juratzkana*** (Limpr.) Trevis.

H16 1968: earthy ledge amongst mica schist boulders, W-facing slope at 1200 ft alt., Muckanaght, Twelve Pins, AR Perry (Paton 1969a: 867).

H27 1987: earthy bank above stream at *ca* 500 ft [alt.], W of Keem Strand, Achill I., JA Paton (Long 1988: 32).

H34 1968: soil in rock crevices at 1500 ft alt., Bulbin Mt., Inishowen, JW Fitzgerald (Paton 1969a: 867).

H35 1962: bare ground at *ca* 1800 ft alt., E shoulder of Errigal, EF Warburg (BBS exc.) (Paton 1963: 488).

H39 1999: on steep damp surface of crumbling basalt at base of N-facing crag, Knock Dhu, D30, DT Holyoak 99-864 (BBSUK) (Blackstock 2000: 41).

21/2 ***Barbilophozia kunzeana*** (Huebener) Müll.Frib.
(syn. *Lophozia kunzeana* (Huebener) A. Evans)

H(28) 1880: mixed with *Lophozia Mulleri*, Benbulbin [*sic* = Ben Bulben], Co. Sligo, D McArdle, comm. H Beesley, received from MB Slater, det. Dr Spruce; conf. SM Macvicar and WH Pearson (D.A.J.[ones] in anon. 1923: 33-34).

21/3 ***Barbilophozia floerkei*** (F.Weber & D. Mohr) Loeske
(syn. *Lophozia floerkei* (F.Weber & D. Mohr) Schiffn.)

H(1) 1905: Brandon Mt., CH Waddell (BEL) (Paton 1967c: 398).
H2 1951: boggy ground, alt. *ca* 2000 ft, Mangerton, Killarney, EW Jones (Castell 1952: 92).
H3 1979: humus in heath on N slope of Sugarloaf Mountain, HMH van Melick (Corley 1981: 19).
H(6) no date: among *Dicranum* etc., Boola, CH Waddell (BEL) (Paton 1967c: 398).
H6 1999: on peaty humus under boulder, *ca* 530 m alt., Lough Coumfea, Comeragh Mountains, S20, TL Blockeel 28/234 (Blackstock 2000: 41).
H7 1983: mossy turf amongst sandstone blocks on exposed ridge, O'Loughnan's Castle, Galty Mts, DG Long (Corley 1984: 23).
H8 1966: on damp rock at 2200 ft alt., Temple Hill, Galtee Mts, MFV Corley & JS Parker (Paton 1967c: 398).
H10 1986: blanket bog, Silvermines, J Cross (Corley 1987: 18).
H13 1975: under *Calluna*, The Black Banks, Mt Leinster, PH Pitkin (BBS exc.) (Paton 1976: 18).
H16 1970: wet hillside *ca* 1000 ft alt., valley above Leenaun Hotel, AR Perry & HJ Perry (Paton 1974b: 163).
H(20) 1949: at 2000-2700 ft alt., Lugnacullia, AW Stelfox, comm. JS Thomson (Castell 1951: 493).
†H20 listed by Blockeel & Long (1998: 36).
H21 1952: shady rocks, *ca* 700 ft alt., Ballinascorney Gap, ALK King (Castell 1953: 299).
H(27) listed by Macvicar (1905: 14).
†H27 listed by Blockeel & Long (1998: 36).
H28 1963: moist depression at 1400 ft alt. in limestone hillside, Gleniff, Dartry Mts, AR Perry & JW Fitzgerald (Paton 1964: 715).
H29 2001: forming part of hepatic mat on N side of sandstone block on rocky W-facing hillslope, *ca* 384 m alt., W slope of Slieve Anierin, H01, DT Holyoak 01-848 (Blackstock: 2002: 39).
H30 1965: in turf on Cuilcagh, *ca* 900 ft alt., EM Lobley & JW Fitzgerald (Paton 1966: 183).
H33 1959: sparingly in turf among scree, Cuilcagh, at 1800 ft [alt.], JW Fitzgerald (Castell 1960: 765).
H34 1967: among rocks above L. Inn, Inishowen, JW Fitzgerald (Paton 1968: 622).
H(35) listed by Macvicar (1905: 14).
†H35 listed by Blockeel & Long (1998: 36).
H36 1956: turf beside stream, Sawel Mt., JW Fitzgerald & MPH Kertland (Castell 1957: 324).
H38 1960: the Eagle Rock, 1500 ft [alt.], NW side of Slieve Donard, AW Stelfox, comm. JW Fitzgerald (Paton 1961: 153).
H39 1952: mossy boulders on hillside, 600 ft alt., Loughan Bay, ALK King (Castell 1953: 299).
H40 1964: among rocks at 1400 ft alt., Benbradagh, JW Fitzgerald (Paton 1964: 854).

21/4 ***Barbilophozia atlantica*** (Kaal.) Müll. Frib.

H6 1999: on peaty humus on rock in river, *ca* 530 m alt., Lough Coumfea, Comeragh Mts, S20, TL Blockeel 28/233 (Blackstock 2000: 41).
H(34) 1914: Ben Bulben [*sic*], J Hunter (NMW), comm. JW Fitzgerald (Paton 1962: 359, Fitzgerald & Fitzgerald 1966a). Locality in H34 ('Ben Bulben' in Paton 1962: 359) corrected to Bulbin Mountain (Paton 1963: 485).

21/5 ***Barbilophozia attenuata*** (Mart.) Loeske (syn. *Lophozia attenuata* (Mart.) Dumort, *L. gracilis* Steph.)

[H(1) listed by Macvicar (1905: 14). H1 deleted because voucher specimen (1898: Anniscaul Lough, Dingle Peninsula, HW Lett & D McArdle, DBN) is indeterminable, replaced by following record (Long 1990a: 24)].
H1 1951: on 'cornice' of humus beneath overhanging *Calluna* at top of low rock outcrop, 50 ft [alt.], rocky knoll on shore of Lough Currane, Waterville, EW Jones 75 (Long 1990a: 24).
H3 1979: humus under over-hanging heather near Glengarriff Wood, HMH van Melick (Corley 1981: 19).
H6 1966: boulders in wood by R. Nier nr Shanballyanne, JW Fitzgerald *et al.* (BBS exc.) (Paton 1967c: 398).
H(7) listed by Macvicar (1905: 14). H(7) listed by Blockeel & Long (1998: 36).
H12 1969: among block scree *ca* 1400 ft alt., Caher Roe's Den, Blackstairs Mt, JW Fitzgerald (Paton 1972a: 133).
H13 1969: block scree below Caher Roe's Den, Blackstairs Mt., JW Fitzgerald (Paton 1970: 189).
H16 1961: boulders nr Toombeola Bridge, nr Roundstone, EM Lobley (Paton 1962: 359).
H20 1952: among quartzite rocks, E slope of Little Sugarloaf, ALK King (Castell 1953: 299).
[H(21) listed by Macvicar (1905: 14)].
H21 1959: Slievenabawnoge Mountain, ALK King (DBN) (Long 1999b: 26).
H25 1972: among *Campylopus flexuosus* on peat, Slieve Bawn NW of Lanesborough, WV Rubers (Paton 1974b: 163).
H(27) 1909: Clare I., HW Lett (anon. 1911b: 31), as *Lophozia gracilis*.
†H27 listed by Blockeel & Long (1998: 36).
H28 1970: siliceous boulders on hillside by road S of Masshill, SW of Tullyvellia Loughs, [The] Ox Mts, AR Perry & HJ Perry (BBS exc.) (Paton: 1974: 163).
H29 1965: boulders beside L. Mahanagh E of Drumkeeran, JW Fitzgerald & EM Lobley (Paton 1966: 183).
H31 1966: N side of Trumpet Hill, Carlingford Peninsula, DM Synnott (Paton 1967c: 398).
H33 1961: growing through mosses in rock crevices, Big Dog 6 miles W of Derrygonnelly, JW Fitzgerald (Paton 1962: 359).
H34 1968: among rocks, Kindrohid nr Clonmany, Inishowen, JW Fitzgerald (Paton 1969a: 870).
H(35) listed by Macvicar (1905: 14).
†H35 listed by Blockeel & Long (1998: 36).
H36 1951: with *Scapania gracilis*, at base of rock, Black Bog, nr Omagh, JW Fitzgerald (Castell 1952: 92).
H(37) listed by Macvicar (1905: 14).
†H37 listed by Blockeel & Long (1998: 36).
H(38) listed by Macvicar (1905: 14). H(38) listed by Blockeel & Long (1998: 36).
H39 1952: moss-covered boulders, Loughan Bay, JW Fitzgerald (Castell 1955: 579).
H40 1959: moss-covered tree trunk, Glenedra, nr Dungiven, JW Fitzgerald (Castell 1960: 765).

21/8 ***Barbilophozia barbata*** (Schmidel ex Schreb.) Loeske

H(1) listed by Macvicar (1905: 13). H(1) listed by Blockeel & Long (1998: 37).
[H(6) listed by Macvicar (1905: 13). H6 deleted because no record or voucher traced, comm. MM Yeo (Long 1990a: 24)].
H(12) 1913: Great Saltee I., HW Lett (*Irish Nat.* **22**, 194, 1913), comm. JW Fitzgerald (Castell 1952: 92).
H(20) listed by Macvicar (1905: 13).
†H20 listed by Blockeel & Long (1998: 37).
H(21) listed by Macvicar (1905: 13). H(21) listed by Blockeel & Long (1998: 37).
H(27) listed by Macvicar (1905: 13). H(27) listed by Blockeel & Long (1998: 37).
H(30) listed by Macvicar (1905: 13). H(30) listed by Blockeel & Long (1998: 37).
H(35) listed by Macvicar (1905: 13). H(35) listed by Blockeel & Long (1998: 37).
[H(37) listed by Macvicar (1905: 13). H37 deleted because no record or voucher traced, comm. MM Yeo (Long 1990a: 24)].
H(40) listed by Macvicar (1905: 13).
†H40 listed by Blockeel & Long (1998: 37).

22/1 ***Anastrepta orcadensis*** (Hook.) Schiffn.

H(1) listed by Macvicar (1905: 14).
†H1 listed by Blockeel & Long (1998: 37).
H(2) 1925: Horses Glen, Mangerton, JB

Duncan, comm. UK Duncan (Paton 1963: 486).
H2 1972: damp heath on steep NW-facing slope, Mangerton, EC Mhic Daeid (Paton 1974b: 163).
H3 1979: among *Herberta* on bank in corrie above Gouganebarra L., AC Crundwell (Corley 1980a: 28).
[H(6) listed by Macvicar (1905: 14). H6 deleted because no record or voucher traced, comm. MM Yeo (Long 1990a: 24)].
†H16 listed by Blockeel & Long (1998: 37).
H20 1975: amongst turf on rocky slope, North Prison, Lugnaquillia Mt., JA Paton (BBS exc.) (Paton 1976: 18).
H(27) listed by Macvicar (1905: 14).
†H27 listed by Blockeel & Long (1998: 37).
H29 1965: amongst *Calluna* on slopes below crags, 1000 ft alt., nr Aghadunvane S of L. Melvin, AR Perry & EF Warburg (Paton 1966: 183).
H33 1957: scattered stems among *Plagiothecium undulatum* and *Bazzania tricrenata* at 1750 ft among boulders on NE side of Tiltinbane, AC Crundwell (Castell 1958: 465).
H35 1961: shaded heathery slopes facing N at *ca* 1000 ft [alt.], Slieve Tooey nr Ardara, DA Ratcliffe (Paton 1962: 360).
1961: with other hepatics beneath *Calluna* on damp N-facing slope at 1500 ft [alt.], Slieve League, nr Carrick, DA Ratcliffe (Paton 1962: 360).

23/2 ***Lophozia ventricosa*** (Dicks.) Dumort. (syn. *Lophozia silvicola* H.Buch, *L. ventricosa* var. *silvicola* (H.Buch) E.W. Jones ex R.M. Schust. [but see note below], *L. ventricosa* var. *confertifolia* (Schiffn.) Husn., *L. ventricosa* var. *longiflora* auct. non (Nees) Macoun)

[H(1) listed by Macvicar (1905: 13)].
H1 1951: at base of boulder on grassy hillside, alt. 400 ft, nr Glenbeigh, *leg.* & det. AD Banwell (Castell 1952: 92), as *Lophozia silvicola*.
1983: heathy bank nr road onto Rossmore I., W of Kenmare, JA Paton (Corley 1984: 24), as var. *ventricosa*.
H(2) listed by Macvicar (1905: 13).
†H2 listed by Blockeel & Long (1998: 37).
H(3) listed by Macvicar (1905: 13).
H3 H3 record confirmed as var. *ventricosa* (Paton 1963: 485).
1989: on peaty N-facing slope by sea, 30 m, Garnish Point, V54, DG Long 15463 (Long 1990a: 25).
H4 1966: shady rock face, Ringnanean Wood, nr mouth of Stick R., MFV Corley (Corley 1980a: 27).
†H5 listed by Blockeel & Long (1998: 37).
H(6) listed by Macvicar (1905: 13).
†H6 listed by Blockeel & Long (1998: 37).
H(7) listed by Macvicar (1905: 13).
H7 1966: streambank, Knockastakeen, Galtee Mts, JA Paton (Corley 1984: 24), as var. *ventricosa*.
H8 1966: among *Sphagnum*, peaty bank on moor, Slievereagh nr Ballylanders, MFV Corley & Parker (Paton 1967c: 397).
H9 1968: peaty bank nr Shandangan L., NE of Corrofin, JA Paton (Corley 1984: 24), as var. *ventricosa*.
H10 1979: moorland on south side of Keeper Hill, AC Crundwell (Corley 1980a: 27).
H(12) 1913: Great Saltee I., HW Lett (*Irish Nat.* **22**, 193, 1913), comm. JW Fitzgerald (Castell 1952: 92).
H12 1975: heathy banks W of Cloroge, Mt Leinster, JA Paton (Corley 1984: 24), as var. *ventricosa*.
[H13 deleted because no record traced, comm. MM Yeo, replaced by next record (Long 1990a: 25)].
H13 1975: bank by stream, The Black Banks, Mt Leinster, JA Paton (Corley 1980a: 28), as var. *silvicola*.
1975: on bank by stream, The Black Banks, Mt Leinster, JA Paton (Long 1990a: 25).
H14 1955: side of bog cutting, Abbeyleix, JS Thomson, conf. as 'a weak state' by EC Wallace (Castell 1956: 147).
H15 1962: growing through *Sphagnum*, raised bog nr Woodford, AJE Smith, as var. *ventricosa* (Paton 1963: 485, Long 1990a: 25).
H(16) listed by Macvicar (1905: 13).
H16 1985: blanket bog W of Ballinaboy, AC Bouman (Corley 1987: 18), as var. *ventricosa*.
[H(17) listed by Macvicar (1905: 13)].
H18 1955: with *Sphagnum* spp., birchwood on Cloncreen Bog, ALK King (Castell 1956: 147).
H(20) listed by Macvicar (1905: 13).
H20 1988: on peaty bank by forestry road, 180 m, Glenmalur Valley E of

Lugnaquilla, DG Long 14907 (Long 1989: 21), as var. *silvicola*.
1993: amongst boulders at foot of waterfall, 210 m alt., Powerscourt Waterfall, O11, DG Long 23198 (Long 1994: 34).

H(21) listed by Macvicar (1905: 13).

†H21 listed by Blockeel & Long (1998: 37).

H22 1978: bog S of Teevurcher, N of Moynalty, DM Synnott (Corley 1980a: 27).

H23 1952: mixed with *Sphagnum* in bog, nr Ballinafid Lake, NE end of L. Owel, JS Thomson (Castell 1954: 473).

†H24 listed by Blockeel & Long (1998: 37).

H25 1972: peat on old red sandstone rock, Slieve Bawn, N of Lanesborough, W Rubers (U) (Corley 1980a: 27-28).

H26 1957: growing through *Dicranella heteromalla*, W slope of [The] Ox Mts, ALK King (Castell 1958: 464).
1987: on peaty tussock on open slope, woodland E of Cloon River nr Partry, DG Long & JA Paton (Long 1988: 30), as var. *ventricosa*.
1987: on peat in clearing in woodland, E bank of Cloon River nr Partry, DG Long (Long 1988: 30), as var. *silvicola*.

H(27) listed by Macvicar (1905: 13).

H27 1987: amongst *Sphagnum* on damp peaty slope, lower E slope of Slievemore, Achill I., DG Long (Long 1988: 30), as var. *ventricosa*.
1987: on wet peaty NE-facing slope, E corrie of Slievemore, Achill I., DG Long (Long 1988: 30), as var. *silvicola*.

H(28) listed by Macvicar (1905: 13).

H28 1970: peaty bank near summit of Ben Bulbin, JA Paton 4039 (Corley 1984: 24, Long 1990a: 25), as var. *ventricosa*.

[H29 deleted because probable voucher (1875: Glenade, D Moore, DBN) is not determinable to variety, replaced by next record (Long 1990a: 25)].

H29 1963: peaty ground among limestone boulders, Peakadaw, Glenade, JW Fitzgerald & AR Perry, NMW (Long 1990a: 25).

H(30) listed by Macvicar (1905: 13).

†H30 listed by Blockeel & Long (1998: 37).

H31 1999: on peaty humus among rocks, *ca* 175 m alt., Two Mile River, Carlingford Mountain, J11, TL Blockeel 28/157 (Blackstock 2000: 41).

H32 2002: on *Sphagnum* in blanket bog flush, 350 m alt., E of Three Counties Hollow, Eshbrack, H54, N Lockhart (Blackstock 2003: 41).

H(33) 1919: Lavilly, nr Enniskillen, WN Tetley (BBSUK) (Castell 1953: 299).

H33 1960: edge of peat drain below scarp N of Lough Navar, JW Fitzgerald (Paton 1961: 152-153).
1969: cutover bog, W of Carricknagower L., SE of Belleek, JA Paton (Corley 1984: 24).

H34 1962: on peat, Croaghconnellagh, Tawnawully Mts, J Appleyard & EC Wallace, det. JA Paton as var. *ventricosa* (Paton 1963: 485, Long 1990a: 25).

H(35) listed by Macvicar (1905: 13).

H35 H35 record confirmed as var. *ventricosa* (Paton 1963: 485).
1990: peaty soil at base of tree, *ca* 60 m alt., head of L. Beagh, Glenveagh, B91, Blockeel 19/409 (Long 1991: 38).
1990: on peaty bank, *ca* 300 m alt., bank of stream running NW from L. Feeane, Aghla More, B92, TL Blockeel 19/460 (Long 1991: 38), as var. *silvicola*.

H36 1952: Lough Bradan, JW Fitzgerald (Castell 1953: 299). H36 record confirmed as var. *ventricosa* (Paton 1963: 485).
1958: creeping over *Dicranum scoparium* in old oak wood, Drumlea Wood, nr Gortin, JW Fitzgerald (Castell 1960: 765), as var. *silvicola*.

H(37) listed by Macvicar (1905: 13).

†H37 listed by Blockeel & Long (1998: 37).

H(38) listed by Macvicar (1905: 13).

†H38 listed by Blockeel & Long (1998: 37).

H(39) listed by Macvicar (1905: 13).

†H39 listed by Blockeel & Long (1998: 37).

[H40 1952: *Sphagnum* bog, Benbradagh, EM Lobley & J Taylor, comm. EM Lobley, conf. (with notes concluding 'I should not care to name these plants definitely at present') by EW Jones, record placed in brackets (Castell 1953: 299)].

†H40 listed by Blockeel & Long (1998: 37).

L. ventricosa var. *silvicola* was treated as a synonym of *L. ventricosa* by Paton (1999: 190) because it seemed to be only a minor variant without taxonomic or ecological sdignificance, differing only in the form of the oil bodies. However, Bakalin (2001) maintains *L. silvicola* at species rank and argues that there are other differentiating characters, so further study is needed.

[23/3 **Lophozia longiflora** (Nees) Schiffn.]
(syn. *Lophozia guttulata* (Lindb.) A. Evans, *L. porphyroleuca* Nees nom. illeg.)

[H(12) 1913: Great Saltee I., HW Lett (*Irish Nat.* **22**, 194, 1913), comm. JW Fitzgerald (Castell 1952: 92), as *L. porphyroleuca*].
[H(20) listed by Macvicar (1905: 13) as *L. porphyroleuca*].
[H(27) listed by Macvicar (1905: 13) as *L. porphyroleuca*. H27 deleted because voucher is *L. ventricosa*, det. JA Paton (Long 1996: 42)].
[H(31) listed by Macvicar (1905: 13) as *L. porphyroleuca*].
[H32 1961: creeping over *Sphagnum*, Killyneill, nr Monaghan, JW Fitzgerald (Paton 1961: 358). H32 record confirmed as *L. porphyroleuca* by checking specimen (Paton 1963: 485). H32 deleted because voucher is *L. ventricosa*, det. JA Paton (Long 1996: 42)].
[H33 1961: among bryophytes on sandstone, Braade Scarp, Navar Forest, JW Fitzgerald (Paton 1961: 358). H33 record confirmed as *L. porphyroleuca* by checking specimen (Paton 1963: 485). H33 deleted because voucher is *L. ventricosa*, det. JA Paton (Long 1996: 42)].
[H(35) listed by Macvicar (1905: 13) as *L. porphyroleuca*].
[H36 1952: Lough Bradan, JW Fitzgerald (Castell 1953: 299), as *L. porphyroleuca*. H36 record confirmed as *L. porphyroleuca* by checking specimen (Paton 1963: 485). H36 deleted because voucher is *L. ventricosa*, det. JA Paton (Long 1996: 42)].
[H(37) listed by Macvicar (1905: 13) as *L. porphyroleuca*].
[H(38) listed by Macvicar (1905: 13) as *L. porphyroleuca*].
[H(39) listed by Macvicar (1905: 13) as *L. porphyroleuca*].

[All Irish records are errors (JA Paton in Long 1996: 42-43)].

23/5 **Lophozia sudetica** (Nees ex Huebener) Grolle
(syn. *Lophozia alpestris* auct. non (Schleich. ex F.Weber) Evans)

H(1) listed by Macvicar (1905: 13). H(1) listed by Blockeel & Long (1998: 37).
[H(2) listed by Macvicar (1905: 13)].
H2 1953: turf bank on summit, Ballincollig Hill, AP Fanning 1478 (DBN) (Long 1999b: 26).
H3 1979: top of boulder beside NE tributary of Glengarriff R., JA Paton (Corley 1980a: 28).
[H(9) listed by Macvicar (1905: 13). H9 deleted as no record or voucher traced, comm. MM Yeo (Long 1990a: 25)].
H(12) 1913: Great Saltee I., HW Lett (*Irish Nat.* **22**, 194, 1913), comm. JW Fitzgerald (Castell 1952: 92).
†H12 listed by Blockeel & Long (1998: 37).
H(13) listed by Macvicar (1905: 13). H(13) listed by Blockeel & Long (1998: 37).
H16 1970: rock on NE slope, Muckanaght, The Twelve Pins, JA Paton (Paton 1971a: 370).
H(20) listed by Macvicar (1905: 13).
†H20 listed by Blockeel & Long (1998: 37).
H(21) listed by Macvicar (1905: 13). H(21) listed by Blockeel & Long (1998: 37).
H25 2002: dry heath on hillside below megalithic tomb, *ca* 200 m alt., Kilronan Mountain, Arigna, G91, HG Hodgetts 4147 (Blackstock 2003: 41).
†H27 listed by Blockeel & Long (1998: 37).
H(28) listed by Macvicar (1905: 13). H(28) listed by Blockeel & Long (1998: 37).
[H(30) listed by Macvicar (1905: 13)].
H30 1955: Carrigasimon Hill near Virginia, ALK King (DBN) (Long 1999b: 26).
H35 2001: N-facing siliceous rocks on small 'tor' on hillside, *ca* 500 m alt., Binnacally, Lavagh Beg, G99, NG Hodgetts 3869 (Blackstock 2003: 41).
H36 1957: among boulders, Cloughmore, nr Glenhull, JW Fitzgerald (Castell 1959: 627).
†H37 listed by Blockeel & Long (1998: 37).
H(38) listed by Macvicar (1905: 13). H(38) listed by Blockeel & Long (1998: 37).
H(39) listed by Macvicar (1905: 13).
†H39 listed by Blockeel & Long (1998: 37).
H40 1968: on blocks below Benbradagh, HH Birks & JW Fitzgerald (Paton 1969a: 869).

23/6 *Lophozia excisa* (Dicks.) Dumort.

H(1) listed by Macvicar (1905: 13). H(1) listed by Blockeel & Long (1998: 37).
†H2 listed by Blockeel & Long (1998: 37).
H(3) listed by Macvicar (1905: 13).
†H3 listed by Blockeel & Long (1998: 37).
H4 1967: crevices on wall of bridge over R. Sullane, E of Macroom, JW Fitzgerald (Paton 1968: 622).
H6 1966: earthy track through old copper mines on cliffs E of Bunmahon, JA Paton & ERB Little (BBS exc.) (Paton 1967c: 397).
H(7) listed by Macvicar (1905: 13). H(7) listed by Blockeel & Long (1998: 37).
H(16) listed by Macvicar (1905: 13). H(16) listed by Blockeel & Long (1998: 37).
H20 1972: beside path, dunes N of Arcklow [*sic* = Arklow] WV Rubers (Paton 1974b: 163).
†H22 listed by Blockeel & Long (1998: 37).
H(27) listed by Macvicar (1905: 13).
†H27 listed by Blockeel & Long (1998: 37).
H(28) listed by Macvicar (1905: 13).
†H28 listed by Blockeel & Long (1998: 37).
H29 1963: shaded rocks, bog E of Sriff Cottage nr Dromahair, JW Fitzgerald & AR Perry (Paton 1964: 714).
H33 1960: in shaded crevice among boulders, growing through *Dicranum scoparium*, Doagh Lough, JW Fitzgerald (Paton 1961: 153).
H34 2002: on unshaded thin soil among rocks on track edge with patchy low *Calluna*, *ca* 50 m alt., Dunree Head, C23, DT Holyoak 02-783 (Blackstock 2003: 41).
H(35) listed by Macvicar (1905: 13).
†H35 listed by Blockeel & Long (1998: 37).
H36 1956: floor of sand pit, nr Coalisland, JW Fitzgerald & MPH Kertland (Castell 1957: 324).
H(37) listed by Macvicar (1905: 13).
†H37 listed by Blockeel & Long (1998: 37).
H(38) listed by Macvicar (1905: 13).
†H38 listed by Blockeel & Long (1998: 37).
H(39) 1928: Giant's Causeway (BBS exc.) (Duncan 1928: 116).
†H39 listed by Blockeel & Long (1998: 37).
H40 1965: wet shaded rocks, Mullaghmore nr Dungiven, JW Fitzgerald (Paton 1966: 183).

[23/10 *Lophozia capitata* (Hook.) Macoun]

[H(3) pre 1816: on rock, dry mountainous situation near Bantry, E Hutchins (in WJ Hooker, 1816, *Brit. Jung*. p. 80, [EW Jones in] *Trans. BBS* **1**, 355) (Castell 1951: 493). H3 deleted because the Irish specimen, probably E Hutchins' specimen from Bantry Bay (GL), is *Acrobolbus wilsonii*, comm. EW Jones & AC Crundwell (Paton 1975: 10)].

23/11 *Lophozia incisa* (Schrad.) Dumort.

H(1) listed by Macvicar (1905: 13).
†H1 listed by Blockeel & Long (1998: 38).
[H(2) listed by Macvicar (1905: 13)].
H2 1973: quarry SE of Killarney nr Danesfort, WV Rubers (Corley 1980a: 28).
H(3) listed by Macvicar (1905: 13).
†H3 listed by Blockeel & Long (1998: 38).
H(6) 1933: Poolvona, E Armitage (anon. 1934c: 143).
†H6 listed by Blockeel & Long (1998: 38).
H7 1966: on peat and soil, rocky slopes above L. Curra, Galtee Mts, ERB Little & JG Duckett (BBS exc.) (Paton 1967c: 397).
H8 1959: bog nr Castleconnell, ALK King (Castell 1960: 765).
H9 1959: blanket bog on Carboniferous shales, Slieve Elva nr Lisdoonvarna, MCF Proctor (Paton 1967c: 397).
H10 1965: in cut-away bog by L. Nahinch, ALK King (Paton 1966: 183).
H11 1966: bog, Derryfadda, W of Johnstown, J Appleyard *et al.* (BBS exc.) (Paton 1967c: 397).
H13 1975: moist slope, The Black Banks, Mt Leinster, N Kirby (BBS exc.) (Paton 1976: 18).
H(14) listed by Macvicar (1905: 13). H(14) listed by Blockeel & Long (1998: 37).
H(16) listed by Macvicar (1905: 13).
†H16 listed by Blockeel & Long (1998: 38).
H(17) listed by Macvicar (1905: 13).
†H17 listed by Blockeel & Long (1998: 38).
H(18) listed by Macvicar (1905: 13).
†H18 listed by Blockeel & Long (1998: 38).
H19 1949: turfy ground, Ballymount Bog nr Calverstown, JS Thomson, comm. ALK King (Paton 1964: 714).
H(20) listed by Macvicar (1905: 13).
†H20 listed by Blockeel & Long (1998: 38).

H(21) listed by Macvicar (1905: 13).
†H21 listed by Blockeel & Long (1998: 38).
H22 1952: Clonycavan Bog, nr Ballivor ALK King (Castell 1953: 299).
1978: sand dune bank, Mornington, DM Synnott (Corley 1980a: 28).
H23 1970: bog S of Doonis L., N of Glassan, JA Paton (Paton 1971a: 370).
H24 1957: bog, Newtownforbes [*sic* = Newton Forbes], MPH Kertland & ALK King, comm. ALK King (Castell 1958: 465).
H25 1965: moorland bog at 700 ft alt., Kilronan Mt. nr Ballyfarnan, JW Fitzgerald & EM Lobley (Paton 1966: 183).
H26 1957: W slope, [The] Ox Mts, ALK King (Castell 1958: 465).
H(27) listed by Macvicar (1905: 13).
†H27 listed by Blockeel & Long (1998: 38).
H(28) listed by Macvicar (1905: 13).
†H28 listed by Blockeel & Long (1998: 38).
H29 1963: peat overlying limestone, Boggaun nr Manorhamilton, JW Fitzgerald & AR Perry (Paton 1964: 714).
H30 1957: peaty bànk, SW side of Tiltinbane, AC Crundwell (Castell 1958: 465).
H32 1961: creeping over sphagnum bog at Killyneill, nr Monaghan, JW Fitzgerald (Paton 1962: 359).
H(33) 1913: bog, Five Crossroads, nr Florence Court, WN Tetley (BBSUK) (Castell 1953: 299).
†H33 listed by Blockeel & Long (1998: 38).
H34 1962: on peat, Croaghconnellagh, Tawnawully Mts, J Appleyard & EC Wallace (BBS exc.) Paton 1963: 485).
H(35) listed by Macvicar (1905: 13).
†H35 listed by Blockeel & Long (1998: 38).
H36 1952: flaccid form, Lough Bradan, JW Fitzgerald (Castell 1953: 299).
H(37) listed by Macvicar (1905: 13).
†H37 listed by Blockeel & Long (1998: 38).
H(38) listed by Macvicar (1905: 13). H(38) listed by Blockeel & Long (1998: 38).
H(39) listed by Macvicar (1905: 13).
†H39 listed by Blockeel & Long (1998: 38).
H(40) listed by Macvicar (1905: 13).
†H40 listed by Blockeel & Long (1998: 38).

23/12 ***Lophozia opacifolia*** Culm. ex Meyl.

H16 1994: wet rocks in gully on N-facing cliffs, 420 m alt., NE corrie of Bengower, Twelve Bens, L75, DG Long 25486 (Long 1995b: 38).
H27 1987: mossy slope on exposed ridge, 730 m, nr middle summit of Mweelrea, GP Rothero & DG Long (Long 1988: 30).
H35 1978: on peat amongst *Calluna*, Muckish Mt., JW Fitzgerald & HH Birks (Fitzgerald 1969, Paton 1969a: 869).

23/13 ***Lophozia bicrenata*** (Schmidel ex Hoffm.) Dumort.

H(1) listed by Macvicar (1905: 13). H(1) listed by Blockeel & Long (1998: 38).
H(2) 1935: Mangerton, no collector named (BBS exc.) (Watson 1936: 265, anon. 1937b: 369).
H(4) listed by Macvicar (1905: 13). H(4) listed by Blockeel & Long (1998: 38).
H6 1966: peaty wall top, Knockmealdown Mts, JG Duckett & J Appleyard (Paton 1967c: 397).
H(7) listed by Macvicar (1905: 13). H(7) listed by Blockeel & Long (1998: 38).
H8 1966: damp ground in plantation, Paradise Hill, Galtee Mts, MFV Corley & JS Parker (Paton 1967c: 397).
H10 1979: soil bank, Keeper Hill, N Lockhart (Corley 1980a: 28).
H(12) 1913: Great Saltee I., HW Lett (*Irish Nat.* **22**, 194, 1913), comm. JW Fitzgerald (Castell 1952: 92).
†H12 listed by Blockeel & Long (1998: 38).
H13 1969: bank of track to old quarry, Lackan nr Old Leighlin, JW Fitzgerald (Paton 1979: 189).
H(16) listed by Macvicar (1905: 13). H(16) listed by Blockeel & Long (1998: 38).
H(20) listed by Macvicar (1905: 13). H(20) listed by Blockeel & Long (1998: 38).
H(21) listed by Macvicar (1905: 13). H(21) listed by Blockeel & Long (1998: 38).
H22 1978: wet clay bank, Hill 426, Greenanstown, Naul, DM Synnott (Corley 1979: 23).
H28 1970: roadside quarry nr Masshill, JA Paton (BBS exc.) (Paton 1971a: 371, Appleyard 1971: 389).
H35 1969: roadside bank, Croaghmuckross nr Kilcar, JA Paton (Paton 1970: 189).
H36 1957: bare peat, Wolf Hill, nr Cookstown, JW Fitzgerald (Castell 1959: 627).
H37 1966: dry peat among rocks, Cashel

Lakes, Silverbridge, JW Fitzgerald & MPH Kertland (Paton 1967c: 397).
H(38) listed by Macvicar (1905: 13).
†H38 listed by Blockeel & Long (1998: 38).
†H39 listed by Blockeel & Long (1998: 38).

24/1a ***Leiocolea rutheana*** (Limpr.) Müll.Frib., **var.** ***rutheana***

H27 1987: amongst *Ctenidium molluscum,* Campylium *stellatum* in a *Schoenus*-dominated rich flush, *ca* 200 ft alt., ½ mile SW of Brackloon Lough, N Lockhart (BBSUK), det. & comm. JA Paton (Lockhart 1989b, Long 1989: 21, Paton 1995, Long 1996: 43).

24/2 ***Leiocolea gillmanii*** (Austin) A.Evans

H27 1987: in wet sandy fenny pasture, N end of Lough Doo, nr Valley, Achill I., AR Perry & BM Murray (Long 1988: 31).

24/3 ***Leiocolea bantriensis*** (Hook.) Jörg. (syn. *Lophozia bantriensis* auct., *L. bantryensis* Steph., *L. muelleri* Dumort. Non (Nees ex Lindb.) Jörg., *L. muelleri* var. *bantriensis* Hook.).

H(1) listed by Macvicar (1905: 13).
†H1 listed by Blockeel & Long (1998: 38).
H(2) 1911: Eagle's Nest, Killarney, JB Duncan (anon.1912b: 57), as *Lophozia muelleri* var. *bantryensis.*
†H2 listed by Blockeel & Long (1998: 38).
H(3) listed by Macvicar (1905: 13). H(3) listed by Blockeel & Long (1998: 38).
H7 1966: calcareous flush beside stream, Knockastackeen, Galtee Mts, JW Fitzgerald *et al.* (BBS exc.) (Paton 1967c: 398).
[H(14) listed by Macvicar (1905: 13)].
H14 1966: in calcareous flush, Derry Hills, Leix, JW Fitzgerald (Paton 1967c: 398).
†H15 listed by Blockeel & Long (1998: 38).
†H16 listed by Blockeel & Long (1998: 38).
H(20) listed by Macvicar (1905: 13). H(20) listed by Blockeel & Long (1998: 38).
H(27) listed by Blockeel & Long (1998: 38).
[H(28) listed by Macvicar (1905: 13)].
H(28) 1928: Gleniff, Ben Bulben (BBS exc.) (Duncan 1928: 118).
†H28 listed by Blockeel & Long (1998: 38).
H(29) 1937: Glenade, no collector named (BBS exc.) (Armitage 1938: 13). 1937: Glenade, W Watson (anon. 1938e: 43).
†H29 listed by Blockeel & Long (1998: 38).
H31 1968: with *Conocephalum*, waterfall gorge, S side of Carnavaddy, Carlingford peninsula, DM Synnott (Paton 1969a: 869).
H(33) 1905: on rocks, Correl Glen, very scarce, D McArdle (*Irish Nat.* **16**, 238, 1907), comm. JW Fitzgerald (Castell 1952: 92).
†H33 listed by Blockeel & Long (1998: 38).
H35 1969: margin of Sessiagh L., Dunfanaghy, JA Paton (Paton 1970: 189).
H36 1956: marsh beside Lough More, nr Favor Royal, JW Fitzgerald & MPH Kertland (Castell 1957: 324).
H(38) listed by Macvicar (1905: 13). H(38) listed by Blockeel & Long (1998: 38).
[H(39) listed by Macvicar (1905: 13)].
H(39) 1928: Cave Hill, Belfast (BBS exc.) (Duncan 1928: 115).
†H39 listed by Blockeel & Long (1998: 38).
H40 1964: rocks by stream, Legananam Pot, nr Dungiven, JW Fitzgerald (Paton 1965a: 853).

24/4 ***Leiocolea fitzgeraldiae*** Paton & A.R. Perry

H27 1994: on irrigated ledges of ± basic sea cliffs, 300 m alt., Clare I., L68, GP Rothero 94/078 (Long 1996: 43).
H(28) 1928: Gleniff, [13/74], HH Knight (NMW) (Paton & Perry 1995: 476, Long 1996: 43).
H28 1987: moist limestone rocks and boulders, Gleniff, 13/7246, JA Paton 7521 & 7522 (E) (Paton & Perry 1995: 477, Long 1996: 43).
H29 1963: limestone boulder and calcareous rock face, Peakadaw, Glenade, 13/8046, AR Perry, Hb. Perry (Paton & Perry 1995: 477, Long 1996: 43).
H33 1951: Braade Scarp, Navar Forest, [23/05], JW Fitzgerald (NMW) (Paton & Perry 1995: 477, [& Errata] 863, Long 1996: 43).

24/5 ***Leiocolea collaris*** (Nees) Schljakov (syn. *Leiocolea alpestris* (Schleich. ex F. Weber) Isov., *L. muelleri* (Nees ex Lindb.) Jörg., *Lophozia alpestris* (Schleich. ex F.Weber) Evans)

H(1) 1935: above L. Cruttia, no collector named (BBS exc.) (Watson 1936: 265, anon. 1937b: 369).
†H1 listed by Blockeel & Long (1998: 39).
H2 1968: small fen on margin of L. Leane nr Muckross Abbey, Killarney, JA Paton (Paton 1969a: 869).
H16 1957: basic rocks at 700 ft [alt.], above Glencorbet, Twelve Pins, AC Crundwell (BBS exc.) (Castell 1958: 464).
H26 1957: shore of Lough Conn, AC Crundwell & RE Parker, comm. AC Crundwell (Castell 1958: 464).
1987: NE shore of Lough Mask, Ballygarry Pier, S of Partry, JA Paton (Long 1988: 31).
†H27 listed by Blockeel & Long (1998: 39).
†H28 listed by Blockeel & Long (1998: 39).
H(29) listed by Macvicar (1905: 13).
†H29 listed by Blockeel & Long (1998: 39).
H33 1957: boulder in bed of Cladagh R., L. Macnean Lower, AC Crundwell (Castell 1958: 464).
H35 1967: stones in stream, W side of L. Eske, HH Birks, HJB Birks & DA Ratcliffe (Paton 1968: 622).
H36 1961: wet ground nr spring, Binnawooda, JW Fitzgerald (Castell 1952: 92).
H37 1964: on earth-topped wall below tower, Slieve Gullion, JW Fitzgerald & MPH Kertland (Paton 1965a: 854). Record apparently omitted in error from Corley & Hill (1981: 32) and Blockeel & Long (1998).
†H39 listed by Blockeel & Long (1998: 39).

The name *Leiocolea collaris* is adopted for this species in place of *L. alpestris* following Grolle & Long (2000: 107, 118).

24/6 ***Leiocolea heterocolpos*** (Thed. ex Hartm.) H.Buch

H39 1969: amongst mosses on shaded basalt rocks, Glenariff Glen, S of Cushendall, JA Paton (Paton 1970: 189, 1972b).

24/7 ***Leiocolea badensis*** (Gottsche) Jörg. (syn. *Lophozia badensis* (Gottsche) Schiffn.)

H9 1957: roadside ditch, Black Head, AC Crundwell (BBS exc.) (Castell 1958: 464).
H11 2000: amongst *Gymnostomum calcareum* and *Aneura pinguis*, encrusted with tufa in disused quarry, 50 m alt., 1 km N of Thomastown, S54, N Lockhart 00/8a (Blackstock 2001: 34).
H15 1994: vertical calcareous bank of streamlet nr Boleyneendorish River, Slieve Aughty, M50, JA Paton 7632 (Long 1995b: 38).
H16 1970: in sandy turf on rocks by sea, Ballyconneely Bay, MFV Corley (Paton 1971a: 371).
H17 1957: marl clay, turlough, Killower, nr Tuam, EM Lobley (BBS exc.) (Castell 1958: 464).
H18 1973: wet calcareous loam, sandpit in esker, Longford, between Roscrea and Kinnitty, WV Rubers (Corley 1980a: 28).
H20 1969: vertical face of sand pit in Ballyman Glen, S of boundary stream, ALK King (Paton 1970: 189).
H22 1966: sandy bank of stream, Stalleen, Dunore, Drogheda, DM Synnott (Paton 1967c: 398).
H23 1970: fen on E shore of L. Ennell, S of Mullingar, JA Paton (Paton 1971a: 371).
H25 1970: calcareous flush above L. Ree, Portrunny Bay, JA Paton (Paton 1971a: 371).
H26 1981: calcareous grassland, shore of L. Carra, nr Moorehall, N Lockhart (Corley 1983: 48).
†H27 listed by Blockeel & Long (1998: 39).
H(28) 1928: nr Rosses Point, Sligo (BBS exc.) (Duncan 1928: 119).
†H28 listed by Blockeel & Long (1998: 39).
H33 1960: moist calcareous clay, Hanging Rock, JW Fitzgerald (Paton 1961: 152).
H(34) 1914: sandhills, Ballyliffen, J Hunter (NMW), comm. AJE Smith (Paton 1963: 485).
H35 1962: calcareous turf, Tramore Strand, Murral, EM Lobley (BBS exc.) (Paton 1963: 485).
H36 1957: moist calcareous soil, Butterlope, JW Fitzgerald (Castell 1958: 464).
H(39) 1928: sandhills, Portrush (BBS exc.)

(Duncan 1928: 116). H(39) listed by Blockeel & Long (1998: 39).
H(40) no date: Downhill, JD Houston, per WR Megaw (anon. 1938e: 43).
†H40 listed by Blockeel & Long (1998: 39).

24/8 ***Leiocolea turbinata*** (Raddi) H.Buch (syn. *Lophozia turbinata* (Raddi) Steph.)

H(1) listed by Macvicar (1905: 13). H(1) listed by Blockeel & Long (1998: 39).
H(2) listed by Macvicar (1905: 13).
†H2 listed by Blockeel & Long (1998: 39).
H4 1951: roadside bank NW of Mallow, AC Crundwell (Castell 1952: 92).
H5 1956: bank of ditch in lane, Tourig, nr Youghal, EC Wallace (Castell 1957: 324).
[H(6) listed by Macvicar (1905: 13). H6 deleted because no record or voucher traced, comm. MM Yeo (Long 1990a: 25)].
H6 1999: on vertical tufa in shaded streamside, Ballymacart River, X28, DH Wrench (Blackstock 2000: 41).
H7 1966: side of ditch, Tower, Palatine Street, Slieve Ardagh Hills, JW Fitzgerald *et al.* (BBS exc.) (Paton 1967c: 397).
H8 1966: on calcareous bank by stream, Slievereagh nr Ballylanders, MFV Corley & JS Parker (Paton 1967c: 397).
H9 1957: calcareous tufa below limestone rocks, Blackhead [*sic* = Black Head], EM Lobley (BBS exc.) (Castell 1958: 464).
H10 1979: old red sandstone rock ledge, Clare Glens, nr Newport, AC Crundwell (Corley 1980a: 28).
H11 1966: ditch-bank, Foulkscourt House nr Johnstown, JG Duckett & ERB Little (BBS exc.) (Paton 1967c: 397).
H12 1954: heavily shaded bank of well, Duncannon, ALK King (Castell 1955: 579).
H(13) listed by Macvicar (1905: 13).
†H13 listed by Blockeel & Long (1998: 39).
H(14) listed by Macvicar (1905: 13).
†H14 listed by Blockeel & Long (1998: 39).
H15 1968: bank above river, The Punchbowl, Gort, JA Paton (Paton 1969a: 869).
H16 1988: damp hollow on sandy slope by sea, N side of Omey I., DG Long 14868 (Long 1989: 21).
H(17) listed by Macvicar (1905: 13). H(17) listed by Blockeel & Long (1998: 39).
H(18) listed by Macvicar (1905: 13). H(18) listed by Blockeel & Long (1998: 39).
[H(19) listed by Macvicar (1905: 13)].
H19 1969: on stone beside old sulphur spring, near Leixlip, ALK King (DBN) (Long 1999b: 26).
H(20) listed by Macvicar (1905: 13). H(20) listed by Blockeel & Long (1998: 39).
H(21) listed by Macvicar (1905: 13).
†H21 listed by Blockeel & Long (1998: 39).
H22 1978: wet rocks and tufa by the road, SE of Stackallen Bridge, Slane, DM Synnott (Corley 1979: 23).
H24 1980: clay bank above Royal Canal, Drapers Bridge, DM Synnott (Corley 1982: 20).
H25 1968: lime-rich clay loam bank under hedge 1 mile W of Lanesborough, WV Rubers, P Hessell & J Klein (Paton 1970: 189).
H26 1970: W bank of the Pollagh R., NE of Balla, JA Paton (Paton 1971a: 371).
H27 1987: amongst *Fossombronia* angulosa on steep sandy bank above stream, Trawmore Sand nr Dookinelly, Achill I., JA Paton (Long 1988: 31).
H(28) 1928: rocks above Glencar Lough, N side (BBS exc.) (Duncan 1928: 119).
†H28 listed by Blockeel & Long (1998: 39).
H(29) 1928: wooded glen, NE end of Glencar Lough (BBS exc.) (Duncan 1928: 118).
†H29 listed by Blockeel & Long (1998: 39).
H31 1966: tufa in limestone quarry N of Dunalk [*sic* = Dundalk], DM Synnott (Paton 1967c: 397).
H32 1954: damp ground in shade, Glaslough Woods, ALK King (Castell 1955: 579).
H(33) 1914: Bohoo Caves, WN Tetley (BBSUK) (Castell 1953: 299).
†H33 listed by Blockeel & Long (1998: 39).
H(34) listed by Macvicar (1905: 13).
†H34 listed by Blockeel & Long (1998: 39).
H(35) listed by Macvicar (1905: 13).
†H35 listed by Blockeel & Long (1998: 39).
H36 1953: sandstone rocks, Adairs Quarry, nr Cookstown, MPH Kertland & EM Lobley (Castell 1955: 579).
H37 1964: earth bank above old canal, Carrickaness, nr Benburb, JW Fitzgerald & MPH Kertland (Paton 1965a: 853).
H(38) listed by Macvicar (1905: 13). H(38) listed by Blockeel & Long (1998: 39).
H(39) listed by Macvicar (1905: 13).
†H39 listed by Blockeel & Long (1998: 39).

H40 1959: wet calcareous ground, Banagher Glen, nr Dungiven, JW Fitzgerald (Castell 1960: 765).

25/1 ***Gymnocolea inflata*** (Huds.) Dumort. (syn. *Gymnocolea inflata* var. *heterostipa* (Carrington. & Spruce) Müll.Frib., *Lophozia inflata* M.Howe, *L. inflata* var. *compacta* Nees, *L. inflata* var. *heterostipa* Carrington & Spruce, *L. inflata* var. *laxa* Nees)

H(1) listed by Macvicar (1905: 12). H(1) listed by Blockeel & Long (1998: 39).
[H(2) listed by Macvicar (1905: 13) as var. *laxa*].
H2 1950: in tuft of *Dicranodontium denudatum*, stream side N slope of Mangerton, LMH & FJ Taylor (Castell 1952: 91).
H(3) listed by Macvicar (1905: 12).
†H3 listed by Blockeel & Long (1998: 39).
H5 1967: track in bog, Lyrenamon, NW of Carrignavar, JW Fitzgerald (Paton 1968: 623).
†H6 listed by Blockeel & Long (1998: 39).
H(7) listed by Macvicar (1905: 12).
†H7 listed by Blockeel & Long (1998: 39).
H9 1964: on bare peat, Hag's Head, ERB Little (Paton 1966: 184).
H10 1951: on *Campylopus* sp. in peat bog, alt. 1300 ft [alt.], Silvermines Mt., AD Banwell, EV Watson & PJ Wanstall (Castell 1952: 91).
H12 1958: under *Calluna*, Forth Mt., ALK King (Castell 1959: 627).
H13 1969: side of bog drain, Sculloge Gap nr Ballymurphy, JW Fitzgerald (Paton 1970: 190).
H14 1956: moorland above Johnsborough, Slieve Bloom Mts, AA Cridland (Castell 1958: 464).
H15 1957: moorland, hills E of Gort, RE Parker (Castell 1958: 464).
H(16) listed by Macvicar (1905: 12).
†H16 listed by Blockeel & Long (1998: 39).
H(18) listed by Macvicar (1905: 12). H(18) listed by Blockeel & Long (1998: 39).
H(20) listed by Macvicar (1905: 12).
†H20 listed by Blockeel & Long (1998: 39).
H(21) listed by Macvicar (1905: 12, 13). H(21) listed by Blockeel & Long (1998: 39).
H23 1979: Corracullin Bog, S of Moate, DM Synnott (Corley 1982: 20), as var. *inflata*.
H24 1955: with *Sphagnum*, on bog surface, Edera Bog, nr Ballymahon, TA Barry, comm. ALK King (Castell 1956: 147).
H25 1965: among *Sphagnum*, Kilronan nr Ballyfarnan, EM Lobley & JW Fitzgerald (Paton 1966: 184).
H26 1965: wet ledges, cliffs S of Glendaduff, [The] Ox Mts, JW Fitzgerald (Paton 1966: 184).
H(27) listed by Macvicar (1905: 12).
†H27 listed by Blockeel & Long (1998: 39).
H(28) 1904: Collooney, D McArdle (DBN), comm. ALK King (Paton 1964: 714).
†H28 listed by Blockeel & Long (1998: 39).
H29 1963: bog E of Sriff Cottage nr Dromahair, JW Fitzgerald & AR Perry (Paton 1964: 714).
H(30) listed by Macvicar (1905: 12).
†H30 listed by Blockeel & Long (1998: 39).
H33 1957: boggy moorland, Belmore Mt., AC Crundwell (Castell 1958: 464).
†H34 listed by Blockeel & Long (1998: 39).
H(35) listed by Macvicar (1905: 12, 13).
†H35 listed by Blockeel & Long (1998: 39).
H36 1956: steep bank of mica schist detritus, Glen Curry Bridge, nr Omagh, JW Fitzgerald & MPH Kertland (Castell 1957: 323).
H(37) listed by Macvicar (1905: 12).
†H37 listed by Blockeel & Long (1998: 39).
H(38) listed by Macvicar (1905: 12, 13).
†H38 listed by Blockeel & Long (1998: 39).
H(39) listed by Macvicar (1905: 12).
†H39 listed by Blockeel & Long (1998: 39).
†H40 listed by Blockeel & Long (1998: 39).

26/1 ***Eremonotus myriocarpus*** (Carrington) Pearson

H1 1968: sheltered rock, SE corrie, Brandon Mt., Dingle, JA Paton (Paton 1969a: 870).
H2 1951: sloping top of boulder just below main fall, Torc Waterfall, EW Jones (Castell 1952: 94).
H16 1968: dripping mica schist at 1400 ft alt., W-facing cliffs, Muckanaght, Twelve Pins, AR Perry (Paton 1970: 190).
H27 1970: ravine, NW slope, The Devil's Mother, N of Killary Harbour, JA Paton (Paton 1971a: 371).
H(34) 1911: rocks, Bulbein [*sic* = Bulbin] Mt., Inishowen, Hunter, *teste* Pearson (*Irish Nat.* 1914, **23**, No. 6), comm. JW Fitzgerald (Paton 1961: 155).

†H34 listed by Blockeel & Long (1998: 39).
H40 1990: on damp, N-facing rock in Big Cleft, Binevenagh, DM Synnott (Long 1991: 38).

27/1 ***Sphenolobopsis pearsonii*** (Spruce) R. M.Schust.
(syn. *Cephaloziella pearsonii* (Spruce) Douin, *Sphenolobus pearsonii* (Spruce) Steph.)

H1 1955: shaded boulder, NE corrie, Brandon Mountain, H Milne-Redhead (Castell 1957: 324).
H2 1972: steep slope above cliffs S of Punch Bowl, Mangerton, EC Mhic Daeid (Paton 1974b: 164).
H3 1955: steeply sloping rocks by waterfall, Lough Nambrackderg, H Milne-Redhead (Castell 1957: 324).
H6 1966: damp rocks on cliffs above Sgilloge Loughs, Comeragh Mts, JA Paton & JG Duckett (BBS exc.) (Paton 1967c: 400).
H7 1966: moist rocks nr L. Curra, Galtee Mts, JA Paton (BBS exc.) (Paton 1967c: 400).
H16 1968: shaded mica schist boulder on W-facing slope at 1200 ft alt., Muckanaght, Twelve Pins, AR Perry (Paton 1969a: 872).
†H27 listed by Blockeel & Long (1998: 40).
H(31) 1900: Carlingford Mt., HW Lett & CH Waddell (DBN), comm. ALK King (Paton 1964: 715).
H35 1967: shaded granite blocks on slopes of The Poisoned Glen, nr Dunlewy, HH Birks, HJB Birks & DA Ratcliffe (Paton 1968: 625).
H40 1965: basalt boulders at 1500 ft alt., Mullaghmore nr Dungiven, JW Fitzgerald (Paton 1966: 185).

28/1 ***Anastrophyllum minutum*** (Schreb.) R. M.Schust.
(syn. *Sphenolobus minutus* (Schreb.) Berggr.)

H(1) listed by Macvicar (1905: 14). H(1) listed by Blockeel & Long (1998: 40).
H(2) listed by Macvicar (1905: 14).
†H2 listed by Blockeel & Long (1998: 40).
H(3) listed by Macvicar (1905: 14).
†H3 listed by Blockeel & Long (1998: 40).
H(6) listed by Macvicar (1905: 14).
†H6 listed by Blockeel & Long (1998: 40).
H(7) listed by Macvicar (1905: 14).
†H7 listed by Blockeel & Long (1998: 40).
H13 1969: peat among block scree below Caher Roe's Den, Blackstairs Mt., JW Fitzgerald (Paton 1970: 189).
H16 1965: raw peat by Lettercraffroe Lough, S of Oughterard, AJE Smith (Paton 1966: 183).
H(20) listed by Macvicar (1905: 14).
†H20 listed by Blockeel & Long (1998: 40).
[H(21) listed by Macvicar (1905: 14)].
H21 1970: bare peat in *Callunetum* on N-facing slope, Dodder Valley, DM Synnott (DBN) (Long 1999b: 26).
H25 1965: on peat in bog at 700 ft alt., Kilronan Mt. nr Ballyfarnan, JW Fitzgerald & EM Lobley (Paton 1966: 183).
H(27) listed by Macvicar (1905: 14).
†H27 listed by Blockeel & Long (1998: 40).
H28 1970: peaty ground among rocks, W ridge of Bricklieve Mts, JA Paton (BBS exc.) (Paton 1971a: 371, Appleyard 1971: 389).
H29 1965: amongst *Calluna* on slopes below crags, 1000 ft alt., nr Aghadunvane, S of L. Melvin, EF Warburg & AR Perry (Paton 1966: 183).
H30 2001: on steep wet peat of low bank in gritstone block-scree, slightly shaded by *Vaccinium myrtillus*, *ca* 314 m alt., S of Englishman's House, H03, DT Holyoak 01-711 (Blackstock: 2002: 39).
H(33) 1905: peaty bank, Correll Glen, very scarce, D McArdle (*Irish Nat.* **16**, 238, 1907), comm. JW Fitzgerald (Castell 1952: 92).
H33 1999: on ledge of N-facing sandstone escarpment, 300 m alt., Letter Scarp, Lough Navar Forest, H05, RD Porley (Blackstock 2000: 41).
H34 1962: peaty overhung bank by Barnes Lough, EF Warburg (BBS exc.) (Paton 1963: 486).
H35 1962: peaty bank, NE slope of Muckish Mountain, RE Longton (BBS exc.) (Paton 1963: 486).
H36 1952: peat shaded by *Calluna*, Lough Bradan, JW Fitzgerald (Castell 1953: 300).
[H(38) listed by Macvicar (1905: 14)].
H38 record (from White River Glen) transferred from H39 to H38 (Paton 1977a: 13).

[H39 deleted because locality on which record was probably based (White River Glen) is in H38, comm. DM Synnott (Paton 1977a: 13)].

28/2 ***Anastrophyllum hellerianum*** (Nees ex Lindenb.) R.M.Schust.
(syn. *Sphenolobus hellerianus* (Nees ex Lindenb.) Steph.)

H33 1961: on rotting *Sorbus* wood, Meenamen Scarp, Navar Forest, JW Fitzgerald (Paton 1962: 359).
H40 1959: large rotting log nr river at first bridge, Banagher Glen, nr Dungiven, JW Fitzgerald (Castell 1960: 765).

29/1 ***Tritomaria exsectiformis*** (Breidl.) Loeske
(syn. *Sphenolobus exsectiformis* (Breidl.) Steph.)

[H1 deleted because no record or voucher traced, comm. MM Yeo (Long 1990a: 25)].
†H2 listed by Blockeel & Long (1998: 40).
†H3 listed by Blockeel & Long (1998: 40).
[H4 deleted because no record or voucher traced, comm. MM Yeo (Long 1990a: 25)].
†H6 listed by Blockeel & Long (1998: 40).
H7 1966: peaty bank by Cooper's Wood S of Galtymore, Galtee Mts, JW Fitzgerald *et al.* (BBS exc.) (Paton 1967c: 398).
H8 1966: peaty bank on hillside above Monabrack, Galtee Mts, JA Paton (Paton 1967c: 398).
H9 1959: on peat under *Calluna*, Slieve Elva, MCF Proctor (Paton 1964: 715).
H10 1965: with *Pohlia nutans*, etc., on cut-away bog at L. Nahinch, ALK King (Paton 1966: 183).
H13 1969: peat among rocks *ca* 2100ft alt., above Caher Roe's Den, Blackstairs Mt., JW Fitzgerald (Paton 1970: 189).
H(17) listed by Macvicar (1905: 14).
†H17 listed by Blockeel & Long (1998: 40).
H(20) listed by Macvicar (1905: 14).
†H20 listed by Blockeel & Long (1998: 40).
H22 1952: bank, Clonycavan Bog, nr Ballivor, ALK King (Castell 1953: 300).
H23 1971: bogland nr Rosemount, AG Side (Paton 1972a: 133).
H24 1957: bog, Newtownforbes [*sic* = Newtown Forbes], MPH Kertland & ALK King, comm. ALK King (Castell 1958: 465).
H25 1966: peat bog 2 miles SW of Termonbarry, W side of R. Shannon, G Halliday & GCG Argent (Paton 1967c: 398).
H26 1970: thin peaty soil on top of boulder, Glendaduff, NE of Foxford, MFV Corley (Paton 1971a: 371).
†H27 listed by Blockeel & Long (1998: 40).
H28 1959: summit of Knocknarea, nr Sligo, ALK King (Castell 1960: 765).
H29 1965: turf on rocks, *ca* 1000 ft alt., S of Lough Melvin, EM Lobley & JW Fitzgerald (Paton 1966: 183).
H30 1965: dry peat at 1500 ft alt., S side of Cuilcagh, JW Fitzgerald & EM Lobley (Paton 1966: 183).
H33 1957: peaty bank, Belmore Mt., AC Crundwell (Castell 1958: 465).
H34 1962: among scree at 900 ft alt., Gap of Mamore 6 m.[iles] N of Buncrana, RD Fitzgerald (Paton 1963: 486).
†H35 listed by Blockeel & Long (1998: 40).
H36 1957: rotting logs in wood, Sheskinawaddy, nr Castlederg, JW Fitzgerald (Castell 1959: 628).
H37 1964: on peat, bog S of Derrycrow, NW of Lough Gullion, JW Fitzgerald (Paton 1965a: 854).
[H38 deleted because no record or voucher traced, comm. MM Yeo (Long 1990a: 25)].
†H39 listed by Blockeel & Long (1998: 40).
H40 1959: moss-covered boulder, shaded by trees, Altnaheglish nr Dungiven, JW Fitzgerald (Castell 1960: 765).

29/2 ***Tritomaria exsecta*** (Schrad.) Loeske
(syn. *Sphenolobus exsectus* (Schrad.) Steph.)

H1 1951: Finglas River, JW Fitzgerald (Castell 1952: 92).
1951: rock covered with moss, top end of Currane Lake, JW Fitzgerald (Castell 1952: 92).
[H2 record (1951: moss covered boulder, Derrycunihy Wood, Killarney, AC Crundwell, JW Fitzgerald & EW Jones: Castell 1952: 92) should be deleted because the locality is in H1 (see Kelly 1984b)].
H3 1979: rock in wood, Glengarriff, AC Crundwell (Corley 1980a: 28).

H16 1968: rotten log on S-facing wooded slope nr Kylemore Castle, Letterfrack, JA Paton (Paton 1969a: 870).
†H27 listed by Blockeel & Long (1998: 40).
H35 1967: blocks in birch/hazel wood, Mulroy Bay, nr Milford, HH Birks, HJB Birks & DA Ratcliffe (Paton 1968: 622).

Old records listed by Macvicar (1905: 14) with ? are ignored because most were probably based on specimens of *T. exsectiformis*.

29/3 ***Tritomaria quinquedentata*** (Huds.) H. Buch
(syn. *Lophozia quinquedentata* (Huds.) Cogn.)

H(1) listed by Macvicar (1905: 13).
†H1 listed by Blockeel & Long (1998: 40).
[H2 record (1951: Derrycunihy Woods, AC Crundwell: Castell 1952: 92) should be deleted because the locality is in H1 (see Kelly 1984b)].
H3 1955: cliffs above Lough Nambrackderg, H Milne-Redhead (Castell 1957: 324).
H(6) listed by Macvicar (1905: 13).
†H6 listed by Blockeel & Long (1998: 40).
H(7) no date: Lough Dineen, Galtee Mts, HW Lett (DBN), comm. ALK King (Paton 1964: 715).
†H7 listed by Blockeel & Long (1998: 40).
H8 1966: among other bryophytes on basic rock at 2000 ft alt., Temple Hill, Galtee Mts, MFV Corley & JS Parker (Paton 1967c: 398).
H9 1967: shaded rocks in hazel scrub, Den of Clab, nr Borton [*sic* = Glen of Clab, nr Boston], F Rose (Paton 1968: 622).
H16 1957: growing over mosses in rock crevice, NE side of Benchoona, nr Killary Harbour, AC Crundwell (BBS exc.) (Castell 1958: 465).
H(20) listed by Macvicar (1905: 13).
†H20 listed by Blockeel & Long (1998: 40).
†H27 listed by Blockeel & Long (1998: 40).
H(28) 1928: Strand Hill, nr Sligo (BBS exc.) (Duncan 1928: 119).
†H28 listed by Blockeel & Long (1998: 40).
H(29) 1913: E Truskmore, WN Tetley (BBSUK) (Castell 1953: 299).
1918: Kinlough Mt., WN Tetley (*Report MEC Sect. II,* for 1918, p. 23) (Castell 1953: 299).
†H29 listed by Blockeel & Long (1998: 40).
H30 1970: among boulder scree, below Englishman's House, Glenfarne, nr Belcoo, JA Paton (BBS exc.) (Paton 1971a: 371, Appleyard 1971: 389-390).
[H(31) listed by Macvicar (1905: 13)].
H31 1966: by Two Mile River, N side of Carlingford Mountain, DM Synnott (DBN) (Long 1999b: 27).
H(33) listed by Blockeel & Long (1998: 40).
H33 2000: on unshaded top of low sandstone boulder forming part of low wall of cashel in open grassland, S of Crossmurrin Nature Reserve, H13, DT Holyoak 00-413 (BBSUK) (Blackstock 2001: 34-35).
H34 1955: with *Herberta hutchinsiae*, Bulbin Mt., AW Stelfox, comm. JS Thomson (Castell 1956: 148).
H35 1955: Horn Head, AW Stelfox, comm. JS Thomson (Castell 1956: 148).
H36 1958: shady bank, hazel coppice, Glenlark, 4 miles E of Gortin, JW Fitzgerald (Castell 1959: 627).
H(37) 1898: on *Dicranum*, Camlough Mt, HW Lett (NMW), comm. JW Fitzgerald (Paton 1975: 11).
H(38) listed by Macvicar (1905: 13).
†H38 listed by Blockeel & Long (1998: 40).
H(39) listed by Macvicar (1905: 13).
†H39 listed by Blockeel & Long (1998: 40).
H40 1952: creeping over *Plagiochila asplenioides*, *Encalypta streptocarpa*, etc., alt. 700 ft, Benbradagh, EM Lobley & J Taylor, comm. EM Lobley (Castell 1953: 299).
1952: moss-covered rock nr waterfall, Downhill, JW Fitzgerald (Castell 1953: 299).

31/1 ***Mylia taylorii*** (Hook.) Gray
(syn. *Leptoscyphus taylorii* (Hook.) Mitt.)

H(1) listed by Macvicar (1905: 15).
†H1 listed by Blockeel & Long (1998: 41).
H(2) listed by Macvicar (1905: 15).
†H2 listed by Blockeel & Long (1998: 41).
H(3) listed by Macvicar (1905: 15).
†H3 listed by Blockeel & Long (1998: 41).
H4 1966: on peat cuttings on moor at 1200 ft alt., Seefin, Boggeragh Mts, MFV Corley & JS Parker (Paton 1967c: 399).
H(6) listed by Macvicar (1905: 15).
†H6 listed by Blockeel & Long (1998: 41).

H7 1966: limestone boulders, Knockeenatoung, Galtee Mts, EM Lobley & RJ Murphy (BBS exc.) (Paton 1967c: 399).
H8 1966: on peaty soil among rocks on moor, Slievereagh nr Ballylanders, MFV Corley & JS Parker (Paton 1967c: 399).
H9 1963: amongst *Sphagnum*, blanket bog on summit of Slieve Elva at 1100 ft alt., Lisdoonvarna, G Halliday (Paton 1964: 715).
H10 1979: wet heath nr summit of Keeper Hill, HMH van Melick (Corley 1980a: 29).
H14 1956: amongst *Sphagnum*, moorland, Mt Knochanastumba, Slieve Bloom, AA Cridland (Castell 1958: 465).
H(16) listed by Macvicar (1905: 15).
†H16 listed by Blockeel & Long (1998: 41).
H17 1957: bog between R. Clare and R. Cregg, RE Parker (Castell 1958: 465).
H(18) 1949: amongst heather, top of Glendine Pass, Kinitty, AP Fanning (Castell 1951: 493).
H19 1955: with *L. anomalus* and *Cephalozia* sp. on bare peat among *Calluna*, bog, Baronstown East, nr Newbridge, ALK King (Castell 1956: 148).
H(20) listed by Macvicar (1905: 15).
†H20 listed by Blockeel & Long (1998: 41).
H(21) listed by Blockeel & Long (1998: 41).
H25 1965: peat banks, bog at 700 ft alt., Kilronan Mt. nr. Ballyfarnan, JW Fitzgerald & EM Lobley (Paton 1966: 185).
H26 1957: W slope, [The] Ox Mts, ALK King (Castell 1958: 465).
H(27) listed by Macvicar (1905: 15).
†H27 listed by Blockeel & Long (1998: 41).
H(28) 1913: Truskmore, WN Tetley (BBSUK) (Castell 1953: 300).
1937: Ben Bulben, no collector named (BBS exc.) (Armitage 1938: 13).
1937: summit of Ben Bulben, EM Lobley (anon. 1938c: 35).
1937: Ben Bulben (*J. Bot., Lond.*, 1938, p.174) (Castell 1953: 300).
†H28 listed by Blockeel & Long (1998: 41).
H29 1963: wet heath SE of Sriff Cottage, E end of Lough Gill, AR Perry & JW Fitzgerald (Paton 1964: 715).
H(30) 1912: Cuilcagh Mt., WN Tetley (BBSUK) (Castell 1953: 300).
†H30 listed by Blockeel & Long (1998: 41).
H(31) listed by Macvicar (1905: 15). H(31) listed by Blockeel & Long (1998: 41).
†H33 listed by Blockeel & Long (1998: 41).
†H34 listed by Blockeel & Long (1998: 41).
H(35) listed by Macvicar (1905: 15).
†H35 listed by Blockeel & Long (1998: 41).
H36 1951: peat bog, Lough Bradan nr Castlederg, JW Fitzgerald (Castell 1952: 93).
H(37) listed by Macvicar (1905: 15).
†H37 listed by Blockeel & Long (1998: 41).
H(38) listed by Macvicar (1905: 15).
†H38 listed by Blockeel & Long (1998: 41).
H(39) listed by Macvicar (1905: 15).
†H39 listed by Blockeel & Long (1998: 41).
H(40) listed by Macvicar (1905: 15).
†H40 listed by Blockeel & Long (1998: 41).

31/2 ***Mylia anomala*** (Hook.) Gray
(syn. *Leptoscyphus anomalus* (Hook.) Lindb.)

H(1) listed by Macvicar (1905: 15). H(1) listed by Blockeel & Long (1998: 41).
H(2) listed by Macvicar (1905: 15).
†H2 listed by Blockeel & Long (1998: 41).
H(3) listed by Macvicar (1905: 15).
†H3 listed by Blockeel & Long (1998: 41).
H7 1966: bog between Seefin and Knockeenatoung, Galtee Mts, EM Lobley & RJ Murphy (BBS exc.) (Paton 1967: 399).
H8 1966: heathy ground N of Monabrack, Galtee Mts, JA Paton (BBS exc.) (Paton 1967c: 399).
H9 1959: blanket bog on Carboniferous shales, Knockaunsmountain nr Lisdoonvarna, MCF Proctor (Paton 1967c: 399).
H10 1959: cut-away bog W of Newport, ALK King (Castell 1960: 765).
H11 1966: bog, Derryfadda, W of Johnstown, J Appleyard *et al.* (BBS exc.) (Paton 1967c: 399).
H13 1969: on *Sphagnum* bog at Crannagh, foot of Mt Leinster, JW Fitzgerald (Paton 1970: 191).
H14 1957: with *Lepidozia setacea*, recolonizing cut edge of bog, Ballypickas, AA Cridland (Castell 1958: 466).
H17 1957: peaty bankside, nr raised bog between R. Clare and R. Cregg, EM Lobley (BBS exc.) (Castell 1958: 466).
H18 1951: big overgrown drain, base of disused turf bank, Galns bog, Birr, AP

Fanning (Castell 1953: 300).
H(19) 1949: Ballymore Bog nr Calverstown, JS Thomson (Castell 1951: 493).
†H19 listed by Blockeel & Long (1998: 41).
H(20) listed by Macvicar (1905: 15).
†H20 listed by Blockeel & Long (1998: 41).
H22 1952: Clonycavan Bog, nr Ballivor, ALK King (Castell 1953: 300).
H23 1952: bog, nr NE end of L. Owel, JS Thomson (Castell 1954: 473).
H24 1965: raised bog S of Roosky, JW Fitzgerald & EM Lobley (Paton 1966: 185).
H25 1966: peat bog 2 miles SW of Termonbarry, W side of R. Shannon, G Halliday & GCG Argent (Paton 1967c: 399).
H26 1986: raised bog, Flughany, H Grogan & C Douglas (Corley 1987: 18).
†H27 listed by Blockeel & Long (1998: 41).
H28 1963: wet peat between limestone outcrops at 800 ft alt., NE of Carrowkeel, Bricklieve Mts, AR Perry & JW Fitzgerald (Paton 1964: 716).
H29 1969: cutover bog E of Cliffony nr Bundoran, JA Paton (Paton 1970: 191).
H30 1965: bog W of Carricknacrannoge Lough, W of Dowra, JW Fitzgerald & EM Lobley (Paton 1966: 185).
H31 1955: in *Sphagnum*, Clack Bog, SW of Ardee, ALK King (Castell 1956: 148).
H32 1961: on *Sphagnum* in bog, Killyneill, nr Monaghan, JW Fitzgerald (Paton 1962: 360).
H33 1959: wet peat in bog, Garvany Bridge, nr Belleek, JW Fitzgerald (Castell 1960: 765).
H34 1967: boggy ground below Illies Hill, E of Buncrana, JW Fitzgerald (Paton 1968: 624).
H35 1962: among *Sphagna* on NE shoulder of Muckish Mt., EF Warburg (BBS exc.) (Paton 1963: 486).
H36 1953: with *Odontoschisma denudatum*, bog, Tannamore, MPH Kertland & EM Lobley (Castell 1955: 580).
H(37) listed by Macvicar (1905: 15).
†H37 listed by Blockeel & Long (1998: 41).
H(38) listed by Macvicar (1905: 15). H(38) listed by Blockeel & Long (1998: 41).
H(39) listed by Macvicar (1905: 15).
†H39 listed by Blockeel & Long (1998: 41).
H40 1952: bogs on summit of Benevenagh, EW Jones (Castell 1953: 300).

32/2 ***Jungermannia atrovirens*** Dumort. (syn. *Aplozia riparia* (Taylor) Dumort., *Solenostoma atrovirens* var. *sphaerocarpoidea* (De Not.) C.Massal., *S. sphaerocarpoideum* (De Not.) Paton & E.F.Warb., *S. triste* (Nees) K.Müll.)

H(1) listed by Macvicar (1905: 12).
†H1 listed by Blockeel & Long (1998: 41).
H(2) listed by Macvicar (1905: 12).
†H2 listed by Blockeel & Long (1998: 41).
H(3) 1939: Cousaniska, L Porter, comm. FA Sowter (Castell 1950: 376).
†H3 listed by Blockeel & Long (1998: 41).
H(4) listed by Macvicar (1905: 12). H(4) listed by Blockeel & Long (1998: 41).
H(5) listed by Macvicar (1905: 12).
†H5 listed by Blockeel & Long (1998: 41).
H6 1966: on river boulders in little glen towards R. Nier, S of Clonmel, JW Fitzgerald *et al.* (BBS exc.) (Paton 1967c: 398).
H(7) 1902: Lough Muskry, HW Lett (DBN), comm. ALK King (Paton 1964: 714).
†H7 listed by Blockeel & Long (1998: 41).
H8 1979: rock at foot of waterfall, Glenastar, W of Ardagh, JA Paton (Corley 1980a: 28).
H9 1956: bank of R. Caher, Fanore Bridge, ALK King (Castell 1957: 323).
1956: Spa Glen, Lisdoonvarna, ALK King (Castell 1957: 323), as var. *sphaerocarpoidea*.
H10 1967: rocks in stream, Devil's Bit Mt., JW Fitzgerald (Paton 1968: 623).
H(16) listed by Macvicar (1905: 12).
†H16 listed by Blockeel & Long (1998: 41).
H(20) listed by Macvicar (1905: 12).
†H20 listed by Blockeel & Long (1998: 41).
H22 1978: crevices of limestone boulder, shore of L. Sheelin, Ross, DM Synnott (Corley 1980a: 28).
H23 1970: fen, E shore of L. Ennell, S of Mullingar, JA Paton (Paton 1971a: 371).
H25 1968: limestone boulder, shore of L. Ree at St Johns Wood, 3 miles SE of Knockcroghery, WV Rubers, P Hessell & J Klein (Paton 1970: 190).
H26 1981: soil amongst limestone rocks, shore of L. Carra, nr Moorehall, N Lockhart (Corley 1983: 48).
†H27 listed by Blockeel & Long (1998: 41).
[H(28) listed by Macvicar (1905: 12)].
H28 1963: on stones in calcareous scree, Gleniff, Ben Bulben Range, JW

Fitzgerald & AR Perry (Paton 1964: 714), as var. *sphaerocarpoidea*.
H(29) 1928: wooded glen, NE end of Glencar Lough (BBS exc.) (Duncan 1928: 118).
H29 1963: on calcareous rocks nr Glencar waterfall, Glencar, JW Fitzgerald & AR Perry (Paton 1974: 714), as var. *sphaerocarpoidea*.
H(30) listed by Macvicar (1905: 12).
†H30 listed by Blockeel & Long (1998: 41).
H31 1966: rock in Two-mile R., Carlingford Mt., DM Synnott (Paton 1968: 623).
H33 1957: boulders, bed of Cladagh R., L. Macnean Lower, AC Crundwell (Castell 1958: 464).
1959: shaded limestone rocks, Buggan nr Knockmore Cliff, JW Fitzgerald (Castell 1960: 765), as var. *sphaerocarpoidea*.
H34 1967: rocks in R. Crana, E of Ballymagan, JW Fitzgerald (Paton 1968: 623).
1969: rocks beside stream, ravine SW of L. Inn, W of Moville, JA Paton (Paton 1970: 190), as *Solenostoma sphaerocarpoidea*.
H(35) listed by Macvicar (1905: 12).
†H35 listed by Blockeel & Long (1998: 41).
H36 1951: limestone rocks in stream below spring, Binnawooda, JW Fitzgerald (Castell 1952: 91).
1958: vertical rock face beside stream, Glenlark, 4 miles E of Gortin, JW Fitzgerald (Castell 1959: 627), as var. *sphaerocarpoidea*.
H37 1966: stones on path in wood, Carrickaness nr Benburb, JW Fitzgerald (Paton 1967c: 398), as *S. sphaerocarpoideum*. H37 added because of transfer from *S. sphaerocarpoidea*, no longer considered distinct from *S. triste* (Váňa 1973, Corley 1980a: 28).
H(38) listed by Macvicar (1905: 12). H(38) listed by Blockeel & Long (1998: 41).
[H(39) listed by Macvicar (1905: 12)].
H39 1952: wet rocks by stream, Glenarm, JW Fitzgerald & EW Jones (Castell 1953: 299), as var. *sphaerocarpoidea*.
[H(40) listed by Macvicar (1905: 12)].
H40 1968: on stone in calcareous flush, Mullaghmore nr Dungiven, HH Birks & JW Fitzgerald (Paton 1969a: 870), as *Solenostoma sphaerocarpoidea*.

32/3 ***Jungermannia pumila*** With.
(syn. *Aplozia pumila* (With.) Dumort., *Solenostoma pumilum* (With.) K.Müll.)

H(1) listed by Macvicar (1905: 12).
†H1 listed by Blockeel & Long (1998: 41).
H(2) listed by Macvicar (1905: 12).
†H2 listed by Blockeel & Long (1998: 41).
†H3 listed by Blockeel & Long (1998: 41).
H4 1967: sandy bank of stream, Mushera, JW Fitzgerald (Paton 1968: 623).
H5 1966: river gravel, R. Araglin, Araglin, JG Duckett *et al.* (BBS exc.) (Paton 1967c: 398).
H6 1966: rocks by stream E of the Punchbowl, Comeragh Mts, ERB Little (BBS exc.) (Paton 1967c: 398).
H7 1966: damp rocks above L. Curra, Galtee Mts, JA Paton *et al.* (BBS exc.) (Paton 1967c: 398).
H8 1979: rock on S side of Clare R., Clare Glens, S of Newport, JA Paton (Corley 1980a: 28).
H10 1979: silt-covered rocks on N bank, Clare R., Clare Glens, S of Newport, JA Paton (Corley 1980a: 28).
H11 1968: track in woods on W bank of R. Nore, SE of Thomastown, JA Paton (Paton 1969a: 870).
H13 1969: stones in stream, Sculloge Gap nr Ballymurphy, JW Fitzgerald (Paton 1970: 190).
H16 1957: Benchoona, J Appleyard (Castell 1958: 464).
1957: rocks in wood, Ballynahinch, EM Lobley (BBS exc.) (Castell 1958: 464).
H(20) listed by Macvicar (1905: 12).
†H20 listed by Blockeel & Long (1998: 41).
[H21 deleted because probable voucher (1890: Glencullen, D McArdle, DBN) is *J. sphaerocarpa* (Long 1990a: 25)].
H26 1987: E bank of Cloon River between Srah and Partry, DM Synnott (Long 1988: 31).
H(27) listed by Macvicar (1905: 12).
†H27 listed by Blockeel & Long (1998: 41).
H28 1969: wet limestone rocks, Gleniff above Clough, Benbulbin [*sic* = Ben Bulben], JA Paton (Paton 1970: 190).
H(29) listed by Macvicar (1905: 12).
†H29 listed by Blockeel & Long (1998: 41).
H(30) listed by Macvicar (1905: 12).
†H30 listed by Blockeel & Long (1998: 41).
H(31) 1883: by stream, Anglesey Mt., CH Waddell (DBN), comm. ALK King

(Paton 1964: 714).
H33 1960: shaded rocks by Correl Glen, JW Fitzgerald (Paton 1961: 152).
H34 1962: bank by path below E side of Bulbin [Mt.], EF Warburg, AC Crundwell & EC Wallace (BBS exc.) (Paton 1963: 484).
H35 1962: damp rock, N side of Muckish Mt., EF Warburg (BBS exc.) (Paton 1963: 484).
H36 1957: wet rocks by stream, Willmount Glen, nr Drumquin, JW Fitzgerald (Castell 1959: 627).
H(37) listed by Macvicar (1905: 12).
†H37 listed by Blockeel & Long (1998: 41).
H(38) listed by Macvicar (1905: 12).
†H38 listed by Blockeel & Long (1998: 41).
H(39) listed by Macvicar (1905: 12).
†H39 listed by Blockeel & Long (1998: 41).
H(40) listed by Macvicar (1905: 12).
†H40 listed by Blockeel & Long (1998: 41).

32/6 ***Jungermannia exsertifolia*** Steph. **subsp. *cordifolia*** (Dumort.) Váňa
(syn. *Aplozia cordifolia* Dumort., *Solenostoma cordifolium* (Dumort.) Steph.)

H(1) listed by Macvicar (1905: 12).
†H1 listed by Blockeel & Long (1998: 42).
H(2) listed by Macvicar (1905: 12).
†H2 listed by Blockeel & Long (1998: 42).
H3 1968: rocky stream on NE slope, Lackawee, Slieve Miskish Mts, JA Paton (Paton 1969a: 870).
H6 1966: rocks in R. Nier nr Shanballyanne, JA Paton & ERB Little (BBS exc.) (Paton 1967c: 398).
H16 1970: wet siliceous rocks *ca* 800 ft alt., stream on N side of Benbeg, AR Perry & HJ Perry (Paton 1974b: 163).
H27 1987: in stream, E slopes of N corrie of Mweelrea, MAS Burton (Long 1988: 31).
H33 2000: on pebble just above shallow flowing water of unshaded inlet stream at edge of lake, by NW edge of Lough Macnean Lower, H03, DT Holyoak 00-297 (BBSUK) (Blackstock 2001: 35).
H34 2002: on slightly shaded rock at water-level in small stream in ravine, *ca* 30 m alt., S of Soldiers Hill, NW of Malin, C45, DT Holyoak 02-558 (Blackstock 2003: 41).
H35 1955: Horn Head, AW Stelfox, comm. JS Thomson (Castell 1956: 147).
H36 2002: on damp rock in edge of small stream shaded by ferns and grasses, *ca* 195 m, Butterlope Glen, H49, DT Holyoak 02-1117 (Blackstock 2003: 41).
H(38) listed by Macvicar (1905: 12). H(38) listed by Blockeel & Long (1998: 42).
H(39) listed by Macvicar (1905: 12). H(39) listed by Blockeel & Long (1998: 42).
H(40) listed by Macvicar (1905: 12).
†H40 listed by Blockeel & Long (1998: 42).

32/7 ***Jungermannia sphaerocarpa*** Hook.
(syn. *Aplozia sphaerocarpa* (Hook.) Dumort., *Jungermannia sphaerocarpa* var. *lurida* Pearson, *Solenostoma sphaerocarpum* (Hook.) Steph.)

H(1) listed by Macvicar (1905: 12). H(1) listed by Blockeel & Long (1998: 42).
H(2) listed by Macvicar (1905: 12). H(2) listed by Blockeel & Long (1998: 42).
H(3) listed by Macvicar (1905: 12) as var. *lurida*. H(3) listed by Blockeel & Long (1998: 42).
[H(6) listed by Macvicar (1905: 12). H6 deleted because no record or voucher traced, comm. MM Yeo (Long 1990a: 25)].
H9 1985: boulder in Caher River, AC Bouman (Corley 1987: 18).
†H16 listed by Blockeel & Long (1998: 42).
H(20) listed by Macvicar (1905: 12).
†H20 listed by Blockeel & Long (1998: 42).
H(21) listed by Macvicar (1905: 12).
†H21 listed by Blockeel & Long (1998: 42).
H(27) listed by Macvicar (1905: 12).
†H27 listed by Blockeel & Long (1998: 42).
[H(29) listed by Macvicar (1905: 12). H29 deleted because only record traced (1875, Glenade, D Moore, DBN) is of *Solenostoma triste* (Paton 1971a: 371)].
H29 1970: boulders in a stream, N-facing cliffs or hill slopes of Glenfarne, nr Belcoo, J Appleyard (BBS exc.) (Paton 1971a: 371, Appleyard 1971: 389-390).
H(31) listed by Macvicar (1905: 12). H(31) listed by Blockeel & Long (1998: 42).
H33 1959: in large swelling tufts on shale beside stream, Cuilcagh, JW Fitzgerald (Castell 1960: 764).
H36 1952: mica schist, Glenhordial R., JW Fitzgerald (Castell 1953: 298).
H(37) listed by Macvicar (1905: 12). H(37) listed by Blockeel & Long (1998: 42).

H(38) listed by Macvicar (1905: 12). H(38) listed by Blockeel & Long (1998: 42).
H(39) listed by Macvicar (1905: 12). H(39) listed by Blockeel & Long (1998: 42).
H(40) listed by Macvicar (1905: 12).
†H40 listed by Blockeel & Long (1998: 42).

32/9 ***Jungermannia gracillima*** **Sm.**
(syn. *Aplozia crenulata* (Mitt.) Lindb., *A. crenulata* var. *gracillima* (Sm.) Heeg., *A. crenulata* var. *inundata* (Schiffn.) Macvicar, *Solenostoma crenulatum* (Sm.) Mitt.)

H(1) listed by Macvicar (1905: 12).
†H1 listed by Blockeel & Long (1998: 42).
H(2) listed by Macvicar (1905: 12).
†H2 listed by Blockeel & Long (1998: 42).
H(3) listed by Macvicar (1905: 12).
†H3 listed by Blockeel & Long (1998: 42).
H5 1966: floor of old quarry, Castle Cooke, Kilworth, JG Duckett *et al.* (BBS exc.) (Paton 1967c: 399).
H6 1966: bank by path in wooded valley N of the Punchbowl, Comeragh Mts, RJ Murphy (BBS exc.) (Paton 1967c: 399).
H(7) listed by Macvicar (1905: 12).
†H7 listed by Blockeel & Long (1998: 42).
H8 1979: pathside nr top of waterfall, Glenastar, W of Ardagh, JA Paton (Corley 1980a: 29).
H(9) listed by Macvicar (1905: 12).
†H9 listed by Blockeel & Long (1998: 42).
H10 1951: earth bank on hillside, alt. 600 ft, above Silvermines, AD Banwell, EV Watson & PJ Wanstall (Castell 1952: 91), as *A. crenulata* var. *gracillima*.
H(12) listed by Macvicar (1905: 12).
†H12 listed by Blockeel & Long (1998: 42).
H13 1969: earthy bank, The Nine Stones, N of Mt Leinster, JW Fitzgerald (Paton 1970: 190).
H(14) listed by Macvicar (1905: 12). H(14) listed by Blockeel & Long (1998: 42).
H15 1957: woodland ride, Chevy Chase, nr Gort, AC Crundwell (BBS exc.) (Castell 1958: 464).
H(16) listed by Macvicar (1905: 12).
†H16 listed by Blockeel & Long (1998: 42).
H(20) listed by Macvicar (1905: 12).
H20 1952: very wet sandy ground, head of Upper Lake Glendalough, JS Thomson (Castell 1958: 464), as *A. crenulata* var. *inundata*.
H(21) listed by Macvicar (1905: 12).
†H21 listed by Blockeel & Long (1998: 42).
H25 1965: damp bankside, Kilronan nr Ballyfarnan, JW Fitzgerald & EM Lobley (Paton 1966: 184).
H26 1987: woodland track on E side of Cloon River W of Partry, JA Paton (Long 1988: 31).
H(27) listed by Macvicar (1905: 12).
†H27 listed by Blockeel & Long (1998: 42).
H(28) listed by Macvicar (1905: 12).
H28 1965: bank of track in wood at mouth of Bonnet R., L. Gill, JW Fitzgerald (Paton 1966: 184).
H29 1963: path below limestone crags, Ballinlig, Glenade, AR Perry & JW Fitzgerald (Paton 1964: 714).
H(30) listed by Macvicar (1905: 12).
†H30 listed by Blockeel & Long (1998: 42).
H(31) listed by Macvicar (1905: 12). H(31) listed by Blockeel & Long (1998: 42).
H32 1965: side of field ditch, Cavanagarvan nr Monaghan, JW Fitzgerald & EM Lobley (Paton 1966: 184).
†H33 listed by Blockeel & Long (1998: 42).
H34 1962: vertical bank of stream, Croaghconnellagh, Tawnawully Mts, J Appleyard & EC Wallace (BBS exc.) (Paton 1963: 484).
H(35) listed by Macvicar (1905: 12).
†H35 listed by Blockeel & Long (1998: 42).
H36 1950: Sandpit, Coalisland, JW Fitzgerald (Castell 1951: 492).
1952: Curraghmulkin, JW Fitzgerald (Castell 1953: 298).
H(37) listed by Macvicar (1905: 12).
†H37 listed by Blockeel & Long (1998: 42).
H(38) listed by Macvicar (1905: 12).
†H38 listed by Blockeel & Long (1998: 42).
H(39) listed by Macvicar (1905: 12).
†H39 listed by Blockeel & Long (1998: 42).
H40 1964: rocks by stream nr top of Glenshane Pass, JW Fitzgerald (Paton 1965a: 853).

32/11 ***Jungermannia hyalina*** **Lyell**
(syn. *Eucalyx hyalinus* (Lyell) F.Lees, *Plectocolea hyalina* (Lyell) Mitt.)

H(1) listed by Macvicar (1905: 11). H(1) listed by Blockeel & Long (1998: 42).
[H(2) listed by Macvicar (1905: 11)].
H2 1983: stream above L. Managh, Horse's Glen, Mangerton Mt., JA Paton (Corley 1984: 24).
H3 1968: roadside bank nr Dunboy Castle,

Castletownbere, JA Paton (Paton 1969a: 871).
H5 1966: gravelly track, Castle Cooke, Kilworth, J Appleyard & JW Fitzgerald (BBS exc.) (Paton 1967c: 399).
H8 1979: edge of field above waterfall, Glenastar, W of Ardagh, JA Paton (Corley 1980a: 29).
H9 1968: bank of R. Aille below Spectacle Bridge, 1 mile SW of Lisdoonvarna, MP Jones (Paton 1970: 190).
H10 1979: by spring in farmyard, E of Toor, Keeper Hill, EW Jones (Corley 1980a: 29).
[H(13) listed by Macvicar (1905: 11)].
H15 1994: stone on bank beside Boleyneendorish River, Slieve Aughty, M50, JA Paton 7638 (Long 1995b: 38).
[H(16) listed by Macvicar (1905: 11)].
H16 1968: bank of lane *ca* 4 miles NW of Oughterard, AR Perry (Paton 1969a: 871).
H(20) listed by Macvicar (1905: 11).
†H20 listed by Blockeel & Long (1998: 42).
[H(21) listed by Macvicar (1905: 11)].
H25 2002: by stream and small waterfall on NE-facing crags, *ca* 150 m alt., Kilronan Mountain, Arigna, G91, NG Hodgetts 4153 (Blackstock 2003: 41).
[H(27) listed by Macvicar (1905: 11)].
H27 1972: cattle-trampled site on transition zone dune-bog, L. Doo, E of Doogort, Achill I., WV Rubers (Corley 1980a: 29).
H28 1970: roadside quarry nr Masshill, JA Paton (BBS exc.) (Paton 1971a: 371, Appleyard 1971: 389).
H(30) listed by Macvicar (1905: 11).
†H30 listed by Blockeel & Long (1998: 42).
H(31) listed by Macvicar (1905: 11). H(31) listed by Blockeel & Long (1998: 42).
H33 1959: clay bank by roadside, Aghahoorin, nr Boho, JW Fitzgerald (Castell 1960: 764).
H34 1962: grassy field below E side of Bulbin, EF Warburg, AC Crundwell & EC Wallace (BBS exc.) (Paton 1963: 484).
[H(35) listed by Macvicar (1905: 11)].
H35 1969: damp roadside above Dunlewy L., Gweedore, JA Paton (Paton 1970: 190).
H36 1956: floor of sand pit, nr Coalisland, JW Fitzgerald & MPH Kertland (Castell 1957: 323).
[H(37) listed by Macvicar (1905: 11)].
H37 1967: stony flush at roadside, Daaikilmore, S of Slieve Gullion, JW Fitzgerald & MPH Kertland (Paton 1968: 623).
[H(38) listed by Macvicar (1905: 11)].
H(39) listed by Macvicar (1905: 11).
†H39 listed by Blockeel & Long (1998: 42).
H40 1950: Dunalis Reservoir nr Coleraine, JW Fitzgerald (Castell 1951: 492).

32/12 ***Jungermannia paroica*** (Schiffn.) Grolle (syn. *Eucalyx paroicus* (Schiffn.) Macvicar, *Plectocolea paroica* (Schiffn.) Evans)

H1 1968: river bank above Blackwater Bridge, W of Kenmare, JA Paton (Paton 1969a: 871).
H6 1972: detritus-covered boulders in stream, Owenashad R., at quarry N of Lismore, WV Rubers (Corley 1980a: 29).
H8 1966: sides of stream S of Galtymore, Galtee Mts, JW Fitzgerald *et al.* (BBS exc.) (Paton 1967c: 399).
H16 1970: bank above S shore of Killary Harbour nr the Bunowen R., JA Paton (Paton 1971a: 371).
H25 2002: rocks in stream and small waterfall on NE-facing crags, *ca* 150 m alt., Kilronan Mt., Arigna, G91, NG Hodgetts 4150 (Blackstock 2003).
H27 1987: sandy side of stream in the floor of the North Corrie, Mweelrea, DM Synnott (Long 1988: 31).
H34 2001: on rocks by river, *ca* 70 m alt., Cloghan More, W bank of River Finn by road bridge, H09, NG Hodgetts 3860 (Blackstock 2003: 41).
H35 1969: rocks beside stream, Fintragh Bay, W of Killybegs, JA Paton (Paton 1970: 190).
H36 1952: moist mica schist detritus, Glen Curry, nr Omagh, JW Fitzgerald (Castell 1956: 147, Fitzgerald 1958).
H(38) 1887: Tollymore Park, CH Waddell (DBN) (as *Nardia obovata)*, comm. JW Fitzgerald (Castell 1960: 764).
1891: Tollymore Park, CH Waddell (BFT) (as *Eucalyx hyalinus*), comm. JW Fitzgerald (Castell 1960: 764).
†H38 listed by Blockeel & Long (1998: 42).
H39 1969: gravelly bank above stream nr Drumfresky, Glensun R., Cushendun, JA Paton (Paton 1970: 190).

H40 1961: mica schist detritus on rocks beside river, Glenedra nr Dungiven, JW Fitzgerald (Paton 1961: 358).

32/13 ***Jungermannia obovata*** Nees
(syn. *Eucalyx obovatus* (Nees) F.Lees, *Plectocolea obovata* (Nees) Mitt.)

H(1) listed by Macvicar (1905: 12).
†H1 listed by Blockeel & Long (1998: 42).
H(2) listed by Macvicar (1905: 12).
†H2 listed by Blockeel & Long (1998: 42).
H3 1967: wet rocks by roadside, Coom Wood, JW Fitzgerald (Paton 1968: 623).
H4 1967: rocks by stream, Mushera, JW Fitzgerald (Paton 1968: 623).
[H(6) listed by Macvicar (1905: 12). H6 deleted because specimen on which record was probably based (DBN) too poor to determine (Paton 1977a: 13)].
H6 1966: bank of stream, Laghtnafrankee, S of Clonmel, JW Fitzgerald (Corley 1978: 14).
H(7) listed by Macvicar (1905: 12).
†H7 listed by Blockeel & Long (1998: 42).
H(9) listed by Macvicar (1905: 12). H(9) listed by Blockeel & Long (1998: 42).
[H(16) listed by Macvicar (1905: 12). H16 deleted because specimen from Kylemore on which record was probably based (DBN) is *Nardia scalaris* (Paton 1977a: 13)].
H16 1986: damp peaty overhang by sea, Sallerna, nr Cleggan, DG Long (Corley 1987: 18).
H(20) listed by Macvicar (1905: 12).
†H20 listed by Blockeel & Long (1998: 42).
H21 1950: Upper Dodder River, AW Stelfox, comm. King (Paton 1964: 714).
H(27) listed by Macvicar (1905: 12).
†H27 listed by Blockeel & Long (1998: 42).
H29 1965: stream below waterfall, Dergvone N of L. Allen, JW Fitzgerald & EM Lobley (Paton 1966: 184).
H(30) listed by Macvicar (1905: 12).
†H30 listed by Blockeel & Long (1998: 42).
H33 2002: on unshaded thin damp soil on ledge at base of N-facing gritstone crag, *ca* 578 m alt., high on NE slope of Cuilcagh, H12, DT Holyoak 02-912 (Blackstock 2003: 41).
H34 1967: rocks on stream bank below Barnan More, N of Buncrana, JW Fitzgerald (Paton 1968).
H(35) listed by Macvicar (1905: 12).
†H35 listed by Blockeel & Long (1998: 42).
H36 1957: wet detritus nr stream, Willmount Glen, nr Drumquin, JW Fitzgerald (Castell 1959: 627).
H(38) listed by Macvicar (1905: 12).
†H38 listed by Blockeel & Long (1998: 42).
H39 1952: Sallagh Braes, EW Jones (Castell 1953: 298).
H40 1968: rocks by Burntollet R., Ness Glen, NW of Claudy, JW Fitzgerald & HH Birks (Paton 1969a: 870).

32/14 ***Jungermannia subelliptica*** (Lindb. ex Kaal.) Levier
(syn. *Plectocolea subelliptica* (Lindb. ex Kaal.) A.Evans)

H16 1970: soil on calcareous schist in ravine, N slope Benbaun, The Twelve Pins, JA Paton (Paton 1971a: 371).
H27 1970: stream, S slope of Bengorm, N of Killary Harbour, JA Paton (Paton 1972a: 133).
H28 1970: on a bit of sandy limestone, corrie to NE of Benbulbin [*sic* = Ben Bulben], JA Paton (BBS exc.) (Paton 1971a: 371, Appleyard 1971: 389).
H34 1969: calcareous schist, Bulbin Mt., Inishowen, JA Paton (Paton 1970: 190, 1971b).
H35 1969: stream, Fintragh Bay, Killybegs, JA Paton (Paton 1972a: 133).
H39 1969: rock beside stream, E slope of Knocklayd, Ballycastle, JA Paton (Paton 1973b: 505).

33/1 ***Nardia compressa*** (Hook.) Gray
(syn. *Alicularia compressa* (Hook.) Nees, *A. compressa* var. *rigida* Lindb.)

H(1) listed by Macvicar (1905: 11).
†H1 listed by Blockeel & Long (1998: 43).
H(2) listed by Macvicar (1905: 11).
†H2 listed by Blockeel & Long (1998: 43).
†H3 listed by Blockeel & Long (1998: 43).
H6 1963: wet rocks in gully at 2000 at. alt., N corrie of Fauscoum, Comeragh Mts, DA Ratcliffe (Paton 1964: 713).
H(7) 1851: sandstone rocks by the Funcheon River at base of Galtymore, ex Hb. T Chandlee (DBN), comm. ALK King (Paton 1964: 713).
H8 1966: banks of stream S of Galtymore, Galtee Mts, JW Fitzgerald *et al.* (BBS exc.) (Paton 1967c: 399).

H10 1979: rocks in stream, S slope of Keeper Hill, JA Paton (Corley 980: 29).
H12 1969: rocks in stream below Caher Roe's Den, Blackstairs Mt., JW Fitzgerald (Paton 1970: 190).
H13 1975: rocks in stream, The Black Banks, Mt Leinster, JA Paton & AR Perry (BBS exc.) (Paton 1976: 19).
H(16) listed by Macvicar (1905: 11).
†H16 listed by Blockeel & Long (1998: 43).
H(20) listed by Macvicar (1905: 11). H(20) listed by Macvicar (1905: 11) as var. *rigida*.
†H20 listed by Blockeel & Long (1998: 43).
H(21) listed by Macvicar (1905: 11). H(21) listed by Blockeel & Long (1998: 43).
H26 1965: boulders in stream W of L. Talt, [The] Ox Mts, JW Fitzgerald (Paton 1966: 184).
H(27) listed by Macvicar (1905: 11). H(27) listed by Macvicar (1905: 11) as var. *rigida*.
†H27 listed by Blockeel & Long (1998: 43).
H28 1967: submerged in small streams draining into L. Gill, HH Birks, HJB Birks & DA Ratcliffe (Paton 1968: 623).
H29 1970: boulders in a stream, E slopes of Benbo, SW of Manorhamilton, E Hegewald (BBS exc.) (Paton 1971a 371, Appleyard 1971: 390).
H30 1965: rocks in stream at 1700 ft alt., S side of Cuilcagh, JW Fitzgerald & EM Lobley (Paton 1966: 184).
H33 1959: in swelling tufts on rocks in stream, at 1700 ft [alt.], Cuilcagh, JW Fitzgerald (Castell 1960: 764).
H34 1962: in stream, Croaghconnellagh, Tawnawully Mts, J Appleyard & EC Wallace (BBS exc.) (Paton 1963: 484).
H(35) listed by Macvicar (1905: 11).
†H35 listed by Blockeel & Long (1998: 43).
H36 1957: in swelling tufts at side of river, Sheskinawaddy, nr Castlederg, JW Fitzgerald & MPH Kertland (Castell 1959: 627).
H(38) listed by Macvicar (1905: 11).
†H38 listed by Blockeel & Long (1998: 43).
H(39) listed by Macvicar (1905: 11).
H39 1951: wet ground by stream, 800 ft alt., Owennaglush River, Glendun, JW Fitzgerald (DBN) (Long 1999b: 27).

33/2 ***Nardia scalaris*** Gray
(syn. *Alicularia scalaris* (Gray) Corda, *A. scalaris* var. *distans* Carrington, *A. scalaris* var. *rivularis* Lindb.)

H(1) listed by Macvicar (1905: 11). H(1) listed by Macvicar (1905: 11) as var. *distans*.
†H1 listed by Blockeel & Long (1998: 43).
H(2) listed by Macvicar (1905: 11).
†H2 listed by Blockeel & Long (1998: 43).
H(3) listed by Macvicar (1905: 11).
†H3 listed by Blockeel & Long (1998: 43).
H4 1966: on rocks by road, Shipool, S of Innishannon, MFV Corley & JS Parker (Paton 1967c: 399).
H5 1967: track in bog, Lyrenamon, NW of Carrignavar, JW Fitzgerald (Paton 1968: 623).
H(6) listed by Macvicar (1905: 11).
†H6 listed by Blockeel & Long (1998: 43).
H(7) listed by Macvicar (1905: 11).
†H7 listed by Blockeel & Long (1998: 43).
H(8) listed by Macvicar (1905: 11).
†H8 listed by Blockeel & Long (1998: 43).
H(9) listed by Macvicar (1905: 11).
†H9 listed by Blockeel & Long (1998: 43).
H10 1951: earth bank on hillside, alt. 1000 ft, Silvermines Mt., ADV [*sic* = AD Banwell ?], EV Watson & PJ Wanstall (Castell 1952: 91).
H(12) listed by Macvicar (1905: 11).
†H12 listed by Blockeel & Long (1998: 43).
H(13) listed by Macvicar (1905: 11).
†H13 listed by Blockeel & Long (1998: 43).
H(14) listed by Macvicar (1905: 11).
†H14 listed by Blockeel & Long (1998: 43).
H(16) listed by Macvicar (1905: 11).
†H16 listed by Blockeel & Long (1998: 43).
[H(17) listed by Macvicar (1905: 11). H17 deleted because no record or voucher traced, comm. MM Yeo (Long 1990a: 25-26)].
[H(18) listed by Macvicar (1905: 11). H18 deleted because no record or voucher traced, comm. MM Yeo, replaced by next record (Long 1990a: 25-26)].
H(18) 1949: bank under heather, Glendine, AP Fanning (DBN), comm. DM Synnott (Long 1990a: 26).
[H(19) listed by Macvicar (1905: 11). H19 deleted because no record or voucher traced, comm. MM Yeo (Long 1990a: 25-26)].
H(20) listed by Macvicar (1905: 11). H(20)

listed by Macvicar (1905: 11) as var. *rivularis*.
†H20 listed by Blockeel & Long (1998: 43).
H(21) listed by Macvicar (1905: 11).
†H21 listed by Blockeel & Long (1998: 43).
H22 1978: quarry, Teevurcher, N of Moynalty, DM Synnott (Corley 1980a: 29).
H25 1968: loamy bank under *Calluna*, Slieve Bawn, WV Rubers, P Hessel & J Klein (Paton 1970: 190).
H(26) listed by Macvicar (1905: 11).
†H26 listed by Blockeel & Long (1998: 43).
H(27) listed by Macvicar (1905: 11).
†H27 listed by Blockeel & Long (1998: 43).
H(28) listed by Macvicar (1905: 11).
†H28 listed by Blockeel & Long (1998: 43).
H(29) listed by Macvicar (1905: 11).
†H29 listed by Blockeel & Long (1998: 43).
H(30) listed by Macvicar (1905: 11).
†H30 listed by Blockeel & Long (1998: 43).
H31 1963: Carlingford Mt., DM Synnott (Paton 1964: 713).
†H33 listed by Blockeel & Long (1998: 43).
H(34) listed by Macvicar (1905: 11).
†H34 listed by Blockeel & Long (1998: 43).
†H35 listed by Blockeel & Long (1998: 43).
H36 1951: wet bank beside road, abundant with *Eucalyx* spp., Leagh's Bridge, Draperstown-Plumbridge Road, JW Fitzgerald (Castell 1952: 91).
H(37) listed by Macvicar (1905: 11).
†H37 listed by Blockeel & Long (1998: 43).
H(38) listed by Macvicar (1905: 11).
†H38 listed by Blockeel & Long (1998: 43).
H(39) listed by Macvicar (1905: 11).
†H39 listed by Blockeel & Long (1998: 43).
†H40 listed by Blockeel & Long (1998: 43).

33/3 ***Nardia geoscyphus*** (De Not.) Lindb.

[Record from H2 (1973: on rotting wood under *Quercus* and *Ilex*, Lady's View, Killarney, V98, DL Kelly: DL Kelly in Hackney 1980, Long 1991: 38) should be deleted because the specimen is *Odontoschisma denudatum* redet. MFV Corley (Kelly 1984c). H2 is thus apparently listed in error in Blockeel & Long (1998)].

H13 1969: rock crevice, The Nine Stones, N of Mt Leinster, JW Fitzgerald (Paton 1970: 190).
H16 1968: shaded bank at edge of lane *ca* 4 miles NW of Oughterard, AR Perry (Paton 1969a: 871).
H27 1970: floor of quarry nr L. Nahatora, S of Louisburgh, JA Paton (Paton 1971a: 371).
H34 1966: shaded bank at Kinnagoe Bay, Inishowen, N Chuter, comm. ALK King (Paton 1967c: 399, King 1968).
H35 1969: roadside bank, Croaghmuckross nr Kilcar, JA Paton (Paton 1970: 190).

Paton (1999: 293-296) established that this species is represented by two forms in Britain that apparently represent distinct taxa, distinguished by large and small leaf cells. Only the small-celled form is known in Ireland.

34/1a ***Marsupella emarginata*** (Ehrh.) Dumort. **var. *emarginata***
(syn. *Marsupella emarginata* var. *minor* Carrington)

H(1) listed by Macvicar (1905: 11).
†H1 listed by Blockeel & Long (1998: 43).
H(2) listed by Macvicar (1905: 11). H(2) listed by Macvicar (1905: 11), as var. *minor*.
†H2 listed by Blockeel & Long (1998: 43).
H3 1953: bank of stream, Valley Desmond, Gougane Barra, ALK King (Castell 1954: 472).
H5 1967: rocks in wood, Coolgreen Glen, SW of Waterglasshill, JW Fitzgerald (Paton 1968: 624).
H(6) listed by Macvicar (1905: 11).
†H6 listed by Blockeel & Long (1998: 43).
H(7) listed by Macvicar (1905: 11).
†H7 listed by Blockeel & Long (1998: 43).
H8 1966: on damp rocks at 2200 ft alt., Temple Hill, Galtee Mts, MFV Corley & JS Parker (Paton 1967c: 399).
H(9) listed by Macvicar (1905: 11).
†H9 listed by Blockeel & Long (1998: 43).
H10 1979: damp rock in gully on S side of Keeper Hill, AC Crundwell (Corley 1980a: 29).
H(12) listed by Macvicar (1905: 11). H(12) listed by Macvicar (1905: 11), as var. *minor*.
†H12 listed by Blockeel & Long (1998: 43).
H(13) listed by Macvicar (1905: 11). †H13 listed by Blockeel & Long (1998: 43).
H(14) listed by Macvicar (1905: 11). H(14) listed by Blockeel & Long (1998: 43).
H(16) listed by Macvicar (1905: 11).

†H16 listed by Blockeel & Long (1998: 43).
[H(18) listed by Macvicar (1905: 11). H18 deleted because no localised record or voucher traced, comm. MM Yeo (Long 1990a: 26)].
H(20) listed by Macvicar (1905: 11).
†H20 listed by Blockeel & Long (1998: 43).
H(21) listed by Macvicar (1905: 11).
†H21 listed by Blockeel & Long (1998: 43).
H22 1978: Hill 426, Greenanstown, Naul, DM Synnott (Corley 1979: 24).
H25 2002: rocks in stream and small waterfall on NE-facing crags, *ca* 150 m alt., Kilronan Mt., Arigna, G91, NG Hodgetts 4150 (Blackstock 2003: 41).
H26 1965: on shaded rock face W of L. Talt, [The] Ox Mts, JW Fitzgerald (Paton 1966: 184).
H(27) listed by Macvicar (1905: 11). H(27) listed by Macvicar (1905: 11), as var. *minor*.
†H27 listed by Blockeel & Long (1998: 43).
H(28) listed by Macvicar (1905: 11).
†H28 listed by Blockeel & Long (1998: 43).
H29 1965: banks of stream, Dergvone N of L. Allen, JW Fitzgerald & EM Lobley (Paton 1966: 184).
H(30) listed by Macvicar (1905: 11). H(30) listed by Macvicar (1905: 11), as var. *minor*.
†H30 listed by Blockeel & Long (1998: 43).
H(31) listed by Macvicar (1905: 11). H(31) listed by Blockeel & Long (1998: 43).
H31 1999: on derelict wall in conifer plantation, *ca* 120 m alt., Two Mile River, Carlingford Mt., J11, TL Blockeel 28/147 (Blackstock 2000: 42).
H(33) 1914: Cuilcagh Mt., WN Tetley (BBSUK) (Castell 1954: 472).
H33 2000: on damp vertical gritstone at base of block scree on N-facing hillside, 500 m alt., SE of Lough Atona, H12, DT Holyoak 00-171A (BBSUK) (Blackstock 2001: 35).
H(34) listed by Macvicar (1905: 11).
†H34 listed by Blockeel & Long (1998: 43).
H(35) listed by Macvicar (1905: 11). H(35) listed by Macvicar (1905: 11), as var. *minor*.
†H35 listed by Blockeel & Long (1998: 43).
H36 1951: Lough Bradan, nr Castlederg, JW Fitzgerald (Castell 1952: 91).
H(37) listed by Macvicar (1905: 11). H(37) listed by Macvicar (1905: 11), as var. *minor*.
†H37 listed by Blockeel & Long (1998: 43).
H(38) listed by Macvicar (1905: 11). H(38) listed by Macvicar (1905: 11), as var. *minor*.
†H38 listed by Blockeel & Long (1998: 43).
H(39) listed by Macvicar (1905: 11).
†H39 listed by Blockeel & Long (1998: 43).
†H40 listed by Blockeel & Long (1998: 43).

34/1b *Marsupella emarginata* var. *aquatica* (Lindenb.) Dumort.
(syn. *Marsupella aquatica* (Lindenb.) Schiffn.)

H1 1951: in stream below L. Coomeeneragh, ALK King (Castell 1952: 91).
1951: in top tarn, Coomasaharn, Glenbeigh, MPH Kertland (Castell 1952: 91).
H(2) listed by Blockeel & Long (1998: 43).
H3 1953: rock in stream, Foulastookeen Mt., ALK King (Castell 1954: 472).
H4 1966: edge of stream at 1200 ft alt., Musheramore, Bogeragh Mts, MFV Corley & JS Parker (Paton 1968: 624).
H6 1966: wet rocks in stream, narrow gorge above L. Coumshingaun, Comeragh Mts, EM Lobley (BBS exc.) (Paton 1967c: 399).
H(13) 1867: rocks in the Clody R., Mt Leinster, R Clayton-Browne (DBN) (Paton 1968: 624).
H16 1957: carrying epiphytic growth of *Lejeunea patens*, on rock slabs subjected to constant trickle of water, N slopes of Benchoona, above Loch Muck, EV Watson (Castell 1958: 463).
H(20) listed by Macvicar (1905: 11). H(20) listed by Blockeel & Long (1998: 43).
H(21) 1949: wet calcareous tufa, E side of Lower Pond, Glenasmole, JP Brunker per JS Thomson (Castell 1950: 375).
H26 1965: boulders in stream W of L. Talt, [The] Ox Mts, JW Fitzgerald (Paton 1966: 184).
H(27) listed by Blockeel & Long (1998: 43).
H27 1999: growing as mats on flushed base of quartzite crag on S side of corrie, *ca* 500 m alt., NE side of Slievemore, Achill I., F60, DT Holyoak 99-384 (BBSUK) (Blackstock 2000: 42).
H28 1959: heavily shaded cleft on submerged rock, Slish Wood, ALK King (Castell 1960: 764).

H29 2001: on sandstone block in stream on N-facing hillside, *ca* 425 m alt., NW slope of Slieve Anierin, H01, DT Holyoak 01-852 (Blackstock: 2002: 39).
H30 1965: boulders in stream at 1100 ft alt., Englishman's House, 3 miles S of Glenfarne, JW Fitzgerald (Paton 1966: 184).
H33 2000: on unshaded gritstone boulders shallowly submerged in and just above water of quick-flowing stream, *ca* 475 m alt., outlet from Lough Atona, H12, DT Holyoak 00-179 (BBSUK) (Blackstock 2001: 35).
H34 1955: Bulbin Mt., AW Stelfox, comm. JS Thomson (Castell 1956: 147).
H35 1950: granite, alt. 800 ft, Douish [*sic* = Dooish], JW Fitzgerald (Castell 1951: 492).
H36 1956: submerged, Lough Lack, nr Drumquin, JW Fitzgerald & MPH Kertland (Castell 1957: 323).
H(38) listed by Macvicar (1905: 11). H(38) listed by Blockeel & Long (1998: 43).
H39 1952: boulders in Glenariff River, EM Lobley & J Taylor (Castell 1954: 472).

34/1c *Marsupella emarginata* var. *pearsonii* (Schiffn.) M.F.V.Corley
(syn. *Marsupella aquatica* var. *pearsonii* (Schiffn.) E.W.Jones, *M. pearsonii* Schiffn.)

H1 1952: wet rocks under cliff, *ca* 1500 ft alt., Connor Pass, Dingle, ALK King (Castell 1953: 298).
H(2) listed by Blockeel & Long (1998: 43).
H16 1970: stone in stream, NE slope of Muckanaght, The Twelve Pins, JA Paton (Paton 1971a: 372).
H(20) listed by Blockeel & Long (1998: 43).
H(27) listed by Blockeel & Long (1998: 43).
H(31) listed by Blockeel & Long (1998: 43).
H34 2002: in bryophyte mat over unshaded flushed schist rock on NW-facing slope, *ca* 480 m alt., just NW of summit of Bulbin Mt.,C34, DT Holyoak 02-509 (Blackstock 2003: 41).
H35 2001: in stream draining into Lough Agh, *ca* 300 m alt., Slieve League, G57, NG Hodgetts 3807 (Blackstock: 2002: 39).
H(38) 1915: Mourne Mts, HW Lett (DBN), comm. ALK King (Paton 1964: 713).
H39 1951: wet rocks by river edge, Owennaglush, Glendun, JW Fitzgerald (Paton 1968: 624).

34/3 *Marsupella sphacelata* (Gieseke ex Lindenb.) Dumort.
(syn. *Marsupella erythrorhiza* Schiffn., *M. sphacelata* var. *media* (Gottsche) E. W.Jones, *M. sullivantii* (De Not.) A. Evans)

[H(1) listed by Macvicar (1905: 11)].
[H(2) listed by Macvicar (1905: 11)].
H6 1966: wet drip in rock crevice at 1400 ft alt., L. Coumshingaun, Comeragh Mts, JW Fitzgerald & J Appleyard (BBS exc.) (Paton 1968: 624).
[H10 1979, wet rock in stream, S slope of Keeper Hill, HMH van Melick (BBSUK) (Corley 1980a: 29) deleted because voucher specimen is *M. emarginata*, comm. JA Paton (Long 1995b: 38)].
H(20) listed by Macvicar (1905: 11) as *M. sphacelata*. H(20) listed by Macvicar (1905: 11) as *M. erythrorhiza*.
†H20 listed by Blockeel & Long (1998: 44).
H(27) listed by Macvicar (1905: 11).
†H27 listed by Blockeel & Long (1998: 44).
H33 1959: on rocks in outlet stream, Lough Atona, Cuilcagh, JW Fitzgerald (Paton 1964: 713).
H(35) listed by Blockeel & Long (1998: 44).
H35 2001: wet stony, peaty flush in summit heath, *ca* 500 m alt., Binacally, Lavagh Beg, G99, NG Hodgetts 3875 (Blackstock 2003: 41).
[H(38) listed by Macvicar (1905: 11)].

34/4 *Marsupella funckii* (F.Weber & D. Mohr) Dumort

H(2) 1930: nr Upper Lake, Killarney, RL Praeger (DBN), comm. ALK King (Paton 1964: 713).
H3 1979: loamy soil on a path on N slope of Sugarloaf Mountain, Bantry I., HMH van Melick (Corley 1981: 19).
[H(6) listed by Macvicar (1905: 11)].
H7 1966: sandy ground beside road, Seefin, Galtee Mts, JW Fitzgerald *et al.* (BBS exc.) (Paton 1967c: 399).
H12 1975: heathy bank W of Cloroge, Mt Leinster, JA Paton (BBS exc.) (Paton 1976: 19).
†H16 listed by Blockeel & Long (1998: 44).

H(20) 1939: deerpark, Powerscourt demesne, Enniskerry, ALK King, comm. JS Thomson (Castell 1950: 375).
†H20 listed by Blockeel & Long (1998: 44).
H(27) listed by Macvicar (1905: 11).
†H27 listed by Blockeel & Long (1998: 44).
H31 1968: stone wall by old road, Ballymakellett, Dundalk, DM Synnott (Paton 1969a: 871).
†H35 listed by Blockeel & Long (1998: 44).
H(37) listed by Macvicar (1905: 11). H(37) listed by Blockeel & Long (1998: 44).
H(38) listed by Macvicar (1905: 11). H(38) listed by Blockeel & Long (1998: 44).
H(39) listed by Macvicar (1905: 11).
†H39 listed by Blockeel & Long (1998: 44).

34/5 ***Marsupella sprucei*** (Limpr.) Bernet (syn. *Marsupella ustulata* Spruce non (Huebener) Spruce ex Pears.)

H1 1973: on wet siliceous rock face, Boughill, WV Rubers (Corley 1980a: 29).
H(2) listed by Blockeel & Long (1998: 44).
H16 1970: sandstone in quartzite scree, NW slope of Benbaun, The Twelve Pins, JA Paton (Paton 1971a: 372).
H20 1975: soft rock on slope above L. Ouler, Tonelagee, JA Paton (BBS exc.) (Paton 1976: 19).
H27 1987: on thin soil on rock, 300 m, NE-facing Coire, Slievemore, Achill I., GP Rothero (Long 1988: 31).
H35 2001: on peat among rocks on N side of summit, *ca* 500 m alt., Binacally, Lavagh Beg, G99, NG Hodgetts 3872 (Blackstock 2003: 41).
H36 1957: sparingly, rocks at 1750 ft Dart Mt., Sperrin Mts, JW Fitzgerald (Castell 1959: 627).
H39 1952: on flat inclined surface of very large block with abundant *Andreaea*, The Undercliff, nr Grey Man's Path, Fair Head, EW Jones (Castell 1953: 298).
[H40 1957: sloping rock faces facing NW at 1900 [ft], Dart Mt., Sperrin Mts, JW Fitzgerald (Castell 1959: 627). H40 deleted because specimen (1958: Dart Mt., JW Fitzgerald, BBSUK) is *M. adusta*, redet. JA Paton, comm. DT Holyoak (Blackstock 2000: 42)].

34/11 ***Marsupella adusta*** (Nees emend. Limpr.) Spruce

H1 1968: sheltered rock in SE corrie, Brandon Mt., Dingle, JA Paton (Paton 1969a: 871, 1969b).
H27 1987: on small bits of sandstone in scree, N corrie, Croagh Patrick, JA Paton (Long 1988: 31).
H35 2001: on thin peat and rocks on N side of summit, *ca* 500 m alt., Binnacally, Lavagh Beg, G99, NG Hodgetts 3873 (Blackstock 2003: 42).
H36 1999: on steep unshaded base of small outcrop of metamorphic rock on exposed summit, *ca* 610 m alt., just SW of summit of Dart Mt., H69, DT Holyoak 99-698, conf. JA Paton, comm. DT Holyoak (BBSUK) (Blackstock 2001: 35; this record was erroneously given for H40 in Blackstock 2000: 42).
H38 2002: in small crevices of unshaded sloping surface of granitic rock on N-facing hillside, *ca* 485 m alt., E of Slievenaglogh, J32, DT Holyoak 02-1023 (Blackstock 2003: 42).
H39 1999: on vertical surfaces of dolerite block on N-facing slope beneath crags, Fair Head, D14, DT Holyoak 99-791, conf. JA Paton (Blackstock 2000: 42).
H40 1958: on sloping rock faces facing NW, 1900 ft alt., Dart Mt., JW Fitzgerald (BBSUK), originally identified as *M. sprucei*, redet. JA Paton, comm. DT Holyoak (Blackstock 2000: 42).
H40 1999: on low unshaded sloping metamorphic rock on exposed summit, *ca* 600 m alt., just NW of summit of Dart Mt., H69, DT Holyoak 99-697, conf. JA Paton (Blackstock 2000: 42).

35/1 ***Gymnomitrion concinnatum*** (Lightf.) Corda

H(16) listed by Blockeel & Long (1998: 44).
H34 1968: rocks at 1500 ft alt., Bulbin Mt., Inishowen, JW Fitzgerald (Paton 1969a: 871).
H35 1961: rocky slope at 1500 ft [alt.], Slieve League, nr Carrick, DA Ratcliffe (Paton 1962: 357).
H39 1951: shallow hollow on large basalt boulder, undercliff, alt. 250 ft, Fair Head, JW Fitzgerald (Castell 1952: 91).

35/2 ***Gymnomitrion obtusum*** Lindb.

H(1) 1840: Brandon, D Moore (DBN), comm. ALK King (Paton 1964: 713).
†H1 listed by Blockeel & Long (1998: 45).
H6 1963: sandstone cliffs facing N at 2000 ft alt., N corrie of Fauscoum, Comeragh Mts, DA Ratcliffe (Paton 1964: 713).
H13 1969: schistose rocks *ca* 2000 ft alt., above Caher Roe's Den, Blackstairs Mt., JW Fitzgerald (Paton 1970: 191).
H16 1951: N side, Muckanaght, H Milne-Redhead (Castell 1952: 91).
H20 1975: side of granite boulder, ridge N of North Prison, Lugnaquillia Mt., JA Paton & N Kirby (BBS exc.) (Paton 1976: 19).
H(27) listed by Macvicar (1905: 10).
†H27 listed by Blockeel & Long (1998: 45).
H35 1962: boulders, upper part of Slieve Snaght, EF Warburg (BBS exc.) (Paton 1963: 484).
H(38) listed by Macvicar (1905: 10).
†H38 listed by Blockeel & Long (1998: 45).
H40 1965: basalt boulders at 1500 ft alt., Mullaghmore nr Dungiven, JW Fitzgerald (Paton 1966: 184).

35/3 ***Gymnomitrion corallioides*** Nees

[H(1) listed with ? by Macvicar (1905: 10)].
H(1) Old record (1840: Brandon Mt., D Moore, DBN) placed in brackets (Paton 1971b, 1972: 133).
H34 1969: schistose rocks, Bulbin Mt., Inishowen, JA Paton (Paton 1970: 191, 1971b).

35/4 ***Gymnomitrion crenulatum*** Gottsche ex Carrington

H(1) listed by Macvicar (1905: 10).
†H1 listed by Blockeel & Long (1998: 45).
H(2) listed by Macvicar (1905: 10).
†H2 listed by Blockeel & Long (1998: 45).
H(3) listed by Macvicar (1905: 10).
†H3 listed by Blockeel & Long (1998: 45).
H6 1963: sandstone cliffs facing N at 2000 ft alt., N corrie of Fauscoum, Comeragh Mts, DA Ratcliffe (Paton 1964: 713).
H(7) listed by Macvicar (1905: 10).
†H7 listed by Blockeel & Long (1998: 45).
H12 1969: schistose rocks *ca* 2000 ft alt., above Caher Roe's Den, Blackstairs Mt., JW Fitzgerald (Paton 1970: 191).
H13 1969: schistose rocks *ca* 2000 ft alt., above Caher Roe's Den, Blackstairs Mt., JW Fitzgerald (Paton 1970: 191).
†H16 listed by Blockeel & Long (1998: 45).
H(20) listed by Macvicar (1905: 10). H(20) listed by Blockeel & Long (1998: 45).
H(21) listed by Macvicar (1905: 10). H(21) listed by Blockeel & Long (1998: 45).
†H27 listed by Blockeel & Long (1998: 45).
†H28 listed by Blockeel & Long (1998: 45).
†H29 listed by Blockeel & Long (1998: 45).
H30 1965: boulders at summit, 2000 ft alt., S side of Cuilcagh, JW Fitzgerald & EM Lobley (Paton 1966: 185).
H(31) listed by Macvicar (1905: 10). H(31) listed by Blockeel & Long (1998: 45).
H33 1959: very sparingly on cliff face above Lough Atona, Cuilcagh, JW Fitzgerald (Castell 1960: 764).
H34 1962: Croaghconnellagh, Tawnawully Mts, J Appleyard & EC Wallace (BBS exc.) (Paton 1963: 484).
H35 1961: dry granite rocks at 1000 ft [alt.], Glenbeagh, nr Dunlewy, DA Ratcliffe (Paton 1962: 357).
H36 1957: rocks at 1750 ft Dart Mt., Sperrin Mts, JW Fitzgerald (Castell 1959: 627).
[H(38) listed by Macvicar (1905: 10)].
H38 1958: *ca* 2000 ft alt., The Eagle's Rocks, Slieve Donard, AW Stelfox (DBN) (Long 1999b: 27).
H(39) listed by Macvicar (1905: 10).
†H39 listed by Blockeel & Long (1998: 45).
H(40) listed by Macvicar (1905: 10).
†H40 listed by Blockeel & Long (1998: 45).

36/1 ***Douinia ovata*** (Dicks.) H.Buch (syn. *Diplophyllum ovatum* (Dicks.) Waddell)

H(1) listed by Macvicar (1905: 19).
†H1 listed by Blockeel & Long (1998: 45).
H2 1973: block scree on steep S-facing slope, Horse's Glen, Mangerton, EC Mhic Daeid (Paton 1974b: 164).
H6 1966: rocks on N side of Coumshingaun L., Comeragh Mts, JA Paton, GCG Argent & ERB Little (BBS exc.) (Paton 1967c: 402).
H12 1969: among block scree at 1400 ft alt., below Caher Roe's Den, Blackstairs Mt., JW Fitzgerald (Paton 1970: 193).
H16 1965: block scree, S slope of Ben Cullagh, Twelve Bens, EC Mhic Daeid (Paton 1974b: 164).

H(20) listed by Macvicar (1905: 19).
†H20 listed by Blockeel & Long (1998: 45).
H(21) listed by Macvicar (1905: 19). H(21) listed by Blockeel & Long (1998: 45).
H(27) listed by Macvicar (1905: 19).
†H27 listed by Blockeel & Long (1998: 45).
[H(29) listed by Macvicar (1905: 19)].
H(31) listed by Macvicar (1905: 19). H(31) listed by Blockeel & Long (1998: 45).
H(34) listed by Blockeel & Long (1998: 45).
H(35) listed by Macvicar (1905: 19).
†H35 listed by Blockeel & Long (1998: 45).
H(38) listed by Macvicar (1905: 19). H(38) listed by Blockeel & Long (1998: 45).
H40 1968: blocks in scree below Benbradagh, HH Birks & JW Fitzgerald (Paton 1969a: 874).

37/1 ***Diplophyllum albicans*** (L.) Dumort.

H(1) listed by Macvicar (1905: 19).
†H1 listed by Blockeel & Long (1998: 45).
H(2) listed by Macvicar (1905: 19).
†H2 listed by Blockeel & Long (1998: 45).
H(3) listed by Macvicar (1905: 19).
†H3 listed by Blockeel & Long (1998: 45).
H4 1966: peaty bank, Seefin, Boggeragh Mts, MFV Corley & JS Parker (Paton 1967c: 402).
H5 1961: in *Sphagnum* in bog nr Inch, NW of Youghal, MJP Scannell, comm. ALK King (Paton 1962: 362).
H(6) listed by Macvicar (1905: 19).
†H6 listed by Blockeel & Long (1998: 45).
H(7) listed by Macvicar (1905: 19).
†H7 listed by Blockeel & Long (1998: 45).
H8 1966: on shady stream bank, Glenbrohane nr Ballyanders [*sic* = Ballylanders], MFV Corley & Parker (Paton 1967c: 402).
H(9) listed by Macvicar (1905: 19).
†H9 listed by Blockeel & Long (1998: 45).
H10 1951: earth bank on hillside, alt. 600 ft, above Silvermines, AD Banwell, EV Watson & PJ Wanstall (Castell 1952: 95).
H11 1954: on granite, Mt Brandon, ALK King (Castell 1955: 581).
H(12) listed by Macvicar (1905: 19).
†H12 listed by Blockeel & Long (1998: 45).
H(13) listed by Macvicar (1905: 19).
†H13 listed by Blockeel & Long (1998: 45).
H(14) listed by Macvicar (1905: 19).
†H14 listed by Blockeel & Long (1998: 45).
H(15) listed by Macvicar (1905: 19).
†H15 listed by Blockeel & Long (1998: 45).
H(16) listed by Macvicar (1905: 19).
†H16 listed by Blockeel & Long (1998: 45).
H(18) listed by Macvicar (1905: 19).
†H18 listed by Blockeel & Long (1998: 45).
[H(19) listed by Macvicar (1905: 19). H19 deleted because no record or voucher traced, comm. MM Yeo (Long 1990a: 26)].
H(20) listed by Macvicar (1905: 19).
†H20 listed by Blockeel & Long (1998: 45).
H(21) listed by Macvicar (1905: 19).
†H21 listed by Blockeel & Long (1998: 45).
H(22) listed by Macvicar (1905: 19).
†H22 listed by Blockeel & Long (1998: 45).
H(23) listed by Macvicar (1905: 19).
†H23 listed by Blockeel & Long (1998: 45).
H24 1965: raised bog nr Roosky, JW Fitzgerald & EM Lobley (Paton 1966: 187).
H25 1965: bog at 700 ft alt., Kilronan Mountain nr Ballyfarnan, JW Fitzgerald & EM Lobley (Paton 1966: 187).
H(26) listed by Macvicar (1905: 19).
†H26 listed by Blockeel & Long (1998: 45).
H(27) listed by Macvicar (1905: 19).
†H27 listed by Blockeel & Long (1998: 45).
H(28) listed by Macvicar (1905: 19).
†H28 listed by Blockeel & Long (1998: 45).
H(29) listed by Macvicar (1905: 19).
†H29 listed by Blockeel & Long (1998: 45).
H(30) listed by Macvicar (1905: 19).
†H30 listed by Blockeel & Long (1998: 45).
H(31) listed by Macvicar (1905: 19). H(31) listed by Blockeel & Long (1998: 45).
H31 1999: on derelict wall in conifer plantation, *ca* 120 m alt., Two Mile River, Carlingford Mountain, J11, TL Blockeel 28/146 (Blackstock 2000: 42).
H32 1961: boulder in ditch, Darraghlan, S of Monaghan, JW Fitzgerald (Paton 1962: 362).
†H33 listed by Blockeel & Long (1998: 45).
H(34) listed by Macvicar (1905: 19).
†H34 listed by Blockeel & Long (1998: 45).
H(35) listed by Macvicar (1905: 19).
†H35 listed by Blockeel & Long (1998: 45).
†H36 listed by Blockeel & Long (1998: 45).
H(37) listed by Macvicar (1905: 19).
†H37 listed by Blockeel & Long (1998: 45).
H(38) listed by Macvicar (1905: 19).
†H38 listed by Blockeel & Long (1998: 45).
H(39) listed by Macvicar (1905: 19).
†H39 listed by Blockeel & Long (1998: 45).
H(40) listed by Macvicar (1905: 19).

†H40 listed by Blockeel & Long (1998: 45).

37/3 ***Diplophyllum obtusifolium*** (Hook.) Dumort.

H(1) listed by Macvicar (1905: 19). H(1) listed by Blockeel & Long (1998: 45).
H(3) listed by Macvicar (1905: 19). H(3) listed by Blockeel & Long (1998: 45).
H(4) listed by Macvicar (1905: 19). H(4) listed by Blockeel & Long (1998: 45).
H6 1966: gravelly track through plantation, Glenshelane, N of Cappoquin, JA Paton & ERB Little (BBS exc.) (Paton 1967c: 402).
H13 2002: on partly bare soil among sparse low herbs and grasses at almost unshaded edge of gravelly bank in young spruce plantation, *ca* 303 m alt., S slope of Croaghaun, S85, DT Holyoak 02-362 (Blackstock 2003: 42).
H20 1969: forestry track, Devil's Glen nr Ashford, JW Fitzgerald & DM Synnott (Paton 1970: 193).
H(21) listed by Macvicar (1905: 19).
†H21 listed by Blockeel & Long (1998: 45).
H32 1961: in earthy crevice in rock in quarry, Cashlan, NE of Newbliss, JW Fitzgerald (Paton 1962: 362).
H34 1967: soil in rock clefts, roadside quarry nr Illies Hill, E of Buncrana, JW Fitzgerald (Paton 1968: 626).
H(37) listed by Macvicar (1905: 19). H(37) listed by Blockeel & Long (1998: 45).

38/1 ***Scapania compacta*** (A.Roth) Dumort.

H(1) listed by Macvicar (1905: 20).
†H1 listed by Blockeel & Long (1998: 45).
H(2) listed by Macvicar (1905: 20).
†H2 listed by Blockeel & Long (1998: 45).
H3 1964: on bare soil, Bearhaven copper mines, Allihies, ERB Little (Paton 1966: 187).
H(4) listed by Macvicar (1905: 20).
†H4 listed by Blockeel & Long (1998: 45).
H6 1966: on old mine waste, cliffs E of Bunmahon, ERB Little (BBS exc.) (Paton 1967c: 403).
H8 1966: on basalt rocks, Knockroe nr Caherconlish, MFV Corley & JS Parker (Paton 1967c: 403).
H12 1969: rocks at side of ditch, Sculloge Gap nr Kiltealy, JW Fitzgerald (Paton 1970: 193).
H(13) listed by Macvicar (1905: 20).
†H13 listed by Blockeel & Long (1998: 45).
†H16 listed by Blockeel & Long (1998: 45).
H(20) listed by Macvicar (1905: 20).
†H20 listed by Blockeel & Long (1998: 45).
H(21) 1905: bank on N side, Lambay, rare, D McArdle (*Irish Nat.* **16**, 104, 1907), comm. JW Fitzgerald (Castell 1952: 95).
†H21 listed by Blockeel & Long (1998: 45).
H(27) listed by Macvicar (1905: 20).
†H27 listed by Blockeel & Long (1998: 45).
H28 1965: tops of sandy hillocks behind sand dunes on coast W of Strandhill, AR Perry & EF Warburg (Paton 1966: 186).
H(31) listed by Macvicar (1905: 20). H(31) listed by Blockeel & Long (1998: 45).
[H(32) listed by Macvicar (1905: 20). H32 deleted because no record or voucher traced, comm. MM Yeo (Long 1990a: 27)].
H34 2002: near low *Calluna* on unshaded damp peaty soil over schist rock on low hill near coast, *ca* 10 m alt., S coast of Doagh Isle W of Balloor, C44, DT Holyoak 02-548 (Blackstock 2003: 42).
H35 1962: on bank by seashore, Rossbeg, ALK King (Paton 1963: 489).
H(37) listed by Macvicar (1905: 20).
†H37 listed by Blockeel & Long (1998: 45).
H(38) listed by Macvicar (1905: 20).
†H38 listed by Blockeel & Long (1998: 45).
H(39) listed by Macvicar (1905: 20).
†H39 listed by Blockeel & Long (1998: 45).
†H40 listed by Blockeel & Long (1998: 45).

38/2 ***Scapania gymnostomophila*** Kaal.

H26 1987: in mossy hollow on limestone pavement, Keel Bridge, Lough Carra, DG Long (Long 1988: 32).
H34 1969: ledge on schistose rocks, Bulbin Mt., Inishowen, JA Paton (Paton 1970: 193, 1971b).
H35 2001: scattered on very steep, heavily grazed slopes above beach, among other bryophytes, *ca* 10 m alt., Trabane, Malin Beg, G57, NG Hodgetts 3788 (Blackstock: 2002: 39).

[38/3 ***Scapania calcicola*** (Arnell & J.Perss.) Ingham]

[H(40) 1900: on heathy mossy patches at edge of damp spots amongst sand dunes, Magilligan, HW Lett & CH Waddell (in

HW Lett, *Irish Nat.* **14**, 176, 1905), comm. JW Fitzgerald (Castell 1952: 95). H40 deleted because identification mistaken (Macvicar 1926: 372, Castell 1955: 581)].

38/4 ***Scapania cuspiduligera*** (Nees) Müll. Frib.

H28 1963: limestone rock face at 1500 ft alt., Gleniff, AR Perry & JW Fitzgerald (Paton 1969a: 874).
H35 2001: short turf in dune heath, with *Ditrichum gracile* etc., *ca* 15 m alt., Maghera Strand, G69, NG Hodgetts 3830 (Blackstock 2003: 42).

38/5 ***Scapania scandica*** (Arnell & H.Buch) Macvicar

H1 1966: peaty bank above L. Nalacken, Brandon Mt., Dingle, JA Paton (Paton 1967c: 402).
H2 1983: earthy slope on S side of L. Erhogh, Horse's Glen, Mangerton Mt., JA Paton (Corley 1984: 24).
H6 1966: heathy bank on hillside N of the Punchbowl, Comeragh Mts, JA Paton (BBS exc.) (Paton 1967c: 402).
H7 1966: on rotting vegetation, rocky slope above L. Curra, Galtee Mts, JA Paton (BBS exc.) (Paton 1967c: 402).
H20 1988: on tree trunk on N-facing rocky slope, 450 m, below Arts Lough, Glenmalur Valley E of Lugnaquillia, DG Long 14915 (Long 1989: 22).
H27 1987: soil below cliffs, NE corrie, Slievemore, Achill I., JA Paton (Long 1988: 32).
H28 1970: on the way to King's Mt., JA Paton (BBS exc.) (Paton 1971a: 373, Appleyard 1971: 389).
†H34 listed by Blockeel & Long (1998: 46).
H36 1957: on floor of disused sand-pit, near Trillick, JW Fitzgerald (BEL) (Long 1993b: 45).

38/6 ***Scapania curta*** (Mart.) Dumort.

[H(1) listed by Macvicar (1905: 21)].
[H(2) listed by Macvicar (1905: 21)].
[H(6) listed by Macvicar (1905: 21)].
[H(16) listed by Macvicar (1905: 21)].
[H(20) listed by Macvicar (1905: 21)].
[H(27) listed by Macvicar (1905: 21)].
H27 1987: on sandy soil in old quarry, roadside 4 km E of Keel, Achill I., DG Long (E) (Long 1988: 32).
[H(28) listed by Macvicar (1905: 21)].
[H(29) listed by Macvicar (1905: 21)].
[H(30) listed by Macvicar (1905: 21)].
[H(35) listed by Macvicar (1905: 21)].
[H36 1957: disused sandpit nr Trillick, JW Fitzgerald (Castell 1959: 630). Record later rejected following revision of specimens by AR Perry (Paton 1965b: 43, 49)].
[H(39) listed by Macvicar (1905: 21)].
[H(40) listed by Macvicar (1905: 21)].

Old records of this species (e.g. in Macvicar 1905: 21) included allied species such as *S. scandica*.

38/7 ***Scapania lingulata*** H.Buch

†H10 listed by Blockeel & Long (1998: 46).
H27 1987: on calcareous boulder on slope of deep ravine W of Croaghaun, Achill I., DG Long (Long 1988: 32).

38/10 ***Scapania umbrosa*** (Schrad.) Dumort.

H(1) listed by Macvicar (1905: 21).
†H1 listed by Blockeel & Long (1998: 46).
H(2) listed by Macvicar (1905: 21).
†H2 listed by Blockeel & Long (1998: 46).
H4 1967: peaty ground above stream, Mushera, JW Fitzgerald (Paton 1968: 626).
H(6) listed by Macvicar (1905: 21).
†H6 listed by Blockeel & Long (1998: 46).
†H7 listed by Blockeel & Long (1998: 46).
H8 1966: on rocks on moor at 1400 ft alt., Slievereagh nr Ballylanders, MFV Corley & JS Parker (Paton 1967c: 402).
H10 1979: heathy slope, S side of Keeper Hill, JA Paton (Corley 1980a: 31).
H12 1975: peat under *Calluna*, moorland nr Cloroge, SE. side of Mt Leinster, AR Perry (BBS exc.) (Paton 1977a: 15).
H13 1969: rocks in block scree below Caher Roe's Den, Blackstairs Mt., JW Fitzgerald (Paton 1970: 193).
H(16) listed by Macvicar (1905: 21).
†H16 listed by Blockeel & Long (1998: 46).
H(20) listed by Macvicar (1905: 21).
†H20 listed by Blockeel & Long (1998: 46).
H(21) listed by Macvicar (1905: 21).
†H21 listed by Blockeel & Long (1998: 46).

[H(25) listed by Macvicar (1905: 21). H25 deleted because no record or voucher traced, comm. MM Yeo (Long 1990a: 26)].
H25 2002: peaty soil below small waterfall on NE-facing crags, with *Kurzia trichoclados*, *ca* 150 m alt., Kilronan Mt., Arigna, G91, NG Hodgetts 4154 (Blackstock 2003: 42).
H26 1965: on peat W of L. Talt, [The] Ox Mts, JW Fitzgerald (Paton 1966: 187).
H(27) listed by Macvicar (1905: 21).
†H27 listed by Blockeel & Long (1998: 46).
H(28) 1892: Ben Bulben, CH Waddell (BFT), comm. JW Fitzgerald (JW Fitzgerald 1952, Castell 1953: 303).
1937: Ben Bulben, no collector named (BBS exc.) (Armitage 1938: 13).
1937: Ben Bulben (*J. Bot., Lond.*, 1938, p. 174) (Castell 1953: 303).
†H28 listed by Blockeel & Long (1998: 46).
H(29) 1928: wooded glen, NE end of Glencar Lough (BBS exc.) (Duncan 1928: 118).
†H29 listed by Blockeel & Long (1998: 46).
H30 1965: on peat among scree, Englishman's House, 3 miles S of Glenfarne, JW Fitzgerald (Paton 1966: 187).
†H33 listed by Blockeel & Long (1998: 46).
H34 1962: rock surface, N side of Croaghconnellagh, EF Warburg (BBS exc.) (Paton 1963: 490).
H(35) listed by Macvicar (1905: 21).
†H35 listed by Blockeel & Long (1998: 46).
H36 1956: by banks of stream, Sawel Mt., JW Fitzgerald & MPH Kertland (Castell 1957: 326).
H(37) listed by Macvicar (1905: 21).
†H37 listed by Blockeel & Long (1998: 46).
H(38) listed by Macvicar (1905: 21). H(38) listed by Blockeel & Long (1998: 46).
H(39) listed by Macvicar (1905: 21).
†H39 listed by Blockeel & Long (1998: 46).
H(40) listed by Macvicar (1905: 21).
†H40 listed by Blockeel & Long (1998: 46).

38/11 ***Scapania nemorea*** (L.) Grolle
(syn. *Scapania nemorosa* (L.) Dumort. nom. illeg.)

H(1) listed by Macvicar (1905: 20).
†H1 listed by Blockeel & Long (1998: 46).
H(2) listed by Macvicar (1905: 20).
†H2 listed by Blockeel & Long (1998: 46).
H(3) listed by Macvicar (1905: 20).
†H3 listed by Blockeel & Long (1998: 46).
H(4) no date: nr Brandon, WK (BEL) (Paton 1967c: 403).
†H4 listed by Blockeel & Long (1998: 46).
H5 1956: wood on hillside, nr Park House, Tourig river valley, nr Youghal, EC Wallace (Castell 1957: 326).
H(6) 1933: Strancall Castle, E Armitage (anon. 1934c: 147).
†H6 listed by Blockeel & Long (1998: 46).
H(7) listed by Macvicar (1905: 20).
†H7 listed by Blockeel & Long (1998: 46).
H8 1979: pathside nr top of waterfall, Glenastar, W of Ardagh, JA Paton (Corley 1980a: 31).
H(9) listed by Macvicar (1905: 20).
†H9 listed by Blockeel & Long (1998: 46).
H10 1967: blocks in wooded valley, Clare Glen, nr Newport, HH Birks, HJB Birks & DA Ratcliffe (Paton 1968: 626).
H(12) listed by Macvicar (1905: 20).
†H12 listed by Blockeel & Long (1998: 46).
H(13) listed by Macvicar (1905: 20).
†H13 listed by Blockeel & Long (1998: 46).
H(16) listed by Macvicar (1905: 20).
†H16 listed by Blockeel & Long (1998: 46).
H(20) listed by Macvicar (1905: 20).
†H20 listed by Blockeel & Long (1998: 46).
H(21) listed by Macvicar (1905: 20). H(21) listed by Blockeel & Long (1998: 46).
H25 1981: on clay, sandstone quarry, Derreenargan, SE of Keadew, DM Synnott (Corley 1982: 21).
H26 1987: on boulder on wooded river bank, E bank of Cloon River nr Partry, DG Long (Long 1988: 32).
H(27) listed by Macvicar (1905: 20).
†H27 listed by Blockeel & Long (1998: 46).
H(28) listed by Macvicar (1905: 20).
†H28 listed by Blockeel & Long (1998: 46).
H29 1963: on rotting wood in glen, Glencar, JW Fitzgerald & AR Perry (Paton 1964: 719).
H(30) listed by Macvicar (1905: 20).
†H30 listed by Blockeel & Long (1998: 46).
[H(31) listed by Macvicar (1905: 20)].
H31 1966: N side of Trumpet Hill, Carlingford Peninsula, DM Synnott (DBN) (Long 1999b: 27).
†H33 listed by Blockeel & Long (1998: 46).
H(34) listed by Macvicar (1905: 20).
†H34 listed by Blockeel & Long (1998: 46).
H(35) listed by Macvicar (1905: 20).
†H35 listed by Blockeel & Long (1998: 46).
H(36) listed by Macvicar (1905: 20).

†H36 listed by Blockeel & Long (1998: 46).
H37 1964: rocks in wood below the tower, Slieve Gullion, JW Fitzgerald & MPH Kertland (Paton 1965a: 857).
H(38) listed by Macvicar (1905: 20).
†H38 listed by Blockeel & Long (1998: 46).
H(39) listed by Macvicar (1905: 20).
†H39 listed by Blockeel & Long (1998: 46).
H(40) listed by Macvicar (1905: 20).
†H40 listed by Blockeel & Long (1998: 46).

38/12 ***Scapania irrigua*** (Nees) Nees

H(1) listed by Macvicar (1905: 20).
†H1 listed by Blockeel & Long (1998: 46).
H(2) listed by Macvicar (1905: 20).
†H2 listed by Blockeel & Long (1998: 46).
H3 1953: wet bank on Foulastookeen Mt., ALK King, conf. EW Jones (with comments) (Castell 1954: 476).
H4 1967: peaty ground above stream, Mushera, JW Fitzgerald (Paton 1968: 626).
H5 1966: forestry track, Castle Cooke nr Kilworth, JW Fitzgerald *et al.* (BBS exc.) (Paton 1967c: 402).
H(6) listed by Macvicar (1905: 20).
†H6 listed by Blockeel & Long (1998: 46).
H7 1966: roadside, Seefin, Galtee Mts, JW Fitzgerald *et al.* (BBS exc.) (Paton 1967c: 402).
H8 1966: bank on hillside above Monabrack, Galtee Mts, JA Paton (BBS exc.) (Paton 1967c: 402).
H9 1979: wet bank by path, Slievebernagh, N Lockhart (Corley 1980a: 31).
H10 1951: soil by hillside path, alt. 550 ft, hills between Ballina and Newtown, AD Banwell, EV Watson & PJ Wanstall (Castell 1952: 96).
H11 1968: woodland track, W bank of the R. Nore, SE of Thomastown, JA Paton (Paton 1969a: 874).
H12 1975: marshy slope, Croghan, Croghan Mt., JA Paton (BBS exc.) (Paton 1976: 20).
H15 1994: steep wet bank beside Boleyneendorish River, Slieve Aughty, M50, JA Paton 7643 (Long 1995b: 38).
H16 1957: boggy ground, Ben Lettery, EM Lobley (BBS exc.) (Castell 1958: 468).
H(17) 1896: Doon Bog, Clonbrock, D McArdle (DBN) (Long 1990a: 26).
H(20) listed by Macvicar (1905: 20).
†H20 listed by Blockeel & Long (1998: 46).
H21 1966: on moss-covered path in wood at Fern Hill, Sandyford, ALK King (Paton 1967c: 402).
H22 1965: on side of drain by cut-away bog S of Summerhill, ALK King (Paton 1966: 187).
H23 1979: on cut-over bog with *Juncus effusus*, Clonbrickan Bog, S of Moate, DM Synnott (Corley 1980a: 31).
H25 1965: marshy ground, Kilronan nr Ballyfarnan, EM Lobley & JW Fitzgerald (Paton 1966: 187).
H26 1957: wet slope, W side of [The] Ox Mts, ALK King (Castell 1958: 468).
H(27) listed by Macvicar (1905: 20).
†H27 listed by Blockeel & Long (1998: 46).
H(28) listed by Macvicar (1905: 20).
†H28 listed by Blockeel & Long (1998: 46).
H29 1963: path above Glencar waterfall, JW Fitzgerald & AR Perry (Paton 1964: 719).
H30 1956: wet woodland path, Virginia, JS Thomson (Castell 1957: 326).
H31 1955: bank of bog-hole, Coole Bog, SW of Ardee, ALK King (Castell 1956: 149).
H33 1959: peaty track over bog, Garvany Bridge, nr Belleek, JW Fitzgerald (Castell 1960: 767).
1959: marshy ground, Aghahoorin, nr Boho, JW Fitzgerald (Castell 1960: 767).
H34 1968: wet floor of quarry, Crockavishane nr Movill, Inishowen, HH Birks & JW Fitzgerald (Paton 1969a: 874).
H35 1962: stony place at old quarry, Muckish Mt., J Appleyard & RE Longton (BBS exc.) (Paton 1963: 490).
H36 1957: side of path, Baronscourt, JW Fitzgerald (Castell 1959: 630).
†H37 listed by Blockeel & Long (1998: 46).
H(38) listed by Macvicar (1905: 20). H(38) listed by Blockeel & Long (1998: 46).
H38 2002: among stones on unshaded silty mud exposed in inundation zone beside reservoir, with patchy low herbs and grasses, *ca* 290 m alt., S end of Fofanny Dam, J22, DT Holyoak 02-969 (Blackstock 2003: 42).
H(39) 1928: Glenariff (BBS exc.) (Duncan 1928: 117).
†H39 listed by Blockeel & Long (1998: 46).
H40 1953: marshy ground, Blackwater Bridge, N of Lough Fea, MPH Kertland

& EM Lobley (Castell 1955: 581).

38/15 ***Scapania undulata*** (L.) Dumort.
(syn. *Scapania dentata* Dumort., *S. dentata* var. *ambigua* De Not., *S. intermedia* (Husn.) Pearson, *S. purpurascens* (Hook.) Taylor, *S. purpurascens* var. *speciosa* Nees)

H(1) listed by Macvicar (1905: 20).
†H1 listed by Blockeel & Long (1998: 47).
H(2) listed by Macvicar (1905: 20).
†H2 listed by Blockeel & Long (1998: 47).
H(3) listed by Macvicar (1905: 20).
†H3 listed by Blockeel & Long (1998: 47).
H4 1966: submerged on rock in stream nr Carigagulla Bridge, Boggeragh Mts, MFV Corley & JS Parker (Paton 1967c: 403).
H(5) 1851: nr Fermoy, ex Hb. T Chandlee (DBN), comm. ALK King (Paton 1964: 719).
†H5 listed by Blockeel & Long (1998: 47).
H(6) listed by Macvicar (1905: 20).
†H6 listed by Blockeel & Long (1998: 47).
H(7) 1943: Corrig-na-binnia, AW Stelfox, per JS Thomson (Wilson 1944: 221), as *S. dentata* var. *ambigua*.
H(7) listed by Macvicar (1905: 20).
†H7 listed by Blockeel & Long (1998: 47).
H8 1966: on rocks in stream below Paradise Hill, Galtee Mts, MFV Corley & JS Parker (Paton 1967c: 403).
H(9) listed by Macvicar (1905: 20).
†H9 listed by Blockeel & Long (1998: 47).
H10 1951: wet rocks in stream in shaded gully, alt. 900 ft, above Silvermines, AD Banwell, EV Watson & PJ Wanstall, comm. & det. AD Banwell, conf. (with notes) by EW Jones (Castell 1952: 95).
H11 1954: growing through *Pellia* sp., on wet bank by Ballyeogan Rd, Graiguenamanagh, ALK King (Castell 1955: 581), as *S. dentata*.
H(12) 1913: Great Saltee I., HW Lett (*Irish Nat.* **22**, 195, 1913), comm. JW Fitzgerald (Castell 1952: 95).
H(12) listed by Macvicar (1905: 20).
†H12 listed by Blockeel & Long (1998: 47).
H(13) listed by Macvicar (1905: 20).
†H13 listed by Blockeel & Long (1998: 47).
H(14) listed by Macvicar (1905: 20).
†H14 listed by Blockeel & Long (1998: 47).
[H(15) listed by Macvicar (1905: 20). H15 deleted because no record or voucher traced, comm. MM Yeo (Long 1990a: 27)].
H15 1994: silted rocks beside Boleyneendorish River, Slieve Aughty, M50, JA Paton 7678 (Long 1995b: 38).
H(16) listed by Macvicar (1905: 20).
†H16 listed by Blockeel & Long (1998: 47).
[H(17) listed by Macvicar (1905: 20). H17 deleted because probable voucher (1896: Doon Bog, Clonbrock, D McArdle, DBN) is *S. irrigua* (Long 1990a: 27)].
[H(18) listed by Macvicar (1905: 20). H18 deleted because no record or voucher traced, comm. MM Yeo (Long 1990a: 27)].
[H(19) listed by Macvicar (1905: 20). H19 deleted because no record or voucher traced, comm. MM Yeo (Long 1990a: 27)].
H(20) listed by Macvicar (1905: 20).
†H20 listed by Blockeel & Long (1998: 47).
H(21) listed by Macvicar (1905: 20).
†H21 listed by Blockeel & Long (1998: 47).
[H(22) listed by Macvicar (1905: 20). H22 deleted because no record traced (Synnott 1982, Corley 1984: 24)].
[H(23) listed by Macvicar (1905: 20). H23 deleted because no record traced (Synnott 1982, Corley 1984: 24)].
H24 1965: wet flush at 800 ft alt., Cornhill nr Drumlish, JW Fitzgerald & EM Lobley (Paton 1966: 187).
H25 1965: rocks in stream at 700 ft alt., Kilronan Mt. nr Ballyfarnan, JW Fitzgerald & EM Lobley (Paton 1966: 187).
H(26) listed by Macvicar (1905: 20).
†H26 listed by Blockeel & Long (1998: 47).
H(27) listed by Macvicar (1905: 20).
H(27) 1935: Dugort, W Watson (anon. 1938e: 45), as *S. dentata* var. *ambigua*.
1937: Dugort, no collector named (BBS exc.) (Armitage 1938: 13), as *S. dentata* var. *ambigua*.
†H27 listed by Blockeel & Long (1998: 47).
H(28) listed by Macvicar (1905: 20).
H(28) 1915: wet stone in thicket, lower Ben Weeskin, WN Tetley (BBSUK) (Castell 1953: 303), as *S. dentata*.
†H28 listed by Blockeel & Long (1998: 47).
H(29) listed by Macvicar (1905: 20).
H(29) 1913: E Truskmore, WN Tetley (BBSUK) (Castell 1953: 303), as *S. dentata*.
1928: wooded glen, NE end of Glencar

Lough (BBS exc.) (Duncan 1928: 118, Castell 1953: 303), as *S. dentata*.

†H29 listed by Blockeel & Long (1998: 47).

H(30) listed by Macvicar (1905: 20).

†H30 listed by Blockeel & Long (1998: 47).

H(31) listed by Macvicar (1905: 20).

†H31 listed by Blockeel & Long (1998: 47).

H(33) 1913: Correll Glen, WN Tetley (BBSUK) (Castell 1953: 303), as *S. dentata*.

H(33) listed by Macvicar (1905: 20).

†H33 listed by Blockeel & Long (1998: 47).

H(34) listed by Macvicar (1905: 20).

†H34 listed by Blockeel & Long (1998: 47).

H(35) listed by Macvicar (1905: 20).

†H35 listed by Blockeel & Long (1998: 47).

H36 1951: rock in stream, alt. 630 ft, between Draperstown and Plumbridge, JW Fitzgerald (Castell 1952: 95).
1951: in stream, alt. 850 ft, Leagh's Bridge, Draperstown-Plumbridge Road, JW Fitzgerald (Castell 1952: 95), as *S. dentata*.

H(37) listed by Macvicar (1905: 20).

†H37 listed by Blockeel & Long (1998: 47).

H(38) listed by Macvicar (1905: 20).

†H38 listed by Blockeel & Long (1998: 47).

H(39) listed by Macvicar (1905: 20).

H(39) 1928: Glenariff (BBS exc.) (Duncan 1928: 117), as *S. dentata*.

H39 1952: in stream, alt. 1300 ft, Slievenance, JW Fitzgerald (Castell 1954: 476).

H40 1952: by the Bishop's Road, Downhill, EW Jones (Castell 1953: 303).

38/16 ***Scapania subalpina*** (Nees ex Lindenb.) Dumort.
(syn. *Scapania subalpina* var. *undulifolia* Nees)

H(1) listed by Macvicar (1905: 20). H(1) listed by Blockeel & Long (1998: 47).

[H(2) listed by Macvicar (1905: 20). H2 deleted because locality (Slieve Mish) may be in H1 and no localised record or voucher traced, comm. MM Yeo (Long 1990a: 27)].

H(6) listed by Macvicar (1905: 20).

†H6 listed by Blockeel & Long (1998: 47).

H7 1966: sandy detritus by stream, Knockastackeen, Galtee Mts, EM Lobley (BBS exc.) (Paton 1967c: 403).

H16 1968: wet flushed rocks on NE-facing slope, Bengower, Twelve Pins, AR Perry (Paton 1970: 193).

H(20) listed by Macvicar (1905: 20). H(20) listed by Blockeel & Long (1998: 47).

[H(21) listed by Macvicar (1905: 20)].

H(27) listed by Macvicar (1905: 20). H(27) listed by Blockeel & Long (1998: 47).

H34 1967: sandy rock crevices by R. Crana, E of Ballymagan, E of Buncrana, JW Fitzgerald (Paton 1968: 627).

†H35 listed by Blockeel & Long (1998: 47).

H36 1956: sandy detritus beside stream, Corick Bridge, Newtownstewart, MPH Kertland & JW Fitzgerald (Castell 1959: 630).

H38 1952: steep earth bank in side of stone quarry, Scrabo, nr Belfast, JW Fitzgerald, MPH Kertland & EW Jones, comm. EW Jones (Castell 1953: 303).

H(39) listed by Macvicar (1905: 20).

†H39 listed by Blockeel & Long (1998: 47).

H40 1965: on detritus, rocks by Altalacky R., Mullaghmore nr Dungiven, JW Fitzgerald (Paton 1965: 187).

[**38/17** ***Scapania uliginosa*** (Sw. ex Lindenb.) Dumort.

[H(1) listed by Macvicar (1905: 20). H1 deleted because all five specimens traced (1846: Knockavohila near Dunkerron, T Taylor, E; 1894: Anniscaul near Dingle, D McArdle, DBN; 1897: glen near Lough Cruttia, Brandon, HW Lett, DBN; 1900: Mt Brandon, D McArdle, BM & DBN; 1952: in stream on Faha Mt., Brandon, collector unknown, DBN) are all *S. undulata* (Long 1993a, 1994: 34)].

[H(2) listed by Macvicar (1905: 20). H2 deleted because specimen (1866: marshy streams at Cromaglown, Killarney, D Moore, DBN) is *S. undulata* (Long 1993a, 1994: 34)].

[H(12) listed by Macvicar (1905: 20). H12 (record: 1899: banks of a stream, Knockroe, D McArdle) deleted because no specimen traced and McArdle's other material attributed to *S. uliginosa* was misidentified (Long 1993a, 1994: 34)].

[H(20) listed by Macvicar (1905: 20). H20 deleted because specimens (no date: Lough Bray, Dr Moore, BM & DBN; 1952: on rocks in upper Liffey, 1600 ft [alt.], nr Sally Gap, collector unknown, DBN) are *S. undulata* (Long 1993a,

1994: 34)].

[H(27) listed by Macvicar (1905: 20). H27 deleted because specimen (1901 & 1904: Pontoon, D McArdle, DBN) is *S. undulata* (Long 1993a, 1994: 34)].

[H28 deleted because specimen (1904: Hazlewood, D McArdle, DBN) is *S. undulata* (Long 1993a)].

[H(31) listed by Macvicar (1905: 20). H31 deleted because specimens (DBN) are *S. undulata*, comm. JA Paton & DM Synnott (Corley 1986: 17); H31 deleted because specimens (1882: Carlingford Mt., Mrs Henry, DBN; 1883: Anglesey Mountain, CH Waddell, DBN; 1899: Carlingford Mt., Golden River, HW Lett, BM; no date: Anglesey Mt., Louth, HW Lett, DBN) are all *S. undulata* (Long 1993a)].

[H35 deleted because specimen (1910: Tory I., HW Lett, DBN) is *S. undulata* (Long 1993a, 1994: 34)].

[H38 deleted because specimen (1885: Mourne Mts, Deer's Meadow, HW Lett, DBN) is *S. irrigua* (Long 1993a)].

[Long (1993a) shows that records from all Irish vice-counties for which it was listed by Corley & Hill (1981) are errors].

[**38/18** ***Scapania paludosa*** (Müll.Frib.) Müll. Frib.]

[1951: with *Dicranella squarrosa*, wet ground nr roadside bridge below Knocknaman, nr Glenbeigh, JS Thomson (Thomson 1953), comm. JW Fitzgerald (Paton 1965a: 857). H1 discounted because specimen not traced, comm. JA Paton (Corley 1981: 21)].

[1964: in wet flush, 1600 ft alt., Mullaghmore, nr Dungiven, JW Fitzgerald (Paton 1965a: 857, Fitzgerald & Fitzgerald 1966a). H40 deleted because specimen is not this species, comm. JA Paton (Corley 1980a: 31)].

38/19 ***Scapania aequiloba*** (Schwägr.) Dumort.

[H(1) listed by Macvicar (1905: 20). H1 record rejected because voucher specimen (1877: Cromaglown, McArdle, DBN) reidentified as *S. gracilis* by Long (1978: 28)].

[H(2) listed by Macvicar (1905: 20). H2 record rejected because voucher specimen (1893: O'Sullivan's Cascade, McArdle, BM) reidentified as *S. gracilis* by Long (1978: 28)].

[H(3) listed by Macvicar (1905: 20). H3 record rejected because no voucher specimen was found (Long 1978: 29, Corley 1978: 15)].

H7 1966: in *Gymnostomum aeruginosum* on conglomerate rock beside L. Curra, Galtee Mts, JA Paton (BBS exc.) (Paton 1967c: 402). H7 confirmed by Long (1978: 28) and listed by Corley (1978: 15).

[H(8) listed by Macvicar (1905: 20). H8 record rejected because no voucher specimen was found (Long 1978: 29, Corley 1978: 15)].

[H(9) listed by Macvicar (1905: 20). H9 record rejected because no voucher specimen was found (Long 1978: 29, Corley 1978: 15)].

[H(13) listed by Macvicar (1905: 20). H13 record rejected because voucher specimen (1895: Graigne, McArdle, DBN) reidentified as *S. gracilis* by Long (1978: 28), who also points out that locality is in H14].

[H16 1957: rock crevice at 1600 ft [alt.], N side of Muckanaght, Twelve Pins, AC Crundwell (BBS exc.) (Castell 1958: 468). H16 record rejected because voucher specimen reidentified as *S. aspera* by Long (1978: 28)].

[H(20) listed by Macvicar (1905: 20). H20 record rejected because voucher specimen (no date: Lugnaquilla, Moore, MANCH) reidentified as *S. gracilis* by Long (1978: 28)].

[H(21) listed by Macvicar (1905: 20). H21 record rejected because voucher specimen (1894: Howth, McArdle, DBN) reidentified as *S. gracilis* by Long (1978: 28)].

H(28) listed by Macvicar (1905: 20).

H28 listed by Corley (1978: 15).†H28 listed by Blockeel & Long (1998: 47).

[H(29) listed by Macvicar (1905: 20). H29 record rejected because voucher specimen (1875: Glenade, Moore, DBN) reidentified as *S. aspera* by Long (1978: 28)].

H29 1969: limestone crags, Peakadaw, Glenade, JA Paton (Corley 1985: 21).

[H33 1957: limestone rocks, E side of Belmore Mt., AC Crundwell (Castell 1958: 468). H33 record rejected because voucher specimen was reidentified as *S. aspera* by Long (1978: 28)].

[H(34) listed by Macvicar (1905: 20). H34 record rejected because no voucher specimen was found (Long 1978: 29, Corley 1978: 15)].

H34 1969: amongst *Anoectangium aestivum*, schist rocks, Bulbin Mt., Inishowen, JA Paton (Corley 1980a: 31).

[H35 1962: stony ground above cliffs, Black Burrow nr Dunfanaghy, EF Warburg & AC Crundwell (BBS exc.) (Paton 1963: 490). H35 specimen reidentified as *S. aspera* by Long (1978: 28), and should be replaced by following record].

H35 1969: Analoge [*sic* = Anloge] Hill, Dunfanaghy, JA Paton ('Hb. Paton', now at E) (Long 1978: 28).

[H39 record rejected because voucher specimen (1895: Sallagh Braes, Lett, DBN) reidentified as *S. gracilis* by Long (1978: 28)].

H(39) 1928: Glenariff (BBS exc.) (Duncan 1928: 117).

H 39 1952: Sallagh Braes, EW Jones (Corley 1978: 15).

[H(40) 1900 and 1905: 'sand hill form, approaching *aspera*,' sand hills, Magilligan, leg. HW Lett & CH Waddell, comm. CH Waddell (anon. 1914b: 114). H(40) record rejected because voucher specimens (1900: Magilligan, Lett & Waddell, BM, DBN, GL) reidentified as *S. aspera* by Long (1978: 28)].

38/20 ***Scapania aspera*** Bernet & M. Bernet

H1 1979: on limestone nr Inchiquin Lough, HMH van Melick (Corley 1981: 21).

H(2) listed by Macvicar (1905: 20).

H2 record placed in ( ) (Corley 1980a: 31). 1983: exposed limestone rocks, E of Doo L., Muckross Park, Killarney, DG Long (Corley 1984: 24).

[H(6) listed by Macvicar (1905: 20). H6 deleted because no record or voucher traced, comm. MM Yeo (Long 1990a: 27)].

H8 1966: on limestone rocks, N end of L. Gur, MFV Corley & JS Parker (Paton 1967c: 402).

H(9) listed by Macvicar (1905: 20).

†H9 listed by Blockeel & Long (1998: 47).

H10 1979: boulders, shore of L. Derg, nr Gortmore, Ferryglass, EC Wallace (Corley 1980a: 31).

H(13) listed by Macvicar (1905: 20). H(13) listed by Blockeel & Long (1998: 47).

H14 1956: Magnesian Limestone, Ballycuddahy, AA Cridland (Castell 1958: 468).

H15 1957: limestone rocks, wood, nr Punch Bowl, nr Gort, J Appleyard & AC Crundwell (BBS exc.) (Castell 1958: 468).

H(16) listed by Macvicar (1905: 20).

†H16 listed by Blockeel & Long (1998: 47).

H18 1986: on limestone outcrop/boulder on *Corylus*-dominated woodland, Clorhane, between Clonmacnoise and Shannonbridge, DL Kelly (Long 1989: 22).

[H(21) listed by Macvicar (1905: 20). H21 deleted because voucher specimen reidentified as *S. gracilis*, comm. DG Long (Corley 1978: 15)].

H22 1978: sand dunes, Mornington, DM Synnott (Corley 1980a: 31).

H23 1952: limestone, Coosan, nr Athlone, ALK King, det. (with notes) by EW Jones (Castell 1953: 303).

H24 1968: limestone wall in oak/ash wood, Rathcline House 2 miles SW of Lanesborough, WV Rubers, P Hessell & J Klein (Paton 1970: 193).

H25 1968: limestone on shore of L. Ree, Portrunny Bay 2 miles SE of Knockroghery, WV Rubers, P Hessell & J Klein (Paton 1970: 193).

H26 1951: woodland nr Pantry [*sic* = Partry], H Milne-Redhead (Castell 1952: 95).

H(27) listed by Macvicar (1905: 20).

†H27 listed by Blockeel & Long (1998: 47).

H(28) 1913: Glencar, Co. Sligo, J Hunter (anon. 1914b: 115). 1928: rocks above Glencar Lough, N side (BBS exc.) (Duncan 1928: 119).

†H28 listed by Blockeel & Long (1998: 47).

H(29) 1928: wooded glen, NE end of Glencar Lough (BBS exc.) (Duncan 1928: 118).

†H29 listed by Blockeel & Long (1998: 47).

[H(30) listed by Macvicar (1905: 20). H30 deleted because voucher specimen reidentified as *S. nemorea*, comm. DG Long (Corley 1978: 15)].

H30 2001: forming part of bryophyte mat at

base of limestone crag shaded by *Fagus sylvatica* woodland, *ca* 220 m alt., Giant's Leap, S of Blacklion, H03, DT Holyoak 01-762 (Blackstock: 2002: 40).

H33 1951: limestone slopes, Knockmore, H Milne-Redhead (Castell 1952: 95).

H(34) 1937: Bundoran sand-dunes, no collector named (BBS exc.) (Armitage 1938: 13).
1937: Bundoran, E Armitage (anon. 1938c: 37).

†H34 listed by Blockeel & Long (1998: 47).

[H(35) listed by Macvicar (1905: 20)].

H35 1961: blown shell sand on rocky slopes above Loughros Beg Bay, nr Ardara, DA Ratcliffe (Paton 1962: 363).

H36 1951: limestone debris nr spring, Binnawooda, JW Fitzgerald (Castell 1952: 95).

[H38 deleted because locality (NE end of Glencar Lough) is in H28 (Corley 1979: 25)].

H(39) 1913: sand dunes, Portrush, WG Travis (anon. 1914b: 115).
1928: sandhills, Portrush (BBS exc.) (Duncan 1928: 116).

†H39 listed by Blockeel & Long (1998: 47).

H40 1952: basalt cliff, *ca* 1000 ft alt., Benevenagh, EW Jones (Castell 1953: 303).

38/21 ***Scapania gracilis*** **Lindb.**
(syn. *Scapania gracilis* var. *integrifolia* Pearson, *S. gracilis* var. *laxifolia* Carrington)

H(1) listed by Macvicar (1905: 20).

†H1 listed by Blockeel & Long (1998: 47).

H(2) listed by Macvicar (1905: 20).

H(2) 1935: Cromagloun, Killarney, DA Jones & FE Milsom (see *J. Bot.* Jan. 1938) (anon. 1938e: 45), as *S. apiculata* var. *jonesii* (Schiffn. MS) Nicholson. Paton (1999: 354) notes that this specimen was subsequently shown to be referable to *S. gracilis*.

†H2 listed by Blockeel & Long (1998: 47).

†H3 listed by Blockeel & Long (1998: 47).

H4 1966: on rocks on moor at 1300 ft alt., E side of Musherabeg, Boggeragh Mts, MFV Corley & JS Parker (Paton 1967c: 402).

H5 2002: on shaded N-facing rock by path, *ca* 45 m alt., Glenbower Wood, near Killeagh, W97, TL Blockeel 31/303 (Blackstock 2003: 42).

H(6) 1933: Coumshingaun, Comeragh Mts, E Armitage (anon. 1934c: 146).

†H6 listed by Blockeel & Long (1998: 47).

H(7) listed by Macvicar (1905: 20).

†H7 listed by Blockeel & Long (1998: 47).

H8 1966: in mosses on rock face, Slievereagh nr Ballylanders, MFV Corley & JS Parker (Paton 1967c: 492).

H9 1962: slopes of Carn Sefin, Black Head, AJE Smith (Paton 1965a: 857).

H10 1951: boulder on hillside, alt. *ca* 600 ft, above Silvermines, AD Banwell, EV Watson & PJ Wanstall (Castell 1952: 95).

H11 1954: Kaal, Mt Brandon, 1250 ft [alt.], ALK King (Castell 1955: 581).

H(12) listed by Macvicar (1905: 20).

†H12 listed by Blockeel & Long (1998: 47).

H(13) listed by Macvicar (1905: 20).

†H13 listed by Blockeel & Long (1998: 47).

H14 1980: mountain blanket bog, Slieve Bloom Mts, NW slope of Arderin, JR Cross & C Douglas (Corley 1983: 48).

H15 1994: rock on bank above Boleyneendorish River, Slieve Aughty, M50, JA Paton 7675 (Long 1995b: 39).

H(16) listed by Macvicar (1905: 20).

†H16 listed by Blockeel & Long (1998: 47).

H18 1978: hummock, Mongan Bog, Clonmacnoise, M Schouten (Corley 1987: 19).

H(20) listed by Macvicar (1905: 20).

†H20 listed by Blockeel & Long (1998: 47)].

[H(21) listed by Macvicar (1905: 20)].

H21 1959: on Slievenabawnoge, ALK King (DBN) (Long 1999b: 27).

H25 1965: on boulders at 700 ft alt., Kilronan Mt., nr Ballyfarnan, JW Fitzgerald & EM Lobley (Paton 1966: 187).

H26 1965: on rocks W of L. Talt, [The] Ox Mts, JW Fitzgerald (Paton 1966: 187).

H(27) listed by Macvicar (1905: 20).

†H27 listed by Blockeel & Long (1998: 47).

H(28) listed by Macvicar (1905: 20).

†H28 listed by Blockeel & Long (1998: 47).

H(29) 1913: L. Melvin, WN Tetley (BBSUK) (Castell 1953: 303).
1928: Glencar, AM Saunders (Castell 1953: 303).

†H29 listed by Blockeel & Long (1998: 47).

H(30) listed by Macvicar (1905: 20).

†H30 listed by Blockeel & Long (1998: 47).

[H(31) listed by Macvicar (1905: 20)].

H31 1966: rock on Feede Mountain, DM Synnott (DBN) (Long 1999b: 27).

H(33) 1908: huge masses on trees, Correll Glen, WN Tetley (BBSUK) (Castell 1953: 303).
1914: Belcoo Rocks, WN Tetley (*Report MEC Sect. II,* for 1914, p. 21) (Castell 1953: 303).
†H33 listed by Blockeel & Long (1998: 47).
H34 1962: amongst scree, Gap of Mamore 6 miles N of Buncrana, RD Fitzgerald (Paton 1963: 490).
H(35) listed by Macvicar (1905: 20).
†H35 listed by Blockeel & Long (1998: 47).
H36 1951: turf overlying mica schist, alt. 900 ft, Gortin Gap nr Omagh, JW Fitzgerald (Castell 1952: 95).
H(37) listed by Macvicar (1905: 20).
†H37 listed by Blockeel & Long (1998: 47).
H(38) listed by Macvicar (1905: 20).
†H38 listed by Blockeel & Long (1998: 47).
H(39) listed by Macvicar (1905: 20).
H(39) 1893: Slemish Mt., CH Waddell 'This has the habit of var. *minor*, but has the leaves entire or nearly so, and the incumbent antical lobe of the var. *integrifolia*', SM Macvicar (anon. 1917b: 198).
†H39 listed by Blockeel & Long (1998: 47).
H(40) listed by Macvicar (1905: 20).
†H40 listed by Blockeel & Long (1998: 47).

38/22 ***Scapania ornithopodioides*** (With.) Waddell

H(1) listed by Macvicar (1905: 20).
†H1 listed by Blockeel & Long (1998: 47).
H(16) 1933: Mackanaght [*sic* = Muckanaght], PWM Richards (anon. 1938e: 45).
†H16 listed by Blockeel & Long (1998: 47).
H(27) listed by Macvicar (1905: 20).
†H27 listed by Blockeel & Long (1998: 47).
H35 1955: Muckish [Mt.], AW Stelfox, comm. JS Thomson (Castell 1956: 149).

38/23 ***Scapania nimbosa*** Taylor ex Lehm.

H(1) listed by Macvicar (1905: 20).
†H1 listed by Blockeel & Long (1998: 47).
†H27 listed by Blockeel & Long (1998: 47).
H35 1962: among *Calluna* nr col *ca* 1400 ft alt., E side of Errigal, EF Warburg (BBS exc.) (Paton 1963: 490).

39/1 ***Leptoscyphus cuneifolius*** (Hook.) Mitt. (syn. *Clasmatocolea cuneifolia* (Hook.) Spruce, *Mylia cuneifolia* (Hook.) Gray)

H(1) listed by Macvicar (1905: 15).
†H1 listed by Blockeel & Long (1998: 48).
H(2) listed by Macvicar (1905: 15).
†H2 listed by Blockeel & Long (1998: 48).
H(3) listed by Macvicar (1905: 15).
†H3 listed by Blockeel & Long (1998: 48).
H4 1967: alder trees at 1200 ft alt., Musherabeg, JW Fitzgerald (Paton 1968: 624).
H(16) listed by Macvicar (1905: 15).
†H16 listed by Blockeel & Long (1998: 48).
H(27) listed by Macvicar (1905: 15).
†H27 listed by Blockeel & Long (1998: 48).
H29 1970: branches of *Sorbus aucuparia ca* 1200 ft alt., among boulder scree below N-facing cliffs SE of Bronagh, AR Perry & HJ Perry (Paton 1974b: 163).
H33 1993: base of birch tree in wooded ravine, Correl Glen, H05, E Urmi (Long 1994: 34).
H35 1961: on holly in damp waterfall ravine at 800 ft [alt.], Glenbeagh, nr Dunlewy, DA Ratcliffe (Paton 1962: 360).

40/1 ***Lophocolea bidentata*** (L.) Dumort. (syn. *Lophocolea bidentata* var. *rivularis* (Raddi) Warnst., *L. cuspidata* (Nees) Limpr.)

H(1) listed by Macvicar (1905: 15).
†H1 listed by Blockeel & Long (1998: 48).
H(2) listed by Macvicar (1905: 15).
†H2 listed by Blockeel & Long (1998: 48).
H(3) listed by Macvicar (1905: 15).
H3 1967: roadside bank S of Macroom, JW Fitzgerald (Paton 1968: 624), as *L. cuspidata*.
H4 1951: roadside bank NW of Mallow, AC Crundwell, det. EW Jones (with notes) (Castell 1953: 300), as *L. cuspidata*.
1955: on beech nr Knocknagree, MJP Scannell, comm. ALK King (Castell 1956: 148).
H5 1966: R. Douglas nr Kilworth, J Appleyard (BBS exc.) (Paton 1967c: 400), as *L. cuspidata*.
H(6) listed by Macvicar (1905: 15).
H(6) 1933: Poolvona, E Armitage (anon. 1934c: 144), as *L. cuspidata*.
†H6 listed by Blockeel & Long (1998: 48).
H(7) listed by Macvicar (1905: 15).

†H7 listed by Blockeel & Long (1998: 48).
H(8) listed by Macvicar (1905: 15).
H8 1966: among roots on bank, Paradise Hill, Galtee Mts, MFV Corley & JS Parker (Paton 1969a: 400), as *L. cuspidata*.
H(9) listed by Macvicar (1905: 15).
H(9) 1949: swampy ground, Calverstown House, JS Thomson (Castell 1950: 377).
H9 1957: Gratloe Wood, ALK King (Castell 1958: 466), as *L. cuspidata*.
H10 1951: old slate heaps in recently disused quarry, alt. *ca* 500 ft, hills between Ballina and Newtown, AD Banwell, EV Watson & PJ Wanstall (Castell 1952: 93).
1951: branches of trees in shaded gully, alt. 900 ft, above Silvermines, AD Banwell, EV Watson & PJ Wanstall (Castell 1952: 93), as *L. cuspidata*.
H11 1952: Farmley Wood, nr Cuffe's Grange, ALK King & MPH Kertland, comm. ALK King (Castell 1953: 300).
1954: tree root, wood, Graiguenamagh, ALK King (Castell 1955: 580), as *L. cuspidata*.
H(12) listed by Macvicar (1905: 15).
H12 1954: clay bank, Inch, JS Thomson (Castell 1955: 580).
H(13) listed by Macvicar (1905: 15).
H13 1969: tree trunk by the R. Slaney, Aghade Bridge nr Tullow, JW Fitzgerald (Paton 1971a: 372), as *L. cuspidata*.
H(14) listed by Macvicar (1905: 15).
H14 1952: on Sitka Spruce, 1200 ft alt., Ossery State Forest, ALK King (Castell 1953: 300), as *L. cuspidata*.
H(15) listed by Macvicar (1905: 15).
H15 1957: on tree stump, Chevy Chase, nr Gort, AC Crundwell (BBS exc.) (Castell 1958: 466), as *L. cuspidata*.
H(16) listed by Macvicar (1905: 15).
†H16 listed by Blockeel & Long (1998: 48).
H17 1966: soil on upturned tree stump in wood, Ryehill, N of Monivea, MFV Corley & JS Parker (Paton 1967c: 400).
1966: on alder root in damp wood, Derreen, N of Monivea, MFV Corley & JS Parker (Paton 1967c: 400), as *L. cuspidata*.
H18 1954: bank, Gloster Woods, Brosna, Offaly, ALK King (Castell 1955: 580).
†H19 listed by Blockeel & Long (1998: 48).
H(20) listed by Macvicar (1905: 15).
H(20) 1912-1914: decayed wood, Glen of the Downs, Allen, Gunn & DMcArdle (in McArdle, *Irish Nat.* **26**, 73, 1917), comm. JW Fitzgerald (Castell 1952: 93), as *L. cuspidata*.
†H20 listed by Blockeel & Long (1998: 48).
H(21) listed by Macvicar (1905: 15).
H(21) 1906: caves on N side and damp bank nr the Seal Hole, Lambay, D McArdle (*Irish Nat.* **16**, 104, 1907), comm. JW Fitzgerald (Castell 1952: 93), as *L. cuspidata*.
†H21 listed by Blockeel & Long (1998: 48).
H(22) listed by Macvicar (1905: 15).
H22 1950: log of wood, Slane, JS Thomson, comm. ALK King (Paton 1964: 716), as *L. cuspidata*.
H(23) listed by Macvicar (1905: 15).
H23 1952: fallen tree, Clonhugh Denesne, NE end of L. Owel, JS Thomson (Castell 1954: 474), as *L. cuspidata*.
H24 1965: ditch bank, Cornhill nr Drumlish, JW Fitzgerald & EM Lobley (Paton 1966: 185).
H25 1952: bank in lane, Kilyamanagh, nr Athlone, right bank of R. Shannon, ALK King (Castell 1953: 300).
1960: in Rockingham Woods, Boyle, ALK King (Paton 1961: 154), as *L. cuspidata*.
H(26) listed by Macvicar (1905: 15).
H26 1965: cliff ledges S of Glendadaff, [The] Ox Mts, JW Fitzgerald (Paton 1966: 185), as *L. cuspidata*.
H(27) listed by Macvicar (1905: 15).
†H27 listed by Blockeel & Long (1998: 48).
H(28) listed by Macvicar (1905: 15).
H(28) 1928: nr Sligo (BBS exc.) (Duncan 1928: 119), as *L. cuspidata*.
†H28 listed by Blockeel & Long (1998: 48).
H(29) listed by Macvicar (1905: 15).
H(29) 1928: wooded glen, NE end of Glencar Lough (BBS exc.) (Duncan 1928: 118), as *L. cuspidata*.
†H29 listed by Blockeel & Long (1998: 48).
H(30) listed by Macvicar (1905: 15).
H30 1956: on ground amongst grass in wood, Virginia, JS Thomson, conf. EW Jones (Castell 1957: 324), as *L. bidentata*.
1969: boulder in stream, NE slope of Slievenakilla, Cuilcagh Mts, JA Paton (Paton 1970: 191), as *L. cuspidata*.
H31 1952: base of stone wall, Flurry Bridge, JW Fitzgerald (Castell 1953: 300), as *L. cuspidata*.
H32 1961: abundant in marshy ground,

Killyneill, nr Monaghan, JW Fitzgerald (Paton 1962: 360).

H(33) 1905: decayed wood, Poulaphuca & Correl Glen, D McArdle (*Irish Nat.* **16**, 238, 1907), comm. JW Fitzgerald (Castell 1952: 93), as *L. cuspidata*.

†H33 listed by Blockeel & Long (1998: 48).

H(34) listed by Macvicar (1905: 15).

H34 1967: roadside bank, Red Castle, L. Foyle, JW Fitzgerald (Paton 1968: 624), as *L. cuspidata*.

H(35) listed by Macvicar (1905: 15).

†H35 listed by Blockeel & Long (1998: 48).

†H36 listed by Blockeel & Long (1998: 48).

H(37) listed by Macvicar (1905: 15).

H37 1951: stone wall, Rough I. nr Newry, JW Fitzgerald (Castell 1952: 93).
1964: rotting tree trunk, Derrylee, E of Verner's Bridge, JW Fitzgerald & MPH Kertland (Paton 1965a: 854), as *L. cuspidata*.

H(38) listed by Macvicar (1905: 15).

H38 1950: sandstone, Ballyalton quarry, JW Fitzgerald (Castell 1951: 494), as *L. cuspidata*.

H(39) listed by Macvicar (1905: 15).

H(39) 1928: Glenariff (BBS exc.) (Duncan 1928: 117), as *L. cuspidata*.

†H39 listed by Blockeel & Long (1998: 48).

H(40) listed by Macvicar (1905: 15).

H40 1968: wet culvert in forest below Benevenagh, HH Birks & JW Fitzgerald (Paton 1969a: 872), as *L. cuspidata*.

Paton (1999: 389-391) abandoned the attempts to distinguish *L. bidentata* and *L. cuspidata* that had proved so troublesome to successive generations of bryologists. This simpler taxonomic treatment now allows many old records (e.g. those from Macvicar 1905: 15 marked ?) to be referred to *L. bidentata* with little risk of error.

40/2 ***Lophocolea bispinosa*** (Hook.f. & Taylor) Gottsche, Lindenb. & Nees

H36 2002: on unshaded compressed soil in middle of track surfaced with schistose gravel, among sparse grasses and low herbs, *ca* 210 m alt., near Kelly's Bridge, Ardnamona, H07, DT Holyoak 02-1135 (BBSUK) (Blackstock 2003: 42).

This Australasian species was first recorded in Europe in the Isles of Scilly in 1962, since when it has become established in several counties across S England and on Colonsay off W Scotland (Paton 1999: 392).

40/3 ***Lophocolea heterophylla*** (Schrad.) Dumort.

H1 1961: growing through *Lejeunea* sp. in Dromore Woods, nr Kenmare, ALK King (Paton 1962: 360).

H(2) listed by Macvicar (1905: 15).

†H2 listed by Blockeel & Long (1998: 48).

†H3 listed by Blockeel & Long (1998: 48).

H(5) listed by Macvicar (1905: 15).

†H5 listed by Blockeel & Long (1998: 48).

H6 1966: on rotting wood, stream N of the Punchbowl, Comeragh Mts, JW Fitzgerald *et al.* (BBS exc.) (Paton 1967c: 400).

H(7) listed by Macvicar (1905: 15).

†H7 listed by Blockeel & Long (1998: 48).

H8 1992: limestone outcrop, 75 m alt., Lough Gur, R64, E Wiltshire (Long 1993b: 45).

H11 1966: rotten tree stump by R. Nore, Inistioge, JG Duckett *et al.* (BBS exc.) (Paton 1967c: 400).

H12 1961: on shaded roadside bank at Ferrybank, ALK King (Paton 1962: 360).

H13 1969: tree trunk by R. Slaney, Aghade Bridge nr Tullow, JW Fitzgerald (Paton 1971a: 372).

H14 1990: on rotting log in old oak woodland, Park Hill, Abbeyleix Demesne, Abbeyleix, S48, DL Kelly (Long 1993b: 45).

H(16) listed by Macvicar (1905: 15).

†H16 listed by Blockeel & Long (1998: 48).

H(19) 1949: decaying log, Blackhall Castle, nr Calverstown, JS Thomson (Castell 1950: 377).

H(20) listed by Macvicar (1905: 15).

†H20 listed by Blockeel & Long (1998: 48).

H(21) listed by Macvicar (1905: 15).

†H21 listed by Blockeel & Long (1998: 48).

H22 1967: woodland above R. Boyne, Donore, Drogheda, DM Synnott (Paton 1968: 624).

H23 1980: old estate woodland, Ballinlough Castle, DM Synnott (Corley 1982: 21).

H24 1968: trees in wood nr Elfeet Bay 8

miles W of Ballymahon, WV Rubers, P Hessel & J Klein (Paton 1970: 191).

H25 1985: on fallen rotting tree trunk, secondary woodland over cut-over peat, extension of St John's Wood, nr Blackbrink Bay, W shore of L Ree, DL Kelly & G O'Donovan (Corley 1986: 17).

H(27) listed by Blockeel & Long (1998: 48).

H29 1968: on *Pseudotsuga* stump, wood 1 mile NE of Roosky, 6 miles SW of Mohill, WV Rubers, P Hessel & J Klein (Paton 1970: 191).

H(30) listed by Macvicar (1905: 15). H(30) listed by Blockeel & Long (1998: 48).

H30 2001: forming part of bryophyte mat at base of limestone crag shaded by *Fagus sylvatica* woodland, *ca* 220 m alt., Giant's Leap, S of Blacklion, H03, DT Holyoak 01-762 (Blackstock: 2002: 40).

H31 1967: tree stump, pine knoll, Monleek, Monasterboice, DM Synnott (Paton 1968: 624).

H33 2000: on low dead twig of *Salix cinerea* at base of N-facing heathy slope, Meenameen Scarp, H05, DT Holyoak 00-317 (BBSUK) (Blackstock 2001: 35).

H(34) listed by Macvicar (1905: 15). H(34) listed by Blockeel & Long (1998: 48).

H(35) listed by Macvicar (1905: 15). H(35) listed by Blockeel & Long (1998: 48).

H35 2002: on decorticated wood of dead horizontal tree trunk part-shaded in mixed deciduous and coniferous woodland near river, *ca* 5 m alt., *ca* 0.5 km W of Rathmelton, C22, DT Holyoak 02-681 (Blackstock 2003: 42).

H36 1957: stem of old whin bush, Killycolpy Wood, JW Fitzgerald (Castell 1959: 628).

H37 1966: on rotting stump in wood, Acton House, Poyntzpass, JW Fitzgerald & MPH Kertland (Paton 1967c: 400).

H(38) listed by Macvicar (1905: 15). H(38) listed by Blockeel & Long (1998: 48).

H38 2002: on rotting wood of tree stumps and humic soil nearby in mature coniferous plantation, *ca* 50 m alt., Tollymore Forest Park, J33, DT Holyoak 02-920 (Blackstock 2003: 42).

H39 1952: on tree base in ravine, Drumnasole, nr Carnlough, EW Jones (Castell 1953: 300).

H40 1999: low on trunk of dying tree in young woodland, Downhill, C73, DT Holyoak 99-209 (BBSUK) (Blackstock 2000: 42).

40/4 ***Lophocolea semiteres*** (Lehm.) Mitt.

H38 2002: with mosses and lichens at base of patchy low *Erica cinerea* in dune-heath, *ca* 5 m alt., Murlough NNR, J33, DT Holyoak 02-953 (BBSUK) (Blackstock 2003: 42).

An alien species from the Southern Hemisphere, first recorded in Europe in 1955 and now established in England, Scotland, Belgium, Netherlands (Paton 1999: 396) and W Wales (Blackstock 2002: 40).

40/5 ***Lophocolea fragrans*** (Moris & De Not.) Gottsche, Lindenb. & Nees (syn. *Lophocolea spicata* Taylor)

H(1) listed by Macvicar (1905: 15).

†H1 listed by Blockeel & Long (1998: 48).

H(2) listed by Macvicar (1905: 15).

†H2 listed by Blockeel & Long (1998: 48).

H(3) listed by Macvicar (1905: 15).

†H3 listed by Blockeel & Long (1998: 48).

H(5) listed by Macvicar (1905: 15).

†H5 listed by Blockeel & Long (1998: 48).

[H(6) listed by Macvicar (1905: 15)].

H6 1966: on rocks by stream N of the Punchbowl, Comeragh Mts, JW Fitzgerald *et al.* (BBS exc.) (Paton 1967c: 400).

H8 1966: on bank in wood by sea, wood E of Tarbert [*sic* = Tarbet], MFV Corley & JS Parker (Paton 1967c: 400).

H10 1967: soil by small rivulets in wooded valley, Clare Glen, nr Newport, HH Birks, HJB Birks & DA Ratcliffe (Paton 1968: 624).

H11 1954: shady ground under trees, forestry planation, R.[ight] bank of R. Barrow, above Graiguenamanagh, ALK King (Castell 1955: 580).

H12 1975: dead tree stump, roadside nr bridge S of Clonough Bridge, SE of Coolgreeny, AR Perry [BBS Exc.] (Paton 1977a: 14). H12 is apparently bracketed in error in Blockeel & Long (1998: 48).

H(13) listed by Macvicar (1905: 15). H(13) listed by Blockeel & Long (1998: 48).

H15 1957: tree, Garryland Woods, nr Gort,

EM Lobley (BBS exc.) (Castell 1958: 466).

H16 1957: on shady boulder by stream in ravine and rocks in woods, Ballynahinch, J Appleyard & EM Lobley (BBS exc.) (Castell 1958: 466).

H(20) listed by Macvicar (1905: 15).

†H20 listed by Blockeel & Long (1998: 48).

H24 1968: tree nr Rathcline House, 2 miles S of Lanesborough, WV Rubers, P Hessel & J Klein (Paton 1970: 191).

H25 2002: shaded wet limestone rock, with *Eurhynchium pumilum*, *ca* 45 m alt., Tawnytaskin Wood, Lough Key, M80, NG Hodgetts 4099 (Blackstock 2003: 42).

H26 1987: on rotting log in woodland by river, Bridge over Cloon River W of Partry, GP Rothero (Long 1988: 31).

†H27 listed by Blockeel & Long (1998: 48).

H28 1965: boulders in wood nr Innisfree, L. Gill, EM Lobley (Paton 1966: 185).

H29 1961: with *Lejeunea* spp. among bryophytes at base of trees, Glencar, JW Fitzgerald & MPH Kertland (Paton 1962: 360).

H33 1960: on a large boulder in the stream above ravine at Pollawaddy above Marble Arch, JW Fitzgerald (Paton 1961: 154).

H34 1967: wet rocks, Red Castle Glen, L. Foyle, JW Fitzgerald (Paton 1968: 624).

H35 1969: shaded rocks beside stream, Fintragh Bay, W of Killybegs, JA Paton (Paton 1970: 191).

H36 2002: on near-vertical sandstone block *ca* 1 m above water in river gorge below waterfall, part shaded by deciduous woodland, *ca* 160 m alt., Sloughan Glen, H27, DT Holyoak 02-1126 (Blackstock 2003: 42).

H37 2002: on steep bark 0.5 m above ground on old *Acer pseudoplatanus* tree in open woodland above stream, *ca* 65 m alt., Gosford Forest Park, H94, DT Holyoak 02-1081 (Blackstock 2003: 42-43).

H39 1963: among bryophytes at base of trees nr stream, Glenariff, JW Fitzgerald & AR Perry (Paton 1964: 716).

H40 1968: shaded rocks in ravine, Ness Glen, NW of Claudy, HH Birks & JW Fitzgerald (Paton 1969a: 872).

41/1 ***Chiloscyphus polyanthos*** (L.) Corda (*Chiloscyphus polyanthos* var. *polyanthos* (L.) Corda, *C. polyanthos* var. *rivularis* (Schrad.) Gottsche, Lindenb. & Nees)

H(1) listed by Macvicar (1905: 15).

†H1 listed by Blockeel & Long (1998: 48).

H(2) listed by Macvicar (1905: 15).

†H2 listed by Blockeel & Long (1998: 48).

H(3) listed by Macvicar (1905: 15).

†H3 listed by Blockeel & Long (1998: 48).

†H4 listed by Blockeel & Long (1998: 48).

H(5) 1852: nr Fermoy, I Carroll (DBN), comm. ALK King (Paton 1964: 716).

H5 1966: on stones in stream nr Rylane Cross, Boggeragh Mts, MFV Corley & JS Parker (Paton 1967c: 400).

[H(6) listed by Macvicar (1905: 15)].

H6 1962: in stream below Coumshingaun, ALK King (Paton 1963: 486), as var. *rivularis*.

H(7) no date: Galtee Mts, HW Lett (DBN), comm. ALK King (Paton 1964: 716).

†H7 listed by Blockeel & Long (1998: 48).

H8 1966: on rocks in stream below Paradise Hill, Galtee Mts, MFV Corley & JS Parker (Paton 1967c: 400).

[H(9) listed by Macvicar (1905: 15)].

H9 1962: wet rocks in stream nr Doolin, Lisdoonvarna, G Halliday (Paton 1963: 486).

H10 1951: wet clay soil in wooded gully, alt. *ca* 900 ft, N slope, above Silvermines, AD Banwell, EV Watson & PJ Wanstall (Castell 1952: 93).

H11 1966: stones in stream, wood beside R. Nore, Inistioge, JG Duckett (BBS exc.) (Paton 1967c: 400), as var. *rivularis*.
1968: wet rocks on roadside, W of the R. Nore, SE of Thomastown, JA Paton (Paton 1969a: 872).

H12 1954: beside waterspout, Inch, JS Thomson (Castell 1955: 580).

H13 1969: rocks in the Burren R., Sheean nr Myshall, JW Fitzgerald (Paton 1970: 191).

H(14) listed by Macvicar (1905: 15).

†H14 listed by Blockeel & Long (1998: 48).

H15 1994: silted rocks beside Boleyneendorish River, Slieve Aughty, M50, JA Paton 7676 (Long 1995b: 38).

H16 1968: sloping boulder beside Kylemore R., above Glencorbet, Twelve Pins, AR Perry (Paton 1969a: 872).

H18 1973: submerged on sandstone block in stream, Slieve Bloom Mts, WV Rubers (Corley 1980a: 30).
H19 1973: submerged, R. Liffey at Ballymore Eustace, WV Rubers (Corley 1980a: 30).
H(20) listed by Macvicar (1905: 15).
†H20 listed by Blockeel & Long (1998: 48).
H(21) listed by Macvicar (1905: 15). H(21) listed by Blockeel & Long (1998: 48).
H23 1953: side of ditch nr bog, Ballinafid nr Multyfarnham, JS Thomson (Castell 1955: 580).
H25 1965: rocks in stream, copse 1 mile N of Ballyfarnan, JW Fitzgerald & EM Lobley (Paton 1966: 185).
H26 1987: tree roots, E bank of Cloon River, W of Patry [*sic* = Partry], JA Paton (Long 1988: 31).
H(27) listed by Macvicar (1905: 15).
†H27 listed by Blockeel & Long (1998: 48).
H28 1965: between stones at the side of L. Gill E of Innisfree, JW Fitzgerald & EM Lobley (Paton 1966: 185).
H29 1963: dead log in stream, Bawn, 1 mile S of Dromahair, AR Perry & JW Fitzgerald (Paton 1964: 716).
†H30 listed by Blockeel & Long (1998: 48).
H(31) listed by Macvicar (1905: 15). H(31) listed by Blockeel & Long (1998: 48).
H32 1961: in marshy ground, Killyneill nr Monaghan, JW Fitzgerald (Paton 1962: 360).
H33 1957: on boulder in ravine of Gladagh [*sic* = Cladagh] R., L. Macnean Lower, AC Crundwell (Castell 1958: 466).
H34 1967: rocks by R. Crana, E of Ballymagan, E of Buncrana, JW Fitzgerald (Paton 1968: 625).
H(35) listed by Macvicar (1905: 15).
†H35 listed by Blockeel & Long (1998: 48).
H36 1951: rotten mica schist beside stream, Garvagh Bridge, between Draperstown and Plumbridge, JW Fitzgerald (Castell 1952: 93).
H37 1950: submerged in Clay Lake, JW Fitzgerald (Paton 1963: 486).
1966: boulders in stream, Ballinasack Bridge nr Forkhill, JW Fitzgerald & MPH Kertland (Paton 1967c: 400), as var. *rivularis*.
H(38) listed by Macvicar (1905: 15).
†H38 listed by Blockeel & Long (1998: 48).
H(39) listed by Macvicar (1905: 15).
†H39 listed by Blockeel & Long (1998: 48).
[H(40) listed by Macvicar (1905: 15)].
H40 1964: rocks in stream, Altnaheglish, nr Dungiven, JW Fitzgerald (Paton 1965a: 854).

41/2 ***Chiloscyphus pallescens*** (Ehrh. ex Hoffm.) Dumort.
(syn. *Chiloscyphus polyanthos* var. *pallescens* (Ehrh. ex Hoffm.) C.Hartm.)

H(1) listed by Macvicar (1905: 15).
†H1 listed by Blockeel & Long (1998: 48).
H(2) listed by Macvicar (1905: 15).
†H2 listed by Blockeel & Long (1998: 48).
H4 1966: in marsh nr Ballymartle, MFV Corley and JS Parker (Paton 1967c: 400).
H(5) listed by Macvicar (1905: 15). H(5) listed by Blockeel & Long (1998: 48).
H6 1966: basic flush, Knockanaffrin, Nier valley, JW Fitzgerald & EM Lobley (BBS exc.) (Paton 1967c: 400).
H7 1983: grassy basic flush on N-facing slope, Galtybeg, Galty Mts, DG Long (Corley 1984: 24).
H8 1966: on ground in wood E of Tarbert [*sic* = Tarbet], MFV Corley & JS Parker (Paton 1967c: 400).
H9 1979: *Salix* marsh beside L. Burke, W of Ennis, JA Paton (Corley 1980a: 30); repeated as: *Salix* carr, Lough Burke, W of Ennis, R27, JA Paton 6173 (Long 1991: 39).
H12 1969: marshy ground, Pallas Bridge nr Wicklow Gap, JW Fitzgerald (Paton 1970: 191).
H13 1975: fen SW of Yellowford Cross Roads, S of Baltinglass, DM Synnott & N Kirby (BBS exc.) (Paton 1976: 19).
H16 1957: wet place among sand-dunes, nr Roundstone, J Appleyard (Castell 1958: 466).
H20 1975: marshy field NE of Avoca, DM Synnott & JA Paton (BBS exc.) (Paton 1976: 19).
H21 1956: bank of drain, marshy ground, Howth Hill, ALK King (Castell 1957: 324).
H23 1966: flat peaty ground 2 miles N of Ballynagore, JW Fitzgerald & EM Lobley (Paton 1967c: 400).
H24 1968: by L. Gowner, Erne Head, G Drennan, comm. JW Fitzgerald (Paton 1969a: 872).
1968: wood on E shore of L. Forbes,

WV Rubers, P Hessel & J Klein (Paton 1970: 191).

H25 2002: very wet lough shore at woodland edge, below tall herbs and willow carr, *ca* 35 m alt., St John's Wood, Lough Ree, M95, NG Hodgetts 4062 (Blackstock 2003: 43).

H26 1981: wet pasture on peat, Kilskeagh Townland, nr L. Carra, N Lockhart (Corley 1983: 48).

H27 1968: marsh behind Dooniver Strand, Achill I., JA Paton (Paton 1969a: 872).

H28 1963: fen at 800 ft alt., NE of Carrowkeel, Bricklieve Mts, AR Perry & JW Fitzgerald (Paton 1964: 716).

H29 1963: wet field below limestone scarp, Boggaun, Manorhamilton, AR Perry & JW Fitzgerald (Paton 1964: 716).

H30 1965: marshy ground above Corrakeeldrum Lough, Dowra, JW Fitzgerald & EM Lobley (Paton 1966: 185).

H32 1980: wet grassy bank, L. Rafinny, N Lockhart (Corley 1983: 48).

H33 1960: moist ground between stones nr the lake edge nr Belcoo, JW Fitzgerald (Paton 1961: 154).

H34 1969: marsh nr L. Inn, W of Moville, JA Paton (Paton 1970: 191).

H35 1963: rock in streamlet on shore in bay N of Rossarrell Point nr Malin Beg, AR Perry & JW Fitzgerald (Paton 1964: 716).

H36 1958: rocks by stream, Mullagh Carn, nr Gortin, JW Fitzgerald (Castell 1959: 628).

H37 1964: stumps beside Derryadd Lough E of Verner's Bridge, JW Fitzgerald & MPH Kertland (Paton 1965a: 855).

H38 1950: wet ground, Clea Lake at 70 ft [alt.], JW Fitzgerald (Castell 1951: 494).

H40 1965: wet ground, lower slopes of Benbradagh, Dungiven, JW Fitzgerald (Paton 1966: 185).

[41a/1] ***Heteroscyphus fissistipus*** (Hook.f. & Taylor) Schiffn.

H1 1999: well established on partly shaded rocks in both cultivated and natural woodland areas within a woodland garden, *ca* 10 m alt., Garinish I., nr Sneem, V66, DG Long 28527 (DBN, E, JE), conf. R Grolle (Blackstock & Long 2002, Blackstock 2003: 43); an Australasian species, for which this was the first record from the Northern Hemisphere.

42/1 ***Geocalyx graveolens*** (Schrad.) Nees

H1 1967: on heather-shaded, N-facing peaty bank E of Hogs Head, Ballinskelligs Bay, HH Birks, HJB Birks & DA Ratcliffe (Paton 1968: 625, HH Birks, HJB Birks & Ratcliffe 1969).

H27 1987: on peaty soil in declivity on damp rocky slope, N coast of Achill I., DG Long (Long 1988: 31-32).

H33 1999: on peaty humus around base of *Mnium thomsonii* growing on more-or-less base-rich ledge, on N-facing sandstone escarpment, Cilcarrick Scarp, Lough Navar Forest, H05, RD Porley 2136, det. GP Rothero (Blackstock 2000: 43).

H35 1991: on shady boulder on steep bank with tall *Calluna* on sea cliffs, 200 m alt., E of Coastguard Hill, Horn Head nr Dunfanaghy, C04, DG Long 20263 (E) (Long 1992: 25).

43/2 ***Harpanthus scutatus*** (F.Weber & D. Mohr) Spruce

H(1) listed by Macvicar (1905: 15).

†H1 listed by Blockeel & Long (1998: 49).

H(2) listed by Macvicar (1905: 15).

†H2 listed by Blockeel & Long (1998: 49).

H(3) listed by Macvicar (1905: 15).

†H3 listed by Blockeel & Long (1998: 49).

H6 1966: on rock in wood, Shanballyanne, Nier valley, ERB Little (BBS exc.) (Paton 1967c: 400).

H16 1968: shaded rocks by L. Corrib, 1 mile NE of Maumwee L., AR Perry (Paton 1969a: 872).

H(20) listed by Macvicar (1905: 15). H(20) listed by Blockeel & Long (1998: 49).

H(27) listed by Macvicar (1905: 15).

†H27 listed by Blockeel & Long (1998: 49).

H28 1965: old stump, Slish Wood, L. Gill, JW Fitzgerald & EM Lobley (Paton 1966: 185).

H29 1965: shaded rocks, Mahanagh nr Drumkeeran, EM Lobley & JW Fitzgerald (Paton 1966: 185).

H33 1960: on rocks by old *Calluna*, scarp N of Lough Achork, JW Fitzgerald (Paton 1961: 154).

H(35) listed by Macvicar (1905: 15).
†H35 listed by Blockeel & Long (1998: 49).
H36 1958: mossy boulders, N-facing oakwood beside Owenkillew River, Drunlea Wood, 3 miles E of Gortin, JW Fitzgerald (Castell 1959: 628).
H39 1964:on rocks in Breen Wood, nr Knocklayd, JW Fitzgerald (Paton 1965a: 855).
H40 1959: shaded mossy boulders, Altnaheglish, nr Dungiven, JW Fitzgerald (Castell 1960: 766).

44/1 ***Saccogyna viticulosa*** (L.) Dumort.

H(1) listed by Macvicar (1905: 16).
†H1 listed by Blockeel & Long (1998: 49).
H(2) listed by Macvicar (1905: 16).
†H2 listed by Blockeel & Long (1998: 49).
H(3) listed by Macvicar (1905: 16).
†H3 listed by Blockeel & Long (1998: 49).
H4 1966: on shady rock face, Ringnanean Wood nr mouth of R. Stick, MFV Corley & JS Parker (Paton 1967c: 400).
H5 1956: wooded hillside, above Park House, Tourig river, NW of Youghal, EC Wallace (Castell 1957: 325).
H(6) listed by Macvicar (1905: 16).
†H6 listed by Blockeel & Long (1998: 49).
H(7) listed by Macvicar (1905: 16).
†H7 listed by Blockeel & Long (1998: 49).
H8 1966: on ground in wood E of Tarbert, MFV Corley & JS.Parker (Paton 1967c: 400).
H(9) listed by Macvicar (1905: 16).
†H9 listed by Blockeel & Long (1998: 49).
H10 1951: on earthy tree roots in damp wooded gully, N aspect, alt. 900 ft, above Silvermines, AD Banwell, EV Watson & PJ Wanstall (Castell 1952: 93).
H11 1954: shaded wet bank, Ballyeogan, Graiguemanagh, ALK King (Castell 1955: 580).
H(12) listed by Macvicar (1905: 16). H(12) listed by Blockeel & Long (1998: 49).
H(13) listed by Macvicar (1905: 16). H(13) listed by Blockeel & Long (1998: 49).
H(14) listed by Macvicar (1905: 16).
†H14 listed by Blockeel & Long (1998: 49).
H(16) listed by Macvicar (1905: 16).
†H16 listed by Blockeel & Long (1998: 49).
H(18) listed by Macvicar (1905: 16). H(18) listed by Blockeel & Long (1998: 49).
H(20) listed by Macvicar (1905: 16).
†H20 listed by Blockeel & Long (1998: 49).
H(21) listed by Macvicar (1905: 16). H(21) listed by Blockeel & Long (1998: 49).
H25 1968: heath on blanket bog, 800 ft alt., Slieve Bawn, WV Rubers, P Hessel & J Klein (Paton 1970: 191).
H26 1965: ledges on cliffs S of Glendaduff, [The] Ox Mts, JW Fitzgerald (Paton 1966: 185).
H(27) listed by Macvicar (1905: 16).
†H27 listed by Blockeel & Long (1998: 49).
H(28) listed by Macvicar (1905: 16).
†H28 listed by Blockeel & Long (1998: 49).
H29 1961: shaded rocks beside stream, Glencar, JW Fitzgerald & MPH Kertland (Paton 1962: 360).
H(30) listed by Macvicar (1905: 16).
†H30 listed by Blockeel & Long (1998: 49).
[H(31) listed by Macvicar (1905: 16)].
H31 1966: by waterfall, Two-mile River, N side of Carlingford Mt., DM Synnott (DBN) (Long 1999b: 27).
H(32) 1947: with *Hookeria lucens et al.*, woods, Hope Castle, Castleblayney, ALK King (Castell 1957: 325).
H33 1957: among boulders at 1750 ft [alt.], NE side of Tiltinbane, AC Crundwell (Castell 1958: 466).
H34 1961: shaded rocks, Greencastle, RD Fitzgerald (Paton 1963: 487).
†H35 listed by Blockeel & Long (1998: 49).
H36 1957: growing through other bryophytes, edge of wood, Sheskinawaddy, nr Castlederg, JW Fitzgerald (Castell 1959: 628).
H(38) listed by Macvicar (1905: 16).
†H38 listed by Blockeel & Long (1998: 49).
H(39) listed by Macvicar (1905: 16).
†H39 listed by Blockeel & Long (1998: 49).
H40 1951: wet ground beside waterfall, Downhill nr Castlerock, alt. 150 ft, JW Fitzgerald (Castell 1952: 93).

45/1 ***Pedinophyllum interruptum*** (Nees) Kaal.

H(1) listed by Macvicar (1905: 15). H(1) listed by Blockeel & Long (1998: 49).
[H(9) listed by Macvicar (1905: 15)].
H9 1994: on moist shaded limestone cliff, Glen of Clab, M20, TL Blockeel 23/172 (BBSUK) (Long 1999b: 27).
[H(20) 1912-1914: very rare, wet rocks at very low elevation (less than 300 ft), Glen of the Downs, Allen, Gunn & D McArdle

(in D McArdle, *Irish Nat.* **26**, 73, 1917), comm. JW Fitzgerald (Castell 1952: 93). H20 deleted because specimen (DBN) is not this species (Corley 1980a: 29)].
[H(27) listed by Macvicar (1905: 15). H27 regarded as dubious record (Corley 1980a: 29)].
H(28) listed by Macvicar (1905: 15).
†H28 listed by Blockeel & Long (1998: 49).
H(29) listed by Macvicar (1905: 15).
†H29 listed by Blockeel & Long (1998: 49).
H(33) 1905; among damp rocks, shore of Lough Erne, D McArdle (*Irish Nat.* **16**, 238, 1907), comm. JW Fitzgerald (Castell 1952: 93).
†H33 listed by Blockeel & Long (1998: 49).
[H35 deleted because voucher (1910: Tory I., HW Lett, DBN) is *Chiloscyphus polyanthos*, comm. DM Synnott (Long 1992: 25)].
[H(38) listed by Macvicar (1905: 15). H38 deleted because specimen (DBN) is not this species (Corley 1980a: 29)].

46/1 ***Plagiochila carringtonii*** (Balf.) Grolle

H16 1984: in bryophyte turf amongst boulders on exposed hillside, N ridge of Benbaun, Twelve Bens, DG Long (Corley 1985: 21).
H27 1961: with *Herberta hutchinsiae* etc. in hepatic cushions on shaded N-facing cliffs at 2550 ft [alt.], spur of Mweelrea above Doo Lough, DA Ratcliffe (Paton 1961: 358, Ratcliffe 1962).

46/2 ***Plagiochila porelloides*** (Torrey ex Nees) Lindenb.
(syn. *Plagiochila asplenioides* auct. non (L.) Dumort., P. *asplenioides* var. *humilis* Lindenb., P. *asplenioides* var. *minor* Lindenb., *P. dillenii* Taylor)

H(1) listed by Macvicar (1905: 14, 15).
†H1 listed by Blockeel & Long (1998: 49).
H(2) listed by Macvicar (1905: 14, 15).
†H2 listed by Blockeel & Long (1998: 49).
H(3) listed by Macvicar (1905: 14).
†H3 listed by Blockeel & Long (1998: 49).
H4 1967: rocks by R. Laney, Carrigagulla Bridge, JW Fitzgerald (Paton 1968: 624).
†H5 listed by Blockeel & Long (1998: 49).
H(6) listed by Macvicar (1905: 14).
†H6 listed by Blockeel & Long (1998: 49).
H(7) listed by Macvicar (1905: 14).
†H7 listed by Blockeel & Long (1998: 49).
H(8) listed by Macvicar (1905: 14).
†H8 listed by Blockeel & Long (1998: 49).
H(9) listed by Macvicar (1905: 14).
†H9 listed by Blockeel & Long (1998: 49).
H10 1951: on wet soil in wooded gully, N slope, alt. *ca* 900 ft, above Silvermines, AD Banwell, EV Watson & PJ Wanstall (Castell 1952: 92).
H11 1952: Farmley Wood, nr Cuffe's Grange, ALK King & MPH Kertland, comm. ALK King (Castell 1953: 300).
H12 1954: shady ground under trees, Inch, JS Thomson (Castell 1955: 580).
H(13) listed by Macvicar (1905: 14, 15).
†H13 listed by Blockeel & Long (1998: 49).
H(14) listed by Macvicar (1905: 14).
†H14 listed by Blockeel & Long (1998: 49).
H(15) listed by Macvicar (1905: 14).
†H15 listed by Blockeel & Long (1998: 49).
†H16 listed by Blockeel & Long (1998: 49).
H(17) 1896: oakwood, Clonbrock, D McArdle (DBN), comm. ALK King (Paton 1964: 715).
†H17 listed by Blockeel & Long (1998: 49).
H(18) listed by Macvicar (1905: 14).
†H18 listed by Blockeel & Long (1998: 49).
[H(19) listed by Macvicar (1905: 14). H19 deleted because no record or voucher traced, comm. MM Yeo (Long 1990a: 26)].
H(20) listed by Macvicar (1905: 14).
†H20 listed by Blockeel & Long (1998: 49).
[H(21) listed by Macvicar (1905: 14). H21 deleted because no record or voucher traced, comm. MM Yeo (Long 1990a: 26)].
H(22) listed by Macvicar (1905: 14).
†H22 listed by Blockeel & Long (1998: 49).
H23 1952: grassy bank, NE end of L. Owel, JS Thomson (Castell 1954: 473).
H24 1957: rock by bank of R. Inny, Ballymacarrow Bridge, MPH Kertland & ALK King, comm. ALK King (Castell 1958: 465).
H25 1960: in Rockingham Woods, Boyle, ALK King (Paton 1961: 153).
H(26) listed by Macvicar (1905: 14).
†H26 listed by Blockeel & Long (1998: 49).
H(27) listed by Macvicar (1905: 14, 15).
†H27 listed by Blockeel & Long (1998: 49).
H(28) listed by Macvicar (1905: 14).
H(28) 1928: nr Rosses Point, Sligo (BBS exc.) (Duncan 1928: 119), as var. *minor*.

†H28 listed by Blockeel & Long (1998: 49).
H(29) listed by Macvicar (1905: 14).
H(29) 1928: wooded glen, NE end of Glencar Lough (BBS exc.) (Duncan 1928: 118), as var. *minor*.
†H29 listed by Blockeel & Long (1998: 49).
H(30) listed by Macvicar (1905: 14).
†H30 listed by Blockeel & Long (1998: 49).
H(31) listed by Macvicar (1905: 14).
†H31 listed by Blockeel & Long (1998: 49).
H32 1954: dry bank under beech, Glaslough Ho.[use], ALK King (Castell 1955: 580).
H(33) listed by Macvicar (1905: 14).
†H33 listed by Blockeel & Long (1998: 49).
H(34) listed by Macvicar (1905: 14).
H(34) 1937: Erne Valley, no collector named (BBS exc.) (Armitage 1938: 13), as *P. asplenioides* var. *minor*.
1937: Erne Valley, no collector named (BBS exc.) (Armitage 1938: 13), as *P. asplenioides* var. *minor* forma *laxa*.
1937: Erne Valley, no collector named (BBS exc.) (Armitage 1938: 13), as *P. asplenioides* var. *humilis* forma *laxa*.
1937: Erne Valley, E Armitage (anon. 1938c: 35), as var. *minor*.
1937: Erne Valley, E Armitage (anon. 1938c: 35), as var. *minor* f. *laxa*.
1937: sand dunes, Bundoran, E Armitage (anon. 1938c: 35), as var. *humilis* f. *laxa*.
†H34 listed by Blockeel & Long (1998: 49).
H(35) listed by Macvicar (1905: 14).
†H35 listed by Blockeel & Long (1998: 49).
H36 1950: Stewartstown Castle, JW Fitzgerald (Castell 1951: 493).
H(37) listed by Macvicar (1905: 14, 15).
†H37 listed by Blockeel & Long (1998: 49).
H(38) listed by Macvicar (1905: 14).
†H38 listed by Blockeel & Long (1998: 49).
H(39) listed by Macvicar (1905: 14).
H(39) 1928: Glenariff (BBS exc.) (Duncan 1928: 117), as var. *humilis*.
†H39 listed by Blockeel & Long (1998: 49).
H(40) listed by Macvicar (1905: 14).
†H40 listed by Blockeel & Long (1998: 49).

A few records from before the description of *P. britannica* by Paton (1979) might be based on material of that species.

46/3 *Plagiochila asplenioides* (L. emend. Taylor) Dumort.
(syn. *Plagiochila asplenioides* var. *major* Nees)

H1 1951: copse beside L. Currane, nr Waterville, EC Wallace (Castell 1952: 92).
1951: Polewoods nr Caragh Lake, PW Richards (Castell 1952: 92).
H(2) 1935: Muckross, no collector named (BBS exc.) (Watson 1936: 265, anon. 1937b: 369).
H2 1951: Torc, JW Fitzgerald (Castell 1952: 92).
H3 1979: woodland beside Glengarriff R., JA Paton (Corley 1980a: 29).
H4 1966: on stony bank by road under trees by R. Lee nr Innishcarra Bridge, MFV Corley & JS Parker (Paton 1967c: 399).
†H5 listed by Blockeel & Long (1998: 49).
H(6) 1933: valley of the Unishad nr Lismore, E Armitage (BRIST), comm. PE Stanley (Paton 1964: 715).
†H6 listed by Blockeel & Long (1998: 49).
H(8) 1901: Glenstal, E Armitage (BRIST), comm. PE Stanley (Paton 1964: 715).
†H8 listed by Blockeel & Long (1998: 49).
H9 1985: hazelscrub W of Doomore, AC Bouman (Corley 1987: 19).
[H10 deleted because record (1951: above Silvermines) is referable to *P. asplenioides* var. *asplenioides* [= *P. porelloides*] (Paton 1977a: 14)].
H10 1967: bank of wooded stream, Devil's Bit Mt., JW Fitzgerald (Corley 1978: 14).
H11 1966: boulder in wood, Inistioge, J Appleyard *et al.* (BBS exc.) (Paton 1967c: 399).
H12 1975: woodland bank S of Clonough Bridge, E of Inch, JA Paton (BBS exc.) (Paton 1976: 19).
H13 1961: shaded banks of R. Slaney, Coolaphuca Wood nr Bunclody, M McCallum Webster, comm. CC Townsend (Paton 1964: 715).
H14 1955: wet ground, Abbeyleix demesne, JS Thomson (Castell 1956: 148).
H15 1957: ditch bank, Chevy Chase, nr Gort, AC Crundwell (BBS exc.) (Castell 1958: 465).
H16 1957: woodland, Tullywee Bridge, Kylemore, AC Crundwell (BBS exc.) (Castell 1958: 465).

H18 1985: limestone boulder in hazel scrub, Clorhane, nr Clonmacnoise, DL Kelly (Corley 1987: 19).
H20 1969: shaded rocks by river, Devil's Glen nr Ashford, JW Fitzgerald & DM Synnott (Paton 1970: 191).
H21 record from Kelly & Synnott (1993) accepted by Long (1999a).
H22 1978: face of limestone cliff by R. Boyne, Beauparc, DM Synnott (Corley 1982: 21).
H23 1979: limestone quarry, S of Crazy Corner, NE of Mullingar, DM Synnott (Corley 1980a: 29).
H(24) listed by Blockeel & Long (1998: 49).
H25 1965: in copse 1 mile S of Ballyfarnan, JW Fitzgerald & EM Lobley (Paton 1966: 185).
H26 1970: wood W of the Pollagh R., NE of Balla, JA Paton (Paton 1971a: 372).
H27 1987: pathside bank on edge of wood, near Rose Cottage NW of Westport House, JA Paton (Long 1988: 31).
H(28) listed by Macvicar (1905: 14).
†H28 listed by Blockeel & Long (1998: 49).
H(29) 1928: wooded glen, NE end of Glencar Lough (BBS exc.) (Duncan 1928: 118).
†H29 listed by Blockeel & Long (1998: 49).
H30 1969: stream bank, NE slope of Slievenakilla, Cuilcagh Mts, JA Paton (Paton 1970: 191).
H31 1967: woodland, Rathescar, Ardee, DM Synnott (Paton 1968: 624).
H(33) listed by Macvicar (1905: 14).
†H33 listed by Blockeel & Long (1998: 49).
H34 1967: wooded glen above Red Castle, Inishowen, JW Fitzgerald (Paton 1968: 624).
H35 1962: wood nr Mid Town, Mulroy Bay, EF Warburg (BBS exc.) (Paton 1963: 486).
H36 1950: on ground, overlying limestone, Stewartstown Castle, JW Fitzgerald (Castell 1952: 92).
H37 1964: shaded bank above canal, Carrickaness, nr Benburb, JW Fitzgerald & MPH Kertland (Paton 1965a: 854).
H(38) listed by Macvicar (1905: 14).
†H38 listed by Blockeel & Long (1998: 49).
†H39 listed by Blockeel & Long (1998: 49).
H40 1952: Benevenagh, EW Jones (Castell 1953: 300).

A few records from before the description of *P. britannica* by Paton (1979) might be based on material of that species.

46/4 ***Plagiochila britannica*** Paton

H2 1983: shaded limestone near pool, old copper mines, Ross I., Killarney, JA Paton (Corley 1984: 24).
H8 1979: flat rock beside waterfall, Glenastar, W of Ardagh, JA Paton (Corley 1980a: 30).
H9 1968: limestone pavement, N slope of Cappanawalla, Ballyvaughan, JA Paton (Corley 1980a: 30).
H16 1986: bridge parapet in shady woodland, Kylemore Abbey, DG Long (Corley 1987: 19).
H24 1997: on limestone rocks under trees, 50 m alt., Barley Harbour N of Portlick Castle, E side of Lough Ree, N05, DG Long 27320 (Long 1999a: 94).
H25 1981: dry limestone wall at NE edge of Caslan's Wood, 3 km N of Strokestown, DM Synnott (Corley 1982: 21).
H26 1987: stone on woodland floor, E bank of Cloon River between Srah and Partry, DM Synnott, det. JA Paton (Long 1988: 31).
H27 1987: on boulder in woodland in grounds of Westport House, MAS Burton (Long 1988: 31).
H28 1963: base of limestone wall, Ballinphuill Castle, near Lissadell, AR Perry (Long 1991: 38).
H29 2000: on damp limestone wall at N edge of mixed deciduous and coniferous woodland, N of Glencar Lough, G74, DT Holyoak 00-508 (BBSUK) (Blackstock 2001: 35-36).
H33 1993: calcareous sandstone cliff, Lough Navar Forest, H05, NG Hodgetts 2696 (Long 1994: 34).
H35 1990: on stone steps set in concrete, Glenveagh Garden, DM Synnott (Long 1991: 38).
1990: on basic rocks on N-facing slope, 1 km NW of Dunfanaghy, Horn Head, DM Synnott (Long 1991: 38).
H37 1964: wall (probably of limestone), Carrickness, nr Benburb Bridge, JW Fitzgerald (Paton 1979: 254).
H40 1990: base of W-facing cliff, Binevenagh, DM Synnott (Long 1991: 38).

Described new to science by Paton (1979). The species had previously been overlooked among large forms of the commoner *P. porelloides* or small forms of *P. asplenioides*.

46/6 ***Plagiochila atlantica*** E.W.Jones & F. Rose
(syn. *Plagiochila ambagiosa* auct. non Mitt.)

H1 1951: rocks at head of Lough Coomeathcun (NE of Waterville), 180 m alt., in open nearly vertical well-lit crevice wet with spray from waterfall, EW Jones 110 (Jones & Rose 1975: 419, Paton 1976: 19).
H2 1983: base of *Ilex* in shady woodland on river bank, Galway's R. above Galway's Bridge, Killarney, DG Long (Corley 1984: 24).
H(3) pre-1816: specimen lacking locality data, but almost certainly from nr Bantry, E Hutchins (Holotype, NY; Isotype, DBN) (Jones & Rose 1975: 418-419, Paton 1976: 19, Synnott 1976b). H(3) listed by Macvicar (1905: 14) for *P. ambagiosa*.
H3 2002: on rock face on SE-facing crag, *ca* 310 m alt., at the head of the valley, Gougane Barra, W06, TL Blockeel 31/329 (Blackstock 2003: 43).

46/7 ***Plagiochila spinulosa*** (Dicks.) Dumort.

†H1 listed by Blockeel & Long (1998: 50).
†H2 listed by Blockeel & Long (1998: 50).
†H3 listed by Blockeel & Long (1998: 50).
†H4 listed by Blockeel & Long (1998: 50).
H(5) listed by Blockeel & Long (1998: 50).
H5 2002: on shaded crag under conifers, *ca* 40 m alt., Glenbower Wood, near Killeagh, W97, TL Blockeel 31/310 (Blackstock 2003: 43).
H6 1966: Coumshingaun, Comeragh Mountains, DM Synnott (DBN) (Long 1999b: 27).
[H7 deleted because voucher reidentified as *P. punctata* (Corley 1981: 19-20)].
†H8 listed by Blockeel & Long (1998: 50).
[H9 deleted because voucher reidentified as *P. killarniensis* (Corley 1981: 19-20)].
[H10 deleted because specimen is *P. killarniensis* (Corley 1979: 24)].
H10 1979: wet shaded rocks nr a waterfall on the slope of Keeper Hill, HMH van Melick (Corley 1981: 19-20).
†H11 listed by Blockeel & Long (1998: 50).
[H12 discounted because no specimen traced (Corley 1981: 19-20)].
H(13) listed by Blockeel & Long (1998: 50).
[H14 discounted because no specimen traced (Corley 1981: 19-20)].
†H16 listed by Blockeel & Long (1998: 50).
[H18 discounted because no specimen traced (Corley 1981: 19-20)].
†H20 listed by Blockeel & Long (1998: 50).
[H21 discounted because no specimen traced (Corley 1981: 19-20)].
[H22 discounted because no specimen traced (Corley 1981: 19-20)].
†H25 listed by Blockeel & Long (1998: 50).
[H26 discounted because no specimen traced (Corley 1981: 19-20)].
H26 1982: banks in wooded ravine, Barnalyra Wood, N of Kilkelly, M49, DM Synnott (DBN) (Long 1999a: 94).
†H27 listed by Blockeel & Long (1998: 50).
†H28 listed by Blockeel & Long (1998: 50).
†H29 listed by Blockeel & Long (1998: 50).
[H30 discounted because no specimen traced (Corley 1981: 19-20)].
H30 2001: part of bryophyte mat on vertical side of gritstone rock in block scree, partly shaded by *Calluna vulgaris*, *ca* 301 m alt., S of Englishman's House, SW of Monesk, H03, DT Holyoak 01-706 (Blackstock: 2002: 40).
[H31 deleted because specimen is *P. killarniensis* (Corley 1979: 24)].
†H33 listed by Blockeel & Long (1998: 50).
†H34 listed by Blockeel & Long (1998: 50).
†H35 listed by Blockeel & Long (1998: 50).
†H36 listed by Blockeel & Long (1998: 50).
[H37 discounted because no specimen traced (Corley 1981: 19-20)].
H(38) listed by Blockeel & Long (1998: 50).
†H39 listed by Blockeel & Long (1998: 50).
H40 1990: cleft, W-facing cliff, Benevenagh, DM Synnott (DBN) (Long 1999b: 27).

Reliable separation of Irish records of *P. spinulosa* from those of *P. bifaria* (syn. *P. killarniensis*) commenced with the review by Paton (1977c). Most older records (e.g. from Macvicar 1905: 14) cannot be referred to either of these species unless voucher specimens have been re-identified.

46/7 ***Plagiochila spinulosa***
or
46/8 ***P. bifaria***

H4 1966: on tree trunks on moor at 1100 ft alt., E side of Musherabeg, Boggeragh Mts, MFV Corley & JS Parker (Paton 1967c: 400).
H(5) 1851: Glenbower Wood nr Killeagh, I Carroll (BEL) (Paton 1967c: 400).
H11 1954: shaded tree root in wood, Graiguenamanagh, ALK King (Castell 1955: 580).
H25 1968: heath on blanket bog, Slieve Bawn, WV Rubers, P Hessel & J Klein (Paton 1970: 191).
H36 1957: among boulders, Cloughmore, nr Glenhull, JW Fitzgerald (Castell 1959: 628).

See note under the preceding species. Voucher specimens listed above have apparently not been reidentified since the review by Paton (1977c).

46/8 ***Plagiochila bifaria*** (Sw.) Lindenb.
(syn. *Plagiochila killarniensis* Pearson)

H(1) 1900: Brandon valley, D McArdle (BM) (Paton 1977c: 458, Corley 1978: 14). H (1) listed by Macvicar (1905: 14) for *P.* killarniensis.
†H1 listed by Blockeel & Long (1998: 50).
H(2) 1840: Cromaglan, Taylor (GL) (Paton 1977c: 458, Corley 1978: 14).
†H2 listed by Blockeel & Long (1998: 50).
H(3) 1869: Glengarriff, B Carrington (MANCH) (Paton 1977c: 458, Corley 1978: 14).
†H3 listed by Blockeel & Long (1998: 50).
H5 2002: small rock outcrop under conifers, 110 m alt., banks of the River Bride, Ardarou Wood, Glenville, W78, TL Blockeel 31/369 (Blackstock 2003: 43).
H6 1999: coastal cliffs, Mine Head, X28, DH Wrench (Blackstock 2000: 43).
H9 1968: Corkscrew Hill, S of Ballyvaughan, JA Paton (Paton 1977c: 458, Corley 1978: 14).
H10 1957: ledges of recently disused slate quarry, alt. 500 ft, hills between Ballina and Newtown, AD Banwell, EV Watson & PJ Wanstall (BBSUK) (Castell 1952: 93, Corley 1979: 24).
H16 1970: N slope of Benbaun, The Twelve Pins, JA Paton (Paton 1977c: 458, Corley 1978: 14).
H20 1975: Nr waterfall, Devil's Glen, Ashford, JA Paton & AR Perry (Paton 1977c: 458, Corley 1978: 14).
H23 1979: limestone bluff, Fore, DM Synnott (Corley 1980a: 30).
H25 2002: shaded rock crevices in NE-facing crags, *ca* 150 m alt., Kilronan Mountain, G91, NG Hodgetts 4158 (Blackstock 2003: 43).
H27 1970: nr Delphi, N of Killary Harbour, JA Paton (Paton 1977c: 458, Corley 1978: 14).
H29 1969: Peakadaw, Glenade, JA Paton (Paton 1977c: 458, Corley 1978: 14).
H31 1968: damp peaty bank, hazel scrub, [between ?] Monasterboice and Fieldstown, DM Synnott (BBSUK) (Paton 1969a: 872, Corley 1979: 24).
H33 1993: trunk of ash tree in limestone woodland gorge, Marble Arch, H13, C Sérgio (Long 1994: 34).
H35 1969: Glencollumkille, N of Carrick, JA Paton (Paton 1977c: 458, Corley 1978: 14).
H39 1969: Garron Point, N of Glenarm, JA Paton (Paton 1977c: 458, Corley 1978: 14).
H40 1999: on unshaded crumbling basalt of crag, *ca* 200 m alt., Windy Hill, C73, DT Holyoak 99-535 (BBSUK) (Blackstock 2000: 43).

Reliable separation of Irish records of this species from those of *P. spinulosa* commenced with the review by Paton (1977c). Older records (e.g. from Macvicar 1905: 14) can be referred to one or other of these species only when voucher specimens have been reidentified.

The name *Plagiochila bifaria* has been adopted in place of *P. killarniensis* following Heinrichs *et al.* (1998) and Grolle & Long (2000: 109, 120). Nevertheless, some doubt about this taxonomic treatment may remain since Rycroft *et al.* (1999) call attention to possible chemical differences between *P. bifaria* from the Neotropics and material from Europe.

46/9 ***Plagiochila punctata*** (Taylor) Taylor (syn. *Plagiochila owenii* Steph.)

H(1) listed by Macvicar (1905: 14).
†H1 listed by Blockeel & Long (1998: 50).
H(2) listed by Macvicar (1905: 14).
H2 1905: Killarney, SJ Owen, as *P. owenii*, 'First detected as a new species by Mr Macvicar' (anon. 1906: 229).
H(3) listed by Macvicar (1905: 14).
†H3 listed by Blockeel & Long (1998: 50).
H(5) 1851: hill nr Kildorrery, I Carroll (BEL) (Paton 1967c: 400).
H(6) listed by Macvicar (1905: 14).
†H6 listed by Blockeel & Long (1998: 50).
H7 1963: sandstone rocks at 1500 ft alt., N side of Galtymore Mt., DA Ratcliffe (Paton 1964: 715).
H8 1966: on rocks at 1500 ft alt., Slievereagh nr Ballylanders, MFV Corley & JS Parker (Paton 1967c: 400).
H9 1967: oaks and hazels, Den of Clab, nr Borton [*sic* = Glen of Clab, nr Boston], F Rose (Paton 1968: 624).
H10 1979: by waterfall, Keeper Hill, RC Stern (Corley 1980a: 30).
H(13) listed by Macvicar (1905: 14).
†H13 listed by Blockeel & Long (1998: 50).
H16 1961: damp quartzite outcrops at 1700 ft [alt.], Ben Breen, Twelve Bens, DA Ratcliffe (Paton 1962: 360).
H(20) listed by Macvicar (1905: 14).
†H20 listed by Blockeel & Long (1998: 50).
H26 1965: on rocks W of L. Talt, [The] Ox Mts, JW Fitzgerald (Paton 1966: 185).
H(27) listed by Macvicar (1905: 14).
†H27 listed by Blockeel & Long (1998: 50).
[H28 1963: shaded rock clefts, Carrowkeel, nr Lough Arrow, BJ Fitzgerald & AR Perry (Paton 1964: 715). H28 deleted because specimen (BBSUK) is *P. spinulosa*, comm. AJE Smith (Corley 1985: 21)].
H(29) listed by Macvicar (1905: 14).
†H29 listed by Blockeel & Long (1998: 50).
H30 1961: shaded rocks with *Hymenophyllum* spp. at 1900 ft [alt.], S side of Cuilcagh, JW Fitzgerald (Paton 1962: 360).
H33 1959: shaded clefts in rocks, Aghahoorin, at 700 ft [alt.], nr Boho, JW Fitzgerald (Castell 1960: 765).
H34 1962: rock hollow, N side of Croaghconnellagh, EF Warburg (BBS exc.) (Paton 1963: 486).
H(35) listed by Macvicar (1905: 14).
†H35 listed by Blockeel & Long (1998: 50).
H(39) listed by Macvicar (1905: 14).
†H39 listed by Blockeel & Long (1998: 50).
H40 1968: boulders, Banagher Glen nr Dungiven, JW Fitzgerald (Paton 1969a: 872).

46/10 ***Plagiochila exigua*** (Taylor) Taylor (syn. *Plagiochila tridenticulata* auct. non (Hook.) Dumort.)

H(1) listed by Macvicar (1905: 14).
†H1 listed by Blockeel & Long (1998: 50).
H(2) listed by Macvicar (1905: 14).
†H2 listed by Blockeel & Long (1998: 50).
H(3) listed by Macvicar (1905: 14).
†H3 listed by Blockeel & Long (1998: 50).
H(6) 1902: L. Coumshingaun, CH Waddell (BEL) (Paton 1968: 624).
H6 1999: on wet rock face in gully, SW corner of corrie, *ca* 400 m alt., Coumshingaun, Comeragh Mts, S31, TL Blockeel 28/291 (Blackstock 2000: 43).
H16 1961: shaded rocks in oakwood on S-facing slope, Kylemore, nr Letterfrack, DA Ratcliffe (Paton 1962: 360).
H(27) listed by Macvicar (1905: 14).
†H27 listed by Blockeel & Long (1998: 50).
H(28) listed by Macvicar (1905: 14). H(28) listed by Blockeel & Long (1998: 50).
H(35) listed by Macvicar (1905: 14).
†H35 listed by Blockeel & Long (1998: 50).
H(39) listed by Macvicar (1905: 14). H(39) listed by Blockeel & Long (1998: 50).
H40 1959: shaded mossy boulders, Altnaheglish, nr Dungiven, JW Fitzgerald (Castell 1960: 765).

47/1 ***Southbya tophacea*** (Spruce) Spruce

H20 1988: on limy mortar of damp shady wall in old conifer plantation, 160 m [alt.], Baravore, Glenmalur Valley E of Lugnaquillia, DG Long 14903 (Long 1989: 22).
H28 1963: growing over *Eucladium* with *Leiocolea turbinata* on tufa, dripping limestone wall, Knocknarea Glen, nr Sligo, JW Fitzgerald & AR Perry (Paton 1964: 713, Fitzgerald & Fitzgerald 1966a).

49/1 *Acrobolbus wilsonii* Nees

H(1) listed by Macvicar (1905: 14).
†H1 listed by Blockeel & Long (1998: 50).
H(2) listed by Macvicar (1905: 14).
†H2 listed by Blockeel & Long (1998: 50).
H(3) listed by Macvicar (1905: 14).
†H3 listed by Blockeel & Long (1998: 50).
H16 1994: wet N-facing crag at *ca* 1600 ft alt., Bengower, Twelve Bens, L75, JA Paton 7636 (Long 1995b: 38).
H(27) listed by Macvicar (1905: 14).
†H27 listed by Blockeel & Long (1998: 50).
H35 1991: amongst boulders on steep bank with tall *Calluna* on sea cliffs, 200 m alt., E of Coastguard Hill, Horn Head nr Dunfanaghy, C04, DG Long 20270 (Long 1992: 25).

50/1 *Pleurozia purpurea* Lindb.

H(1) listed by Macvicar (1905: 21).
†H1 listed by Blockeel & Long (1998: 51).
H(2) listed by Macvicar (1905: 21).
†H2 listed by Blockeel & Long (1998: 51).
H3 1953: sandstone boulder in shade, Valley Desmond, Gougane Barra, ALK King (Castell 1954: 476).
H9 1962: in *Sphagnum-Rhynchospora alba* bog N of Lough Goller, S of Lisdoonvarna, G Halliday (Paton 1963: 490).
H(16) listed by Macvicar (1905: 21).
†H16 listed by Blockeel & Long (1998: 51).
H(17) listed by Macvicar (1905: 21).
†H17 listed by Blockeel & Long (1998: 51).
H(18) 1949: Edenderry, nr Portarlington, H Gams & H Osvald, comm. H Gams per EC Wallace (Castell 1950: 379).
†H18 listed by Blockeel & Long (1998: 51).
H(20) listed by Macvicar (1905: 21). H(20) listed by Blockeel & Long (1998: 51).
H(21) listed by Macvicar (1905: 21). H(21) listed by Blockeel & Long (1998: 51).
H23 1952: The Derries Bog, Athlone, ALK King (Castell 1953: 303).
H24 1955: Derryad Bog, nr Killashee, TA Barry, comm ALK King (Castell 1956: 150).
H(25) 1935: Athlone bog, H Osvald (*Acta Phyt. Suecica* **26**, pp. 24, 40, 42, 1949) (Castell 1950: 379).
1937: raised moss in Shannon Valley, 3 miles, NW of Lanesborough, H Osvald (*Acta Phyt. Suecica* **26**, pp. 24, 40, 42, 1949) (Castell 1950: 379).
†H25 listed by Blockeel & Long (1998: 51).
H26 1986: among mosses on raised bog, Flughany, C Douglas & H Grogan (Corley 1987: 20).
H(27) listed by Macvicar (1905: 21).
†H27 listed by Blockeel & Long (1998: 51).
H28 1963: wet peaty slopes by roadside, Castleore, Slish Mt., AR Perry & JW Fitzgerald (Paton 1964: 720).
H29 1963: plentiful in bog E of Sriff Cottage nr Dromahair, JW Fitzgerald & AR Perry (Paton 1964: 720).
H30 1961: sparingly among *Sphagnum*, Bellavally, Cuilcagh, JW Fitzgerald (Paton 1962: 363).
†H33 listed by Blockeel & Long (1998: 51).
H(34) listed by Macvicar (1905: 21).
†H34 listed by Blockeel & Long (1998: 51).
H(35) listed by Macvicar (1905: 21).
†H35 listed by Blockeel & Long (1998: 51).
H36 1951: peat bank, roadside, alt. 630 ft, Lough Bradan nr Castlederg, JW Fitzgerald (Castell 1952: 96).
H(38) listed by Macvicar (1905: 21). H(38) listed by Blockeel & Long (1998: 51).
[H(39) listed by Macvicar (1905: 21)].
H39 1990: Garra Plateau above Carnlough, DM Synnott (DBN) (Long 1999b: 27).
[H40 deleted because no localised record or voucher traced, comm. MM Yeo (Long 1990a: 28)].
[H(40) listed by Macvicar (1905: 21)].
H40 1999: on open wet blanket bog, Windy Hill, C73, DT Holyoak 99-545 (BBSUK) (Blackstock 2000: 43).

51/1 *Radula complanata* (L.) Dumort.

H(1) listed by Macvicar (1905: 21).
†H1 listed by Blockeel & Long (1998: 51).
H(2) listed by Macvicar (1905: 21).
†H2 listed by Blockeel & Long (1998: 51).
H(3) listed by Macvicar (1905: 21).
†H3 listed by Blockeel & Long (1998: 51).
H4 1955: on beech nr Knocknagree, MJP Scannell, comm ALK King (Castell 1956: 149).
H5 1956: on willows, fen W of Youghal, EC Wallace (Castell 1957: 326).
H(6) listed by Macvicar (1905: 21).
†H6 listed by Blockeel & Long (1998: 51).
H(7) listed by Macvicar (1905: 21).
†H7 listed by Blockeel & Long (1998: 51).
†H8 listed by Blockeel & Long (1998: 51).

H(9) listed by Macvicar (1905: 21).
†H9 listed by Blockeel & Long (1998: 51).
H10 1951: branches of Alder in shaded gully, alt. 900 ft, above Silvermines, AD Banwell, EV Watson & PJ Wanstall (Castell 1952: 96).
H11 1954: on larch, in wood, Graiguenamanagh, ALK King (Castell 1955: 581).
H(12) listed by Macvicar (1905: 21).
†H12 listed by Blockeel & Long (1998: 51).
H(13) listed by Macvicar (1905: 21).
†H13 listed by Blockeel & Long (1998: 51).
H(14) listed by Macvicar (1905: 21).
†H14 listed by Blockeel & Long (1998: 51).
H(15) listed by Macvicar (1905: 21).
†H15 listed by Blockeel & Long (1998: 51).
H(16) listed by Macvicar (1905: 21).
†H16 listed by Blockeel & Long (1998: 51).
H(17) listed by Macvicar (1905: 21).
†H17 listed by Blockeel & Long (1998: 51).
[H(18) listed by Macvicar (1905: 21). H18 deleted because no record traced, comm. MM Yeo, replaced by next record (Long 1990a: 28)].
H(18) 1889: near Geashill, CD Russell (DBN), comm, DM Synnott (Long 1990a: 28).
H(19) listed by Macvicar (1905: 21).
†H19 listed by Blockeel & Long (1998: 51).
H(20) listed by Macvicar (1905: 21).
†H20 listed by Blockeel & Long (1998: 51).
H(21) listed by Macvicar (1905: 21).
†H21 listed by Blockeel & Long (1998: 51).
H(22) listed by Macvicar (1905: 21).
†H22 listed by Blockeel & Long (1998: 51).
H23 1952: trunk of fallen tree, Clonhugh Demense, NE end of L. Owel, JS Thomson (Castell 1954: 476).
H24 1957: on Hawthorn, Ballymacarrow Bridge, MPH Kertland & ALK King, comm. ALK King (Castell 1958: 468).
H25 1959: fallen beech, shore of L. Funshinagh, ALK King (Castell 1969: 768).
H(26) listed by Macvicar (1905: 21).
†H26 listed by Blockeel & Long (1998: 51).
H(27) listed by Macvicar (1905: 21).
†H27 listed by Blockeel & Long (1998: 51).
H(28) listed by Macvicar (1905: 21).
†H28 listed by Blockeel & Long (1998: 51).
H(29) listed by Macvicar (1905: 21).
†H29 listed by Blockeel & Long (1998: 51).
H(30) listed by Macvicar (1905: 21).
†H30 listed by Blockeel & Long (1998: 51).
H31 1965: trunk of fallen chestnut tree, bank of R. Boyne opposite gate of Townley Hall, Tullyallen, DM Synnott (Paton 1966: 187).
H32 1952: gorse stem, *ca* 250 ft alt., Lisgall, nr Carrickmacross, JW Fitzgerald (Castell 1953: 303).
†H33 listed by Blockeel & Long (1998: 51).
H(34) listed by Macvicar (1905: 21).
†H34 listed by Blockeel & Long (1998: 51).
†H35 listed by Blockeel & Long (1998: 51).
†H36 listed by Blockeel & Long (1998: 51).
H(37) listed by Macvicar (1905: 21).
†H37 listed by Blockeel & Long (1998: 51).
[H(38) listed by Macvicar (1905: 21). H38 deleted because no record traced, comm. MM Yeo, replaced by next record (Long 1990a: 28)].
H(38) 1884: trees, Tollymore Park, HW Lett (DBN), comm. DM Synnott (Long 1990a: 28).
H38 2002: on bark of oak in open planted woodland, *ca* 45 m alt., just S of Shimna River in Tollymore Forest Park, J33, DT Holyoak 02-941 (Blackstock 2003: 43).
H(39) listed by Macvicar (1905: 21).
†H39 listed by Blockeel & Long (1998: 51).
H(40) listed by Macvicar (1905: 21).
†H40 listed by Blockeel & Long (1998: 51).

51/2 ***Radula lindenbergiana*** Gottsche ex C. Hartm.
(syn. *Radula lindbergiana* Gottsche)

H1 1951: Derrynane, EW Jones (Castell 1952: 96).
†H2 listed by Blockeel & Long (1998: 51).
H3 1979: rock on hillside between streams, Lackawee, Slieve Miskish Mts, JA Paton (Corley 1980a: 31).
H6 1966: on boulders by lake, Sgilloge Loughs, Comeragh Mts, J Appleyard & JW Fitzgerald (BBS exc.) (Paton 1967c: 403).
H8 1979: Glenastar ravine, nr Ardagh, EW Jones (Corley 1980a: 31).
H16 1994: in crevice formed by crack in huge boulder on open moorland, above Lough Nalawney, Errisbeg, L64, TL Blockeel 23/203 (Long 1995b: 39).
†H27 listed by Blockeel & Long (1998: 51).
H(28) 1928: Gleniff, Ben Bulben (BBS exc.) (Duncan 1928: 118).
†H28 listed by Blockeel & Long (1998: 51).
H29 1963: limestone face at 800 ft alt., Peakadaw, Glenade, AR Perry & JW

Fitzgerald (Paton 1964: 720).

51/3 ***Radula voluta*** Taylor ex Gottsche, Lindenb. & Nees

H(1) listed by Macvicar (1905: 21).
†H1 listed by Blockeel & Long (1998: 51).
H(2) listed by Macvicar (1905: 21).
†H2 listed by Blockeel & Long (1998: 51).
H3 1955: wet rocks in ravine, NE slope of Lackawee, H Milne-Redhead (Castell 1957: 326).
H(6) listed by Macvicar (1905: 21).
†H6 listed by Blockeel & Long (1998: 51).
H7 1966: sheltered rocks above L. Curra, Galtee Mts, JA Paton & J Appleyard (BBS exc.) (Paton 1967c: 403).
H(16) 1933: Kylemore, PWM Richards (anon. 1939c: 111).
†H16 listed by Blockeel & Long (1998: 51).
H(27) listed by Macvicar (1905: 21). H(27) listed by Blockeel & Long (1998: 51).
H28 1965: growing over *Cinclidotus*, boulders beside L. Gill E of Innisfree, JW Fitzgerald & EM Lobley (Paton 1966: 187).
H(30) listed by Macvicar (1905: 21). H(30) listed by Blockeel & Long (1998: 51).
H35 1969: shaded rocks in gorge, Fintragh Bay, W of Killybegs, JA Paton (Paton 1970: 193).

51/4 ***Radula holtii*** Spruce

H1 1951: Lough Coomeathcun nr Glenbeigh, EW Jones (BBS exc.) (Paton 1963: 490).
H(2) listed by Macvicar (1905: 21).
†H2 listed by Blockeel & Long (1998: 51).
H3 1955: rivulet, NE slope of Lackawee, H Milne-Redhead (Castell 1957: 326).
H(27) listed by Macvicar (1905: 21).
†H27 listed by Blockeel & Long (1998: 51).

51/5 ***Radula aquilegia*** (Hook.f. & Taylor) Gottsche, Lindenb. & Nees

H(1) listed by Macvicar (1905: 21).
†H1 listed by Blockeel & Long (1998: 51).
H(2) listed by Macvicar (1905: 21).
†H2 listed by Blockeel & Long (1998: 51).
H(3) listed by Macvicar (1905: 21).
†H3 listed by Blockeel & Long (1998: 51).
H(6) listed by Macvicar (1905: 21).
†H6 listed by Blockeel & Long (1998: 51).
H(7) listed by Macvicar (1905: 21).
†H7 listed by Blockeel & Long (1998: 51).
†H16 listed by Blockeel & Long (1998: 51).
H(27) listed by Macvicar (1905: 21).
†H27 listed by Blockeel & Long (1998: 51).
H28 1963: siliceous rocks at 1000 ft alt., Knockachree, Slieve Gamph, AR Perry & JW Fitzgerald (Paton 1964: 720).
H29 1967: shaded dry N-facing limestone cliffs, Peakadaw, Glenade, HH Birks, HJB Birks & DA Ratcliffe (Paton 1968: 627).
H(34) listed by Blockeel & Long (1998: 51).
H34 2002: with mosses on overhanging schist of outcrop on N-facing slope near summit, *ca* 488 m alt., just NW of summit of Bulbin Mt.,C34, DT Holyoak 02-511 (Blackstock 2003: 43).
H35 1961: shaded rocks in small stream ravine at 500 ft [alt.], Slieve Tooey, nr Ardara, DA Ratcliffe (Paton 1962: 363).
[H(38) listed by Macvicar (1905: 21). H38 deleted because no record or voucher traced (Long 1999a: 95)].

51/6 ***Radula carringtonii*** J.B.Jack

H(1) listed by Macvicar (1905: 21).
†H1 listed by Blockeel & Long (1998: 51).
H(2) listed by Macvicar (1905: 21).
†H2 listed by Blockeel & Long (1998: 51).
H3 1956: wet rocks in ravine, NE slope of Lackawee, H Milne-Redhead (Castell 1957: 326).
H(27) listed by Macvicar (1905: 21).
H27 1994: in mats on wall of shallow gully in crag above sea, 300 m alt., the high sea cliffs on Clare I., L68, GP Rothero (BBSUK) (Long 1999b: 27).
[H(33) 1905: damp rocks, shore of Lough Erne, very scarce, D McArdle (*Irish Nat.* **16**, 237, 1907), comm. JW Fitzgerald (Castell 1952: 96). H33 deleted because no voucher traced (Long 1999a: 95)].

52/1 ***Ptilidium ciliare*** (L.) Hampe

H(1) listed by Macvicar (1905: 19). H(1) listed by Blockeel & Long (1998: 51).
H(2) listed by Macvicar (1905: 19). H(2) listed by Blockeel & Long (1998: 51).
H8 1966: on basalt rocks, Knockroe, nr Caherconlish, MFV Corley & JS Parker (Paton 1967c: 396).
H(20) 1932: rock nr Glenmacross Waterfall,

MC Knowles (DBN), comm. JW Fitzgerald (Castell 1959: 629).

H20 1999: on gently sloping granite boulder on steep E-facing slope, The Scalp (W side), N of Enniskerry, O22, DL Kelly (Blackstock 2000: 43).

H21 1952: growing with *Lophozia ventricosa* in cleft of non-siliceous igneous rock, facing N, *ca* 900 ft alt., Slieve na Bawnoge, ALK King (Castell 1953: 302).

H22 1977: damp rocks, N side of Bellewstown, DM Synnott (Corley 1979: 23).

†H27 listed by Blockeel & Long (1998: 51).

H35 1969: amongst mosses, S slope of Muckish Mt., JA Paton (Paton 1970: 188).

H36 1957: in turf on rock ledges, Barnes Gap, JW Fitzgerald (Castell 1959: 629).

H(39) 1928: Colin Top or Colin Glen (BBS exc.) (Duncan 1928: 116). H(39) listed by Blockeel & Long (1998: 51).

H40 1999: with mosses on low basalt boulder in unshaded scree/grassy slope, *ca* 300 m alt., SW slope of Benbradagh, C71, DT Holyoak 99-674 (BBSUK) (Blackstock 2000: 43).

52/2 ***Ptilidium pulcherrimum*** (Weber) Vain.

H31 1953: mixed with *Metzgeria furcata* on Scots Pine in Ravensdale State Forest, ALK King (Castell 1954: 475).

53/1 ***Porella platyphylla*** (L.) Pfeiff.
(syn. *Madotheca platyphylla* (L.) Dumort.)

H(1) listed by Macvicar (1905: 21).

†H1 listed by Blockeel & Long (1998: 52).

H(2) listed by Macvicar (1905: 21).

†H2 listed by Blockeel & Long (1998: 52).

H(4) no date: Blarney, I Carroll (DBN), comm. ALK King (Paton 1964: 720).

†H4 listed by Blockeel & Long (1998: 52).

H5 1956: limestone rock, Carrigshane Hill, EC Wallace (Castell 1957: 326).

H(6) listed by Macvicar (1905: 21).

†H6 listed by Blockeel & Long (1998: 52).

H(7) listed by Macvicar (1905: 21).

†H7 listed by Blockeel & Long (1998: 52).

H(8) listed by Macvicar (1905: 21).

†H8 listed by Blockeel & Long (1998: 52).

H(9) listed by Macvicar (1905: 21).

†H9 listed by Blockeel & Long (1998: 52).

H11 1966: limestone wall, Dysart Castle, Inistioge, JG Duckett *et al.* (BBS exc.) (Paton 1967c: 403).

H(12) listed by Macvicar (1905: 21). H(12) listed by Blockeel & Long (1998: 52).

H13 1958: walls of ruins, St Mullin's, ALK King (Castell 1969: 768).

H14 1956: Magnesian Limestone, E of Graigueadrisley, S of Rathdowney, AA Cridland (Castell 1958: 468).

H(16) 1906: rocks in wood nr Cong, D McArdle (DBN) (Paton 1977a: 15).

†H16 listed by Blockeel & Long (1998: 52).

H17 1970: limestone boulder, wall in lane nr L.Corrib NW of Annaghdown, AR Perry & HJ Perry (Paton 1974b: 164).

H18 1986: limestone wall in mixed woodland, Clorhane, between Clonmacnoise and Shannonbridge, DL Kelly (Corley 1987: 20).

H(19) listed by Blockeel & Long (1998: 52).

H(20) listed by Macvicar (1905: 21).

H20 1997: on wall by lagoon, 5 m alt., E side of Broad Lough N of Wicklow, T39, DG Long 27350 (E) (Long 1999b: 27).

H21 1952: shaded tree trunk, Lucan Demesne, ALK King (DBN) (Long 1999b: 27).

H(22) listed by Macvicar (1905: 21).

†H22 listed by Blockeel & Long (1998: 52).

H23 1979: N-facing limestone bluff, Fore, DM Synnott (Corley 1982: 23).

H24 1968: limestone wall in oak/ash wood, Rathcline House 2 miles S of Lanesborough, WV Rubers, P Hessell & J Klein (Paton 1970: 193).

H25 2002: limestone exposure in pasture, *ca* 90 m alt., Carrigan More, M95, NG Hodgetts 4074 (Blackstock 2003: 43).

H26 1953: stone wall, by Loch Carra, E shore, opposite Otter Point, R Mackechnie and EC Wallace (Castell 1954: 476).

[H27 deleted because record (McArdle 1907) may have been based on material from H16 (Paton 1977a: 15)].

H(28) listed by Macvicar (1905: 21).

†H28 listed by Blockeel & Long (1998: 52).

H(29) listed by Macvicar (1905: 21).

†H29 listed by Blockeel & Long (1998: 52).

H(30) listed by Macvicar (1905: 21).

†H30 listed by Blockeel & Long (1998: 52).

H31 1968: limestone outcrop, Castle Roche, NW of Dundalk, DM Synnott (Paton

1969a: 875).
H32 1950: on limestone, Lough Aphnea, JW Fitzgerald (Castell 1951: 495).
†H33 listed by Blockeel & Long (1998: 52).
H36 1956: on shaded limestone rocks, Loughry, nr Cookstown, JW Fitzgerald & MPH Kertland (Castell 1957: 326).
H37 1966: limestone boulders in wood 1 mile E of Allistragh, 3 miles N of Armagh, JW Fitzgerald & MPH Kertland (Paton 1967c: 403).
H(38) listed by Macvicar (1905: 21). H(38) listed by Blockeel & Long (1998: 52).
H(39) listed by Macvicar (1905: 21).
†H39 listed by Blockeel & Long (1998: 52).
†H40 listed by Blockeel & Long (1998: 52).

53/2 ***Porella cordaeana*** (Huebener) Moore (syn. *Madotheca cordaeana* (Huebener) Dumort., *M. rivularis* Nees, *P. cordaeana* var. *faroensis* (C.E.O. Jensen) E.W.Jones, *Porella cordaeana* var. *simplicior* (J.E.Zetterst.) S.W. Arnell)

H(5) listed by Blockeel & Long (1998: 52).
H6 1966: rocks in stream below Coumshingaun L., Comeragh Mts, JA Paton *et al.* (BBS exc.) (Paton 1967c: 403).
H9 1968: stones on bank of R. Fergus nr Elmvale House, W of Killinaboy, AR Perry (Paton 1969a: 875).
H13 1969: rocks by R. Slaney at Aghade Bridge nr Tullow, JW Fitzgerald (Paton 1970: 193).
H15 1957: on stone at edge of turlough, Garryland Wood, nr Gort, AC Crundwell (BBS exc.) (Castell 1958: 469).
H20 1969: rocks by the river, Devil's Glen nr Ashford, JW Fitzgerald & DM Synnott (Paton 1970: 193).
H22 1978: siliceous rock by road, Hill 426, Greenanstown, Naul, DM Synnott (Corley 1979: 25).
H23 1970: rocks in wood, E shore of Killinure L., S of Glassan, JA Paton (Paton 1971a: 373).
H28 1965: boulders beside L. Gill, Slish Wood, JW Fitzgerald & EM Lobley (Paton 1966: 187).
H29 1965: limestone boulders, mouth of Bonnet River, L. Gill, JW Fitzgerald (Paton 1966: 187).
H31 1967: wall of old Abbey, Drogheda, DM Synnott (DBN), det. JA Paton (Long 1999b: 27).
[H32 var. *simplicior* deleted because voucher specimen (1900: Castlesham, CH Waddell, NMW) is var. *cordaeana* (Long 1990a: 28)].
H(32) listed by Macvicar (1905: 21). H(32) listed by Blockeel & Long (1998: 52).
H(33) listed by Blockeel & Long (1998: 52).
H36 1953: sandstone rocks, Adairs Quarry, Cookstown, MPH Kertland & EM Lobley (Castell 1955: 581).
H37 1967: stones in side of ditch, Killevy Old Church, Slieve Gullion, JW Fitzgerald & MPH Kertland (Paton 1968: 627).
[H38 var. *simplicior* deleted because no localised record or voucher traced, comm. MM Yeo (Long 1990a: 28)].
H(38) listed by Macvicar (1905: 21). H(38) listed by Blockeel & Long (1998: 52).
H(39) listed by Macvicar (1905: 21).
[H39 var. *simplicior* deleted because voucher specimen (1898: Colin Glen, CH Waddell, DBN) is var. *cordaeana* (Long 1990a: 28)].
†H39 listed by Blockeel & Long (1998: 52).
H40 1966: on wet basalt rocks, Knockloughrim Orange Hall, *ca* 3 miles SE of Maghera, JW Fitzgerald (Paton 1967c: 403).

53/3 ***Porella arboris-vitae*** (With.) Grolle (syn. *Madotheca laevigata* (Schrad.) Dumort., *Porella arboris-vitae* var. *killarniensis* (Pearson) M.F.V.Corley, *Porella arboris-vitae* var. *obscura* (Nees) M.F.V.Corley, *P. laevigata* (Schrad.) Pfeiff.)

H(1) listed by Macvicar (1905: 21).
†H1 listed by Blockeel & Long (1998: 52).
H(2) listed by Macvicar (1905: 21).
†H2 listed by Blockeel & Long (1998: 52).
H(3) listed by Macvicar (1905: 21). H(3) listed by Blockeel & Long (1998: 52).
H(5) 1851: Templemichael Glen, I Carroll (BEL) (Paton 1967c: 403).
H6 1961: shaded rocks by stream below Coumshingaun, Comeragh Mts, DA Ratcliffe (Paton 1962: 363).
H7 1966: rocks on cliff above L. Muskry, Galtee Mts, ERB Little (BBS exc.) (Paton 1967c: 403).

H9 1951: woodland below cliffs, Slieve Carran, H Milne-Redhead (Castell 1952: 96).
H16 1957: rocks, Muckanaght, Twelve Pins, RE Parker (Castell 1958: 468).
H(20) listed by Macvicar (1905: 21).
†H20 listed by Blockeel & Long (1998: 52).
H23 1978: limestone rock, Hare I., Lough Ree, J Russell comm. PH Pitkin (Corley 1979: 25).
H26 1966: limestone pavement by L. Mask, E end of bridge leading to Inishcoog, G Halliday & GCG Argent (Paton 1967c: 403).
H27 1968: boulders beside L. Cullin, W of Foxford, JA Paton (Paton 1969a: 875).
H(28) 1928: Gleniff, Ben Bulben (BBS exc.) (Duncan 1928: 118).
†H28 listed by Blockeel & Long (1998: 52).
H(29) 1928: wooded glen, NE end of Glencar Lough (BBS exc.) (Duncan 1928: 118).
†H29 listed by Blockeel & Long (1998: 52).
H(30) 1909: Lenliss Hill, WN Tetley (BBSUK) (Castell 1953: 303).
H30 1966: under trees in heavy shade, E shore of Lough Gowna, ALK King (DBN) (Long 1999b: 28).
H(33) 1909: Belmore Crags, WN Tetley (BBSUK) (Castell 1953: 303).
H33 1951: cliffs, Knockmore, H Milne-Redhead (Castell 1953: 303).
H(34) 1937: lime rocks, Erne Valley, no collector named (BBS exc.) (Armitage 1938: 13).
1937: Erne Valley, E Armitage (anon. 1938c: 37).
H35 1951: Slieve League, alt. *ca* 1300 ft, H Milne-Redhead, conf. EW Jones (Castell 1952: 96).
[H(36) listed by Macvicar (1905: 21)].
H(39) listed by Macvicar (1905: 21).
†H39 listed by Blockeel & Long (1998: 52).
H40 1952: wet rock beside waterfall, Downhill, JW Fitzgerald (Castell 1953: 303).

53/4 ***Porella obtusata*** (Taylor) Trevis.
(syn. *Madotheca thuja* auct. non (Dicks.) Dumort., *Porella thuja* auct. Non (Dicks.) Lindb.)

H(1) listed by Macvicar (1905: 21).
†H1 listed by Blockeel & Long (1998: 52).
H(2) listed by Macvicar (1905: 21).
†H2 listed by Blockeel & Long (1998: 52).
H(3) listed by Macvicar (1905: 21).
†H3 listed by Blockeel & Long (1998: 52).
H5 1956: S facing wall, hill above Youghal, EC Wallace (Castell 1957: 326).
H(6) listed by Macvicar (1905: 21).
†H6 listed by Blockeel & Long (1998: 52).
H8 1966: basalt rocks, Knockseefin, Pallas Green, JW Fitzgerald & JG Duckett (BBS exc.) (Paton 1967c: 403).
H16 1951: dry rocks by shore, Bunowen Hill, H Milne-Redhead (Castell 1952: 96).
H18 1962: on basalt, Croghan Hill, Offaly, ALK King (Paton 1963: 490).
H(20) listed by Macvicar (1905: 21).
†H20 listed by Blockeel & Long (1998: 52).
H27 1965: on stones in dried up stream bed nr L. Aun, Currane Achill, DF Chamberlain (Paton 1966: 187).
H34 2002: on unshaded sloping quartzite rock on low coastal headland, *ca* 7 m [alt.], Culoort, NW of Malin, C45, DT Holyoak 02-572 (Blackstock 2003: 43).
H35 1998: on steep side of boulder in unshaded river, 10 m alt., Lackagh River, Glen Lough, 9 km W of Millford, B02, A Orange 11753 (Blackstock 1999: 38).
H(38) 1910: Kirkcubbin, J Glover (anon. 1911d: 16), labelled as *Madotheca platyphylla* but redet. as *M. thuja* by SJ Owen.
1914: Ballyhalbert, HW Lett (DBN), comm. JW Fitzgerald (Castell 1959: 630).
H(39) listed by Macvicar (1905: 21). H(39) listed by Blockeel & Long (1998: 52).

53/5 ***Porella pinnata*** L.
(syn. *Madotheca porella* (Dicks.) Nees)

†H1 listed by Blockeel & Long (1998: 52).
†H2 listed by Blockeel & Long (1998: 52).
H4 1966: partially submerged on rock in stream, Owenagearagh R. below Cloghroe, MFV Corley & JS Parker (Paton 1967c: 403).
H(5) listed by Blockeel & Long (1998: 52).
H5 2002: on tree roots at edge of stream, 40 m alt., Glenbower Wood, near Killeagh, W97, TL Blockeel 31/308 (Blackstock 2003: 43).
H6 1966: Owennashad R., N of Lismore, J Appleyard & JG Duckett (BBS exc.) (Paton 1967c: 403).
H9 1968: stones in stream by R. Fergus,

Elmvale House, W of Killinaboy, AR Perry (Paton 1969a: 875).

H10 1972: rocks on N bank of river, Clare Glen, D Kelly (Paton 1973b: 506).

H12 1975: alder trunks nr R. Bann, Camolin, JA Paton (BBS exc.) (Paton 1976: 21).

H13 1999: on rock and tree roots near water level on shaded stream bank, *ca* 35 m alt., N bank of Pollymounty River, Ballyknockcrumpin, S73, TL Blockeel 28/308 (Blackstock 2000: 43).

H15 1957: shaded moist rocks in calcareous stream, nr Punch Bowl, 1 mile S of Gort, RE Parker (Castell 1958: 469).

†H20 listed by Blockeel & Long (1998: 52).

H28 1965: boulders at water level, L. Gill, Slish Wood, JW Fitzgerald & EM Lobley (Paton 1966: 188).

H30 1955: rocky cleft by river, State Forest, Virginia, ALK King (Castell 1956: 150).

H37 1966: boulders in stream, Ballinasack Bridge nr Forkhill, JW Fitzgerald & MPH Kertland (Paton 1967c: 403).

54/1 ***Frullania tamarisci*** (L.) Dumort.
(syn. *Frullania tamarisci* var. *atrovirens* Carrington, *F. tamarisci* var. *cornubica* Carrington, *F. tamarisci* var. *robusta* Lindb.)

H(1) listed by Macvicar (1905: 23).

†H1 listed by Blockeel & Long (1998: 52).

H(2) listed by Macvicar (1905: 23).

†H2 listed by Blockeel & Long (1998: 52).

H3 1968: sheltered rocks in ravine, NE slope of Lackawee, Slieve Miskish Mts, JA Paton (Paton 1969a: 876), as var. *cornubica*.

H4 1967: rocks by Shournagh R., nr Blarney, JW Fitzgerald (Paton 1968: 628), as var. *robusta*.

H5 1956: rock in old quarry, Youghal, EC Wallace (Castell 1957: 326).

H(6) listed by Macvicar (1905: 23).

H6 1966: cliffs above Sgilloge Loughs, Comeragh Mts, JA Paton (BBS exc.) (Paton 1967c: 405), as var. *robusta*.
1972: basic conglomerate, Coumshingaun L., Comeragh Mts, WV Rubers (Paton 1974b: 164), as var. *cornubica*.

H(7) listed by Macvicar (1905: 23).

H7 1966: boulders beside stream E of Knockastackeen, Galtee Mts, JA Paton *et al.* (BBS exc.) (Paton 1967c: 405), as var. *robusta*.
1966: rocks by L. Curra, Galtee Mts, J Appleyard & JA Paton (BBS exc.) (Paton 1967c: 405), as var. *cornubica*.

H(8) listed by Macvicar (1905: 23).

H(9) listed by Macvicar (1905: 23).

†H8 listed by Blockeel & Long (1998: 52).

†H9 listed by Blockeel & Long (1998: 52).

H10 1951: ledges of recently disused slate quarry, alt. 500 ft, hills between Ballina and Newtown, AD Banwell, EV Watson & PJ Wanstall (Castell 1952: 96).

H11 1954: tree trunk in wood, Graiguenamanagh, ALK King (Castell 1955: 582).

H(12) listed by Macvicar (1905: 23).

†H12 listed by Blockeel & Long (1998: 52).

H(13) listed by Macvicar (1905: 23).

H13 1969: rocks in old quarry, Lackan nr Old Leighlin, JW Fitzgerald (Paton 1970: 194), as var. *robusta*.

H(14) listed by Macvicar (1905: 23).

†H14 listed by Blockeel & Long (1998: 52).

H(15) listed by Macvicar (1905: 23).

†H15 listed by Blockeel & Long (1998: 52).

H(16) listed by Macvicar (1905: 23).

H16 1957: Lissoughter Mt., E of Twelve Pins, J Appleyard (BBS exc.) (Castell 1960: 769), as var. *cornubica*.
1970: rocks in old quarry 1 mile E of Clifden, JA Paton (Paton 1971a: 373), as var. *robusta*.

H(17) 1896: oakwood, Clonbrock, D McArdle (DBN), comm. ALK King (Paton 1964: 721).

†H17 listed by Blockeel & Long (1998: 52).

H(18) listed by Macvicar (1905: 23).

†H18 listed by Blockeel & Long (1998: 52).

H20 1975: large boulder in Vartry R., Devil's Glen, Ashford, JA Paton (Paton 1976: 21), as var. *cornubica*.

H(20) listed by Macvicar (1905: 23).

H(21) no date: Lambay I., D McArdle [*Irish Nat.* **16**, 103, 1907] (Castell 1955: 582).

H21 1951: granite, Kilmashogue Mt., ALK King (Castell 1953: 304).

H(22) listed by Macvicar (1905: 23).

†H22 listed by Blockeel & Long (1998: 52).

H23 1979: limestone quarry, S of Crazy Corner, Mullingar, DM Synnott (Corley 1982: 23).

H24 1965: on boulders at 800 ft alt., Cornhill nr Drumlish, JW Fitzgerald & EM Lobley (Paton 1966: 188), as var. *robusta*.

H25 1960: in Rockingham Woods, Boyle, ALK King (Paton 1961: 157).
H(26) listed by Macvicar (1905: 23).
†H26 listed by Blockeel & Long (1998: 52).
H(27) listed by Macvicar (1905: 23).
H27 1970: rocks in ravine, S slope Ben Gorm, N of Killary Harbour, JA Paton (Paton 1971a: 373), as var. *robusta*.
H(28) listed by Macvicar (1905: 23).
H28 1963: siliceous rocks at 1000 ft alt., S of Knockachree, Slieve Gamph, AR Perry & JW Fitzgerald (Paton 1964: 721), as var. *cornubica*.
1969: boulder beside path, Slish Wood, SE of Sligo, JA Paton (Paton 1970: 194), as var. *robusta*.
H(29) listed by Macvicar (1905: 23).
H29 1969: limestone crags, Peakadaw, Glenade, JA Paton (Paton 1970: 194), as var. *cornubica*.
H(30) listed by Macvicar (1905: 23).
H30 1965: ash bole, Moneygashel Fort nr Blacklion, AR Perry & ER Warburg (Paton 1966: 188), as var. *robusta*.
H31 1951: abundant on stone wall, Flurry Bridge, JW Fitzgerald (Castell 1957: 326).
1963: on siliceous rock nr the sea, Clogher Head, DM Synnott (Paton 1965a: 858).
H32 1954: tree trunk, Glaslough Woods, ALK King (Castell 1955: 582).
H(33) 1911: Claddagh [*sic* = Cladagh], Florence Court, WN Tetley (BBSUK) (Castell 1954: 477).
H33 1959: on trees, Correll Glen, JW Fitzgerald (Castell 1960: 769), as var. *robusta*.
H(34) listed by Macvicar (1905: 23).
H34 1967: rocks above L. Inn, Innishowen [*sic* = Inishowen], JW Fitzgerald (Paton 1968: 628), as var. *robusta*.
1969: on bryophytes on schist rocks, Bulbin Mt., Inishowen, JA Paton (Paton 1971a: 373), as var. *cornubica*.
H35 1950: beside river, Lough Veagh, JW Fitzgerald (Castell 1951: 496).
1950: on oak, Barnes Gap, nr Creeslough, JW Fitzgerald (Castell 1951: 496), as var. *cornubica*.
H36 1951: mica schist, alt. 900 ft, with var. *robusta*, Gortin Gap nr Omagh, JW Fitzgerald (Castell 1952: 96).
1951: abundant on same rock as *F. tamarisci*, mica schist, alt. 900 ft, Gortin Gap nr Omagh, JW Fitzgerald (Castell 1952: 96), as var. *robusta*.
H(37) listed by Macvicar (1905: 23).
†H37 listed by Blockeel & Long (1998: 52).
H(38) listed by Macvicar (1905: 23). H(38) listed by Blockeel & Long (1998: 52).
H38 1999: on bole of oak tree, *ca* 55 m alt., Tollymore Forest Park, *ca* 4 km W of Newcastle, J33, TL Blockeel & DH Wrench 28/334 (Blackstock 2000: 43).
H(39) listed by Macvicar (1905: 23).
H39 1967: rocks, Long Mt., Rasharkin, JW Fitzgerald (Paton 1968: 628), as var. *robusta*.
H(40) listed by Macvicar (1905: 23).
H40 1964: on rocks at 1500 ft alt., Benbradagh nr Dungiven, JW Fitzgerald (Paton 1967c), as var. *cornubica*.

54/2 ***Frullania teneriffae*** (F.Weber) Nees (syn. *Frullania germana* (Tayl.) Gottsche, Lindenb. & Nees)

H(1) listed by Macvicar (1905: 23).
†H1 listed by Blockeel & Long (1998: 52).
H(2) listed by Macvicar (1905: 23).
†H2 listed by Blockeel & Long (1998: 52).
H(3) listed by Macvicar (1905: 23).
†H3 listed by Blockeel & Long (1998: 52).
H4 1966: on birch trunks at 1200 ft alt., E side of Musherabeg, MFV Corley & JS Parker (Paton 1967c: 405).
H6 1966: boulders beside Coumshingaun L. Comeragh Mts, JA Paton (BBS exc.) (Paton 1967c: 405).
H8 1966: on basalt rocks, Knockroe nr Caherconlish, MFV Corley & JS Parker (Paton 1967c: 405).
H(9) listed by Macvicar (1905: 23).
†H9 listed by Blockeel & Long (1998: 52).
†H16 listed by Blockeel & Long (1998: 52).
H17 1966: on tree stumps in grass field, Derreen N of Monivea, MFV Corley & JS Parker (Paton 1967c: 405).
H18 1962: on basalt on Croghan Hill, Offaly, ALK King (Paton 1963: 491).
H19 1954: on boulder, hillside facing SE, alt. 700 ft, Glending, Kildare side of road, ALK King (Castell 1955: 582).
H(20) listed by Macvicar (1905: 23).
†H20 listed by Blockeel & Long (1998: 52).
H21 2001: on vertical rock face in cove, *ca* 20 m alt., Howth Peninsula, N of Baily Lighthouse, O23, TL Blockeel 30/255 (Blackstock: 2002: 40).

H22 1978: rocks E of Carnbane West, Oldcastle, DM Synnott (Corley 1980a: 32).
H25 2002: epiphytic on willow growing out of crevices in NE-facing crags, *ca* 150 m alt., Kilronan Mt., Arigna, G91, NG Hodgetts 4159 (Blackstock 2003: 43).
H26 1957: on pine trees, nr Lough Carra, RE Parker (Castell 1958: 470).
H(27) listed by Macvicar (1905: 23).
†H27 listed by Blockeel & Long (1998: 52).
H(28) 1937: Ben Bulben, no collector named (BBS exc.) (Armitage 1938: 13).
†H28 listed by Blockeel & Long (1998: 52).
H(29) 1913: rocks, L. Melvin, WN Tetley (BBSUK) (Castell 1954: 477).
†H29 listed by Blockeel & Long (1998: 52).
H(30) listed by Macvicar (1905: 23).
†H30 listed by Blockeel & Long (1998: 52).
H31 1965: on Silurian rock, Clogher Head E of pier, DM Synnott (Paton 1966: 189).
†H33 listed by Blockeel & Long (1998: 52).
H34 1967: trees below Illies Hill, E of Buncrana, JW Fitzgerald (Paton 1968: 628).
H(35) listed by Macvicar (1905: 23).
†H35 listed by Blockeel & Long (1998: 52).
H36 1957: on trees nr stream, Sheskinawaddy, nr Castlederg, JW Fitzgerald (Castell 1959: 630).
[H38 record discounted (Birks & Ratcliffe 1976a, Paton 1977a: 16)].
H(39) listed by Macvicar (1905: 23).
†H39 listed by Blockeel & Long (1998: 52).
H40 1952: rocks, Benevenagh, EW Jones (Castell 1953: 304).

54/3a ***Frullania microphylla*** (Gottsche) Pearson **var.** ***microphylla***

H(1) listed by Macvicar (1905: 23).
†H1 listed by Blockeel & Long (1998: 53).
H(2) listed by Macvicar (1905: 23).
†H2 listed by Blockeel & Long (1998: 53).
H(3) listed by Macvicar (1905: 23).
†H3 listed by Blockeel & Long (1998: 53).
H6 1999: on vertical surface of small crag on coastal cliff, *ca* 50 m alt., Mine Head, *ca* 11 km S of Dungarvan, X28, TL Blockeel 28/219 (Blackstock 2000: 43).
H(7) listed by Macvicar (1905: 23).
†H7 listed by Blockeel & Long (1998: 53).
H16 1951: loose stone wall nr Slyne Head, H Milne-Redhead (Castell 1952: 96).
H(27) listed by Macvicar (1905: 23).
†H27 listed by Blockeel & Long (1998: 53).
H28 1967: shaded boulders by L. Gill, HH Birks, HJB Birks & DA Ratcliffe (Paton 1968: 629).
H29 1967: shaded dry N-facing limestone cliffs, Peakadaw, Glenade, HH Birks, HJB Birks & DA Ratcliffe (Paton 1968: 629).
H33 1959: closely appressed to NW-facing rock face, at 900 ft [alt.], Rossinure More, JW Fitzgerald (Castell 1960: 769).
H(34) listed by Macvicar (1905: 23).
†H34 listed by Blockeel & Long (1998: 53).
H(35) listed by Macvicar (1905: 23).
†H35 listed by Blockeel & Long (1998: 53).
H39 1999: on vertical N-facing dolerite at base of crags, Fair Head, D14, DT Holyoak 99-784B (BBSUK) (Blackstock 2000: 43).
H40 1990: on vertical rock-face, at base of W-facing cliffs, Binevenagh, DM Synnott (Long 1991: 39).

54/4 ***Frullania fragilifolia*** (Taylor) Gottsche, Lindenb. & Nees

H(1) listed by Macvicar (1905: 23).
†H1 listed by Blockeel & Long (1998: 53).
H(2) listed by Macvicar (1905: 23).
†H2 listed by Blockeel & Long (1998: 53).
H(3) listed by Macvicar (1905: 23).
†H3 listed by Blockeel & Long (1998: 53).
H6 1966: rock by stream below Coumshingaun L., Comeragh Mts, JG Duckett *et al.* (BBS exc.) (Paton 1967c: 405).
[H(7) listed by Macvicar (1905: 23). H7 deleted because no record or voucher traced, comm. MM Yeo (Long 1990a: 28)].
H16 1957: on pine, Kylemore, J Appleyard & AC Crundwell (BBS exc.) (Castell 1958: 470).
H(20) listed by Macvicar (1905: 23).
†H20 listed by Blockeel & Long (1998: 53).
H21 2001: on vertical rock face in cove, *ca* 20 m alt., Howth Peninsula, N of Baily Lighthouse, O23, TL Blockeel 30/256 (Blackstock: 2002: 40).
H(27) listed by Macvicar (1905: 23).
†H27 listed by Blockeel & Long (1998: 53).
†H29 listed by Blockeel & Long (1998: 53).
H(33) 1905: on alders, shore of Lough Erne nr Church Hill, D McArdle (*Irish Nat.* **16**,

237, 1907), comm. JW Fitzgerald (Castell 1952: 97).
†H33 listed by Blockeel & Long (1998: 53).
H34 1968: rocks by the sea, Tremone Bay, SE of Culdaff, Inishowen, HH Birks & JW Fitzgerald (Paton 1970: 194).
H(35) listed by Macvicar (1905: 23).
†H35 listed by Blockeel & Long (1998: 53).
H(36) 1887: HW Lett (NMW) (Paton 1970: 194).
H(38) listed by Macvicar (1905: 23). H(38) listed by Blockeel & Long (1998: 53).
H(39) listed by Macvicar (1905: 23).
†H39 listed by Blockeel & Long (1998: 53).
H40 1968:basalt rocks at 1000 ft alt., Benevenagh, HH Birks & JW Fitzgerald (Paton 1970: 194).

54/5 ***Frullania dilatata*** (L.) Dumort.

H(1) listed by Macvicar (1905: 23).
†H1 listed by Blockeel & Long (1998: 53).
H(2) listed by Macvicar (1905: 23).
†H2 listed by Blockeel & Long (1998: 53).
H(3) listed by Macvicar (1905: 23).
†H3 listed by Blockeel & Long (1998: 53).
H4 1951: trunk of roadside tree, NW of Mallow, AC Crundwell (Castell 1952: 97).
†H5 listed by Blockeel & Long (1998: 53).
H(6) listed by Macvicar (1905: 23).
†H6 listed by Blockeel & Long (1998: 53).
†H7 listed by Blockeel & Long (1998: 53).
H(8) listed by Macvicar (1905: 23).
†H8 listed by Blockeel & Long (1998: 53).
H(9) listed by Macvicar (1905: 23).
†H9 listed by Blockeel & Long (1998: 53).
H10 1951: face of recently disused slate quarry, alt. 500 ft, hills between Ballina and Newtown, AD Banwell, EV Watson & PJ Wanstall (Castell 1952: 97).
H11 1952: Farmley Wood, nr Cuffe's Grange, ALK King & MPH Kertland (Castell 1953: 304).
H(12) listed by Macvicar (1905: 23).
†H12 listed by Blockeel & Long (1998: 53).
H(13) listed by Macvicar (1905: 23).
†H13 listed by Blockeel & Long (1998: 53).
H(14) listed by Macvicar (1905: 23).
†H14 listed by Blockeel & Long (1998: 53).
H(15) listed by Macvicar (1905: 23).
†H15 listed by Blockeel & Long (1998: 53).
†H16 listed by Blockeel & Long (1998: 53).
H17 1957: on alders in small wood 5 miles S of Headford, AC Crundwell (BBS exc.) (Castell 1958: 470).
[H(18) listed by Macvicar (1905: 23). H18 deleted because no record traced, comm. MM Yeo, replaced by next record (Long 1990a: 28)].
H(18) 1949: Elm tree in copse at Black Bull, Sharavogue, AP Fanning (DBN), comm. DM Synnott (Long 1990a: 28).
H(19) listed by Macvicar (1905: 23).
†H19 listed by Blockeel & Long (1998: 53).
H(20) listed by Macvicar (1905: 23).
†H20 listed by Blockeel & Long (1998: 53).
H(21) listed by Macvicar (1905: 23).
†H21 listed by Blockeel & Long (1998: 53).
H(22) listed by Macvicar (1905: 23).
†H22 listed by Blockeel & Long (1998: 53).
†H23 listed by Blockeel & Long (1998: 53).
H24 1957: on hawthorn, Ballymacarrow Bridge, MPH Kerland & ALK King, comm. ALK King (Castell 1958: 470).
H(25) 1949: by well, roadside nr Roscommon Town, ALK King (Castell 1953: 304).
†H25 listed by Blockeel & Long (1998: 53).
H(26) listed by Macvicar (1905: 23).
†H26 listed by Blockeel & Long (1998: 53).
H(27) listed by Macvicar (1905: 23).
†H27 listed by Blockeel & Long (1998: 53).
H(28) listed by Macvicar (1905: 23).
†H28 listed by Blockeel & Long (1998: 53).
H(29) listed by Macvicar (1905: 23).
H29 1972: siliceous outcrop, E end of L. Gill N of Dromahair, WV Rubers (Paton 1974b: 165).
H(30) listed by Macvicar (1905: 23).
†H30 listed by Blockeel & Long (1998: 53).
H(31) listed by Macvicar (1905: 23). H(31) listed by Blockeel & Long (1998: 53).
H32 1954: on poplar, woods, Glaslough Ho. [use], ALK King (Castell 1955: 582).
†H33 listed by Blockeel & Long (1998: 53).
†H34 listed by Blockeel & Long (1998: 53).
H35 1962: rock nr the sea opposite Cruit I., The Rosses, EF Warburg (BBS exc.) (Paton 1963: 491).
†H36 listed by Blockeel & Long (1998: 53).
H(37) listed by Macvicar (1905: 23).
†H37 listed by Blockeel & Long (1998: 53).
H(38) listed by Macvicar (1905: 23).
†H38 listed by Blockeel & Long (1998: 53).
H(39) listed by Macvicar (1905: 23).
†H39 listed by Blockeel & Long (1998: 53).
H40 1951: growing with *Metzgeria furcata*, Downhill nr Castlerock, JW Fitzgerald (Castell 1952: 97).

55/1 ***Jubula hutchinsiae*** (Hook.) Dumort. (syn. *Jubula hutchinsiae* var. *integrifolia* Moore)

H(1) listed by Macvicar (1905: 22).
†H1 listed by Blockeel & Long (1998: 53).
H(2) listed by Macvicar (1905: 22).
†H2 listed by Blockeel & Long (1998: 53).
H(3) listed by Macvicar (1905: 22).
†H3 listed by Blockeel & Long (1998: 53).
H(4) listed by Macvicar (1905: 22). H(4) listed by Blockeel & Long (1998: 53).
H4 2002: one large patch on vertical rock face in small stream, 10 m alt., E bank of River Brandon, *ca* 3 km SE of Inishannon, W55, TL Blockeel 31/375 (Blackstock 2003: 43).
H6 1961: shady recesses amongst rocks in cascading stream below Coumshingaun, Comeragh Mts, DA Ratcliffe (Paton 1962: 364).
H8 1979: NE side of Knockanimpaha and Sugar Hill, W of Newcastle West, HMH van Melick (Corley 1981: 21).
H(16) listed by Macvicar (1905: 22).
†H16 listed by Blockeel & Long (1998: 53).
H(20) listed by Macvicar (1905: 22).
†H20 listed by Blockeel & Long (1998: 53).
H(27) listed by Macvicar (1905: 22).
†H27 listed by Blockeel & Long (1998: 53).
H28 1967: shaded dripping hole on N slopes of Knockachree, Slieve Gamph, HH Birks, HJB Birks & DA Ratcliffe (Paton 1968: 628).
H29 1967: wet shaded rocks nr Glencar L., HH Birks, HJB Birks & DA Ratcliffe (Paton 1967: 628).
H34 1967: wet rocks by stream, Red Castle Glen, L. Foyle, JW Fitzgerald (Paton 1968: 628).
H35 1951: W side, Lough Eske, H Milne-Redhead (Castell 1952: 96).
H36 1958: base of mossy boulder beside stream in shaded glen, Altadavan, nr Favor Royal, JW Fitzgerald (Castell 1959: 630).
H(38) listed by Macvicar (1905: 22).
†H38 listed by Blockeel & Long (1998: 53).
†H39 listed by Blockeel & Long (1998: 53).

56/1 ***Marchesinia mackaii*** (Hook.) Gray

H(1) listed by Macvicar (1905: 22).
†H1 listed by Blockeel & Long (1998: 53).
H(2) listed by Macvicar (1905: 22).
†H2 listed by Blockeel & Long (1998: 53).
H(3) listed by Macvicar (1905: 22).
†H3 listed by Blockeel & Long (1998: 53).
H(4) listed by Macvicar (1905: 22).
†H4 listed by Blockeel & Long (1998: 53).
H(5) 1852: nr Fermoy, T Chandlee (DBN), comm. ALK King (Paton 1964: 721).
H6 1972: basic conglomerate at 1500 ft alt., Coumshingaun L., Comeragh Mts, WV Rubers (Paton 1974b: 164).
H7 1966: limestone rocks in quarry, Ardfinnan, JA Paton, GCG Argent & ERB Little (BBS exc.) (Paton 1967c: 403).
H8 1967: dry slightly basic outcrops in steep N-facing wooded valley, Clare Glen, nr Newport, HJB Birks & DA Ratcliffe (Paton 1968: 627).
H(9) listed by Macvicar (1905: 22).
†H9 listed by Blockeel & Long (1998: 53).
H10 1967: slightly basic outcrops by small waterfall in wooded valley, Clare Glen nr Newport, HH Birks, HJB Birks & DA Ratcliffe (Paton 1968: 627).
H11 1991: on cliffy slope on Devonian old red sandstone, in small wood of mixed broadleaved species, 0.5 miles SW of Thomastown, S54, DL Kelly & RN Goodwillie (Long 1993b: 46).
H14 1980: on bark, Clopook Wood, nr Timahoe, DL Kelly (Corley 1981: 21).
H15 1957: with *Metzgeria furcata* var. *fruticulosa*, on tree, Garryland Woods, nr Gort, EM Lobley (BBS exc.) (Castell 1958: 470).
1957: shaded rocks by calcareous stream, nr Punch Bowl, 1 mile S of Gort, RE Parker (Castell 1958: 470).
H(16) listed by Macvicar (1905: 22).
†H16 listed by Blockeel & Long (1998: 53).
H17 1950: on limestone, with *Bryum capillare* and *Brachythecium rutabulum*, nr Menlo, ALK King (Castell 1954: 477).
H(20) listed by Macvicar (1905: 22).
†H20 listed by Blockeel & Long (1998: 53).
H(21) listed by Macvicar (1905: 22). H(21) listed by Blockeel & Long (1998: 53).
H(22) 1912: Beauparc, HW Lett (DBN), comm. ALK King (Paton 1964: 721).
†H22 listed by Blockeel & Long (1998: 53).
H23 1957: limestone, Hill of Fore, ALK King (Castell 1958: 470).
H26 1951: wood, Lough Carra, H Milne-Redhead (Castell 1952: 96).

†H27 listed by Blockeel & Long (1998: 53).
H(28) 1928: rocks above Glencar Lough, N side (BBS exc.) (Duncan 1928: 119).
†H28 listed by Blockeel & Long (1998: 53).
H(29) 1918: Kinlough Mt., WN Tetley (BBSUK)(Castell 1953: 304).
1928: wooded glen, NE end of Glencar Lough (BBS exc.) (Duncan 1928: 118, Castell 1953: 304).
†H29 listed by Blockeel & Long (1998: 53).
H31 1966: vertical rock by Two-mile R., Carlingford Mt., DM Synnott (Paton 1967c: 403).
H(33) 1913: Belmore crags, WN Tetley (BBSUK) (Castell 1953: 304).
H33 1951: Knockmore, H Milne-Redhead (Castell 1952: 96).
H(34) 1937: lime rocks, Erne Valley, no collector named (BBS exc.) (Armitage 1938: 13).
1937: rocks, Erne Valley, E Armitage (anon. 1938c: 38).
H35 1962: rock in crevice nr Mullaghderg Lough, The Rosses, EF Warburg (BBS exc.) (Paton 1963: 491).
H(38) listed by Macvicar (1905: 22). H(38) listed by Blockeel & Long (1998: 53).
H(39) listed by Macvicar (1905: 22).
†H39 listed by Blockeel & Long (1998: 53).
H40 1968: basalt rocks at 1000 ft alt., Benevenagh, JW Fitzgerald (Paton 1969a: 875).

57/1 ***Drepanolejeunea hamatifolia*** (Hook.) Schiffn.

H(1) listed by Macvicar (1905: 22).
†H1 listed by Blockeel & Long (1998: 53).
H(2) listed by Macvicar (1905: 22).
†H2 listed by Blockeel & Long (1998: 53).
†H3 listed by Blockeel & Long (1998: 53).
H4 1966: on trunk of sallow in wood by Rathmore House nr Summercove, MFV Corley & JS Parker (Paton 1967c: 404).
H5 2002: plentifully on trunks of poplar trees, 110 m alt., banks of River Bride, Ardarou Wood, Glenville, W78, TL Blockeel 31/363 (Blackstock 2003: 43).
H6 1966: on laurel tree, thick woodland, Glendine Bridge nr Youghal, JG Duckett (BBS exc.) (Paton 1967c: 404).
H8 1975: hazel branch, wooded ravine, Glenistar, PH Pitkin (Paton 1976: 21).
H(9) listed by Macvicar (1905: 22).
†H9 listed by Blockeel & Long (1998: 53).
H(14) listed by Macvicar (1905: 22). H(14) listed by Blockeel & Long (1998: 53).
H15 1957: trees, Chevy Chase Forest, Owendalulleegh, nr Gort, RE Parker (Castell 1958: 470).
H(16) listed by Macvicar (1905: 22).
†H16 listed by Blockeel & Long (1998: 53).
H(17) listed by Macvicar (1905: 22). H(17) listed by Blockeel & Long (1998: 53).
H(20) listed by Macvicar (1905: 22). H(20) listed by Blockeel & Long (1998: 53).
H(21) listed by Macvicar (1905: 22). H(21) listed by Blockeel & Long (1998: 53).
H25 1968: trees on margin of St Johns Wood, 3 miles SE of Knockcroghery, WV Rubers, P Hessell & J Klein (Paton 1970: 194).
H26 1970: willow by pool W of the Pollagh R., NE of Balla, JA Paton (Paton 1971a: 373).
H(27) listed by Macvicar (1905: 22).
†H27 listed by Blockeel & Long (1998: 53).
H28 1965: boulders, Slish Wood. L. Gill, JW Fitzgerald & EM Lobley (Paton 1966: 188).
H(29) listed by Macvicar (1905: 22).
†H29 listed by Blockeel & Long (1998: 53).
H(31) listed by Macvicar (1905: 22). H(31) listed by Blockeel & Long (1998: 53).
H33 1957: rocks and organic debris on rocks, Correll Glen, nr Derrygonnelly (Castell 1958: 470).
H(34) listed by Macvicar (1905: 22). H(34) listed by Blockeel & Long (1998: 53).
H34 2001: willow bough in swampy woodland by lough, *ca* 20 m alt., NE of Lough Eske Bridge, G98, NG Hodgetts 3887 (Blackstock 2003: 43).
H(35) listed by Macvicar (1905: 22).
†H35 listed by Blockeel & Long (1998: 53).
H(38) listed by Macvicar (1905: 22). H(38) listed by Blockeel & Long (1998: 53).
H(39) listed by Macvicar (1905: 22).
†H39 listed by Blockeel & Long (1998: 53).
H40 1990: Big Cleft, Binevenagh, DM Synnott (Long 1991: 39).

58/1 ***Harpalejeunea molleri*** (Steph.) Grolle (syn. *Harpalejeunea ovata* auct. non (Hook.) Schiffn.)

H(1) listed by Macvicar (1905: 22).
†H1 listed by Blockeel & Long (1998: 53).
H(2) listed by Macvicar (1905: 22).
†H2 listed by Blockeel & Long (1998: 53).

H(3) listed by Macvicar (1905: 22).
†H3 listed by Blockeel & Long (1998: 53).
H(6) listed by Macvicar (1905: 22).
†H6 listed by Blockeel & Long (1998: 53).
†H7 listed by Blockeel & Long (1998: 53).
H(9) listed by Macvicar (1905: 22). H(9) listed by Blockeel & Long (1998: 53).
H15 1957: Chevy Chase, nr Gort, J Appleyard (Castell 1958: 470).
†H16 listed by Blockeel & Long (1998: 53).
H(27) listed by Macvicar (1905: 22).
†H27 listed by Blockeel & Long (1998: 53).
H28 1967: shaded rocks, N slopes of Knockachree, Slieve Gamph, HH Birks, HJB Birks & DA Ratcliffe (Paton 1968: 628).
†H29 listed by Blockeel & Long (1998: 53).
H33 1959: with *Drepanolejeunea hamatifolia* and *Lejeunea ulicina*, on old hazel tree overhanging R. Cladagh, nr Marble Arch, JW Fitzgerald (Castell 1960: 768).
H(34) listed by Blockeel & Long (1998: 53).
H(35) listed by Macvicar (1905: 22).
†H35 listed by Blockeel & Long (1998: 53).
H(38) listed by Macvicar (1905: 22). H(38) listed by Blockeel & Long (1998: 53).
H(39) listed by Macvicar (1905: 22). H(39) listed by Blockeel & Long (1998: 53).
H40 1990: rock face in Big Cleft, Binevenagh, DM Synnott (Long 1991: 39).

59/1 ***Microlejeunea ulicina*** (Taylor) A.Evans (syn. *Lejeunea ulicina* (Taylor) Gottsche, Lindenb. & Nees)

H(1) listed by Macvicar (1905: 22).
†H1 listed by Blockeel & Long (1998: 54).
H(2) listed by Macvicar (1905: 22).
†H2 listed by Blockeel & Long (1998: 54).
H3 1955: creeping over *Frullania* on willow, Coomhola Coppermine, H Milne-Redhead (Castell 1958: 470).
H(4) listed by Macvicar (1905: 22).
†H4 listed by Blockeel & Long (1998: 54).
H5 1956: on *Ulex europaeus*, wooded hillside, above Park House, Tourig R., nr Youghal, EC Wallace (Castell 1958: 470).
H(6) listed by Macvicar (1905: 22).
†H6 listed by Blockeel & Long (1998: 54).
H(7) listed by Macvicar (1905: 22).
†H7 listed by Blockeel & Long (1998: 54).
H9 1957: trunk of spruce, Tuamgraney Woods, ALK King (Castell 1958: 470). 1957: on *Prunus spinosa* in scrub, SW side of Slievecarran, AC Crundwell (BBS exc.) (Castell 1958: 470).
H10 1967: base of old larch trees, Knockfine, Keeper Hill, JW Fitzgerald (Paton 1968: 628).
H11 1954: on larch in plantation, R.[ight] bank of R. Barrow, above Graiguenamanagh, ALK King (Castell 1955: 582).
H(12) listed by Macvicar (1905: 22).
†H12 listed by Blockeel & Long (1998: 54).
H13 1999: on *Salix* in damp scrubby woodland, *ca* 35 m alt., N bank of Pollymounty River, Ballyknockcrumpin, S73, TL Blockeel 28/307 (Blackstock 2000: 44).
H(14) listed by Macvicar (1905: 22).
†H14 listed by Blockeel & Long (1998: 54).
H15 1957: trunks of spruce, Owendalulleegh, nr Gort, RE Parker (Castell 1958: 470).
H(16) listed by Macvicar (1905: 22).
†H16 listed by Blockeel & Long (1998: 54).
H(18) listed by Macvicar (1905: 22). H(18) listed by Blockeel & Long (1998: 54).
H(20) listed by Macvicar (1905: 22).
†H20 listed by Blockeel & Long (1998: 54).
H(21) listed by Macvicar (1905: 22). H(21) listed by Blockeel & Long (1998: 54).
H21 2001: on rhododendron bark in shelter of N-facing crag, *ca* 80 m alt., Muck Rock, Howth Peninsula, O23, TL Blockeel (Blackstock: 2002: 40).
H22 1978: on birch in wet woodland, Fletcherstown, DM Synnott (Corley 1982: 23).
H23 1970: shrubs on E shore of Killinure L., S of Glassan (Paton 1971a: 373).
H24 1965: trees in wood nr Cloonart Bridge S of Roosky, EM Lobley & JW Fitzgerald (Paton 1966: 188).
H(25) 1897: on *Frullania tamarisci*, Mote Park, Johnson (DBN), comm. ALK King (Paton 1964: 721).
†H25 listed by Blockeel & Long (1998: 54).
H26 1968: alders beside L. Corrib nr Cong Quay, JA Paton (Paton 1969a: 875).
H(27) listed by Macvicar (1905: 22).
†H27 listed by Blockeel & Long (1998: 54).
H(28) 1914: among *Frullania dilatata* and *Metzgeria furcata*, on tree, Slishwood, WN Tetley (BBSUK) (Castell 1954: 477).
†H28 listed by Blockeel & Long (1998: 54).
H(29) listed by Macvicar (1905: 22).

†H29 listed by Blockeel & Long (1998: 54).
H30 1956: on tree, shore of L. Ramor, Virginia, JS Thomson (Castell 1957: 326).
H31 1953: trunk of Scots Pine, Ravensdale State Forest, ALK King (Castell 1954: 477).
H32 1965: on bark of coniferous trees nr Cootehill, JW Fitzgerald & EM Lobley (Paton 1966: 188).
H(33) 1905: decayed logs, Correl Glen, D McArdle (*Irish Nat.* **16**, 237, 1907), comm. JW Fitzgerald (Castell 1952: 96).
†H33 listed by Blockeel & Long (1998: 54).
H34 1967: on *Calluna* stems in scree, Gap of Mamore, N of Buncrana, JW Fitzgerald (Paton 1968: 628).
H(35) listed by Macvicar (1905: 22).
†H35 listed by Blockeel & Long (1998: 54).
H36 1953: creeping over *Metzgeria*, on trees, Ranfurley Park, Dungannon, MPH Kertland & EM Lobley (Castell 1955: 582).
H37 1964: on trees in wood, Derrylee E of Verner's Bridge, JW Fitzgerald & MPH Kertland (Paton 1965a: 858).
H(38) listed by Macvicar (1905: 22). H(38) listed by Blockeel & Long (1998: 54).
H38 2002: *ca* 1.5 m above ground on almost unshaded bark of *Betula pubescens* tree beside clearing at edge of river, *ca* 95 m alt., by N bank of Shimna River just W of Parnell's Bridge, Tollymore Forest Park, J33, DT Holyoak 02-1034 (Blackstock 2003: 43).
H(39) listed by Macvicar (1905: 22).
†H39 listed by Blockeel & Long (1998: 54).
H40 1964: on birch trees, Altnaheglish, nr Dungiven, JW Fitzgerald (Paton 1965a: 858).

60/1 ***Lejeunea cavifolia*** (Ehrh.) Lindb. (syn. *Lejeunea cavifolia* var. *planiuscula* auct. non (Lindb.) Lindb.)

[H(1) listed by Macvicar (1905: 22)].
[H(1) no date: no locality, no collector named (anon. 1937b: 370), for *L. cavifolia* var. *planiuscula*. Record unacceptable without data].
H1 1966: rocks on NE side of Brandon Mt., Dingle, JA Paton (Paton 1968: 627).
[H(2) listed by Macvicar (1905: 22)].
[H(2) no date: no locality, WE Nicholson (anon. 1937b: 370). Record unacceptable without data].
H2 record confirmed (Paton 1963: 490). †H2 listed by Blockeel & Long (1998: 54).
[H(3) listed by Macvicar (1905: 22)].
H3 1967: wet rocks by river, Ballyfinnane Bridge, JW Fitzgerald (Paton 1968: 627).
H4 1967: trees in woods, Dripsey Castle, nr Cork, JW Fitzgerald (Paton 1968: 627).
H(5) no date: Templemichael Glen, I Carroll (DBN), comm. ALK King (Paton 1965a: 858).
H5 2002: on trunk of poplar tree, 110 m alt., banks of River Bride, Ardarou Wood, Glenville, W78, TL Blockeel 31/365 (Blackstock 2003: 44).
[H(6) listed by Macvicar (1905: 22)].
H6 1966: rock beside R. Nier nr Shanballyanne, JA Paton (BBS exc.) (Paton 1967c: 403).
[H(7) listed by Macvicar (1905: 22)].
H7 1966: rocks nr L. Curra, Galtee Mts, J Appleyard & JA Paton (BBS exc.) (Paton 1967c: 403).
[H(8) listed by Macvicar (1905: 22)].
H8 1979: *Salix* trunk near S bank of Clare R., Clare Glens, S of Newport, JA Paton (Corley 1980a: 31).
[H(9) listed by Macvicar (1905: 22)].
H10 1967: rocks in wooded valley, Clare Glen, nr Newport, HH Birks, HJB Birks & DA Ratcliffe (Paton 1968: 627).
[H(12) listed by Macvicar (1905: 22)].
[H(13) listed by Macvicar (1905: 22)]. H13 deleted because no record traced, comm. MM Yeo, replaced by next record (Long 1990a: 28)].
H13 H13 record confirmed (Paton 1964: 720). 1954: on rock by towpath, left bank of R. Barrow above Graiguenamanagh, ALK King, conf. JA Paton (Long 1990a: 28).
[H(14) listed by Macvicar (1905: 22)].
H14 1972: tree base in woodland, Abbeyleix, D Kelly (Paton 1973b: 506).
[H(15) listed by Macvicar (1905: 22)].
H15 1994: on ash tree in swampy woodland, Garryland Wood, M40, NG Hodgetts 2949 (Long 1995b: 39).
[H(16) listed by Macvicar (1905: 22)].
H16 1970: wet, slightly basic rocks, corrie on N side of Benbeg S of L. Nafooey, AR Perry & HJ Perry (Paton 1974b: 164).
H(17) 1896: oakwood, Clonbrock, D McArdle

(DBN), comm. ALK (Paton 1966: 720).
[H(18) listed by Macvicar (1905: 22)].
[H(20) listed by Macvicar (1905: 22)].
H20 record confirmed (Paton 1964: 720). †H20 listed by Blockeel & Long (1998: 54).
[H(21) listed by Macvicar (1905: 22)].
H21 record confirmed (Paton 1964: 720). †H21 listed by Blockeel & Long (1998: 54).
[H(22) listed by Macvicar (1905: 22)].
H23 1980: base of ash tree in estate woodland, Ballinlough Castle S of L. Shesk, Clonmellon, DM Synnott (Corley 1982: 23).
H25 1968: *Salix* on margin of St Johns Wood, 3 miles SE of Knockcroghery, WV Rubers, P Hessell & J Klein (Paton 1970: 193).
[H(26) listed by Macvicar (1905: 22)].
H26 1970: tree by pool W of the Pollagh R., NE of Balla, JA Paton (Paton 1971a: 373).
[H(27) listed by Macvicar (1905: 22)].
H27 record confirmed (Paton 1963: 490). †H27 listed by Blockeel & Long (1998: 54).
[H(28) listed by Macvicar (1905: 22)].
H28 1965: on boulders by L. Gill, Slish Wood, JW Fitzgerald & EM Lobley (Paton 1966: 188).
[H(29) listed by Macvicar (1905: 22)].
H29 record confirmed (Paton 1964: 720). †H29 listed by Blockeel & Long (1998: 54).
[H(30) listed by Macvicar (1905: 22)].
H30 2001: on mortared-stone wall of bridge over stream in deciduous woodland, partly shaded by trees, *ca* 95 m alt., Deerpark, W of Virginia, N58, DT Holyoak 01-663 (Blackstock: 2002: 40).
H33 1957: boulder in ravine of Cladagh R., Lough Macnean Lower, AC Crundwell (Castell 1958: 469). H33 record confirmed (Paton 1962: 363, 1963: 490).
[H(34) listed by Macvicar (1905: 22)].
H34 1967: on *Thamnium*, wet rocks, Red Castle Glen, L. Foyle, JW Fitzgerald (Paton 1968: 627).
H35 1950: river at Lough Veagh, JW Fitzgerald (Castell 1951: 495). H35 record confirmed (Paton 1963: 490).
H36 1957: moss covered tree by stream, Aghintain, nr Fivemiletown, JW Fitzgerald (Castell 1958: 469). H36 record confirmed (Paton 1962: 363, 1963: 490).
H37 1966: boulders in stream, Ballinasack Bridge nr Forkhill, JW Fitzgerald & MPH Kertland (Paton 1967c: 403).
[H(38) listed by Macvicar (1905: 22)].
[H(38) no date: no locality, JB Duncan (anon. 1937b: 370). Record unacceptable without data].
H38 record confirmed (Paton 1963: 490). †H38 listed by Blockeel & Long (1998: 54).
[H(39) listed by Macvicar (1905: 22)].
H39 1950: wet tree trunk, amongst moss, Lower Crow Glen, JW Fitzgerald (Castell 1951: 495). H39 record confirmed (Paton 1963: 490).
H40 1964: on rocks, Legananam Pot, nr Dungiven, JW Fitzgerald (Paton 1965a: 858).

Old records (e.g. from Macvicar 1905: 22) should not be accepted unless specimens have been reidentified.

60/2 ***Lejeunea lamacerina*** (Steph.) Schiffn. (syn. *Lejeunea cavifolia* var. *heterophylla* Carrington, *L. heterophylla* Carrington, *L. lamacerina* var. *azorica* (Steph.) Greig-Sm., *L. planiuscula* Lindb.)

[H(1) listed by Macvicar (1905: 22)].
H(1) 1936: Derrycunihy Woods, PWM Richards (anon. 1938e: 45), as *L. planiuscula*.
H1 listed (Greig-Smith 1954: 469), for var. *azorica* and var. *lamacerina*. †H1 listed by Blockeel & Long (1998: 54).
[H(2) listed by Macvicar (1905: 22)].
[H(2) no date: no locality, WE Nicholson (anon. 1937b: 370), as *L. planiuscula*. Record unacceptable without data].
H(2) 1935: among mosses, Muckross Demesne, nr Lower Lake, Killarney, DA Jones (BBSUK) (Castell 1955: 582), as var *azorica*.
H2 listed (Greig-Smith 1954: 469), for var. *lamacerina*. †H2 listed by Blockeel & Long (1998: 54).
H(3) 1936: Glengarriff, PWM Richards (anon. 1938e: 45), as *L. planiuscula*.
H3 H3 listed (Greig-Smith 1954: 469), for var. *lamacerina*.
1979: shaded rock, W side of Adrigole

harbour, JA Paton (Corley 1980a: 32), as var. *azorica*.

H4 1966: among mosses on bank by road in wood, Ringnanean Wood nr mouth of R. Stick, MFV Corley & Parker (Paton 1967c: 404), as var. *azorica*.

H5 1956: bank in lane, Youghal, EC Wallace (Castell 1958: 469).
1966: on rocks and mosses by R. Douglas nr Kilworth, JG Duckett (BBS exc.) (Paton 1967c: 404), as var. *azorica*.

H6 1956: bank in wood, Deelish, nr Dungarvan, EC Wallace (Castell 1958: 469-470), as var. *azorica*.
1961: shaded recesses amongst large blocks, nr stream below Coumshingaun, Comeragh Mts, DA Ratcliffe (Paton 1962: 363), as var. *azorica*.
1961: shaded recesses amongst large blocks nr stream below Coumshingaun, Comeragh Mts, DA Ratcliffe (Paton 1963: 490).

H7 1966: rocks in stream, Knockastackeen, Galtee Mts, JW Fitzgerald (BBS exc.) (Paton 1967c: 404).
1966: rocks beside stream below Bay L., Knockmealdown Mts, JA Paton (BBS exc.) (Paton 1967c: 404), as var. *azorica*.

H8 1966: on rotten tree stump in wood E of Tarbert [*sic* = Tarbet], MFV Corley & JS Parker (Paton 1967c: 404), as var. *azorica*.

H9 1959: hazel in scrub on escarpment N of Killinaboy, MCF Proctor (Paton 1964: 720).
1979: stream bank, wood on SE. side of Woodcock Hill, Sixmilebridge, JA Paton (Corley 1980a: 32).

H10 listed (Greig-Smith 1954: 469), for var. *azorica* and var. *lamacerina*. †H10 listed by Blockeel & Long (1998: 54).

H11 1954: growing through *Saccogyna viticulosa* on wet shaded bank, Ballyeogan, Graiguenamanagh, ALK King (Castell 1955: 582), as var *azorica*.

H12 1963: on roadside bank S of Inch, ALK King (Paton 1964: 720), as var. *azorica*.

H13 1969: under arch of bridge over stream, Sculloge Gap, JW Fitzgerald (Paton 1970: 194), as var. *azorica*.

H15 1957: rocks by stream, nr Punch Bowl, nr Gort, J Appleyard (Castell 1958: 469-470), as var. *azorica*.
1957: trees, Chevey Chase Forest, Owendalulleegh, nr Gort, RE Parker (submitted as *L. patens*, redet. P Greig-Smith) (Castell 1958: 469).

H16 1957: on stones, wet place, Ballynahinch, J Appleyard (Castell 1958: 469).
1968: shaded rocks, wood E of Kylemore Castle, AR Perry (Paton 1974b: 164), as var. *azorica*.

[H(20) listed by Macvicar (1905: 22)].

H20 1969: boulder in stream, Black's Bridge nr Aughrim, JW Fitzgerald (Paton 1970: 194), as var. *azorica*.

H21 1963: on vertical face of shaded granite rock in Mt Merrion Wood, ALK King (Paton 1964: 720), as var. *azorica*.

H25 1965: copse by roadside, Ballyfarnan, JW Fitzgerald & EM Lobley (Paton 1966: 188).
1965: boulders in stream 1 mile N of Ballyfarnan, JW Fitzgerald & EM Lobley (Paton 1966: 188), as var *azorica*.

[H(27) listed by Macvicar (1905: 22)].

H27 1960: with *Lophocolea fragans*, Old Head Wood, AW Stelfox, comm. JW Fitzgerald (Paton 1962: 363), as var. *azorica*.
1962: rocks in stream under dense *Salix aurita* below Lough Acorrymore, Achill I., EF Warburg (Paton 1963: 490-491).

H28 1963: shaded rocks, Knocknarea Glen, JW Fitzgerald & AR Perry (Paton 1964: 720), as var. *azorica*.

H29 1961: on *Thamnium* at base of trees, Glencar, JW Fitzgerald & MPH Kertland (Paton 1962: 363).
1963: on rocks on E shore of Lough Gill, JW Fitzgerald & AR Perry (Paton 1964: 720), as var. *azorica*.

H31 1999: in cleft of rock near edge of stream, *ca* 150 m alt., Two Mile River, Carlingford Mountain, J11, TL Blockeel 28/154 (Blackstock 2000: 44).

H33 1957: earth-covered limestone rock, E side of Belmore Mountain, AC Crundwell (Castell 1958: 469-470), as var. *azorica*.
1960: rock crevice by waterfall, Corraderrybrock, N of L. Macnean, JW Fitzgerald (Paton 1966: 188).

H34 1961: on shaded rocks, Greencastle, RD Fitzgerald (Paton 1962: 363), as var. *azorica*.

1967: rocks by R. Crana, E of Ballymagan, E of Buncrana, JW Fitzgerald (Paton 1968: 627).

[H(35) listed by Macvicar (1905: 22)].

[H35 1950: waterfalls, Muckish, at 1000 ft [alt.], JW Fitzgerald (Castell 1951: 495). Publication of following record presumably implies this record was later doubted].

H35 1962: rock crevice, Maghery nr Dunglow, EF Warburg & J Appleyard (BBS exc.) (Paton 1963: 490-491).
1962: on rocks nr the sea, The Rosses, J Appleyard (BBS exc.) (Paton 1963: 490-491), as var. *azorica*.

H36 1957: wet rocks beside waterfall, Burn Dennett, JW Fitzgerald (Castell 1958: 469).
1957: shaded rocks, nr stream, Strabane Glen, JW Fitzgerald (Castell 1958: 469-470), as var. *azorica*.

H37 1950: on stone at water's edge, tidal estuary, Rough I., JW Fitzgerald (Castell 1951: 495, Paton 1964: 720).

[H(38) listed by Macvicar (1905: 22)].

H38 1962: rocks beside stream, Tollymore Park, Newcastle, JW Fitzgerald & MPH Kertland (Paton 1963: 490-491).

[H(39) listed by Macvicar (1905: 22)].

H39 1950: wet rock, nr river, Crow Glen, JW Fitzgerald (Castell 1951: 495)].
1963: on mosses in ravine, Glenariff, JW Fitzgerald & AR Perry (Paton 1964: 720), as var. *azorica*.

H40 listed (Greig-Smith 1954: 469), for var. *azorica*. †H40 listed by Blockeel & Long (1998: 54).

Old records (e.g. of *L. heterophylla* from Macvicar 1905: 22) should not be accepted unless specimens have been reidentified.

60/3 ***Lejeunea patens*** Lindb.

[H(1) listed by Macvicar (1905: 22)].

H1 listed (Greig-Smith 1954: 468). H1 record confirmed (Paton 1962: 364, 1963: 491). †H1 listed by Blockeel & Long (1998: 54).

[H(2) listed by Macvicar (1905: 22)].

H2 record confirmed (Paton 1962: 364, 1963: 491). †H2 listed by Blockeel & Long (1998: 54).

[H(3) listed by Macvicar (1905: 22)].

H3 record confirmed (Paton 1963: 491). †H3 listed by Blockeel & Long (1998: 54).

H4 1967: rocks by stream, Mushera, JW Fitzgerald (Paton 1968: 627).

H(5) 1850: Lota [*sic* = Fota, i.e. Foaty Island] nr Cork, I Carroll (BEL) (Paton 1967c: 404).

†H5 listed by Blockeel & Long (1998: 54).

[H(6) listed by Macvicar (1905: 22)].

H6 1966: rocks beside stream below Coumshingaun L., Comeragh Mts, JA Paton *et al.* (BBS exc.) (Paton 1967c: 404).

H7 1966: rocks above L. Curra, Galtee Mts, JA Paton *et al.* (BBS exc.) (Paton 1967c: 404).

H8 1966: on ground in wood E of Tarbert, MFV Corley & JS Parker (Paton 1967c: 404).

[H(9) listed by Macvicar (1905: 22)].

H9 record confirmed (Paton 1964: 721). †H9 listed by Blockeel & Long (1998: 54).

H10 listed (Greig-Smith 1954: 468). H10 record confirmed (Paton 1962: 364, 1963: 491). †H10 listed by Blockeel & Long (1998: 54).

H11 1966: on rocks, wood by R. Nore, Inistioge, JW Fitzgerald *et al.* (BBS exc.) (Paton 1967c: 404).

H12 1969: rocks in stream, Wicklow Gap, JW Fitzgerald (Paton 1970: 193).

[H(13) listed by Macvicar (1905: 22)]. H13 record confirmed (Paton 1964: 721). H13 deleted because no localised record or voucher traced, comm. MM Yeo (Long 1990a: 28)].

[H(14) listed by Macvicar (1905: 22)].

†H15 listed by Blockeel & Long (1998: 54).

[H(16) listed by Macvicar (1905: 22)].

H16 record confirmed (Paton 1963: 491). †H16 listed by Blockeel & Long (1998: 54).

H17 1965: on decaying vegetation amongst heath on blanket bog by T.40 road between Cregg R. and R. Clare, AJE Smith (Paton 1966: 188).

[H(20) listed by Macvicar (1905: 22)].

H20 record confirmed (Paton 1964: 721). †H20 listed by Blockeel & Long (1998: 54).

H21 record confirmed (Paton 1964: 721). †H21 listed by Blockeel & Long (1998: 54).

H25 1960: growing through *Zygodon* in Rockingham Woods, Boyle, ALK King (Paton 1961: 157). H25 record confirmed (Paton 1962: 364, 1963: 491).
H26 1965: on *Salix* below cliffs S of Glendaduff, [The] Ox Mts, JW Fitzgerald (Paton 1966: 188).
[H27 deleted because voucher specimen (1962: near Sraheens Lough, Achill I., EF Warburg, BBSUK) is *L. lamacerina*, det. & comm. JA Paton (Long 1995b: 39)].
[H(27) listed by Macvicar (1905: 22)].
H27 H27 record confirmed (Paton 1963: 491).
1987: rock in ravine below N ridge of Devil's Mother, L96, JA Paton 7604 (E), det. & comm. JA Paton (Long 1995b: 39).
[H(28) listed by Macvicar (1905: 22)].
H28 record confirmed (Paton 1963: 491). †H28 listed by Blockeel & Long (1998: 54).
[H(29) listed by Macvicar (1905: 22)].
H29 record confirmed (Paton 1962: 364, 1963: 491). †H29 listed by Blockeel & Long (1998: 54).
H30 1965: on boulders beside Corrakeeldrum Lough nr Dowra, JW Fitzgerald & EM Lobley (Paton 1966: 188).
[H(31) listed by Macvicar (1905: 22)].
H31 record confirmed (Paton 1964: 721). †H31 listed by Blockeel & Long (1998: 54).
H33 record confirmed (Paton 1963: 491). †H33 listed by Blockeel & Long (1998: 54).
[H(34) listed by Macvicar (1905: 22)].
H34 record confirmed (Paton 1963: 491). †H34 listed by Blockeel & Long (1998: 54).
[H(35) listed by Macvicar (1905: 22)].
H35 record confirmed (Paton 1962: 364, 1963: 491). †H35 listed by Blockeel & Long (1998: 54).
H36 1957: shaded moist rocks, Willmount Glen, nr Drumquin, JW Fitzgerald (Castell 1958: 470). H36 record confirmed (Paton 1962: 364, 1963: 491).
H37 1951: granite side of wet drain, alt. 25 ft, Rough I. nr Newry, JW Fitzgerald (Castell 1952: 96). H37 record confirmed (Paton 1963: 491).
[H(38) listed by Macvicar (1905: 22)]. H38 record confirmed (Paton 1962: 364, 1963: 491). H38 deleted because voucher specimen (1962: Shimna River, Tollymore Park, Newcastle, MPH Kertland & JW Fitzgerald, BBSUK) is *L. lamacerina*, det. & comm. JA Paton (Long 1995b: 39)].
[H(39) listed by Macvicar (1905: 22)].
H39 listed (Greig-Smith 1954: 468). H39 record confirmed (Paton 1962: 364, 1963: 491). †H39 listed by Blockeel & Long (1998: 54).
H40 1952: Benevenagh, EW Jones (Castell 1953: 304). H40 record confirmed (Paton 1963: 491).

Old records (e.g. from Macvicar 1905: 22) should not be accepted unless specimens have been reidentified.

60/4 ***Lejeunea flava*** (Sw.) Nees **subsp. *moorei*** (Lindb.) R.M.Schust.

H(1) listed by Macvicar (1905: 22).
†H1 listed by Blockeel & Long (1998: 54).
H(2) listed by Macvicar (1905: 22).
†H2 listed by Blockeel & Long (1998: 54).
H(3) 1900: Glengarriff, CH Binstead, comm. HH Knight (anon. 1919b: 267).
†H3 listed by Blockeel & Long (1998: 54).
H6 1967: dry rocks in wooded valley nr Lismore, DA Ratcliffe, HH Birks & HJB Birks (Paton 1968: 628).
H16 1961: dry shaded rocks in oak woods on S-facing slope at 200 ft [alt.], Kylemore, nr Letterfrack, DA Ratcliffe (Paton 1962: 363).
H27 1987: vertical wet rocks in ravine, 50 m [alt.], small ravine on S side of Ben Gorm above Killary Harbour, GP Rothero (Long 1988: 33).

60/5 ***Lejeunea hibernica*** Bischl. *et al.* ex Grolle
(syn. *Lejeunea diversiloba* auct. non Spruce)

H(1) listed by Macvicar (1905: 22).
†H1 listed by Blockeel & Long (1998: 54).
H(2) listed by Macvicar (1905: 22).
†H2 listed by Blockeel & Long (1998: 54).
H3 1955: wet rocks in ravine, NE slope of Lackawee, H Milne-Redhead (Castell 1956: 150).
H16 1994: by waterfall at foot of small ravine, 40 m alt., N side of Kylemore

Lough, L75, DG Long *et al.* 25582 (E) (Long 1999b: 28).
H27 1987: creeping over *Fissidens* in subterranean burn in large block scree, 250 m [alt.], E-facing slope of coire of Mweelrea, above Doo Lough, GP Rothero (Long 1988: 33).

60/6 ***Lejeunea eckloniana*** Lindenb. (syn. *Lejeunea holtii* Spruce)

H(1) listed by Macvicar (1905: 22).
†H1 listed by Blockeel & Long (1998: 54).
H(2) listed by Macvicar (1905: 22).
†H2 listed by Blockeel & Long (1998: 54).
H3 1955: wet rocks, ravine, NE slope of Lackawee, H Milne-Redhead (Castell 1958: 469).
H4 1967: on *Porella pinnata*, rocks in stream, Dripsey Castle, JW Fitzgerald (Paton 1968: 628).
H5 2002: on thin layer of muddy silt on shaded rock at edge of stream, 40 m alt., Glenbower Wood, near Killeagh, W97, TL Blockeel 31/309 (Blackstock 2003: 44).
H6 1961: wet shaded rocks beside a cascade below Coumshingaun, Comeragh Mts, DA Ratcliffe (Paton 1962: 363).
H10 1967: blocks near water in wooded valley, Clare Glen, nr Newport, HH Birks, HJB Birks & DA Ratcliffe (Paton 1968: 628).
H13 1999: on rock near water level on shaded stream bank, *ca* 35 m alt., N bank of Pollymounty River, Ballyknockcrumpin, S73, TL Blockeel 28/309 (Blackstock 2000: 44).
H16 1933: shaded rocks, ravine, Lough Fee, Connemara, PW Richards (Castell 1956: 150).

The name *Lejeunea eckloniana* is adopted in place of *L. holtii* following Grolle & Long (2000: 112-125).

60/7 ***Lejeunea mandonii*** (Steph.) Müll.Frib.

H1 1967: among boulders S of Brandon Mt., Dingle, JW Fitzgerald (Paton 1968: 628).
H2 1966: shaded rock below Torc Cascade, Killarney, JA Paton (Paton 1967c: 404).
H29 1963: with *Cololejeunea rossettiana*, shaded limestone rock crevices at 900 ft alt., Peakadaw, Glenade, JW Fitzgerald & AR Perry (Paton 1964: 721, Fitzgerald & Fitzgerald 1966a).

61/1 ***Colura calyptrifolia*** (Hook.) Dumort. (syn. *Colurolejeunea calyptrifolia* (Hook.) Schiffn.)

H(1) listed by Macvicar (1905: 22).
†H1 listed by Blockeel & Long (1998: 54).
H(2) listed by Macvicar (1905: 22).
†H2 listed by Blockeel & Long (1998: 54).
H(3) listed by Macvicar (1905: 22).
†H3 listed by Blockeel & Long (1998: 54).
H4 1967: growing over moss on trees by stream, Mount Hillary, JW Fitzgerald (Paton 1968: 628).
H(6) listed by Macvicar (1905: 22).
†H6 listed by Blockeel & Long (1998: 54).
[H(7) listed by Macvicar (1905: 22)].
H7 1966: on damp rocks nr L. Curra, Galtee Mts, JA Paton & J Appleyard (BBS exc.) (Paton 1967c: 404).
H8 1979: on ash tree, Glenastar ravine, nr Ardagh, EW Jones (Corley 1980a: 32).
H9 1959: on *Frullania tamarisci* in *Empetrum-Dryas* heath facing NW, on spur of hill between Ballyvaughan and Turlough, MCF Proctor (Paton 1961: 157).
H10 1951: branches of small trees in sheltered gully, N slope, alt. 900 ft, above Silvermines, AD Banwell, EV Watson & PJ Wanstall (Castell 1952: 96).
H13 2002: lightly shaded near-vertical bark of branch on felled *Picea sitchensis* at edge of clearing in plantation, *ca* 310 m alt., S slope of Croaghaun, S85, DT Holyoak 02-359 (Blackstock 2003: 44).
H15 1960: on *Ulex europaeus* by roadside between Gort and Derrybrien, *ca* 5 miles E of Gort, Slieve Aughty, MCF Proctor (Paton 1961: 157).
†H16 listed by Blockeel & Long (1998: 54).
H(21) listed by Macvicar (1905: 22). H(21) listed by Blockeel & Long (1998: 54).
H24 1965: stems of old whin in wood, Cloonart Bridge nr Roosky, JW Fitzgerald & EM Lobley (Paton 1966: 188).
H25 1981: on spruce, E side of Slieve Bawn, Strokestown, DM Synnott (Corley 1982: 23).
H26 1968: on *Frullania* on alder beside L.

Corrib nr Cong Quay, JA Paton (Paton 1969a: 875).
H(27) listed by Macvicar (1905: 22).
†H27 listed by Blockeel & Long (1998: 54).
H28 1967: on *Frullania* on shaded rocks, N slopes of Knockachree, Slieve Gamph, HH Birks, HJB Birks & DA Ratcliffe (Paton 1968: 628).
H29 1965: stems of old whin beside stream, Dergvone N of Allen, JW Fitzgerald & EM Lobley (Paton 1966: 188).
H30 2001: epiphyte on twigs of tall *Calluna vulgaris* and *Vaccinium myrtillus* in gritstone block-scree, *ca* 301 m alt., S of Englishman's House, SW of Monesk, H03, DT Holyoak 01-708 (Blackstock: 2002: 40).
H33 1957: on heather stem at 1750 ft [alt.], NE side of Tiltinbane, AC Crundwell (Castell 1958: 469).
1957: rocks and organic debris on rocks, Correll Glen, nr Derrygonelly, RE Parker (Castell 1958: 469).
H35 1961: dry shaded rocks in waterfall ravine at 700 ft [alt.], Glenbeagh, nr Dunlewy, DA Ratcliffe (Paton 1962: 363).
H(38) listed by Macvicar (1905: 22). H(38) listed by Blockeel & Long (1998: 54).
H(39) 1928: Glenariff (BBS exc.) (Duncan 1928: 114, 117). H(39) listed by Blockeel & Long (1998: 54).

62/1 ***Cololejeunea calcarea*** (Lib.) Schiffn.

H(1) listed by Macvicar (1905: 22).
†H1 listed by Blockeel & Long (1998: 55).
H(2) listed by Macvicar (1905: 22).
†H2 listed by Blockeel & Long (1998: 55).
H7 1966: conglomerate rock beside L. Curra, Galtee Mts, JA Paton (BBS exc.) (Paton 1967c: 404).
H9 1957: limestone rock, Black Head, AC Crundwell (BBS exc.) (Castell 1958: 469).
H10 1979: vertical old red sandstone face, Clare Glens, N side, AC Crundwell (Corley 1980a: 32).
H15 1968: shaded rocks on N side of river, The Punchbowl, Gort, JA Paton (Paton 1969a: 875).
H16 1957: basic rocks at 800 ft [alt.], above Glencorbet, Twelve Pins, AC Crundwell (BBS exc.) (Castell 1958: 469).
H(21) listed by Macvicar (1905: 22). H(21) listed by Blockeel & Long (1998: 55).
H27 1994: on N-facing basic crag, Knockaveen, Clare I., L78, TL Blockeel 23/216 (Long 1995b: 39).
H(28) 1928: Gleniff, Ben Bulben (BBS exc.) (Duncan 1928: 118).
†H28 listed by Blockeel & Long (1998: 55).
H29 1963: limestone outcrop on scarp, *ca* 950 ft alt., Boggaun, S of Manorhamilton, AR Perry & JW Fitzgerald (Paton 1964: 720).
H30 2001: on steep damp limestone at base of low crag, partly shaded by *Corylus avellana* scrub, *ca* 208 m alt., nr Giant's Leap, S of Blacklion, H03, DT Holyoak 01-749 (Blackstock 2002: 41).
H(31) listed by Macvicar (1905: 22). H(31) listed by Blockeel & Long (1998: 55).
H33 1957: rocks in wood, nr Hanging Rock, L. Macnean Lower, AC Crundwell (Castell 1958: 469).
H34 1969: amongst mosses on schistose rocks, Bulbin Mt., Inishowen, JA Paton (Paton 1970: 194).
H35 1965: E side of Banagher Hill, *ca* 700 ft alt., above L. Eske, EW Jones (Paton 1966: 188).
H36 2002: with other bryophytes on steep damp limestone *ca* 2 m above water on N bank of river, shaded by *Corylus* and saplings of *Fraxinus*, *ca* 95 m alt., just below Carrickaness Bridge (W of Drumquin), H27, DT Holyoak 02-1122 (Blackstock 2003: 44).
H(38) listed by Macvicar (1905: 22). H(38) listed by Blockeel & Long (1998: 55).
H(39) listed by Macvicar (1905: 22).
†H39 listed by Blockeel & Long (1998: 55).
H(40) listed by Macvicar (1905: 22).
†H40 listed by Blockeel & Long (1998: 55).

62/2 ***Cololejeunea rossettiana*** (C.Massal.) Schiffn.

H(2) listed by Macvicar (1905: 22).
†H2 listed by Blockeel & Long (1998: 55).
H4 2002: on shaded limestone boulders, 40 m alt., in the castle grounds, Blarney, W67, TL Blockeel 31/293 (Blackstock 2003: 44).
H6 1961: with *Lejeunea* on *Thamnium*, rocks below Coumshingaun, Comeragh Mts, DA Ratcliffe (Paton 1962: 363).
H8 1966: deep crevices in limestone, L. Gur nr Kilteely, JG Duckett (BBS exc.)

(Paton 1967c: 404).

H9 1957: shaded rocks, limestone cave, Slievecarran, DG Catcheside & EM Lobley (BBS exc.), comm. EM Lobley (Castell 1958: 469).

H14 1980: on *Marchesinia* on bark, Clopook Wood, nr Timahoe, DL Kelly (Corley 1981: 21).

H16 1968: on *Thamnium* and on rock face, damp shaded limestone rift, Pigeon Hole, W of Cong, AR Perry (Paton 1969a: 875).

H(21) listed by Macvicar (1905: 22). H(21) listed by Blockeel & Long (1998: 55).

H22 1967: limestone cliffs, Beauparc, DM Synnott (Paton 1968: 628).

H28 1959: limestone, Knocknarea Glen, ALK King (Castell 1969: 768).

H29 1963: shaded limestone boulder, shore on E side of Lough Gill, AR Perry & JW Fitzgerald (Paton 1964: 720).

H33 1959: with *C. calcarea*, creeping over *Metzgeria conjugata* and *Neckera complanata*, under overhanging rock, Knockmore Cliff, JW Fitzgerald (Castell 1960: 768).

H36 1957: creeping over moss, limestone rocks beside waterfall, Carrickaness Bridge, JW Fitzgerald (Castell 1958: 469).

62/3 *Cololejeunea minutissima* (Sm.) Schiffn.

H(1) listed by Macvicar (1905: 22).

†H1 listed by Blockeel & Long (1998: 55).

H(2) listed by Macvicar (1905: 22).

†H2 listed by Blockeel & Long (1998: 55).

H(3) listed by Macvicar (1905: 22).

†H3 listed by Blockeel & Long (1998: 55).

H4 1966: on hazel in wood by river, Shipool, S of Innishannon, MFV Corley & JS Parker (Paton 1967c: 404).

H5 1956: on sallows, fen W of Youghal and on thorn trees, Tourig, nr Youghal, EC Wallace (Castell 1958: 469).

H6 1956: on willow, nr Ardmore, EC Wallace (Castell 1958: 469).

H8 1959: very sparingly amongst *Radula complanata* on oak, Castleconnell, ALK King (Castell 1969: 768).

H9 1951: small tree, Poulsallagh, Burren, H Milne-Redhead (Castell 1952: 96).

H10 1967: bark of ash and hazel trees in wooded valley, Clare Glen, nr Newport, HH Birks, HJB Birks & DA Ratcliffe (Paton 1968: 628).

H11 1966: on trees by the R. Nore, Dysart Castle nr Thomastown, JW Fitzgerald *et al.* (BBS exc.) (Paton 1967c: 404).

H13 1999: on *Salix* in wet ground, *ca* 8 m alt., by canal by River Barrow, 1 km NW of Saint Mullin's, S73, TL Blockeel 28/73 (Blackstock 2000: 44).

[H(14) listed by Macvicar (1905: 22)].

H15 1957: trunk of ash, Garryland Wood, nr Gort, AC Crundwell & EM Lobley (BBS exc.) (Castell 1958: 469).

H16 1957: scrub in old railway cutting, Recess, RE Parker (Castell 1958: 469).

H17 1957: mixed with *Radula complanata* and mosses on moist limestone wall, Fens, Cloonboo, RE Parker (Castell 1958: 469).

1957: trees, small wood, nr Kilgarriff, Headford, EM Lobley (BBS exc.) (Castell 1958: 469).

H18 1951: with *Tortula papillosa*, *Cryphaea heteromalla*, *Metzgeria furcata* and *Radula complanata*, on tree in grove nr Derrinlough House, Birr, AP Fanning (Castell 1953: 304).

H(21) listed by Blockeel & Long (1998: 55).

H23 1970: shrubs on E shore of Killinure L., S of Glassan, JA Paton (Paton 1971a: 373).

H24 1968: trees in wood nr Elfeet Bay, 8 miles W of Ballymahon, WV Rubers, P Hessell & J Klein (Paton 1970: 194).

H25 1968: *Salix* on margin of St Johns Wood, 3 miles SE of Knockcroghery, WV Rubers, P Hessell & J Klein (Paton 1970: 194).

H26 1965: on stems of hawthorn, W shore of L. Carra nr Partry, A McG Stirling (Paton 1967c: 404).

[H(27) listed with ? by Macvicar (1905: 22)].

†H27 listed by Blockeel & Long (1998: 55).

H28 1963: bole of conifer in wooded gorge nr Grange S of Knocknarea, AR Perry & JW Fitzgerald (Paton 1964: 720).

[H(29) listed with ? by Macvicar (1905: 22)].

H29 1963: elm in wooded W-facing slope of limestone scarp, Boggaun, Manorhamilton, AR Perry & JW Fitzgerald (Paton 1964: 720).

[H(30) listed with ? by Macvicar (1905: 22)].

H30 1969: elder on E shore of Brackley L., S of Swanlinbar, JA Paton (Paton 1970: 194).

H33 1957: on hazel, wood, nr Hanging Rock, L. Macnean Lower, AC Crundwell (Castell 1958: 469).
H34 2001: on roadside holly tree in hedgerow, *ca* 20 m alt., NE of Lough Eske Bridge, G98, NG Hodgetts 3888 (Blackstock 2003: 44).
H35 1962: wet rock crevice nr Mullaghderg Lough, The Rosses, EF Warburg (BBS exc.) (Paton 1963: 490).
[H(39) listed with ? by Macvicar (1905: 22)].
H40 1999: on bark of old *Taxus baccata* tree at edge of clearing in ornamental woodland, Downhill Forest, C73, DT Holyoak 99-291 (BBSUK) (Blackstock 2000: 44)

63/1 ***Aphanolejeunea microscopica*** (Taylor) A.Evans
(syn. *Cololejeunea microscopica* (Taylor) Schiffn.)

H(1) listed by Macvicar (1905: 22).
†H1 listed by Blockeel & Long (1998: 55).
H(2) listed by Macvicar (1905: 22).
†H2 listed by Blockeel & Long (1998: 55).
H3 1955: creeping over *Diplophyllum*, rocks on cliff, NE slope of Lackawee, H Milne-Redhead (Castell 1958: 469).
H6 1966: on rock face in quarry by Owennashad R., N of Lismore, J Appleyard & JG Duckett (BBS exc.) (Paton 1967c: 404).
H7 1966: on rocks and on *Frullania*, cliffs above L. Muskry, Galtee Mts, JA Paton & JG Duckett (BBS exc.) (Paton 1967c: 404).
H8 1975: hazel branch, wooded ravine, Glenistar, PH Pitkin (Paton 1976: 21).
[H(9) listed by Macvicar (1905: 22). H9 deleted because no record traced (Milne-Redhead 1969, Paton 1970: 194)].
H9 1994: on *Corylus* on shady limestone cliff, 180 m alt., S side of Glen of Clab, The Burren, M20, DG Long 25451 (Long 1995b: 40).
H10 1951: branches of small trees in sheltered gully, N slope, alt. 900 ft, above Silvermines, AD Banwell, EV Watson & PJ Wanstall (Castell 1952: 96).
H15 1994: with *Metzgeria fruticulosa* and *Colura* on *Salix* branch, Boleyneendorish River, Slieve Aughty, M50, JA Paton 7655 (Long 1995b: 40).
H(16) 1933: Kylemore, PWM Richards (anon. 1939c: 111).
†H16 listed by Blockeel & Long (1998: 55).
H26 1965: on rocks W of L. Talt, [The] Ox Mts, JW Fitzgerald (Paton 1966: 188).
H(27) listed by Macvicar (1905: 22).
†H27 listed by Blockeel & Long (1998: 55).
H28 1963: on shaded rocks S of Knockachree, [The] Ox Mts, JW Fitzgerald & AR Perry (Paton 1964: 720).
H29 1963: rotting log in stream above Glencar waterfall, AR Perry & JW Fitzgerald (Paton 1964: 720).
H33 1957: rocks and organic debris on rocks, Correll Glen, nr Derrygonnelly, RE Parker (Castell 1958: 469).
1957: alder root by Cladagh R., L. Macnean Lower, AC Crundwell (Castell 1958: 469).
H35 1962: creeping over mosses in gorge of R. Devlin, Dunlewy, EM Lobley & MPH Kertland (BBS exc.) (Paton 1963: 490).
H36 1957: wet rock face, Butterlope, nr Plumbridge, JW Fitzgerald (Castell 1958: 469).
H(39) listed by Macvicar (1905: 22).
†H39 listed by Blockeel & Long (1998: 55).
H40 1968: shaded rock face by stream, Nanagher Glen nr Dungiven, HH Birks & JW Fitzgerald (Paton 1969a: 875).

64/1 ***Fossombronia foveolata*** Lindb.
(syn. *Fossombronia dumortieri* Huebener & Genth. ex Lindb.)

H1 1951: damp ground at edge of Finglas R., Dreenan Lake, Waterville, JW Fitzgerald, det. EW Jones (Castell 1952: 91).
1951: on peat in boggy area in native oakwood, S end of L. Caragh, RKG Vaughan, comm. PJ Wanstall, det. EW Jones (Castell 1952: 91).
H(2) listed by Macvicar (1905: 10).
†H2 listed by Blockeel & Long (1998: 55).
H3 1979: marshy field N of car park, Sheep's Head, JA Paton (Corley 1980a: 26-27).
H9 1963: shady damp bank nr cliff top, N end of cliffs of Moher, G Halliday (Paton 1964: 713).
H(16) 1933: near Letterfrack, PWM Richards (anon. 1938e: 43).

†H16 listed by Blockeel & Long (1998: 55).
H20 1975: mud exposed on margin of Vartry Reservoir, JA Paton & PH Pitkin (BBS exc.) (Paton 1976: 17).
H26 1987: amongst *Leiocolea alpestris*, NE shore of Lough Mask, Ballygarry Pier, S of Partry, JA Paton (Long 1988: 30).
H(27) 1909: Clare I., HW Lett (DBN), comm. ALK King (Paton 1964: 713).
1932: peaty bank, SW shore of L. Conn, RL Praeger (DBN), comm. ALK King (Paton 1964: 713).
†H27 listed by Blockeel & Long (1998: 55).
H35 1972: moist gravel, E shore, L. Meela nr Dunglow, JA Paton (Paton 1973b: 504).
H37 1966: wet ground among stones at edge of lake, Aughnagurgan Lake, SE of Keady, JW Fitzgerald & MPH Kertland (Paton 1967c: 395).
H39 1952: bare peaty patches nr shore, Lough Neagh, Selshan, JW Fitzgerald (Castell 1953: 298).

64/2 ***Fossombronia angulosa*** (Dicks.) Raddi

H(1) listed by Macvicar (1905: 10).
†H1 listed by Blockeel & Long (1998: 55).
[H(2) listed by Macvicar (1905: 10). H2 deleted because no localised record traced (Ratcliffe 1965, Paton 1967c: 395)].
H(3) listed by Macvicar (1905: 10).
†H3 listed by Blockeel & Long (1998: 55).
H16 1959: wet shady recesses and overhangs of sea cliff in inlet opposite Cleggan, Connemara, MCF Proctor (Paton 1961: 151).
†H27 listed by Blockeel & Long (1998: 55).
[H34 deleted because no localised record traced (Ratcliffe 1965, Paton 1967c: 395)].
H(34) 1911: Ardagh, J Hunter (anon. 1912b: 56, Paton 1968: 620); reinstates record previously deleted.
H35 1962: bank of stream nr the sea, Crohy Head nr Dunglow, J Appleyard (BBS exc.) (Paton 1963: 484).

[64/3 ***Fossombronia caespitiformis*** De Not. ex Rabenh.]

[H1 1951: Currane Lake, JW Fitzgerald, det. EW Jones (Castell 1952: 90), and 1951: Staigue Fort, Castlecove, JW Fitzgerald, det. EW Jones (Castell 1952: 90). H1 deleted because specimen (from Staigue Fort) is *F. husnotii* (Paton 1975: 10)].
[H3 1962: path among copper mines, Allihies, AJE Smith (Paton 1963: 484). H3 deleted because specimen (from Allihies) is *F. husnotii* (Paton 1975: 10)].
[H16 1957: fertile, damp stony ground by road to Ballynahinch Castle Hotel, *ca* 2 miles E of forester's lodge, Connemara, EV Watson (Castell 1958: 463). H16 deleted because specimen (from road to Ballynahinch Castle Hotel) is *F. husnotii* (Paton 1975: 10)].
[H(34) listed by Macvicar (1905: 10). H34 deleted because no specimen traced to support record by J Hunter from Ned's Point, Buncrana (Paton 1977a: 12)].

64/4 ***Fossombronia husnotii*** Corb.
(syn. *Fossombronia husnotii* var. *anglica* W.E.Nicholson)

H1 1951: Currane Lake, and Staigue Fort nr Castle Cove, JW Fitzgerald (BBS exc.) (Paton 1975: 10), originally identified as *F. caespitiformis*.
H3 1968: tracks nr old copper mines above Allihies, JA Paton (Paton 1969a: 867, 1969b).
H5 2002: on bare peaty humus by gravelly path, 55 m alt., Glenbower Wood, W97, TL Blockeel 31/307 (Blackstock 2003: 44).
H9 1979: flat earthy rock nr Inagh R., W of L. Burke, W of Ennis, JA Paton & AC Crundwell (Corley 1980a: 27).
H16 1970: damp track E of Kylemore Castle, Letterfrack, JA Paton (Paton 1971a: 369).
H27 1970: roadside bank nr L. Nahatora, S of Louisburgh, JA Paton (Paton 1971a: 369).
H34 2002: on unshaded compressed stony soil of bare patches in old track above sea cliffs, *ca* 40 m alt., Dunree Head, C23, DT Holyoak 02-790 (Blackstock 2003: 44).

64/5 ***Fossombronia pusilla*** (L.) Nees
(syn. *Fossombronia pusilla* var. *pusilla* (L.) Nees)

H(1) listed by Macvicar (1905: 10).
†H1 listed by Blockeel & Long (1998: 56).

H(2) listed by Macvicar (1905: 10). H(2) listed by Blockeel & Long (1998: 56).
H(3) listed by Macvicar (1905: 10).
†H3 listed by Blockeel & Long (1998: 56).
[H(4) or [H(5) no date but before 1880: nr Cork, I Carroll (OXF), comm. AR Perry (Paton 1963: 484)].
H4 1966: muddy river bank, R. Lee, Innishcarra Bridge, MFV Corley & JS Parker (Paton 1967c: 395).
H(5) 1852: Fermoy, T Chandlee (DBN), comm. ALK King (Paton 1964: 712).
†H5 listed by Blockeel & Long (1998: 56).
H6 1966: edge of field nr R. Nier, Shanballyanne, JA Paton, GCG Argent & ERB Little (BBS exc.) (Paton 1967c: 395).
H8 1966: boggy ground, Knockseefin, Nicker, J Appleyard (BBS exc.) (Paton 1967c: 395).
H9 1994: earthy slope in scrub, N-facing side of Glen of Clab, Gortaclare Mt., M20, JA Paton 7679 (Long 1995b: 37).
H10 1967: sandy bank, Devil's Bit Mt., JW Fitzgerald (Paton 1968: 620).
H11 1954: damp shaded bank, wood, R.[ight] bank of R. Barrow, above Graiguenamanagh, ALK King (Castell 1955: 579).
H12 1975: marshy woodland S of Clonough Bridge, E of Inch, JA Paton (BBS exc.) (Paton 1976: 17).
H13 2002: on near-vertical clay soil at base of bank beside track, slightly shaded by *Prunus laurocerasus* scrub, *ca* 65 m alt., just W of Bunclody, S95, DT Holyoak 02-364 (Blackstock 2003: 44).
H16 1957: woodland ride, Ballynahinch, AC Crundwell & EM Lobley (BBS exc.), comm. AC Crundwell (Castell 1958: 463).
H19 1953: shady roadside bank, Cupidstown Hill, ALK King (Castell 1954: 472).
H20 1975: path in Devil's Glen, Ashford, PH Pitkin (BBS exc.) (Paton 1976: 17).
H(21) listed by Blockeel & Long (1998: 56).
H21 2002: in wheat stubble, 60 m alt., SE of Hazelhatch Station, N93, CD Preston (Blackstock 2003: 44).
H23 1952: path in wood, nr Ballinafid, NE end of L. Owel, JS Thomson (Castell 1954: 472).
H24 1980: side of drain by L. Gowna, N of Inchmore, DM Synnott (Corley 1982: 19).
H25 1973: ash/oak wood, St John's Wood 3 miles SE of Knockeroghery, WV Rubers (Paton 1974b: 162).
H27 1970: roadside bank N of Killary Harbour, JA Paton (Paton 1971a: 369).
H28 1970: wet sandy lane cutting in forestry plantation, Slish Wood, AR Perry & HJ Perry (BBS exc.) (Paton 1974b: 162).
H29 1970: on a bank by the track below Peakadaw, J Appleyard (BBS exc.) (Paton 1971a: 369, Appleyard 1971: 388).
H31 1966: stubble field, Cluide, Dunleer, DM Synnott (Paton 1967c: 395).
H(33) listed by Blockeel & Long (1998: 56).
H33 1959: clay path, Rossinure More, nr Knockmore Cliff, JW Fitzgerald (Castell 1960: 764). The updated record was apparently omitted in error from Blockeel & Long (1998: 56).
2000: on soil exposed in flush with patchy *Juncus effusus* on damp grassland near *Corylus* scrub, W of Marble Arch, H13, DT Holyoak 00-168 (BBSUK) (Blackstock 2001: 36).
H34 1968: clay bank by sea cliff, Tremone Bay, SE of Culdaff, Inishowen, HH Birks & JW Fitzgerald (Paton 1969a: 867).
H(35) listed by Macvicar (1905: 10). H(35) listed by Blockeel & Long (1998: 56).
H35 2002: almost unshaded on steep loamy soil of low bank at edge of track, *ca* 47 m alt., NE of Mevagh, Rosguill, C14, DT Holyoak 02-604 (Blackstock 2003: 44).
H36 1953: damp sandy bankside nr Annahavil Hill nr Dungannon, MPH Kertland & EM Lobley (Castell 1955: 579).
H37 1964: fallow field, SE corner of Lough Gullion, JW Fitzgerald (Paton 1965a: 852).
H(38) listed by Macvicar (1905: 10).
†H38 listed by Blockeel & Long (1998: 56).
H(39) listed by Macvicar (1905: 10).
†H39 listed by Blockeel & Long (1998: 56).
H40 1968: ditch by forestry track, Benevenagh, JW Fitzgerald & HH Birks (Paton 1969a: 867).

Not all voucher specimens of *F. pusilla* have been checked since the description of *F. maritima* (Paton 1973a). Hence records of *F. pusilla* from before 1973 may include a few of *F. maritima*, although the latter species is rarer and known only from coastal localities.

64/6 ***Fossombronia maritima*** (Paton) Paton (syn. *Fossombronia pusilla* var. *maritima* Paton)

H3 1968: heathy cliff slopes, Garinish Head, W of Allihies, JA Paton (Paton 1973a: 247, 1974b: 162).
H27 1987: flat sandy area behind strand, Trawmore Sand nr Dookinelly, Achill I., JA Paton (Long 1988: 30).

64/7 ***Fossombronia wondraczekii*** (Corda) Lindb.

H1 1951: L. Caragh, RE Parker (Castell 1952: 90).
1951: on soil, grassy bank, garden of Towers Hotel, AD Banwell (Castell 1952: 90).
1951: damp bank by road, Glenbeigh, EW Jones (Castell 1952: 90).
H3 1979: marshy woodland beside Glengarriff R., JA Paton (Corley 1980a: 27).
H4 1967: forestry track, Carrigagulla, S of Mushera, JW Fitzgerald (Paton 1968: 620).
H5 1966: on forestry track, Castle Cooke nr Kilworth, JW Fitzgerald *et al.* (BBS exc.) (Paton 1967c: 395-396).
H6 1966: open drain on track N of the Punchbowl, Comeragh Mts, EM Lobley *et al.* (BBS exc.) (Paton 1967c: 395-396).
H9 1979: wet track near Killuran R., NW slope of Slieve Bernagh, N of Broadford, JA Paton (Corley 1980a: 27).
H10 1979: marshy field above Clare Glens, S of Newport, JA Paton (Corley 1980a: 27).
H12 1969: cattle track in marshy field, Pallas Bridge nr Wicklow Gap, JW Fitzgerald (Paton 1970: 187).
H13 1969: side of peat drain, bog at St Mullins nr Graiguenamanagh, JW Fitzgerald (Paton 1970: 187).
H15 1957: damp ground, Chevy Chase Woods, Owendalulleegh, nr Gort, J Appleyard, DG Catcheside & EM Lobley (BBS exc.), comm. J Appleyard & EM Lobley (Castell 1958: 463).
H16 1965: rough damp meadow nr the sea *ca* ½ mile S of Lettermullan village, Lettermullan I., DF Chamberlain (Paton 1966: 181).
1965: bank of roadside ditch nr Ballynahinch Castle Hotel, AJE Smith (Paton 1966: 181).
H20 1975: marshy field nr bridge over R. Ow, S of Aghavannagh, JA Paton & WD Foster (BBS exc.) (Paton 1976: 17).
H21 1974: wet peaty mud, drained valley bog, Golden Ball, Kilternan, PH Pitkin (Paton 1975: 10).
H24 1968: peaty pasture *ca* 2½ miles N of Killashee, W of Longford, WV Rubers, P Hessel & J Klein (Paton 1970: 187).
H25 1968: pasture on edge of raised bog nr Drumdaff House, 6 miles W of Lanesborough, WV Rubers, P Hessel & J Klein (Paton 1970: 187).
H26 1987: in tractor rut on woodland path, E side of Cloon River between Srah and Partry, DM Synnott (Long 1988: 30).
H27 1965: amongst tall grass nr the sea, Currane Achill, DF Chamberlain (Paton 1966: 181).
H29 1970: small marsh N of Dromahair, JA Paton (BBS exc.) (Paton 1971a: 369, Appleyard 1971: 390).
H31 1967: stubble field nr White River Cross, Tenure, DM Synnott (Paton 1968: 620).
H(33) 1919: ditch, L. Avilly, nr Eniskillen, WN Tetley (BBSUK) (Castell 1954: 472).
H34 1965: in stubblefield SW of Grianan of Aileach, Burt, EW Jones (Paton 1966: 181).
H35 1962: fallow field between Dunfanaghy and Falcarragh, JHG Peterken (BBS exc.) (Paton 1963: 484).
H37 1966: wet clay track in oakwood 1 mile E of Allistragh, 3 miles N of Armagh, JW Fitzgerald & MPH Kertland (Paton 1967c: 395-396).
H(38) listed by Macvicar (1905: 10). H(38) listed by Blockeel & Long (1998: 56).

64/9 ***Fossombronia incurva*** Lindb.

H1 1983: damp sandy track between dunes and estuary, Rossbehy, nr Glenbeigh, JA Paton (Corley 1984: 23).
H3 1979: on track S of road, S of League Point, Sheep's Head Peninsula, JA Paton

(Corley 1980a: 27).

H6 1966: gravelly path in wood, Glenshelane, N of Cappoquin, JA Paton & ERB Little (BBS exc.) (Paton 1967c: 395).

H16 1969: gravelly lay-by 3 miles E of Lettercrafroe L., AR Perry & HJ Perry (Paton 1970: 187).

H27 1967: on waste ground in layby, Beltra nr Newport, HH Birks & HJB Birks (Paton 1969a: 867).

H28 1970: roadside quarry nr Masshill, JA Paton (BBS exc.) (Paton 1971a: 369, Appleyard 1971: 389).

H30 1969: floor of old quarry, Blackrocks Cross, Cuilcagh Mts, SW of Swanlinbar, JA Paton (Paton 1970: 187).

H35 2002: on unshaded partly bare compressed soil at edge of car park near lake, *ca* 260 m alt., just W of Lough Salt, C12, DT Holyoak 02-686 (Blackstock 2003: 44).

H36 2002: on unshaded partly bare damp gravelly sand in disused sand and gravel quarry, *ca* 170 m alt., Killucan, H67, DT Holyoak 02-1099 (Blackstock 2003: 44).

H38 2002: on unshaded partly bare damp sand by edge of pool in old sand quarry, *ca* 20 m alt., SW of Kilkeel, J21, DT Holyoak 02-1060 (Blackstock 2003: 44).

H39 1999: on damp, partly bare, compressed sand of pathway in dunes with very short vegetation, E of Portballintrae, C94, DT Holyoak 99-242 (BBSUK) (Blackstock 2000: 44).

H40 1999: on small bare patches in very short grassland of little-used trackway in dunes, Ballymaclary NNR, C73, DT Holyoak 99-204 (BBSUK) (Blackstock 2000: 44).

64/10 ***Fossombronia fimbriata*** Paton

H27 1987: on damp sandy ground by sea, Trawmore Sand near Dookinelly, Achill I., DG Long (Long 1988: 30).

H28 1970: old quarry nr Masshill, [The] Ox Mts, W of Cloonacool, JA Paton & J Appleyard (BBS exc.) (Paton 1974a: 4, 1975: 10).

65/1 ***Petalophyllum ralfsii*** (Wils.) Nees & Gottsche ex Lehm.

H(1) listed by Macvicar (1905: 10).

†H1 listed by Blockeel & Long (1998: 56).

H2 1954: margin of moist dune slack, Banna, AP Fanning, comm. EC Wallace (Paton 1964: 712).

H9 1994: damp soil on limestone at edge of sand dunes, 2 m alt., Fanore, M10, DG Long 25469 (Long 1995b: 37).

H16 1988: damp hollow on sandy flats, W of Doon Hill near Ballyconneely, DG Long 14882 (Long 1989: 20).

H(21) listed by Macvicar (1905: 10).

†H21 listed by Blockeel & Long (1998: 56).

†H27 listed by Blockeel & Long (1998: 56).

H28 1970: old quarry nr Derry, on L. Arrow, JA Paton (BBS exc.) (Paton 1971a: 369, Appleyard 1971: 389).

H35 1962: dune slack, coast opposite Cruit I., The Rosses, AC Crundwell, J Appleyard & EF Warburg (BBS exc.) (Paton 1963: 483).

H(39) 1928: sandhills, Portrush (BBS exc.) (Duncan 1928: 113, 116). H(39) listed by Blockeel & Long (1998: 56).

H(40) listed by Macvicar (1905: 10).

†H40 listed by Blockeel & Long (1998: 56).

The author citation for the name of this species follows Stotler *et al.* (2002).

66/1 ***Pellia epiphylla*** (L.) Corda (syn. *Pellia borealis* Lorb.)

H(1) listed by Macvicar (1905: 9).

†H1 listed by Blockeel & Long (1998: 56).

H(2) listed by Macvicar (1905: 9).

H(2) no date: Killarney, DG Catcheside ([Book review by DG Catcheside], *Trans. B.B.S.* **1**, 131, 1948) (Castell 1950: 374), as *P. borealis*.
pre 1947: nr Killarney, K Müller (*Beitr. Kryptogamenfl. Schweiz*, **10**, no. 2, 44, 1947; also Schiffner, *Hep. Europ. exsic.* 1321 as *P. epiphylla* var. *cataractarum*) (Castell 1951: 492), as *P. borealis*. [H2 listed under *P. borealis* in *CC* by Paton 1965b: 24, but this taxon deleted from list by Paton 1968: 620; see Paton 1999: 527 for discussion of this taxon which differs from *P. epiphylla* only in cytological characters].

†H2 listed by Blockeel & Long (1998: 56).

H(3) listed by Macvicar (1905: 9).

†H3 listed by Blockeel & Long (1998: 56).

H4 1966: shady bank by stream nr Kilculleh House, Rylane Cross, Boggeragh Mts,

MFV Corley & JS Parker (Paton 1967c: 394).
H5 1951: base of wall, Mallow, EC Wallace & EF Warburg (Castell 1952: 90).
H(6) listed by Macvicar (1905: 9).
†H6 listed by Blockeel & Long (1998: 56).
H(7) listed by Macvicar (1905: 9).
†H7 listed by Blockeel & Long (1998: 56).
H(8) listed by Macvicar (1905: 9).
†H8 listed by Blockeel & Long (1998: 56).
H(9) listed by Macvicar (1905: 9).
†H9 listed by Blockeel & Long (1998: 56).
H10 1951: damp soil in wooded fully, N slope, alt. *ca* 900 ft, above Silvermines, AD Banwell, EV Watson & PJ Wanstall (Castell 1952: 90).
H11 1958: stone floor, first story of Norman castle ruin, Coolhill, ALK King (Castell 1959: 626).
H(12) listed by Macvicar (1905: 9).
†H12 listed by Blockeel & Long (1998: 56).
H(13) listed by Macvicar (1905: 9).
†H13 listed by Blockeel & Long (1998: 56).
H(14) listed by Macvicar (1905: 9).
†H14 listed by Blockeel & Long (1998: 56).
H(15) listed by Macvicar (1905: 9).
†H15 listed by Blockeel & Long (1998: 56).
†H16 listed by Blockeel & Long (1998: 56).
[H17 deleted because no record traced, comm. MM Yeo, replaced by following record (Long 1990a: 24)].
[H(17) listed by Macvicar (1905: 9)].
H (17) 1896: Doon Bog, Clonbrock, D McArdle (DBN), comm. DM Synnott (Long 1990a: 24).
[H(18) listed by Macvicar (1905: 9). H18 deleted because no record traced, comm. MM Yeo, replaced by following record (Long 1990a: 24)].
H(18) 1890: Geashill, CD Russell & HW Lett (DBN), comm. DM Synnott (Long 1990a: 24).
[H(19) listed by Macvicar (1905: 9). H19 deleted because no record or voucher traced, comm. MM Yeo (Long 1990a: 24)].
H(20) listed by Macvicar (1905: 9).
†H20 listed by Blockeel & Long (1998: 56).
H(21) listed by Macvicar (1905: 9).
†H21 listed by Blockeel & Long (1998: 56).
H(22) listed by Macvicar (1905: 9).
†H22 listed by Blockeel & Long (1998: 56).
H(23) listed by Macvicar (1905: 9).
†H23 listed by Blockeel & Long (1998: 56).
H24 1965: side of ditch, Cornhill nr Drumlish, JW Fitzgerald & EM Lobley (Paton 1966: 181).
H25 1965: bank of stream in copse at 400 ft alt., 1 mile N of Ballyfarnan, JW Fitzgerald & EM Lobley (Paton 1966: 181).
H(26) listed by Macvicar (1905: 9).
†H26 listed by Blockeel & Long (1998: 56).
H(27) listed by Macvicar (1905: 9).
†H27 listed by Blockeel & Long (1998: 56).
H(28) listed by Macvicar (1905: 9).
†H28 listed by Blockeel & Long (1998: 56).
H(29) listed by Macvicar (1905: 9).
†H29 listed by Blockeel & Long (1998: 56).
H(30) listed by Macvicar (1905: 9).
†H30 listed by Blockeel & Long (1998: 56).
H31 1966: bank of Two-mile R., Carlingford Mt., DM Synnott (Paton 1967c: 394).
H32 1965: side of field ditch, Cavanagarvan, nr Monaghan, JW Fitzgerald & EM Lobley (Paton 1966: 181).
H(33) 1913: 'Dolerite Hill Wood', Castle Hume, Enniskillen, WN Tetley (BBSUK) (Castell 1954: 471).
†H33 listed by Blockeel & Long (1998: 56).
H(34) listed by Macvicar (1905: 9).
†H34 listed by Blockeel & Long (1998: 56).
†H35 listed by Blockeel & Long (1998: 56).
H36 1951: wet bank beside road, Leagh's Bridge, alt. 850 ft, between Draperstown and Plumbridge, JW Fitzgerald (Castell 1952: 90).
H37 1952: sides of wet ditch beside road, *ca* 1050 ft alt., Carrigatuke, nr Newtown Hamilton, JW Fitzgerald (Castell 1953: 298).
H(38) listed by Macvicar (1905: 9).
†H38 listed by Blockeel & Long (1998: 56).
H(39) listed by Macvicar (1905: 9).
†H39 listed by Blockeel & Long (1998: 56).
H40 1951: wet ground beside waterfall, alt. 150 ft, Downhill nr Castlerock, JW Fitzgerald (Castell 1952: 90).

66/2 ***Pellia neesiana*** (Gottsche) Limpr.

H1 record confirmed by examination of specimen (Paton 1962: 357). †H1 listed by Blockeel & Long (1998: 56).
H2 1966: marshy woodland nr road N of Galways Bridge, Killarney, JA Paton, GCG Argent & EM Lobley (Paton 1967c: 394).
H(3) listed by Macvicar (1905: 9). H3 record confirmed by examination of specimen

(Paton 1962: 357).
†H3 listed by Blockeel & Long (1998: 56).
H6 1966: marshy ground nr stream E of the Punchbowl, Comeragh Mts, JA Paton (BBS exc.) (Paton 1967c: 394).
H7 1966: fen carr nr Bansha, J Appleyard, JG Duckett & DM Synnott (BBS exc.) (Paton 1967c: 394).
H8 1979: *Salix* marsh nr top of waterfall, Glenastar, W of Ardagh, JA Paton (Corley 1980a: 26).
H9 1979: marsh nr stream, S slope, Keeper Hill, JA Paton & AC Crundwell (Corley 1980a: 26).
†H10 listed by Blockeel & Long (1998: 56).
H12 1969: marshy ground at Pallas Bridge nr Wicklow Gap, JW Fitzgerald (Paton 1970: 187).
H13 1969: marshy ground among alders, Crannagh, foot of Mt Leinster, JW Fitzgerald (Paton 1970: 187).
H15 1994: steep bank below flush, above Boleyneendorish River, Slieve Aughty, M50, JA Paton 7677 (Long 1995b: 37).
H16 1970: marshy ground E of Kylemore Castle, Letterfrack, JA Paton (Paton 1971a: 369).
H20 1975: margin of Upper Lake, Vale of Glendalough, WD Foster (BBS exc.) (Paton 1976: 17).
H21 1975: wet flush, N-facing slope, Ben of Howth, PH Pitkin (Paton 1976:17).
H23 1968: moist pasture nr Bethlehem House, 5 miles SW of Ballymahon, WV Rubers, P Hessel & J Klein (Paton 1970: 187).
H24 1968: by L. Gowna, Erne Head, G Drennan, comm. JW Fitzgerald (Paton 1969a: 866).
H25 1968: loamy bank of brook, Slieve Bawn, WV Rubers, P Hessel & J Klein (Paton 1970: 187).
H26 1987: on soil in open woodland nr Cloon River nr Partry, MAS Burton (Long 1988: 30).
H27 1970: flush in wood nr Erriff Bridge, N of Maumtrasna, JA Paton (Paton 1971a: 369).
H28 1970: roadside quarry nr Masshill, J Appleyard (BBS exc.) (Paton 1971a: 369, Appleyard 1971: 389).
H29 1969: marsh on S margin of L. Melvin nr Ross Pt, JA Paton (Paton 1970: 187).
H30 1970: flush below crags, below Englishman's House, Glenfarne, nr Belcoo, JA Paton (BBS exc.) (Paton 1971a: 369, Appleyard 1971: 389-390).
H33 1969: wet woodland on margin of Lower L. Erne, NE of Monea, JA Paton (Paton 1970: 187).
H34 1969: edge of pool, The Well, Gap of Mamore, N of Buncrana, JA Paton (Paton 1970: 187).
H35 1969: marsh in field N of Sessiagh L., Dunfanaghy, JA Paton (Paton 1970: 187).
H36 1956: wet bank, edge of stream, Oughtvabeg, Sperrin Mts, JW Fitzgerald & MPH Kertland, conf. EC Wallace (Castell 1957: 323). H36 record confirmed by examination of specimen (Paton 1962: 357).
H37 1964: base of stumps by Derryadd Lough, E of Verner's Bridge, JW Fitzgerald & MPH Kertland (Paton 1965a: 852).
H(38) listed by Blockeel & Long (1998: 56).
H39 1969: flushed bank above Glendum R., W of Cushendun Viaduct, JA Paton (Paton 1970: 187).
H40 1999: on moist humic soil nr stream in shade of deciduous trees, nr Altalacky River, NW of Moneyneany, H79, DT Holyoak 99-721 (BBSUK) (Blackstock 2000: 44).

66/3 ***Pellia endiviifolia*** (Dicks.) Dumort. (syn. *Pellia fabbroniana* Raddi, *P. fabbroniana* var. *lorea* Nees)

H(1) listed by Macvicar (1905: 9).
†H1 listed by Blockeel & Long (1998: 57).
H(2) listed by Macvicar (1905: 9).
†H2 listed by Blockeel & Long (1998: 57).
H(3) 1893: banks of the Puleen River, D McArdle (DBN), comm. ALK King (Paton 1964: 712).
†H3 listed by Blockeel & Long (1998: 57).
H4 1951: side of ditch, NW of Mallow, AC Crundwell (Castell 1952: 90).
H5 1967: base of bridge, Waterglasshill, JW Fitzgerald (Paton 1968: 620).
†H6 listed by Blockeel & Long (1998: 57).
H7 1966: calcareous flush by stream, Knockastackeen, Galtee Mts, JW Fitzgerald *et al.* (BBS exc.) (Paton 1967c: 395).
H8 1966: shady calcareous bank, Knockainy nr Hospital, MFV Corley & JS Parker (Paton 1967c: 395).

H(9) listed by Macvicar (1905: 9).
†H9 listed by Blockeel & Long (1998: 57).
H10 1951: damp roadside bank, Silvermines, AD Banwell, EV Watson & PJ Wanstall (Castell 1952: 90).
H11 1954: wet bank, Ballyeogan Rd, Graiguenamanagh, ALK King (Castell 1955: 579).
H(12) listed by Macvicar (1905: 9).
†H12 listed by Blockeel & Long (1998: 57).
H13 1969: moist bank, Lucys Wood, Bunclody, EM Booth (Paton 1970: 187).
H(14) listed by Macvicar (1905: 9).
†H14 listed by Blockeel & Long (1998: 57).
H15 1957: earthy bank by the Punchbowl, Gort, AC Crundwell (BBS exc.) (Castell 1958: 463).
H16 1957: roadside bank, Tullywee Bridge, Kylemore, AC Crundwell (BBS exc.) (Castell 1958: 463).
H17 1957: Turlough, Killower, nr Tuam, AC Crundwell (BBS exc.) (Castell 1958: 463).
H(18) listed by Macvicar (1905: 9).
†H18 listed by Blockeel & Long (1998: 57).
H(19) listed by Macvicar (1905: 9).
†H19 listed by Blockeel & Long (1998: 57).
H(20) listed by Macvicar (1905: 9).
†H20 listed by Blockeel & Long (1998: 57).
H(21) listed by Macvicar (1905: 9).
†H21 listed by Blockeel & Long (1998: 57).
H(22) listed by Macvicar (1905: 9).
†H22 listed by Blockeel & Long (1998: 57).
†H23 listed by Blockeel & Long (1998: 57).
H25 1968: lime-rich loamy bank, Hind R. at Cloonsellan, 5 miles SE of Roscommon, WV Rubers, P Hessel & J Klein (Paton 1970: 187).
H26 1970: wet depression, Keel Bridge, 3 miles N of Ballinrobe, DM Synnott (BBS exc.) (Paton 1971a: 369, Appleyard 1971: 388).
†H27 listed by Blockeel & Long (1998: 57).
[H(28) listed by Macvicar (1905: 9)].
H(28) 1928: nr Rosses Point, Sligo (BBS exc.) (Duncan 1928: 119).
†H28 listed by Blockeel & Long (1998: 57).
H(29) 1928: wooded glen, NE end of Glencar Lough (BBS exc.) (Duncan 1928: 118).
†H29 listed by Blockeel & Long (1998: 57).
H30 1957: ditch, Cornahaw, SW of Black Lion [*sic* = Blacklion], AC Crundwell (Castell 1958: 463).
H31 1953: bank of drain, Ravensdale State Forest, ALK King (Castell 1954: 472).
H32 1954: damp ground, Glaslough Woods, ALK King (Castell 1955: 579).
†H33 listed by Blockeel & Long (1998: 57).
H(34) 1937: Bundoran, no collector named (BBS exc.) (Armitage 1938: 13).
†H34 listed by Blockeel & Long (1998: 57).
H(35) listed by Macvicar (1905: 9).
†H35 listed by Blockeel & Long (1998: 57).
H36 1956: banks beside stream, Glen Curry Bridge, nr Omagh, JW Fitzgerald & MPH Kertland (Castell 1957: 323).
H37 1964: bank of old canal, Carrickaness, nr Benburb, JW Fitzgerald & MPH Kertland (Paton 1965a: 852).
[H(38) listed by Macvicar (1905: 9)].
H(38) 1887: bog between Hilltown and Rathfriland, CH Waddell & HW Lett, DBN (Paton 1977a: 11).
H38 2002: with other bryophytes on steep flushed rock of bank *ca* 2.5 m above river, partly shaded by deciduous trees, *ca* 45 m alt., edge of Shimna River in Tollymore Forest Park, J33, DT Holyoak 02-938 (Blackstock 2003: 44).
[H(39) listed by Macvicar (1905: 9)].
H39 1952: wet weathered basalt, Cranny Falls, Carnlough, EM Lobley & J Taylor, comm. J Taylor (Castell 1953: 298), as var. *lorea*.
H40 1952: by stream, Benbradagh, EM Lobley & J Taylor, comm. J Taylor (Castell 1953: 298).

67/1 ***Pallavicinia lyellii*** (Hook.) Carruth.

H(1) listed by Macvicar (1905: 9).
†H1 listed by Blockeel & Long (1998: 57).
H(2) listed by Macvicar (1905: 9). H(2) listed by Blockeel & Long (1998: 57).
H(3) before 1815: nr Bantry, E Hutchins (BM) (Paton 1977a: 11).
H8 1979: hollow in cutover bog, Sugar Hill, S of Knockanimpaha, JA Paton (Corley 1980a: 26).
H11 1966: side of peat drain, Derryfadda, W of Johnstown, JW Fitzgerald (BBS exc.) (Paton 1967c: 395).
H(19) listed by Macvicar (1905: 9). H(19) listed by Blockeel & Long (1998: 57).
H(20) listed by Macvicar (1905: 9). H(20) listed by Blockeel & Long (1998: 57).
[H21 deleted because no record or voucher traced, comm. DM Synnott & MM Yeo (Long 1990a: 24)].
H27 1962: wet part of bog nr the Harbour,

Keel, Achill I., EF Warburg (Paton 1963: 483).

68/1 ***Moerckia hibernica*** (Hook.) Gottsche (syn. *Moerckia flotoviana* (Nees) Schiffn., *M. flotowiana* auct.)

H1 1983: bank of small stream, Ballaghbeana Gap, Mullachanattin Mt., A Schaepe (Corley 1984: 23).
H9 1977: Roche's Marsh, at road junction 2 miles E of Kilfenora, PH Pitkin (Corley 1979: 23).
H14 1966: growing on *Eucladium* under bridge, Derry Hills, Leix, JW Fitzgerald (Paton 1967c: 395).
H16 1970: lay-by nr L. Bofin, W of Oughterard, JA Paton (Paton 1971a: 369).
H17 1957: open turf on marl, nr turlough, nr Tuam, RE Parker (Castell 1958: 463).
H18 1973: sandpit in esker, Longford, between Roscrea and Kinnitty, WV Rubers (Corley 1980a: 26).
H(20) listed by Macvicar (1905: 9). [Corley 1980a: 26 adds H20 by transferring record from *M. hibernica* to *M. flotoviana*].
H(21) listed by Macvicar (1905: 9). H(21) listed by Blockeel & Long (1998: 57).
H23 1970: amongst *Schoenus nigricans*, E shore, Killinure L., JA Paton (Paton 1972a: 131).
†H27 listed by Blockeel & Long (1998: 57).
H28 1999: on small areas of partly bare damp sand in dune slack, Bunduff, G75, DT Holyoak 99-746 (BBSUK) (Blackstock 2000: 44).
H33 1959: marshy ground, Dog Big, 3 miles W of Knockmore Cliff, JW Fitzgerald (Castell 1960: 764).
H34 1968: flush at 1000 ft alt., Bulbin Mt., Inishowen, JW Fitzgerald (Paton 1969a: 867).
†H35 listed by Blockeel & Long (1998: 57).
H(38) listed by Macvicar (1905: 9).
†H38 listed by Blockeel & Long (1998: 57).
H(39) listed by Macvicar (1905: 9). H(39) listed by Blockeel & Long (1998: 57).
H(40) 1938: Portstewart, WR Megaw (anon. 1940b: 177).
†H40 listed by Blockeel & Long (1998: 57).

69/1 ***Blasia pusilla*** L.

H(1) listed by Macvicar (1905: 10). H(1) listed by Blockeel & Long (1998: 57).
H(2) listed by Macvicar (1905: 10). H(2) listed by Blockeel & Long (1998: 57).
†H3 listed by Blockeel & Long (1998: 57).
H5 1966: gravelly detritus by river, Araglin, J Appleyard (BBS exc.) (Paton 1967c: 395).
H6 1966: damp gravelly bank, Glenshelane N of Cappoquin, JG Duckett *et al.* (BBS exc.) (Paton 1967c: 395).
H(7) listed by Macvicar (1905: 10).
†H7 listed by Blockeel & Long (1998: 57).
H(12) listed by Macvicar (1905: 10). H(12) listed by Blockeel & Long (1998: 57).
H16 1957: marshy ground, Ben Lettery, EM Lobley (BBS exc.) (Castell 1958: 463).
H(18) listed by Macvicar (1905: 10).
†H18 listed by Blockeel & Long (1998: 57).
H(19) listed by Macvicar (1905: 10). H(19) listed by Blockeel & Long (1998: 57).
H(20) listed by Macvicar (1905: 10).
†H20 listed by Blockeel & Long (1998: 57).
H(21) listed by Macvicar (1905: 10).
†H21 listed by Blockeel & Long (1998: 57).
[H(22) listed by Macvicar (1905: 10). H22 deleted because record not traced (Synnott 1982, Corley 1984: 23)].
H26 1970: ditch bank W of the Pollagh R., NE of Balla, JA Paton (Paton 1971a: 369).
H(27) listed by Macvicar (1905: 10).
†H27 listed by Blockeel & Long (1998: 57).
H(28) 1928: Gleniff, Ben Bulben (BBS exc.) (Duncan 1928: 118).
†H28 listed by Blockeel & Long (1998: 57).
H(29) listed by Macvicar (1905: 10).
†H29 listed by Blockeel & Long (1998: 57).
H(30) listed by Macvicar (1905: 10). H(30) listed by Blockeel & Long (1998: 57).
H30 2001: on almost unshaded damp soil of track between felled coniferous plantations, *ca* 315 m alt., just S of R200, W of Bellavally Gap, H12, DT Holyoak 01-641 (Blackstock 2002: 41).
H(31) listed by Macvicar (1905: 10). H(31) listed by Blockeel & Long (1998: 57).
H32 1961: beside pool in floor of quarry, Cashlan, NE of Newbliss, JW Fitzgerald (Paton 1962: 357).
†H33 listed by Blockeel & Long (1998: 57).
†H34 listed by Blockeel & Long (1998: 57).
H(35) listed by Macvicar (1905: 10).

†H35 listed by Blockeel & Long (1998: 57).
H36 1956: wet mica schist detritus beside stream, Glen Curry Bridge, nr Omagh, JW Fitzgerald & MPH Kertland (Castell 1957: 323).
H(37) listed by Macvicar (1905: 10).
†H37 listed by Blockeel & Long (1998: 57).
H(38) listed by Macvicar (1905: 10).
†H38 listed by Blockeel & Long (1998: 57).
H(39) listed by Macvicar (1905: 10).
†H39 listed by Blockeel & Long (1998: 57).
H40 1961: on mica schist detritus on rocks by river, Glenedra, nr Dungiven, JW Fitzgerald (Paton 1962: 357).

70/1 ***Aneura pinguis*** (L.) Dumort.
(syn. *Riccardia pinguis* (L.) Gray)

H(1) listed by Macvicar (1905: 8).
†H1 listed by Blockeel & Long (1998: 57).
H(2) listed by Macvicar (1905: 8).
†H2 listed by Blockeel & Long (1998: 57).
H3 1953: bank of streamlet, 1200 ft alt., Foulastookeen Mt., ALK King (Castell 1954: 471).
H4 1966: wet calcareous rock face, Ringnanean Wood, Belgooly, MFV Corley & JS Parker (Paton 1967c: 394).
H5 1956: old quarry, N of Youghal, EC Wallace (Castell 1957: 322).
H(6) listed by Macvicar (1905: 8).
H6 1961: among wet rocks N of Errisbeg, Connemara, EM Lobley (Paton 1961: 356).
H(7) listed by Macvicar (1905: 8).
†H7 listed by Blockeel & Long (1998: 57).
†H8 listed by Blockeel & Long (1998: 57).
H(9) listed by Macvicar (1905: 8).
†H9 listed by Blockeel & Long (1998: 57).
H10 1951: wet rocks by stream in wooded gully, alt. 900 ft, above Silvermines, AD Banwell, EV Watson & PJ Wanstall (Castell 1952: 89).
H11 1966: side of ditch in bog, Derryfadda, W of Johnstown, JW Fitzgerald *et al.* (BBS exc.) (Paton 1967c: 394).
H12 1966: bog by roadside, Kiltealy, Blackstairs Mts, A Folan, J Appleyard & JG Duckett (Paton 1967c: 394).
H(13) listed by Macvicar (1905: 8).
†H13 listed by Blockeel & Long (1998: 57).
H(14) listed by Macvicar (1905: 8).
†H14 listed by Blockeel & Long (1998: 57).
H15 1962: fen nr Cregg Point by Lough Derg, AJE Smith (Paton 1963: 483).
†H16 listed by Blockeel & Long (1998: 57).
H17 1957: fen, Ballindooly, nr Galway City, RE Parker (Castell 1958: 462).
H(18) listed by Macvicar (1905: 8).
†H18 listed by Blockeel & Long (1998: 57).
H(19) listed by Macvicar (1905: 8). H(19) listed by Blockeel & Long (1998: 57).
H19 1999: damp calcareous clayey ground, on W side of Motorway, near Newbridge, DL Kelly (Blackstock 2000: 44).
H(20) listed by Macvicar (1905: 8).
†H20 listed by Blockeel & Long (1998: 57).
H(21) listed by Macvicar (1905: 8). H(21) listed by Blockeel & Long (1998: 57).
H22 1978: tufa by the sea shore, Gormanstown, DM Synnott (Corley 1979: 22).
H23 1967: Scraw Bog, nr Mullingar, ALK King (Paton 1968: 620).
H24 1966: in marsh on E shore of L. Ree, ALK King (Paton 1967c: 394).
H25 1968: peat covered marl, Annaghmore L., 3 miles NW of Strokestown, WV Rubers, P Hessel & J Klein (Paton 1970: 186).
H26 1965: growing through *Campylopus atrovirens*, bog W of L. Talt, [The] Ox Mts, JW Fitzgerald (Paton 1966: 181).
H(27) listed by Macvicar (1905: 8).
†H27 listed by Blockeel & Long (1998: 57).
†H28 listed by Blockeel & Long (1998: 57).
H(29) 1928: wooded glen, NE end of Glencar Lough (BBS exc.) (Duncan 1928: 118).
†H29 listed by Blockeel & Long (1998: 57).
H30 1965: marshy ground nr Corrakeeldrum Lough, Dowra, JW Fitzgerald & EM Lobley (Paton 1966: 181).
H(31) listed by Macvicar (1905: 8).
H31 1966: side of peat cutting, Ardee Bog, DM Synnott (Paton 1967c: 394).
H32 1961: on moist bank in sandpit, Castleshane, nr Monaghan, JW Fitzgerald, originally published (Paton 1962: 356) in error as record from H33, later corrected (Paton 1963: 483).
[H33 record deleted because locality (Castleshane nr Monaghan, Paton 1962: 356) is in H32 (Paton 1963: 483)].
[†H33 listed by Blockeel & Long (1998: 57), but apparently in error in view of deletion of preceding record].
H(34) 1937: Bundoran sand-dunes, no collector named (BBS exc.) (Armitage 1938: 13). 1937: Bundoran sandhills, E Armitage

(anon. 1938c: 28).
†H34 listed by Blockeel & Long (1998: 57).
H(35) listed by Macvicar (1905: 8).
†H35 listed by Blockeel & Long (1998: 57).
H36 1951: wet ground over mica schist, Leagh's Bridge, alt. 850 ft, Draperstown-Plumbridge Road, JW Fitzgerald (Castell 1952: 89).
H(37) listed by Macvicar (1905: 8).
†H37 listed by Blockeel & Long (1998: 57).
H(38) listed by Macvicar (1905: 8). H(38) listed by Blockeel & Long (1998: 57).
H38 2002: with other bryophytes on unshaded damp near-horizontal granite in flush, *ca* 465 m alt., E of Slievenaglogh, J32, DT Holyoak 02-1022 (Blackstock 2003: 44).
H(39) listed by Macvicar (1905: 8).
†H39 listed by Blockeel & Long (1998: 57).
H(40) listed by Macvicar (1905: 8).
†H40 listed by Blockeel & Long (1998: 57).

71/1 ***Cryptothallus mirabilis*** Malmb.

H2 1968: under *Sphagnum fimbriatum* in woodland beside Doo L., nr Muckross House, Killarney, JH Dickson (Paton 1969a: 866, Dickson 1969).
H16 1970: under birch-shaded *Sphagnum*, W of Bunowen R., S of Killary Harbour, JA Paton (Paton 1971a: 369).
H20 1975: beneath *Sphagnum recurvum* in willow/birch wood, S end of L. Dan, PH Pitkin (BBS exc.) (Paton 1976: 17).
H35 1991: under *Sphagnum* and *Betula* near path above W side of Glenlack, Glenveagh, C01, NF Stewart (DBN) (Long 1992: 24).

72/1 ***Riccardia multifida*** (L.) Gray
(syn. *Aneura ambrosioides* Pearson, *A. multifida* (L.) Dumort.)

H(1) listed by Macvicar (1905: 9) as *A. multifida*. H(1) listed by Macvicar (1905: 9) as *A. ambrosioides*.
†H1 listed by Blockeel & Long (1998: 57).
H(2) listed by Macvicar (1905: 9) as *A. multifida*. H(2) listed by Macvicar (1905: 9) as *A. ambrosioides*.
†H2 listed by Blockeel & Long (1998: 57).
[H(3) listed by Macvicar (1905: 9)].
H3 1953: growing with *A. pinguis* on bank of stream, 1200 ft alt., Foulastookeen Mt., ALK King (Castell 1954: 471).
H4 1966: boggy ground on moor, Musheramore, Boggeragh Mts, MFV Corley & JS Parker (Paton 1967c: 394).
H(5) listed by Macvicar (1905: 9) as *A. ambrosioides*.
†H5 listed by Blockeel & Long (1998: 57).
†H6 listed by Blockeel & Long (1998: 57).
[H(7) listed by Macvicar (1905: 9)].
H7 1966: flush on slopes above L. Curra, Galtee Mts, ERB Little & JA Paton (BBS exc.) (Paton 1967c: 394).
[H(8) listed by Macvicar (1905: 9)].
H8 1966: wet drip at 1300 ft alt., S of Galtymore, Galtee Mts, JW Fitzgerald *et al.* (BBS exc.) (Paton 1967c: 394).
[H(9) listed by Macvicar (1905: 9)].
H9 1956: damp shaded bank, Spa Glen, Lisdoonvarna, ALK King (Castell 1957: 322).
H10 1951: wet rocks by stream in shaded gully, alt. 900 ft, above Silvermines, AD Banwell, EV Watson & PJ Wanstall (Castell 1952: 90).
H11 1954: ditch by Ballyeogan Rd, Graiguenamanagh, ALK King (Castell 1955: 578).
[H(12) listed by Macvicar (1905: 9)].
H(12) 1913: Great Saltee I., HW Lett (*Irish Nat.* **22**, 194, 1913), comm JW Fitzgerald (Castell 1952: 90).
†H12 listed by Blockeel & Long (1998: 57).
[H(13) listed by Macvicar (1905: 9)].
H13 1975: bank by stream, The Black Banks, Mt Leinster, JA Paton (BBS exc.) (Paton 1976: 16).
[H(14) listed by Macvicar (1905: 9)].
H15 1994: mildly base-rich flush, above Boleyneendorish River, Slieve Aughty, M50, JA Paton 7622 (Long 1995b: 37).
[H(16) listed by Macvicar (1905: 9)].
H16 1957: roadside bank, Tullywee Bridge, Kylemore, AC Crundwell (BBS exc.) (Castell 1958: 462).
H(17) listed by Macvicar (1905: 9).
†H17 listed by Blockeel & Long (1998: 57).
H(18) listed by Macvicar (1905: 9).
†H18 listed by Blockeel & Long (1998: 57).
H(19) listed by Macvicar (1905: 9). H(19) listed by Blockeel & Long (1998: 57).
H(20) listed by Macvicar (1905: 9).
†H20 listed by Blockeel & Long (1998: 57).
H(21) listed by Macvicar (1905: 9). H(21) listed by Blockeel & Long (1998: 57).
[H(22) listed by Macvicar (1905: 9)].
H(23) listed by Macvicar (1905: 9).

†H23 listed by Blockeel & Long (1998: 57).
H24 1957: bog, Newtownforbes [*sic* = Newtown Forbes], MPH Kertland & ALK King, comm. ALK King (Castell 1958: 462).
H25 1968: loamy bank, Slieve Bawn, WV Rubers, P Hessel & J Klein (Paton 1970: 186).
[H(26) listed by Macvicar (1905: 9)].
H26 1970: wet ground on edge of bog pool, Glendaduff, NE of Foxford, MFV Corley (Paton 1971a: 368).
H(27) listed by Macvicar (1905: 9).
†H27 listed by Blockeel & Long (1998: 57).
[H(28) listed by Macvicar (1905: 9)].
H28 1970: steep acid outcrops of Knockalongy, above L. Minnaun, [The] Ox Mts, DM Synnott (BBS exc.) (Paton 1971a: 368, Appleyard 1971: 387).
[H(29) listed by Macvicar (1905: 9)].
H(29) 1928: wooded glen, NE end of Glencar Lough (BBS exc.) (Duncan 1928: 118).
†H29 listed by Blockeel & Long (1998: 57).
[H(30) listed by Macvicar (1905: 9)].
H30 1965: wet rocks at Englishman's House, 3 miles S of Glenfarne, JW Fitzgerald (Paron 1966: 180).
H(31) listed by Blockeel & Long (1998: 57).
H31 1999: among *Fissidens osmundoides* in weakly base-rich flush on moorland slope, *ca* 250-300 m alt., Two Mile River, Carlingford Mt., J11, TL Blockeel 28/166 (Blackstock 2000: 44).
H32 1954: damp ground, woods, Glaslough Ho.[use], ALK King (Castell 1955: 578).
†H33 listed by Blockeel & Long (1998: 57).
[H(34) listed by Macvicar (1905: 9)].
H34 1969: damp bank on coast, Balloor, Doagh Isle, W of Malin, JA Paton (Paton 1979: 186).
†H35 listed by Blockeel & Long (1998: 57).
H36 1951: in crevice with *Hookeria lucens*, alt. 950 ft, Lough Lee, JW Fitzgerald (Castell 1952: 90).
H(37) listed by Macvicar (1905: 9).
†H37 listed by Blockeel & Long (1998: 57).
H(38) 1928: Slieve Donard (BBS exc.) (Duncan 1928: 114, 117).
†H38 listed by Blockeel & Long (1998: 57).
[H(39) listed by Macvicar (1905: 9)].
H(39) 1928: Glenariff (BBS exc.) (Duncan 1928: 117).
†H39 listed by Blockeel & Long (1998: 57).
H40 1964: in drip below rocks, Altnaheglish, nr Dungiven, JW Fitzgerald (Paton 1965a: 851).

72/2 ***Riccardia chamedryfolia*** (With.) Grolle (syn. *Aneura major* (Lindb.) Müll.Frib., *A. sinuata* Dumort, *A. sinuata* var. *major* (Lindb.) Macvicar, *Riccardia major* Lindb., *R. sinuata* (Hook.) Trevis, *R. sinuata* var. *major* (Nees) Arnell)

[H(1) listed by Macvicar (1905: 9)].
H(1) 1935: Dunmore Head, no collector named (BBS exc.) (Watson 1936: 265), as *Aneura major*.
1935: Dunmore Head, no collector named (BBS exc.) (anon. 1937b: 369), as *Aneura sinuata*.
†H1 listed by Blockeel & Long (1998: 58).
H(2) listed by Macvicar (1905: 9).
†H2 listed by Blockeel & Long (1998: 58).
†H3 listed by Blockeel & Long (1998: 58).
H(4) 1851: Inniscarra, I Carroll (BEL) (Paton 1967c: 394).
H4 1966: flush in old quarry, Shipool, S of Innishannon, MFV Corley & JS Parker (Paton 1967c: 394).
H(5) listed by Macvicar (1905: 9).
†H5 listed by Blockeel & Long (1998: 58).
H6 1956: wet roadside rocks, Glendine, nr Youghal, EC Wallace (Castell 1957: 322).
H(7) listed by Macvicar (1905: 9).
†H7 listed by Blockeel & Long (1998: 58).
H8 1966: below waterfall, stream S of Galtymore, Galtee Mts, JW Fitzgerald *et al.* (BBS exc.) (Paton 1967c: 394).
H9 1964: on wet shale beside stream, Lisdoonvarna, ERB Little (Paton 1966: 180).
H10 1967: wet shaded rocks in wooded valley, Clare Glen, nr Newport, HH Birks, HJB Birks & DA Ratcliffe (Paton 1968: 619).
H11 1966: old sandpit, Dysart Castle, Inistioge, JG Duckett *et al.* (BBS exc.) (Paton 1967c: 394).
H(12) 1913: Great Saltee I., HW Lett (*Irish Nat.* **22**, 194, 1913) comm. JW Fitzgerald (Castell 1952: 90).
†H12 listed by Blockeel & Long (1998: 58).
H13 1969: leaf mould at edge of disused quarry, Kilcarry Bridge nr Clonegal, JW Fitzgerald (Paton 1970: 186).
H14 1957: rotting wood, bog cutting, Kylee Bog, AA Cridland (Castell 1958: 462).

H15 1970: bank in old limestone quarry 4 miles W of Ballinasloe, JA Paton (Paton 1971a: 368).
H16 1957: submerged in stream, gully below Benchollaghduff, J Appleyard (Castell 1958: 462).
H19 1969: wet side of track through Derryvullagh Bog nr Athy, JW Fitzgerald (Paton 1971a: 368).
H(20) listed by Macvicar (1905: 9).
†H20 listed by Blockeel & Long (1998: 58).
H(21) listed by Blockeel & Long (1998: 58).
H21 1999: on flat wet grassy ground, upper part of Dalkey Quarry, Dalkey, O22, DL Kelly (Blackstock 2000: 44).
H22 1978: wet rocks by the road, SE of Stackallen Bridge, Slane, DM Synnott (Corley 1979: 22).
H23 1966: bog at Newell's Bridge, 2 miles N of Ballynagore, JW Fitzgerald & EM Lobley (Paton 1967c: 394).
H24 1968: peaty ditch bank, bog 1 mile SE of Cloondara, WV Rubers, P Hessel & J Klein (Paton 1970: 186).
H25 1968: lime-rich loamy soil, pasture on shores of L. Ree at Lanesborough, WV Rubers, P Hessel & J Klein (Paton 1970: 186).
H26 1965: wet peaty flush, S of Glendaduff, [The] Ox Mts, JW Fitzgerald (Paton 1966: 180).
†H27 listed by Blockeel & Long (1998: 58).
†H28 listed by Blockeel & Long (1998: 58).
H29 1963: on shaded rocks above Glencar, JW Fitzgerald & AR Perry (Paton 1964: 712).
H(30) listed by Macvicar (1905: 9). H(30) listed by Blockeel & Long (1998: 58).
H30 2001: on almost unshaded steep damp soil of bank above ditch, beside track, *ca* 219 m alt., N of Legeelan, H03, DT Holyoak 01-741 (Blackstock 2002: 41).
H33 1957: damp bank, roadside N of Cuilcagh, AC Crundwell (Castell 1958: 462).
H34 1962: field, E side of Bulbin [Mt.], AC Crundwell, EC Wallace & EF Warburg (BBS exc.) (Paton 1963: 483).
†H35 listed by Blockeel & Long (1998: 58).
H36 1950: on limestone, wet place by water's edge, Stewartstown Castle, JW Fitzgerald (Castell 1951: 491).
H37 1964: fallow field SE corner of Lough Gullion, JW Fitzgerald (Paton 1965a: 851).
H(38) 1917: Scrobo [*sic* = Scrabo] Quarries, J Glover (anon. 1918b: 14), labelled as *Aneura multifida*, but material in four packets redet. as *Aneura major* by DA Jones.
H(38) listed by Macvicar (1915: 9). H(38) listed by Blockeel & Long (1998: 58).
H38 2002: on thin soil over horizontal sandstone in floor of old quarry, part-shaded by scrub, *ca* 100 m alt., Scrabo quarry, J47, DT Holyoak 02-1026 (Blackstock 2003: 44).
H(39) 1928: Glenariff (BBS exc.) (Duncan 1928: 117), as *Aneura sinuata* var. *major*.
H39 1950: very wet, partially submerged peat, Big Frosses, JW Fitzgerald (Castell 1951: 491).
H40 1969: sandy cliffs, Downhill, NW of Coleraine, JA Paton (Paton 1970: 186).

72/3 *Riccardia incurvata* Lindb.

H1 1983: sandy soil in marsh behind shore, L. Leane, NW of Tomies Wood, JA Paton (Corley 1984: 23).
H9 1968: peat in old cutting nr Shandangan L., NE of Corofin, JA Paton (Paton 1969a: 866, 1969b).
H16 1969: gravelly lay-by 3 miles E of Lettercrafroe L., AR Perry & HJ Perry (Paton 1970: 182).
H20 1973: roadside pit, nr Sally Gap, Wicklow Mts, WV Rubers (Corley 1980a: 26).
H27 1968: gravelly layby, Killary Harbour, SW of Aasleagh, JA Paton (Paton 1969a: 866, 1969b).
H35 1969: E shore of L. Meela, Dunglow, JA Paton (Paton 1975: 9).
H38 2002: on unshaded partly bare damp sand by edge of pool in old sand quarry, *ca* 20 m alt., SW of Kilkeel, J21, DT Holyoak 02-1058 (Blackstock 2003: 44).

72/4 *Riccardia palmata* (Hedw.) Carruth.
(syn. *Aneura palmata* (Hedw.) Dumort.)

H(1) listed by Macvicar (1905: 9).
†H1 listed by Blockeel & Long (1998: 58).
H(2) listed by Macvicar (1905: 9).
†H2 listed by Blockeel & Long (1998: 58).
H(3) listed by Macvicar (1905: 9).
†H3 listed by Blockeel & Long (1998: 58).
H6 1999: on rotting log in oak woodland, *ca*

90 m alt., Owennashad River, just N of Drumber Bridge, Lismore, S00, TL Blockeel 28/208 (Blackstock 2000: 44).

H7 1966: wet peat, bog W of Longfordpass Bridge, Urlingford, JA Paton (BBS exc.) (Paton 1967c: 394).

H9 1979: vertical peat wall NE of Lough Cullaunyheeda, nr Derrymore House, HMH van Melick (Corley 1981: 17).

H11 1966: on peat, bog at Derryfadda W of Johnstown, ERB Little (BBS exc.) (Paton 1967c: 394).

H15 1957: fallen tree trunk, Chevy Chase Woods, Owendalulleegh, nr Gort, DG Catcheside & EM Lobley (BBS exc.), comm. EM Lobley (Castell 1958: 462).

H(16) listed by Macvicar (1905: 9).

†H16 listed by Blockeel & Long (1998: 58).

[H(18) listed by Macvicar (1905: 9). H18 deleted because voucher specimen (1897: Geashill, CD Russell, DBN) is *R. latifrons* (Long 1990a: 24)].

H(20) listed by Macvicar (1905: 9).

†H20 listed by Blockeel & Long (1998: 58).

H23 1970: rotten wood, carr S of Doonis L., N of Glassan, JA Paton (Paton 1971a: 369).

H24 1986: among *Sphagnum* in *Betula* flush on raised bog, Clooneen, H Grogan & C Douglas (Corley 1987: 18).

H25 1970: bog nr Kilteevan House, E of Roscommon, JA Paton (Paton 1971a: 369).

H26 1965: on peat on cliff ledges S of Glendaduff, [The] Ox Mts, JW Fitzgerald (Paton 1966: 181).

H(27) listed by Macvicar (1905: 9).

†H27 listed by Blockeel & Long (1998: 58).

H28 1965: on ditch bank by track, Slish Wood, Lough Gill, JW Fitzgerald & EM Lobley (Paton 1966: 181).

H(29) 1928: wooded glen, NE end of Glencar Lough (BBS exc.) (Duncan 1928: 118).

†H29 listed by Blockeel & Long (1998: 58).

H(30) listed by Macvicar (1905: 9).

†H30 listed by Blockeel & Long (1998: 58).

H33 1959: on thin peat over shaded rock, Aghahoorin, nr Boho, JW Fitzgerald (Castell 1960: 763).

H34 1962: on peaty bank, N side of Croaghconnellagh, EF Warburg (BBS exc.) (Paton 1963: 483).

H35 1961: rotten log in damp woods facing NW at 500 ft [alt.], Glenbeagh, nr Dunlewy, DA Ratcliffe (Paton 1962: 356).

H36 1957: rotten logs in wood, Sheskinawaddy, nr Castlederg, JW Fitzgerald (Castell 1959: 626).

H39 1969: damp sandstone cliffs, W side of Murlough Bay, E of Ballycastle, JA Paton (Paton 1970: 186).

H40 1968: rotting wood, Banagher Glen nr Dungiven, JW Fitzgerald & HH Birks (Paton 1969a: 866).

72/5 ***Riccardia latifrons*** (Lindb.) Lindb. (syn. *Aneura latifrons* Lindb.)

H(1) listed by Macvicar (1905: 9).

†H1 listed by Blockeel & Long (1998: 58).

[H(2) listed by Macvicar (1905: 9)].

H2 1966: on *Sphagnum*, heathy slope nr Galways Bridge, Killarney, JA Paton, GCG Argent & EM Lobley (Paton 1967c: 394).

[H(3) listed by Macvicar (1905: 9)].

H3 1968: peaty bank on coast SW of Dog's Point, Kenmare R., JA Paton (Paton 1969a: 866).

[H(6) listed by Macvicar (1905: 9)].

H6 1966: on *Leucobryum* and *Sphagnum*, bog nr road E of the Punchbowl, Comeragh Mts, ERB Little & JA Paton (BBS exc.) (Paton 1967c: 394).

H7 1966: on peat, bog W of Longfordpass Bridge, Urlingford, ERB Little *et al.* (BBS exc.) (Paton 1967c: 394).

H8 1959: bog E of Castleconnell, ALK King (Castell 1960: 763).

H9 1962: vertical peat face, Lough Goller SW of Lisdoonvarna, G Halliday (Paton 1963: 483).

H10 1959: bog W of Newport, ALK King (Castell 1960: 763).

H11 1966: on peat, bog at Derryfadda W of Johnstown, ERB Little (BBS exc.) (Paton 1967c: 394).

H12 1969: peat in bog, Sculloge Gap, Kiltealy, JW Fitzgerald (Paton 1970: 186).

H13 1969: bog at Knockullard nr Borris, JW Fitzgerald (Paton 1971a: 368).

H(14) listed by Macvicar (1905: 9). H(14) listed by Blockeel & Long (1998: 58).

H15 1962: decaying tree stump, raised bog nr Woodford, AJE Smith (Paton 1963: 483).

H16 1968: rotten pine log, roadside E of Kylemore Castle, DM Synnott (Paton

1969a: 866).
[H(17) listed by Macvicar (1905: 9)].
[H(18) listed by Macvicar (1905: 9)].
H18 1952: Rahan Bog, ALK King (Paton 1967c: 394).
H19 1955: on ground in bog, Baronstown East, nr Newbridge, ALK King (Castell 1956: 147).
[H(20) listed by Macvicar (1905: 9)].
H20 1975: boggy slope nr Ballycayle, Glencree R., JA Paton & PH Pitkin (BBS exc.) (Paton 1976: 16).
H(21) listed by Macvicar (1905: 9). H(21) listed by Blockeel & Long (1998: 58).
H22 1952: bank, Clonycavan Bog, nr Ballivor, ALK King (Castell 1953: 297).
H23 1952: Derries Bog, ALK King (Castell 1953: 297).
H24 1965: on peat in raised bog S of Roosky, JW Fitzgerald & EM Lobley (Paton 1966: 180).
H25 1967: Cleaheen Bog, R.[ight] bank of R. Shannon above Carrick-on-Shannon, ALK King (Paton 1968: 619-620).
H(27) listed by Macvicar (1905: 9).
†H27 listed by Blockeel & Long (1998: 58).
H(28) 1937: Creevykeel, Cliffony, CV Marquand & EM Lobley (E) (Paton 1965a: 852).
†H28 listed by Blockeel & Long (1998: 58).
H29 1961: on rotting wood with *Lejeunea patens*, Glencar, JW Fitzgerald & MPH Kertland (Paton 1962: 356).
[H(30) listed by Macvicar (1905: 9)].
H33 1959: peat, Immeroo Bog, nr Tempo, JW Fitzgerald (Castell 1960: 763).
H34 1968: peat on bog at Gorey nr Culdaff, Inishowen, JW Fitzgerald & HH Birks (Paton 1969a: 866).
†H35 listed by Blockeel & Long (1998: 58).
H36 1957: wet detritus beside stream, Willmount Glen, nr Drumquin, JW Fitzgerald (Castell 1959: 626).
[H(38) 1917: Scrobo [*sic* = Scrabo] Quarries, J Glover (anon. 1918b: 14), labelled as *Aneura multifida*, but material in two packets redet. as *A. latifrons* by DA Jones].
H37 1952: on peat, Lough Gullion, JW Fitzgerald (Paton 1963: 483).
H39 1969: wet peat below sandstone cliffs, W side of Murlough Bay, E of Ballycastle, JA Paton (Paton 1970: 186).
H40 1952: *Sphagnum* peat, Benbradagh, EM Lobley & J Taylor, comm. J Taylor (Castell 1953: 297).

73/1 ***Metzgeria fruticulosa*** (Dicks.) A.Evans (syn. *Metzgeria furcata* var. *fruticulosa* (Dicks.) Lindb., *M. furcata* var. *aeruginosa* (Hook.) Gottsche, Lindenb. & Nees)

[H1 records not confirmed as *M. fruticulosa s.s.* in revision by Paton 1977b: 447].
H1 1979: on tree by Roughty R., near Kenmare, RC Stern (Corley 1980a: 26).
[H2 listed by Paton 1977b: 447 and Corley 1978: 12, but deleted because locality of record (1894: Ventry, D McArdle, DBN) is in H1, comm. DM Synnott & MM Yeo, replaced with following record (Long 1990a: 23-24)].
H2 1983: Ross I., Killarney, DM Synnott (DBN), comm. DM Synnott & MM Yeo (Long 1990a: 23-24).
H3 listed by Paton (1977b: 447) and Corley (1978: 12). †H3 listed by Blockeel & Long (1998: 58).
H4 listed by Paton (1977b: 447) and Corley (1978: 12). †H4 listed by Blockeel & Long (1998: 58).
H5 listed by Paton (1977b: 447) and Corley (1978: 12). †H5 listed by Blockeel & Long (1998: 58).
H6 listed by Paton (1977b: 447) and Corley (1978: 12). †H6 listed by Blockeel & Long (1998: 58).
[H7 records not confirmed as *M. fruticulosa s.s.* in revision by Paton 1977b: 447].
H8 listed by Paton (1977b: 447) and Corley (1978: 12). †H8 listed by Blockeel & Long (1998: 58).
H9 listed by Paton (1977b: 447) and Corley (1978: 12). †H9 listed by Blockeel & Long (1998: 58).
H10 listed by Paton (1977b: 447) and Corley (1978: 12). †H10 listed by Blockeel & Long (1998: 58).
H11 listed by Paton (1977b: 447) and Corley (1978: 12). †H11 listed by Blockeel & Long (1998: 58).
[H12 records not confirmed as *M. fruticulosa s.s.* in revision by Paton 1977b: 447].
H(13) listed by Paton (1977b: 447), Corley (1978: 12) and Blockeel & Long (1998: 58).
H13 1999: on *Salix* in scrubby woodland on bank of stream, *ca* 35 m alt., N bank of Pollymounty River, Ballyknockcrumpin,

S73, TL Blockeel 28/306 (Blackstock 2000: 44).

[H14 records not confirmed as *M. fruticulosa s.s.* in revision by Paton 1977b: 447].

H15 listed by Paton (1977b: 447) and Corley (1978: 12). [Record of var. *ulvula* deleted because specimen (NMW) is *M. temperata*, comm. DG Long (Corley 1978: 12)].

[H16 records not confirmed as *M. fruticulosa s.s.* in revision by Paton 1977b: 447].

H(16) 1860: on trees, Oughterard, Connemara, W Sutcliffe, Hb. Bankfield Museum [Halifax] (Corley 1979: 22).

†H16 listed by Blockeel & Long (1998: 58).

H17 listed by Paton (1977b: 447) and Corley (1978: 12). †H17 listed by Blockeel & Long (1998: 58).

H(18) listed by Paton (1977b: 447), Corley (1978: 12) and Blockeel & Long (1998: 58).

H(19) 1857: Ballyton, JH Davis (E) (Paton 1977b: 447, Corley 1978: 12).

[H20 records not confirmed as *M. fruticulosa s.s.* in revision by Paton 1977b: 447].

H20 1994: on *Sambucus* by old farm buildings, 190 m alt., Knockaphrumpa, SE of Roundwood, T29, DG Long 25430 (Long 1995b: 37).

[H21 records not confirmed as *M. fruticulosa s.s.* in revision by Paton 1977b: 447].

†H21 listed by Blockeel & Long (1998: 58).

[H22 1969: willows beside R. Boyne, W of Donor nr Drogheda, JA Paton (Paton 1970: 187). H22 records not confirmed as *M. fruticulosa s.s.* in revision by Paton 1977b: 447].

H23 listed by Paton (1977b: 447) and Corley (1978: 12). †H23 listed by Blockeel & Long (1998: 58).

H24 listed by Paton (1977b: 447) and Corley (1978: 12). †H24 listed by Blockeel & Long (1998: 58).

H25 listed by Paton (1977b: 447) and Corley (1978: 12). †H25 listed by Blockeel & Long (1998: 58).

H26 listed by Paton (1977b: 447) and Corley (1978: 12). †H26 listed by Blockeel & Long (1998: 58).

[H27 records not confirmed as *M. fruticulosa s.s.* in revision by Paton 1977b: 447].

H27 1987: on flaky bark of *Fuchsia* in hedge, lane below Slievemore, Dugort, Achill I., DG Long (Long 1988: 30).

H28 listed by Paton (1977b: 447) and Corley (1978: 12). †H28 listed by Blockeel & Long (1998: 58).

H29 listed by Paton (1977b: 447) and Corley (1978: 12). †H29 listed by Blockeel & Long (1998: 58).

[H30 listed by Paton (1977b: 447) and Corley 1978: 12, but deleted because record is unlocalised, comm. MM Yeo, replaced by next record (Long 1990a: 24)].

H30 1969: on willow by stream, NE slope of Slievenakilla, NE of Ballinagleragh, JA Paton (NMW) (Long 1990a: 24).

H31 listed by Paton (1977b: 447) and Corley (1978: 12). †H31 listed by Blockeel & Long (1998: 58).

H32 listed by Paton (1977b: 447) and Corley (1978: 12). †H32 listed by Blockeel & Long (1998: 58).

H33 listed by Paton (1977b: 447) and Corley (1978: 12). †H33 listed by Blockeel & Long (1998: 58).

[H34 records not confirmed as *M. fruticulosa s.s.* in revision by Paton 1977b: 447].

H34 2002: on bark of *Salix cinerea* by small stream in scrub edge on N-facing slope above sandy beach, *ca* 15 m alt., Kinnoge Bay, C64, DT Holyoak 02-541 (Blackstock 2003: 45).

H35 listed by Paton (1977b: 447) and Corley (1978: 12). †H35 listed by Blockeel & Long (1998: 58).

H36 listed by Paton (1977b: 447) and Corley (1978: 12). †H36 listed by Blockeel & Long (1998: 58).

H37 listed by Paton (1977b: 447) and Corley (1978: 12). †H37 listed by Blockeel & Long (1998: 58).

H38 listed by Paton (1977b: 447) and Corley (1978: 12). †H38 listed by Blockeel & Long (1998: 58).

H39 listed by Paton (1977b: 447) and Corley (1978: 12). †H39 listed by Blockeel & Long (1998: 58).

H40 listed by Paton (1977b: 447) and Corley (1978: 12). †H40 listed by Blockeel & Long (1998: 58).

See Paton (1977b) for separation of Irish records of this species and the next. Older records of '*M. furcata* var. *aeruginosa*' and 'var. *prolifera*' (e.g. in Macvicar 1905: 9) and '*M. fruticulosa*' can only be referred to the aggregate of these two species (see next entry) unless specimens have been revised since 1977.

73/1 ***Metzgeria fruticulosa***
or
73/2 ***M. temperata***

H3 1966: ash trunks on edge of wood W of Kilmurry, MFV Corley & JS Parker (Paton 1967c: 395).
H4 1966: ash trunk on roadside nr Rylane Cross, Boggeragh Mts, MFV Corley & JS Parker (Paton 1967c: 395).
H5 1966: on sycamore, 5 miles E of Fermoy, J Appleyard & JG Duckett (BBS exc.) (Paton 1967c: 395).
H6 1964: on fallen *Salix* by R. Glendine, ALK King (Paton 1966: 181).
H8 1966: ash trunk by road, Ballylanders, MFV Corley & JS Parker (Paton 1967c: 395).
H9 1957: on hazel in scrub, SE side of Slievecarran, AC Crundwell (BBS exc.) (Castell 1958: 462).
H10 1951: branches of alder in damp shaded gully, alt. *ca* 900 ft, above Silvermines, AD Banwell, EV Watson & PJ Wanstall (Castell 1952: 90).
H11 1966: on trees nr Foulkscourt House, W of Johnstown, ERB Little (BBS exc.) (Paton 1967c: 395).
H15 1957: trunk of ash, Garryland Wood, nr Gort, AC Crundwell (BBS exc.) (Castell 1958: 462).
H17 1957: on alders in small wood 5 miles S of Hedford, AC Crundwell (BBS exc.) (Castell 1958: 462).
H23 1961: trees N of Castle Pollard, EM Lobley (Paton 1962: 357).
H24 1957: on trees, Ballymacarrow Bridge, MPH Kertland & ALK King, comm. ALK King (Castell 1958: 462).
H26 1965: on *Salix* below cliffs S of Glendaduff, [The] Ox Mts, JW Fitzgerald (Paton 1966: 181).
H32 1961: on elder trees in small wood, Castleshane, nr Monaghan, JW Fitzgerald (Paton 1962: 357).
H35 1955: on willow nr Glenties, UK Duncan (Castell 1956: 147).
H37 1962: elder tree in shady wood, Tannyoki nr Poyntz Pass, EM Lobley & MPH Kertland (BBS exc.) (Paton 1963: 483).
H40 1951: on blackthorn, 630 ft alt., Altikeeragh, nr Castlerock, JW Fitzgerald (Castell 1953: 298).

Some of records listed above will be based on specimens later redet. as *M. fruticulosa* s.s. by Paton (1977b: 447) and listed by Corley (1978: 12), for which only vice-county numbers were published.

73/2 ***Metzgeria temperata*** Kuwah.
(syn. *Metzgeria fruticulosa* auct. pro parte non (Dicks.) A.Evans)

H3 1968: NE slope of Lackawee, Slieve Miskish Mts, JA Paton (Paton 1977b: 449, Corley 1978: 12).
H4 1967: Musherabeg, JW Fitzgerald (BBSUK) (Paton 1977b: 449, Corley 1978: 12).
H5 1979: on *Salix*, Fota I., N Kirby (Corley 1980a: 26).
H6 1966: N of Punchbowl, S of Clonmel, JW Fitzgerald (BBSUK) (Paton 1977b: 449, Corley 1978: 12).
H7 1966: Coopers Wood, S of Galtymore, Galtee Mts, JW Fitzgerald *et al.* (BBS exc.) (BBSUK) (Paton 1967c: 395, 1977b: 449, Corley 1978: 12).
H9 1957: Maghera Wood, Tulla, ALK King (NMW) (Paton 1977b: 449, Corley 1978: 12).
H12 1969: trees by stream, Wicklow Gap, JW Fitzgerald (BBSUK) (Paton 1970: 187, 1977b: 449, Corley 1978: 12).
H13 2002: bark on almost unshaded branch on felled *Picea sitchensis* at edge of clearing in plantation, *ca* 310 m alt., S slope of Croaghaun, S85, DT Holyoak 02-358 (Blackstock 2003: 45).
H15 1957: Chevy Chase 8 km ESE of Gort, DH Dalby (BM) (Paton 1977b: 449, Corley 1978: 12).
H16 1957: trunk of alder, Tullywee Bridge, Kylemore, AC Crundwell (BBS exc.) (BBSUK) (Castell 1958: 462, Paton 1977b: 449, Corley 1978: 12).
H22 1978: beech bole in fringe woodland, by Moate Farm, Moynalty, DM Synnott (Corley 1980a: 26).
H24 1965: Cloonart Bridge nr Roosky, JW Fitzgerald (Paton 1977b: 449, Corley 1978: 12).
H25 1965: trees, Kilronan nr Ballyfarnan, EM Lobley & JW Fitzgerald (BBSUK) (Paton 1966: 181, 1977b: 449, Corley 1978: 12).
H27 1987: on sycamore trunk, N of

Slievemore Hotel, Dugort, Achill I., JA Paton (Long 1988: 30).

H29 1984: on *Salix* in damp wooded valley below Corglass, Glencar Lough, DG Long (Corley 1985: 20).

H31 1953: on Scots Pine, Ravensdale State Forest, ALK King (BBSUK) (Castell 1954: 471, Paton 1977b: 449, Corley 1978: 12).

H33 1957: trunk of *Alnus incana*, wood on SE. side of Belmore Mt., AC Crundwell (BBSUK) (Castell 1958: 462, Paton 1977b: 449, Corley 1978: 12).

H34 2001: on *Salix cinerea* in swampy woodland by river, *ca* 70 m alt., Cloghan More, H09, NG Hodgetts 3859 (Blackstock 2003: 45).

H35 1990: on bole of ornamental evergreen, *ca* 60 m alt., Glenveagh Castle, Glenveagh, C02, Blockeel 19/423 (Long 1991: 37).

H36 1950: Drum Manor, nr Cookstown, MPH Kertland (BEL) (Corley 1979: 22).

H38 2002: on base of *Pinus radiata* trunk near edge of young plantation of that species, *ca* 295 m alt., near S end of Fofanny Dam, J22, DT Holyoak 02-972 (Blackstock 2003: 45).

H39 1990: on *Salix caprea* trunk, Breen Wood, D13, DM Synnott (Long 1991: 37).

Irish records of this species had been confused with those of *M. fruticulosa* prior to the paper by Paton (1977b).

73/3 ***Metzgeria furcata*** (L.) Dumort.
(syn. *Metzgeria furcata* var. *ulvula* Nees)

H(1) listed by Macvicar (1905: 9).

H1 1951: large cushions on trees, L. Currane, EW Jones, comm. JW Fitzgerald (Castell 1952: 90), as var. *ulvula*.

H(2) listed by Macvicar (1905: 9).

†H2 listed by Blockeel & Long (1998: 58).

H(3) listed by Macvicar (1905: 9).

H3 1968: rhododendron stems, coast nr Dunboy Castle, Castletownbere, JA Paton (Paton 1969a: 866), as var. *ulvula*.

H4 1951: trunk of tree by roadside, NW of Mallow, AC Crundwell (Castell 1952: 90).

†H5 listed by Blockeel & Long (1998: 58).

H(6) listed by Macvicar (1905: 9).

†H6 listed by Blockeel & Long (1998: 58).

H(7) listed by Macvicar (1905: 9).

†H7 listed by Blockeel & Long (1998: 58).

H8 1966: oak trunk in wood by sea, wood E of Tarbert, MFV Corley & JS Parker (Paton 1967c: 395).

H(9) 1907: Ballyvaughan, HW Lett (anon. 1909b: 319).

H9 1957: on Spruce, Maghera Wood, Tulla, ALK King (Castell 1958: 462).

H10 1951: face of recently disused quarry, alt. 500 ft, hills between Ballina and Newtown, AD Banwell, EV Watson & PJ Wanstall (Castell 1952: 90).

H11 1952: on beech, Farmley Wood, nr Cuffe's Grange, ALK King & MPH Kertland, comm. ALK King (Castell 1953: 298).

H(12) 1907: Killanne, HW Lett (anon. 1909b: 319).

†H12 listed by Blockeel & Long (1998: 58).

H(13) listed by Macvicar (1905: 9).

†H13 listed by Blockeel & Long (1998: 58).

H(14) listed by Macvicar (1905: 9).

†H14 listed by Blockeel & Long (1998: 58).

H15 1952: on trees, Ross Quay, Lough Derg, ALK King (Castell 1953: 298).
1957: stems of spruce, Owendalulleegh, RE Parker (Castell 1958: 462), as var. *ulvula*.

†H16 listed by Blockeel & Long (1998: 58).

[H17 deleted because no record traced, comm. MM Yeo, replaced by following record (Long 1990a: 24)].

H(17) 1896: oak wood, Clonbrock, D McArdle (DBN), comm. DM Synnott (Long 1990a: 24).

[H(17) listed by Macvicar (1905: 9)].

[H18 deleted because no record traced, comm. MM Yeo, replaced by following record (Long 1990a: 24)].

H(18) 1949: copse by road near Black Bull, Sharavogue, AP Fanning (DBN), comm. DM Synnott (Long 1990a: 24).

[H(18) listed by Macvicar (1905: 9)].

H(19) listed by Macvicar (1905: 9).

†H19 listed by Blockeel & Long (1998: 58).

H(20) listed by Macvicar (1905: 9).

†H20 listed by Blockeel & Long (1998: 58).

H(21) listed by Macvicar (1905: 9).

†H21 listed by Blockeel & Long (1998: 58).

H(22) listed by Macvicar (1905: 9).

†H22 listed by Blockeel & Long (1998: 58).

†H23 listed by Blockeel & Long (1998: 58).

H24 1965: on trees in wood, Cloonart Bridge nr Roosky, JW Fitzgerald & EM Lobley (Paton 1966: 181).
†H25 listed by Blockeel & Long (1998: 58).
H(26) listed by Macvicar (1905: 9).
†H26 listed by Blockeel & Long (1998: 58).
H(27) listed by Macvicar (1905: 9).
†H27 listed by Blockeel & Long (1998: 58).
H(28) listed by Macvicar (1905: 9).
†H28 listed by Blockeel & Long (1998: 58).
H(29) listed by Macvicar (1905: 9).
†H29 listed by Blockeel & Long (1998: 58).
H(30) listed by Macvicar (1905: 9).
†H30 listed by Blockeel & Long (1998: 58).
H31 1953: Ravensdale State Forest, ALK King (Castell 1954: 471).
H32 1954: on box bole, Glaslough Woods, ALK King (Castell 1955: 578).
†H33 listed by Blockeel & Long (1998: 58).
H(34) listed by Macvicar (1905: 9).
†H34 listed by Blockeel & Long (1998: 58).
H35 1969: elder in valley, Fintragh Bay, W of Killybegs, JA Paton (Paton 1970: 187), as var. *ulvula*.
H36 1951: abundant on beech, Anahoe nr Ballygawley, JW Fitzgerald (Castell 1952: 90).
H(37) listed by Macvicar (1905: 9).
†H37 listed by Blockeel & Long (1998: 58).
H(38) listed by Macvicar (1905: 9). H(38) listed by Blockeel & Long (1998: 58).
H38 1999: on bole of sycamore, *ca* 55 m alt., Tollymore Forest Park, *ca* 4 km W of Newcastle, J33, TL Blockeel 28/332 (Blackstock 2000: 44).
H(39) listed by Macvicar (1905: 9).
†H39 listed by Blockeel & Long (1998: 58).
H40 1951: with *Frullania dilatata*, Downhill nr Castlerock, JW Fitzgerald (Castell 1952: 90).

73/4 ***Metzgeria conjugata*** Lindb.

H(1) listed by Macvicar (1905: 9).
†H1 listed by Blockeel & Long (1998: 58).
H(2) listed by Macvicar (1905: 9).
†H2 listed by Blockeel & Long (1998: 58).
H(3) listed by Macvicar (1905: 9).
†H3 listed by Blockeel & Long (1998: 58).
H(6) listed by Macvicar (1905: 9).
†H6 listed by Blockeel & Long (1998: 58).
H(7) listed by Macvicar (1905: 9).
†H7 listed by Blockeel & Long (1998: 58).
H(8) listed by Macvicar (1905: 9).
†H8 listed by Blockeel & Long (1998: 58).
H(9) listed by Macvicar (1905: 9). H(9) listed by Blockeel & Long (1998: 58).
H10 1979: Clare Glen, EW Jones (Corley 1980a: 26).
H11 1966: shaded rocks, wood by the R. Nore, Inistioge, JW Fitzgerald *et al.* (BBS exc.) (Paton 1967c: 395).
H(12) listed by Macvicar (1905: 9). H(12) listed by Blockeel & Long (1998: 58).
H(13) 1895: trees nr R. Burren, Graigue, D McArdle (DBN), comm. JW Fitzgerald (Castell 1959: 626).
[H(15) record given as 'I. 15*' (1915: Quantock, W Watson, anon.1916b: 169) is probably in error for vc5 in England (South Somerset) where there are Quantock Hills and Quantock Forest; W Watson was active in Somerset around 1915. H(15) is not listed for this species by Blockeel & Long 1998: 58].
H(16) 1933: Lough Fee, PWM Richards (anon. 1938e: 43).
†H16 listed by Blockeel & Long (1998: 58).
H(17) listed by Macvicar (1905: 9). H(17) listed by Blockeel & Long (1998: 58).
H(18) listed by Macvicar (1905: 9). H(18) listed by Blockeel & Long (1998: 58).
H(20) listed by Macvicar (1905: 9).
†H20 listed by Blockeel & Long (1998: 58).
H(21) listed by Macvicar (1905: 9). H(21) listed by Blockeel & Long (1998: 58).
H(22) listed by Macvicar (1905: 9).
†H22 listed by Blockeel & Long (1998: 58).
H(27) listed by Macvicar (1905: 9).
†H27 listed by Blockeel & Long (1998: 58).
H(28) 1928: Gleniff, Ben Bulben (BBS exc.) (Duncan 1928: 118).
†H28 listed by Blockeel & Long (1998: 58).
H(29) 1937: Glenade, no collector named (BBS exc.) (Armitage 1938: 13).
†H29 listed by Blockeel & Long (1998: 58).
H(30) listed by Macvicar (1905: 9). H(30) listed by Blockeel & Long (1998: 58).
H30 2001: forming part of pendent bryophyte mat over wet base of limestone crag shaded by *Fagus sylvatica* woodland, *ca* 220 m alt., Giant's Leap, S of Blacklion, H03, DT Holyoak 01-758 (Blackstock 2002: 41).
†H33 listed by Blockeel & Long (1998: 58).
H34 1961: on shaded rocks, Greencastle, RD Fitzgerald (Paton 1962: 357).
H(35) listed by Macvicar (1905: 9).
†H35 listed by Blockeel & Long (1998: 58).
H36 1956: moss-covered rocks in stream,

Altadavan, nr Favor Royal, JW Fitzgerald & MPH Kertland, comm. JW Fitzgerald (Castell 1958: 462).
H37 1966: rocks by waterfall, Corkley R., Aughnaguran nr Keady, JW Fitzgerald & MPH Kertland (Paton 1967c: 395).
H(38) listed by Macvicar (1905: 9).
†H38 listed by Blockeel & Long (1998: 58).
H(39) listed by Macvicar (1905: 9).
†H39 listed by Blockeel & Long (1998: 58).
H40 1951: ash tree with *Lejeunea* spp., alt. 630 ft, Altikeeragh nr Castlerock, JW Fitzgerald (Castell 1952: 90).

73/5 ***Metzgeria leptoneura*** Spruce
(syn. *Metzgeria hamata* Lindb. nom. illeg.)

H(1) listed by Macvicar (1905: 9).
†H1 listed by Blockeel & Long (1998: 59).
H(2) listed by Macvicar (1905: 9).
†H2 listed by Blockeel & Long (1998: 59).
H3 1955: wet rocks, ravine, NE slope of Lackawee, H Milne-Redhead (Castell 1957: 323).
H(7) 1902: Lough Muskry, Galtee Mts, HW Lett (OXF), comm. AR Perry (Paton 1963: 483).
H(16) listed by Macvicar (1905: 9).
†H16 listed by Blockeel & Long (1998: 59).
H(27) listed by Macvicar (1905: 9).
†H27 listed by Blockeel & Long (1998: 59).
H28 1967: rock crevice in cascading stream above L. Achree, [The] Ox Mts, DA Ratcliffe, HH Birks & HJB Birks (Paton 1968: 620).
H29 1967: damp shady cleft in limestone cliffs, Glenade, DA Ratcliffe, HH Birks & HJB Birks (Paton 1968: 620).
†H35 listed by Blockeel & Long (1998: 59).
H(39) 1928: Glenariff (BBS exc.) (Duncan 1928: 114, 117).
†H39 listed by Blockeel & Long (1998: 59).

74/1 ***Apometgeria pubescens*** (Schrank) Kuwah.
(syn. *Metzgeria pubescens* Schrank)

H(39) listed by Macvicar (1905: 9).
†H39 listed by Blockeel & Long (1998: 59).
H40 1999: with mosses on top of boulders nr stream below waterfall in entrance to ravine, Umbra, C73, DT Holyoak 99-101 (BBSUK) (Blackstock 2000: 44).

[75/1 ***Sphaerocarpos michelii*** Bellardi]

[H(39) listed by Macvicar (1905: 8), but no Irish record is accepted by Blockeel & Long (1998) or Paton (1999)].

76/1 ***Targionia hypophylla*** L.

H(1) listed by Macvicar (1905: 7). H(1) listed by Blockeel & Long (1998: 59).
H(2) listed by Macvicar (1905: 7). H(2) listed by Blockeel & Long (1998: 59).
H(4) listed by Macvicar (1905: 7). H(4) listed by Blockeel & Long (1998: 59).
H(39) listed by Macvicar (1905: 7). H(39) listed by Blockeel & Long (1998: 59).

77/1 ***Lunularia cruciata*** (L.) Lindb.

H(1) listed by Macvicar (1905: 8).
†H1 listed by Blockeel & Long (1998: 59).
H(2) listed by Macvicar (1905: 8).
†H2 listed by Blockeel & Long (1998: 59).
†H3 listed by Blockeel & Long (1998: 59).
H4 1951: roadside bank NW of Mallow, AC Crundwell (Castell 1952: 89).
†H5 listed by Blockeel & Long (1998: 59).
H(6) listed by Macvicar (1905: 8).
†H6 listed by Blockeel & Long (1998: 59).
†H7 listed by Blockeel & Long (1998: 59).
H8 1966: soil by stream, Glenbrohane, Ballylanders, MFV Corley & JS Parker (Paton 1967c: 392).
†H9 listed by Blockeel & Long (1998: 59).
H10 1951: on soil by garden path, Ballina, AD Banwell, EV Watson & PJ Wanstall (Castell 1952: 89).
H11 1954: shaded corner of graveyard, Duiske Abbey, Graiguenamanagh, ALK King (Castell 1955: 578).
H(12) listed by Macvicar (1905: 8).
†H12 listed by Blockeel & Long (1998: 59).
H13 1969: stones under bridge over Burren R., Sheean nr Myshall, JW Fitzgerald (Paton 1979: 185).
H14 1956: side of ditch by Barranagh's Bridge, nr Mountmellick, AA Cridland (Castell 1958: 461).
†H16 listed by Blockeel & Long (1998: 59).
H17 1966: on top of limestone wall, Ryehill, N of Monivea, MFV Corley & JS Parker (Paton 1967c: 392).
H(18) listed by Macvicar (1905: 8). H(18) listed by Blockeel & Long (1998: 59).
H19 1967: crumbling rock in stream at

Castletown, Celbridge, ALK King (Paton 1968: 618).
H(20) listed by Macvicar (1905: 8).
†H20 listed by Blockeel & Long (1998: 59).
H(21) listed by Macvicar (1905: 8).
†H21 listed by Blockeel & Long (1998: 59).
H(22) listed by Macvicar (1905: 8).
†H22 listed by Blockeel & Long (1998: 59).
H24 1968: wall, station yard, Longford, WV Rubers *et al.* (Paton 1971a: 368).
H25 1965: stream bank, Ballyfarnan, JW Fitzgerald & EM Lobley (Paton 1966: 180).
H26 1970: nr pool in wood W of the Pollagh R., NE of Balla, JA Paton (Paton 1971a: 368).
H27 1962: floor of ruin, Claghmore, Achill I., EF Warburg (Paton 1963: 482).
H(28) 1928: nr Sligo (BBS exc.) (Duncan 1928: 119).
†H28 listed by Blockeel & Long (1998: 59).
H29 1963: earth-covered boulder in stream below waterfall, Glencar, JW Fitzgerald & AR Perry (Paton 1964: 711).
H(30) listed by Macvicar (1905: 8). H(30) listed by Blockeel & Long (1998: 59).
H30 2001: on thin compressed soil among limestone fragments of track, partly shaded by *Fagus sylvatica* plantation, *ca* 95 m alt., N58, DT Holyoak 01-656 (Blackstock 2002: 41).
H31 1966: pathway in woodland, Castlebellingham, DM Synnott (Paton 1967c: 392).
H(32) listed by Blockeel & Long (1998: 59).
H33 1957: roadside bank, Enniskillen, AC Crundwell (Castell 1958: 461).
H(34) listed by Macvicar (1905: 8).
†H34 listed by Blockeel & Long (1998: 59).
H35 1962: between stones of pavement, Dunfanaghy, AC Crundwell (Paton 1963: 482).
†H36 listed by Blockeel & Long (1998: 59).
H37 1952: between cobblestones in yard, Lurgan, JW Fitzgerald (Castell 1953: 297).
H(38) listed by Macvicar (1905: 8).
†H38 listed by Blockeel & Long (1998: 59).
H(39) listed by Macvicar (1905: 8).
†H39 listed by Blockeel & Long (1998: 59).
†H40 listed by Blockeel & Long (1998: 59).

78/1 ***Dumortiera hirsuta*** (Sw.) Nees

H(1) listed by Macvicar (1905: 8).
†H1 listed by Blockeel & Long (1998: 59).
H(2) listed by Macvicar (1905: 8).
†H2 listed by Blockeel & Long (1998: 59).
†H3 listed by Blockeel & Long (1998: 59).
H(4) listed by Macvicar (1905: 8).
†H4 listed by Blockeel & Long (1998: 59).
H6 1961: partly submerged on rocks by a cascade in stream below Coumshingaun, Comeragh Mts, DA Ratcliffe (Paton 1962: 356).
H7 1963: wet rocks in small ravine, stream on N side of Galtymore Mt., DA Ratcliffe (Paton 1963: 711).
H8 1966: on shady damp rocks by steam, Carrignabinnia, Galtee Mts, MFV Corley & JS Parker (Paton 1967c: 393).
H9 1962: on slumped clay in mouth of cave above L. Inchiquin, ALK King (Paton 1963: 483).
H10 1967: on dripping rocks and in wet caves in wooded valley, Clare Glen, nr Newport, HH Birks, HJB Birks & DA Ratcliffe (Paton 1968: 618).
H11 1966: on rocks by the R. Nore, Inistioge, JW Fitzgerald *et al.* (BBS exc.) (Paton 1967c: 393).
H(20) listed by Macvicar (1905: 8).
†H20 listed by Blockeel & Long (1998: 59).
H(29) 1928: on dripping roacks by the margin of stream, wooded glen, NE end of Glencar Lough (BBS exc.) (Duncan 1928: 114, 118).
†H29 listed by Blockeel & Long (1998: 59).
H39 1952: dripping rock by river, wooded ravine, Glenarm Glen, JW Fitzgerald & EW Jones, comm. JW Fitzgerald (Castell 1953: 297).

79/1 ***Conocephalum conicum*** (L.) Dumort.

H(1) listed by Macvicar (1905: 8).
†H1 listed by Blockeel & Long (1998: 59).
H(2) listed by Macvicar (1905: 8).
†H2 listed by Blockeel & Long (1998: 59).
H(3) listed by Macvicar (1905: 8).
†H3 listed by Blockeel & Long (1998: 59).
H4 1966: muddy river bank, R. Lee, Innishcarra Bridge, MFV Corley & JS Parker (Paton 1967c: 392).
H5 1956: by stream, Glenally, Youghal, EC Wallace (Castell 1957: 322).
H(6) listed by Macvicar (1905: 8).
†H6 listed by Blockeel & Long (1998: 59).
H(7) listed by Macvicar (1905: 8).
†H7 listed by Blockeel & Long (1998: 59).

H8 1966: bank by stream, Glenbrohane, Ballylanders, MFV Corley & JS Parker (Paton 1967c: 392).
H9 1956: bank nr Corkscrew Hill, above Ballyvaughan, ALK King (Castell 1957: 322).
H10 1951: wet soil in wooded gully, N slope, alt. 900 ft, above Silvermines, AD Banwell, EV Watson & PJ Wanstall (Castell 1952: 89).
H11 1958: stone floor of first story of Norman castle ruin, Coolhill, ALK King (Castell 1959: 626).
H(12) listed by Macvicar (1905: 8).
†H12 listed by Blockeel & Long (1998: 59).
H(13) listed by Macvicar (1905: 8).
†H13 listed by Blockeel & Long (1998: 59).
H(14) listed by Macvicar (1905: 8).
†H14 listed by Blockeel & Long (1998: 59).
[H(15) listed by Macvicar (1905: 8). H15 deleted because no record or voucher traced, comm. MM Yeo (Long 1990a: 23)].
H(16) listed by Macvicar (1905: 8).
†H16 listed by Blockeel & Long (1998: 59).
H17 1966: ground in damp wood, Derreen nr Monivea, MFV Corley & JS Parker (Paton 1967c: 392).
H(18) listed by Macvicar (1905: 8).
†H18 listed by Blockeel & Long (1998: 59).
[H(19) listed by Macvicar (1905: 8). H19 deleted because no record or voucher traced, comm. MM Yeo, replaced by following record (Long 1990a: 23)].
H19 1968: bank in woods at St Catherine's, Leixlip, ALK King (DBN), comm. DM Synnott (Long 1990a: 23).
H(20) listed by Macvicar (1905: 8).
†H20 listed by Blockeel & Long (1998: 59).
H(21) listed by Macvicar (1905: 8).
†H21 listed by Blockeel & Long (1998: 59).
H(22) listed by Macvicar (1905: 8).
†H22 listed by Blockeel & Long (1998: 59).
H23 1953: wet path in woods, Pakenham Hall, Castlepollard, ALK King (Castell 1954: 471).
H24 1957: bank of ditch, nr Carrickboy, ALK King (Castell 1958: 461).
H(25) listed by Macvicar (1905: 8).
†H25 listed by Blockeel & Long (1998: 59).
H(26) listed by Macvicar (1905: 8).
†H26 listed by Blockeel & Long (1998: 59).
H(27) listed by Macvicar (1905: 8).
†H27 listed by Blockeel & Long (1998: 59).
H(28) listed by Macvicar (1905: 8).
†H28 listed by Blockeel & Long (1998: 59).
H(29) listed by Macvicar (1905: 8).
†H29 listed by Blockeel & Long (1998: 59).
H(30) listed by Macvicar (1905: 8).
†H30 listed by Blockeel & Long (1998: 59).
H(31) listed by Macvicar (1905: 8).
†H31 listed by Blockeel & Long (1998: 59).
H32 1954: bank in woods, Glaslough Ho. [use], ALK King (Castell 1955: 578).
H(33) listed by Macvicar (1905: 8).
†H33 listed by Blockeel & Long (1998: 59).
H(34) listed by Macvicar (1905: 8).
†H34 listed by Blockeel & Long (1998: 59).
H(35) listed by Macvicar (1905: 8).
†H35 listed by Blockeel & Long (1998: 59).
H(36) listed by Macvicar (1905: 8).
†H36 listed by Blockeel & Long (1998: 59).
H37 1964: bank of disused canal, Carrickaness, nr Benburb, JW Fitzgerald & MPH Kertland (Paton 1965a: 851).
H(38) listed by Macvicar (1905: 8).
†H38 listed by Blockeel & Long (1998: 59).
H(39) listed by Macvicar (1905: 8).
†H39 listed by Blockeel & Long (1998: 59).
H40 1951: earth bank of stream, alt. 420 ft, Ballinrees nr Coleraine, JW Fitzgerald (Castell 1952: 89).

80/1 ***Reboulia hemisphaerica*** (L.) Raddi

H(1) listed by Macvicar (1905: 8).
†H1 listed by Blockeel & Long (1998: 60).
H(2) listed by Macvicar (1905: 8). H(2) listed by Blockeel & Long (1998: 60).
H(4) listed by Macvicar (1905: 8).
†H4 listed by Blockeel & Long (1998: 60).
H(5) listed by Macvicar (1905: 8). H(5) listed by Blockeel & Long (1998: 60).
H7 1966: earth-covered ledges in limestone rocks, Rock of Cashel, JG Duckett & J Appleyard (BBS exc.) (Paton 1967c: 392).
H8 1966: earth-covered ledges in limestone, L. Gur nr Kilteely, JG Duckett (BBS exc.) (Paton 1967c: 392).
H(9) listed by Macvicar (1905: 8). H(9) listed by Blockeel & Long (1998: 60).
H11 1966: earth-covered crevices in limestone, bank of R. Nore, Dysart Castle, Inistioge, JG Duckett *et al.* (BBS exc.) (Paton 1967c: 392).
H(16) listed by Macvicar (1905: 8). H(16) listed by Blockeel & Long (1998: 60).
H(17) listed by Macvicar (1905: 8). H(17) listed by Blockeel & Long (1998: 60).

H(21) listed by Macvicar (1905: 8). H(21) listed by Blockeel & Long (1998: 60).
H23 1979: crevice of limestone/chert bluff, Fore, DM Synnott (Corley 1980a: 25).
H25 1968: dry sandy railway bank *ca* 1 mile N of Athlone, WV Rubers *et al.* (Paton 1971a: 368).
H26 1994: Killasser near Swinford, G30, G O'Donovan (Long 1995b: 37).
†H27 listed by Blockeel & Long (1998: 60).
H(28) 1928: Gleniff, Ben Bulben (BBS exc.) (Duncan 1928: 118).
†H28 listed by Blockeel & Long (1998: 60).
H29 1963: in shaded earthy crevice in limestone rocks, Peakadaw, Glenade, JW Fitzgerald & AR Perry (Paton 1964: 711).
H33 1959: earth-topped walls nr Belcoo, JW Fitzgerald (Castell 1960: 763).
H(35) listed by Macvicar (1905: 8). H(35) listed by Blockeel & Long (1998: 60).
H(38) listed by Macvicar (1905: 8).
†H38 listed by Blockeel & Long (1998: 60).
H(39) listed by Macvicar (1905: 8). H(39) listed by Blockeel & Long (1998: 60).
H(40) listed by Macvicar (1905: 8). H(40) listed by Blockeel & Long (1998: 60).

81/1 ***Preissia quadrata*** (Scop.) Nees

H(1) listed by Macvicar (1905: 8).
†H1 listed by Blockeel & Long (1998: 60).
H(2) listed by Macvicar (1905: 8).
†H2 listed by Blockeel & Long (1998: 60).
H3 1967: rocks at 1400 ft alt., Foilanumera, JW Fitzgerald (Paton 1968: 618).
H(6) listed by Macvicar (1905: 8). H(6) listed by Blockeel & Long (1998: 60).
†H8 listed by Blockeel & Long (1998: 60).
H9 1957: roadside, on soil on limestone rocks, Black Head, AC Crundwell (BBS exc.) (Castell 1958: 462).
H14 1963: calcareous mire below esker, by the Tullamore-Rosscrea road, NW of Clonaslee, G Halliday (Paton 1964: 711).
H(15) 1865: side of L. Derg, D Moore (DBN), comm. ALK King (Paton 1964: 711).
H(16) listed by Macvicar (1905: 8).
†H16 listed by Blockeel & Long (1998: 60).
H17 1957: fen, Ballindooly, nr Galway City, RE Parker (Castell 1958: 462).
H18 1973: on marl, sandpit in esker, Longford, between Roscrea and Kinnitty, WV Rubers (Corley 1980a: 25).
H(19) listed by Macvicar (1905: 8). H(19) listed by Blockeel & Long (1998: 60).
H(21) listed by Macvicar (1905: 8). H(21) listed by Blockeel & Long (1998: 60).
H22 1969: fen on The Commons, N of Duleek, SW of Drogheda, DM Synnott & JA Paton (Paton 1970: 185).
H23 1957: limestone, nr Fore Abbey, ALK King (Castell 1958: 462).
†H25 listed by Blockeel & Long (1998: 60).
H(26) listed by Macvicar (1905: 8).
†H26 listed by Blockeel & Long (1998: 60).
†H27 listed by Blockeel & Long (1998: 60).
H(28) listed by Macvicar (1905: 8).
†H28 listed by Blockeel & Long (1998: 60).
H(29) 1928: wooded glen, NE end of Glencar Lough (BBS exc.) (Duncan 1928: 118).
†H29 listed by Blockeel & Long (1998: 60).
H31 1966: by waterfall, Two-mile R., Carlingford Mt., DM Synnott (Paton 1967c: 393).
H33 1957: moist sandstone rocks, nr Lough Achork, Lough Navar Forest, RE Parker (Castell 1958: 462).
1957: moist bank, ravine of Gladagh [*sic* = Cladagh] River, Lough Macnean Lower, AC Crundwell (Castell 1958: 462).
H(34) listed by Macvicar (1905: 8).
†H34 listed by Blockeel & Long (1998: 60).
H(35) listed by Macvicar (1905: 8).
†H35 listed by Blockeel & Long (1998: 60).
H36 1956: crevices of rock beside Lough More, nr Favor Royal (Castell 1957: 322).
1956: bank beside stream, Sawel Mt., JW Fitzgerald & MPH Kertland (Castell 1957: 322).
H(38) listed by Macvicar (1905: 8). H(38) listed by Blockeel & Long (1998: 60).
H38 2002: in unshaded crevices in mortared-stone wall of bridge over river, *ca* 50 m alt., by Shimna River in Tollymore Forest Park, J33, DT Holyoak 02-922 (Blackstock 2003: 45).
H(39) listed by Macvicar (1905: 8).
†H39 listed by Blockeel & Long (1998: 60).
H40 1952: sandhills, Magilligan, JW Fitzgerald (Castell 1954: 471).

82/1a *Marchantia polymorpha* L. subsp. *polymorpha*
(syn. *Marchantia polymorpha* var. *aquatica* (Nees) Gottsche, Lindenb. & Nees)

H(1) 1955: rocks under bank of Finglas River, Camp [Q70], AP Fanning 1908 (DBN) (Long 1995a: 35, 1996: 42).

H1 1979: rocks by the Roughty River, nr Kilgarvan [W07], EW Jones (NMW) (DG Long MS). H1 listed by Blockeel & Long (1998: 60).

H(2) 1936: submerged, Ross I., Killarney [V98], WB Turrill (BM) (Long 1995a: 35, 1996: 42).

H(6) 1933: Knockmealdown Mts [S00], E Armitage (BBSUK) (Long 1995a: 35, 1996: 42).

H6 1966: on rocks in R. Nier nr Shanballyanne, ERB Little (BBS exc.) (Paton 1967c: 393, as var. *aquatica*; DG Long MS; specimen not listed by Long 1995a, 1996).

H7 1966: among boulders by the stream, Knockastakeen, Galtee Mts [R92], JW Fitzgerald *et al.* (BBS exc.) (BBSUK) (Paton 1967c: 393, as var. *aquatica*; Long 1995a: 35, 1996: 42).

H10 1967: on wet rocks by river in wooded valley, Clare Glen nr Newport [R75], HH Birks, HJB Birks & DA Ratcliffe (BBSUK) (Paton 1968: 618, as var. *aquatica*; Long 1995a: 35, 1996: 42).

H11 1966: rocks in R. Nore, Dysart Castle, Inistioge [S53], JG Duckett *et al.* (BBS exc.) (BBSUK) (Paton 1967c: 393, Long 1995a: 35, 1996: 42).

H13 1969: earth bank by stream, Farranafreney, Leighlinbridge [S66], JW Fitzgerald (BBSUK) (Paton 1970: 185, Long 1995a: 35, 1996: 42).
1969: detritus on rocks below Aghade Bridge nr Tullow, JW Fitzgerald (Paton 1970: 185, as var. *aquatica*; DG Long MS; not listed by Long 1995a, 1996).

H15 1994: silted rocks beside Boleyneendorish River, Slieve Aughty, 12/5506, JA Paton (BBSUK) (Long 1995a: 35-36, 1996: 42).

[H(16) record, 1872: nr Cong, D Moore (DBN), comm. ALK King (Paton 1964: 712), not revised by DG Long MS, Long 1995a, 1996].

H16 1957: Muckanaght, [L75], M Forsyth (BEL) (Paton 1968: 618, Long 1995a: 36, 1996: 42).

H(18) 1949: growing upright amongst tall grasses at edge of bog pool, Sharavogue bog, Birr [S09], AP Fanning (BBSUK, BM, DBN), as var. *aquatica* (Castell 1952: 89; DG Long MS, Long 1996: 42, Blockeel & Long 1998: 60).

H20 1975: Glencullen River, Enniskerry [O21], DM Synnott (DBN), as var. *aquatica* (Long 1995a: 36, 1996: 42).

H(21) no date: nr Dublin [O13], T Taylor (BM) (Long 1995a: 36, 1996: 42).

H21 1967: on rotten calf in stream in ravine at Luttrellstown [O03], ALK King (DBN) (DG Long MS). H21 listed by Blockeel & Long (1998: 60).

H22 1978: on fallen mud-covered tree at water level, R. Nanny, E of Cooper Hill Bridge, Julianstown [O17], DM Synnott (DBN) (Long 1995a: 36, 1996: 42).

[H24 record, 1968: limestone pit 1 mile S of Lanesborough, WV Rubers, P Hessel & J Klein (Paton 1970: 185), not revised by DG Long MS, Long 1995a, 1996].

H25 1971: marsh nr Knockvicar Bridge, Boyle River [G80], L Farrell (DBN), as var. *aquatica* (Long 1995a: 36, 1996: 42).

H(27) 1909: Clare I. [L68], RL Praeger (DBN) (Long 1995a: 36, 1996: 42).

H27 1968: marsh by lough behind Dooniver Strand nr Bulls Mouth, Achill I. [F70], JA Paton (Hb. JA Paton, now at E) (DG Long MS). H27 listed by Blockeel & Long (1998: 60).

H28 1963: in running water, stream at 900 ft [alt.], Gleniff, Ben Bulben range [G74], BJ Fitzgerald & AR Perry (BBSUK), as var. *aquatica* (Paton 1964: 712; DG Long MS). H28 listed by Long (1996: 42) and Blockeel & Long (1998: 60).

H29 1963: on dripping tufa in spray zone of waterfall, Glencar [G74], JW Fitzgerald & AR Perry (BBSUK), as var. *aquatica* (Paton 1964: 712; DG Long MS). H29 listed by Long (1996: 42), Blockeel & Long (1998: 60).

H(30) 1911: Killykeen [H30], HW Lett (DBN) (DG Long MS). H(30) listed by Long (1996: 42) and Blockeel & Long (1998: 60).
1911: Farnham Lake, CH Waddell (BBSUK, BEL), comm. JW Fitzgerald (Paton 1963: 483), as var. *aquatica* (DG

Long MS).

H30 2001: on unshaded partly bare horizontal clay soil on bank of stream, *ca* 313 m alt., just S of R200, W of Bellavally Gap, H12, DT Holyoak 01-645 (Blackstock 2002: 41).

H32 1980: in standing water in calcareous marsh, Lough Duff [H63], N Lockhart (BBSUK), as var. *aquatica* (Corley 1983: 47, Long 1995a: 36, 1996: 42).

H(33) 1920: marsh by docks, Portora, Enniskillen [H24], WN Tetley (BBSUK) (Castell 1953: 297, DG Long MS).

H33 1961: in marshy ground, at base of Braade Scarp, Navar Forest [H05], JW Fitzgerald (BBSUK), as var. *aquatica* (Paton 1962: 356; DG Long MS). H33 listed by Long (1996: 42) and Blockeel & Long (1998: 60).

H34 1967: on rocks in river, Crana River, Ballymagan, E of Buncrana [C33], JW Fitzgerald (BBSUK), as var. *aquatica* (Paton 1968: 618, Long 1995a: 36, 1996: 42). [Corley 1980a: 25 adds H34 by transferring records from 'var. *aquatica*'].

H35 1969: on edge of Sessiagh Lough, Dunfanaghy [C03], JA Paton (NMW) (Long 1995a: 36, 1996: 42).

H36 1956: on limestone pavement at edge of river, Corick Bridge nr Newtown Stewart [H48], MPH Kertland & JW Fitzgerald (BBSUK, BEL) (Castell 1957: 322, Long 1995a: 36, 1996: 42).
1966: in river, Washing Bay, L. Neagh, F Rose (Paton 1967c: 393, as var. *aquatica*; DG Long MS; not listed by Long 1995a, 1996).

H37 1966: on wall of mill leat, Carrickaness nr Benburb, [H85], JW Fitzgerald (BBSUK), as var. *aquatica* (Paton 1967c: 393, Long 1995a: 36, 1996: 42).

H(38) 1887: among rushes etc., Rathfriland [J23], CH Waddell (BEL, BM) (Paton 1967c: 393, Long 1995a: 36, 1996: 42).

H(39) 1895: rocks in river nr R.C. Chapel, Cushendall [D22], HW Lett (DBN) (DG Long MS).

H39 1952: rocks at edge of river, Glenarm [D31], EW Jones & JW Fitzgerald (BBSUK), as var. *aquatica* (Castell 1953: 297; DG Long MS). H39 listed by Long (1996: 42) and Blockeel & Long (1998: 60).

H40 1952: rocks by stream, Downhill [C73], EW Jones (BBSUK), as var. *aquatica* (Castell 1953: 297; DG Long MS). H40 listed by Long (1996: 42) and Blockeel & Long (1998: 60). [Corley 1980a: 25 adds H40 by transferring records from 'var. *aquatica*'].

Records were revised by Long (1995a) based on the taxonomic interpretation of the three subspecies by Bischler-Causse & Boisselier-Dubayle (1991); old reports were discounted when no voucher specimens were available. Details that were not published for some records are taken from DG Long (MS). Old records (e.g. in Macvicar 1905: 8) cannot be assigned to subspp. unless the specimens have been revised.

82/1b *Marchantia polymorpha* subsp. *ruderalis* Bischl. & Boisselier

H(1) 1861: Dingle Bay, B Carrington (BM) (DG Long MS). H(1) listed by Long (1996: 42) and Blockeel & Long (1998: 60).

[H3 deleted (Long 1995a: 36)].

H4 2002: on bare ground at foot of limestone wall, 40 m alt., Blarney, W67, TL Blockeel 31/290 (Blackstock 2003: 45).

[H5 deleted (Long 1995a: 36)].

H5 2002: in flower bed, *ca* 10 m alt., Fota House, Foaty I., W77, TL Blockeel 31/344 (Blackstock 2003: 45).

[H6 deleted (Long 1995a: 36)].

H7 1966: forestry road in woods N of Knockastockeen, Galtee Mts [R92], JA Paton (BBSUK) (Paton 1967c: 393; Long 1995a: 36, 1996: 42).

[H8 deleted (Long 1995a: 36)].

H9 1957: cut bog surface, nr Clare River, Kinvarra, M Forsyth (NMW) (DG Long MS). H9 listed by Long (1996: 42) and Blockeel & Long (1998: 60).

[H10 deleted (Long 1995a: 36)].

H16 1970: burnt soil in deciduous woodland, Hill of Doon, L. Corrib [M04], AR Perry (NMW) (DG Long MS). H16 listed by Long (1996: 42) and Blockeel & Long (1998: 60).

H(17) 1896: Doon Bog, Clonbrock [M73], D McArdle (DBN) (DG Long MS). H(17) listed by Long (1996: 42) and Blockeel & Long (1998: 60).

[H18 deleted (Long 1995a: 36)].
[H19 deleted (Long 1995a: 36)].
[H20 deleted (Long 1995a: 36)].
H(21) 1876: abundant on the surface of pots in the Garden [O13], D Moore (DBN) (DG Long MS).
H21 1988: enclosed garden, Lambay [O35], DM Synnott (DBN) (DG Long MS). H21 listed by Long (1996: 42) and Blockeel & Long (1998: 60).
H22 1952: bank in Clonycavan Bog nr Ballivor [N65], ALK King (BBSUK, DBN) (Castell 1953: 297; DG Long MS). H22 listed by Long (1996: 42) and Blockeel & Long (1998: 60).
H23 1957: on marshy ground at N end of L. Ennell, Mullingar [N44], ALK King (BBSUK, DBN) (Castell 1958: 462; DG Long MS). H23 listed by Long (1996: 42) and Blockeel & Long (1998: 60).
H25 1962: yard, Boyle [G80], PW Warburg (BBSUK) (Paton 1963: 483; DG Long MS). H25 listed by Long (1996: 42) and Blockeel & Long (1998: 60).
[H27 deleted (Long 1995a: 36)].
[H28 deleted (Long 1995a: 36)].
H29 1963: side of stream below Glencar Waterfall [G74], AR Perry & JW Fitzgerald (BBSUK) (Paton 1964: 712; DG Long MS). H29 listed by Long (1996: 42) and Blockeel & Long (1998: 60).
H(30) 1911: nr the tea house, Farnham Wood [H30], J Glover (NMW) (DG Long MS). H(30) listed by Long (1996: 42) and Blockeel & Long (1998: 60).
[H31 deleted (Long 1995a: 36)].
H33 1993: in plant-pot in garden, Cloghtogle N of Lisbellaw [H34], DG Long 24684 (E) (DG Long MS). H33 listed by Long (1996: 42) and Blockeel & Long (1998: 60).
H34 2002: on unshaded partly bare soil of flower borders in camping grounds, *ca* 5 m alt., Quigley's Point (C53), DT Holyoak 02-775 (Blackstock 2003: 45).
[H35 deleted (Long 1995a: 36)].
[H36 deleted (Long 1995a: 36)].
H37 1965: Castledillon, MPH Kertland (NMW) (DG Long MS). H37 listed by Long (1996: 42) and Blockeel & Long (1998: 60).
H(38) 1891: Miller's house in Loughbrickland [J14], HW Lett (DBN) (DG Long MS).
H38 1950: Scrabo, JW Fitzgerald (NMW) (DG Long MS). H38 listed by Long (1996: 42) and Blockeel & Long (1998: 60).
H(39) 1928: Gawley's Gate [J06], M Duff (BEL) (DG Long MS).
H39 1983: lime rich Quaternary clay exposed by pressure of quarry waste on shore of lough, 0 m alt., Larne Lough at Magheramore Quarry tip (J49), P Hackney (BEL) (DG Long MS). H39 listed by Long (1996: 42) and Blockeel & Long (1998: 60).

See note under subsp. *polymorpha*. Records of '*M. polymorpha*' from Paton (1965b) were placed as this form by Long (1995a: 36). Details of specimens assigned to subsp. *ruderalis* are from an unpublished list by DG Long (MS).

82/1c *Marchantia polymorpha* subsp. *montivagans* Bischl. & Boisselier
(syn. *Marchantia alpestris* (Nees) Burgeff)

H28 1871: Benbulbin [*sic* = Ben Bulben], [G74], D Moore (DBN, NMW) (Long 1995a: 36, 1996: 42).

See note under subsp. *polymorpha*.

83/1 *Ricciocarpos natans* (L.) Corda

H7 1991: floating in small ponds in poor fen, Ballydonagh Townland, nr Grange, R94, N Lockhart & A O'Suillivan (Long 1992: 24).
1991: in calcareous stream dammed by wall, with *Berula* and *Lemna minor*, The Wilderness, Clonmel, S22, R Fitzgerald & P Clancy, DBN (Long 1992: 24).
H(8) listed by Macvicar (1905: 7).
†H8 listed by Blockeel & Long (1998: 61).
H9 1979: soil by inflowing stream, N end of Fin Lough, NW of Sixmilebridge, AC Crundwell *et al.* (Corley 1980a: 26).
H(15) listed by Macvicar (1905: 7). H(15) listed by Blockeel & Long (1998: 61).
H(19) listed by Macvicar (1905: 7).
†H19 listed by Blockeel & Long (1998: 61).
H(20) pre-1874: Wicklow, W Archer (BM), comm. CD Preston (Long 1990a: 23).
H(21) listed by Macvicar (1905: 7).
†H21 listed by Blockeel & Long (1998: 61).
H(22) listed by Macvicar (1905: 7).

†H22 listed by Blockeel & Long (1998: 61). Caffrey (1987) gives details of a record in 1986 from a ditch beside the Martry River.
H(23) 1892: bog drain, quarry, Knockdrin, HC Levinge (BRIST), comm. PE Stanley (Paton 1964: 711).
†H23 listed by Blockeel & Long (1998: 61).
H(25) listed by Blockeel & Long (1998: 61).
H30 2001: drying mud beneath *Phragmites australis* and *Schoenoplectus lacustris* beside dried pool at lake edge, *ca* 70 m alt., NW shore of Lough Sheelin, nr Kilnahard, N48, DT Holyoak 01-674 (Blackstock 2002: 42).
H(31) listed by Macvicar (1905: 7). H(31) listed by Blockeel & Long (1998: 61).

84/1 ***Riccia cavernosa*** Hoffm.

H1 1952: damp sand behind dunes, coast 2 miles E of Castlegregory, 'yellowish masses', NY Sandwith (Castell 1953: 297), as *R. crystallina*. Specimen formerly placed as *R. crystallina* redet. as this species (Paton 1967a: 224, 1968: 619).
H3 1983: exposed lake mud with *Littorella* and *Elatine*, The Gearagh, nr Macroom, N McGough, conf. JA Paton (Long 1994: 33).
H15 1979: on mud in turlough, L. Coole, Gort, N Lockhart (Corley 1980a: 26).
H25 1968: wet organic clay, Portrunny Bay, 2 miles NE of Knockcroghery, WV Rubers, P Hessel & J Klein (Paton 1970: 186).
H30 2001: on unshaded partly bare sandy mud in shallow depression on lake shore *ca* 1 m above water-level, *ca* 46 m alt., shore of Lough Oughter, W of Inishconnell, H30, DT Holyoak 01-685 (Blackstock 2002: 42).
H35 1999: on sandy mud of dried shallow pool in old sand quarry at edge of dunes, SW of Carrickart, C13, DT Holyoak 99-758 (BBSUK) (Blackstock 2000: 45).
H38 1956: mud, lake margin, L. Henney, 4 miles N of Ballynahinch, JS Pate & BS Gunning, comm. RE Parker (Castell 1957: 322), as *R. crystallina*. Specimen formerly placed as *R. crystallina* redet. as this species (Paton 1967a: 224, 1968: 619).
[H39 listed by Macvicar (1905: 7), as *R. crystallina*].
H39 1999: on damp mud of drained reservoir, with sparse herbaceous vegetation, Copeland Reservoir, J49, DT Holyoak 99-848 (BBSUK) (Blackstock 2000: 45).

[84/2 ***Riccia crystallina*** L.]

[Irish and British records from Paton (1965b: 23) *CC* were mainly reidentified as *R. cavernosa*; the H39 record from *CC* was deleted (Paton 1967a: 224, 1968: 619)].

84/3 ***Riccia huebeneriana*** Lindenb.

H20 1973: mud exposed at edge of Vartry Reservoir, Roundwood, PH Pitkin (Paton 1974b: 161).

84/4 ***Riccia fluitans*** L.

H7 1991: floating and submerged amongst *Iris* in swamp, 100 m alt., Doonoor Townland, 1 km S of Grange, R94, N Lockhart & A O'Suillivan (Long 1992: 24).
[H(8) listed by Macvicar (1905: 7). H8 deleted because record inadequately localised and no voucher traced (Long 1990a: 23)].
H8 1999: pond in corner of wet field, *ca* 1 km W of Oola, R84, S Reynolds (Blackstock 2000: 45).
1999: abundant in Lough Agoule, W of Ballingarry, R33, S Reynolds (Blackstock 2000: 45).
H10 1991: in small marsh, Culacussane, S of Annacarty, NE of Tipperary Town, R94, MPJ Scannell (DBN) (Long 1992: 24).
1991: submerged amongst *Carex rostrata*, 120 m alt., around Glassdrum Lough, S of Cappaghwhite, R84, N Lockhart & A O'Suillivan (Long 1992: 24).
H13 1965: lake at Oak Park Agricultural Institute, JGD Lamb, comm. DM Synnott (Paton 1966: 180).
H19 1954: at edge of still pond in Townland of Redbog, nr Blessington, ALK King (Castell 1955: 578).
H20 1961: in pond at Lemonstown, ALK King (Paton 1962: 356).
H(21) listed by Macvicar (1905: 7). H(21) listed by Blockeel & Long (1998: 61).

H23 1968: peat ditch, L. Doonis, 5 miles N of Glassan, WV Rubers, P Hessel & J Klein (Paton 1970: 186).
H25 1980: in reedswamp at lake margin, Smutternagh, L. Key, DL Kelly (Corley 1986: 17).
H(29) listed by Macvicar (1905: 7). H(29) listed by Blockeel & Long (1998: 61).
H31 1993: swampy fen beside lake near monastery NE of Collon, O08, NF Stewart (Long 1994: 33).
[H(32) listed by Macvicar (1905: 7). H32 deleted because no record or voucher traced, comm. MM Yeo (Long 1990a: 23)].
H32 1956: Smithborough, N53, MPH Kertland, comm. NF Stewart (Long 1994: 33).
H36 1956: abundant in ditch with *Lemna* spp., Derrymeen, nr Verner's Bridge, JW Fitzgerald & MPH Kertland (Castell 1957: 322).
H(37) listed by Macvicar (1905: 7).
†H37 listed by Blockeel & Long (1998: 61).
H(38) listed by Macvicar (1905: 7). H(38) listed by Blockeel & Long (1998: 61).
H39 1955: by lake shore, Selshan, Lough Neagh, Richards, comm. JW Fitzgerald (Paton 1963: 482).
H40 1992: old flooded sand pit, Traad Point, H98, S Wolfe-Murphy, det. R Weyl, comm. DT Holyoak (BBSUK) (Blackstock 2001: 37).

84/7 ***Riccia sorocarpa*** Bisch.

H(1) listed by Macvicar (1905: 7). H(1) listed by Blockeel & Long (1998: 61).
H2 1966: track on N shore of Muckross Lake, Killarney, JA Paton & GCG Argent (Paton 1967c: 393).
H3 1964: soil in garden, Glengarriff Castle Hotel, Glengarriff, ERB Little (Paton 1967c: 393).
H4 1967: forestry track, Carrigafroca, S of Ballyvoge, JW Fitzgerald (Paton 1968: 619).
H5 1966: wet gravel track, Castle Cooke, Kilworth, JG Duckett *et al.* (BBS exc.) (Paton 1967c: 393).
H6 1966: gravelly path, Glenshelane N of Cappoquin, JA Paton *et al.* (BBS exc.) (Paton 1967c: 393).
H8 1966: on damp earth by stream, Nicker, Pallas Green, ERB Little (BBS exc.) (Paton 1967c: 393).
H9 1963: bare limestone soil in depression by path 1½ miles N of Feenagh, Ballyvaughan, G Halliday (Paton 1964: 711).
H10 1979: field on N side of Clare R., 3 km E of Clare Glens, AC Crundwell (Corley 1980a: 25).
H12 1966: earth bank by road, Kiltealy, Blackstairs Mts, JG Duckett, J Appleyard & A Folan (Paton 1967c: 393).
H13 1969: track to old quarry, Lackan nr Old Leighlin, JW Fitzgerald (Paton 1970: 186).
H15 1957: ride, Garrylands Wood, J Appleyard (Castell 1958: 461).
H16 1957: roadside waste ground, Ballynahinch, AC Crundwell & EV Watson (BBS exc.), comm. AC Crundwell (Castell 1958: 461).
H19 2002: in stubble field (barley), 80 m alt., N of R445, W of Newhall Cross Roads, N81, HF Fox & CD Preston (Blackstock 2003: 45).
H20 1950: side of path, Bray Head, AW Stelfox, comm. JS Thomson (Castell 1951: 491).
H(21) 1930: Glenasmole, Dublin, leg. AW Stelfox, comm. M Buchanan (anon. 1931b: 281).
H22 1950: soil on rocky ground, Slane, JS Thomson, comm. ALK King (Paton 1964: 711).
H25 1973: shaded path, shore of L. Ree, St John's Wood, WV Rubers (Paton 1974b: 161).
H26 1970: mixed with a little *R. beyrichiana*, shore of L. Carra, nr Partry House, collector not recorded (BBS exc.) (Paton 1971a: 368, Appleyard 1971: 388).
†H27 listed by Blockeel & Long (1998: 61).
H28 1963: limestone outcrop at 1300 ft alt., Lugnagall, Glencar, AR Perry & JW Fitzgerald (Paton 1964: 711).
H31 1970: sandy stubble field, Big Strand, Clogher Head, DM Synnott (Paton 1971a: 368).
H32 1980: muddy wheelruts of trackway, White Lake, N Lockhart (Corley 1983: 47).
H33 1960: thin soil overlying limestone, scarp behind Knockmore Cliff, JW Fitzgerald (Paton 1961: 150).
†H34 listed by Blockeel & Long (1998: 61).

H35 1962: earthy wall-top by path to Menagh Church, Rosguill Peninsula, EF Warburg (BBS exc.) (Paton 1963: 482).
H36 1956: abundant on waste ground beside road, Artrea Bridge, nr Cookstown, JW Fitzgerald & MPH Kertland (Castell 1957: 322).
H37 1962: stubble field between Moy and Portadown, J Appleyard (BBS exc.) (Paton 1963: 482).
H38 1952: on path, Scrabo quarry, JW Fitzgerald, EW Jones & MPH Kertland (Castell 1954: 471).
H(39) 1928: Fair Head (BBS exc.) (Duncan 1928: 116).
†H39 listed by Blockeel & Long (1998: 61).
H(40) listed by Macvicar (1905: 7).
†H40 listed by Blockeel & Long (1998: 61).

84/9 ***Riccia glauca*** L.

H(1) listed by Macvicar (1905: 7). H1 record confirmed by checking specimen (Paton 1963: 482).
†H1 listed by Blockeel & Long (1998: 61).
H2 1966: track on N shore of Muckross Lake, Killarney, JA Paton & GCG Argent (Paton 1967c: 393).
H3 1964: soil in garden, Glengarriff Castle Hotel, Glengarriff, ERB Little (Paton 1967c: 393).
H4 1967: forestry track, Carrigafroca, S of Ballyvoge, JW Fitzgerald (Paton 1968: 619).
H5 1966: sandy river gravel by R. Araglin nr Kilworth, JW Fitzgerald *et al.* (BBS exc.) (Paton 1967c: 393).
H6 1966: gravelly path in wood, Glenshelane, N of Cappoquin, JA Paton *et al.* (BBS exc.) (Paton 1967c: 393).
H7 1966: cornfield W of Longfordpass Bridge, Urlingford, JA Paton & ERB Little (BBS exc.) (Paton 1967c: 393).
H9 1979: wet track nr Killuran R., NW slope of Slieve Bernagh, N of Broadford, JA Paton & N Lockhart (Corley 1980a: 25).
H10 1979: bank of Clare R., Clare Glens, S of Newport, JA Paton (Corley 1980a: 25).
H11 1966: stubble field, Inistioge, JW Fitzgerald *et al.* (BBS exc.) (Paton 1967c: 393).
H14 1966: marshy field nr Owenbeg R., E of Abbeyleix, JA Paton & GCG Argent (Paton 1967c: 393).
H15 1957: woodland ride, Chevy Chase, nr Gort, AC Crundwell (BBS exc.) (Castell 1958: 461). H15 record confirmed by checking specimen (Paton 1963: 482).
H16 1957: roadside wall-top, Ballynahinch, J Appleyard (Castell 1958: 461). H16 record confirmed by checking specimen (Paton 1963: 482).
H19 2002: abundant in stubble field (winter wheat), 70 m alt., 'Furry Field', NE of Coursetown House, Courttown East townland, Athy, S69, HF Fox & CD Preston (Blackstock 2003: 45).
H(20) listed by Macvicar (1905: 7).
H20 1969: forestry track, Devil's Glen nr Ashford, JW Fitzgerald & DM Synnott (Paton 1970: 185).
H(21) listed by Macvicar (1905: 7).
H21 2002: stubble field (wheat), 60 m alt., SE of Hazelhatch Station, N93, CD Preston (Blackstock 2003: 45).
H25 1970: field beside L. Ree, Portrunny Bay, JA Paton (Paton 1971a: 368).
H26 1987: on mud under *Salix* by river, E bank of Cloon River near Partry, DG Long, conf. JA Paton (Long 1988: 30).
H28 1970: roadside verge, Templehouse Lake, S of Coolaney, JA Paton (BBS exc.) (Paton 1971a: 368, Appleyard 1971: 389).
H33 1957: rut in quarry, S side of Lough Macnean Lower, AC Crundwell (Castell 1958: 461). H33 record confirmed by checking specimen (Paton 1963: 482).
[H(34) listed by Macvicar (1905: 7)].
H34 1967: farm track, Red Castle, L. Foyle, JW Fitzgerald (Paton 1968: 619).
[H(35) listed by Macvicar (1905: 7)].
H37 1962: stubble field between Moy and Portadown, J Appleyard (BBS exc.) (Paton 1963: 482).
[H(38) listed by Macvicar (1905: 7)].
H38 1966: path in garden, Tullybrannigan Rd, Newcastle, AW Stelfox, comm. JW Fitzgerald (Paton 1967c: 393).
H(39) listed by Macvicar (1905: 7). H39 record confirmed by checking specimen (Paton 1963: 482).
†H39 listed by Blockeel & Long (1998: 61).
H(40) listed by Macvicar (1905: 7). H40 record confirmed (Paton 1964: 711).
†H40 listed by Blockeel & Long (1998: 61).

84/10 ***Riccia subbifurca*** Warnst. ex Croz. (syn. *Riccia warnstorfii* auct. non Limpr. ex Warnst.)

H1 1951: walls, Glenbeigh, Blackstones Bridge, Caherdaniel and Ross-Behy (all H1), EW Jones (Castell 1952: 89).
H2 1966: track on N shore of Muckross Lake, Killarney, JA Paton & GCG Argent (Paton 1967c: 393).
H3 1964: soil in garden, Glengarriff Castle Hotel, Glengarriff, ERB Little (Paton 1967c: 393).
H4 1967: forestry track, Carrigafroca, S of Ballyvoge, JW Fitzgerald (Paton 1968: 618).
H5 1966: sandy river gravel by R. Araglin nr Kilworth, JW Fitzgerald *et al.* (BBS exc.) (Paton 1967c: 393).
H6 1966: gravel track in wood, Glenshelane, N of Cappoquin, JG Duckett (BBS exc.) (Paton 1967c: 393).
H9 1979: wet track nr Killuran R., NW slope of Slieve Bernagh, N of Broadford, JA Paton (Corley 1980a: 25).
H14 1966; marshy field nr Owenbeg River E of Abbeyleix, JA Paton & GCG Argent 3172-b (Paton 1990: 6, Long 1990a: 23).
H16 1957: waste ground by roadside, Ballynahinch, AC Crundwell & EV Watson (BBS exc.), comm. AC Crundwell (Castell 1958: 461).
H27 1987: track below wood, below Lough Greney, nr Knappagh, S of Westport, JA Paton (Long 1988: 30).
H28 1970: roadside quarry nr Masshill, JA Paton (BBS exc.) (Paton 1971a: 368, Appleyard 1971: 389).
H33 1960: potato field, Tullykelter, nr Monea, JW Fitzgerald (Paton 1961: 150).
H34 2002: unshaded partly bare loamy soil of flower beds in camping ground, *ca* 8 m alt., Quigley's Point, C53, DT Holyoak 02-555 (Blackstock 2003: 45).
H35 1962: grassy track on cliff, Crohy Head nr Dunglow, AC Crundwell (BBS exc.) (Paton 1963: 482).
H36 1956: damp sand, side of sandpit nr Coalisland, JW Fitzgerald & MPH Kertland (Castell 1957: 322).
H37 1966: pool of disused quarry, Tullydonnell, 2 miles W of Forkhill, JW Fitzgerald & MPH Kertland (Paton 1967c: 393).
H38 1966: path in garden, Tullybrannigan Rd, Newcastle, AW Stelfox, comm. JW Fitzgerald (Paton 1967c: 393).
H39 1952: floor of quarry, Ballintoy, EW Jones (Castell 1954: 471).
[H40 1952: ride in felled woodland, Benevenagh, EW Jones (Castell 1954: 471), and 1952: in ditch at side of the Bishop's Road, Downhill, EW Jones (Castell 1954: 471). H40 deleted (Paton 1990: 5-6, Long 1990a: 23)].
H40 1999: on thin compressed soil on stony track in *Picea* plantation, Garvagh Forest, C81, DT Holyoak 99-296 (BBSUK) (Blackstock 2000: 45).

Paton (1990) showed that *R. warnstorfii* of British authors should be referred to *R. subbifurca*.

84/11 ***Riccia crozalsii*** Levier

[H3 1968: track nr Dunboy Castle, Castletownbere, JA Paton (Paton 1969a: 865). H3 record deleted because voucher reidentified as '*R. warnstorfii*' (Paton 1980: 3, Corley 1981: 17)].
H3 1993: soil among rocks above end of South Harbour, Clear I., V92, NF Stewart, RJ Stewart & R Fitzgerald, conf. JA Paton (Long 1994: 33).
[H16 1970: bank by road nr the sea, nr Cashel, Bertraghboy Bay, MFV Corley (Paton 1971a: 368); H16 deleted because voucher reidentified as '*R. warnstorfii*' (Paton 1980: 3, Corley 1981: 17)].
[H27 deleted because specimens (1987: on damp gravelly roadside, lane below Slievemore, Achill I., DG Long & JA Paton, det. JA Paton: Long 1988: 30) collected and cultivated by JA Paton have proved not to be this species, comm. JA Paton (Long 1989: 20)].
[H35 1969: track below road S of Rinnafaghla Pt., Rosguill, JA Paton (Paton 1970: 185). The H35 record deleted because voucher reidentified as '*R. warnstorfii*' (Paton 1980: 3, Corley 1981: 17)].
[H36 1957: waste ground beside road, with *R. warnstorfii*, 2 miles S of Newtownstewart, JW Fitzgerald (Castell 1958: 461, Fitzgerald & Fitzgerald 1960a). H36 deleted because voucher

reidentified as '*R. warnstorfii*' (Paton 1980: 3, Corley 1981: 17)].

[84/12 ***Riccia bifurca*** Hoffm]

[H16 discounted because no specimen traced and record regarded as extremely doubtful (Paton 1980: 3, Corley 1981: 17)].

84/13 ***Riccia beyrichiana*** Hampe ex Lehm. (syn. *Riccia glaucescens* Carrington, *R. lescuriana* Austin)

H1 1951: sandy ground at base of rocks, Abbey I., Derrynane, JW Fitzgerald (Castell 1952: 89).
H3 1968: track to old copper mine above Allihies, JA Paton (Paton 1969a: 865).
H9 1957: on pocket of soil in limestone pavement, Black Head, AC Crundwell (Castell 1958: 461).
H15 1994: on soil at edge of limestone pavement, 2 km SE of Cappaghmore, M30, TL Blockeel & CD Preston 23/173 (Long 1995b: 37).
H16 1965: on earth-covered rock, track to Killary Harbour Youth Hostel nr Leenane, DF Chamberlain (Paton 1966: 180).
H(20) listed by Blockeel & Long (1998: 62).
[H(23) no date: Co. Westmeath, D Moore (DBN), comm. ALK King (Paton 1964: 711). H23 deleted because record is unlocalised, comm. MM Yeo (Long 1990a: 23)].
H26 1962: soil on limestone pavement by Keel Bridge between Ballinrobe and Partry, AJE Smith (Paton 1963: 482).
H27 1987: beside track below Slievemore, N of Slievemore Hotel, Dugort, Achill I., JA Paton (Long 1988: 30).
H34 2002: on exposed soil of flushed bank on N-facing slope of coastal headland, *ca* 7 m [alt.], Culoort, NW of Malin, C45, DT Holyoak 02-573 (Blackstock 2003: 45).
[H(35) listed by Macvicar (1905: 7)].
†H35 listed by Blockeel & Long (1998: 62).
H37 1967: stony flush by roadside, Daaikilmore, S of Slieve Gullion, JW Fitzgerald & MPH Kertland (Paton 1968: 619).
H38 2002: among low grasses and herbs on unshaded mainly bare gravelly and gritty sediment high in inundation zone beside reservoir, *ca* 125 m alt., NW edge of Lough Island Reavy Reservoir, J23, DT Holyoak 02-964 (Blackstock 2003: 45).
H(39) listed by Macvicar (1905: 7).
†H39 listed by Blockeel & Long (1998: 62).

HORNWORTS
(ANTHOCEROTOPSIDA)

85/1 ***Anthoceros punctatus*** L.
(syn. *Anthoceros husnotii* Steph.)

H1 1951: ditch by road, S side of Lough Currane, J Appleyard & EF Warburg (BBS exc.) (Paton 1963: 491).
H2 1966: bank of road through woods nr Torc Cascade, Killarney, JA Paton (Paton 1967c: 392).
H(3) listed by Blockeel & Long (1998: 62).
H3 1998: Beara, Castletownbere, W Labeij (Blackstock 2000: 45).
H5 1966: gravelly detritus by river, Araglin, J Appleyard *et al.* (BBS exc.) (Paton 1967c: 392).
H6 1966: clay ditch bank, Ballin L. nr Bunmahon, JG Duckett & DM Synnott (Paton 1967c: 392).
H8 1966: cattle-trodden soil in wet meadow, L. Gur nr Kilteely, JG Duckett, JW Fitzgerald & J Appleyard (BBS exc.) (Paton 1967c: 393).
H9 1979: marshy field beside L. Burke, W of Ennis, JA Paton (Corley 1980a: 25).
H12 1975: forestry track SE of Killinierin, N of Gorey, JA Paton (BBS exc.) (Paton 1976: 16).
H13 2002: with *Phaeoceros laevis* on near-vertical clay soil at base of bank beside track, slightly shaded by *Prunus laurocerasus* scrub, *ca* 65 m alt., just W of Bunclody, S95, DT Holyoak 02-365, det. TH Blackstock (Blackstock 2003: 45).
H16 1969: soil at edge of field, Farravaun, Glann, Oughterard, AR Perry & HJ Perry (Paton 1970: 185).
H27 1962: bank on cliffs, E end of Keel Bay, Achill I., EF Warburg (Paton 1963: 491).
H29 2001: on vertical loamy soil of edge of lawn/flower border in garden, slightly shaded, *ca* 45 m alt., SE of Loughrinn, N09, DT Holyoak 01-862 (Blackstock 2002: 42).
H34 1962: stubble field nr Castleforward nr Newtown Cunningham, EF Warburg *et al.* (BBS exc.) (Paton 1963: 491).
H(35) 1910: Catlagh Wood nr Milford, HW Lett (DBN), comm. ALK King (Paton 1964: 721).
H38 1950: side of stubble field, Netherleigh, JW Fitzgerald (Paton 1963: 491).

This species was known as *A. husnotii* in several *CC* up to and including that by Paton (1965b: 21), whereas the following species was known as *A. punctatus*. However, '*A. punctatus*' of Macvicar (1905: 23) probably consisted mainly of records of the present species, although all of the voucher specimens need to be reidentified.

85/2 ***Anthoceros agrestis*** Paton
(syn. *Anthoceros punctatus* auct. non L.)

[H(12) 1913: Great Saltee I., HW Lett (*Irish Nat.* **22**, 194, 1913), comm. JW Fitzgerald (Castell 1952: 97). H12 rejected in *CC* by Paton (1965b: 21)].
[H27 deleted to correct misprint in *CC* (Paton 1971a: 368)].
H35 1969: marshy field nr Doe Castle, N of Cresslough [*sic* = Creeslough], JA Paton (Paton 1970: 185).
H36 1957: side of field drain, Butterlope, JW Fitzgerald (Castell 1959: 630). H36 record confirmed by examination of specimen (Paton 1963: 491).

86/1 ***Phaeoceros laevis*** (L.) Prosk.
(syn. *Anthoceros laevis* L., *Phaeoceros laevis* subsp. *laevis*)

H(1) listed by Macvicar (1905: 23).
†H1 listed by Blockeel & Long (1998: 62).
H(3) 1930: clay face above Eccles Hotel, Glengarriff, M Buchanan (DBN), comm. ALK King (Paton 1964: 721).
†H3 listed by Blockeel & Long (1998: 62).
†H4 listed by Blockeel & Long (1998: 62).
H5 1966: wet track, Castle Cooke, Kilworth, JG Duckett *et al.* (BBS exc.) (Paton 1967c: 392).
H6 1966: field nr Clogheen, N of Ballymacarbry, JA Paton, GCG Argent & ERB Little (BBS exc.) (Paton 1967c: 392).
H7 1966: cornfield W of Longfordpass Bridge, Urlingford, JA Paton & ERB Little (BBS exc.). (Paton 1967c: 392).
H8 1966: soil in grass field, Glenbrohane, Ballylanders, MFV Corley & JS Parker (Paton 1967c: 392).
H9 1962: ditch by path from Fisherstreet to cliffs of Moher, J Lane, comm. G Halliday (Paton 1963: 491).
H12 1975: forestry track SE of Killinierin, N of Gorey, JA Paton (BBS exc.) (Paton

1976: 16).

H13 2002: on near-vertical clay soil at base of bank beside track, slightly shaded by *Prunus laurocerasus* scrub, *ca* 65 m alt., just W of Bunclody, S95, DT Holyoak 02-365 (Blackstock 2003: 45-46).

H14 1966: damp ground amongst grass on farm track nr Owenbeg R., E of Abbeyleix, GCG Argent (Paton 1967c: 392).

H16 1957: roadside bank, Tullywee Bridge, Kylemore, AC Crundwell (BBS exc.) (Castell 1958: 470).

H19 2002: (male), stubble field (winter wheat), 70 m alt., 'Furry Field', NE of Coursetown House, Courttown East townland, Athy, S69, HF Fox & CD Preston (Blackstock 2003: 46).

H20 1975: gravel path, Devil's Glen, Ashford, JA Paton (BBS exc.) (Paton 1976: 16).

H(21) 1930: Glenasmole, M Buchanan (anon. 1931b: 288).

H21 2002: (male), stubble field (wheat), 60 m alt., SE of Hazelhatch Station, N93, CD Preston (Blackstock 2003: 46).

H22 1978: side of ditch, Petersville Crossroads, N of Moynalty, DM Synnott (Corley 1980a: 25).

H24 1980: side of ditch, roadside by L. Gowna, N of Inchmore, DM Synnott (Corley 1982: 19).

H26 1970: ditch bank W of the Pollagh R., NE of Balla, JA Paton (Paton 1971a: 368).

H27 1970: earthy track bank W of Bundorragha, N of Killary Harbour, JA Paton (Paton 1971a: 368).

[H(28) record (1928, Glencar, FE Milsom, comm. G Halliday: Paton 1963: 491) omitted from *CC* by Paton (1965b: 21) because it was based on the specimen from H29 cited in the next entry, *fide* JA Paton MS note in Recorder's Notebook, comm. TH Blackstock].

H(29) 1928: Cottage garden, NE end of Glencar Lough (BBS exc.) (Duncan 1928: 118).

†H29 listed by Blockeel & Long (1998: 62).

H31 1966: stubble field S of Dromiskin, DM Synnott (Paton 1967c: 392).

H32 1961: moist bank in field, Castleshane, nr Monaghan, JW Fitzgerald (Paton 1962: 364).

H34 1962: stubble field, Newtown Cunningham, J Appleyard *et al.* (BBS exc.) (Paton 1963: 491).

H35 1962: stubble field, Ards Peninsula, J Appleyard *et al.* (BBS exc.) (Paton 1963: 491).

H36 1956: wet mica schist detritus beside stream, Glen Curry Bridge, nr Omagh, JW Fitzgerald & MPH Kertland (Castell 1957: 326).

H37 1962: stubble field between Moy and Portadown, J Appleyard, AC Crundwell & EC Wallace (BBS exc.) (Paton 1963: 491).

H(38) 1903: damp pasture, Saintfield, CH Waddell (DBN), comm. ALK King (Paton 1964: 721).

H38 2002: (male), on soil part shaded by crop of oats in field, *ca* 14 m alt., W of B1 road NW of Ballyhosset (SE of Downpatrick), J54, DT Holyoak 02-1012 (Blackstock 2003: 46).

H(39) 1928: stream at Derriaghy (BBS exc.) (Duncan 1928: 116).

†H39 listed by Blockeel & Long (1998: 62).

H40 1952: stubble field, Coleraine, EW Jones (Castell 1953: 304).

MOSSES
(SPHAGNOPSIDA)

1/1 ***Sphagnum austinii*** Sull. ex Aust. (syn. *Sphagnum austinii* var. *imbricatum* (Russ.) Lindb. nom. illeg., *S. imbricatum* Hornsch. ex Russow subsp. *austinii* (Sull. ex Aust.) Flatberg)

H1 1955: Reenacollee Bog, nr Kenmare, TA Barry, comm. ALK King (BBSUK, DBN) (Warburg 1956: 151, Hill 1986: 19).
H2 1971: wet bog on peninsula separating Upper Lake from Long Range, Killarney, C Mhic Daeid (BBSUK) (Crundwell 1973: 507, Hill 1986: 19).
H9 1960: hummock in blanket bog by Lough Coller, nr Lisdoonvarna, MCF Proctor (BBSUK) (Warburg 1961: 158, Hill 1986: 19).
H(10) 1949: Annagh Bog, Annagh, ALK King (DBN) (Hill 1986: 19). [Another record H(10), 1911: nr Roscrea, HW Lett (DBN), Crundwell 1969: 876 not assigned to segregate species as recognised by Hill 1986].
H14 1956: Monettia Bog, AA Cridland (BBSUK) (Warburg 1958b: 471, Hill 1986: 19).
H15 1961: raised bog nr Aughrim, 5 km SW of Ballinasloe, EM Lobley (BBSUK) (Warburg 1962: 364, Hill 1986: 19).
[H(16) no date: Kylemore, EM Lind, det. A Thompson (Thompson 1944: 207), as *S. imbricatum*. Specimen apparently not revised by Hill (1986)].
H16 1982: flat bog between the N and NW outlines of Errisbeg Mt, Roundstone, DM Synnott (DBN) (Hill 1986: 19).
H(17) listed by Lett (1915: 90).
H17 1957: bog on S side of Clare River, W of Claregalway, AC Crundwell (Hill 1986: 19).
H(18) listed by Lett (1915: 90).
H18 1984: Curraboy Bog, Woodfield House, Clara, DM Synnott (DBN) (Hill 1986: 19). [An older record of *S. imbricatum* var. *cristatum* f. *congestum* (H(18), 1903: Geashill, HW Lett, comm. JA Wheldon, anon. 1917a: 183) may also have been referable to this species].
H20 1975: on raised bog, Rathduffmore, DM Synnott (BBS exc.) (BBSUK, DBN) (Crundwell 1976: 21, Hill 1986: 19).
H22 1956: Rossan Bog, 1 km SE of Kinnegad, ALK King (BBSUK, DBN) (Warburg 1957: 327, Hill 1986: 19).
H23 1959: Lisclogher Bog, near Devlin, ALK King (BBSUK) (Warburg 1960: 769, Hill 1986: 19).
H24 1968: Erne Head, G Drennan (Crundwell 1969: 876, Blockeel 1987: 20).
H25 1981: raised bog, Cloonshannagh, S of Roosky, DM Synnott (BBSUK, DBN) (Hill 1982: 23, 1986: 19).
H26 1982: raised bog between Kiltinagh and Knock, DM Synnott (DBN) (Hill 1986: 19).
[H(27) 1937: near Keel Lough, no collector named (BBS exc.) (A Thompson in Armitage 1938: 11), as *S. imbricatum* var. *cristatum*. H(27), no date: Keel, Achill I., GH Allison (Thompson 1944: 207), as *S. imbricatum*. Specimen apparently not revised by Hill (1986)].
H27 1982: ridge W of Corranbinnia Lough, Nephin Beg Mts, DM Synnott (DBN) (Hill 1986: 19).
H29 1963: hummocks in roadside bog, Fluganagh, 3 miles SE of Dromahair, AR Perry & RD Fitzgerald (BBSUK) (Warburg 1964: 722, Hill 1986: 19).
H30 1968: Fartrin Bog, S of Ballyconnell, G Drennan (Crundwell 1969: 876, Blockeel 1987: 20).
H33 1956: a single large hummock on deep very wet bog, hill NE of Killy Beg, near Belleek, RE Parker (BBSUK) (Warburg 1957: 327, Hill 1986: 19).
H35 1962: raised bog, 2 miles N of Dunglow, EM Lobley & MPH Kertland (BBSUK, DBN) (Warburg 1963b: 492, Hill 1986: 19).
H36 1954: Fairywater, S of Botow's Court Bog, nr Drumquin, MES Morrison (BBSUK) (Warburg 1957: 327, Hill 1986: 19).
(H39) 1889: mountain between Cushendall and Ballymena, HW Lett (DBN) (Hill 1986: 19).
H(39) listed by Lett (1915: 90).
H39 1953: forming hummocks on raised bog, Clogh Mills, nr Ballymena, EM Lobley (Blockeel 1987: 20).
H40 1969: in tussocks, Maghera, T Dilks (BBSUK) (Crundwell 1974: 165, Hill 1986: 19).

1/2 ***Sphagnum affine*** Renauld & Cardot (syn. *Sphagnum imbricatum* Hornsch. ex Russow subsp. *affine* (Renauld & Cardot) Flatberg)

H1 1983: edge of small pool with *Rhynchospora fusca*, between Looscannagh and Derrycanagh Water, DM Synnott (DBN) (Hill 1986: 19).
H2 1959: Cromaglan Bridge Bog, Killarney, SB Chapman (Hill 1986: 19).
H(37) 1898: Camlough Mt., HW Lett (DBN) (Crundwell 1969: 876, Hill 1986: 19).

1/3 ***Sphagnum papillosum*** Lindb. (syn. *Sphagnum hakkodense* Warnst. & Cardot, *S. papillosum* var. *confertum* Lindb., *S. papillosum* var. *normale* Warnst., *S. papillosum* var. *sublaeve* Limpr.)

H(1) listed by Lett (1915: 90) without details.
†H1 listed by Blockeel & Long (1998: 63).
H(2) 1935: Eagle's Nest, no collector named (BBS exc.) (Watson 1936: 264), as var. *sublaeve*.
†H2 listed by Blockeel & Long (1998: 63).
H(3) listed by Lett (1915: 90) without details.
†H3 listed by Blockeel & Long (1998: 63).
H4 1966: boggy ground at 1200 ft alt., Seefin, Boggeragh Mts, MFV Corley & JS Parker (Perry 1967: 405).
H5 1967: in bog, *ca* 800 ft [alt.], Lyrenamon, RD Fitzgerald (Crundwell 1968: 629).
†H6 listed by Blockeel & Long (1998: 63).
H(7) listed by Lett (1915: 90) without details.
†H7 listed by Blockeel & Long (1998: 63).
H(8) listed by Lett (1915: 90) without details.
†H8 listed by Blockeel & Long (1998: 63).
H(9) listed by Lett (1915: 90) without details.
†H9 listed by Blockeel & Long (1998: 63).
H(10) listed by Lett (1915: 90) without details.
†H10 listed by Blockeel & Long (1998: 63).
H(11) listed by Lett (1915: 90) without details.
†H11 listed by Blockeel & Long (1998: 63).
H(12) listed by Lett (1915: 90) without details.
†H12 listed by Blockeel & Long (1998: 63).
H(13) listed by Lett (1915: 90) without details.
†H13 listed by Blockeel & Long (1998: 63).
H(14) listed by Lett (1915: 90) without details.
†H14 listed by Blockeel & Long (1998: 63).
H15 1957: blanket bog, hills E of Gort, RE Parker (Warburg 1958b: 471).
H(16) listed by Lett (1915: 90) without details.
H(16) no date: Kylemore, EM Lind, det. A Thompson (Thompson 1944: 207), as var. *normale*.
†H16 listed by Blockeel & Long (1998: 63).
H(17) listed by Lett (1915: 90) without details.
†H17 listed by Blockeel & Long (1998: 63).
H(18) listed by Lett (1915: 90) without details.
H(18) 1949: Rathlumber, A Jackson (Thompson & Lobley 1950: 382), as var. *normale*.
†H18 listed by Blockeel & Long (1998: 63).
H(19) 1949: Ballymount Bog, Calverstown, JS Thomson (Thompson & Lobley 1950: 382), as var. *normale*.
†H19 listed by Blockeel & Long (1998: 63).
H(20) listed by Lett (1915: 90), as var. *confertum*.
H(20) 1949: Ballyreagh Bog, AEA Dunston (Thompson & Lobley 1950: 382), as var. *sublaeve*.
†H20 listed by Blockeel & Long (1998: 63).
H(21) listed by Lett (1915: 90) without details.
H(21) 1948: Pine Forest, Co. Dublin, AEA Dunston, det. A Thompson (anon. 1949b: 216), as *S. papillosum* var. *normale*.
1948: Pine Forest, Co. Dublin, AEA Dunston, det. A Thompson (anon. 1949b: 216), as *S. papillosum* var. *sublaeve*.
1949: side of road to Mahoney Bog, AEA Dunston (Thompson & Lobley 1950: 382), as *S. hakkodense*.
H22 1956: Rossan Bog, nr Kinnegad, ALK King (Warburg 1957: 326).
H(23) listed by Lett (1915: 90) without details.
†H23 listed by Blockeel & Long (1998: 63).
H(24) listed by Lett (1915: 90) without details.
†H24 listed by Blockeel & Long (1998: 63).
H(25) listed by Lett (1915: 90) without details.
†H25 listed by Blockeel & Long (1998: 63).
H(26) listed by Lett (1915: 90) without details.
†H26 listed by Blockeel & Long (1998: 63).
H(27) listed by Lett (1915: 90) without details.
H(27) 1937: nr Keel, no collector named (BBS exc.) (A Thompson in Armitage 1938: 11), as var. *sublaeve*.
no date: nr Keel Lough, A Thompson (Thompson 1944: 207), as var. *sublaeve*.
†H27 listed by Blockeel & Long (1998: 63).
H(28) listed by Lett (1915: 90) without details.
H(28) 1937: Ben Bulben, no collector named (BBS exc.) (A Thompson in Armitage 1938: 11), as var. *normale*.
no date: Ben Bulbin, EM Lobley & A

Thompson (Thompson 1944: 207), as var. *normale*.
†H28 listed by Blockeel & Long (1998: 63).
H(29) listed by Lett (1915: 90) without details.
H(29) 1937: Glenade, no collector named (BBS exc.) (A Thompson in Armitage 1938: 11), as var. *normale*.
1937: Tullaghan, no collector named (BBS exc.) (A Thompson in Armitage 1938: 11), as var. *normale*.
1937: Bog, Tullaghan, EM Lobley (anon. 1938a: 22), as var. *normale*.
no date: Tullaghan, EM Lobley (Thompson 1944: 207), as var. *normale*.
no date: Glenade, A Thompson (Thompson 1944: 207), as var. *normale*.
†H29 listed by Blockeel & Long (1998: 63).
H(30) listed by Lett (1915: 90) without details.
†H30 listed by Blockeel & Long (1998: 63).
[H(31) listed by Lett (1915: 90) without details. H31 deleted because no valid record or voucher specimen traced (Blockeel 1999: 3)].
H31 1999: on peaty bank in *Schoenus* flush, 300 m alt., Two Mile River, Carlingford, J11, TL Blockeel 28/168 (Rothero 2000: 45).
[H(32) listed by Lett (1915: 90) without details. H32 deleted because no valid record or voucher specimen traced (Blockeel 1999: 3)].
H(33) listed by Lett (1915: 90).
H(33) 1937: Castle Caldwell, no collector named (BBS exc.) (A Thompson in Armitage 1938: 11), as var. *normale*.
no date: Castle Caldwell, A Thompson (Thompson 1944: 207), as var. *normale*.
†H33 listed by Blockeel & Long (1998: 63).
†H34 listed by Blockeel & Long (1998: 63).
H(35) listed by Lett (1915: 90) without details.
H(35) 1946: nr L. Birrog, Portnoo, JS Thomson, det. A Thompson (anon. 1949b: 216), as *S. papillosum* var. *normale*.
†H35 listed by Blockeel & Long (1998: 63).
H(36) listed by Lett (1915: 90) without details.
†H36 listed by Blockeel & Long (1998: 63).
H(37) listed by Lett (1915: 90) without details.
†H37 listed by Blockeel & Long (1998: 63).
H(38) listed by Lett (1915: 90) without details.
†H38 listed by Blockeel & Long (1998: 63).
H(39) listed by Lett (1915: 90) without details.
†H39 listed by Blockeel & Long (1998: 63).
†H40 listed by Blockeel & Long (1998: 63).

1/4a ***Sphagnum palustre*** **L. var.** ***palustre***
(syn. *Sphagnum cymbifolium* Hedw., *S. cymbifolium* var. *congestum* Schimp., *S. cymbifolium* var. *flavescens* Wheldon, *S. cymbifolium* var. *squarrosulum* Wheldon)

H(1) listed by Lett (1915: 90) without details.
†H1 listed by Blockeel & Long (1998: 63).
H(2) listed by Lett (1915: 90) without details.
†H2 listed by Blockeel & Long (1998: 63).
H(3) listed by Lett (1915: 90) without details.
†H3 listed by Blockeel & Long (1998: 63).
H(4) listed by Lett (1915: 90) without details.
†H4 listed by Blockeel & Long (1998: 63).
H(6) listed by Lett (1915: 90) without details.
†H6 listed by Blockeel & Long (1998: 63).
H(7) listed by Lett (1915: 90) without details.
†H7 listed by Blockeel & Long (1998: 63).
H(8) listed by Lett (1915: 90) without details.
†H8 listed by Blockeel & Long (1998: 63).
H(9) listed by Lett (1915: 90) without details.
†H9 listed by Blockeel & Long (1998: 63).
H(10) listed by Lett (1915: 90) without details.
†H10 listed by Blockeel & Long (1998: 63).
H(11) listed by Lett (1915: 90) without details.
†H11 listed by Blockeel & Long (1998: 63).
H(12) listed by Lett (1915: 90) without details.
†H12 listed by Blockeel & Long (1998: 63).
H(13) listed by Lett (1915: 90) without details.
†H13 listed by Blockeel & Long (1998: 63).
H(14) listed by Lett (1915: 90) without details.
†H14 listed by Blockeel & Long (1998: 63).
H(15) listed by Lett (1915: 90) without details.
†H15 listed by Blockeel & Long (1998: 63).
H(16) listed by Lett (1915: 90).
†H16 listed by Blockeel & Long (1998: 63).
[H(17) listed by Lett (1915: 90) without details. H17 deleted because no valid record or voucher specimen traced (Blockeel 1999: 3)].
H(18) listed by Lett (1915: 90) without details.
†H18 listed by Blockeel & Long (1998: 63).
[H(19) listed by Lett (1915: 90) without details. H19 deleted because no valid record or voucher specimen traced (Blockeel 1999: 3)].
H(20) listed by Lett (1915: 90).
†H20 listed by Blockeel & Long (1998: 63).
H(21) listed by Lett (1915: 90) without details.
†H21 listed by Blockeel & Long (1998: 63).
H22 1952: Clonycavan Bog, nr Ballivor, ALK King (Warburg 1953: 305).
H23 1957: by the S shore of L. Ennell, nr Mullingar, ALK King (Warburg 1958b:

471).
H(24) listed by Lett (1915: 90) without details.
†H24 listed by Blockeel & Long (1998: 63).
H(25) listed by Lett (1915: 90) without details.
†H25 listed by Blockeel & Long (1998: 63).
H(26) listed by Lett (1915: 90) without details.
†H26 listed by Blockeel & Long (1998: 63).
H(27) listed by Lett (1915: 90) without details.
†H27 listed by Blockeel & Long (1998: 63).
H(28) listed by Lett (1915: 90) without details.
†H28 listed by Blockeel & Long (1998: 63).
H(29) listed by Lett (1915: 90) without details.
†H29 listed by Blockeel & Long (1998: 63).
H(30) listed by Lett (1915: 90) without details.
H30 1955: bog, ½ mile N of Virginia, ALK King (Warburg 1956: 150).
[H(31) listed by Lett (1915: 90) without details. H31 deleted because no valid record or voucher specimen traced (Blockeel 1999: 3)].
H31 1999: in *Juncus* flush on moorland, 350 m alt., Two Mile River, Carlingford, J11, TL Blockeel 28/182 (Rothero 2000: 45).
[H(32) listed by Lett (1915: 90) without details. H32 deleted because no valid record or voucher specimen traced (Blockeel 1999: 3)].
H32 2002: in blanket bog flush, 350 m alt., E of Three Counties Hollow, Eshbrack, H54, N Lockhart 2002/07a (Rothero 2003: 46).
H(33) listed by Lett (1915: 90) without details.
H(33) 1905: Rossinver More, HW Lett (Wheldon 1924: 55), as *S. cymbifolium* var. *flavescens* Wheldon var. nov.
†H33 listed by Blockeel & Long (1998: 63).
H(34) listed by Lett (1915: 90) without details.
†H34 listed by Blockeel & Long (1998: 63).
H(35) listed by Lett (1915: 90) without details.
†H35 listed by Blockeel & Long (1998: 63).
H36 1953: bog, Tamnamore, MPH Kertland & EM Lobley (Warburg 1955: 582).
H(37) 1901: Parish of Montiaghs, HW Lett (Wheldon 1924: 55), as *S. cymbifolium* var. *flavescens* Wheldon var. nov.
H(37) listed by Lett (1915: 90) without details.
†H37 listed by Blockeel & Long (1998: 63).
H(38) listed by Lett (1915: 90).
†H38 listed by Blockeel & Long (1998: 63).
H(39) listed by Lett (1915: 90) without details.
†H39 listed by Blockeel & Long (1998: 63).
†H40 listed by Blockeel & Long (1998: 63).

1/5 ***Sphagnum magellanicum*** Brid.
(syn. *Sphagnum medium* Limpr., *S. medium* var. *obscurum* Warnst., *S. medium* var. *purpurascens* (Russow) Warnst., *S. medium* var. *roseum* (Roell) Warnst.)

H(1) 1892: mts NE of Waterville, RW Scully (DBN) (Crundwell 1969: 876).
†H1 listed by Blockeel & Long (1998: 63).
H(2) 1936: wood by Upper Lake, Killarney, PWM Richards (anon. 1938d: 41), as *S. medium.*
†H2 listed by Blockeel & Long (1998: 63).
H(3) listed by Lett (1915: 90), without detail.
†H3 listed by Blockeel & Long (1998: 63).
H7 1966: raised bog W of Longford Pass Bridge, Urlingford, EM Lobley (BBS exc.) (Crundwell 1970: 195).
[H(8) listed by Lett (1915: 90), without detail. H8 deleted because no valid record or voucher specimen traced (Blockeel 1999: 3)].
H8 1992: in bog, 1 km N of Blane Bridge, between Glin and Athea, R13, E Wiltshire, conf. A Eddy (Rothero 2000: 45).
H(9) listed by Lett (1915: 90), without detail.
†H9 listed by Blockeel & Long (1998: 63).
H(10) listed by Lett (1915: 90). H(10) listed by Blockeel & Long (1998: 63).
H11 1966: in bog, Derryfadda, nr Johnstown, RD Fitzgerald (Crundwell 1968: 629).
H14 1956: bog E of Clonaddadoran, AA Cridland (Warburg 1958b: 471).
H15 1962: raised bog nr Woodford, AJE Smith (Warburg 1963b: 492).
H(16) no date: Shenanagh, Kylemore, EM Lind, det. A Thompson (Thompson 1944: 207).
†H16 listed by Blockeel & Long (1998: 63).
H17 1957: bog between R. Clare and R. Cregg, RE Parker (Warburg 1958b: 471).
H(18) listed by Lett (1915: 90).
†H18 listed by Blockeel & Long (1998: 63).
H(19) 1949: Ballymount Bog, nr Calverstown, JS Thomson (Thompson & Lobley 1950: 382).
†H19 listed by Blockeel & Long (1998: 63).
H(20) no date: mountain bog, Kippure, A Jackson (Thompson & Lobley 1950: 382).
†H20 listed by Blockeel & Long (1998: 63).
H22 1956: Rossan Bog, nr Kinnegad, ALK

King (Warburg 1957: 326).
H(23) 1935: nr Mullingar, AR Clapham & AG Tansley, per JPM Brenan (anon. 1949b: 216).
†H23 listed by Blockeel & Long (1998: 63).
H24 1955: Edera Bog, nr Ballymahon, TA Barry, comm. ALK King (Warburg 1957: 326).
H(25) 1920: Elphin, JD Houston (anon. 1921: 273), new record as *S. medium* var. *purpurascens*.
†H25 listed by Blockeel & Long (1998: 63).
H(26) no date: Lough Mask, Miss Bagwell, det. U Duncan (Thompson 1944: 207).
†H26 listed by Blockeel & Long (1998: 63).
H(27) no date: W West (Wheldon 1919: 251), new record as *S. medium* var. *roseum* f. *abbreviatum*.
1937: nr Keel Lough, no collector named (BBS exc.) (A Thompson in Armitage 1938: 11).
no date: Keel, Achill I., GH Allison (Thompson 1944: 207).
†H27 listed by Blockeel & Long (1998: 63).
H(28) 1937: Cliffony, no collector named (BBS exc.) (A Thompson in Armitage 1938: 11).
1937: Lough Cloenty, near Cliffeny [*sic* = Cliffony], EM Lobley (anon. 1938a: 21).
no date: nr Cliffony, EM Lobley (Thompson 1944: 207).
†H28 listed by Blockeel & Long (1998: 63).
H(29) 1937: Tullaghan, no collector named (BBS exc.) (A Thompson in Armitage 1938: 11).
no date: Tullaghan, EM Lobley (Thompson 1944: 207).
†H29 listed by Blockeel & Long (1998: 63).
H(30) listed by Lett (1915: 90). H(30) listed by Blockeel & Long (1998: 63).
H31 1955: Coole Bog, W of Ardee, ALK King (Warburg 1956: 150).
H32 2002: in blanket bog flush, 350 m alt., E of Three Counties Hollow, Eshbrack, H54, C Douglas & N Lockhart 2002/06a (Rothero 2003: 46).
H(33) listed by Lett (1915: 90).
†H33 listed by Blockeel & Long (1998: 63).
H(34) listed by Lett (1915: 90).
H34 1968: in bog, Gorey, nr Culdaff, JW Fitzgerald (Crundwell 1969: 876).
H(35) listed by Lett (1915: 90), without locality.
†H35 listed by Blockeel & Long (1998: 63).
H36 1953: bog, Tamnamore, nr Verner's Bridge, MPH Kertland & EM Lobley (Warburg 1954: 477).
H(37) no date: JD Houston (Wheldon 1919: 251), new record as *S. medium* var. *obscurum* f. *fuscescens*.
H(37) listed by Lett (1915: 90).
†H37 listed by Blockeel & Long (1998: 63).
H(38) listed by Lett (1915: 90).
†H38 listed by Blockeel & Long (1998: 63).
†H39 listed by Blockeel & Long (1998: 63).
†H40 listed by Blockeel & Long (1998: 63).

1/6 ***Sphagnum squarrosum*** Crome
(syn. *Sphagnum squarrosum* var. *imbricatum* Schimp., *S. squarrosum* var. *spectabile* Russow in Warnst., *S. squarrosum* var. *subsquarrosum* Russow)

H(1) 1892: Kilgobban Bog, nr Camp, Dingle, RW Scully (DBN) (Crundwell 1969: 877).
H(2) listed by Lett (1915: 92) without details.
†H2 listed by Blockeel & Long (1998: 63).
H3 1950: L. Ordree, Sherkin I., PJ Newbould (Warburg 1952: 97).
H(4) listed by Lett (1915: 92). H(4) listed by Blockeel & Long (1998: 63).
H(5) listed by Lett (1915: 92) without details.
†H5 listed by Blockeel & Long (1998: 63).
H6 1966: edge of Ballin Lough, Kill, EM Lobley & RD Fitzgerald (BBS exc.) (Perry 1967: 405).
H(7) listed by Lett (1915: 92).
†H7 listed by Blockeel & Long (1998: 63).
[H(8) listed by Lett (1915: 92) without locality. H8 deleted because no valid record or voucher specimen traced (Blockeel 1999: 3)].
H9 1963: slightly flushed area by road, W side of Slieve Elva, *ca* 750 ft [alt.], Lisdoonvarna, G Halliday (Warburg 1964: 722).
H12 1961: bank of glacial kettlehole nr Curracloe, ALK King (Warburg 1962: 365).
H(13) listed by Lett (1915: 92).
†H13 listed by Blockeel & Long (1998: 63).
H14 1965: stream in bogland nr Derry Hills, DM Synnott (Warburg 1966: 189).
H(16) listed by Lett (1915: 92).
†H16 listed by Blockeel & Long (1998: 63).
H17 1968: in marginal lagg of raised bog, Addergoule North, R. Suck, nr

Ballinasloe, HJB Birks (Crundwell 1969: 877).

H18 1986: minerotrophic soak, Clara Bog, C O'Connell (Blockeel 1987: 20, O'Connell & Foss 1987).

H(19) 1949: Ballymount Bog, nr Calverstown, JS Thomson (Thompson & Lobley 1950: 380), as var. *spectabile*.
1949: Ballmount [*sic* = Ballymount] Bog, nr Calverstown, JS Thomson (Thompson & Lobley 1950: 380), as var. *subsquarrosum*.

H(20) listed by Lett (1915: 92).

†H20 listed by Blockeel & Long (1998: 63).

H(21) listed by Lett (1915: 92). H(21) listed by Blockeel & Long (1998: 63).

H(22) listed by Lett (1915: 92) without locality.

†H22 listed by Blockeel & Long (1998: 63).

H23 1957: bog, Ballinafid, JS Thomson (Warburg 1958b: 471).

H24 1957: Newtownforbes [*sic* = Newtown Forbes] bog, MPH Kertland & ALK King (Warburg 1958b: 471).

H25 1981: raised bog, Cloonlarge, 8 km E of Roscommon, DM Synnott (Hill 1982: 23).

H(27) listed by Lett (1915: 92).

H(27) 1937: near Lough Keel no collector named (BBS exc.) (A Thompson in Armitage 1938: 10), as var. *spectabile*.
no date: nr Keel Lough, Achill I., A Thompson (Thompson 1944: 202), as *S. squarrosum* var. *spectabile*.

†H27 listed by Blockeel & Long (1998: 63).

H28 1965: wood at mouth of R. Bonnet, RD Fitzgerald (Warburg 1966: 189).

H(29) 1937: Tullaghan, no collector named (BBS exc.) (A Thompson in Armitage 1938: 10), as var. *spectabile*.
1937: Tullaghan, no collector named (BBS exc.) (A Thompson in Armitage 1938: 10), as var. *subsquarrosum*.
1937: Tullaghan, EM Lobley (anon. 1938a: 20), as var. *subsquarrosum*.
no date: Tullaghan, EM Lobley (Thompson 1944: 202), as *S. squarrosum* var. *spectabile*.
no date: Tullaghan, EM Lobley (Thompson 1944: 202), as *S. squarrosum* var. *subsquarrosum*.

†H29 listed by Blockeel & Long (1998: 63).

H30 1965: bog, Carricknacrannoge, EM Lobley & RD Fitzgerald (Warburg 1966: 189).

H(31) listed by Lett (1915: 92) without details.

[H31 record (1950: corner of railway bridge, Co. Louth, JS Thomson: Thompson 1951: 496, as var. *spectabile*) has such poor locality data that the record should be dismissed as unlocalised].

†H31 listed by Blockeel & Long (1998: 63), but notes with previous record suggest it should be rejected.

H(32) listed by Lett (1915: 92).

†H32 listed by Blockeel & Long (1998: 63).

H(33) listed by Lett (1915: 92).

†H33 listed by Blockeel & Long (1998: 63).

H(34) listed by Lett (1915: 92).

H(34) 1937: Bundoran, no collector named (BBS exc.) (A Thompson in Armitage 1938: 10), as var. *subsquarrosum*.
no date: nr Bundoran, GH Allison (Thompson 1944: 202), as *S. squarrosum* var. *subsquarrosum*.

†H34 listed by Blockeel & Long (1998: 63).

H35 1970: in boggy ditch nr Portnoo, N of Ardara, MFV Corley (Crundwell 1971b: 374).

H(36) listed by Lett (1915: 92).

†H36 listed by Blockeel & Long (1998: 63).

H(37) listed by Lett (1915: 92).

H(37) 1917: Annalost, JD Houston, det . as 'f. *elegans*' by JA Wheldon (anon. 1918a: 207), as var. *spectabile*.

†H37 listed by Blockeel & Long (1998: 63).

H(38) 1905: in bog, Lisbane, Saintfield, CH Waddell det. JA Wheldon (anon. 1917a: 183-184), as *S. squarrosum* var. *imbricatum*.

H(38) listed by Lett (1915: 92).

†H38 listed by Blockeel & Long (1998: 63).

H(39) listed by Lett (1915: 92).

†H39 listed by Blockeel & Long (1998: 63).

H40 1953: Maghera, MES Morrison (BEL) (Crundwell 1971b; 374).

1/7 ***Sphagnum teres*** (Schimp.) Ångstr.
(syn. *Sphagnum squarrosum* var. *teres* Schimp.)

H1 1961: bog by R. Caragh, nr Glencar Hotel, EM Lobley (Warburg 1962: 364).

H(20) listed by Lett (1915: 92). H(20) listed by Blockeel & Long (1998: 64).

H22 1978: cut-over bog between L. Bane and Dromone, Oldcastle, DM Synnott (Hill 1980b: 32).

H23 1985: open woodland over peat, Clonhugh Wood, nr L. Owel, DL Kelly

(Hill 1986: 20).

H25 1985: fen at bog margin, Carrowbehy, H Grogan, C Douglas & JC Cross (Blockeel 1987: 20).

H27 1957: iron flush in blanket bog, nr Dooleeg, ALK King (Warburg 1958b: 471, King 1958a).

H30 2000: amongst *S. palustre* and *Aulacomnium palustre* on peat under birch, 60 m alt., N of Annagh Lough, H31, J Cross, det. N Lockhart (BBSUK) (Rothero 2001: 37).

H33 2000: in fen beside lough with *Carex rostrata*, Meenameen Lough, W end, H05, DT Holyoak 00-224 (BBSUK) (Rothero 2001: 37).

H(34) listed by Lett (1915: 92). H(34) listed by Blockeel & Long (1998: 64).

H35 1998: in mesotrophic flush, 150 m alt., Meentygrannagh Bog, 2 km S of Altinierin, C00, N Lockhart (Rothero 1999b: 39).

†H37 listed by Blockeel & Long (1998: 64).

[H38 record from Ingham (in Barker *et al.* 1907) deleted because no specimen traced (Lobley & Fitzgerald 1970: 360, Crundwell 1971b: 374)].

[H(38) listed by Lett (1915: 92)].

H38 1993: Lough Moss, J25, M Bailey (Blockeel 1994: 35).

†H39 listed by Blockeel & Long (1998: 64).

H40 1953: bog nr Blackwater Bridge, N of L. Fea, MPH Kertland & EM Lobley (Warburg 1955: 582).

1/8 ***Sphagnum fimbriatum*** Wilson
(syn. *Sphagnum fimbriatum* var. *intermedium* Russow, *S. fimbriatum* var. *laxifolium* Warnst., *S. fimbriatum* var. *robustum* Braithw., *S. fimbriatum* var. *validus* Cardot)

H1 1951: marshy ground in wood, nr Glenbeigh, UK Duncan (BBS exc.) (Warburg 1952: 97).

H4 1967: woodland, Old Park House, nr Bandon, RD Fitzgerald (Crundwell 1968: 630).

H6 1966: *Juncus* marsh S of Kill, Bunmahon, JA Paton, GCG Argent & ERB Little (BBS exc.) (Perry 1967: 406).

H7 1966: under *Rhododendron* by stream running into Bay Lough, Knockmealdown Mts, ERB Little & JA Paton (BBS exc.) (Perry 1967: 406).

H8 1991: under Birch on cutaway bog, 60 m alt., 3 km NW of Cappamore, R73, N Lockhart & A O'Suillivan (Blockeel 1992: 25).

H9 1963: slightly flushed area by road, W side of Slieve Elva, *ca* 750 ft [alt.], Lisdoonvarna, G Halliday (Warburg 1964: 722).

H10 1979: heathy ground among *Molinia*, Keeper Hill, S of Silvermine Mts, HMH van Melick (Hill 1981: 22).

H13 1969: edge of bog, St Mullins, nr Craiguenamanagh [*sic* = Graiguenamanagh], RD Fitzgerald (Crundwell 1970: 195).

H18 1957: Annagharvey Bog, nr Tullymore, JS Thomson (Warburg 1958b: 472).

H(19) 1949: Ballymount Bog, nr Calverstown, JS Thomson (Thompson & Lobley 1950: 380), as var. *intermedium*.

H(20) listed by Lett (1915: 92).

H(20) 1949: Ballyreagh Bog, AEA Dunston (Thompson & Lobley 1950: 380), as var. *robustum*.
1949: Ballyreagh Bog, AEA Dunston (Thompson & Lobley 1950: 380), as var. *validus*.

†H20 listed by Blockeel & Long (1998: 64).

H(21) 1949: Featherbed Mt., AEA Dunston (Thompson & Lobley 1950: 380), as var. *laxifolium*.

H22 1969: birch wood, Thomastown Bog, Duleek, DM Synnott (Crundwell 1970: 195).

H23 1986: *Molinia* flush on raised bog, Cloncrow, H Grogan & C Douglas (Blockeel 1987: 21).

H24 1980: small bog S of Currygrane Lough, Ballinalea, DM Synnott (Hill 1981: 22).

H25 1965: bog on moors, Kilronan, nr Ballyfarnan, EM Lobley & RD Fitzgerald (Warburg 1966: 190).

H27 1987: on grassy bank in coastal gully, Trawmore Sand, E end of Keel Bay, Achill I., TL Blockeel (Blockeel 1988: 33).

H28 1965: among rocks, Slish Wood, L. Gill, EM Lobley & RD Fitzgerald (Warburg 1966: 190).

H29 1963: roadside bog, Flughanagh, 3 miles SE of Dromahair, AR Perry & RD Fitzgerald (Warburg 1964: 722).

H(30) listed by Lett (1915: 92). H(30) listed by Blockeel & Long (1998: 64).

H32 1961: bog, Killyneill, nr Monaghan, RD Fitzgerald (Warburg 1962: 365).
H(33) listed by Lett (1915: 92). H(33) listed by Blockeel & Long (1998: 64).
[H(34) listed by Lett (1915: 92) without details. H34 deleted because no valid record or voucher specimen traced (Blockeel 1999: 3)].
H(35) listed by Lett (1915: 92).
†H35 listed by Blockeel & Long (1998: 64).
H36 1953: bog under birch, Tamnamore, nr Verner's Bridge, MPH Kertland & EM Lobley (Warburg 1954: 478).
H(37) listed by Blockeel & Long (1998: 64).
H(38) listed by Lett (1915: 92).
†H38 listed by Blockeel & Long (1998: 64).
H(39) listed by Lett (1915: 92) without details.
†H39 listed by Blockeel & Long (1998: 64).
H(40) listed by Blockeel & Long (1998: 64).

1/9 *Sphagnum girgensohnii* Russow

H1 1955: sward on bank nr river, Owencashla, Glenteenassig, AP Fanning (DBN), comm. DM Synnott (Blockeel 1989: 24).
H3 1962: boggy ground nr Coomhola Bridge, N of T65 between Glengarriff and Bantry, AJE Smith (Warburg 1963b: 492).
H(20) listed by Lett (1915: 92).
†H20 listed by Blockeel & Long (1998: 64).
H29 1965: among rocks by stream, Dergvone, NE of Drumkeeran, EM Lobley & RD Fitzgerald (Warburg 1966: 190).
H(34) listed by Lett (1915: 92). H(34) listed by Blockeel & Long (1998: 64).
H35 1990: in damp hollow in Oak/Birch woodland, 60 m alt., Ballyarr Wood, *ca* 5 km E of Kilmacrenan, C12, TL Blockeel 19/511 (Blockeel 1991c: 40).
H36 1957: bog, Shestinawaddy [*sic* = Sheskinawaddy], RD Fitzgerald (Warburg 1958b: 472).
H37 1962: raised bog, Clady Beg nr Clady Milltown, EM Lobley & MPH Kertland (Warburg 1963b: 492).
H(38) listed by Lett (1915: 92). H(38) listed by Blockeel & Long (1998: 64).
[H39 deleted because a specimen (1890: Glendun, SA Brenan, DBN) is *S. robustum* (Crundwell 1970: 195)].
H(39) 1890: Glendun [= D2030], SA Brenan (BIRM) (Lett 1915: 92, Lobley & Fitzgerald 1970: 363, Crundwell 1971b: 374) [reinstatement of record deleted by A.C. Crundwell in 1970].
H39 1988: in poor fen by lake with *S. subnitens*, Loughnabrook, Garron Plateau, D21, R Weyl (BBSUK) (Rothero 2001: 37).
H40 1999: on bank above track in woodland, Banagher Glen, C60, DT Holyoak 99-636 (BBSUK) (Rothero 2000: 46).

1/10 *Sphagnum russowii* Warnst.
(syn. *Sphagnum robustum* (Warnst.) Card., *S. russowii* var. *girgensohnioides* Russow)

H(3) 1912: Glengarrif, HW Lett (DBN) (Crundwell 1969: 877).
H7 1966: flush bog by stream at *ca* 1000 ft alt., Knockastakeen, Galtee Mts, EM Lobley (BBS exc.) (Perry 1967: 406).
H10 1979: in wet flush on mountain slope, Keeper Hill, N Lockhart (Hill 1980b: 33).
H(13) 1867: Mt Leinster, RC Browne (DBN) (Crundwell 1968: 630).
†H13 listed by Blockeel & Long (1998: 64).
H(20) 1949: Ballyreagh Bog, AEA Dunston (Thompson & Lobley 1950: 380).
1949: Ballyreagh Bog, AEA Dunston (Thompson & Lobley 1950: 380), as var. *girgensohnioides*.
†H20 listed by Blockeel & Long (1998: 64).
H(21) 1948: bog at Pine Forest, Dublin, AEA Dunston, det. A Thompson (DBN) (anon. 1949b: 215, Crundwell 1969: 877).
1949: side of road to Mahoney Bog, AEA Dunston (Thompson & Lobley 1950: 380), as var. *girgensohnioides*.
H28 1962: bog below dripping limestone rocks, Gleniff, Dartry Mts, EM Lobley (BBS exc.) (Warburg 1963b: 493).
H29 1970: N-facing hillside nr county boundary S of Glencar Lough, AR Perry & HJ Perry (Crundwell 1974: 165).
H(30) 1909: top of Cuilcagh, 'W.N. Y' (MANCH) (Crundwell 1976: 22).
H33 1960: boggy ground under scarp, *ca* 750 ft [alt.], Carricknagower Lough, RD Fitzgerald (Warburg 1961: 158).
H(34) listed by Lett (1915: 94). H(34) listed by Blockeel & Long (1998: 64).
H35 2001: hummock in *Molinia* and *Juncus* in N-facing coire, 410 m alt., Lavagh

More, G99, NG Hodgetts 3862 (Rothero 2003: 46).

H36 no date: Borin Wood, Gorton, MPH Kertland (Crundwell, 1969: 877).

H37 1962: raised bog, Clady Bog, nr Clady Milltown, EM Lobley & MPH Kertland (Warburg 1963b: 493).

H38 1952: Deers Meadows, nr source of R. Bann, Mourne Mts, JW Fitzgerald & EM Lobley (Warburg 1954: 478).

H(39) listed by Lett (1915: 94).

†H39 listed by Blockeel & Long (1998: 64).

H40 1952: bog, Benbradagh, EM Lobley & J Taylor (Warburg 1954: 478).

1/11 ***Sphagnum quinquefarium*** (Lindb. ex Braithw.) Warnst.
(syn. *Sphagnum acutifolium* var. *quinquefarium* Lindb.)

H(1) listed by Lett (1915: 93).

†H1 listed by Blockeel & Long (1998: 64).

H(2) listed by Lett (1915: 93) without details.

†H2 listed by Blockeel & Long (1998: 64).

H(3) listed by Lett (1915: 93).

†H3 listed by Blockeel & Long (1998: 64).

H(6) listed by Lett (1915: 93).

†H6 listed by Blockeel & Long (1998: 64).

H(7) listed by Lett (1915: 93).

†H7 listed by Blockeel & Long (1998: 64).

H(14) listed by Lett (1915: 93). H(14) listed by Blockeel & Long (1998: 64).

H(16) listed by Lett (1915: 93).

†H16 listed by Blockeel & Long (1998: 64).

H(20) 1949: Ballyreagh, AEA Dunston (Thompson & Lobley 1950: 380).

†H20 listed by Blockeel & Long (1998: 64).

H(21) 1949: Pine Forest East, AEA Dunston (Thompson & Lobley 1950: 380).

H(27) listed by Lett (1915: 93).

†H27 listed by Blockeel & Long (1998: 64).

H(28) 1937: Ben Bulben, no collector named (BBS exc.) (A Thompson in Armitage 1938: 10).
1937: Gleniff, no collector named (BBS exc.) (A Thompson in Armitage 1938: 10).
no date: Glen Iff [*sic* = Gleniff], A Thompson (Thompson 1944: 202).
no date: Ben Bulbin, A Thompson (Thompson 1944: 202).

†H28 listed by Blockeel & Long (1998: 64).

H(29) listed by Lett (1915: 93).

†H29 listed by Blockeel & Long (1998: 64).

H30 1965: by stream *ca* 700 ft alt., Cuilcagh, EM Lobley & RD Fitzgerald (Warburg 1966: 190).

H(33) listed by Lett (1915: 93).

†H33 listed by Blockeel & Long (1998: 64).

H(34) listed by Lett (1915: 93). H(34) listed by Blockeel & Long (1998: 64).

H34 2001: on shaded wooded bank in disused railway cutting, 100 m alt., Barnesmore Gap, SE of Ardinawark, H08, NG Hodgetts 3876 (Rothero 2003: 46).

H(35) listed by Lett (1915: 93).

†H35 listed by Blockeel & Long (1998: 64).

H(36) listed by Lett (1915: 93).

†H36 listed by Blockeel & Long (1998: 64).

H(37) 1917: Camlough Mt., JD Houston (GL) (Crundwell 1969: 877).

[H(38) listed by Lett (1915: 93), from Mourne Mts.].

[H38 record deleted because specimen (1903, Saintfield, HW Lett, BBSUK) is *S. recurvum* (Lobley & Fitzgerald 1970: 364, Crundwell 1971b: 374)].

H(39) listed by Lett (1915: 93).

†H39 listed by Blockeel & Long (1998: 64).

[H40 deleted because specimen (1936: Kilrea, Houston, BEL) is *S. capillaceum* (Crundwell 1970: 195)].

H40 1999: on ground on edge of coniferous plantation, Binevenagh Forest, C63, DT Holyoak 99-583 (BBSUK) (Rothero 2000: 46).

1/12 ***Sphagnum warnstorfii*** Russow
(syn. *Sphagnum warnstorfianum* Du Rietz)

[H(9) 1948: Co. Clare, AAJ (Thompson & Lobley 1950: 380). H9 not accepted for *CC* by Corley & Hill (1981: 56)].

H14 1966: calcareous flush, Derry Hills, nr Clonaslee, RD Fitzgerald (Perry 1967: 406).

H16 2000: in *Schoenus* fen, 40 m alt., Errisbeg, NE side of Lough Nalawney, L64, DG Long 28458, conf. MO Hill (Rothero 2001: 37).

[H(19) 1949: Ballymount Bog, nr Calverstown, JS Thomson (Thompson & Lobley 1950: 380). H19 not accepted for *CC* by Corley & Hill (1981: 56)].

[H(20) 1948: Kippure, AAJ (Thompson & Lobley 1950: 380). H20 not accepted for *CC* by Corley & Hill (1981: 56)].

H25 2002: in fen at edge of raised bog, 90 m alt., Carrowbehy/Caher Bog, M58, NG

Hodgetts 4123 (Rothero 2003: 46).

H27 1961: basic flush bogs in wet meadows, 300 ft [alt.], Knappagh, nr Westport, DA Ratcliffe (Warburg 1962: 365).

[H(28) 1937: Benbulben, no collector named (BBS exc.) (A Thompson in Armitage 1938: 10). H(28), no date: Ben Bulbin, A Thompson (Thompson 1944: 201). H28 not accepted for *CC* by Corley & Hill (1981: 56)].

H32 1980: Lisarilly, H52, N Lockhart, Hb. Forest & Wildlife Service [at Newtown Mount Kennedy], comm. NF Stewart (Blockeel 1995c: 40).

[H(34) 1937: Bundoran, no collector named (BBS exc.) (A Thompson in Armitage 1938: 10). H(34), no date: nr Bundoran, GH Allison (Thompson 1944: 201). H34 not accepted for *CC* by Corley & Hill (1981: 56)].

H(40) 1936: Glenshane Pass, JD Houston (BEL) (Crundwell 1968: 630).

1/13b ***Sphagnum capillifolium*** (Ehrh.) Hedw. **subsp. *rubellum*** (Wilson) M.O.Hill
(syn. *Sphagnum acutifolium* Ehrh. ex Schrad., *S. acutifolium* var. *deflexum* Schimp., *S. acutifolium* var. *elegans* Braithw., *S. acutifolium* var. *purpureum* Schimp., *S. acutifolium* var. *rubellum* (Wilson) Russow, *S. capillaceum* (Weiss) Schrank, *S. capillifolium* var. *rubellum* (Wilson) A.Eddy, *S. nemoreum* auct., *S. rubellum* Wilson, *S. subtile* (Russow) Warnst.)

H(1) listed by Lett (1915: 92, 93) without details.
†H1 listed by Blockeel & Long (1998: 64).
H(2) listed by Lett (1915: 92, 93) without details.
†H2 listed by Blockeel & Long (1998: 64).
H(3) listed by Lett (1915: 93) without details.
†H3 listed by Blockeel & Long (1998: 64).
H(4) listed by Lett (1915: 92, 93) without details.
H4 1966: boggy ground at 1200 ft alt., Seefin, Boggeragh Mts, MFV Corley & JS Parker (Perry 1967: 406), as *S. rubellum*.
H(5) listed by Lett (1915: 92) without details.
†H5 listed by Blockeel & Long (1998: 64).
H(6) listed by Lett (1915: 93).
†H6 listed by Blockeel & Long (1998: 64).
H(7) listed by Lett (1915: 92, 93) without details.
†H7 listed by Blockeel & Long (1998: 64).
H(8) listed by Lett (1915: 92, 93) without details.
†H8 listed by Blockeel & Long (1998: 64).
H(9) listed by Lett (1915: 92, 93) without details.
†H9 listed by Blockeel & Long (1998: 64).
H(10) listed by Lett (1915: 92, 93).
H10 record of *S. rubellum* transferred to *S. capillaceum* (Hill 1978: 16). †H10 listed by Blockeel & Long (1998: 64).
H(11) listed by Lett (1915: 92) without details.
H11 1954: Mt Brandon, *ca* 1250 ft [alt.], ALK King (Warburg 1955: 583), as *S. rubellum*.
1966: bog, Derryfadda, nr Johnstown, RD Fitzgerald (BBS exc.) (Perry 1967: 406).
H(12) listed by Lett (1915: 92) without details.
H12 record of *S. rubellum* transferred to *S. capillaceum* (Hill 1978: 16). †H12 listed by Blockeel & Long (1998: 64).
H(13) listed by Lett (1915: 92, 93) without details.
H13 1969: in bog, Crannagh, foot of Mt Leinster, RD Fitzgerald (Crundwell 1970: 195).
H(14) listed by Lett (1915: 92, 93) without details.
H14 record of *S. rubellum* transferred to *S. capillaceum* (Hill 1978: 16). †H14 listed by Blockeel & Long (1998: 64).
H(15) listed by Lett (1915: 92) without details.
H15 1957: blanket bog, hills E of Gort, RE Parker (Warburg 1958b: 472).
H(16) listed by Lett (1915: 92, 93) without details.
†H16 listed by Blockeel & Long (1998: 64).
H(17) listed by Lett (1915: 92, 93) without details.
†H17 listed by Blockeel & Long (1998: 64).
H(18) listed by Lett (1915: 92, 93).
†H18 listed by Blockeel & Long (1998: 64).
H(19) listed by Lett (1915: 92) without details.
H19 1955: bog, Baronstown East, ALK King (Warburg 1956: 151), as *S. rubellum*.
H(20) listed by Lett (1915: 92, 93) without details.
†H20 listed by Blockeel & Long (1998: 64).
[H(21) listed by Lett (1915: 92, 93) without details. H21 deleted because no valid record or voucher specimen traced (Blockeel 1999: 3)].
H22 1952: Clonycavan Bog, nr Ballivor,

ALK King (Warburg 1953: 306), as *S. nemoreum*.
1952: Clonycavan Bog, nr Ballivor, ALK King (Warburg 1953: 306), as *S. rubellum*.

H(23) listed by Lett (1915: 93).

H23 1971: fen bog, Fore, DM Synnott (conf. EM Lobley: Crundwell 1972: 135).

H24 1955: Edera Bog, nr Ballymahon, TA Barry, comm. ALK King (Warburg 1957: 327), as *S. rubellum*.
1965: bog S of Roosky, EM Lobley & RD Fitzgerald (Warburg 1966: 190).

H(25) listed by Lett (1915: 92) without details.

H25 1957: raised bog, Ballymoe, ALK King (Warburg 1958b: 472), as *S. rubellum*
1957: bog above Chevy Chase Wood, Owendalulleegh, nr Gort, EM Lobley (Warburg 1958b: 472), as *S. capillaceum*.

H(26) listed by Lett (1915: 92, 93) without details.

†H26 listed by Blockeel & Long (1998: 64).

H(27) listed by Lett (1915: 92, 93).

H(27) 1937: Slievemore, no collector named (BBS exc.) (A Thompson in Armitage 1938: 10), as *S. subtile*.
no date: Slievemore, Achill Isle [= I.], A Thompson (Thompson 1944: 201), as *S. subtile*.

†H27 listed by Blockeel & Long (1998: 64).

H(28) listed by Lett (1915: 92, 93) without details.

†H28 listed by Blockeel & Long (1998: 64).

H(29) listed by Lett (1915: 92).

H(29) 1937: bog, Tullaghan, no collector named (BBS exc.) (A Thompson in Armitage 1938: 10), as *S. rubellum*.
1937: bog, Tullaghan, EM Lobley (anon. 1938a: 19), as *S. rubellum*.
no date: Tullaghan, EM Lobley (Thompson 1944: 201), as *S. rubellum*.

†H29 listed by Blockeel & Long (1998: 64).

H(30) listed by Lett (1915: 92, 93) without details.

†H30 listed by Blockeel & Long (1998: 64).

[H(31) listed by Lett (1915: 92, 93) without details. H31 deleted because no valid record or voucher specimen traced (Blockeel 1999: 3)].

H31 1999: edge of gravelly flush on slope above stream, 300 m alt., Two Mile River, Carlingford, J11, TL Blockeel 28/171 (Rothero 2000: 46).

H(32) listed by Lett (1915: 92) without details.

H(32) 1947: Black I., Lough Muckno, Castlebury, JS Thomson, det. A Thompson (anon. 1948a: 117), as *S. rubellum*.

H(33) listed by Lett (1915: 92, 93) without details.

†H33 listed by Blockeel & Long (1998: 64).

H(34) listed by Lett (1915: 92, 93) without details.

†H34 listed by Blockeel & Long (1998: 64).

H(35) listed by Lett (1915: 92, 93).

†H35 listed by Blockeel & Long (1998: 64).

H(36) listed by Lett (1915: 93).

†H36 listed by Blockeel & Long (1998: 64).

H(37) listed by Lett (1915: 92, 93).

†H37 listed by Blockeel & Long (1998: 64).

H(38) listed by Lett (1915: 92, 93).

†H38 listed by Blockeel & Long (1998: 64).

H(39) listed by Lett (1915: 92, 93).

†H39 listed by Blockeel & Long (1998: 64).

H(40) listed by Lett (1915: 93).

†H40 listed by Blockeel & Long (1998: 64) without details.

1/14 ***Sphagnum fuscum*** (Schimp.) H. Klinggr.
(syn. *Sphagnum acutifolium* var. *fuscum* Schimp.)

[H2 record dismissed as doubtful (Birks & Ratcliffe 1976b, Hill 1977a: 16)].

H2 1983: Cores Bog, W side of Mangerton Mt., DM Synnott (Hill 1984b: 25).

H9 1979: waved peat NE of L. Callaunyheeda, nr Derrymore House, HMH van Melick (Hill 1981: 22).

H10 1965: bog at Carrig, SW of Birr, ALK King (Warburg 1966: 190).

H15 1962: raised bog nr Woodford, AJE Smith (Warburg 1963b: 493).

H16 1957: forming hummocks in blanket bog, nr Conga Lough, RE Parker (Warburg 1958b: 472).

H17 1957: bog between R. Clare and R. Cregg, RE Parker (Warburg 1958b: 472).

H(18) listed by Lett (1915: 93).

†H18 listed by Blockeel & Long (1998: 64).

H19 1956: Mouds Bog, nr Newbridge, ALK King (Warburg 1957: 327).

H22 1956: Rossan Bog, nr Kinnegad, ALK King (Warburg 1957: 327).

H23 1952: The Derries Bog, Athlone, ALK King (Warburg 1953: 305).

H24 1966: Cloontirm Bog nr Longford, ALK

King (Perry 1967: 406).

H25 1966: peat bog 2 miles SW of Termonbarry, W side of R. Shannon, G Halliday (Perry 1967: 406).

H27 1951: blanket bog nr L. Namucka, Louisberg, DH Dalby (Warburg 1953: 305).

H29 1986: hummock on raised bog, South Cashel, H Grogan & C Douglas (Blockeel 1987: 21).

H30 1986: hummock on raised bog, Kilconny, H Grogan & C Douglas (Blockeel 1987: 21).

H(32) listed by Lett (1915: 93). H(32) listed by Blockeel & Long (1998: 64).

H(33) 1909: bog nr Florence Court, WN Tetley (anon. 1911c: 7).

H(33) listed by Lett (1915: 93).

†H33 listed by Blockeel & Long (1998: 64).

H(34) listed by Lett (1915: 93). H(34) listed by Blockeel & Long (1998: 64).

[H35 1966: raised bog, Faery Water, Omagh, F Rose (Perry 1967: 406). H35 record from Perry 1967: 406 deleted because the locality is in H36 (Crundwell 1969: 877)].

H36 1966: raised bog, Faery Water, Omagh, F Rose, comm. PD Coker [erroneously attributed to H35] (Perry 1967: 406, Crundwell 1969: 877).

[H38 record from Warburg 1963a deleted because no specimen traced (Lobley & Fitzgerald 1970: 363, Crundwell 1971b: 374)].

H(39) listed by Lett (1915: 93) without details.

†H39 listed by Blockeel & Long (1998: 64).

†H40 listed by Blockeel & Long (1998: 64).

1/15a ***Sphagnum subnitens*** Russow & Warnst. **var.** ***subnitens***
(syn. *Sphagnum acutifolium* var. *subnitens* (Russow & Warnst.) Hérib., *S. acutifolium* var. *luridum* Huebener, *S. plumulosum* Röll, *S. plumulosum* var. *flavofuscescens* Warnst. nom. illeg., *S. plumulosum* var. *lilacinum* Spruce ex Warnst., *S. plumulosum* var. *viride* (Warnst.) Warnst)

H(1) listed by Lett (1915: 93).

†H1 listed by Blockeel & Long (1998: 65).

H(2) 1935: Eagle's Nest, no collector named (BBS exc.) (Watson 1936: 264).

†H2 listed by Blockeel & Long (1998: 65).

H(3) listed by Lett (1915: 93).

†H3 listed by Blockeel & Long (1998: 65).

H5 1967: on moor, Watergrasshill, RD Fitzgerald (Crundwell 1968: 630).

H(6) listed by Lett (1915: 93).

†H6 listed by Blockeel & Long (1998: 65).

H(7) listed by Lett (1915: 93).

†H7 listed by Blockeel & Long (1998: 65).

H(8) listed by Lett (1915: 93) without locality.

†H8 listed by Blockeel & Long (1998: 65).

H(9) listed by Lett (1915: 93).

†H9 listed by Blockeel & Long (1998: 65).

H10 1959: bog W of Newport, ALK King (Warburg 1960: 770).

H(11) listed by Lett (1915: 93).

†H11 listed by Blockeel & Long (1998: 65).

H(12) listed by Lett (1915: 93) without details.

†H12 listed by Blockeel & Long (1998: 65).

H(13) listed by Lett (1915: 93).

†H13 listed by Blockeel & Long (1998: 65).

H14 1956: Monettia Bog, N side of Clonaslee, AA Cridland (Warburg 1958b: 472).

H(15) listed by Lett (1915: 93).

†H15 listed by Blockeel & Long (1998: 65).

H(16) listed by Lett (1915: 93).

†H16 listed by Blockeel & Long (1998: 65).

H17 1957: bog between R. Clare and R. Cregg, RE Parker (Warburg 1958b: 472).

H(18) listed by Lett (1915: 93).

†H18 listed by Blockeel & Long (1998: 65).

H(19) 1949: Ballmount [*sic* = Ballymount] Bog, nr Calverstown, JS Thomson (Thompson & Lobley 1950: 380).

†H19 listed by Blockeel & Long (1998: 65).

†H20 listed by Blockeel & Long (1998: 65).

H(21) 1949: side of road to Mahoney Bog, AEA Dunston (Thompson & Lobley 1950: 380).

†H21 listed by Blockeel & Long (1998: 65).

H22 1952: Clonycavan Bog, nr Ballivor, ALK King (Warburg 1953: 306).

H23 1952: The Derries Bog, Athlone, ALK King (Warburg 1953: 306).

H24 1955: cut-away surface of Edera Bog, nr Ballymahon, TA Barry, comm. ALK King (Warburg 1957: 327).

H(25) listed by Lett (1915: 93).

†H25 listed by Blockeel & Long (1998: 65).

H(26) listed by Lett (1915: 93).

†H26 listed by Blockeel & Long (1998: 65).

H(27) listed by Lett (1915: 93).

†H27 listed by Blockeel & Long (1998: 65).

H(28) listed by Lett (1915: 93).

†H28 listed by Blockeel & Long (1998: 65).

H(29) 1937: Glenade, no collector named (BBS exc.) (A Thompson in Armitage 1938: 10).
1937: Tullaghan, no collector named (BBS exc.) (A Thompson in Armitage 1938: 10).
no date: Tullaghan, EM Lobley (Thompson 1944: 202).
no date: Glenade, A Thompson (Thompson 1944: 202).

†H29 listed by Blockeel & Long (1998: 65).

H(30) listed by Lett (1915: 93).

†H30 listed by Blockeel & Long (1998: 65).

H(31) listed by Lett (1915: 93). H(31) listed by Blockeel & Long (1998: 65).

H31 1999: on damp peaty bank amongst rocks, 200 m alt., Two Mile River, Carlingford, J11, TL Blockeel 28/158 (Rothero 2000: 46).

[H(32) listed by Lett (1915: 93) without locality. H32 deleted because no valid record or voucher specimen traced (Blockeel 1999: 3)].

H(33) listed by Lett (1915: 93).

†H33 listed by Blockeel & Long (1998: 65).

H(34) listed by Lett (1915: 93).

†H34 listed by Blockeel & Long (1998: 65).

H(35) listed by Lett (1915: 93).

†H35 listed by Blockeel & Long (1998: 65).

H(36) listed by Lett (1915: 94).

†H36 listed by Blockeel & Long (1998: 65).

H(37) listed by Lett (1915: 94).

H(37) 1917: Ranghlan, JD Houston (anon. 1918a: 206), as *S. plumulosum* var. *viride*.

†H37 listed by Blockeel & Long (1998: 65).

H(38) 1907: Slieve Donard, CH Waddell (anon. 1918a: 206), as *S. plumulosum* var. *flavo-fuscescens*.

H(38) listed by Lett (1915: 93, 94).
New record in H(38), no date: W West (Wheldon 1919: 248), as *S. plumulosum* var. *lilacinum* f. *orthocladum*.

†H38 listed by Blockeel & Long (1998: 65).

H(39) listed by Lett (1915: 94).

†H39 listed by Blockeel & Long (1998: 65).

†H40 listed by Blockeel & Long (1998: 65).

1/15b ***Sphagnum subnitens* var. *ferrugineum*** (Flatberg) M.O.Hill
(syn. *Sphagnum subfulvum* auct. non Sjörs, *S. subnitens* subsp. *ferrugineum* Flatberg)

H16 1980: in small hummocks with *S. subnitens*, Errisbeg, Roundstone, 200 m alt., A Moen, comm. DM Synnott, conf. RE Andrus (Hill 1982: 23); same record also reported as: flat fen, 150 m alt., Errisbeg, L7040, A Moen 80305 (TRH) (Moen & Synnott 1983, Flatberg 1985: 53).

H25 1982: small hummock on edge of raised bog, 1 km W of Clonallis House, Cloonallis Bog, Castlerea, M6481, DM Synnott (Hill 1983: 49, Moen & Synnott 1983).

H27 1980: flush below the large corrie on the N side of Mweelrea, DM Synnott (Hill 1982: 23); same record also reported as: W facing slopes below the corrie on N side of Mweelrea Mt., *ca* 60 m alt., L8168, A Moen, DM Synnott (DBN) (Moen & Synnott 1983, Flatberg 1985: 53).

H39 1990: flat fen/bog complex, Garron Plateau above Carnlough, DM Synnott, conf. MO Hill (Blockeel 1991c: 40).

1/17 ***Sphagnum molle*** Sull.

H1 1966: grassy bog at *ca* 500 ft alt., L. Avoonane below Brandon Peak, EM Lobley (Perry 1967: 406-407).

H2 1967: in large bog complex by Owneykeagh River, nr Barraduff, HH Birks, HJB Birks & DA Ratcliffe (Crundwell 1968: 630).

H3 1951: hillside, Pass of Keimaneigh, ALK King (Warburg 1954: 478).

H15 1957: bog above Chevy Chase Woods, Owendalulleegh, EM Lobley (BBS exc.) (Warburg 1958b: 473).

H16 1957: grassy bog, Ben Lettery, EM Lobley (BBS exc.) (Warburg 1958b: 473).

H20 1975: heath at S end of L. Dan, N of Laragh, JA Paton (BBS exc.) (Crundwell 1976: 22).

H25 2002: nr edge of raised bog, 90 m alt., Derrynabrock Bog, G50, NG Hodgetts 4107 (Rothero 2003: 46).

H27 1958: blanket-bog, N of Sheskin, ALK

King (Warburg 1960: 770).
H28 1965: bog by L. Gill nr Ennisfree, EM Lobley & RD Fitzgerald (Warburg 1966: 190).
H29 1963: wet heath SE of Sriff Cottage, E end of L. Gill, AR Perry & RD Fitzgerald (Warburg 1964: 722).
H30 1965: bog, Carricknacrannoge, EM Lobley & RD Fitzgerald (Warburg 1966: 190).
H33 1961: peat bog, Tully South, nr Lisnaskea, RD Fitzgerald (Warburg 1962: 365).
H(34) listed by Lett (1915: 91).
†H34 listed by Blockeel & Long (1998: 65).
†H35 listed by Blockeel & Long (1998: 65).
H36 1966: raised bog S of Washing Bay, F Rose, comm. PD Coker (Perry 1967: 407).
H(37) listed by Lett (1915: 91). H(37) listed by Blockeel & Long (1998: 65).
H(38) listed by Lett (1915: 91). H(38) listed by Blockeel & Long (1998: 65).
H(39) listed by Lett (1915: 91).
†H39 listed by Blockeel & Long (1998: 65).
H(40) listed by Blockeel & Long (1998: 65).
H40 1987: Moneystachan Bog, C90, P Corbett, det. R Weyl (BBSUK) (Rothero 2001: 37).

1/18 ***Sphagnum strictum*** Sull.

H1 1967: amongst *Molinia* in soligenous bog by Inchiquin Lough, nr Kenmare, HH Birks, HJB Birks & DA Ratcliffe (Crundwell 1968: 629).
H2 1966: sloping hillside of deep grass tussocks below Galway's Bridge, Upper Lake, EM Lobley & JA Paton (Perry 1967: 405).
†H3 listed by Blockeel & Long (1998: 65).
H16 1957: grassy bog on lower slopes of Ben Lettery, *ca* 700 ft [alt.], EM Lobley (BBS exc.) (Warburg 1958b: 471).
[H27 1957: grassy bog on lower slopes of Maumtrasna, *ca* 500 ft [alt.], EM Lobley (BBS exc.) (Warburg 1958b: 471). H27 record deleted because specimen (from Maumtrasna) was from H16 (Crundwell 1970: 195)].
H(27) 1901: Pontoon, HW Lett (DBN, as *S. compactum* var. *squarrosum*) (Crundwell 1970: 195).
†H27 listed by Blockeel & Long (1998: 65).
H34 1962: bog nr Barnes Bridge, EM Lobley (BBS exc.) (Warburg 1963b: 492).
H35 1961: shallow peat at 800 ft [alt.], Poisoned Glen, nr Dunlewy, DA Ratcliffe, (Warburg 1962: 364).
H39 1952: bog, 1000 ft [alt.], Pollen Burn, Granny Water, Carnlough, EM Lobley & J Taylor (Warburg 1953: 305).
H40 1952: grassy moorland, *ca* 1500 ft [alt.], Benbradagh, EM Lobley & J Taylor (Warburg 1953: 305).

1/19 ***Sphagnum compactum*** Lam. & DC.
(syn. *Sphagnum compactum* var. *imbricatum* Warnst., *S. compactum* var. *subsquarrosum* Warnst., *S. rigidum* (Nees & Hornsch.) Schimp., *S. rigidum* var. *compactum* (Lam. & DC.) Schimp., *S. rigidum* var. *squarrosum* Russow)

H(1) listed by Lett (1915: 91, 92).
H(1) 1935: near Loch Cruttia, no collector named (BBS exc.) (Watson 1936: 264), as var. *subsquarrosum.*
†H1 listed by Blockeel & Long (1998: 65).
H(2) listed by Lett (1915: 92) without details.
H(2) 1935: Garygarry, no collector named (BBS exc.) (Watson 1936: 264), as var. *imbricatum.*
†H2 listed by Blockeel & Long (1998: 65).
†H3 listed by Blockeel & Long (1998: 65).
H4 1966: boggy ground at 1300 ft alt., Musheramore, Boggeragh Mts, MFV Corley & JS Parker (Perry 1967: 405).
H5 1967: in bog, *ca* 800 ft [alt.], Lyrenamon, NW of Carrignavar, RD Fitzgerald (Crundwell 1968: 629).
H(6) 1933: Poolvona, E Armitage, ['The var. is not well marked,' EM Lobley] (anon. 1934a: 104), as var. *squarrosum.*
1933: Poolvona, E Armitage (anon. 1934a: 104), as var. *subsquarrosum.*
1933: Knockmealdown, E Armitage (anon. 1934a: 104), as var. *imbricatum.*
†H6 listed by Blockeel & Long (1998: 65).
H7 1953: N slope of Slievenamuck Mt., Bansha State Forest, ALK King (Warburg 1954: 477).
†H8 listed by Blockeel & Long (1998: 65).
H9 1964: peat, Hag's Head, ERB Little (Warburg 1966: 189).
H10 1986: blanket bog, Tauntinna Mt., J Cross, comm. H Grogan (Blockeel 1987: 21).
H12 1958: Forth Mt., ALK King (Warburg 1959: 630).

H(14) listed by Lett (1915: 91). H(14) listed by Blockeel & Long (1998: 65).
H15 1957: bog above Chevy Chase woods, Owendalulleegh, nr Gort, EM Lobley (BBS exc.) (Warburg 1958b: 471).
H(16) listed by Lett (1915: 91, 92).
†H16 listed by Blockeel & Long (1998: 65).
[H(17) listed by Lett (1915: 91) without locality. H17 deleted because no valid record or voucher specimen traced (Blockeel 1999: 3)].
[H18 deleted because no valid record or voucher specimen traced (Blockeel 1999: 3)].
[H19 deleted because no valid record or voucher specimen traced (Blockeel 1999: 3)].
H(20) listed by Lett (1915: 91, 92). H(20) listed by Blockeel & Long (1998: 65).
H(21) listed by Lett (1915: 91, 92).
H(21) 1949: side of road to Mahoney Bog, AEA Dunston (Thompson & Lobley 1950: 380), as var. *subsquarrosum*.
H24 1965: bog, Corn Hill, *ca* 700 ft alt., nr Drumlish, EM Lobley & RD Fitzgerald (Warburg 1966: 189).
H25 2002: in wet heath near summit of hill, 250 m alt., Slieve Bawn, near radio mast, M97, NG Hodgetts 4092 (Rothero 2003: 47).
H26 1957: W slope of [The] Ox Mts, ALK King (Warburg 1958b: 471).
H(27) listed by Lett (1915: 91, 92).
H(27) no date: W West (Wheldon 1919: 248), new record as *S. compactum* var. *imbricatum* f. *purpurascens*.
†H27 listed by Blockeel & Long (1998: 65).
H(28) listed by Lett (1915: 92) without details.
†H28 listed by Blockeel & Long (1998: 65).
H(29) 1937: Glenade, no collector named (BBS exc.) (A Thompson in Armitage 1938: 10), as var. *imbricatum*.
no date: Glenade, A Thompson (Thompson 1944: 202), as *S. compactum* var. *imbricatum*.
†H29 listed by Blockeel & Long (1998: 65).
H(30) listed by Lett (1915: 91).
†H30 listed by Blockeel & Long (1998: 65).
H(31) listed by Lett (1915: 91, 92). H(31) listed by Blockeel & Long (1998: 65).
[H(32) listed by Lett (1915: 91, 92) without locality. H32 deleted because no valid record or voucher specimen traced (Blockeel 1999: 3)].
H(33) listed by Lett (1915: 92).
H(33) 1937: Castle Caldwell, no collector named (BBS exc.) (A Thompson in Armitage 1938: 10), as var. *imbricatum*.
no date: Castle Caldwell, A Thompson (Thompson 1944: 202), as *S. compactum* var. *imbricatum*.
†H33 listed by Blockeel & Long (1998: 65).
H(34) listed by Lett (1915: 92).
†H34 listed by Blockeel & Long (1998: 65).
H(35) listed by Lett (1915: 92).
†H35 listed by Blockeel & Long (1998: 65).
H(36) listed by Lett (1915: 92).
†H36 listed by Blockeel & Long (1998: 65).
H(37) listed by Lett (1915: 92).
†H37 listed by Blockeel & Long (1998: 65).
H(38) listed by Lett (1915: 92). H(38) listed by Blockeel & Long (1998: 65).
H38 2002: on peat on hillside with *Nardus* and *Carex panicea*, 205 m alt., W slope of Slievenabrock, J33, DT Holyoak 02-1018 (Rothero 2003: 47).
H(39) listed by Lett (1915: 92).
H(39) 1928: Fair Head (BBS exc.) (Duncan 1928: 116), as var. *subsquarrosum*.
†H39 listed by Blockeel & Long (1998: 65).
†H40 listed by Blockeel & Long (1998: 65).

1/20 ***Sphagnum subsecundum*** Nees
(syn. *Sphagnum subsecundum* subsp. *subsecundum*)

[H(1) listed by Lett (1915: 91), without locality].
[H1 1961: bog by R. Caragh, nr Glencar Hotel, EM Lobley (Warburg 1962: 365). H1 record not accepted by Corley & Hill 1981: 57, following revision of specimens by MO Hill].
[H(3) listed by Lett (1915: 91)].
[H(4) listed by Lett (1915: 91)].
[H(6) listed by Lett (1915: 91), without locality].
[H7 1966: marshy ground by Bay Lough, Knockmealdown Mts, ERB Little (BBS exc.) (Perry 1967: 406). H7 record not accepted by Corley & Hill 1981: 57, following revision of specimens by MO Hill].
[H(11) listed by Lett (1915: 91)].
[H(16) listed by Lett (1915: 91)].
[H16 1957: immersed in bog, L. Fee, EM Lobley (BBS exc.) (Warburg 1958b: 472). H16 record not accepted by Corley & Hill 1981: 57, following revision of specimens by MO Hill].

H16 1987: *Carex lasiocarpa* flush on blanket bog, E of Orrid Lough, Maam Cross, H Grogran & C Douglas (Blockeel 1988: 33).
[H(17) listed by Lett (1915: 91)].
H18 1986: in sedge-dominated meadow, Clonmacnoise Callows, N Lockhart (Blockeel 1989: 24).
[H(20) listed by Lett (1915: 91)].
[H(21) listed by Lett (1915: 91)].
[H(25) listed by Lett (1915: 91)].
H25 1985: fen at bog margin, Carrowbehy, H Grogan, C Douglas & JC Cross (Blockeel 1987: 21).
[H(26) listed by Lett (1915: 91)].
[H(27) listed by Lett (1915: 91)].
H27 1987: flush on blanket bog, Derrakillew, H Grogan *et al.* (Blockeel 1988: 33).
[H(28) listed by Lett (1915: 91)].
[H28 1965: bog by L. Gill nr Ennisfree, EM Lobley & RD Fitzgerald (Warburg 1966: 189). H(28) record not accepted by Corley & Hill 1981: 57, following revision of specimens by MO Hill].
[H(29) 1937: Tullaghan, no collector named (BBS exc.) (A Thompson in Armitage 1938: 11), as *S. subsecundum.* H(29), 1937: Tullaghan, EM Lobley (anon. 1938a: 21), as *S. subsecundum.* H(29) record not accepted by Corley & Hill 1981: 57, following revision of specimens by MO Hill].
[H(30) listed by Lett (1915: 91)].
[H(31) listed by Lett (1915: 91)].
[H(33) listed by Lett (1915: 91)].
[H(35) listed by Lett (1915: 91), without locality].
H35 1991: floating scraw, Meenaguse Lough, G98, R Goodwillie (Blockeel 1993: 47).
[H(37) listed by Lett (1915: 91)].
[H(38) listed by Lett (1915: 91)].
[H(39) listed by Lett (1915: 91)].
[H(40) listed by Lett (1915: 91)].

MO Hill (MS) revised specimens from Ireland and Britain for the *CC* (Corley & Hill 1981: 57), but found no correctly identified gatherings from Ireland. Five records of the species have subsequently been obtained from Irish vice-counties.

1/21 ***Sphagnum inundatum*** Russow
(syn. *Sphagnum auriculatum* var. *inundatum* (Russow) M.O.Hill, *S. denticulatum* var. *inundatum* (Russow) Karttunen, *S. inundatum var. densum* (Warnst.) Sherrin, *S. inundatum* var. *diversifolium* Warnst., *S. inundatum* var. *eurycladum* Warnst., *S. inundatum* var. *lancifolium* Warnst., *S. inundatum* var. *ovalifolium* Warnst., *S. inundatum* var. *robustum* Warnst., *S. subsecundum* Nees subsp. *inundatum* (Russow) A. Eddy)

H(1) no date: nr L. Crutta, A Thompson (Thompson 1944: 204-205), as *S. inundatum* var. *densum.*
no date: Conner Hill Road, A Thompson (Thompson 1944: 204-205), as *S. inundatum* var. *densum.*
†H1 listed by Blockeel & Long (1998: 65).
H(2) no date: Killarney, A Thompson (Thompson 1944: 204-205), as *S. inundatum* var. *diversifolium.*
1935: Torc Mt., no collector named (BBS exc.) (Watson 1936: 264), as var. *lancifolium.*
†H2 listed by Blockeel & Long (1998: 65).
†H3 listed by Blockeel & Long (1998: 65).
H4 1966: marshy ground by stream nr Kilcullen House, Rylane Cross, Boggeragh Mts, MFV Corley & JS Parker (Perry 1967: 406).
H(6) 1933: Knockmealdown, E Armitage (anon. 1934a: 105).
†H6 listed by Blockeel & Long (1998: 65).
H7 1966: bog at *ca* 1000ft alt., between Seefin and Knockeenatoung, Galtee Mts, EM Lobley (BBS exc.) (Perry 1967: 406).
H9 1957: Maghera Woods, Tulla, ALK King (Warburg 1958b: 472).
H10 1991: wet meadow by stream, 200 m alt., W of Kilcommon, R86, N Lockhart & A O'Suillivan (Blockeel 1992: 25).
H12 1958: bank of stream E slope of Blackstairs Mts, nr Kilteely, ALK King (Warburg 1959: 631).
H15 1957: bog above Chevy Chase Wood, Owendalulleegh, EM Lobley (BBS exc.) (Warburg 1958b: 472).
H16 1957: bogs, nr Roundstone, EM Lobley (BBS exc.) (Warburg 1958b: 472).
H17 1957: open drain of bog betwen R. Clare and R. Cregg, EM Lobley (BBS exc.)

(Warburg 1958b: 472).

H18 2002: in flush in blanket bog, 300 m alt., Glenletter, Slieve Bloom Mountains, N20, N Lockhart 2002/14a (Rothero 2003: 47).

H(19) 1949: Ballymount Bog, nr Calverstown, JS Thomson (Thompson & Lobley 1950: 381), as *S. inundatum* var. *lancifolium*.

H(20) 1949: Ballyreagh Bog, AEA Dunston (Thompson & Lobley 1950: 381), as *S. inundatum* var. *eurycladum*.
1949: Ballyreagh Bog, AEA Dunston (Thompson & Lobley 1950: 381), as *S. inundatum* var. *lancifolium*.
1949: Ballyreagh Bog, AEA Dunston (Thompson & Lobley 1950: 381), as *S. inundatum* var. *diversifolium*.

†H20 listed by Blockeel & Long (1998: 65).

H(21) 1948: Pine Forest, Co. Dublin, AEA Dunston, det. A Thompson (anon. 1949b: 216), as *S. inundatum* var. *diversifolium*.
1949: side of road to Mahoney Bog, AEA Dunston (Thompson & Lobley 1950: 381), as *S. inundatum* var. *robustum*.
1949: Pine Forest East, AEA Dunston (Thompson & Lobley 1950: 381), as *S. inundatum* var. *lancifolium*.

H22 1978: fen, 3 km N of Oldcastle, DM Synnott (Hill 1980b: 32).

H24 1957: Carn Clonhugh Hill, 800 ft [alt.], ALK King (Warburg 1958b: 472).

H(25) no date: Elphin, JD Houston (anon. 1921: 272), new record as *S. inundatum* var. *ovalifolium* f. *densum*.

H25 1965: bog *ca* 700 ft alt., Kilronan, nr Ballyfarnan, EM Lobley & RD Fitzgerald (Warburg 1966: 189).

H(27) no date: Keel, Achill I., GH Allison (Thompson 1944: 204).

†H27 listed by Blockeel & Long (1998: 65).

H(28) 1937: Cliffony, no collector named (BBS exc.) (A Thompson in Armitage 1938: 11), as var. *robustum*.
no date: nr Cliffony, EM Lobley (Thompson 1944: 204-205), as *S. inundatum* var. *robustum*.

†H28 listed by Blockeel & Long (1998: 65).

H(29) 1937: Tullaghan, no collector named (BBS exc.) (A Thompson in Armitage 1938: 11), as var. *lancifolium*.
1937: Glenade, no collector named (BBS exc.) (A Thompson in Armitage 1938: 11), as var. *diversifolium*.
1937: Tullaghan, EM Lobley (anon. 1938a: 21), as var. *lancifolium*.
no date: Tullaghan, EM Lobley (Thompson 1944: 204-205), as *S. inundatum* var. *lancifolium*.
no date: Glenade, A Thompson (Thompson 1944: 204-205), as *S. inundatum* var. *diversifolium*.

†H29 listed by Blockeel & Long (1998: 65).

H30 1957: edge of ditch, roadside on NW side of Tiltinbane, AC Crundwell (Warburg 1959: 631).

H(31) 1945: Feed Wood, nr Ravensdale, JS Thomson, det. A Thompson (anon. 1946b: 278), as *S. inundatum* var. *lancifolium*.

H32 2002: in blanket bog flush with *S. inundatum*, *Drepanocladus cossonii*, 250 m alt., 1 km downstream of outflow from Lough Bradan, H54, N Lockhart 2002/02a (Rothero 2003: 47).

H(33) 1937: Castle Caldwell, no collector named (BBS exc.) (A Thompson in Armitage 1938: 11), as var. *robustum*.
1937: Castle Caldwell, no collector named (BBS exc.) (A Thompson in Armitage 1938: 11), as var. *eurycladum*.
1937: Castle Caldwell, no collector named (BBS exc.) (A Thompson in Armitage 1938: 11), as var. *lancifolium*.
no date: Castle Caldwell, A Thompson (Thompson 1944: 204-205), as *S. inundatum* var. *robustum*.
no date: Castle Caldwell, A Thompson (Thompson 1944: 204-205), as *S. inundatum* var. *eurycladum*.
no date: Castle Caldwell, A Thompson (Thompson 1944: 204-205), as *S. inundatum* var. *lancifolium*.

†H33 listed by Blockeel & Long (1998: 65).

H(34) 1937: Bundoran, no collector named (BBS exc.) (A Thompson in Armitage 1938: 11), as var. *eurycladum*.
1937: Bundoran, no collector named (BBS exc.) (A Thompson in Armitage 1938: 11), as var. *densum*.
no date: Bundoran, EM Lobley (Thompson 1944: 204-205), as *S. inundatum* var. *eurycladum*.
no date: nr Bundoran, GH Allison (Thompson 1944: 204-205), as *S. inundatum* var. *densum*.

†H34 listed by Blockeel & Long (1998: 65).

H(35) no date: Lough Nacung, EM Lind, det. A Thompson (Thompson 1944: 204-

205), as *S. inundatum* var. *robustum*.

†H35 listed by Blockeel & Long (1998: 65).

H36 1953: bog, Tamnamore, nr Verner's Bridge, MPH Kertland & EM Lobley (Warburg 1954: 477).

H(37) 1917: margin of pool, Carnlough Mts, JD Houston, det. JA Weldon (anon. 1919a: 232), as var. *ovalifolium*.

H37 1952: Lough Gullion, nr Lough Neagh, RD Fitzgerald & EM Lobley (Warburg 1954: 477).

H(38) 1928: Slieve Donard (BBS exc.) (Duncan 1928: 114, 117), as var. *diversifolium*.

†H38 listed by Blockeel & Long (1998: 65).

†H39 listed by Blockeel & Long (1998: 65).

†H40 listed by Blockeel & Long (1998: 65).

1/22 ***Sphagnum denticulatum*** Brid.
(syn. *Sphagnum auriculatum* Schimp., *S. auriculatum* var. *auriculatum* Schimp., *S. auriculatum* var. *canovirescens* auct., *S. auriculatum* var. *laxifolium* Warnst., *S. auriculatum* var. *ovatum* Warnst., *S. auriculatum* var. *racemosum* Warnst., *S. auriculatum* var. *submersum* Warnst., *S. auriculatum* var. *tenellum* Warnst., *S. crassicladum* Warnst., *S. crassicladum* var. *diversifolium* Warnst., *S. crassicladum* var. *intermedium* Warnst., *S. crassicladum* var. *magnifolium* Warnst., *S. obesum* (Wilson) Warnst., *S. obesum* var. *canovirens* Warnst., *S. obesum* var. *hemi-isophyllum* Warnst., *S. obesum* var. *mastigocladum* Warnst., *S. obesum* var. *plumosum* Warnst., *S. obesum* var. *teretiramosum* Warnst., *S. rufescens* (Nees & Hornsch.) Warnst., *S. subsecundum* var. *auriculatum* (Schimp.) Schlieph., *S. subsecundum* var. *contortum* sensu Lett 1915)

H(1) listed by Lett (1915: 91).

H(1) 1935: Connor Hill, no collector named (BBS exc.) (Watson 1936: 264), as *S. obesum* var. *teretiramosum*.

H(1) 1935: Connor Hill, no collector named (BBS exc.) (Watson 1936: 264), as *S. obesum* var. *hemi-isophyllum*.

H(1) 1935: Brandon Headland, no collector named (BBS exc.) (Watson 1936: 264), as *S. auriculatum* var. *ovatum*.
1935: Connor Hill, no collector named (BBS exc.) (Watson 1936: 264), as *S. crassifolium* [*sic* = *crassicladum*] var. *diversfolium* [*sic*].

†H1 listed by Blockeel & Long (1998: 66).

H(2) listed by Lett (1915: 91) without details.

H(2) no date: W West (Wheldon 1919: 251), new record as *S. crassicladum* var. *intermedium* f. *lanceolatum*.
1935: Torc Mt., no collector named (BBS exc.) (Watson 1936: 264), as *S. auriculatum* var. *canovirescens*.
1935: Old Weir Bridge, no collector named (BBS exc.) (Watson 1936: 264), as *S. crassifolium* [*sic* = *crassicladum*] var. *magnifolium*.
no date: Killarney, A Thompson (Thompson 1944: 205), as *S. auriculatum* var. *ovatum*.

†H2 listed by Blockeel & Long (1998: 66).

H(3) no date: JD Houston (Wheldon 1919: 251), new record as *S. crassicladum* var. *diversifolium* f. *inundatum*.
no date: Sugarloaf Mt., nr Glengarriff, A Thompson (Thompson 1944: 204), as *S. obesum* var. *teretiramosum*.

†H3 listed by Blockeel & Long (1998: 66).

H(4) listed by Lett (1915: 91) without details.

H4 1967: Musherabeg, Bogheragh Mts, RD Fitzgerald (Crundwell 1968: 630).

H5 1961: bog nr Inch, NW of Youghal, MJP Scannell, comm. ALK King (Warburg 1962: 365).

H(6) listed by Lett (1915: 91).

[H(6) 1933: Knockmealdown, E Armitage, 'The stem I examined was *S. inundatum*. It looks like a mixture,' A Thompson (anon. 1934a: 105). In view of A Thompson's comments this gathering should not be accepted as a vice-county record without checking the specimen].

H(6) 1933: Poolvona, E Armitage ['Near var. *ovatum*,' A Thompson] (anon. 1934a: 105).
1933: Poolvona, E Armitage, conf. A Thompson (with notes) (anon. 1934a: 105), as *S. auriculatum* var. *ovatum*.

†H6 listed by Blockeel & Long (1998: 66).

H7 1966: bog between Seefin and Knockeenatoung, Galtee Mts, EM Lobley (BBS exc.) (Perry 1967: 406).

H(8) listed by Lett (1915: 91).

H8 1966: bog on moor, Slievereagh, nr Ballylanders, MFV Corley & JS Parker (Perry 1967: 406).

H9 1960: peat cutting in derelict bog by Castlelodge River, nr Little Templebannagh Lough, leg. & det. MCF

Proctor (Warburg 1961: 158).
H10 1979: wet heath, W slope of Keeper Hill, S of Silvermine Mts, HMH van Melick (Hill 1981: 21).
H(11) listed by Lett (1915: 91).
H11 1966: ditch on bog, Derryfadda, W of Johnstown, ERB Little (BBS exc.) (Perry 1967: 406).
H(12) listed by Lett (1915: 91).
H12 1958: bank of stream, E slope of Blackstairs Mts, nr Kilteely, ALK King (Warburg 1959: 631).
H(13) listed by Lett (1915: 91).
H13 1966: bog in Deer Park, E Booth, comm. DM Synnott (Perry 1967: 406).
H(14) listed by Lett (1915: 91).
H(14) 1912: mountain stream, The Cones, Slieve Bloom, WN Tetley (BBSUK), comm. AA Cridland (Warburg 1958b: 472).
†H14 listed by Blockeel & Long (1998: 66).
H15 1957: blanket bog, hills E of Gort, RE Parker (Warburg 1958b: 472).
H(16) listed by Lett (1915: 91).
H(16) no date: Kylemore, EM Lind, det. A Thompson (Thompson 1944: 204), as *S. obesum* var. *canovirens*.
no date: Kylemore, EM Lind, det. A Thompson (Thompson 1944: 205), as *S. auriculatum* var. *ovatum*.
†H16 listed by Blockeel & Long (1998: 66).
H(17) 1909: Cloonlusk Bog, S of Tuam, WN Tetley (anon. 1911c: 6), as *S. crassicladum*.
H(17) listed by Lett (1915: 91).
H(17) no date: WN Tetley (Wheldon 1919: 251), new record as *S. crassicladum* var. *magnifolium* f. *fluctuans*.
H17 1957: bog between R. Clare and R. Cregg, RE Parker (Warburg 1958b: 472).
H(18) 1949: Rathlumber Bog, A Jackson (Thompson & Lobley 1950: 382), as *S. crassicladum* var. *magnifolium*.
H18 1967: Ballyduff bog nr Clonmacnoise, MP Horan (Crundwell 1968: 630).
H19 1968: on edge of cut-away bog, Allenwood, ALK King (Crundwell 1969: 877).
H(20) listed by Lett (1915: 91).
H(20) no date: Wicklow Gap, A Thompson (Thompson 1944: 204), as *S. obesum* var. *mastigocladum*.
1949: Ballyreagh Bog, AEA Dunston (Thompson & Lobley 1950: 382), as *S. auriculatum* var. *tenellum*.
†H20 listed by Blockeel & Long (1998: 66).
H(21) listed by Lett (1915: 91).
H(21) 1948: Pine Forest, Co. Dublin, AEA Dunston, det. A Thompson (anon. 1949b: 216).
1949: side of road to Mahoney Bog, AEA Dunston (Thompson & Lobley 1950: 381), as *S. obesum* var. *canovirens*.
1949: road to Mahoney Bog, AEA Dunston (Thompson & Lobley 1950: 382), as *S. auriculatum* var. *ovatum*.
1949: Pine Forest East, AEA Dunston (Thompson & Lobley 1950: 382), as *S. auriculatum* var. *submersum*.
1949: side of road to Mahoney Bog, AEA Dunston (Thompson & Lobley 1950: 382), as *S. crassicladum* var. *magnifolium*.
1949: Featherbed Mt., AEA Dunston (Thompson & Lobley 1950: 382), as *S. crassicladum* var. *diversifolium*.
†H21 listed by Blockeel & Long (1998: 66).
H22 1965: drain by edge of cut-away bog S of Summerhill, ALK King (Warburg 1966: 189).
H23 1961: bog *ca* 4 miles N of Castlepollard, EM Lobley (Warburg 1962: 365).
H24 1955: Edera Bog, nr Ballymahon, TA Barry, comm. ALK King (Warburg 1957: 327).
H(25) 1910: Curlew Hills, WN Tetley (anon. 1911c: 6), as *S. crassicladum*.
H(25) listed by Lett (1915: 91).
H25 1957: raised bog, Ballymoe, ALK King (Warburg 1958b: 472).
H(26) listed by Lett (1915: 91).
H26 1957: below L. Talt, W slope of [The] Ox Mts, ALK King (Warburg 1958b: 472).
H(27) listed by Lett (1915: 91).
H(27) 1937: Achill I., no collector named (BBS exc.) (A Thompson in Armitage 1938: 10), as *S. obesum* var. *teretiramosum*.
1937: near Keel Lough, no collector named (BBS exc.) (A Thompson in Armitage 1938: 10-11), as *S. obesum* var. *canovirens*.
1937: Slievemore, no collector named (BBS exc.) (A Thompson in Armitage 1938: 10-11), as *S. obesum* var. *hemi-isophyllum*.
1937: near Keel Lough, no collector

named (BBS exc.) (A Thompson in Armitage 1938: 11), as var. *ovatum*.
1937: Slievemore, no collector named (BBS exc.) (A Thompson in Armitage 1938: 11), as var. *ovatum*.
1937: Meenaun Cliffs, no collector named (BBS exc.) (A Thompson in Armitage 1938: 11), as *S. auriculatum* var. *submersum*.
1937: bog nr Keel, no collector named (BBS exc.) (A Thompson in Armitage 1938: 11), as *S. auriculatum* var. *submersum*.
1937: Slievemore, no collector named (BBS exc.) (A Thompson in Armitage 1938: 11), as *S. auriculatum* var. *submersum*.
1937: nr Keel Lough, no collector named (BBS exc.) (A Thompson in Armitage 1938: 11), as *S. crassicladum* var. *diversifolium*.
no date: Slievemore, Achill I., A Thompson (Thompson 1944: 204), as *S. obesum* var. *plumosum*.
no date: Achill I., GH Allison (Thompson 1944: 204), as *S. obesum* var. *teretiramosum*.
no date: nr Keel Lough, Achill I., A Thompson (Thompson 1944: 204), as *S. obesum* var. *canovirens*.
no date: Slievemore, Achill I., A Thompson (Thompson 1944: 204), as *S. obesum* var. *hemi-isophyllum*.
no date: nr Keel Lough, Achill I., GH Allison & A Thompson (Thompson 1944: 205), as *S. auriculatum* var. *ovatum*.
no date: Meenawn [*sic* = Meenaun] Cliffs, Achill I., A Thompson (Thompson 1944: 205-206), as *S. auriculatum* var. *submersum*.
no date: nr Keel Loch, Achill I., A Thompson (Thompson 1944: 206), as *S. crassicladum* var. *diversifolium*.

†H27 listed by Blockeel & Long (1998: 66).

H(28) 1909: Slishwood, Co. Sligo [erroneously given as I 30], WN Tetley (anon. 1911c: 6), as *S. crassicladum*.

H(28) listed by Lett (1915: 91).

H(28) 1937: Ben Bulben, no collector named (BBS exc.) (A Thompson in Armitage 1938: 10), as *S. obesum* var. *teretiramosum*.
1937: Ben Bulben, no collector named (BBS exc.) (A Thompson in Armitage 1938: 11), as *S. auriculatum* var. *racemosum*.
no date: Ben Bulbin [*sic* = Bulben], A Thompson (Thompson 1944: 204), as *S. obesum* var. *teretiramosum*.
no date: Ben Bulbin [*sic* = Bulben], A Thompson (Thompson 1944: 205-206), as *S. auriculatum* var. *racemosum*.

†H28 listed by Blockeel & Long (1998: 66).

H(29) listed by Lett (1915: 91).

H(29) 1937: Tullaghan, no collector named (BBS exc.) (A Thompson in Armitage 1938: 10), as *S. obesum*.
1937: Slievemore, no collector named (BBS exc.) (A Thompson in Armitage 1938: 10), as *S. obesum* var. *plumosum*.
1937: Glenade, no collector named (BBS exc.) (A Thompson in Armitage 1938: 10), as *S. obesum* var. *canovirens*.
no date: Glenade, A Thompson (Thompson 1944: 204), as *S. obesum* var. *canovirens*.
no date: Tullaghan, EM Lobley (Thompson 1944: 205), as *S. auriculatum*.

†H29 listed by Blockeel & Long (1998: 66).

H(30) 1910: Cuilcagh Mts, WN Tetley (anon. 1911c: 6), as *S. rufescens*.

H(30) listed by Lett (1915: 91).

H30 1957: roadside ditch on NW side of Tiltinbane, AC Crundwell (Warburg 1959: 631).

H(31) listed by Lett (1915: 91) without details.

H(31) 1945: Feede Woode, nr Ravensdale, JS Thomson, det. A Thompson (anon. 1946b: 278), as *S. auriculatum* var. *racemosum*.

H31 1999: among dwarf shrubs on moist, rocky stream bank, 300 m alt., Two Mile River, Carlingford, J11, TL Blockeel 28/169 (Rothero 2000: 46).

H(33) 1909: Lisblake bog, WN Tetley (anon. 1911c: 6), labelled as *S. rufescens* var. *aquatile* but redet. by WR Sherrin as *S. crassicladum*.
1909: Barr of Whealt, WN Tetley (anon. 1911c: 6), as *S. obesum*.

H(33) listed by Lett (1915: 91).

H(33) 1937: Castle Caldwell, no collector named (BBS exc.) (A Thompson in Armitage 1938: 11), as var. *ovatum*.
1937: Castle Caldwell, no collector named (BBS exc.) (A Thompson in Armitage 1938: 11), as var. *laxifolium*.
1937: Castle Caldwell, no collector

named (BBS exc.) (A Thompson in Armitage 1938: 11), as *S. crassicladum* var. *diversifolium*.
no date: Castle Caldwell, A Thompson (Thompson 1944: 205), as *S. auriculatum* var. *ovatum*.
no date: Castle Caldwell, A Thompson (Thompson 1944: 205), as *S. auriculatum* var. *laxifolium*.
no date: Castle Caldwell, A Thompson (Thompson 1944: 206), as *S. crassicladum* var. *diversifolium*.

†H33 listed by Blockeel & Long (1998: 66).

H(34) no date: Bundoran, EM Lobley (Thompson 1944: 205), as *S. auriculatum*.
1937: Bundoran, EM Lobley (anon. 1938a: 21), as *S. auriculatum*.

†H34 listed by Blockeel & Long (1998: 66).

H(35) 1910: nr Bunlin Waterfall, NW Donegal, J Glover (anon. 1912c: 6), labelled as *S. crassicladum* but redet. as *S. obesum* by WR Sherrin.

H(35) listed by Lett (1915: 91).

H35 1962: boggy heath nr Rossbeg, ALK King (Warburg 1963b: 492).

H(36) listed by Lett (1915: 91).

H36 1953: bog, Tamnamore, nr Verner's Bridge, MPH Kertland & EM Lobley (Warburg 1954: 477).

H(37) listed by Lett (1915: 91).

H(37) 1917: Camlough Mts, JD Houston (anon. 1918a: 209), as *S. rufescens*.
no date: I.37 without locality, JD Houston (Wheldon 1919: 251), as *S. rufescens* f. *bicolor* W., subf. *intortum*.

H37 1952: Lough Gullion, nr Lough Neagh, RD Fitzgerald & EM Lobley (Warburg 1954: 477).

H(38) listed by Lett (1915: 91).

H(38) 1928: Slieve Donard (BBS exc.) (Duncan 1928: 114, 117), as *S. obesum* var. *cano-virens*.

†H38 listed by Blockeel & Long (1998: 66).

H(39) listed by Lett (1915: 91).

H(39) 1928: Fair Head (BBS exc.) (Duncan 1928: 116).

†H39 listed by Blockeel & Long (1998: 66).

H(40) listed by Lett (1915: 91) without details.

†H40 listed by Blockeel & Long (1998: 66).

1/23 ***Sphagnum contortum*** Schultz
(syn. *Sphagnum laricinum* (Wilson) Spruce)

H1 1961: bog by R. Caragh, nr Glencar Hotel, EM Lobley (Warburg 1962: 365).

[H2 deleted because no valid record or voucher specimen traced (Blockeel 1999: 3)].

H(3) listed by Lett (1915: 90). H(3) listed by Blockeel & Long (1998: 66).

H(6) listed by Lett (1915: 90).

†H6 listed by Blockeel & Long (1998: 66).

[H(8) listed by Lett (1915: 90) without locality. H8 deleted because no valid record or voucher specimen traced (Blockeel 1999: 3)].

H9 1959: margin of derelict bog nr Kinroe, Corofin, MCF Proctor (DBN) (Crundwell 1969: 877).

H(12) listed by Lett (1915: 90).

†H12 listed by Blockeel & Long (1998: 66).

H15 1957: bog above Chevy Chase woods, Owendalulleegh, EM Lobley (BBS exc.) (Warburg 1958b: 472).

H(16) listed by Lett (1915: 90). H(16) listed by Blockeel & Long (1998: 66).

H16 2001: in rich flushes at edge of peaty moorland, 260 m alt., corrie above Knappagh Lough, L76, DG Long 29961, conf. MO Hill (Rothero 2002: 43).

H17 1990: on fen peat in mire, 20 m alt., by side of N84 road, N of Galway, M33, TL Blockeel 19/563 (Blockeel 1991c: 40).

H(20) listed by Lett (1915: 90) without locality. H(20) listed by Blockeel & Long (1998: 66).

H(21) listed by Lett (1915: 90). H(21) listed by Blockeel & Long (1998: 66).

H22 1978: cut-over bog between L. Bane and Dromone, Oldcastle, DM Synnott (Hill 1980b: 32).

H23 1966: Scraw Bog, Portnashangan, ALK King (Perry 1967: 406).

H25 1985: fen at bog margin, Carrowbehy, H Grogan, C Douglas & JC Cross (Blockeel 1987: 21).

H26 1981: base-rich fen, nr L. Beg, 10 km S of Castlebar, N Lockhart (Hill 1983: 50).

H(27) listed by Lett (1915: 90).

†H27 listed by Blockeel & Long (1998: 66).

[H(28) listed by Lett (1915: 90)].

H(29) listed by Lett (1915: 90). H(29) listed by Blockeel & Long (1998: 66).

H29 2000: in damp runnel in calcareous flush, 335 m alt., SW of Aghavogil, G85, DT Holyoak 00-699 (BBSUK) (Rothero 2001: 37).
H(30) listed by Blockeel & Long (1998: 66).
H(31) listed by Lett (1915: 90). H(31) listed by Blockeel & Long (1998: 66).
H33 2000: in wet fen beside lough, Meenameen Lough, W end, H05, DT Holyoak 00-227 (BBSUK) (Rothero 2001: 37).
H(34) listed by Lett (1915: 90). H(34) listed by Blockeel & Long (1998: 66).
H(35) listed by Lett (1915: 90).
†H35 listed by Blockeel & Long (1998: 66).
H36 1956: L. Lee, MPH Kertland (Crundwell 1969: 877).
H37 1964: *ca* 800 ft [alt.], Annacloghmullin Hill, MPH Kertland, comm. EM Lobley (Warburg 1965: 859).
H(38) listed by Lett (1915: 90).
†H38 listed by Blockeel & Long (1998: 66).
H(39) listed by Lett (1915: 90).
†H39 listed by Blockeel & Long (1998: 66).
H40 1953: bog nr Blackwater Bridge, N of L. Fea, MPH Kertland & EM Lobley (Warburg 1955: 583).

1/24 ***Sphagnum platyphyllum*** (Lindb. ex Braithw.) Sull. ex Warnst.

H1 1988: muddy, base-rich 'small sedge' flush, nr S end of Lough Coomeathcun, NE of Waterville, M Yeo (Blockeel 1989: 24).
H16 1980: rich fen, Errisbeg, A Moen (Moen & Synnott 1983: 334, Hill 1984b: 25).
H27 1987: flushed slopes, Glenlaur Valley just above Sheeffry Bridge, DM Synnott (Blockeel 1988: 33).
H(33) 1937: Castle Caldwell, no collector named (BBS exc.) (A Thompson in Armitage 1938: 11).
no date: bog by L. Erne, Castle Caldwell, A Thompson (BBSUK), conf. MO Hill (Thompson 1944: 206; MO Hill MS).

1/25 ***Sphagnum tenellum*** (Brid.) Bory (syn. *Sphagnum molluscum* Bruch)

H(1) listed by Lett (1915: 90).
†H1 listed by Blockeel & Long (1998: 66).
H(2) listed by Lett (1915: 90), without details.
†H2 listed by Blockeel & Long (1998: 66).
†H3 listed by Blockeel & Long (1998: 66).
H4 1966: boggy ground on moor at 1200 ft alt., Seefin, Boggeragh Mts, MFV Corley & JS Parker (Perry 1967: 406).
H(6) listed by Lett (1915: 90).
†H6 listed by Blockeel & Long (1998: 66).
H7 1964: hillside N of watershed on The Vee pass, ALK King (Warburg 1965: 859).
H8 1959: bog Castleconnell, ALK King (Warburg 1960: 769).
H9 1963: W side of Slieve Elva at 800 ft [alt.], Lisdoonvarna, G Halliday (Warburg 1964: 722).
H10 1959: bog 2 miles W of Newport, ALK King (Warburg 1960: 769).
H11 1954: Mt Brandon, Co. Kilkenny, *ca* 1250 ft [alt.], ALK King (Warburg 1955: 583).
H12 1958: Forth Mt., ALK King (Warburg 1959: 631).
H13 1969: in bog, St Mullins, nr Graiguenamanagh, RD Fitzgerald (Crundwell 1970: 195).
H(14) listed by Lett (1915: 90).
†H14 listed by Blockeel & Long (1998: 66).
H15 1957: blanket bog on hills E of Gort, RE Parker (Warburg 1958b: 472).
H(16) listed by Lett (1915: 90).
†H16 listed by Blockeel & Long (1998: 66).
H17 1957: bog between R. Clare and R. Cregg, RE Parker (Warburg 1958b: 472).
H(18) listed by Lett (1915: 90).
†H18 listed by Blockeel & Long (1998: 66).
H(19) 1949: Ballymount Bog, Calverstown, JS Thomson (Thompson & Lobley 1950: 381).
†H19 listed by Blockeel & Long (1998: 66).
H(20) listed by Lett (1915: 90).
†H20 listed by Blockeel & Long (1998: 66).
[H(21) listed by Lett (1915: 90) without details. H21 deleted because no valid record or voucher specimen traced (Blockeel 1999: 3)].
H22 1952: Clonycavan Bog, nr Ballivor, ALK King (Warburg 1953: 305).
H23 1952: The Derries Bog, Athlone, ALK King (Warburg 1953: 305).
H24 1955: Edera Bog, nr Ballymahon, TA Barry, comm. ALK King (Warburg 1957: 327).
H25 1952: Carrigynachten Bog, nr Athlone, ALK King (Warburg 1953: 305).
H(26) listed by Lett (1915: 90).

†H26 listed by Blockeel & Long (1998: 66).
H(27) listed by Lett (1915: 90).
†H27 listed by Blockeel & Long (1998: 66).
H(28) listed by Lett (1915: 90).
†H28 listed by Blockeel & Long (1998: 66).
H(29) 1937: Glenade, no collector named (BBS exc.) (A Thompson in Armitage 1938: 10).
no date: Glenade, A Thompson (Thompson 1944: 204).
†H29 listed by Blockeel & Long (1998: 66).
H(30) listed by Lett (1915: 90).
†H30 listed by Blockeel & Long (1998: 66).
H31 1963: N side of Carlingford Mt., DM Synnott (Warburg 1965: 859).
[H(32) listed by Lett (1915: 90) without locality. H32 deleted because no valid record or voucher specimen traced (Blockeel 1999: 3)].
H(33) listed by Lett (1915: 90).
†H33 listed by Blockeel & Long (1998: 66).
H(34) listed by Lett (1915: 90).
†H34 listed by Blockeel & Long (1998: 66).
H(35) listed by Lett (1915: 90).
†H35 listed by Blockeel & Long (1998: 66).
H(36) listed by Lett (1915: 90).
†H36 listed by Blockeel & Long (1998: 66).
H(37) listed by Lett (1915: 90).
†H37 listed by Blockeel & Long (1998: 66).
H(38) listed by Lett (1915: 90).
†H38 listed by Blockeel & Long (1998: 66).
H(39) listed by Lett (1915: 90).
†H39 listed by Blockeel & Long (1998: 66).
†H40 listed by Blockeel & Long (1998: 66).

1/26 ***Sphagnum cuspidatum*** Ehrh. ex Hoffm. (syn. *Sphagnum cuspidatum* var. *falcatum* Russow, *S. cuspidatum* var. *plumosum* Nees & Hornsch., *S. cuspidatum* var. *serrratum* (Austin) Austin, *S. cuspidatum* var. *submersum* Schimp., *S. viride* Flatberg)

H(1) listed by Lett (1915: 94).
†H1 listed by Blockeel & Long (1998: 66).
H(2) listed by Lett (1915: 94) without details.
†H2 listed by Blockeel & Long (1998: 66).
†H3 listed by Blockeel & Long (1998: 66).
H4 1966: partially submerged in bog at 1200 ft alt., Seefin, Boggeragh Mts, MFV Corley & JS Parker (Perry 1967: 406).
H5 1967: in bog, *ca* 700 ft [alt.], Lyrenamon, NW of Carrignavar, RD Fitzgerald (Crundwell 1968: 630).
H(6) 1933: Knockmealdown, E Armitage (anon. 1934a: 104).
1933: Poolvona, E Armitage (anon. 1934a: 104), as var. *falcatum*.
†H6 listed by Blockeel & Long (1998: 66).
H7 1966: bog between Seefin and Knockeenatoung, Galtee Mts, EM Lobley & RJ Murphy (BBS exc.) (Perry 1967: 406).
H(8) listed by Lett (1915: 94).
†H8 listed by Blockeel & Long (1998: 66).
H(9) listed by Lett (1915: 94) without details.
H9 1963: *Menyanthes*-pool by roadside, W side of Slieve Elva, *ca* 750 ft [alt.], Lisdoonvarna, G Halliday (Warburg 1964: 722).
H(10) listed by Lett (1915: 94).
H10 1959: cut-away bog W of Newport, ALK King (Warburg 1960: 770).
H(11) listed by Lett (1915: 94).
†H11 listed by Blockeel & Long (1998: 66).
H(12) listed by Lett (1915: 94).
H12 1961: Forth Mt, at 600 ft [alt.], ALK King (Warburg 1962: 365).
H(13) listed by Lett (1915: 94).
†H13 listed by Blockeel & Long (1998: 66).
H(14) listed by Lett (1915: 94, 95).
†H14 listed by Blockeel & Long (1998: 66).
H15 1952: marsh nr Ross Quay, L. Derg, ALK King (Warburg 1953: 305).
H(16) listed by Lett (1915: 94).
H(16) no date: Shenanagh nr Kylemore, EM Lind, det. A Thompson (Thompson 1944: 203), as *S. cuspidatum* var. *falcatum*.
†H16 listed by Blockeel & Long (1998: 66).
H(17) listed by Lett (1915: 95).
†H17 listed by Blockeel & Long (1998: 66).
H(18) listed by Lett (1915: 94, 95).
H(18) 1949: Rathlumber, AAJ (Thompson & Lobley 1950: 381), as var. *plumosum*.
†H18 listed by Blockeel & Long (1998: 66).
H(19) 1949: Ballymount Bog, nr Calverstown JS Thomson (Thompson & Lobley 1950: 381), as var. *falcatum*.
1949: Ballymount Bog, nr Calverstown, JS Thomson (Thompson & Lobley 1950: 381), as var. *plumosum*.
†H19 listed by Blockeel & Long (1998: 66).
H(20) listed by Lett (1915: 95).
†H20 listed by Blockeel & Long (1998: 66).
H(21) listed by Lett (1915: 94).
H(21) 1948: Pine Forest, Co. Dublin, AEA Dunston, det. A Thompson (anon. 1949b: 215), as *S. cuspidatum* var.

falcatum.
1949: Featherbed Mt., AEA Dunston (Thompson & Lobley 1950: 381), as var. *submersum.*
H22 1952: Clonycavan Bog, Ballivor, ALK King (Warburg 1953: 305).
H23 1952: The Derries Bog, nr Athlone, ALK King (Warburg 1953: 305).
H24 1955: Derryad Bog, TA Barry, comm. ALK King (Warburg 1957: 327).
H(25) listed by Lett (1915: 94).
†H25 listed by Blockeel & Long (1998: 66).
H(26) listed by Lett (1915: 94, 95).
†H26 listed by Blockeel & Long (1998: 66).
H(27) listed by Lett (1915: 94, 95).
H(27) no date: 'I.27' with no locality, W West (Wheldon 1919: 249), as var. *falcatum, f. polyphyllum.*
1937: nr Keel Lough, no collector named (BBS exc.) (A Thompson in Armitage 1938: 10), as var. *submersum.*
1937: Slievemore, no collector named (BBS exc.) (A Thompson in Armitage 1938: 10), as var. *plumulosum.*
no date: nr Keel Lough, Achill I., A Thompson (Thompson 1944: 203-204), as *S. cuspidatum* var. *submersum.*
no date: Slievemore, Achill I., A Thompson (Thompson 1944: 203-204), as *S. cuspidatum* var. *plumulosum.*
†H27 listed by Blockeel & Long (1998: 66).
H(28) listed by Lett (1915: 94, 95).
H(28) 1937: Ben Bulben [*sic* = Bulben], no collector named (BBS exc.) (A Thompson in Armitage 1938: 10), as var. *falcatum.*
1937: Cliffony, no collector named (BBS exc.) (A Thompson in Armitage 1938: 10), as var. *falcatum.*
1937: Ben Bulben, no collector named (BBS exc.) (A Thompson in Armitage 1938: 10), as var. *submersum.*
no date: nr Cliffony, EM Lobley (Thompson 1944: 203), as *S. cuspidatum* var. *falcatum.*
no date: Ben Bulbin [*sic* = Bulben], A Thompson (Thompson 1944: 203-204), as *S. cuspidatum* var. *submersum.*
†H28 listed by Blockeel & Long (1998: 66).
H(29) listed by Lett (1915: 94, 95).
†H29 listed by Blockeel & Long (1998: 66).
H(30) listed by Lett (1915: 94, 95).
†H30 listed by Blockeel & Long (1998: 66).
H(31) listed by Lett (1915: 94).
H31 1964: submerged in pool, Corcreeagh Bog, DM Synnott (Warburg 1965: 859).
H(32) listed by Lett (1915: 94, 95).
H(32) 1947: Black I., Lough Muckno, Castlebury, JS Thomson, det. A Thompson (anon. 1948a: 118), as var. *serratum.*
H(33) listed by Lett (1915: 94, 95).
†H33 listed by Blockeel & Long (1998: 66).
H(34) listed by Lett (1915: 94) without details.
H(34) 1937: Bundoran, no collector named (BBS exc.) (A Thompson in Armitage 1938: 10), as var. *falcatum.*
1937: Bundoran, no collector named (BBS exc.) (A Thompson in Armitage 1938: 10), as var. *serratum.*
no date: nr Bundoran, GH Allison (Thompson 1944: 203-204), as *S. cuspidatum* var. *falcatum.*
no date: nr Bundoran, GH Allison (Thompson 1944: 203-204), as *S. cuspidatum* var. *serratum.*
†H34 listed by Blockeel & Long (1998: 66).
H(35) listed by Lett (1915: 94, 95).
†H35 listed by Blockeel & Long (1998: 66).
H(36) listed by Lett (1915: 94, 95).
†H36 listed by Blockeel & Long (1998: 66).
H(37) 1918: ditch in bog, Derryloste, JS Houston (anon. 1919a: 232), as var. *falcatum.*
H(37) listed by Lett (1915: 94, 95).
†H37 listed by Blockeel & Long (1998: 66).
H(38) listed by Lett (1915: 94, 95).
†H38 listed by Blockeel & Long (1998: 66).
H(39) 1928: Fair Head (BBS exc.) (Duncan 1928: 116), as var. *plumulosum.*
H(39) listed by Lett (1915: 94, 95).
†H39 listed by Blockeel & Long (1998: 66).
†H40 listed by Blockeel & Long (1998: 66).

1/29 ***Sphagnum pulchrum*** (Lindb. ex Braithw.) Warnst.

H1 1972: edges of pools, Coomnacarig Bog, Glencar, C Mhic Daeid (Crundwell 1973: 507).
H2 1970: edges of pools in blanket bog, 650 ft alt., Killarney, C MhicDaeid (Crundwell 1971b: 374).
H16 1957: hummocks of blanket bog, nr Roundstone, JH Tallis (BBS exc.) (Warburg 1958b: 471).
H17 1985: in pools on raised bog, Cloonmore, H Grogan & C Douglas (Blockeel 1987: 21, Douglas 1987).
[H(20) 1949: Ballyreagh Bog, AEA Dunston

(Thompson & Lobley 1950: 381). Not accepted for H20 in *CC* by Corley & Hill (1981: 57)].

[H(21) 1949: Pine Forest East, AEA Dunston (Thompson & Lobley 1950: 381). Not accepted for H21 in *CC* by Corley & Hill (1981: 57)].

H23 1986: large pools on raised bog, Cross Wood, H Grogan & C Douglas (Blockeel 1987: 21, Douglas 1987).

H25 1982: edge of pool on remnant of raised bog, Garranlahan, S of Ballinlough, DM Synnott (Hill 1983: 50).

[H(29) 1937: Glenade, no collector named (BBS exc.) (A Thompson in Armitage 1938: 10). H(29), no date: Glenade, A Thompson (Thompson 1944: 203). Not accepted for H29 in *CC* by Corley & Hill (1981: 57)].

H35 1965: seepage area in blanket bog W of Dermot & Grania's Bed, Maas, MCF Proctor (Warburg 1966: 189).

†H38 listed by Blockeel & Long (1998: 66).

H39 1953: raised bog nr Clogh Mills, nr Ballymena, MPH Kertland & EM Lobley (Warburg 1954: 477).

H40 1985: edge of pool on raised bog, Ballynahone, H89, R Weyl (BBSUK) (Rothero 2001: 38).

1/30a *Sphagnum fallax* (H.Klinggr.) H. Klinggr. **subsp.** ***fallax***
(syn. *Sphagnum intermedium* auct. non Hoffm., *S. recurvum* P.Beauv. var. *mucronatum* (Russow) Warnst.)

[H(1) listed by Lett (1915: 94), as *S. intermedium*].

†H1 listed by Blockeel & Long (1998: 66).

†H2 listed by Blockeel & Long (1998: 66).

†H3 listed by Blockeel & Long (1998: 66).

H4 1966: boggy ground at 1300 ft alt., Musheramore, Boggeragh Mts, MFV Corley & JS Parker, conf. MO Hill (Perry 1967: 406; MO Hill MS), as *S. recurvum*.

[H(6) listed by Lett (1915: 94), as *S. intermedium*].

†H6 listed by Blockeel & Long (1998: 66).

[H(7) listed by Lett (1915: 94), as *S. intermedium*].

†H7 listed by Blockeel & Long (1998: 66).

H8 1966: boggy ground on moor, Slievereagh, nr Ballylanders, MFV Corley & JS Parker, conf. MO Hill (Perry 1967: 406; MO Hill MS), as *S. recurvum*.

†H9 listed by Blockeel & Long (1998: 66).

H10 1979: moorland on S side of Keeper Hill, AC Crundwell (Hill 1980b: 32).

[H(11) listed by Lett (1915: 94), as *S. intermedium*].

H11 1966: in bog, Derryfadda, nr Johnstown, RD Fitzgerald (BBS exc.) (Crundwell 1968: 629), as *S. recurvum*.

[H(12) listed by Lett (1915: 94), as *S. intermedium*].

H12 1958: pool on Forth Mt, ALK King (Warburg 1959: 631), as *S. recurvum*.

H(13) 1867: Mt Leinster, RC Browne (DBN) (Lett 1915: 94 as *S. intermedium*; Crundwell 1968: 629 as *S. recurvum*).

†H13 listed by Blockeel & Long (1998: 66).

[H(14) listed by Lett (1915: 94), as *S. intermedium*].

H14 1956: by edge of Gortahile Bog, AA Cridland (Warburg 1958b: 471), as *S. recurvum*.

[H(16) listed by Lett (1915: 94), as *S. intermedium*].

H16 1955: roadside drain, Ballinahinch, ALK King (Warburg 1956: 151), as *S. recurvum*.

H17 1968: in *Molinia*-dominated flush in raised bog at Addergoule North, R. Suck nr Ballinasloe, HJB Birks (Crundwell 1969: 877), as *S. recurvum*.

H(18) listed by Blockeel & Long (1998: 66).

[H18 1965: bog at Letter crossroads, Slieve Bloom Mts, ALK King (Warburg 1966: 189), as *S. recurvum*. *S. recurvum* var. *mucronatum* listed for H18 by Corley & Hill 1981: 57, but post-1949 record not accepted for H18 by Blockeel & Long 1998: 66].

[H(20) listed by Lett (1915: 94), as *S. intermedium*].

H20 1949: Fromanallison valley, Kippune [*sic* = Kippure], A Jeffares (BBSUK), det. MO Hill (MO Hill MS) [Same specimen was apparently listed by Thompson & Lobley (1950: 381) as *S. amblyphyllum* var. *mesophyllum*].

[H21 deleted because the record was based on *S. robustum* (Crundwell 1969: 877)].

[H21 1958: Glenasmole, ALK King (DBN) (Crundwell 1969: 877), as *S. recurvum*. Taxon was not accepted for H21 by Corley & Hill 1981: 57 or Blockeel & Long 1998: 66, possibly because the

record was overlooked].
H22 1978: bog margin, NW of Petersville Cross Roads, N of Moynalty, DM Synnott (Hill 1979: 26).
H23 1966: Scraw Bog, Portnashangan, ALK King (Perry 1967: 406), as *S. recurvum.*
H24 1957: Ardagh Hill, MPH Kertland & ALK King (Warburg 1958b: 471), as *S. recurvum.*
[H(25) listed by Lett (1915: 94), as *S. intermedium*].
H25 1965: bog, *ca* 700 ft alt., Kilronan, nr Ballyfarnan, EM Lobley & RD Fitzgerald (Warburg 1966: 189), as *S. recurvum.*
[H(26) listed by Lett (1915: 94), as *S. intermedium*].
H26 1970: on edge of bog pool, Glendaduff, NE of Foxford, MFV Corley, conf. MO Hill (Crundwell 1971b: 374; MO Hill MS), as *S. recurvum.*
[H(27) listed by Lett (1915: 94), as *S. intermedium*].
†H27 listed by Blockeel & Long (1998: 66).
[H(28) listed by Lett (1915: 94), as *S. intermedium*].
†H28 listed by Blockeel & Long (1998: 66).
[H(29) listed by Lett (1915: 94), as *S. intermedium*].
†H29 listed by Blockeel & Long (1998: 66).
[H(30) listed by Lett (1915: 94), as *S. intermedium*].
H30 1955: bog on Ballyjamesduff road, W of Virginia, ALK King (Warburg 1956: 151), as *S. recurvum.*
[H(31) listed by Lett (1915: 94), as *S. intermedium*].
H31 1966: Ardee Bog, DM Synnott (Perry 1967: 406), as *S. recurvum.*
H32 2002: in blanket bog flush with *S. inundatum*, *Drepanocladus cossonii*, 250 m alt., 1 km downstream of outflow from Lough Bradan, H54, N Lockhart 2002/03a (Rothero 2003: 47).
H33 1957: moorland on NE side of Tiltinbane, AC Crundwell (Warburg 1959: 631), as *S. recurvum.*
†H34 listed by Blockeel & Long (1998: 66).
[H(35) listed by Lett (1915: 94), as *S. intermedium*].
†H35 listed by Blockeel & Long (1998: 66).
[H(36) listed by Lett (1915: 94), as *S. intermedium*].
†H36 listed by Blockeel & Long (1998: 66).
[H(37) listed by Lett (1915: 94), as *S. intermedium*].
†H37 listed by Blockeel & Long (1998: 66).
[H(38) listed by Lett (1915: 94), as *S. intermedium*].
†H38 listed by Blockeel & Long (1998: 66).
[H(39) listed by Lett (1915: 94), as *S. intermedium*].
†H39 listed by Blockeel & Long (1998: 66).
†H40 listed by Blockeel & Long (1998: 66).

A few specimens were revised by MO Hill (MS) for the *CC* (Corley & Hill 1981: 57). Older records of *S. recurvum* have apparently also been referred to this taxon, although a few might conceivably be attributable to any of the following three much rarer taxa.

1/30b *Sphagnum fallax* subsp. *isoviitae* (Flatberg) M.O.Hill

H8 1992: at edge of forestry plantation, Cloonahard, S of Ballykahill, R14, E Wiltshire, det. A Eddy (Rothero 2000: 46).

1/31 *Sphagnum flexuosum* Dozy & Molk.
(syn. *Sphagnum amblyphyllum* (Russow) Warnst., *S. amblyphyllum* var. *macrophyllum* Warnst., *S. amblyphyllum* var. *mesophyllum* Warnst., *S. recurvum* P.Beauv. var. *amblyphyllum* (Russow) Warnst.)

H(3) 1934: wet place under a willow, nr Sugar Loaf Mt., Glengarriff, A Thompson (BBSUK), conf. MO Hill (Hill 1977b: 19, 1978: 16, MO Hill MS).
H3 2002: on wet ground in mixed woodland, 20 m alt., Glengarriff Woods, V95, TL Blockeel 31/138 (Rothero 2003: 47).
H16 1957: bog by L. Inach, Connemara, EM Lobley (Hb. EM Lobley), conf. MO Hill (Hill 1977b: 19, 1978: 16, MO Hill MS).
[H(21) 1949: Pine Forest East, AEA Dunston (Thompson & Lobley 1950: 381), as *S. amblyphyllum* var. *mesophyllum.* Not accepted for H21 in *CC* by Corley & Hill (1981: 57)].
H25 2002: at edge of raised bog with *S. subnitens*, 90 m alt., Carrowbehy/Caher Bog, M58, NG Hodgetts 4122 (Rothero 2003: 47).
[H(27) 1937: nr Keel Lough, no collector

named (BBS exc.) (A Thompson in Armitage 1938: 10), as *S. amblyphyllum* var. *macrophyllum*. H(27), 1937: nr Keel Lough, no collector named (BBS exc.) (A Thompson in Armitage 1938: 10), as *S. amblyphyllum* var. *mesophyllum*. H(27), no date: nr Keel Lough, Achill I., A Thompson (Thompson 1944: 203), as *S. amblyphyllum* var. *macrophyllum*. H (27), no date: nr Keel Lough, Achill I., A Thompson (Thompson 1944: 203), as *S. amblyphyllum* var. *mesophyllum*. Not accepted for H27 in *CC* by Corley & Hill (1981: 57)].

[H(28) 1937: Ben Bulben, no collector named (BBS exc.) (A Thompson in Armitage 1938: 10), as *S. amblyphyllum* var. *macrophyllum*. H(28), no date: Ben Bulbin [*sic* = Bulben], EM Lobley & A Thompson (Thompson 1944: 203), as *S. amblyphyllum* var. *macrophyllum*. Not accepted for H28 in *CC* by Corley & Hill (1981: 57)].

[H(29) 1937: Tullaghan, no collector named (BBS exc.) (A Thompson in Armitage 1938: 10), as *S. amblyphyllum* var. *mesophyllum*. H(29), no date: Tullaghan, EM Lobley (Thompson 1944: 203), as *S. amblyphyllum* var. *mesophyllum*. H(29), 1937: Tullaghan, EM Lobley (anon. 1938a: 20), as *S. amblyphyllum* var. *mesophyllum*. Not accepted for H29 in *CC* by Corley & Hill (1981: 57)].

[H(39) 1928: Fair Head (BBS exc.) (Duncan 1928: 116), as *S. amblyphyllum* var. *macrophyllum*. Not accepted for H39 in *CC* by Corley & Hill (1981: 57)].

Specimens were revised by MO Hill (MS) for *CC* (Corley & Hill 1981: 57).

1/32 *Sphagnum angustifolium* (C.E.O. Jensen ex Russow) C.E.O.Jensen (syn. *Sphagnum recurvum* P.Beauv. var. *tenue* H.Klinggr.)

H2 1987: *Betula* flush on raised bog, Ardagh, H Grogan & C Douglas (Blockeel 1988: 33).

H3 1979: flush in corrie, alt. 300 m, Gouganebarra Lake, AC Crundwell (Hill 1980b: 32).

H10 1986: slight flush draining from *Racomitrium* heath on N facing slope, Keepers Hill, JC Cross, comm. H Grogan (Blockeel 1987: 21).

H16 1987: small flush on blanket bog, E of Orrid Lake, adjacent to road, Maam Cross, H Grogan & C Douglas (Blockeel 1988: 33).

H23 1986: small *Betula* flush along channel on raised bog, Wooddown, H Grogan & C Douglas (Blockeel 1987: 21).

H25 1985: flush on raised bog, Carrowbehy, H Grogan, C Douglas & JC Cross (Blockeel 1987: 21).

H26 1986: small *Betula* flushes on western raised bog, Gowlaun, H Grogan, C Douglas & JC Cross (Blockeel 1987: 21).

H27 1987: swallow hole area on blanket bog, 3 km E of Glenkeen Bridge, S of Loursborg, H Grogan & E McGee (Blockeel 1988: 33).

H33 1999: at base of sandstone escarpment with *Luzula sylvatica, Vaccinium myrtillus*, 250 m alt., Carricknagower Scarp, Lough Navar Forest, H05, RD Porley 1526, det. MO Hill (Rothero 2000: 46).

H39 1988: with *S. fallax*, Dungonnel Dam, Garron Plateau, D21, K Anderson, det. R Weyl (BBSUK) (Rothero 2001: 38).

[1/34 *Sphagnum riparium* Ångstr.]

[H6 deleted because no published record or specimen traced (Duncan 1967, Crundwell 1968: 629)].

[1/?] *Sphagnum* of uncertain identity

[H(1) 1935: Brandon Headland, no collector named (BBS exc.) (Watson 1936: 264), as *S. fallax* var. *laxifolium*].

[H(1) 1935: Brandon Headland, no collector named (BBS exc.) (Watson 1936: 264), as *S. fallax* var. *schultzii*].

[H(1) 1935: near Loch Cruttia, no collector named (BBS exc.) (Watson 1936: 264), as *S. aquatile* var. *intortum*].

[H(1) 1935: Loch Cruttia, no collector named (BBS exc.) (Watson 1936: 264), as *S. aquatile* var. *sanguinale*].

[H(1) 1935: Connor Hill, no collector named (BBS exc.) (Watson 1936: 264), as *S. aquatile* var. *remotum*].

[H(1) 1935: Connor Hill, no collector named (BBS exc.) (Watson 1936: 264), as *S. Camussii*].

[H(2) no date: W West (Wheldon 1919: 250), new record as *S. holtii*].
[H(2) no date: W West (Wheldon 1919: 252), new record as *S. cymbifolium* var. *pallescens* f. *confertum*. Wijk *et al.* (1967: 443) list *S. cymbifolium* var. *pallescens* Warnst. as a synonym of both *S. magellanicum* and *S. palustre*].
[H(2) 1935: Mangerton, no collector named (BBS exc.) (Watson 1936: 264), as *S. recurvum* var. *robustum*].
[H(2) 1935: Mangerton, no collector named (BBS exc.) (Watson 1936: 264), as *S. aquatile* var. *intortum*].
[H(2) 1935: Mangerton, no collector named (BBS exc.) (Watson 1936: 264), as *S. aquatile* var. *remotum*].
[H(2) 1935: Old Weir Bridge, no collector named (BBS exc.) (Watson 1936: 264), as *S. aquatile* var. *remotum*].
[H(2) 1935: Eagle's Nest, no collector named (BBS exc.) (Watson 1936: 264), as *S. Camussii*].
[H(6) 1933: Knockmealdown, E Armitage (anon. 1934a: 104), as *S. recurvum* var. *majus*].
[H(9) 1948: Co. Clare, A Jackson (Thompson & Lobley 1950: 381), as *S. recurvum* var. *majus* Ångstr.].
[H(9) 1945: Co. Clare, JS Thomson, det. A Thompson (anon. 1946b: 278), as *S. recurvum* var. *robustum* Breidl.].
[H(16) no date: Kylemore, EM Lind, det. A Thompson (Thompson 1944: 207), as *S. centrale*].
[H(20) 1949: Ballyreagh Bog, AEA Dunston (Thompson & Lobley 1950: 381), as *S. recurvum* var. *parvulum* Warnst.].
[H(20) 1949: Ballyreagh Bog, AEA Dunston (Thompson & Lobley 1950: 381), as *S. subsecundum* var. *intermedium* Warnst.].
[H(21) 1948: Pine Forest, Co. Dublin, AEA Dunston, det. A Thompson (anon. 1949b: 215), as *S. recurvum* var. *robustum* Breidl.].
[H(21) 1948: Pine Forest, Co. Dublin, AEA Dunston, det. A Thompson (anon. 1949b: 215), as *S. recurvum* var. *majus* Ångstr.].
[H(21) 1948: Pine Forest, Co. Dublin, AEA Dunston, det. A Thompson (anon. 1949b: 215), as *S. recurvum* var. *parvulum* Warnst.].
[H(21) 1948: Pine Forest, Co. Dublin, AEA Dunston, det. A Thompson (anon. 1949b: 215), as *S. fallax* var. *laxifolium* Warnst.].
[H(21) 1948: Pine Forest, Co. Dublin, AEA Dunston, det. A Thompson (anon. 1949b: 215), as *S. fallax* var. *Schultzii* Warnst.].
[H(21) 1949: side of road to Mahoney Bog, AEA Dunston (Thompson & Lobley 1950: 381), as *S. fallax* var. *robustum* Warnst.].
[H(21) 1949: Pine Forest East, AEA Dunston (Thompson & Lobley 1950: 382), as *S. camusii*].
[H(25) no date: Elphin, collector not named (anon. 1921: 273), new record as *S. cymbifolium* f. *confertum*. According to Wijk *et al.* (1967: 441) *S. cymbifolium* var. *confertum* is a synonym of *S. papillosum*, but the identity of *S. cymbifolium* f. *confertum* may not be the same].
[H(27) 1937: Slievemore, no collector named (BBS exc.) (A Thompson in Armitage 1938: 10), as *S. recurvum* var. *majus*].
[H(27) 1937: nr Keel Lough, no collector named (BBS exc.) (A Thompson in Armitage 1938: 10), as *S. recurvum* var. *majus*].
[H(27) 1937: Slievemore, no collector named (BBS exc.) (A Thompson in Armitage 1938: 10), as *S. Holtii*].
[H(27) 1937: Slievemore, no collector named (BBS exc.) (A Thompson in Armitage 1938: 11), as *S. Camusii*].
[H(27) 1937: nr Keel Lough, no collector named (BBS exc.) (A Thompson in Armitage 1938: 11), as *S. Camusii*].
[H(27) no date: nr Keel, Achill I., A Thompson (Thompson 1944: 203), as *S. recurvum* var. *majus*].
[H(27) no date: on Slievemore, Achill I., A Thompson (Thompson 1944: 203), as *S. recurvum* var. *majus* Ångstr.].
[H(27) no date: nr Keel Lough, GH Allison & A Thompson (Thompson 1944: 206), as *S. camusii*].
[H(28) 1937: Ben Bulben, no collector named (BBS exc.) (A Thompson in Armitage 1938: 10), as *S. recurvum* var. *robustum*].
[H(28) 1937: Gleniff, no collector named (BBS exc.) (A Thompson in Armitage 1938: 10), as *S. recurvum* var. *majus*].
[H(28) 1937: Ben Bulben, no collector named (BBS exc.) (A Thompson in Armitage

1938: 10), as *S. recurvum* var. *majus*].

[H(28) 1937: Cliffony, no collector named (BBS exc.) (A Thompson in Armitage 1938: 11), as *S. Camusii*].

[H(28) 1937: Ben Bulbin [*sic* = Bulben], A Thompson. et. EM Lobley, comm. EM Lobley (anon. 1938a: 21), as *S. recurvum* var. *majus*].

[H(28) no date: Ben Bulbin [*sic* = Bulben], EM Lobley & A Thompson (Thompson 1944: 203), as *S. recurvum* var. *robustum* Breidl.].

[H(28) no date: Ben Bulbin [*sic* = Bulben], EM Lobley and A Thompson (Thompson 1944: 203), as *S. recurvum* var. *majus* Ångstr.].

[H(28) no date: Gleniff, A Thompson (Thompson 1944: 203), as *S. recurvum* var. *majus* Ångstr.].

[H(28) no date: nr Cliffony, EM Lobley (Thompson 1944: 206), as *S. camusii*].

[H(29) 1937: Glenade, no collector named (BBS exc.) (A Thompson in Armitage 1938: 10), as *S. recurvum* var. *majus*].

[H(29) 1937: Tullaghan, no collector named (BBS exc.) (A Thompson in Armitage 1938: 10), as *S. recurvum* var. *majus*].

[H(29) 1937: Glenade, no collector named (BBS exc.) (A Thompson in Armitage 1938: 10), as *S. fallax* var. *robustum*].

[H(29) 1937: Tullaghan, no collector named (BBS exc.) (A Thompson in Armitage 1938: 11), as *S. Camusii*].

[H(29) no date: Tullaghan, EM Lobley (Thompson 1944: 203), as *S. recurvum* var. *majus* Ångstr.].

[H(29) no date: Glenade, A Thompson (Thompson 1944: 203), as *S. recurvum* var. *majus* Ångstr.].

[H(29) no date: Glenade, A Thompson (Thompson 1944: 203), as *S. fallax* var. *robustum* Warnst.].

[H(29) no date: Tullaghan, EM Lobley (Thompson 1944: 204), as *S. subsecundum* var. *intermedium* Warnst.].

[H(29) no date: Tullaghan, EM Lobley (Thompson 1944: 206), as *S. camusii*].

[H(31) 1912: Clennont Mts, HW Lett & CH Waddell, comm. CH Waddell, as *S. recurvum*, but redet. by JA Wheldon as '*S. pulchrum* W., var. *fuscoflavens* W., *f. brachyanocladum* W.' (anon. 1918a: 207)].

[H(38) 1928: Slieve Donard (BBS exc.) (Duncan 1928: 114, 117), as *S. aquatile* var. *turgidum*].

[H(38) 1928: Slieve Donard (BBS exc.) (Duncan 1928: 114, 117), as *S. aquatile* var. *intortum*].

[H(38) 1928: Slieve Donard (BBS exc.) (Duncan 1928: 114, 117), as *S. aquatile* var. *pauperatum*].

[H(38) 1928: Slieve Donard (BBS exc.) (Duncan 1928: 114, 117), as *S. aquatile* var. *mastigocladum*].

[H(39) 1928: Fair Head (BBS exc.) (Duncan 1928: 116), as *S. recurvum* var. *majus*].

[H(39) 1928: Fair Head (BBS exc.) (Duncan 1928: 116), as *S. aquatile* var. *mastigocladum*].

[H(39) 1928: Fair Head (BBS exc.) (Duncan 1928: 116), as *S. aquatile* var. *remotum*].

[H(40) 1913: margin of lake, Kilrea, JD Houston, det. by JA Wheldon as *S. recurvum* var. *majus*, *f. silvaticum* Russ. (anon. 1919a: 231)].

Without revision of specimens the records listed above apparently cannot be safely attributed to any of the species of *Sphagnum* now recognised as occurring in Ireland.

MOSSES
(ANDREAEOPSIDA)

2/1 ***Andreaea alpina*** Hedw.

H(1) listed by Lett (1915: 95).
H1 (Murray 1988: 61). †H1 listed by Blockeel & Long (1998: 67).
H(2) listed by Lett (1915: 95).
H2 (Murray 1988: 61). †H2 listed by Blockeel & Long (1998: 67).
H3 2002: on wet rock face, 310 m alt., Gougane Barra at head of valley, W06, TL Blockeel 31/331 (Rothero 2003: 47).
H(7) listed by Lett (1915: 95).
H7 (Murray 1988: 61). †H7 listed by Blockeel & Long (1998: 67).
H(16) listed by Lett (1915: 95).
H16 (Murray 1988: 61). †H16 listed by Blockeel & Long (1998: 67).
H(20) listed by Lett (1915: 95).
H20 (Murray 1988: 61). †H20 listed by Blockeel & Long (1998: 67).
H(21) listed by Lett (1915: 95). H(21) listed (Murray 1988: 61, Blockeel & Long 1998: 67).
H27 1965: rocks at 1500 ft alt., E end of Sheeffry Hills, nr Gortmore, A McG Stirling (Warburg 1966: 190). Listed for H27 (Murray 1988: 61). †H27 listed by Blockeel & Long (1998: 67).
[H(28) listed by Lett (1915: 95). H28 deleted by Blockeel 1989: 24 because no specimen was recorded during review by Murray 1988: 61].
H(31) listed by Lett (1915: 95).
H31 (Murray 1988: 61). †H31 listed by Blockeel & Long (1998: 67).
H(35) listed by Lett (1915: 95).
H35 (Murray 1988: 61). †H35 listed by Blockeel & Long (1998: 67).
[H(36) listed by Lett (1915: 95)].
[H(37) listed by Lett (1915: 95). H37 deleted by Blockeel 1989: 24 because no specimen was recorded during review by Murray 1988: 61].
H(38) listed by Lett (1915: 95).
H38 (Murray 1988: 61). †H38 listed by Blockeel & Long (1998: 67).
H(39) listed by Lett (1915: 95). H(39) listed (Murray 1988: 61, Blockeel & Long 1998: 67).
[H(40) listed by Lett (1915: 95). H40 deleted by Blockeel 1989: 24 because no specimen was recorded during review by Murray 1988: 61].
H40 1999: on steep basalt at base of crag, 490 m alt., Mullaghmore, NW side, C70, DT Holyoak 99-681 (BBSUK) (Rothero 2000: 46).

2/2a ***Andreaea rupestris*** Hedw. **var. *rupestris***
(syn. *Andreaea petrophila* Ehrh., *A. petrophila* var. *acuminata* Schimp., *A. petrophila* var. *gracilis* Bruch, Schimp. & W.Gümbel)

[H(1) listed by Lett (1915: 95), without details].
[H(2) listed by Lett (1915: 95)].
H3 1967: on rocks, *ca* 1400 ft [alt.], Gougane Barra, RD Fitzgerald (Crundwell 1968: 630). H3 listed (Murray 1988: 72, Blockeel 1989: 24).
H(4) 1851: Musheragh Mt., [10/3285], Carroll s.n. (BM) (Murray 1988: 72, Blockeel 1989: 24).
H(6) listed by Lett (1915: 95).
H6 (Murray 1988: 72, Blockeel 1989: 24). †H6 listed by Blockeel & Long (1998: 67).
[H(7) 1945: moraine at Loch Diheen, Galtees, RD Meikle (anon. 1947: 28). Specimen not seen by Murray (1988), so excluded from *CC* by Blockeel & Long (1998: 67)].
H8 1966: rocks at 2400 ft alt., Temple Hill, Galtee Mts, MFV Corley & JS Parker (Perry 1967: 407). H8 listed (Murray 1988: 72, Blockeel 1989: 24). †H8 listed by Blockeel & Long (1998: 67).
[H(11) listed by Lett (1915: 95)].
[H(12) listed by Lett (1915: 95)].
H13 1969: on wall in old quarry, Lackan, nr Oldleighlin, RD Fitzgerald (Crundwell 1970: 196; H13 also listed by Murray 1988: 72, Blockeel 1989: 24). †H13 listed by Blockeel & Long (1998: 67).
H(16) listed by Lett (1915: 95).
H16 (Murray 1988: 72, Blockeel 1989: 24). †H16 listed by Blockeel & Long (1998: 67).
H(20) listed by Lett (1915: 95).
H20 (Murray 1988: 72, Blockeel 1989: 24). †H20 listed by Blockeel & Long (1998: 67).
H(21) listed (Murray 1988: 72, Blockeel 1989: 24, Blockeel & Long 1998: 67).
[H21 1953: Ballymorphin Hill, AW Stelfox, comm. JS Thomson (Warburg 1954: 478). Specimen apparently not revised by Murray (1988)].

H27 (Murray 1988: 72, Blockeel 1989: 24). †H27 listed by Blockeel & Long (1998: 67).
H(29) listed by Lett (1915: 95). H(29) (Murray 1988: 72, Blockeel 1989: 24, Blockeel & Long 1998: 67).
H30 1961: Millstone Grit boulder, *ca* 1700 ft [alt.], Bellavally, Cuilcagh, RD Fitzgerald (Warburg 1962: 366). H30 listed (Murray 1988: 72, Blockeel 1989: 24).†H30 listed by Blockeel & Long (1998: 67).
H(31) listed by Lett (1915: 95). H(31) (Murray 1988: 72, Blockeel 1989: 24, Blockeel & Long 1998: 67).
H31 1999: on boulder on moorland slope, 300 m alt., Two Mile River, Carlingford, J11, TL Blockeel 28/163 (Rothero 2000: 46).
H(34) no date [= 19th century]: Inishowen Mt., [24/34], R Brown s.n. (BM) (Murray 1988: 72, Blockeel 1989: 24).
H34 2002: on steep schist of NW-facing crag, 425 m alt., NW slope of Bulbin Mt., DT Holyoak 02-821 (Rothero 2003: 47).
H(35) listed by Lett (1915: 95).
H35 (Murray 1988: 72, Blockeel 1989: 24). †H35 listed by Blockeel & Long (1998: 67).
H36 1950: mica schist boulder, *ca* 2050 ft Dart Mt., J Taylor (Warburg 1951: 498). H36 listed (Murray 1988: 72, Blockeel 1989: 24).
H(37) listed by Lett (1915: 95).
H37 (Murray 1988: 72, Blockeel 1989: 24). †H37 listed by Blockeel & Long (1998: 67).
H(38) 1901: Slieve Donard, E Armitage (anon. 1915a: 124), as *A. petrophila* var. *gracilis*, from 'I.18*' (but surely a typographical error for I.38). H(38) listed by Lett (1915: 95).
H38 (Murray 1988: 72, Blockeel 1989: 24). †H38 listed by Blockeel & Long (1998: 67).
H(39) listed by Lett (1915: 95).
H39 (Murray 1988: 72, Blockeel 1989: 24). †H39 listed by Blockeel & Long (1998: 67).
H(40) listed by Lett (1915: 95).
H40 (Murray 1988: 72, Blockeel 1989: 24). †H40 listed by Blockeel & Long (1998: 67).

[**2/2b** ***Andreaea rupestris*** **Hedw. var.** ***papillosa*** (Lindb.) Podp.
(syn. *Andreaea obovata* Thed. var. *papillosa* (Lindb.) Nyholm)]

[All Irish records are errors or based on intermediate specimens: Murray 1988: 72-75, Blockeel 1989: 24]

2/6 ***Andreaea rothii*** F.Weber & D.Mohr subsp. uncertain
(syn. *Andreaea crassinervia* auct., *A. crassinervia* ssp. *huntii* auct., *A. crassinervia* var. *huntii* auct.)

H(1) listed by Lett (1915: 95, 96).
H(2) 1885: nr Cromaglown, GA Holt (MANCH), as *A. crassinervia* ssp. *huntii* conf. MO Hill (MO Hill MS, Corley & Hill 1981: 58).
H(2) listed by Lett (1915: 95, 96).
H3 1953: sandstone, *ca* 1600 ft [alt.], Foulastookeen Mt., ALK King (Warburg 1954: 478).
H(4) listed by Lett (1915: 96).
H(5) listed by Lett (1915: 96).
H(6) listed by Lett (1915: 96).
[H(7) 1945: moraine at Loch Diheen, Galtees, RD Meikle (anon. 1947: 28). No specimen seen by Murray (1988), so excluded from *CC* by Blockeel & Long (1998: 68)].
H8 1966: rocks at 2400 ft alt., Temple Hill, Galtee Mts, MFV Corley & JS Parker (Perry 1967: 407).
H10 1979: on acidic boulders, Keeper Hill, N Lockhart (Hill 1980b: 33).
H(11) listed by Lett (1915: 96).
H(12) listed by Lett (1915: 96).
H(13) listed by Lett (1915: 96).
H(16) listed by Lett (1915: 95).
H16 1957: on siliceous boulders, Lissoughter, DG Catcheside (CAN), as *A. crassinervia, fide* Schultze-Motel (MO Hill MS, Corley & Hill 1981: 58).
H(20) listed by Lett (1915: 95, 96).
H(21) listed by Lett (1915: 95, 96).
H(25) listed by Lett (1915: 96).
H(26) listed by Lett (1915: 96).
H(27) listed by Lett (1915: 95, 96).
H(28) listed by Lett (1915: 96).
H(29) listed by Lett (1915: 96).
H(30) listed by Lett (1915: 96).
H(31) listed by Lett (1915: 96).
H(33) listed by Lett (1915: 96).

H(34) listed by Lett (1915: 96).
H(35) listed by Lett (1915: 96).
H(36) listed by Lett (1915: 96).
H(37) listed by Lett (1915: 96).
H(38) listed by Lett (1915: 95, 96).
H(39) listed by Lett (1915: 96) without locality.
H(40) listed by Lett (1915: 96).

Recognition of subspecies in *A. rothii* was inconsistent until the taxonomic review by Murray (1988) and it remains problematical because intermediate plants occur. It is uncertain whether many of the specimens supporting the records listed above have been revised by Murray or subsequently.

2/6a ***Andreaea rothii*** F.Weber & D.Mohr **subsp. *rothii***
(syn. *Andreaea crassinervia* auct. pro parte)

H1 (BM, DBN: Murray 1988: 47, Blockeel 1989: 24). †H1 listed by Blockeel & Long (1998: 68).
H(2) (BM: Murray 1988: 47, Blockeel 1989: 25). H(2) listed by Blockeel & Long (1998: 68).
H3 2002: on large boulder, 530 m alt., Gougane Barra, below Lough Fadda, W06, TL Blockeel 31/322 (Rothero 2003: 47).
[H5 listed by Murray 1988: 47 on basis of specimens in BM and DBN. H5 later deleted because specimen (Kildorrery, 1857, I Carroll, BM) is intermediate between subsp. *rothii* and subsp. *falcata*, det. BM Murray (Blockeel 1999: 2, amending Blockeel 1989: 25).]
H8 (BBSUK: Murray 1988: 47, Blockeel 1989: 24). †H8 listed by Blockeel & Long (1998: 68).
H(12) (BBSUK: Murray 1988: 47, Blockeel 1989: 24). H(12) listed by Blockeel & Long (1998: 68).
H(13) (DBN: Murray 1988: 47, Blockeel 1989: 24). H(13) listed by Blockeel & Long (1998: 68).
[H16 listed by Murray 1988: 47 on basis of specimen in BM. H16 later deleted because specimen (W Salruck, 1900, Gamble, BM) is intermediate between subsp. *rothii* and subsp. *falcata*, det. BM Murray (Blockeel 1999: 2, amending Blockeel 1989: 25).]
H20 (BM, DBN, MO, NY: Murray 1988: 47, Blockeel 1989: 24). †H20 listed by Blockeel & Long (1998: 68).
H(21) (BM: Murray 1988: 47, Blockeel 1989: 24). H(21) listed by Blockeel & Long (1998: 68).
H27 (DBN: Murray 1988: 47, Blockeel 1989: 24). †H20 listed by Blockeel & Long (1998: 68).
H(30) (BBSUK: Murray 1988: 47, Blockeel 1989: 24). H(30) listed by Blockeel & Long (1998: 68).
H31 1999: on boulder on moorland slope, 300 m alt., Two Mile River, Carlingford, J11, TL Blockeel 28/162 (Rothero 2000: 46).
H34 2001: on siliceous rocks on NW-facing slope above disused railway, 100 m alt., Barnesmore Gap, SE of Ardinawark, H08, NG Hodgetts 3882 (Rothero 2003: 47).
[H35 listed by Murray 1988: 47 on basis of specimen in BM. H35 later deleted because specimen (Poison Glen, 1980, Dixon, BM) is intermediate between subsp. *rothii* and subsp. *falcata*, det. BM Murray (Blockeel 1999: 2, amending Blockeel 1989: 25).]
H35 2001: on rock on N-facing crags, 350 m alt., Common Mountain, Glengesh, G78, NG Hodgetts 3850 (Rothero 2003: 47).
H(36) (DBN: Murray 1988: 47, Blockeel 1989: 24). H(36) listed by Blockeel & Long (1998: 68).
H(38) (BM, DBN: Murray 1988: 47, Blockeel 1989: 24). H(38) listed by Blockeel & Long (1998: 68).

2/6b ***Andreaea rothii* subsp. *falcata*** (Schimp.) Lindb.
(syn. *Andreaea crassinervia* auct. pro parte, *A. crassinervia* subsp. *huntii* (Limpr.) Amann)

H1 (Murray 1988: 54, Blockeel 1989: 24). †H1 listed by Blockeel & Long (1998: 68).
H(2) 1885: nr Cromaglown, GA Holt (MANCH) (Hill 1981: 22), as var. *huntii*.
H2 (Murray 1988: 54, Blockeel 1989: 24). †H2 listed by Blockeel & Long (1998: 68).
H3 (Murray 1988: 54, Blockeel 1989: 24).

†H3 listed by Blockeel & Long (1998: 68).
H(5) listed (Murray 1988: 54, Blockeel 1989: 24, Blockeel & Long 1998: 68).
H6 (Murray 1988: 54, Blockeel 1989: 24). †H6 listed by Blockeel & Long (1998: 68).
H10 (Murray 1988: 54, Blockeel 1989: 24). †H10 listed by Blockeel & Long (1998: 68).
H16 (Murray 1988: 54, Blockeel 1989: 24). †H16 listed by Blockeel & Long (1998: 68).
H16 2001: on rock wall in small rocky valley, 275m alt., Benchoona, N slope, L76, DG Long 29993 (Rothero 2002: 43); apparently not a new or updated vice-county record.
H20 (Murray 1988: 54, Blockeel 1989: 24). †H20 listed by Blockeel & Long (1998: 68).
H(21) listed (Murray 1988: 54, Blockeel 1989: 24, Blockeel & Long 1998: 68).
H(25) listed (Murray 1988: 54, Blockeel 1989: 24, Blockeel & Long 1998: 68).
H25 2002: on rocks by stream, 150 m alt., Kilronan Mt., Arigna, G91, NG Hodgetts 4149 (Rothero 2003: 47).
H(26) listed (Murray 1988: 54, Blockeel 1989: 24, Blockeel & Long 1998: 68).
H27 (Murray 1988: 54, Blockeel 1989: 24). †H27 listed by Blockeel & Long (1998: 68).
H28 (Murray 1988: 54, Blockeel 1989: 24). †H28 listed by Blockeel & Long (1998: 68).
H(29) listed (Murray 1988: 54, Blockeel 1989: 24, Blockeel & Long 1998: 68).
H29 2001: on steep, E-facing sandstone crag, 420 m alt., Coal Pit, E slope of Bencroy, H01, DT Holyoak 01-792 (Rothero 2002: 43).
H30 (Murray 1988: 54, Blockeel 1989: 24). †H30 listed by Blockeel & Long (1998: 68).
H31 (Murray 1988: 54, Blockeel 1989: 24). †H31 listed by Blockeel & Long (1998: 68).
H33 (Murray 1988: 54, Blockeel 1989: 24). †H33 listed by Blockeel & Long (1998: 68).
H34 2001: on siliceous rocks on NW-facing slope above disused railway, 100 m alt., Barnesmore Gap, SE of Ardinawark H08, NG Hodgetts 3879 (Rothero 2003: 47).
H35 (Murray 1988: 54, Blockeel 1989: 24). †H35 listed by Blockeel & Long (1998: 68).
H36 1999: on open rock on ridge, 580 m alt., Dart Mt., W side, H69, DT Holyoak 99-691 (Rothero 2000: 46).
H38 (Murray 1988: 54, Blockeel 1989: 24). †H38 listed by Blockeel & Long (1998: 68).
H39 (Murray 1988: 54, Blockeel 1989: 24). †H39 listed by Blockeel & Long (1998: 68).

2/8 ***Andreaea megistospora*** B.M.Murray

H3 1953: Coomataggart Mt., [10/1068], King s.n. (DBN) (Murray 1988: 57, Blockeel 1989: 24).
H(4) 1851: Musheragh Mt., [10/38], Carroll s. n. (BM) (Murray 1988: 57, Blockeel 1989: 24).
H27 listed by Murray (1988: 79) and Blockeel (1989: 24). †H27 listed by Blockeel & Long (1998: 68).
H34 2001: on siliceous rocks on NW-facing slope above disused railway, 100 m alt., Barnesmore Gap, SE of Ardinawark, H08, NG Hodgetts 3883 (Rothero 2003: 47).
H(38) 1923: Rocky Mt. nr Hilltown, [33/2326], HW Lett s.n. (DBN) (Murray 1988: 57, Blockeel 1989: 24).

MOSSES
(BRYOPSIDA)

3/1 ***Pogonatum nanum*** (Hedw.) P.Beauv. (syn. *Polytrichum nanum* Hedw., *P. subrotundum* Menzies ex Brid., *P. subrotundum* var. *longisetum* (Bruch, Schimp. & W.Gümbel) Lindb.)

[H(1) listed by Lett (1915: 97) without details. H1 deleted because no valid record or voucher specimen traced (Blockeel 1999: 3)].
H(2) listed by Lett (1915: 97). H(2) listed by Blockeel & Long (1998: 68).
[H(3) listed by Lett (1915: 97) without locality. H3 deleted because no valid record or voucher specimen traced (Blockeel 1999: 3)].
H(4) listed by Lett (1915: 97). H(4) listed by Blockeel & Long (1998: 68).
H(5) listed by Lett (1915: 97). H(5) listed by Blockeel & Long (1998: 68).
H(10) listed by Lett (1915: 97). H(10) listed by Blockeel & Long (1998: 68).
H(12) listed by Lett (1915: 97). H(12) listed by Blockeel & Long (1998: 68).
H(13) listed by Lett (1915: 97). H(13) listed by Blockeel & Long (1998: 68).
H(20) listed by Lett (1915: 97). H(20) listed by Blockeel & Long (1998: 68).
H(21) listed by Lett (1915: 97). H(21) listed by Blockeel & Long (1998: 68).
H25 1968: on loamy bank in sandstone pit, Slieve Bawn, WV Rubers *et al.* (U) (Crundwell 1975: 13).
H(27) listed by Lett (1915: 97). H(27) listed by Blockeel & Long (1998: 68).
H(28) listed by Lett (1915: 97). H(28) listed by Blockeel & Long (1998: 68).
H31 1999: on mineral soil on rocky outcrop by stream, 300 m alt., Two Mile River, Carlingford, J11, TL Blockeel 28/173 (Rothero 2000: 46).
H(32) listed by Lett (1915: 97). H(32) listed by Blockeel & Long (1998: 68).
H(33) listed by Lett (1915: 97).
†H33 listed by Blockeel & Long (1998: 68).
[H(34) listed by Lett (1915: 97) without locality. H34 deleted because no valid record or voucher specimen traced (Blockeel 1999: 3)].
H(35) listed by Lett (1915: 97). H(35) listed by Blockeel & Long (1998: 68).
H36 1956: Glen Curry Bridge, nr Omagh, RD Fitzgerald & MPH Kertland (Warburg 1957: 328).
H(37) listed by Lett (1915: 97).
†H37 listed by Blockeel & Long (1998: 68).
H(38) listed by Lett (1915: 97). H(38) listed by Blockeel & Long (1998: 68).
H(39) listed by Lett (1915: 97).
†H39 listed by Blockeel & Long (1998: 68).
H(40) listed by Lett (1915: 97) without locality.
†H40 listed by Blockeel & Long (1998: 68).

3/2 ***Pogonatum aloides*** (Hedw.) P.Beauv. (syn. *Pogonatum aloides* var. *minimum* (Crome) Mol., *Polytrichum aloides* Hedw., *Polytrichum aloides* var. *dicksonii* (Turner) Lilj.)

H(1) listed by Lett (1915: 97) without details.
†H1 listed by Blockeel & Long (1998: 69).
H(2) listed by Lett (1915: 97) without details.
†H2 listed by Blockeel & Long (1998: 69).
H(3) listed by Lett (1915: 97) without details.
†H3 listed by Blockeel & Long (1998: 69).
H(4) listed by Lett (1915: 97) without details.
†H4 listed by Blockeel & Long (1998: 69).
H(5) listed by Lett (1915: 97).
†H5 listed by Blockeel & Long (1998: 69).
H(6) listed by Lett (1915: 97) without details.
†H6 listed by Blockeel & Long (1998: 69).
H(7) 1943: near Carrig-na-binnia, AW Stelfox, per JS Thomson (Duncan 1944: 208).
†H7 listed by Blockeel & Long (1998: 69).
H(8) listed by Lett (1915: 97) without details.
†H8 listed by Blockeel & Long (1998: 69).
H(9) listed by Lett (1915: 97) without details.
†H9 listed by Blockeel & Long (1998: 69).
H10 1951: bank in slate quarry, nr Killaloe, AD Banwell, PJ Wanstall & EV Watson (Warburg 1953: 306).
H(11) listed by Lett (1915: 97) without details.
†H11 listed by Blockeel & Long (1998: 69).
H(12) listed by Lett (1915: 97) without details.
†H12 listed by Blockeel & Long (1998: 69).
H(13) listed by Lett (1915: 97) without details.
†H13 listed by Blockeel & Long (1998: 69).
H(14) listed by Lett (1915: 97) without details.
†H14 listed by Blockeel & Long (1998: 69).
H15 1994: peaty bank by forestry track, near Pollboy, Slieve Aughty, M50, NG Hodgetts 2960 (Blockeel 1995c: 40).
H(16) 1933: Kylemore, PWM Richards (anon. 1938d: 38).
†H16 listed by Blockeel & Long (1998: 69).
[H(18) listed by Lett (1915: 97) without details. H18 deleted because no valid record or voucher specimen traced (Blockeel

1999: 3)].
H19 1953: roadside bank, Cupidstown Hill, ALK King (Warburg 1954: 478).
H(20) listed by Lett (1915: 97) without details.
†H20 listed by Blockeel & Long (1998: 69).
H(21) listed by Lett (1915: 97) without details.
†H21 listed by Blockeel & Long (1998: 69).
H22 1978: quarry, Teevurcher, N of Moynalty, DM Synnott (Hill 1979: 26).
H(24) listed by Lett (1915: 97) without details.
†H24 listed by Blockeel & Long (1998: 69).
H25 1965: clay bank, Kilronan Mt., nr Ballyfarnan, RD Fitzgerald & EM Lobley (Warburg 1966: 190).
H(26) listed by Lett (1915: 97) without details.
†H26 listed by Blockeel & Long (1998: 69).
H(27) listed by Lett (1915: 97) without details.
†H27 listed by Blockeel & Long (1998: 69).
H(28) 1948: Union Rock, Sligo, ALK King (per JS Thomson) (anon. 1949c: 216).
†H28 listed by Blockeel & Long (1998: 69).
H29 1963: clay bank, *ca* 600 ft [alt.], Glencar Waterfall, RD Fitzgerald & AR Perry (Warburg 1964: 722).
H(30) listed by Lett (1915: 97) without details.
†H30 listed by Blockeel & Long (1998: 69).
[H(31) listed by Lett (1915: 97) without details. H31 deleted because no valid record or voucher specimen traced (Blockeel 1999: 3)].
H(32) listed by Lett (1915: 97) without details.
†H32 listed by Blockeel & Long (1998: 69).
H(33) listed by Lett (1915: 97) without details.
†H33 listed by Blockeel & Long (1998: 69).
H(34) listed by Lett (1915: 97) without details.
†H34 listed by Blockeel & Long (1998: 69).
H(35) listed by Lett (1915: 97) without details.
†H35 listed by Blockeel & Long (1998: 69).
H(36) listed by Lett (1915: 97) without details.
†H36 listed by Blockeel & Long (1998: 69).
H(37) listed by Lett (1915: 97) without details.
†H37 listed by Blockeel & Long (1998: 69).
H(38) listed by Lett (1915: 97).
†H38 listed by Blockeel & Long (1998: 69).
H(39) listed by Lett (1915: 97).
†H39 listed by Blockeel & Long (1998: 69).
H(40) listed by Lett (1915: 97) without locality.
†H40 listed by Blockeel & Long (1998: 69).

3/3 ***Pogonatum urnigerum*** (Hedw.) P. Beauv.
(syn. *Polytrichum urnigerum* Hedw.)

H(1) listed by Lett (1915: 97) without details.
†H1 listed by Blockeel & Long (1998: 69).
H(2) listed by Lett (1915: 97) without details.
†H2 listed by Blockeel & Long (1998: 69).
H(3) listed by Lett (1915: 97) without details.
†H3 listed by Blockeel & Long (1998: 69).
H(4) listed by Lett (1915: 97) without details.
†H4 listed by Blockeel & Long (1998: 69).
H(5) listed by Lett (1915: 97) without details.
†H5 listed by Blockeel & Long (1998: 69).
H6 1966: on ground, *ca* 1200 ft [alt.], Sgilloge Loughs, Comeragh Mts, RD Fitzgerald (BBS exc.) (Crundwell 1968: 630).
H(7) listed by Lett (1915: 97) without details.
†H7 listed by Blockeel & Long (1998: 69).
H(8) 1945: below Corrig-na-binna, AW Stelfox, per JS Thomson (anon. 1946c: 279).
†H8 listed by Blockeel & Long (1998: 69).
H9 1979: slate quarry, N side of Knocksise Hill, 2½ km W of Broadford, DM Synnott (Hill 1981: 22).
H(10) listed by Lett (1915: 97) without details.
†H10 listed by Blockeel & Long (1998: 69).
H(12) listed by Lett (1915: 97) without details.
†H12 listed by Blockeel & Long (1998: 69).
H(13) 1867: old quarry, Browne's Hill, Carlow, RC Browne (DBN) (Crundwell 1968: 630).
†H13 listed by Blockeel & Long (1998: 69).
H(14) listed by Lett (1915: 97) without details.
†H14 listed by Blockeel & Long (1998: 69).
H(15) listed by Lett (1915: 97) without details.
†H15 listed by Blockeel & Long (1998: 69).
H(16) listed by Lett (1915: 97) without details.
†H16 listed by Blockeel & Long (1998: 69).
H17 1980: path to raised bog, Ballinamore, JD Sleath (Hill 1981: 22).
[H(18) listed by Lett (1915: 97) without details. H18 deleted because no valid record or voucher specimen traced (Blockeel 1999: 3)].
H(20) listed by Lett (1915: 97) without details.
†H20 listed by Blockeel & Long (1998: 69).
H(21) listed by Lett (1915: 97) without details.
†H21 listed by Blockeel & Long (1998: 69).
H22 1978: quarry, Teevurcher, N of Moynalty, DM Synnott (Hill 1979: 26).
H(25) listed by Lett (1915: 97) without details.
†H25 listed by Blockeel & Long (1998: 69).
[H(26) listed by Lett (1915: 97) without details. H26 deleted because no valid record or voucher specimen traced (Blockeel 1999: 3)].
†H27 listed by Blockeel & Long (1998: 69).

H(28) listed by Lett (1915: 97) without details.
†H28 listed by Blockeel & Long (1998: 69).
H(29) listed by Lett (1915: 97) without details.
†H29 listed by Blockeel & Long (1998: 69).
H(30) listed by Lett (1915: 97) without details.
†H30 listed by Blockeel & Long (1998: 69).
[H(31) listed by Lett (1915: 97) without details. H31 deleted because no valid record or voucher specimen traced (Blockeel 1999: 3)].
H(32) listed by Lett (1915: 97) without details.
†H32 listed by Blockeel & Long (1998: 69).
H(33) listed by Lett (1915: 97) without details.
†H33 listed by Blockeel & Long (1998: 69).
H(34) listed by Lett (1915: 97) without details.
†H34 listed by Blockeel & Long (1998: 69).
H(35) listed by Lett (1915: 97) without details.
†H35 listed by Blockeel & Long (1998: 69).
H(36) listed by Lett (1915: 97) without details.
†H36 listed by Blockeel & Long (1998: 69).
[H(37) listed by Lett (1915: 97) without details. H37 deleted because no valid record or voucher specimen traced (Blockeel 1999: 3)].
H(38) listed by Lett (1915: 97) without details. H(38) listed by Blockeel & Long (1998: 69).
H38 1999: on rocky bank of stream, 50 m alt., Tollymore Forest park, 4 km W of Newcastle, J33, TL Blockeel 28/350 (Rothero 2000: 47).
H(39) listed by Lett (1915: 97) without details.
†H39 listed by Blockeel & Long (1998: 69).
H(40) listed by Lett (1915: 97) without details.
†H40 listed by Blockeel & Long (1998: 69).

4/1 ***Polytrichum alpinum*** Hedw.
(syn. *Polytrichum alpinum* var. *septentrionale* (Sw.) Lindb.)

H(1) listed by Lett (1915: 97).
†H1 listed by Blockeel & Long (1998: 69).
H(2) listed by Lett (1915: 97).
†H2 listed by Blockeel & Long (1998: 69).
H3 2002: on turfy ledge on crag, 310 m alt., Gougane Barra at head of valley, W06, TL Blockeel 31/338 (Rothero 2003: 47).
H6 1966: among rocks above L. Coumshingaun, Comeragh Mts, EM Lobley (BBS exc.) (Perry 1967: 407).
H(7) listed by Lett (1915: 97).
†H7 listed by Blockeel & Long (1998: 69).
H(8) 1944: Corrig-na-binnia, AW Stelfox (per JS Thomson) (anon. 1947: 28). H(8) listed by Blockeel & Long (1998: 69).
H12 1978: summit moorland, 770 m alt., Mt Leinster, MRD Seaward (Hill 1983: 50).
H(13) listed by Lett (1915: 97). H(13) listed by Blockeel & Long (1998: 69).
H(16) listed by Lett (1915: 97).
†H16 listed by Blockeel & Long (1998: 69).
H(20) listed by Lett (1915: 97).
†H20 listed by Blockeel & Long (1998: 69).
H(21) listed by Lett (1915: 97). H(21) listed by Blockeel & Long (1998: 69).
[H(23) listed by Lett (1915: 97) as 1909: Mullingar, HW Lett. H23 discounted because based on dubious literature record (Hill 1981: 22)].
[H(26) listed by Lett (1915: 97) for var. *septentrionale*, without locality].
H(27) listed by Lett (1915: 97).
†H27 listed by Blockeel & Long (1998: 69).
H(28) listed by Lett (1915: 97) without details.
†H28 listed by Blockeel & Long (1998: 69).
H(29) listed by Lett (1915: 97). H(29) listed by Blockeel & Long (1998: 69).
H(30) listed by Lett (1915: 97).
†H30 listed by Blockeel & Long (1998: 69).
[H(31) record of var. *septentrionale* (1890: Slieve League, HN Dixon, anon. 1932: 332) deleted because the locality is in H35 (Crundwell 1968: 630)].
[H(31) listed by Lett (1915: 97) without locality. H31 deleted because no valid record or voucher specimen traced (Blockeel 1999: 3)].
H33 1957: NE side of Tiltinbane, AC Crundwell (Warburg 1958b: 473).
H(34) listed by Lett (1915: 97).
†H34 listed by Blockeel & Long (1998: 69).
H(35 listed by Lett (1915: 97).
†H35 listed by Blockeel & Long (1998: 69).
H(36) listed by Lett (1915: 97).
†H36 listed by Blockeel & Long (1998: 69).
H37 1950: among cairn boulders, Slieve Gullion, J Taylor (Warburg 1954: 478).
H(38) listed by Lett (1915: 97). H(38) listed by Blockeel & Long (1998: 69).
H38 2002: on thin gritty soil over granite on N-facing slope, 485 m alt., E of Slievenaglogh, J32, DT Holyoak 02-1024 (Rothero 2003: 47).
H(39) listed by Lett (1915: 97).
†H39 listed by Blockeel & Long (1998: 69).
H(40) listed by Lett (1915: 97).
†H40 listed by Blockeel & Long (1998: 69).

4/2 ***Polytrichum longisetum*** Sw. ex Brid. (syn. *Polytrichum aurantiacum* Hoppe ex Brid., *P. gracile* Dicks.)

H(1) listed by Lett (1915: 98). H(1) listed by Blockeel & Long (1998: 69).
H(2) listed by Lett (1915: 98). H(2) listed by Blockeel & Long (1998: 69).
H(3) listed by Lett (1915: 98).
†H3 listed by Blockeel & Long (1998: 69).
H(7) listed by Lett (1915: 98). H(7) listed by Blockeel & Long (1998: 69).
H(8) listed by Lett (1915: 98). H(8) listed by Blockeel & Long (1998: 69).
[H(11) listed by Lett (1915: 98). H11 deleted because the locality on which the record is based (1911: nr Bagnalstown, leg. WN Tetley, in Lett 1915: 98) is in H13, *teste* ALK King (Warburg 1955: 583)].
H(12) listed by Lett (1915: 98). H(12) listed by Blockeel & Long (1998: 69).
H(13) listed by Lett (1915: 98). H(13) listed by Blockeel & Long (1998: 69).
H(14) listed by Lett (1915: 98).
†H14 listed by Blockeel & Long (1998: 69).
H15 1957: peaty ground, Chevy Chase Woods, Owendalulleegh, EM Lobley (BBS exc.) (Warburg 1958b: 473).
H16 1994: peat in cleared conifer plantation, 40 m alt., Derryclare Wood, L85, DG Long 25600 (Blockeel 1995c: 40).
H(17) listed by Lett (1915: 98).
†H17 listed by Blockeel & Long (1998: 69).
H(18) listed by Lett (1915: 98).
†H18 listed by Blockeel & Long (1998: 69).
H(19) 1949: Ballymount Bog, nr Calverstown, JS Thomson (Warburg 1950: 382). H (19) listed by Blockeel & Long (1998: 69).
H(20) listed by Lett (1915: 98). H(20) listed by Blockeel & Long (1998: 69).
[H(21) listed by Lett (1915: 98) without locality. H21 deleted because no valid record or voucher specimen traced (Blockeel 1999: 3)].
H(22) 1937: bog nr Navan, MJ Gorman, comm. JS Thomson (Warburg 1957: 328).
H22 1956: Rossal Bog, nr Kinnegad, ALK King (Warburg 1957: 328).
H23 1952: Derries Bog, Athlone, JP Brunker & ALK King (Warburg 1953: 306).
H24 1957: damp ground by beech plantation at edge of bog, Newtownforbes [*sic* = Newtown Forbes], ALK King (Warburg 1958b: 473).
H(25) listed by Lett (1915: 98).
†H25 listed by Blockeel & Long (1998: 69).
H(26) listed by Lett (1915: 98).
†H26 listed by Blockeel & Long (1998: 69).
H27 1965: shelter belt in Peatland Experimental Station, Glenamoy, DM Synnott (Warburg 1966: 190).
H28 1970: c.fr. on the boggy moorland leading to the corrie to the NE of Benbulbin [*sic* = Ben Bulben], collector not recorded (seen by most members of BBS exc.) (Crundwell 1971b: 374, Appleyard 1971: 389).
H(29) listed by Lett (1915: 98). H(29) listed by Blockeel & Long (1998: 69).
H(30) listed by Lett (1915: 98). H(30) listed by Blockeel & Long (1998: 69).
H(32) 1947: boggy ground, Black I., Lough Muckno, Hope Castle demesne, Castleblaney, JS Thomson (anon. 1948b: 118). H(32) listed by Blockeel & Long (1998: 69).
H(33) listed by Lett (1915: 98).
†H33 listed by Blockeel & Long (1998: 69).
H(36) listed by Lett (1915: 98).
†H36 listed by Blockeel & Long (1998: 69).
H(37) listed by Lett (1915: 98).
†H37 listed by Blockeel & Long (1998: 69).
H(38) listed by Lett (1915: 98). H(38) listed by Blockeel & Long (1998: 69).
H(39) listed by Lett (1915: 98). H(39) listed by Blockeel & Long (1998: 69).
H(40) listed by Lett (1915: 98). H(40) listed by Blockeel & Long (1998: 69).

4/3 ***Polytrichum formosum*** Hedw. (syn. *Polytrichum attenuatum* Menzies ex Brid.)

H(1) listed by Lett (1915: 98) without details.
†H1 listed by Blockeel & Long (1998: 69).
H(2) listed by Lett (1915: 98) without details.
†H2 listed by Blockeel & Long (1998: 69).
†H3 listed by Blockeel & Long (1998: 69).
H4 1967: bank of boulders, *ca* 1300 ft [alt.], Musherabeg, Bogeragh Mts, RD Fitzgerald (Crundwell 1968: 631).
H5 1951: hedge-bank, Mallow, EC Wallace & EF Warburg (Warburg 1952: 98).
†H6 listed by Blockeel & Long (1998: 69).
H(7) listed by Lett (1915: 98) without details.
†H7 listed by Blockeel & Long (1998: 69).
H8 1959: bog ½ mile E of Castleconnell, ALK King (Warburg 1960: 771).

H(9) listed by Lett (1915: 98) without details.
†H9 listed by Blockeel & Long (1998: 69).
H(10) listed by Lett (1915: 98) without details.
†H10 listed by Blockeel & Long (1998: 69).
H(11) listed by Lett (1915: 98) without details.
†H11 listed by Blockeel & Long (1998: 69).
H(12) listed by Lett (1915: 98) without details.
†H12 listed by Blockeel & Long (1998: 69).
H(13) listed by Lett (1915: 98) without details.
†H13 listed by Blockeel & Long (1998: 69).
H(14) listed by Lett (1915: 98) without details.
†H14 listed by Blockeel & Long (1998: 69).
H15 1994: on leached soil on hummock in grassland over limestone, 25 m alt., near L. Briskeen, *ca* 5 km W of Gort, M40, TL Blockeel 23/157 (Blockeel 1995c: 40).
H(16) listed by Lett (1915: 98) without details.
†H16 listed by Blockeel & Long (1998: 69).
H(17) listed by Lett (1915: 98) without details.
†H17 listed by Blockeel & Long (1998: 69).
H(18) listed by Lett (1915: 98) without details.
†H18 listed by Blockeel & Long (1998: 69).
H19 1958: shaded bank under beeches, Elverstone, ALK King (Warburg 1959: 631).
H(20) listed by Lett (1915: 98) without details.
†H20 listed by Blockeel & Long (1998: 69).
H(21) 1948: entrance to The Pine Forest, AEA Dunston (anon. 1949c: 216).
[†H21 listed by Blockeel & Long (1998: 69). H21 deleted because no valid record or voucher specimen traced (Blockeel 1999: 3), but apparently deleted in error in view of preceding record].
H22 1950: under trees, Slane, JS Thomson (Warburg 1952: 98).
H(23) listed by Lett (1915: 98) without details.
†H23 listed by Blockeel & Long (1998: 69).
H(24) listed by Lett (1915: 98) without details.
†H24 listed by Blockeel & Long (1998: 69).
H(25) listed by Lett (1915: 98) without details.
†H25 listed by Blockeel & Long (1998: 69).
H(26) listed by Lett (1915: 98) without details.
†H26 listed by Blockeel & Long (1998: 69).
H(27) listed by Lett (1915: 98) without details.
†H27 listed by Blockeel & Long (1998: 69).
H(28) listed by Lett (1915: 98) without details.
†H28 listed by Blockeel & Long (1998: 69).
H(29) listed by Lett (1915: 98) without details.
†H29 listed by Blockeel & Long (1998: 69).
H(30) listed by Lett (1915: 98) without details.
†H30 listed by Blockeel & Long (1998: 69).
H(31) listed by Lett (1915: 98) without details.
†H31 listed by Blockeel & Long (1998: 69).
[H(32) listed by Lett (1915: 98) without details].
H(33) listed by Lett (1915: 98) without details.
†H33 listed by Blockeel & Long (1998: 69).
H34 1967: on bank in wood, Illies, Inishowen, RD Fitzgerald (Crundwell 1968: 631).
H(35) listed by Lett (1915: 98) without details.
†H35 listed by Blockeel & Long (1998: 69).
H(36) listed by Lett (1915: 98) without details.
†H36 listed by Blockeel & Long (1998: 69).
H37 1950: bank, Edenappa, JS Thomson (Warburg 1952: 98).
H(38) listed by Lett (1915: 98) without details.
†H38 listed by Blockeel & Long (1998: 69).
H(39) listed by Lett (1915: 98) without details.
†H39 listed by Blockeel & Long (1998: 69).
H(40) listed by Lett (1915: 98) without details.
†H40 listed by Blockeel & Long (1998: 69).

4/5a *Polytrichum commune* Hedw. **var. *commune***

H(1) listed by Lett (1915: 98) without details.
†H1 listed by Blockeel & Long (1998: 69).
†H2 listed by Blockeel & Long (1998: 69).
H(3) listed by Lett (1915: 98) without details.
†H3 listed by Blockeel & Long (1998: 69).
H4 1966: boggy ground at 1100 ft alt., Seefin, Boggeragh Mts, MFV Corley & JS Parker (Perry 1967: 407).
H(5) listed by Lett (1915: 98) without details.
†H5 listed by Blockeel & Long (1998: 69).
H(6) listed by Lett (1915: 98) without details.
†H6 listed by Blockeel & Long (1998: 69).
H(7) listed by Lett (1915: 98) without details.
†H7 listed by Blockeel & Long (1998: 69).
H(8) listed by Lett (1915: 98) without details.
†H8 listed by Blockeel & Long (1998: 69).
H(9) listed by Lett (1915: 98) without details.
†H9 listed by Blockeel & Long (1998: 69).
H10 1951: moorland above 1000 ft [alt.], Silvermines Mts, AD Banwell, PJ Wanstall & EV Watson (Warburg 1953: 306).
H(11) listed by Lett (1915: 98) without details.
†H11 listed by Blockeel & Long (1998: 69).
H(12) listed by Lett (1915: 98) without details.
†H12 listed by Blockeel & Long (1998: 69).
H(13) listed by Lett (1915: 98) without details.
†H13 listed by Blockeel & Long (1998: 69).
H(14) listed by Lett (1915: 98) without details.
†H14 listed by Blockeel & Long (1998: 69).
H15 1957: moorland flush, nr Owendalulleegh, RE Parker (Warburg 1958b: 473).

H(16) listed by Lett (1915: 98) without details.
†H16 listed by Blockeel & Long (1998: 69).
[H(17) listed by Lett (1915: 98) without details. H17 deleted because no valid record or voucher specimen traced (Blockeel 1999: 3)].
H(18) listed by Lett (1915: 98) without details. H(18) listed by Blockeel & Long (1998: 69).
H(19) 1949: Ballymount Bog, nr Calverstown, JS Thomson (Warburg 1950: 382).
†H19 listed by Blockeel & Long (1998: 69).
H(20) listed by Lett (1915: 98) without details.
†H20 listed by Blockeel & Long (1998: 69).
[H(21) listed by Lett (1915: 98) without details. H21 deleted because no valid record or voucher specimen traced (Blockeel 1999: 3)].
H22 1956: Rossan Bog, nr Kinnegad, ALK King (Warburg 1957: 328).
H23 1952: Derries Bog, Athlone, JP Brunker & ALK King (Warburg 1953: 306).
H(24) 1941: Lough Leeben, JG Finlay (Duncan 1944: 208).
†H24 listed by Blockeel & Long (1998: 69).
H(25) 1948: roadside on right bank of River Shannon, nr Carrick-on-Shannon, ALK King (Warburg 1950: 382).
†H25 listed by Blockeel & Long (1998: 69).
H(26) listed by Lett (1915: 98) without details.
†H26 listed by Blockeel & Long (1998: 69).
H(27) listed by Lett (1915: 98) without details.
†H27 listed by Blockeel & Long (1998: 69).
H(28) listed by Lett (1915: 98) without details.
†H28 listed by Blockeel & Long (1998: 69).
H(29) listed by Lett (1915: 98) without details.
†H29 listed by Blockeel & Long (1998: 69).
H(30) listed by Lett (1915: 98) without details.
†H30 listed by Blockeel & Long (1998: 69).
H(31) listed by Lett (1915: 98) without details.
†H31 listed by Blockeel & Long (1998: 69).
H(32) listed by Lett (1915: 98) without details.
†H32 listed by Blockeel & Long (1998: 69).
H(33) listed by Lett (1915: 98) without details.
†H33 listed by Blockeel & Long (1998: 69).
H(34) listed by Lett (1915: 98) without details.
†H34 listed by Blockeel & Long (1998: 69).
H(35) listed by Lett (1915: 98) without details.
†H35 listed by Blockeel & Long (1998: 69).
H(36) listed by Lett (1915: 98) without details.
†H36 listed by Blockeel & Long (1998: 69).
H(37) listed by Lett (1915: 98) without details.
†H37 listed by Blockeel & Long (1998: 69).
H(38) listed by Lett (1915: 98) without details.
†H38 listed by Blockeel & Long (1998: 69).
H(39) listed by Lett (1915: 98) without details.
†H39 listed by Blockeel & Long (1998: 69).
H(40) listed by Lett (1915: 98) without details.
†H40 listed by Blockeel & Long (1998: 69).

4/5c ***Polytrichum commune* var. *humile*** Sw. (syn. *Polytrichum commune* var. *minus* Weis ex De Not. hom. illeg.)

H(38) 1804: nr Gilford, Davies (Lett 1915: 98). H(38) listed by Blockeel & Long (1998: 69).

Derda & Wyatt (1990) and Wyatt & Derda (1997: 288) found that two of the dwarf varieties of *P. commune* appear to be indistinguishable genetically from var. *commune*. It therefore seems unlikely that var. *humile* is worthy of taxonomic recognition.

4/6 ***Polytrichum piliferum*** Hedw.

H(1) listed by Lett (1915: 98) without details.
†H1 listed by Blockeel & Long (1998: 70).
H(2) listed by Lett (1915: 98) without details.
†H2 listed by Blockeel & Long (1998: 70).
H(3) listed by Lett (1915: 98) without details.
†H3 listed by Blockeel & Long (1998: 70).
H(4) listed by Lett (1915: 98) without details.
†H4 listed by Blockeel & Long (1998: 70).
H5 1967: on rocks, Coolgreen Glen, SW of Watergrasshill, RD Fitzgerald (Crundwell 1968: 630).
H(6) listed by Lett (1915: 98) without details.
†H6 listed by Blockeel & Long (1998: 70).
H(7) listed by Lett (1915: 98) without details.
†H7 listed by Blockeel & Long (1998: 70).
H8 1966: rocks on moor, Slievereagh, nr Ballylanders, MFV Corley & JS Parker (Perry 1967: 407).
H(9) listed by Lett (1915: 98) without details.
†H9 listed by Blockeel & Long (1998: 70).
H(10) listed by Lett (1915: 98) without details.
†H10 listed by Blockeel & Long (1998: 70).
[H(11) listed by Lett (1915: 98) without details. H11 deleted because no valid record or voucher specimen traced (Blockeel 1999: 3)].
H(12) listed by Lett (1915: 98) without details.
†H12 listed by Blockeel & Long (1998: 70).
H(13) listed by Lett (1915: 98) without details.
†H13 listed by Blockeel & Long (1998: 70).
H(14) listed by Lett (1915: 98) without details.
†H14 listed by Blockeel & Long (1998: 70).

[H(15) listed by Lett (1915: 98) without details. H15 deleted because no valid record or voucher specimen traced (Blockeel 1999: 3)].
H(16) listed by Lett (1915: 98) without details.
†H16 listed by Blockeel & Long (1998: 70).
H17 1968: on bare peat at edge of raised bog at Addergoule N[orth], R. Suck, nr Ballinasloe, HJB Birks (Crundwell 1969: 877).
[H(18) listed by Lett (1915: 98) without details. H18 deleted because no valid record or voucher specimen traced (Blockeel 1999: 3)].
H19 1953: Cupidstown Hill, AW Stelfox, comm. JS Thomson (Warburg 1954: 478).
H(20) listed by Lett (1915: 98) without details.
†H20 listed by Blockeel & Long (1998: 70).
[H(21) listed by Lett (1915: 98) without details. H21 deleted because no valid record or voucher specimen traced (Blockeel 1999: 3)].
H22 1978: Lower Palaeozoic rocks, N side of Bellewstown, DM Synnott (Corley 1979: 26).
H24 1965: bank *ca* 900 ft alt., Corn Hill, nr Drumlish, RD Fitzgerald & EM Lobley (Warburg 1966: 190).
H(25) listed by Lett (1915: 98) without details.
†H25 listed by Blockeel & Long (1998: 70).
H(26) listed by Lett (1915: 98) without details.
†H26 listed by Blockeel & Long (1998: 70).
H(27) listed by Lett (1915: 98) without details.
†H27 listed by Blockeel & Long (1998: 70).
H28 1963: dry rocks by roadside, Castleore, Slish Mt., AR Perry & RD Fitzgerald (Warburg 1964: 722).
H29 1963: bog E of Sriff Cottage, nr Dromahair, RD Fitzgerald & AR Perry (Warburg 1964: 722).
H(30) listed by Lett (1915: 98) without details.
†H30 listed by Blockeel & Long (1998: 70).
H(31) listed by Lett (1915: 98) without details.
†H31 listed by Blockeel & Long (1998: 70).
[H(32) listed by Lett (1915: 98) without details. H32 deleted because no valid record or voucher specimen traced (Blockeel 1999: 3)].
H(33) listed by Lett (1915: 98) without details.
†H33 listed by Blockeel & Long (1998: 70).
H(34) listed by Lett (1915: 98) without details.
†H34 listed by Blockeel & Long (1998: 70).
H(35) listed by Lett (1915: 98) without details.
†H35 listed by Blockeel & Long (1998: 70).
H(36) listed by Lett (1915: 98) without details.
†H36 listed by Blockeel & Long (1998: 70).
H(37) listed by Lett (1915: 98) without details.
†H37 listed by Blockeel & Long (1998: 70).
H(38) listed by Lett (1915: 98) without details.
†H38 listed by Blockeel & Long (1998: 70).
H(39) listed by Lett (1915: 98) without details.
†H39 listed by Blockeel & Long (1998: 70).
H(40) listed by Lett (1915: 98) without details.
†H40 listed by Blockeel & Long (1998: 70).

4/7 ***Polytrichum juniperinum*** Hedw.

H(1) listed by Lett (1915: 98) without details.
†H1 listed by Blockeel & Long (1998: 70).
H(2) listed by Lett (1915: 98) without details.
†H2 listed by Blockeel & Long (1998: 70).
H(3) listed by Lett (1915: 98) without details.
†H3 listed by Blockeel & Long (1998: 70).
H(4) listed by Lett (1915: 98) without details.
†H4 listed by Blockeel & Long (1998: 70).
H(5) listed by Lett (1915: 98) without details.
†H5 listed by Blockeel & Long (1998: 70).
H(6) listed by Lett (1915: 98) without details.
†H6 listed by Blockeel & Long (1998: 70).
H(8) 1945: Galtees at 2500 ft [alt.], RD Meikle (anon. 1947: 28).
†H8 listed by Blockeel & Long (1998: 70).
H(9) listed by Lett (1915: 98) without details.
†H9 listed by Blockeel & Long (1998: 70).
H10 1979: bank in wood, N side of Clare Glens, nr Newport, AC Crundwell (Hill 1980b: 33).
H(11) listed by Lett (1915: 98) without details.
†H11 listed by Blockeel & Long (1998: 70).
H(12) listed by Lett (1915: 98) without details.
†H12 listed by Blockeel & Long (1998: 70).
H(13) listed by Lett (1915: 98) without details.
†H13 listed by Blockeel & Long (1998: 70).
H(14) listed by Lett (1915: 98) without details.
†H14 listed by Blockeel & Long (1998: 70).
H15 1957: moorland on hills, E of Gort, RE Parker (Warburg 1958b: 473).
H(16) 1911: Arrishay, CA Cheetham (anon. 1915a: 124).
H(16) listed by Lett (1915: 98) without details.
†H16 listed by Blockeel & Long (1998: 70).
[H(17) listed by Lett (1915: 98) without details. H17 deleted because no valid record or voucher specimen traced (Blockeel 1999: 3)].
H(18) listed by Lett (1915: 98) without details.
†H18 listed by Blockeel & Long (1998: 70).
H(19) listed by Lett (1915: 98) without details.
†H19 listed by Blockeel & Long (1998: 70).

H(20) listed by Lett (1915: 98) without details.
†H20 listed by Blockeel & Long (1998: 70).
H(21) listed by Lett (1915: 98) without details.
†H21 listed by Blockeel & Long (1998: 70).
H22 1950: Slane, JS Thomson (Warburg 1952: 98).
H23 1960: cut-away bog at Lisclogher, ALK King (Warburg 1961: 159).
H(24) listed by Lett (1915: 98) without details.
†H24 listed by Blockeel & Long (1998: 70).
H(25) listed by Lett (1915: 98) without details.
†H25 listed by Blockeel & Long (1998: 70).
H(26) listed by Lett (1915: 98) without details.
†H26 listed by Blockeel & Long (1998: 70).
H(27) listed by Lett (1915: 98) without details.
†H27 listed by Blockeel & Long (1998: 70).
H(28) listed by Lett (1915: 98) without details.
†H28 listed by Blockeel & Long (1998: 70).
H(29) listed by Lett (1915: 98) without details.
†H29 listed by Blockeel & Long (1998: 70).
H(30) listed by Lett (1915: 98) without details.
†H30 listed by Blockeel & Long (1998: 70).
H(31) listed by Lett (1915: 98) without details.
†H31 listed by Blockeel & Long (1998: 70).
H(32) listed by Lett (1915: 98) without details.
†H32 listed by Blockeel & Long (1998: 70).
H(33) listed by Lett (1915: 98) without details.
†H33 listed by Blockeel & Long (1998: 70).
H(34) listed by Lett (1915: 98) without details.
†H34 listed by Blockeel & Long (1998: 70).
H(35) listed by Lett (1915: 98) without details.
†H35 listed by Blockeel & Long (1998: 70).
H(36) listed by Lett (1915: 98) without details.
†H36 listed by Blockeel & Long (1998: 70).
H(37) listed by Lett (1915: 98) without details.
†H37 listed by Blockeel & Long (1998: 70).
H(38) listed by Lett (1915: 98) without details.
†H38 listed by Blockeel & Long (1998: 70).
H(39) listed by Lett (1915: 98) without details.
†H39 listed by Blockeel & Long (1998: 70).
H(40) listed by Lett (1915: 98) without details.
†H40 listed by Blockeel & Long (1998: 70).

4/8 ***Polytrichum strictum*** Brid.
(syn. *Polytrichum alpestre* Hoppe)

H(1) listed by Lett (1915: 98). H(1) listed by Blockeel & Long (1998: 70).
[H(3) listed by Lett (1915: 98) without details. H3 deleted because no valid record or voucher specimen traced (Blockeel 1999: 3)].
H6 1966: in *Sphagnum* by stream below Coumshingaun, Comeragh Mts, ERB Little & JA Paton (BBS exc.) (Perry 1967: 407).
H7 1966: cut-away bog, Longfordpass South, nr Orlingford (*sic* = Urlingford), RD Fitzgerald (Crundwell 1968: 630).
H8 1966: boggy ground on summit ridge at 2500 ft alt., Temple Hill, Galtee Mts, MFV Corley & JS Parker (Perry 1967: 407).
H10 1979: peaty heath, W slope of Keeper Hill, S of Silvermine Mts, HMH van Melick (Hill 1981: 22).
H14 1955: turf bog, Abbyleix, JS Thomson (Warburg 1956: 151).
H16 1966: moorland at head of L. Nadirkmore, Maumtrasma Mts, G Halliday (Perry 1967: 407).
H17 1968: on bare peat in raised bog at Addergoule N[orth], R. Suck, nr Ballinasloe, HJB Birks (Crundwell 1969: 877).
H18 1957: Annagharvey Bog, nr Tullamore, JS Thomson (Warburg 1958b: 473).
H(20) listed by Lett (1915: 98) without locality.
†H20 listed by Blockeel & Long (1998: 70).
H(21) listed by Lett (1915: 98). H(21) listed by Blockeel & Long (1998: 70).
H22 1971: raised bog, Thomastown Bog, Duleek, DM Synnott (Crundwell 1974: 166).
H23 1952: bog nr NE end of L. Owel, JS Thomson (Warburg 1954: 478).
H24 1965: among *Calluna* in wood, Cloonart Bridge, RD Fitzgerald & EM Lobley (Warburg 1966: 190).
H25 1981: raised bog, N of Frenchpark, DM Synnott (Hill 1982: 24).
[H27 1957: blanket bog, nr summit of Maumtrasna, RE Parker (BBS exc.) (Warburg 1958b: 473). H27 deleted because record (from Maumtrasna) is from locality in H16 (Crundwell 1970: 196)].
H27 1962: Central Achill, EF Warburg (Warburg 1963c: 142, Crundwell 1970: 196).
H(28) 1910: Trushmore [*sic* = Truskmore], WN Tetley (anon. 1911c: 7).
H(28) listed by Lett (1915: 98).
†H28 listed by Blockeel & Long (1998: 70).
H(29) listed by Lett (1915: 98).
†H29 listed by Blockeel & Long (1998: 70).
H30 1965: bog *ca* 1500 ft alt., S side of Cuilcagh, RD Fitzgerald & EM Lobley (Warburg 1966: 190).

H32 1980: large tussocks in small acidic marsh, Tld [= Townland] Lisarrilly, N Lockhart (Hill 1983: 50).
H33 1950: open fen-carr nr Colebrooke, J Taylor (Warburg 1951: 498).
H34 1962: boggy ground below E side of Bulbin [Mt.], EF Warburg *et al.* (BBS exc.) (Warburg 1963b: 493).
H35 1962: at 1850 ft [alt.] in gully on N side of Muckish Mt., AC Crundwell (BBS exc.) (Warburg 1963b: 493).
H36 1950: waterlogged peat *ca* 2000 ft [alt.], Dart Mt., J Taylor (Warburg 1951: 498).
H37 1964: moorland, *ca* 1100 ft [alt.], Slieve Gullion, RD Fitzgerald (Warburg 1965: 860).
H(38) listed by Lett (1915: 98).
†H38 listed by Blockeel & Long (1998: 70).
H(39) listed by Lett (1915: 98).
†H39 listed by Blockeel & Long (1998: 70).
H(40) 1936: Kilrea, WR Megaw (anon. 1937a: 366).
†H40 listed by Blockeel & Long (1998: 70).

5/1 ***Oligotrichum hercynicum*** (Hedw.) Lam. & DC.
(syn. *Oligotrichum hercynicum* var. *laxum* (Braithw.) Roth, *O. incurvum* (Brid.) Lindb.)

[H(1) listed by Lett (1915: 97) without details. H1 deleted because no valid record or voucher specimen traced (Blockeel 1999: 3)].
H(2) listed by Lett (1915: 97).
†H2 listed by Blockeel & Long (1998: 70).
H(4) listed by Lett (1915: 97).
†H4 listed by Blockeel & Long (1998: 70).
H(5) listed by Lett (1915: 97). H(5) listed by Blockeel & Long (1998: 70).
H6 1966: roadside bank, pass E of the Punchbowl, Comeragh Mts, ERB Little & JA Paton (BBS exc.) (Perry 1967: 407).
H7 1966: on track, *ca* 1000 ft [alt.], Seefin, Galtee Mts, RD Fitzgerald (BBS exc.) (Crundwell 1968: 630).
H(13) listed by Lett (1915: 97).
†H13 listed by Blockeel & Long (1998: 70).
H(16) 1933: Muckanaght, Twelve Bens, PWM Richards (anon. 1938d: 38).
†H16 listed by Blockeel & Long (1998: 70).
H(20) listed by Lett (1915: 97).
†H20 listed by Blockeel & Long (1998: 70).
H(27) listed by Lett (1915: 97) without locality.
H27 1957: under boulder, Maumtrasna, J Appleyard (BBS exc.) (Warburg 1958b: 473), as var. *laxum.*
H(29) listed by Lett (1915: 97). H(29) listed by Blockeel & Long (1998: 70).
H(31) listed by Lett (1915: 97). H(31) listed by Blockeel & Long (1998: 70).
H33 1957: NE side of Tiltinblane [*sic* = Tiltinbane], AC Crundwell (Warburg 1958b: 473).
H(34) listed by Lett (1915: 97).
†H34 listed by Blockeel & Long (1998: 70).
†H35 listed by Blockeel & Long (1998: 70).
H36 1956: Glen Curry Bridge, nr Omagh, RD Fitzgerald & MPH Kertland (Warburg 1957: 328).
H(38) listed by Lett (1915: 97).
†H38 listed by Blockeel & Long (1998: 70).
H(39) listed by Lett (1915: 97).
†H39 listed by Blockeel & Long (1998: 70).
†H40 listed by Blockeel & Long (1998: 70).

6/1 ***Atrichum crispum*** (James) Sull. & Lesq.

H20 1957: coarse gravel at margin of fast-flowing stream, waterfall on Gleninacnass R., 4 miles N of Laragh, 1200 ft [alt.], RE Parker (Warburg 1958b: 473).
H25 2002: by stream and waterfall on crags, 150 m alt., Kilronan Mt., Arigna, G91, NG Hodgetts 4152 (Rothero 2003: 48).
H29 1970: by stream, N-facing cliffs or hillslopes of Glenfarne, nr Belcoo, JA Paton (BBS exc.) (Crundwell 1971b: 374, Appleyard 1971: 389-390).

6/2 ***Atrichum tenellum*** (Röhl.) Bruch & Schimp.

H1 1983: marshy track, W side of Blackwater River above bridge, W of Kenmare, V76, JA Paton 2536 (Blockeel 1995c: 41).
H3 1979: marshy soil beside track, NE end of Glen Lough, Adrigole, JA Paton (Hill 1980b: 33).
H16 1994: wet gravelly bank, N of Kylemore River, Twelve Bens, L75, JA Paton 2697 (Blockeel 1995c: 41).
H35 1991: on low vertical muddy bank by lake, 60 m alt., E end of Dunlewy Lough, B91, DG Long 20239 (Blockeel 1992: 26).

H38 2002: on open gravelly sediment in inundation zone of reservoir, 125 m alt., NW end of Lough Island Reavy Reservoir, J23, DT Holyoak 02-960 (Rothero 2003: 48).

6/3a ***Atrichum undulatum*** (Hedw.) P.Beauv. **var.** ***undulatum***
(syn. *Catharinea undulata* (Hedw.) F. Weber & D.Mohr)

H(1) listed by Lett (1915: 96) without details.
†H1 listed by Blockeel & Long (1998: 70).
H(2) listed by Lett (1915: 96) without details.
†H2 listed by Blockeel & Long (1998: 70).
H(3) listed by Lett (1915: 96) without details.
†H3 listed by Blockeel & Long (1998: 70).
H(4) listed by Lett (1915: 96) without details.
†H4 listed by Blockeel & Long (1998: 70).
†H5 listed by Blockeel & Long (1998: 70).
H(6) listed by Lett (1915: 96) without details.
†H6 listed by Blockeel & Long (1998: 70).
H7 1953: wood on Slievenamuck Mt., nr Bansha, ALK King (Warburg 1954: 478).
H(8) listed by Lett (1915: 96) without details.
†H8 listed by Blockeel & Long (1998: 70).
H(9) listed by Lett (1915: 96) without details.
†H9 listed by Blockeel & Long (1998: 70).
H(10) listed by Lett (1915: 96) without details.
†H10 listed by Blockeel & Long (1998: 70).
H(11) listed by Lett (1915: 96) without details.
†H11 listed by Blockeel & Long (1998: 70).
H(12) listed by Lett (1915: 96) without details.
†H12 listed by Blockeel & Long (1998: 70).
H(13) listed by Lett (1915: 96) without details.
†H13 listed by Blockeel & Long (1998: 70).
H(14) listed by Lett (1915: 96) without details.
†H14 listed by Blockeel & Long (1998: 70).
H(15) listed by Lett (1915: 96) without details.
†H15 listed by Blockeel & Long (1998: 70).
H(16) listed by Lett (1915: 96) without details.
†H16 listed by Blockeel & Long (1998: 70).
H17 1966: ground in wood, Ryehill, N of Monivea, MFV Corley & JS Parker (Perry 1967: 407).
H(18) listed by Lett (1915: 96) without details.
†H18 listed by Blockeel & Long (1998: 70).
[H(19) listed by Lett (1915: 96) without details. H19 deleted because no valid record or voucher specimen traced (Blockeel 1999: 3)].
H(20) listed by Lett (1915: 96) without details.
†H20 listed by Blockeel & Long (1998: 70).
H(21) listed by Lett (1915: 96) without details.
†H21 listed by Blockeel & Long (1998: 70).
H22 1950: Slane, JS Thomson (Warburg 1952: 98).
H(23) listed by Lett (1915: 96) without details.
†H23 listed by Blockeel & Long (1998: 70).
H24 1957: ditch, nr Carrickboy, ALK King (Warburg 1958b: 473).
H(25) 1940: near Lough Key, JS Thomson (Duncan 1944: 208).
†H25 listed by Blockeel & Long (1998: 70).
H(26) listed by Lett (1915: 96) without details.
†H26 listed by Blockeel & Long (1998: 70).
H(27) listed by Lett (1915: 96) without details.
†H27 listed by Blockeel & Long (1998: 70).
H(28) listed by Lett (1915: 96) without details.
†H28 listed by Blockeel & Long (1998: 70).
H(29) listed by Lett (1915: 96) without details.
†H29 listed by Blockeel & Long (1998: 70).
H(30) listed by Lett (1915: 96) without details.
†H30 listed by Blockeel & Long (1998: 70).
[H(31) listed by Lett (1915: 96) without details. H31 deleted because no valid record or voucher specimen traced (Blockeel 1999: 3)].
H31 1999: on bare soil under beech tree in plantation, 100 m alt., Two Mile River, Carlingford, J11, TL Blockeel 28/186 (Rothero 2000: 47).
H(32) listed by Lett (1915: 96) without details.
†H32 listed by Blockeel & Long (1998: 70).
H(33) listed by Lett (1915: 96) without details.
†H33 listed by Blockeel & Long (1998: 70).
H(34) listed by Lett (1915: 96) without details.
†H34 listed by Blockeel & Long (1998: 70).
H(35) listed by Lett (1915: 96) without details.
†H35 listed by Blockeel & Long (1998: 70).
H(36) listed by Lett (1915: 96) without details.
†H36 listed by Blockeel & Long (1998: 70).
H(37) listed by Lett (1915: 96) without details.
†H37 listed by Blockeel & Long (1998: 70).
H(38) listed by Lett (1915: 96) without details.
†H38 listed by Blockeel & Long (1998: 70).
H(39) listed by Lett (1915: 96) without details.
†H39 listed by Blockeel & Long (1998: 70).
H(40) listed by Lett (1915: 96) without details.
†H40 listed by Blockeel & Long (1998: 70).

6/4 ***Atrichum angustatum*** (Brid.) Bruch & Schimp.
(syn. *Atrichum angustatum* var. *rhystophyllum* (Müll.Hal.) P.W.Richards & E.C.Wallace, *Catharinea angustata* (Brid.) Brid., *C. angustata* var. *rhystophylla* (Müll.Hal.) Dixon)

H36 1957: old sand pit, nr Trillick, RD Fitzgerald (Warburg 1959: 631).
H(38) 1908: large patch fifteen inches across, on top of a mud-capped wall S of Saintfield Demesne, Saintfield, HW Lett (Lett 1915: 96). H(38) listed by Blockeel & Long (1998: 70).

7/1 ***Tetraphis pellucida*** Hedw.
(syn. *Georgia pellucida* (Hedw.) Rabenh.)

H(1) listed by Lett (1915: 96).
†H1 listed by Blockeel & Long (1998: 70).
H(2) listed by Lett (1915: 96).
†H2 listed by Blockeel & Long (1998: 70).
H3 1955: cliffs, NE slope of Lackaher, H Milne-Redhead (Warburg 1956: 151).
H4 1966: peaty soil and rotten tree stumps, E side of Musherabeg, Boggeragh Mts, MFV Corley & JS Parker (Perry 1967: 415).
H5 1966: woodland at Castle Cooke, NE of Fermoy, DM Synnott (BBS exc.) (Perry 1967: 415).
H(6) listed by Lett (1915: 96).
†H6 listed by Blockeel & Long (1998: 70).
H7 1966: rotting tree in wood, Knockastakeen, Galtee Mts, EM Lobley & RD Fitzgerald (BBS exc.) (Perry 1967: 415).
H8 1966: peaty bank on moor, Slievereagh, nr Ballylanders, MFV Corley & JS Parker (Perry 1967: 415).
H10 1967: on rotting stump, Knockfine, Keeper Hill, RD Fitzgerald (Crundwell 1968: 638).
H11 1954: trunk of larch in plantation, R. [ight] bank of R. Barrow above Graiguenamanagh, ALK King (Warburg 1955: 583).
H12 1969: on peat among scree, *ca* 1200 ft [alt.], Caher Roe's Den, Blackstairs Mts, RD Fitzgerald (Crundwell 1970: 203).
H(13) listed by Lett (1915: 96).
†H13 listed by Blockeel & Long (1998: 70).
H16 1970: rotting stump in woodland E of Kylemore Castle, JA Paton (Crundwell 1971b: 379).
H(18) listed by Lett (1915: 96). H(18) listed by Blockeel & Long (1998: 70).
H(20) listed by Lett (1915: 96).
†H20 listed by Blockeel & Long (1998: 70).
H(21) listed by Lett (1915: 96).
†H21 listed by Blockeel & Long (1998: 70).
H23 1957: old tree stump nr Ballinafid, JS Thomson, comm. ALK King (Warburg 1962: 366).
H25 2002: on wet peat by path in shady plantation woodland, 45 m alt., Lough Key Forest Park 'bog garden', G80, NG Hodgetts 4113 (Rothero 2003: 48).
H26 1965: peat *ca* 750 ft alt., cliffs S of Glendaduff, [The] Ox Mts, RD Fitzgerald (Warburg 1966: 197).
H(27) listed by Lett (1915: 96).
†H27 listed by Blockeel & Long (1998: 70).
H(28) listed by Lett (1915: 96).
†H28 listed by Blockeel & Long (1998: 70).
H(29) listed by Lett (1915: 96).
†H29 listed by Blockeel & Long (1998: 70).
†H30 listed by Blockeel & Long (1998: 70).
H(32) listed by Lett (1915: 96). H(32) listed by Blockeel & Long (1998: 70).
H(33) listed by Lett (1915: 96).
†H33 listed by Blockeel & Long (1998: 70).
H(34) listed by Lett (1915: 96).
†H34 listed by Blockeel & Long (1998: 70).
H(35) listed by Lett (1915: 96).
†H35 listed by Blockeel & Long (1998: 70).
H36 1952: peat and sandstone crevices, 600 ft [alt.], L. Bradan, RD Fitzgerald (Warburg 1953: 306).
H37 1952: shaded peat bank, L. Gullion, RD Fitzgerald (Warburg 1953: 306).
H(38) listed by Lett (1915: 96). H(38) listed by Blockeel & Long (1998: 70).
H38 1999: on old log at edge of stream, 50 m alt., Tollymore Forest park, 4 km W of Newcastle, J33, TL Blockeel 28/347 (Rothero 2000: 47).
H(39) listed by Lett (1915: 96).
†H39 listed by Blockeel & Long (1998: 70).
H(40) listed by Lett (1915: 96).
†H40 listed by Blockeel & Long (1998: 70).

8/1 ***Tetrodontium brownianum*** (Dicks.) Schwägr.
(syn. *Georgia brownii* Lindb. nom. illeg., *Tetraphis browniana* (Dicks.) Grev.)

H1 1951: Coomeeneragh, nr Glenbeigh, EW Jones (BBS exc.) (Warburg 1952: 98).
H8 1966: overhang of rocks at waterfall, *ca* 1300 ft alt., S side of Galtymore, RD Fitzgerald (BBS exc.) (Perry 1967: 415).
H16 2001: on shady rock face in gully on steep hillside, 150 m alt., Benchoona, NW slope, L76, DG Long 29988 (Rothero 2002: 43).
H(20) listed by Lett (1915: 96).
†H20 listed by Blockeel & Long (1998: 71).
H(21) listed by Lett (1915: 96) without locality. H(21) listed by Blockeel & Long (1998: 71).
H33 1959: moist sandstone cliffs, 1800 ft [alt.], Quilcagh [*sic* = Cuilcagh], RD Fitzgerald (Warburg 1960: 770).
H(35) listed by Lett (1915: 96).
H35 2002: on underside of quartzite overhang on crag, 570 m alt., N slope of Muckish, C02, DT Holyoak 02-725 (Rothero 2003: 48).
H36 1957: sandstone, Corrick Bridge, nr Plumbridge, RD Fitzgerald (Warburg 1958b: 473).
H(39) listed by Blockeel & Long (1998: 71).
†H40 listed by Blockeel & Long (1998: 71).

9/1 ***Diphyscium foliosum*** (Hedw.) D.Mohr.
(syn. *Webera sessilis* Lindb., *W. sessilis* var. *acutifolia* Lindb. ex Braithw.)

H(1) listed by Lett (1915: 121).
†H1 listed by Blockeel & Long (1998: 71).
H(2) listed by Lett (1915: 121).
†H2 listed by Blockeel & Long (1998: 71).
†H3 listed by Blockeel & Long (1998: 71).
H6 1999: on thin layer of sandy soil in rock crevice on stream bank, 80 m alt., Lismore, Owennashad R. just N of Drumber Bridge, S00, TL Blockeel 28/210 (Rothero 2000: 47).
H7 1966: among rocks on slope above L. Curra at *ca* 2000 ft alt., J Appleyard (BBS exc.) (Perry 1967: 407).
H8 1966: peat among rocks at 2300 ft alt., Temple Hill, Galtee Mts, MFV Corley & JS Parker (Perry 1967: 407).
H13 1975: crevice in rock, streambank, Mt Leinster, DM Synnott (Hill 1977a: 16-17).
H(16) listed by Lett (1915: 121).
†H16 listed by Blockeel & Long (1998: 71).
H(20) listed by Lett (1915: 121).
†H20 listed by Blockeel & Long (1998: 71).
[H(21) listed by Lett (1915: 121) without details. H21 deleted because no valid record or voucher specimen traced (Blockeel 1999: 3)].
H(27) listed by Lett (1915: 121).
†H27 listed by Blockeel & Long (1998: 71).
H28 1970: steep acid outcrops of Knockalongy, above L. Minnaun, N end of [The] Ox Mts, J Appleyard (BBS exc.) (Crundwell 1971b: 374, Appleyard 1971: 387).
H(29) listed by Lett (1915: 121). H(29) listed by Blockeel & Long (1998: 71).
H29 2001: on soil in crevice on steep, E-facing crag, 420 m alt., Coal Pit, E slope of Bencroy, H01, DT Holyoak 01-790 (Rothero 2002: 43).
H(31) listed by Lett (1915: 121). H(31) listed by Blockeel & Long (1998: 71).
H31 1999: on thin humus on rock wall of stream gully, 300 m alt., Two Mile River, Carlingford, J11, TL Blockeel 28/178 (Rothero 2000: 47).
H33 1961: limestone in wood and on ground at base of rocks at *ca* 200 ft [alt.], Stonefort, nr Boa I., RD Fitzgerald (Warburg 1962: 366).
H34 1962: on rock face with *Diplophyllum albicans*, Bulbin [Mt.], J Appleyard (BBS exc.) (Warburg 1963b: 493).
H(35) listed by Lett (1915: 121).
†H35 listed by Blockeel & Long (1998: 71).
H36 1958: rock cleft, 1700 ft [alt.], Mullaghcarbatagh, Sperrin Mts, RD Fitzgerald (Warburg 1959: 631), as var. *acutifolium*.
H(37) listed by Lett (1915: 121). H(37) listed by Blockeel & Long (1998: 71).
H(38) listed by Lett (1915: 121).
†H38 listed by Blockeel & Long (1998: 71).
H(39) listed by Lett (1915: 121).
†H39 listed by Blockeel & Long (1998: 71).
H(40) listed by Lett (1915: 121).
†H40 listed by Blockeel & Long (1998: 71).

10/1 ***Buxbaumia aphylla*** Hedw.

H(1) 1880: Killarney, Purple Mt., Wade (Lett 1915: 96). H(1) listed by Blockeel & Long (1998: 71).

11/1 ***Archidium alternifolium*** (Hedw.) Schimp.

H(1) listed by Lett (1915: 100).
†H1 listed by Blockeel & Long (1998: 71).
H2 1962: decayed wall of bridge above Torc Cascade, AJE Smith (Warburg 1963b: 494).
†H3 listed by Blockeel & Long (1998: 71).
H5 1951: lane, nr Mallow, EC Wallace & EF Warburg (Warburg 1952: 98).
H8 1979: edge of field above waterfall, Glenastar, W of Ardagh, JA Paton (Hill 1980b: 34).
H9 1979: thin soil on flat rocks nr Inagh River, W of L. Burke, W of Ennis, JA Paton & AC Crundwell (Hill 1980b: 34).
H12 1975: roadside gravel, Pallis Bridge nr Wicklow Gap, W of Coolgreany, AR Perry (Hill 1977a: 17).
H13 1969: on track in old quarry, Lackan, nr Oldleighlin, RD Fitzgerald (Crundwell 1971b: 375).
H16 1957: damp ground by stream, L. Muck, nr Killary Harbour, AC Crundwell (BBS exc.) (Warburg 1958b: 473).
H(21) listed by Lett (1915: 100). H(21) listed by Blockeel & Long (1998: 71).
H25 2002: by path, 200 m alt., Kilronan Mt., Arigna, G91, NG Hodgetts 4143 (Rothero 2003: 48).
H26 1987: NE shore of L. Mask, Ballygarry Pier, S of Partry, JA Paton (Blockeel 1988: 33).
†H27 listed by Blockeel & Long (1998: 71).
H28 1970: roadside quarry nr Masshill, J Appleyard (BBS exc.) (Crundwell 1971b: 375, Appleyard 1971: 389).
H29 1965: marshy path, Newton Glen, L. Gill, EM Lobley & RD Fitzgerald (Warburg 1966: 191).
H30 1969: floor of old quarry, Blackrocks Cross, Cuilcagh Mts, JA Paton (Crundwell 1970: 197).
H34 1962: track, E side of Bulbin [Mt.], AC Crundwell & EF Warburg (BBS exc.) (Warburg 1963b: 494).
H35 1962: damp hillside track, Tramore Strand, Murroe, nr Dunfanaghy, EM Lobley (BBS exc.) (Warburg 1963b: 494).
H(38) listed by Lett (1915: 100). H(38) listed by Blockeel & Long (1998: 71).
H38 2002: on open gravelly sediment in inundation zone of reservoir, 125 m alt., NW end of Lough Island Reavy Reservoir, J23, DT Holyoak 02-961 (Rothero 2003: 48).
H(39) listed by Lett (1915: 100). H(39) listed by Blockeel & Long (1998: 71).
H39 1999: on damp compressed sand of pathway in dunes, E of Portballintrae, C94, DT Holyoak 99240 (BBSUK) (Rothero 2000: 47).
H(40) listed by Blockeel & Long (1998: 71).
H40 1999: on gravelly edge of track, Binevenagh Lake, N end, C63, DT Holyoak 99-579 (BBSUK) (Rothero 2000: 47).

12/1 ***Pleuridium acuminatum*** Lindb.
(syn. *Pleuridium subulatum* (Huds.) Rabenh.)

H(1) listed by Lett (1915: 100). H(1) listed by Blockeel & Long (1998: 71).
[H3 deleted because no valid record or voucher specimen traced (Blockeel 1999: 3)].
H(4) listed by Lett (1915: 100). H(4) listed by Blockeel & Long (1998: 71).
H5 1966: clay bank by R. Douglas, N of Kilworth, DM Synnott (BBS exc.) (Perry 1967: 408).
H8 1966: shady bank in wood on sea shore, nr Ballydonohoe House, E of Tarbet, MFV Corley & JS Parker (Perry 1967: 408).
H9 1979: bank in field, W side of Slievebernagh, AC Crundwell (Hill 1980b: 34).
H(14) listed by Lett (1915: 100). H(14) listed by Blockeel & Long (1998: 71).
H16 1970: on bank by road nr sea, Cashel, Bertraghboy Bay, MFV Corley (Crundwell 1971b: 375).
[H18 deleted because no valid record or voucher specimen traced (Blockeel 1999: 3)].
[H(20) listed by Lett (1915: 101) without locality. H20 deleted because no valid record or voucher specimen traced (Blockeel 1999: 3)].
[H(21) listed by Lett (1915: 101) without

locality. H21 deleted because no valid record or voucher specimen traced (Blockeel 1999: 3)].

H22 1960: on sandy floor of quarry at Grangegeeth, ALK King (Warburg 1961: 159).

H25 1968: on peaty soil nr Drumdaff House, 6 miles W of Lanesborough, WV Rubers *et al.* (U) (Crundwell 1975:13).

H27 1987: steep bank in wood, below L. Greney, nr Knappagh, S of Westport, JA Paton (Blockeel 1988: 33).

H28 1969: bank of track in Slish Wood, SE of Sligo, JA Paton (Crundwell 1970: 197).

H29 1963: dry bank, *ca* 600 ft [alt.], Glencar Waterfall, RD Fitzgerald & AR Perry (Warburg 1964: 723).

H30 1961: bare earth, *ca* 1500 ft [alt.], Bellavally, Cuilcagh, RD Fitzgerald (Warburg 1962: 366).

[H(31) listed by Lett (1915: 101) without details. H31 deleted because no valid record or voucher specimen traced (Blockeel 1999: 3)].

H32 1965: clay, Cavanagarvan, nr Monaghan, RD Fitzgerald (Warburg 1966: 191).

H33 2000: on vertical soil of river bank, Sruh Croppa River, H13, DT Holyoak 00-256 (BBSUK) (Rothero 2001: 38).

H(34) listed by Lett (1915: 101). H(34) listed by Blockeel & Long (1998: 71).

H35 1969: roadside bank, Croaghmuckross, nr Kilcar, JA Paton (Crundwell 1970: 197).

H36 1958: floor of sand pit, Craigard, RD Fitzgerald (Warburg 1959: 632).

H(37) listed by Lett (1915: 101).

†H37 listed by Blockeel & Long (1998: 71).

H(38) listed by Lett (1915: 101). H(38) listed by Blockeel & Long (1998: 71).

H(39) listed by Lett (1915: 101). H(39) listed by Blockeel & Long (1998: 71).

H(40) listed by Lett (1915: 101). H(40) listed by Blockeel & Long (1998: 71).

H40 1999: on soil bank above stream in woodland clearing, Downhill Forest, C73, DT Holyoak 99-213 (BBSUK) (Rothero 2000: 47).

12/2 ***Pleuridium subulatum*** (Hedw.) Rabenh. (syn. *Pleuridium alternifolium* auct. non Rabenh.)

H(1) listed by Lett (1915: 101). H(1) listed by Blockeel & Long (1998: 72).

H(2) listed by Lett (1915: 101).

†H2 listed by Blockeel & Long (1998: 72).

H(3) listed by Lett (1915: 101) without details. H(3) listed by Blockeel & Long (1998: 72).

H6 1966: waste ground nr the river, Bunmahon, JA Paton (BBS exc.) (Perry 1967: 408).

H9 1979: track on N slope of Knocksise, W of Broadford, JA Paton (Hill 1980b: 34).

H12 1958: State Forest plantation, Coolmeela, nr Bunclody, ALK King (Warburg 1959: 632).

H(21) listed by Lett (1915: 101).

†H21 listed by Blockeel & Long (1998: 72).

H(31) listed by Lett (1915: 101). H(31) listed by Blockeel & Long (1998: 72).

H36 2002: on soil at edge of path by lough, 225 m alt., by N end of Lough Fea, H78, DT Holyoak 02-1148 (Rothero 2003: 48).

H(38) listed by Lett (1915: 101). H(38) listed by Blockeel & Long (1998: 72).

H38 2002: on open stony soil on floor of old quarry, 100 m alt., Scrabo Quarry, J47, DT Holyoak 02-1032 (Rothero 2003: 48).

H(39) listed by Lett (1915: 101). H(39) listed by Blockeel & Long (1998: 72).

13/1 ***Pseudephemerum nitidum*** (Hedw.) Loeske
(syn. *Pleuridium axillare* (Sm.) Lindb.)

H(1) listed by Lett (1915: 100) without details.

†H1 listed by Blockeel & Long (1998: 72).

H(2) listed by Lett (1915: 100).

†H2 listed by Blockeel & Long (1998: 72).

H3 1979: damp clay by Glengarriff River, DM Synnott (Hill 1981: 23).

H(4) listed by Lett (1915: 100).

†H4 listed by Blockeel & Long (1998: 72).

H5 1966: Castlecooke, nr Kilworth, RD Fitzgerald (Crundwell 1968: 632).

H6 1966: damp sandy track at *ca* 900 ft alt., N of the Punchbowl, Comeragh Mts, EM Lobley (BBS exc.) (Perry 1967: 409).

H8 1966: bare patch in field, Knockseefin, Pallas Grean New, JG Duckett *et al.* (BBS exc.) (Perry 1967: 409).
H9 1957: Maghera woods, Tulla, ALK King (Warburg 1958b: 473).
H10 1979: meadow by Clare River, *ca* 140 m alt., EW Jones (Hill 1980b: 35).
H12 1969: bare ground at roadside, Killinierin, nr Inch, RD Fitzgerald (Crundwell 1970: 197).
H15 1957: clay bank, Chevy Chase Woods, Owendalulleegh, DG Catcheside & EM Lobley (BBS exc.) (Warburg 1958b: 473-474).
H16 1969: soil at edge of field, Farravaun, Glann, Oughterard, AR Perry & HJ Perry (Crundwell 1970: 197).
H20 1969: stubble field, Ballygahan House, nr Avoca, RD Fitzgerald (Crundwell 197).
[H21 deleted because no valid record or voucher specimen traced (Blockeel 1999: 3)].
H25 2002: on open disturbed soil in old campsite, 50 m alt., Lough Keel, near Rockingham Demesne, G80, NG Hodgetts 4139 (Rothero 2003: 48).
H26 1970: ditch bank, field W of Pollagh River, NE of Balla, JA Paton (Crundwell 1971b: 375).
H27 1970: marshy trackside, Bundorragha, N of Killary Harbour, JA Paton (Crundwell 1971b: 375).
H29 1961: potato field, Glencar, RD Fitzgerald & MPH Kertland (Warburg 1962: 366).
H(30) 1941: Sally Point, JG Finlay (Duncan 1944: 208).
H30 2001: on steep clay bank of small stream, 305 m alt., W of Bellavally Gap, H12, DT Holyoak 01-637 (Rothero 2002: 43).
H31 1967: stubble field, Kirwans Cross, Tenure, Dunleer, DM Synnott (Crundwell 1969: 879).
†H33 listed by Blockeel & Long (1998: 72).
H34 1962: stubble field nr Newtown Cunningham, J Appleyard *et al.* (BBS exc.) (Warburg 1963b: 494).
H35 1962: stubble field, Ards Peninsula, J Appleyard *et al.* (BBS exc.) (Warburg 1963b: 494).
H36 1957: Vinegar Hill, RD Fitzgerald (Warburg 1958b: 473-474).
H37 1966: field nr Drumbanagher House, Poyntzpass, RD Fitzgerald (Perry 1967: 409).
H(38) listed by Lett (1915: 100). H(38) listed by Blockeel & Long (1998: 72).
H38 2002: on soil in arable field with oat crop, 14 m alt., W of B1, NW of Ballyhosset, J54, DT Holyoak 02-1013 (Rothero 2003: 48).
H(39) listed by Lett (1915: 100). H(39) listed by Blockeel & Long (1998: 72).
H39 1999: on mud of dried reservoir, Copeland Reservoir, J49, DT Holyoak 99-885 (BBSUK) (Rothero 2000: 47).
H(40) 1939: Toomebridge, WR Megaw (anon. 1940a: 172).
†H40 listed by Blockeel & Long (1998: 72).

14/1 ***Ditrichum cylindricum*** (Hedw.) Grout (syn. *Ditrichum tenuifolium* Lindb.)

H1 1951: earth capped wall by L. Currane, EW Jones (BBS exc.) (Warburg 1952: 98).
†H2 listed by Blockeel & Long (1998: 72).
H3 1979: top of garden wall, house by Glenbeg Lake, G Bloom (Hill 1980b: 34).
H4 1979: bank in field, E of Ballygarvan, S of Cork, JA Paton (Hill 1980b: 34).
H6 1966: bare patch of soil in field by R. Nire, Shanballyanne, ERB Little & JA Paton (BBS exc.) (Perry 1967: 408).
H7 1966: arable field nr Ardfinnan, J Appleyard & JG Duckett (BBS exc.) (Perry 1967: 408).
H8 1979: bank in field above road, E side of Sugar Hill, S of Knockanimpaha, JA Paton (Hill 1980b: 34).
H10 1968: soil in garden, Loughtea House, E side of L. Derg, 4½ miles N of Killaloe, AR Perry (Crundwell 1969: 878).
H11 1966: arable field, Inistioge, JG Duckett *et al.* (BBS exc.) (Perry 1967: 408).
H12 1969: bare ground at roadside, Killinierin, nr Inch, RD Fitzgerald (Crundwell 1970: 197).
H13 1969: earth-topped wall, Crannagh, foot of Mt Leinster, RD Fitzgerald (Crundwell 1970: 197).
H14 2002: in stubble field, 80 m alt., Garrans Crossroads NE of Stradbally, S59, HF Fox & CD Preston (Rothero 2003: 48).
H15 1957: woodland ride, Chevy Chase, nr Gort, AC Crundwell (BBS exc.) (Warburg 1958b: 474).

H16 1957: woodland ride, Ballynahinch, AC Crundwell (BBS exc.) (Warburg 1958b: 474).
H19 2002: in stubble field (winter wheat) 70 m alt., Furry Field, Courttown East townland, Athy, S69, HF Fox & CD Preston (Rothero 2003: 48).
H20 1969: in stubble field, Ballygahan House, nr Avoca, RD Fitzgerald (Crundwell 1970: 197).
H27 1970: marshy trackside, Bundorragha, N of Killary Harbour, JA Paton (Crundwell 1971b: 375).
H29 2000: on old track over moorland, S of Moneyduff, G83, DT Holyoak 00-564 (BBSUK) (Rothero 2001: 38).
H30 2001: on damp soil on track, 315 m alt., W of Bellavally Gap, H12, DT Holyoak 01-640 (Rothero 2002: 43).
H33 1960: potato field, Tullykelter Castle, nr Monea, RD Fitzgerald (Warburg 1961: 159-160).
H34 1962: fallow field N of Lifford, EM Lobley & MPH Kertland (BBS exc.) (Warburg 1963b: 494).
H35 1962: garden soil, Glen Alla, nr Rathmullan, Lough Swilly, EM Lobley & MPH Kertland (BBS exc.) (Warburg 1963b: 494).
H36 1957: fallow field, nr Cookstown, RD Fitzgerald (Warburg 1958b: 474).
H37 1962: stubble field between Moy and Loughall, AC Crundwell, J Appleyard & EC Wallace (Warburg 1963b: 494).
H(38) listed by Blockeel & Long (1998: 72).
H(39) listed by Lett (1915: 101). H(39) listed by Blockeel & Long (1998: 72).
H39 1999: on mud at edge of reservoir, North Woodburn Reservoir, J39, DT Holyoak 99-865 (BBSUK) (Rothero 2000: 47).
H40 1952: stubble field, Coleraine, EW Jones (Warburg 1953: 306).

14/2 ***Ditrichum pusillum*** (Hedw.) Hampe
(syn. *Ditrichum tortile* (Schrad.) Brockm.)

H(5) listed by Lett (1915: 101). H(5) placed in brackets, comm. HLK Whitehouse (Hill 1981: 23). H(5) listed by Blockeel & Long (1998: 72).
H(12) listed by Lett (1915: 101). H(12) placed in brackets, comm. HLK Whitehouse (Hill 1981: 23). H(12) listed by Blockeel & Long (1998: 72).
H(32) listed by Lett (1915: 101). H(32) placed in brackets, comm. HLK Whitehouse (Hill 1981: 23). H(32) listed by Blockeel & Long (1998: 72).
H(35) listed by Lett (1915: 101). H(35) placed in brackets, comm. HLK Whitehouse (Hill 1981: 23). H(35) listed by Blockeel & Long (1998: 72).
H(38) 1908: Scrabo Quarry, Scrabo Hill, HW Lett (anon. 1909a: 304, Lett 1915: 101). H(38) placed in brackets, comm. HLK Whitehouse (Hill 1981: 23).
H(39) listed by Lett (1915: 101). H(39) placed in brackets, comm. HLK Whitehouse (Hill 1981: 23). H(39) listed by Blockeel & Long (1998: 72).

14/4 ***Ditrichum lineare*** (Sw.) Lindb.

H3 1999: on open gravelly area amongst mine spoil, 140 m alt., Allihies old copper mines, V54, DG Long 28498 (Rothero 2000: 47).
H(28) listed by Blockeel & Long (1998: 72).
†H39 listed by Blockeel & Long (1998: 72).

14/6 ***Ditrichum heteromallum*** (Hedw.) E. Britton
(syn. *Ditrichum homomallum* (Hedw.) Hampe)

H(1) listed by Lett (1915: 101) without details.
†H1 listed by Blockeel & Long (1998: 72).
H(2) listed by Lett (1915: 101).
†H2 listed by Blockeel & Long (1998: 72).
H(3) listed by Lett (1915: 101).
†H3 listed by Blockeel & Long (1998: 72).
H(4) listed by Lett (1915: 101).
†H4 listed by Blockeel & Long (1998: 72).
H(5) listed by Lett (1915: 101).
†H5 listed by Blockeel & Long (1998: 72).
H(6) listed by Lett (1915: 101).
†H6 listed by Blockeel & Long (1998: 72).
H(7) no date: near Carrig-na-binnia, AW Stelfox, per JS Thomson (Duncan 1944: 208).
†H7 listed by Blockeel & Long (1998: 72).
H8 1966: damp rocks at 2000 ft alt., Temple Hill, Galtee Mts, MFV Corley & JS Parker (Perry 1967: 408).
H10 1979: loamy soil, W side of Keeper Hill, S of Silvermine Mts, HMH van Melick (Hill 1981: 23).
H(12) listed by Lett (1915: 101).

†H12 listed by Blockeel & Long (1998: 72).
H13 1969: sandy bank, the Nine Sisters, N of Mt Leinster, RD Fitzgerald (Crundwell 1970: 197).
†H16 listed by Blockeel & Long (1998: 72).
H(20) listed by Lett (1915: 101).
†H20 listed by Blockeel & Long (1998: 72).
H(21) listed by Lett (1915: 101).
†H21 listed by Blockeel & Long (1998: 72).
H25 1968: loamy bank, Slieve Bawn, WV Rubers *et al.* (U) (Crundwell 1975: 13).
H(27) listed by Lett (1915: 101).
†H27 listed by Blockeel & Long (1998: 72).
H28 1965: side of track to Deerpark burial chamber, Colgagh Lough, AR Perry & EF Warburg (Warburg 1966: 191).
H(29) listed by Lett (1915: 101).
†H29 listed by Blockeel & Long (1998: 72).
H30 1965: peat on old ramp *ca* 1150 ft alt., Englishman's House, 3 miles S of Glenfarne, RD Fitzgerald (Warburg 1966: 191).
H(31) listed by Lett (1915: 101). H(31) listed by Blockeel & Long (1998: 72).
H(32) listed by Lett (1915: 101). H(32) listed by Blockeel & Long (1998: 72).
H(33) listed by Lett (1915: 101) without details. H(33) listed by Blockeel & Long (1998: 72).
H33 2000: on face of gritstone rock on N-facing hillside, 600 m alt., SE of Lough Atona, H12, DT Holyoak 00-187 (BBSUK) (Rothero 2001: 38).
H(34) listed by Lett (1915: 101).
†H34 listed by Blockeel & Long (1998: 72).
H(35) listed by Lett (1915: 101).
†H35 listed by Blockeel & Long (1998: 72).
H(36) listed by Lett (1915: 101).
†H36 listed by Blockeel & Long (1998: 72).
H37 1962: damp bankside, Tannyoki, nr Poyntz Pass, EM Lobley & MPH Kertland (Warburg 1963b: 494).
H(38) listed by Lett (1915: 101).
†H38 listed by Blockeel & Long (1998: 72).
H(39) listed by Lett (1915: 101).
†H39 listed by Blockeel & Long (1998: 72).
H(40) listed by Lett (1915: 101).
†H40 listed by Blockeel & Long (1998: 72).

14/7a *Ditrichum zonatum* (Brid.) Braithw. **var. *zonatum***

H(39) no date: Ballycastle, Dixon (Lett 1915: 101). H(39) listed by Blockeel & Long (1998: 72).

14/7b *Ditrichum zonatum* (Brid.) Braithw. **var. *scabrifolium*** Dixon

H16 1968: dripping rocks on N-facing mica-schist outcrop at 1600 ft [alt.], Muckanaght, AR Perry (Crundwell 1969: 879).
H35 1972: on detritus, Slieve Snaght, above Dunlewy, EC Wallace (Crundwell 1975: 13).

14/9 *Ditrichum flexicaule* (Schwägr.) Hampe *s.s.*

H10 1957: wall, E bank of R Shannon near Portumna, [12/80], PW Richards (DBN) (Smith 1993: 54, Blockeel 1994: 36).
H(27) 1910: near Louisburgh, [02/88], HW Lett (DBN) (Smith 1993: 54, Blockeel 1994: 36).
H(35) 1916: Rossnowlagh, [12/8569], W Lett (DBN) (Smith 1993: 54, Blockeel 1994: 36).
H(38) 1931: shore at Kirkestown, [31/65], WR Megaw (BBSUK) (Smith 1993: 54, Blockeel 1994: 36).
H(39) 1882: on peat, Divis, [33/27], CH Waddell (DBN) (Smith 1993: 54, Blockeel 1994: 36).

This species and the next were not separated in Ireland and Britain until the revision by Smith (1993).

14/10 *Ditrichum gracile* (Mitt.) Kuntze (syn. *Ditrichum crispatissimum* (Müll. Hal.) Paris, *D. flexicaule* auct. pro parte non (Schwägr.) Hampe)

H(1) listed by Lett (1915: 101) as *D. flexicaule*, without details.
†H1 listed by Blockeel & Long (1998: 73).
[H(2) listed by Lett (1915: 101) as *D. flexicaule*, without details. H2 deleted because no valid record or voucher specimen traced (Blockeel 1999: 3)].
[H(3) listed by Lett (1915: 101) as *D. flexicaule*, without details. H3 deleted because no valid record or voucher specimen traced (Blockeel 1999: 3)].
[H(6) listed by Lett (1915: 101) as *D. flexicaule*, without details. H6 deleted because no valid record or voucher specimen traced (Blockeel 1999: 3)].
H7 1966: limestone, Cashel Rock, Cashel,

ERB Little (BBS exc.) (Perry 1967: 408).
†H7 listed by Blockeel & Long (1998: 73).
H(8) listed by Lett (1915: 101) as *D. flexicaule*, without details.
†H8 listed by Blockeel & Long (1998: 73).
†H9 listed by Blockeel & Long (1998: 73).
H(10) listed by Lett (1915: 101) as *D. flexicaule*, without details.
†H10 listed by Blockeel & Long (1998: 73).
†H11 listed by Blockeel & Long (1998: 73).
H11 1968: turfy bank in old limestone quarry N of Thomastown, JA Paton (Crundwell 1969: 879); H11 listed by Blockeel and Long 1998: 73, but not necessarily on the basis of this specimen.
[H(12) listed by Lett (1915: 101) as *D. flexicaule*, without details. H12 deleted because no valid record or voucher specimen traced (Blockeel 1999: 3)].
[H(13) listed by Lett (1915: 101) as *D. flexicaule*, without details. H13 deleted because no valid record or voucher specimen traced (Blockeel 1999: 3)].
H(14) listed by Lett (1915: 101) as *D. flexicaule*, without details.
†H14 listed by Blockeel & Long (1998: 73).
H15 1957: calcareous grassland, Loughrea, RE Parker (Warburg 1958b: 474).
†H16 listed by Blockeel & Long (1998: 73).
H(17) listed by Lett (1915: 101) as *D. flexicaule*, without details.
†H17 listed by Blockeel & Long (1998: 73).
H(18) listed by Lett (1915: 101) as *D. flexicaule*, without details.
†H18 listed by Blockeel & Long (1998: 73).
H(19) listed by Lett (1915: 101) as *D. flexicaule*, without details.
†H19 listed by Blockeel & Long (1998: 73).
H(20) listed by Lett (1915: 101) as *D. flexicaule*, without details. H(20) listed by Blockeel & Long (1998: 73).
H(21) listed by Lett (1915: 101) as *D. flexicaule*, without details. H(21) listed by Blockeel & Long (1998: 73).
H22 1965: wet calcareous grassland, Commons, Duleek, DM Synnott (Hill 1978: 17), as *D. flexicaule*.
H(23) listed by Lett (1915: 101) as *D. flexicaule*, without details.
†H23 listed by Blockeel & Long (1998: 73).
H24 1966: cleft of rock by canal towpath, Keenagh, ALK King (Perry 1967: 408).
H(25) listed by Lett (1915: 101) as *D. flexicaule*, without details.
†H25 listed by Blockeel & Long (1998: 73).
H(26) listed by Lett (1915: 101) as *D. flexicaule*, without details.
†H26 listed by Blockeel & Long (1998: 73).
H(27) listed by Lett (1915: 101) as *D. flexicaule*, without details.
†H27 listed by Blockeel & Long (1998: 73).
H(28) listed by Lett (1915: 101) as *D. flexicaule*, without details.
†H28 listed by Blockeel & Long (1998: 73).
H(29) listed by Lett (1915: 101) as *D. flexicaule*, without details.
†H29 listed by Blockeel & Long (1998: 73).
[H(30) listed by Lett (1915: 101) as *D. flexicaule*, without details. H30 deleted because no valid record or voucher specimen traced (Blockeel 1999: 3)].
[H(31) listed by Lett (1915: 101) as *D. flexicaule*, without details. H31 deleted because no valid record or voucher specimen traced (Blockeel 1999: 3)].
[H(32) listed by Lett (1915: 101) as *D. flexicaule*, without details. H32 deleted because no valid record or voucher specimen traced (Blockeel 1999: 3)].
H(33) listed by Lett (1915: 101) as *D. flexicaule*, without details.
†H33 listed by Blockeel & Long (1998: 73).
H(34) listed by Lett (1915: 101) as *D. flexicaule*, without details.
†H34 listed by Blockeel & Long (1998: 73).
H(35) listed by Lett (1915: 101) as *D. flexicaule*, without details.
†H35 listed by Blockeel & Long (1998: 73).
H36 1957: limestone boulders, Carrickaness Bridge, nr Drumguin [*sic* = Drumquin], RD Fitzgerald (Warburg 1958b: 474).
H(38) listed by Lett (1915: 101) as *D. flexicaule*, without details. H(38) listed by Blockeel & Long (1998: 73).
H(39) listed by Lett (1915: 101) as *D. flexicaule*, without details.
†H39 listed by Blockeel & Long (1998: 73).
H(40) listed by Lett (1915: 101) as *D. flexicaule*, without details.
†H40 listed by Blockeel & Long (1998: 73).

Smith (1993: 52) found that very few records of specimens labelled as *Ditrichum flexicaule* were referable to *D. flexicaule* s.s., the great majority being *D. gracile* (then known as *D. crispatissimum*). The vice-counties listed for *D. flexicaule* in the *CC* by Corley & Hill (1981) were therefore transferred to

D. gracile in Blockeel & Long (1998: 73).

16/1 ***Distichium capillaceum*** (Hedw.) Bruch, Schimp. & W.Gümbel
(syn. *Swartzia montana* Lindb., *S. montana* var. *compacta* (Huebener) Braithw.)

H(1) listed by Lett (1915: 101).
†H1 listed by Blockeel & Long (1998: 73).
[H(3) listed by Lett (1915: 101) without details. H3 deleted because no valid record or voucher specimen traced (Blockeel 1999: 3)].
H(9) listed by Lett (1915: 101). H(9) listed by Blockeel & Long (1998: 73).
H12 1975: calcareous mortar, bridge 1 mile NE of Knockbrandon, Camolin, AR Perry (Hill 1977a: 17).
H(16) listed by Lett (1915: 101) without details.
†H16 listed by Blockeel & Long (1998: 73).
H(20) listed by Lett (1915: 101). H(20) listed by Blockeel & Long (1998: 73).
[H21 deleted because no valid record or voucher specimen traced (Blockeel 1999: 3)].
H(27) listed by Lett (1915: 101) without locality.
†H27 listed by Blockeel & Long (1998: 73).
H(28) listed by Lett (1915: 101).
†H28 listed by Blockeel & Long (1998: 73).
H(29) listed by Lett (1915: 101).
†H29 listed by Blockeel & Long (1998: 73).
H(33) listed by Lett (1915: 102). H(33) listed by Blockeel & Long (1998: 73).
H33 2000: on thin soil in deep crevice in N-facing sandstone scarp, Meenameen Scarp, W end, H05, DT Holyoak 00-216 (BBSUK) (Rothero 2001: 38).
H(34) listed by Lett (1915: 102).
†H34 listed by Blockeel & Long (1998: 73).
†H35 listed by Blockeel & Long (1998: 73).
H(39) listed by Blockeel & Long (1998: 73).
H(40) listed by Lett (1915: 102).
†H40 listed by Blockeel & Long (1998: 73).

16/2 ***Distichium inclinatum*** (Hedw.) Bruch, Schimp. & W.Gümbel
(syn. *Swartzia inclinata* (Hedw.) P. Beauv.)

H(16) listed by Lett (1915: 102).
†H16 listed by Blockeel & Long (1998: 73).
H26 1965: limestone wall by road, Moore Hall, L. Carra, G Halliday & GCG Argent (Perry 1967: 408).
H(27) listed by Lett (1915: 102).
†H27 listed by Blockeel & Long (1998: 73).
H(28) listed by Lett (1915: 102).
†H28 listed by Blockeel & Long (1998: 73).
H29 1965: Carboniferous limestone outcrop in gully S of Glencar Lough at 700 ft alt., nr county boundary, EF Warburg & AR Perry (Warburg 1966: 191).
[H(33) listed by Lett (1915: 102)].
H(34) listed by Lett (1915: 102). H(34) listed by Blockeel & Long (1998: 73).
H34 2002: on damp sand in grassland, 25 m alt., SW of Lagacurry, Doagh Isle, C45, DT Holyoak 02-554 (Rothero 2003: 48).
H(35) listed by Lett (1915: 102).
†H35 listed by Blockeel & Long (1998: 73).
H(39) listed by Blockeel & Long (1998: 73).
H39 1999: on floor of old chalk quarry, White Rocks, E of Portrush, C94, DT Holyoak 99-617 (BBSUK) (Rothero 2000: 47).
H(40) 1913: damp hollows, sandhills, Magelligan [*sic* = Magilligan], JD Houston (anon. 1914a: 96).
1913: Magilligan, Hunter & Waddell (Lett 1915: 102).
H40 1999: in short, patchy vegetation on damp sand in dune slack, Ballymaclary NNR, C63, DT Holyoak 99-196 (BBSUK) (Rothero 2000: 47).

17/1 ***Ceratodon purpureus*** (Hedw.) Brid.
(syn. *Ceratodon purpureus* subsp. *purpureus* (Hedw.) Brid.)

H(1) listed by Lett (1915: 109) without details.
†H1 listed by Blockeel & Long (1998: 73).
H(2) listed by Lett (1915: 109) without details.
†H2 listed by Blockeel & Long (1998: 73).
H(3) listed by Lett (1915: 109) without details.
†H3 listed by Blockeel & Long (1998: 73).
H(4) listed by Lett (1915: 109) without details.
†H4 listed by Blockeel & Long (1998: 73).
†H5 listed by Blockeel & Long (1998: 73).
H(6) listed by Lett (1915: 109) without details.
†H6 listed by Blockeel & Long (1998: 73).
H7 1966: rock, slopes above L. Curra,

Galtee Mts, ERB Little (BBS exc.) (Perry 1967: 409).
H(8) listed by Lett (1915: 109) without details.
†H8 listed by Blockeel & Long (1998: 73).
H(9) listed by Lett (1915: 109) without details.
†H9 listed by Blockeel & Long (1998: 73).
H(10) listed by Lett (1915: 109) without details.
†H10 listed by Blockeel & Long (1998: 73).
H(11) listed by Lett (1915: 109) without details.
†H11 listed by Blockeel & Long (1998: 73).
H(12) listed by Lett (1915: 109) without details.
†H12 listed by Blockeel & Long (1998: 73).
H(13) listed by Lett (1915: 109) without details.
†H13 listed by Blockeel & Long (1998: 73).
H(14) listed by Lett (1915: 109) without details.
†H14 listed by Blockeel & Long (1998: 73).
H(15) listed by Lett (1915: 109) without details.
†H15 listed by Blockeel & Long (1998: 73).
H(16) listed by Lett (1915: 109) without details.
†H16 listed by Blockeel & Long (1998: 73).
H(17) listed by Lett (1915: 109) without details.
†H17 listed by Blockeel & Long (1998: 73).
H(18) listed by Lett (1915: 109) without details.
†H18 listed by Blockeel & Long (1998: 73).
†H19 listed by Blockeel & Long (1998: 73).
H(20) listed by Lett (1915: 109) without details.
†H20 listed by Blockeel & Long (1998: 73).
H(21) listed by Lett (1915: 109) without details.
†H21 listed by Blockeel & Long (1998: 73).
H(22) listed by Lett (1915: 109) without details.
†H22 listed by Blockeel & Long (1998: 73).
H(23) listed by Lett (1915: 109) without details.
†H23 listed by Blockeel & Long (1998: 73).
H(24) listed by Lett (1915: 109) without details.
†H24 listed by Blockeel & Long (1998: 73).
H(25) listed by Lett (1915: 109) without details.
†H25 listed by Blockeel & Long (1998: 73).
H(26) listed by Lett (1915: 109) without details.
†H26 listed by Blockeel & Long (1998: 73).
H(27) listed by Lett (1915: 109) without details.
†H27 listed by Blockeel & Long (1998: 73).
†H28 listed by Blockeel & Long (1998: 73).
H(29) listed by Lett (1915: 109) without details.
†H29 listed by Blockeel & Long (1998: 73).
H(30) listed by Lett (1915: 109) without details.
†H30 listed by Blockeel & Long (1998: 73).
H(31) listed by Lett (1915: 109) without details.
†H31 listed by Blockeel & Long (1998: 73).
H(32) listed by Lett (1915: 109) without details.
†H32 listed by Blockeel & Long (1998: 73).
H(33) listed by Lett (1915: 109) without details.
†H33 listed by Blockeel & Long (1998: 73).
H(34) listed by Lett (1915: 109) without details.
†H34 listed by Blockeel & Long (1998: 73).
H(35) listed by Lett (1915: 109) without details.
†H35 listed by Blockeel & Long (1998: 73).
H(36) listed by Lett (1915: 109) without details.
†H36 listed by Blockeel & Long (1998: 73).
H37 1951: granite wall, Rough I., RD Fitzgerald (Warburg 1952: 98).
H(38) listed by Lett (1915: 109) without details.
†H38 listed by Blockeel & Long (1998: 73).
H(39) listed by Lett (1915: 109) without details.
†H39 listed by Blockeel & Long (1998: 73).
H(40) listed by Lett (1915: 109) without details.
†H40 listed by Blockeel & Long (1998: 73).

[17/2 ***Ceratodon conicus*** (Hampe ex Müll. Hal.) Lindb.)]

[Old records from H21 and H27 given by Lett (1915: 110) are dismissed as errors].

20/1 ***Rhabdoweisia fugax*** (Hedw.) Bruch, Schimp. & W.Gümbel
(syn. *Oncophorus striatus* (Schrad.) Lindb.)

H(1) listed by Lett (1915: 109). H(1) listed by Blockeel & Long (1998: 74).
H6 1966: rock clefts, *ca* 1400 ft [alt.], Coumshingaun, Comeragh Mts, RD Fitzgerald (BBS exc.) (Crundwell 1968: 632).
H(7) listed by Lett (1915: 109). H(7) listed by Blockeel & Long (1998: 74).
H(16) listed by Lett (1915: 109).
†H16 listed by Blockeel & Long (1998: 74).
H(20) listed by Lett (1915: 109). H(20) listed by Blockeel & Long (1998: 74).
H(21) listed by Lett (1915: 109). H(21) listed by Blockeel & Long (1998: 74).
H(31) listed by Lett (1915: 109). H(31) listed by Blockeel & Long (1998: 74).
H(35) listed by Lett (1915: 109). H(35) listed by Blockeel & Long (1998: 74).
H35 2001: in rock crevice in S-facing cliffs, 400 m alt., Meenaguse, G98, NG Hodgetts 3917 (Rothero 2003: 48).
H(38) listed by Lett (1915: 109).
†H38 listed by Blockeel & Long (1998: 74).
H(39) listed by Lett (1915: 109). H(39) listed by Blockeel & Long (1998: 74).
H(40) listed by Lett (1915: 109).
†H40 listed by Blockeel & Long (1998: 74).

20/2 ***Rhabdoweisia crispata*** (Dicks.) Lindb.
(syn. *Oncophorus crispatus* (With.) Lindb., *Rhabdoweisia denticulata* (Brid.) Bruch, Schimp. & W.Gümbel)

H(1) listed by Lett (1915: 109).
†H1 listed by Blockeel & Long (1998: 74).
H(2) listed by Lett (1915: 109). H(2) listed by Blockeel & Long (1998: 74).
H3 1979: shady rock crevice, S slope of Sugarloaf Mt, nr Lackavane, HMH van Melick (Hill 1981: 23).
H(6) listed by Lett (1915: 109).
†H6 listed by Blockeel & Long (1998: 74).
H(7) listed by Lett (1915: 109).
†H7 listed by Blockeel & Long (1998: 74).
H8 1966: thin soil on rock face at 2200 ft alt., Temple Hill, Galtee Mts, MFV Corley & JS Parker (Perry 1967: 409).
H10 1979: shady rock crevice nr waterfall, W side of Keeper Hill, S of Silvermine Mts, HMH van Melick (Hill 1981: 23).
H12 1969: rock crevices in scree, *ca* 1400 ft [alt.], Caher Roe's Den, Blackstairs Mts, RD Fitzgerald (Crundwell 1970: 198).
H13 1969: rock crevices, *ca* 1000 ft [alt.], below Caher Roe's Den, Blackstairs Mts, RD Fitzgerald (Crundwell 1970: 198).
[H16 deleted because no valid record or voucher specimen traced (Blockeel 1999: 4)].
H(20) listed by Lett (1915: 109). H(20) listed by Blockeel & Long (1998: 74).
†H27 listed by Blockeel & Long (1998: 74).
[H(28) listed by Lett (1915: 109)].
H29 2001: on thin dry soil in crevice of NW-facing gritstone crag, 370 m alt., Slieve Anierin, W slope, H01, DT Holyoak 01-845 (Rothero 2002: 44).
H(31) listed by Lett (1915: 109). H(31) listed by Blockeel & Long (1998: 74).
H(33) listed by Blockeel & Long (1998: 74).
H34 1962: rock, E side of Bulbin [Mt.], AC Crundwell (BBS exc.) (Warburg 1963b: 494).
H35 1951: crevices in conglomerate rocks, *ca* 1800 ft [alt.], Slieve League, H Milne-Redhead (Warburg 1952: 99).
H36 1958: rock crevices, 1100 ft [alt.], Craigatuke, RD Fitzgerald (Warburg 1959: 632).
H(38) listed by Lett (1915: 109).
†H38 listed by Blockeel & Long (1998: 74).
H(39) listed by Lett (1915: 109).
†H39 listed by Blockeel & Long (1998: 74).
H(40) 1937: Inishgore, WR Megaw (anon. 1938d: 39).
†H40 listed by Blockeel & Long (1998: 74).

20/3 ***Rhabdoweisia crenulata*** (Mitt.) H. Jameson
(syn. *Oncophorus crenulatus* (Mitt.) Braithw.)

H1 1951: rock crevice, Coomasaharn, nr Glenbeigh, PR Bell & EF Warburg (BBS exc.) (Warburg 1952: 99).
H(2) listed by Lett (1915: 109).
H2 1983: crevices of rocks on steep N-facing slope, S slope above Lough Erhogh, Mangerton Mt, DG Long (Hill 1984b: 26).
H3 1979: wet rock above stream, N side of Foilastookeen Mt, Gougane Barra, DM Synnott (Hill 1981: 23).
H4 1967: rock cleft, *ca* 1300 ft [alt.],

Musherabeg, Boggeragh Mts, RD Fitzgerald (Crundwell 1968: 633).
H6 1961: damp crevices of acidic sandstone cliffs at 1800 ft [alt.], Coumshingaun, Comeragh Mts, DA Ratcliffe (Warburg 1962: 366).
H7 1983: sandstone ledges on exposed ridge, O'Loughnan's Castle, Galtey Mts, DG Long (Hill 1984b: 26).
H16 1951: N side of Muckanaught [*sic* = Muckanaght], *ca* 1650 ft [alt.], H Milne-Redhead (Warburg 1952: 99).
H20 1979: shaded granite rock crevice, 3 km W of Turlough Hill, N Lockhart (Hill 1981: 23).
H26 1965: rock crevices, *ca* 600 ft alt., W of L. Talt, [The] Ox Mts, RD Fitzgerald (Warburg 1966: 192).
†H27 listed by Blockeel & Long (1998: 74).
H28 1963: clefts of rocks, S of Knockachree, Slieve Gamph, RD Fitzgerald & AR Perry (Warburg 1964: 724).
H(33) listed by Lett (1915: 109). H(33) listed by Blockeel & Long (1998: 74).
H35 1962: Slieve Snaght, J Appleyard (BBS exc.) (Warburg 1963b: 494).
H36 1957: cliff, Baines Gap, nr Gortin, RD Fitzgerald (Warburg 1958b: 474).
H40 1957: rocks, *ca* 1900 ft [alt.], Dart Mt., Sperrin Mts, RD Fitzgerald (Warburg 1958b: 474).

21/1 ***Cynodontium bruntonii*** (Sm.) Bruch, Schimp. & W.Gümbel
(syn. *Oncophorus bruntonii* (Sm.) Lindb.)

H(1) listed by Lett (1915: 109). H(1) listed by Blockeel & Long (1998: 74).
H4 1967: on rocks, *ca* 1300 ft [alt.], Musherabeg, Boggeragh Mts, RD Fitzgerald (Crundwell 1968: 633).
H(5) listed by Lett (1915: 109). H(5) listed by Blockeel & Long (1998: 74).
H(6) listed by Lett (1915: 109).
†H6 listed by Blockeel & Long (1998: 74).
H7 1966: rocks above L. Curra, J Appleyard (BBS exc.) (Perry 1967: 410).
H12 1969: on rocks in scree, *ca* 1400 ft [alt.], Caher Roe's Den, Blackstairs Mts, RD Fitzgerald (Crundwell 1970: 198).
H13 1961: shaded rocks, banks of R. Slaney, Coolaphuca Wood, nr Blunclody, M McCallum Webster, comm. CC Townsend (Warburg 1962: 367).
H(20) listed by Lett (1915: 109).
†H20 listed by Blockeel & Long (1998: 74).
H29 2001: in crevices of open sandstone at base of E-facing crag, 418 m alt., Coal Pit, E slope of Bencroy, H01, DT Holyoak 01-794 (Rothero 2002: 44).
[H(30) listed by Lett (1915: 109) as 1911: Cuilcagh Mt., Swanlinbar R., leg. Tetley. H30 deleted: specimen from Cuilcagh Mt., Swanlinbar R, 1911, leg. WN Tetley (DBN), is *Amphidium mougeotii*, comm. DM Synnott (Blockeel 1989: 25)].
H30 1965: on cliff, 380 m [alt.], Englishman's House, 3 miles S of Glenfarne, RD Fitzgerald (NMW), comm. AR Perry (Blockeel 1990: 29).
H36 1958: mica schist rocks, 1500 ft [alt.], Mullaghcarn, nr Gortin, RD Fitzgerald (Warburg 1959: 632).
H(39) listed by Lett (1915: 109).
H(39) listed by Blockeel & Long (1998: 74).

21/3 ***Cynodontium jenneri*** (Schimp.) Stirt.

H35 2001: in rock crevice on S-facing cliffs, 400 m alt., Meenaguse, G98, NG Hodgetts 3896 (Rothero 2003: 48).

23/1 ***Dichodontium pellucidum*** (Hedw.) Schimp.
(syn. *Dichodontium pellucidum* var. *compactum* Schimp. ex Dixon, *D. pellucidum* var. *fagimontanum* (Brid.) Schimp.)

H(1) listed by Lett (1915: 109) without details.
H(1) 1935: Brandon Mt., no collector named (BBS exc.) (Watson 1936: 264), as var. *compactum.*
†H1 listed by Blockeel & Long (1998: 75).
H(2) listed by Lett (1915: 109) without details.
H2 1951: wet stony shore, Ross I., Killarney, EW Jones (Warburg 1952: 99), as var. *fagimontanum.*
H(3) listed by Lett (1915: 109) without details.
H3 1962: soil by path, copper mines, Allihies, AJE Smith (Warburg 1963b: 494), as var. *fagimontanum.*
H4 1967: stones by stream, *ca* 1200 ft [alt.], Mushera, RD Fitzgerald (Crundwell 1968: 633).

H(5) listed by Lett (1915: 109) without details.
†H5 listed by Blockeel & Long (1998: 75).
H6 1966: streamside, E of the Punchbowl, Comeragh Mts, ERB Little & JA Paton (BBS exc.) (Perry 1967: 410).
H(7) listed by Lett (1915: 109) without details.
†H7 listed by Blockeel & Long (1998: 75).
H(8) listed by Lett (1915: 109) without details.
†H8 listed by Blockeel & Long (1998: 75).
H(9) listed by Lett (1915: 109) without details.
†H9 listed by Blockeel & Long (1998: 75).
H10 1951: stream above Silvermines, AD Banwell, PJ Wanstall & EV Watson (Warburg 1953: 307).
H(12) listed by Lett (1915: 109) without details.
†H12 listed by Blockeel & Long (1998: 75).
H(13) listed by Lett (1915: 109) without details.
†H13 listed by Blockeel & Long (1998: 75).
H(14) listed by Lett (1915: 109) without details.
†H14 listed by Blockeel & Long (1998: 75).
H(16) listed by Lett (1915: 109) without details.
H16 1962: edge of ditch at base of Lissoughter, nr Recess, AJE Smith (Warburg 1963b: 494), as var. *fagimontanum.*
H(18) listed by Blockeel & Long (1998: 75).
†H20 listed by Blockeel & Long (1998: 75).
H(20) listed by Lett (1915: 109) without details.
H(21) listed by Lett (1915: 109) without details. H(21) listed by Blockeel & Long (1998: 75).
H24 1980: boulder on shore of L. Kinale, DM Synnott (DBN) (Blockeel 1989: 25).
H(25) 1940: near Boyle, JS Thomson (Duncan 1944: 209).
†H25 listed by Blockeel & Long (1998: 75).
H(26) listed by Lett (1915: 109) without details.
†H26 listed by Blockeel & Long (1998: 75).
H(27) listed by Lett (1915: 109).
†H27 listed by Blockeel & Long (1998: 75).
H(28) listed by Lett (1915: 109) without details.
H(28) 1937: Gleniff, no collector named (BBS exc.) (Armitage 1938: 11), as var. *compactum.*
H28 1965: dune slacks, Yellow Strand, N of Raghly, EF Warburg & AR Perry (Warburg 1966: 192), as var. *fagimontanum.*
H(29) listed by Lett (1915: 109) without details.
†H29 listed by Blockeel & Long (1998: 75).
H(30) listed by Lett (1915: 109).
†H30 listed by Blockeel & Long (1998: 75).
[H(31) listed by Lett (1915: 109) without details. H31 deleted because no valid record or voucher specimen traced (Blockeel 1999: 4)].
H31 1999: on wet rock wall of gully, 300 m alt., Two Mile River, Carlingford, J11, TL Blockeel 28/177 (Rothero 2000: 47).
H(32) listed by Lett (1915: 109) without details.
†H32 listed by Blockeel & Long (1998: 75).
H(33) listed by Lett (1915: 109) without details.
†H33 listed by Blockeel & Long (1998: 75).
H(34) listed by Lett (1915: 109).
†H34 listed by Blockeel & Long (1998: 75).
H(35) listed by Lett (1915: 109) without details.
H35 1962: dunes, Murroe Strand, nr Dunfanaghy, EF Warburg *et al.* (BBS exc.) (Warburg 1963b: 494), as var. *fagimontanum.*
H(36) listed by Lett (1915: 109) without details.
†H36 listed by Blockeel & Long (1998: 75).
H(37) listed by Lett (1915: 109).
†H37 listed by Blockeel & Long (1998: 75).
H(38) listed by Lett (1915: 109) without details. H(38) listed by Blockeel & Long (1998: 75).
H38 1999: in sand amongst rocks by stream, 50 m alt., Tollymore Forest park, 4 km W of Newcastle, J33, TL Blockeel 28/339 (Rothero 2000: 47).
H(39) 1915: Sallagh Braes, JD Houston (anon. 1916c: 6).
1915: Giant's Causeway, JD Houston (anon. 1916c: 6), det. as var. *compactum* by DA Jones ('I think this might pass for the var. *compactum*').
H(39) listed by Lett (1915: 109).
†H39 listed by Blockeel & Long (1998: 75).
H(40) listed by Lett (1915: 109).
†H40 listed by Blockeel & Long (1998: 75).

23/2 ***Dichodontium flavescens*** (Dicks.) Lindb.
(syn. *Dichodontium pellucidum* var. *flavescens* (Dicks.) Husn.)

[H(1) listed by Lett (1915: 109) without details. Not accepted for H1 by MO Hill (Corley & Hill 1981: 66).
[H(2) listed by Lett (1915: 109). Not accepted for H2 by MO Hill (Corley & Hill 1981: 66)].
[H(3) listed by Lett (1915: 109). Not accepted for H3 by MO Hill (Corley & Hill 1981: 66)].
[H(4) listed by Lett (1915: 109). Not accepted for H4 by MO Hill (Corley & Hill 1981: 66)].
[H(5) listed by Lett (1915: 109). Not accepted for H5 by MO Hill (Corley & Hill 1981: 66)].
[H(6) listed by Lett (1915: 109). Not accepted for H6 by MO Hill (Corley & Hill 1981: 66)].
[H8 1966: edge of stream, *ca* 1300 ft alt., S side of Galtymore, RD Fitzgerald (BBS exc.) (Perry 1967: 410). Not accepted for H8 by MO Hill (Corley & Hill 1981: 66)].
[H11 1958: wooded ravine, Coolhill Castle, ALK King (Warburg 1959: 632). Not accepted for H11 by MO Hill (Corley & Hill 1981: 66)].
[H(13) listed by Lett (1915: 109). Not accepted for H13 by MO Hill (Corley & Hill 1981: 66)].
[H(14) listed by Lett (1915: 109). Not accepted for H14 by MO Hill (Corley & Hill 1981: 66)].
[H(16) 1933: Kylemore, PWM Richards (anon. 1938d: 39). Not accepted for H16 by MO Hill (Corley & Hill 1981: 66)].
H(20) 1812: sand in the river at the Dargle, Dr Taylor (BM), conf. MO Hill (Lett 1915: 109; MO Hill MS).
H(21) 1840: Holly Park nr Dublin, S Foot (GL), conf. MO Hill (MO Hill MS).
H(21) listed by Lett (1915: 109) without details.
[H(27) listed by Lett (1915: 109). Not accepted for H27 by MO Hill (Corley & Hill 1981: 66)].
[H(28) listed by Lett (1915: 109). Not accepted for H28 by MO Hill (Corley & Hill 1981: 66)].
H(29) 1909: Waterfalls, Glencar, WN Tetley (BBSUK), conf. MO Hill (Lett 1915: 109; MO Hill MS).
1928: wooded glen, NE end of Glencar Lough (BBS exc.) (Duncan 1928: 118).
[H(30) listed by Lett (1915: 109). Not accepted for H30 by MO Hill (Corley & Hill 1981: 66)].
[H(31) listed by Lett (1915: 109). Not accepted for H31 by MO Hill (Corley & Hill 1981: 66)].
[H(32) listed by Lett (1915: 109). Not accepted for H32 by MO Hill (Corley & Hill 1981: 66)].
[H(33) listed by Lett (1915: 109). Not accepted for H33 by MO Hill (Corley & Hill 1981: 66)].
[H(34) listed by Lett (1915: 109). Not accepted for H34 by MO Hill (Corley & Hill 1981: 66)].
[H(35) listed by Lett (1915: 109). Not accepted for H35 by MO Hill (Corley & Hill 1981: 66)].
[H37 1964: stones by R. Blackwater, Carrickaness, nr Benburb, RD Fitzgerald (Warburg 1965: 861). Not accepted for H8 by MO Hill (Corley & Hill 1981: 66)].
[H(38) listed by Lett (1915: 109). Not accepted for H38 by MO Hill (Corley & Hill 1981: 66)].
[H(39) listed by Lett (1915: 109). Not accepted for H39 by MO Hill (Corley & Hill 1981: 66)].
[H(40) listed by Lett (1915: 109) as 1895: Roe Park, Limavady, leg. Stewart. This specimen should be checked to confirm identification].
H40 *ca* 1960: rocks in stream below waterfall, Downhill, EW Jones, conf. MO Hill (MO Hill MS).

Irish and British specimens were revised for the *CC* by MO Hill (Corley & Hill 1981: 66); details of records given above are taken from unpublished notes (MO Hill MS). A recent study by Werner (2002) has shown that *D. flavescens* can be distinguished from *D. pellucidum* using characters of the gametophyte, so that some records that have been rejected because of the absence of sporophytes need to be reassessed.

25/1 ***Dicranella palustris*** (Dicks.) Crundw. ex E.F.Warb.
(syn. *Anisothecium squarrosum* (Starke) Lindb., *Dicranella squarrosa* (Starke) Schimp.)

H(1) listed by Lett (1915: 103).
†H1 listed by Blockeel & Long (1998: 75).
H(2) listed by Lett (1915: 103).
†H2 listed by Blockeel & Long (1998: 75).
H(3) listed by Lett (1915: 103).
†H3 listed by Blockeel & Long (1998: 75).
H4 1967: wet ground, *ca* 1300 ft [alt.], Musherabeg, RD Fitzgerald (Crundwell 1968: 632).
H(5) listed by Lett (1915: 103).
†H5 listed by Blockeel & Long (1998: 75).
H(6) listed by Lett (1915: 103).
†H6 listed by Blockeel & Long (1998: 75).
H(7) listed by Lett (1915: 103).
†H7 listed by Blockeel & Long (1998: 75).
H8 1966: boggy ground by stream S of Paradise Hill, Galtee Mts, MFV Corley & JS Parker (Perry 1967: 409).
H9 1957: side of drain, Maghera woods, Tulla, ALK King (Warburg 1958b: 475).
H10 1967: wet moor, Knockfine, Keeper Hill, RD Fitzgerald (Crundwell 1968: 632).
H12 1969: on wall by stream, Pallis Bridge, Wicklow Gap, RD Fitzgerald (Crundwell 1970: 197).
H13 1969: in flush, the Nine Stones, N of Mt Leinster, RD Fitzgerald (Crundwell 1970: 197).
H(14) listed by Lett (1915: 103).
†H14 listed by Blockeel & Long (1998: 75).
H15 1994: wet bank beside Boleyneendorish River, Slieve Aughty, M50, JA Paton 2699 (Blockeel 1995c: 41).
†H16 listed by Blockeel & Long (1998: 75).
H(18) listed by Lett (1915: 103). H(18) listed by Blockeel & Long (1998: 75).
H(20) listed by Lett (1915: 103).
†H20 listed by Blockeel & Long (1998: 75).
H(21) listed by Lett (1915: 103).
†H21 listed by Blockeel & Long (1998: 75).
H25 1968: side of brook, Slieve Bawn, 4 miles NE of Lanesborough, WV Rubers, P Hessel & J Klein (U) (Crundwell 1974: 166).
H(27) listed by Lett (1915: 103).
†H27 listed by Blockeel & Long (1998: 75).
H(28) listed by Lett (1915: 103).
†H28 listed by Blockeel & Long (1998: 75).
H(29) listed by Lett (1915: 103).
†H29 listed by Blockeel & Long (1998: 75).
H(30) listed by Lett (1915: 103).
†H30 listed by Blockeel & Long (1998: 75).
H(31) listed by Lett (1915: 103). H(31) listed by Blockeel & Long (1998: 75).
H31 1999: on wet rock ledge by stream, 300 m alt., Two Mile River, Carlingford, J11, TL Blockeel 28/174 (Rothero 2000: 48).
H(32) listed by Lett (1915: 103).
†H32 listed by Blockeel & Long (1998: 75).
H(33) listed by Lett (1915: 103).
†H33 listed by Blockeel & Long (1998: 75).
H(34) listed by Lett (1915: 103) without locality.
†H34 listed by Blockeel & Long (1998: 75).
H(35) listed by Lett (1915: 103).
†H35 listed by Blockeel & Long (1998: 75).
H36 1950: loose turf, bank of stream, Lislap Forestry Centre, nr Omagh, J Taylor (Warburg 1951: 498).
H(37) listed by Lett (1915: 103).
†H37 listed by Blockeel & Long (1998: 75).
H(38) listed by Lett (1915: 104). H(38) listed by Blockeel & Long (1998: 75).
H38 2002: on rock at edge of stream, 225 m alt., Spinkwee River, W of Slievenabrock, J33, DT Holyoak 02-1020 (Rothero 2003: 49).
H(39) listed by Lett (1915: 104).
†H39 listed by Blockeel & Long (1998: 75).
H(40) listed by Lett (1915: 104).
†H40 listed by Blockeel & Long (1998: 75).

25/2 ***Dicranella schreberiana*** (Hedw.) Dixon
(syn. *Anisothecium crispum* Lindb., *A. crispum* var. *elatum* (Schimp.) Braithw., *Dicranella schreberana* auct., *D. schreberi* var. *elata* Schimp.)

[H(1) listed by Lett (1915: 103) as Mangerton, leg. Miss Hutchins (as var. *crispum* and var. *elatum*). H1 deleted because no valid record or voucher specimen traced (Blockeel 1999: 4)].
H(2) listed by Lett (1915: 103) without details.
†H2 listed by Blockeel & Long (1998: 76).
H3 1967: roadside bank S of Macroom, RD Fitzgerald (Crundwell 1968: 632).
H4 1967: on track in field, Dripsey Castle, nr Cork, RD Fitzgerald (Crundwell 1968: 632).
H5 1966: arable field at 200 ft alt., Kilworth,

JG Duckett *et al.* (BBS exc.) (Perry 1967: 409).

H6 1966: bare soil in field by R. Nire, Shanballyanne, ERB Little & JA Paton (BBS exc.) (Perry 1967: 409).

H7 1966: arable nr Ardfinnan, J Appleyard & JG Duckett (BBS exc.) (Perry 1967: 409).

H8 1966: roadside bank between Barna and Pallas Grean, ERB Little (BBS exc.) (Perry 1967: 409).

H9 1977: Roche's Marsh, at road junction 2 miles E of Kilfenora, PH Pitkin (Hill 1979: 26).

H10 1979: field beside Clare River, S of Derrygareen, E of Newport, JA Paton (Hill 1980b: 35).

H11 1966: soil by road nr Foulkscourt House, W of Johnstown, ERB Little (BBS exc.) (Perry 1967: 409).

†H12 listed by Blockeel & Long (1998: 76).

H13 1975: bank on edge of fen SW of Yellowford Cross Roads, S of Baltinglass, JA Paton (BBS exc.) (Crundwell 1976: 23).

H14 1956: disturbed limey ground, nr Castletown, AA Cridland (Warburg 1958b: 475).

H15 1962: ditch bank nr raised bog by L. Derg, AJE Smith (Warburg 1963b: 494).

H16 1965: ditch bank in conifer plantation nr Lettercraffroe Lough, S of Oughterard, AJE Smith (Warburg 1966: 192).

H18 1987: barley stubble, Derrybrat, 5 km NW of Kilcormac, HLK Whitehouse (Blockeel 1988: 33).

H19 2002: in barley stubble on clay, 95 m alt., 1.5 km W of Kildare railway station, M71, HF Fox & CD Preston (Rothero 2003: 49).

†H20 listed by Blockeel & Long (1998: 76).

H(21) listed by Lett (1915: 103).

†H21 listed by Blockeel & Long (1998: 76).

H22 1978: side of ditch, Petersville Cross Roads, N of Moynalty, DM Synnott (Hill 1979: 26).

H23 1952: old cart track, Clonhugh Demesne, NE end of L. Owel, JS Thomson (Warburg 1953: 307).

H24 1957: Ardagh Hill, MPH Kertland & ALK King (Warburg 1958b: 475).

†H25 listed by Blockeel & Long (1998: 76).

H26 1970: side of track, Keel Bridge, 3 miles N of Ballinrobe, J Appleyard (BBS exc.) (Crundwell 1971b: 375, Appleyard 1971: 388).

H27 1987: on shaded clay bank at edge of woodland near a moist ditch running into nearby lake, Westport House, Westport, DA Newman (Blockeel 1988: 33-34).

H28 1970: forestry road, Knocknarea, W of Sligo, J Appleyard (BBS exc.) (Crundwell 1971b: 375, Appleyard 1971: 387).

H29 1963: shale, Treannatullagh, S of Belhavel Lough, RD Fitzgerald & AR Perry (Warburg 1964: 724).

[H30 deleted because no valid record or voucher specimen traced (Blockeel 1999: 4)].

H30 2001: on thin soil by stump on bank of stream, 315 m alt., W of Bellavally Gap, H12, DT Holyoak 01-646 (Rothero 2002: 44).

H32 1961: ground in old sandpit, Castleshane, nr Monaghan, RD Fitzgerald (Warburg 1962: 367).

H33 1959: calcareous clay at foot of scarp, Magho, Lower Lough Erne, RD Fitzgerald (Warburg 1960: 772).

H(34) listed by Lett (1915: 103) without locality.

†H34 listed by Blockeel & Long (1998: 76).

H35 1962: stubble field, Ards Peninsula, J Appleyard (BBS exc.) (Warburg 1963b: 494).

H36 1958: bare wet ground, L. More, nr Favor Royal, RD Fitzgerald (Warburg 1959: 632).

H37 1962: side of open drain in fen nr Clady Milltown, EM Lobley & MPH Kertland (Warburg 1963b: 494).

H(38) listed by Lett (1915: 103). H(38) listed by Blockeel & Long (1998: 76).

H38 2002: on disturbed soil on moorland slope by stream, 210 m alt., near N end of Silent Valley Reservoir, J32, DT Holyoak 02-979 (Rothero 2003: 49).

H(39) listed by Lett (1915: 103).

†H39 listed by Blockeel & Long (1998: 76).

H(40) 1913: Legavannon, Tarvagh and Kilrea, JD Houston (anon. 1914a: 97).

†H40 listed by Blockeel & Long (1998: 76).

25/3 ***Dicranella grevilleana*** (Brid.) Schimp. (syn. *Anisothecium grevillei* Lindb.)

H(20) 1864: Lugnaquilla, Moore (Lett 1915: 103). H(20) listed by Blockeel & Long (1998: 76).
†H28 listed by Blockeel & Long (1998: 76).
†H29 listed by Blockeel & Long (1998: 76).

25/4 ***Dicranella crispa*** (Hedw.) Schimp.

H1 1951: wet gravelly flush nr sea, between Carrigasheen and Rinneen Point, nr Waterville, J Appleyard (BBS exc.) (Warburg 1952: 99).
H(2) listed by Lett (1915: 102). H(2) listed by Blockeel & Long (1998: 76).
H(5) listed by Lett (1915: 102). H(5) listed by Blockeel & Long (1998: 76).
H(16) listed by Lett (1915: 102). H(16) listed by Blockeel & Long (1998: 76).
H28 1970: roadside quarry nr Masshill, JA Paton (BBS exc.) (Crundwell 1971b: 375, Appleyard 1971: 389).
H29 1963: wet clayey pasture below limestone scarp, Boggaun, nr Manorhamilton, AR Perry & RD Fitzgerald (Warburg 1964: 724).
H(34) listed by Lett (1915: 102).
†H34 listed by Blockeel & Long (1998: 76).
H(38) listed by Lett (1915: 102). H(38) listed by Blockeel & Long (1998: 76).
H(39) listed by Lett (1915: 102).
†H39 listed by Blockeel & Long (1998: 76).
H(40) listed by Lett (1915: 102). H(40) listed by Blockeel & Long (1998: 76).

25/5 ***Dicranella subulata*** (Hedw.) Schimp. (syn. *Dicranella curvata* (Hedw.) Schimp., *D. secunda* Lindb., *D. subulata* var. *curvata* (Hedw.) Rabenh.)

H(1) listed by Lett (1915: 102).
†H1 listed by Blockeel & Long (1998: 76).
H(3) listed by Lett (1915: 102). H(3) listed by Blockeel & Long (1998: 76).
H(5) listed by Lett (1915: 102). H(5) listed by Blockeel & Long (1998: 76).
H6 1966: among boulders above Coumshingaun, J Appleyard (BBS exc.) (Perry 1967: 409), as var. *curvata*.
H(12) listed by Lett (1915: 102). H(12) listed by Blockeel & Long (1998: 76).
H(13) listed by Lett (1915: 102). H(13) listed by Blockeel & Long (1998: 76).
H16 1970: bank of Kylemore River N of Benbaun, Twelve Pins, JA Paton (Crundwell 1971b: 375).
[H(13) listed by Lett (1915: 102) as Howth, leg. Orr. H21 deleted: specimen from Howth, leg. D Orr (DBN), is *D. heteromalla*, comm. DM Synnott (Blockeel 1989: 25)].
[H17 deleted because entry in *CC* is a transcription error (Blockeel 1995c: 41)].
[H(27) listed by Lett (1915: 102) as *D. curvata*].
H34 2002: on thin soil on ledges of steep NW-facing crag, 420 m alt., NW slope of Bulbin Mountain, C34, DT Holyoak 02-804 (Rothero 2003: 49).
H(35) 1907: Killybegs, CA Cheetham (anon. 1915a: 125).
†H35 listed by Blockeel & Long (1998: 76).
H36 1957: sandy detritus, *ca* 1500 ft [alt.], Dart Mt., Sperrin Mts, RD Fitzgerald (Warburg 1958b: 474).
H(38) listed by Lett (1915: 102). H(38) listed by Blockeel & Long (1998: 76).
H(39) listed by Lett (1915: 102). H(39) listed by Blockeel & Long (1998: 76).
H40 2002: on damp soil on floor of old quarry, 275 m alt., above Whitewater Bridge, NE of Lough Fea, H78, DT Holyoak 02-1155 (Rothero 2003: 49).

25/6 ***Dicranella varia*** (Hedw.) Schimp. (syn. *Anisothecium rubrum* Lindb. nom. illeg., *A. rubrum* var. *callistomum* (With.) Braithw., *A. rubrum* var. *tenellum* (Bruch, Schimp. & W.Gümbel) Braithw., *A. rubrum* var. *tenuifolium* (Bruch, Schimp. & W.Gümbel) Braithw.)

H(1) listed by Lett (1915: 102).
†H1 listed by Blockeel & Long (1998: 76).
H(2) listed by Lett (1915: 102).
†H2 listed by Blockeel & Long (1998: 76).
H(3) listed by Lett (1915: 102).
†H3 listed by Blockeel & Long (1998: 76).
H(4) listed by Lett (1915: 102). H(4) listed by Blockeel & Long (1998: 76).
H4 2002: on bare soil on bank, 40 m alt., Blarney in the Castle grounds, W76, TL Blockeel 31/295 (Rothero 2003: 49).
H(5) listed by Lett (1915: 103).
†H5 listed by Blockeel & Long (1998: 76).
H(6) listed by Lett (1915: 102).
†H6 listed by Blockeel & Long (1998: 76).

H(7) listed by Lett (1915: 102).
†H7 listed by Blockeel & Long (1998: 76).
H8 1966: soil among limestone rocks in quarry, Knockainy, MFV Corley & JS Parker (Perry 1967: 409).
H(9) 1945: near Kilnaboy, JS Thomson (anon. 1946c: 280).
†H9 listed by Blockeel & Long (1998: 76).
H(10) listed by Lett (1915: 102).
†H10 listed by Blockeel & Long (1998: 76).
H11 1966: side of road, Foulkscourt House, nr Johnstown, J Appleyard *et al.* (BBS exc.) (Perry 1967: 409).
H(12) listed by Lett (1915: 102, 103).
†H12 listed by Blockeel & Long (1998: 76).
[H(13) 1940: Kilkea Park, JS Thomson (Duncan 1944: 209). H(13) deleted because record transferred to H(19) (Warburg 1953: 307)].
H13 1969: sandy ground, Corrabut Gap, nr Myshall, RD Fitzgerald (Crundwell 1970: 197).
H(14) listed by Lett (1915: 102).
†H14 listed by Blockeel & Long (1998: 76).
H15 1952: bank in marsh, nr Ross Quay, L. Derg, MPH Kertland & ALK King (Warburg 1953: 307).
†H16 listed by Blockeel & Long (1998: 76).
H(17) listed by Lett (1915: 102).
†H17 listed by Blockeel & Long (1998: 76).
H(18) listed by Lett (1915: 102).
†H18 listed by Blockeel & Long (1998: 76).
H(19) 1940: Kilkea Park, JS Thomson (Duncan 1944: 209), published as a record from H(13) but later transferred to H(19) (Warburg 1953: 307).
†H19 listed by Blockeel & Long (1998: 76).
H(20) listed by Lett (1915: 102).
†H20 listed by Blockeel & Long (1998: 76).
H(21) listed by Lett (1915: 102).
†H21 listed by Blockeel & Long (1998: 76).
H22 1961: damp sandy roadside nr Kells, EM Lobley (Warburg 1962: 367).
H23 1955: mud heap by roadside, Ballinafid, nr Multyfarnham, JS Thomson (Warburg 1956: 152).
H24 1957: by Ballymacarrow Bridge, ALK King (Warburg 1958b: 474).
H(25) listed by Lett (1915: 103).
†H25 listed by Blockeel & Long (1998: 76).
†H26 listed by Blockeel & Long (1998: 76).
†H27 listed by Blockeel & Long (1998: 76).
†H28 listed by Blockeel & Long (1998: 76).
H(29) listed by Lett (1915: 103).
†H29 listed by Blockeel & Long (1998: 76).
H(30) listed by Lett (1915: 103).
†H30 listed by Blockeel & Long (1998: 76).
H(31) listed by Lett (1915: 103). H(31) listed by Blockeel & Long (1998: 76).
H(32) listed by Lett (1915: 103). H(32) listed by Blockeel & Long (1998: 76).
H(33) listed by Lett (1915: 103).
†H33 listed by Blockeel & Long (1998: 76).
H(34) listed by Lett (1915: 103) without locality.
†H34 listed by Blockeel & Long (1998: 76).
H(35) listed by Lett (1915: 103).
†H35 listed by Blockeel & Long (1998: 76).
H(36) listed by Lett (1915: 103).
†H36 listed by Blockeel & Long (1998: 76).
H(37) listed by Lett (1915: 103).
†H37 listed by Blockeel & Long (1998: 76).
H(38) listed by Lett (1915: 103).
†H38 listed by Blockeel & Long (1998: 76).
H(39) listed by Lett (1915: 103).
†H39 listed by Blockeel & Long (1998: 76).
H(40) listed by Lett (1915: 103).
†H40 listed by Blockeel & Long (1998: 76).

25/7 *Dicranella staphylina* H.Whitehouse

H3 1968: field at head of Glenbeg L. nr Ardgroom, 82/52, JA Paton (Whitehouse 1969: 765, Crundwell 1970: 197).
H4 2002: at edge of stubble field, 30 m alt., Curraghbinny Wood, E of Carragline, W76, TL Blockeel 31/380 (Rothero 2003: 49).
H5 1979: soil in arboretum, Fota I., N Kirby (Hill 1980b: 35).
H6 1966: arable field nr Clogheen, Ballymacarby, Clonmel, 92/08 [*sic* = 02/08], JA Paton & ERB Little (Whitehouse 1969: 765, Crundwell 1970: 197).
H8 1979: potato field, Beagh Castle, Askeaton, EW Jones (Hill 1980b: 35).
H9 1979: waste ground, W side of Slievebernagh, AC Crundwell (Hill 1980b: 35).
H10 1987: barley field, 2 km SW of Ballinderry, HLK Whitehouse (Blockeel 1988: 34).
H12 1972: timber road, wood at Mountfin House, 2 km W of Ferns, WV Rubers (U) (Crundwell 1974: 166).
H13 1999: on bare soil at edge of path, 8 m alt., R Barrow nr canal, 1 km NW of Saint Mullins, S73, TL Blockeel 28/326 (Rothero 2000: 48).

H14 1987: barley field, 2 km W of Mountmellick, HLK Whitehouse (Blockeel 1988: 34).
H16 1970: soil in field, Gorteen Bay, Roundstone, MFV Corley (Crundwell 1971b: 375).
H18 1987: barley stubble, Derrybrat, 5 km NW of Kilcormac, HLK Whitehouse (Blockeel 1988: 34).
H19 1987: barley field, 2.5 km E of Rathangan, HLK Whitehouse (Blockeel 1988: 34).
H20 1962: roadside nr Rathdangan, HLK Whitehouse (Whitehouse 1969: 765, Crundwell 1970: 197).
H21 1988: side of cart track, E of the farmyard, Lambay I., DM Synnott (Blockeel 1989: 26).
H22 1978: wheat stubble, 1 km W of Julianstown, DM Synnott (Hill 1980b: 35).
H25 1973: on shaded path, shore of L. Ree, St John's Wood, WV Rubers (U) (Crundwell 1974: 166).
H26 1987: in tractor ruts in woodland, E bank of Cloon River near Partry, DG Long (Blockeel 1988: 34).
H27 1987: on peaty soil by track, Dooega, Achill I., TL Blockeel (Blockeel 1988: 34).
H29 1972: on shaded path, NE end of L. Gill, WV Rubers (U) (Crundwell 1974: 166).
H30 2001: on damp soil on track, 315 m alt., W of Bellavally Gap, H12, DT Holyoak 01-641B (Rothero 2002: 44).
H33 2000: on disturbed stony soil, Marble Arch, by visitor centre, H13, DT Holyoak 00-145 (BBSUK) (Rothero 2001: 39).
H34 2002: on disturbed soil of flower bed, 5 m alt., Quigley's Point camping ground, C53, DT Holyoak 02-479 (Rothero 2003: 49).
H35 1990: bare soil under trees in hotel grounds, 5 m alt., Dunfanaghy, C03, TL Blockeel 19/457 (Blockeel 1991c: 41).
H36 2002: on soil at edge of track in woodland, 100 m alt., Drum Manor Forest Park, H77, DT Holyoak 02-1089 (Rothero 2003: 49).
H37 1970: on garden soil, Armagh, MFV Corley (Crundwell 1971b: 375).
H(38) 1909: on spongy patches of *Conferva*, Lenaderg, JH Davies (DBN), comm. DM Synnott (Blockeel 1989: 26).
H38 2002: on stony soil on disturbed ground by estuarine bay, 5 m alt, W of Dundrum, J33, DT Holyoak 02-957 (Rothero 2003: 49).
H39 1999: on mud of drained reservoir, Copeland Reservoir, J49, DT Holyoak 99-849 (BBSUK) (Rothero 2000: 48).
H40 1999: on bare silty mud among grasses on bank of large ditch, Umbra, C73, DT Holyoak 99-110 (BBSUK) (Rothero 2000: 48).

This common but inconspicuous moss was described new to science by Whitehouse (1969). Before then it was apparently overlooked as non-fertile material of other *Dicranella* spp. or *Pseudephemerum nitidum.*

25/8 ***Dicranella rufescens*** (Dicks.) Schimp. (syn. *Anisothecium rufescens* (With.) Lindb.)

H(1) listed by Lett (1915: 103).
†H1 listed by Blockeel & Long (1998: 76).
H(2) listed by Lett (1915: 103). H(2) listed by Blockeel & Long (1998: 76).
H3 1967: clay bank of stream, Foilanumera, RD Fitzgerald (Crundwell 1968: 632).
H4 1967: sandy bank, Carrigagulla Bridge, Bogeragh Mts, RD Fitzgerald (Crundwell 1968: 632).
H5 1967: clay bank, Coolgreen Glen, SW of Watergrasshill, RD Fitzgerald (Crundwell 1968: 632).
H(6) listed by Lett (1915: 103).
†H6 listed by Blockeel & Long (1998: 76).
H7 1966: damp sandy bankside by wood between Seefin and Knockeenatoung, Galtee Mts, EM Lobley & RJ Murphy (BBS exc.) (Perry 1967: 409).
H8 1966: side of ditch, Knockseefin, Nicker, J Appleyard (BBS exc.) (Perry 1967: 409).
H9 1979: waste ground by R. Inagh, 11 km W of Ennis, JA Paton & AC Crundwell (Hill 1980b: 35).
H10 1967: clay bank, Knockfine, Keeper Hill, RD Fitzgerald (Crundwell 1968: 632).
H12 1975: bank nr R. Bann, Camolin, JA Paton (BBS exc.) (Crundwell 1976: 23).
H(14) listed by Lett (1915: 103). H(14) listed by Blockeel & Long (1998: 76).
H15 1994: on muddy stream bank with

Scapania irrigua, nr Pollboy, Slieve Aughty, M50, NG Hodgetts 2965 (Blockeel 1995c: 41).

H16 1970: bank of the Bunowen River, nr Killary Harbour, JA Paton (Crundwell 1971b: 375).

H(20) listed by Lett (1915: 103).

†H20 listed by Blockeel & Long (1998: 76).

H(21) listed by Lett (1915: 103). H(21) listed by Blockeel & Long (1998: 76).

H26 1987: tractor rut on woodland path, E side of Cloon River, between Srah and Partry, DM Synnott (Blockeel 1988: 34).

H27 1965: bank of stream nr Srahillbeg Lough, Achill, EF Warburg (Warburg 1966: 192).

H28 1970: on mud by waterfall, Gleniff, S of Clogh, *ca* 3 miles E of Benbulbin [*sic* = Ben Bulben], J Appleyard (BBS exc.) (Crundwell 1971b: 373, Appleyard 1971: 387-388).

H29 1965: wet clay in flush at 700 ft alt., hillside nr Aghadunvane, S of L. Melvin, EF Warburg & AR Perry (Warburg 1966: 192).

H30 1970: on muddy slopes, below Englishman's House, Glenfarne nr Belcoo, J Appleyard (BBS exc.) (Crundwell 1971b: 375, Appleyard 1971: 389-390).

H(31) listed by Lett (1915: 103). H(31) listed by Blockeel & Long (1998: 76).

[H(32) listed by Lett (1915: 103) as 1910: Eskmore, leg. Bingham. H32 deleted because specimen from Eskmore, 1910, leg. RW Bingham (DBN), is *Ditrichum heteromallum*, comm. DM Synnott (Blockeel 1989: 25-26)].

H34 1962: fallow field N of Lifford, EM Lobley & MPH Kertland (BBS exc.) (Warburg 1963b: 494).

H35 1962: gravelly roadside, Creeslough, EF Warburg & EM Lobley (BBS exc.) (Warburg 1963b: 494).

H36 1957: sandy detritus, Curraghinhalt, nr Gortin, RD Fitzgerald (Warburg 1958b: 474).

H37 2002: on soil on steep bank above stream, Gosford Forest Park, H94, DT Holyoak 02-1085 (Rothero 2003: 49).

H(38) listed by Lett (1915: 103). H(38) listed by Blockeel & Long (1998: 76).

H38 2002: on damp clay bank in inundation zone of reservoir, 290 m alt., S end of Fofanny Dam, J22, DT Holyoak 02-971 (Rothero 2003: 49).

H(39) listed by Lett (1915: 103).

†H39 listed by Blockeel & Long (1998: 76).

H(40) listed by Lett (1915: 103).

†H40 listed by Blockeel & Long (1998: 76).

25/9 ***Dicranella cerviculata*** (Hedw.) Schimp.

H(1) listed by Lett (1915: 102). H(1) listed by Blockeel & Long (1998: 76).

H(2) listed by Lett (1915: 102). H(2) listed by Blockeel & Long (1998: 76).

H(3) listed by Lett (1915: 102). H(3) listed by Blockeel & Long (1998: 76).

H(4) listed by Lett (1915: 102). H(4) listed by Blockeel & Long (1998: 76).

H(5) listed by Lett (1915: 102). H(5) listed by Blockeel & Long (1998: 76).

H(6) listed by Lett (1915: 102). H(6) listed by Blockeel & Long (1998: 76).

[H12 deleted because no valid record or voucher specimen traced (Blockeel 1999: 4)].

H(13) 1949: Essexford Bog, Inniskeen, JP Brunker (Warburg 1950: 382).

H13 1971: peat face nr Hacketstown, AG Side (Crundwell 1972: 137).

H(14) listed by Lett (1915: 102).

†H14 listed by Blockeel & Long (1998: 76).

H(16) listed by Lett (1915: 102). H(16) listed by Blockeel & Long (1998: 76).

H16 1957: peat cutting, lower slopes of Maumtrasna E of Skeltia, EM Lobley (BBS exc.) published by Warburg 1958b: 474 as a record from H27, but re-assigned to H16 by (Crundwell 1970: 198). H16 is therefore apparently given in brackets in error by Blockeel & Long (1998: 76).

H17 1957: raised bog between R. Clare and R. Cregg, EM Lobley (BBS exc.) (Warburg 1958b: 474).

H18 1965: peat bank, Letter Crossroads, Slieve Bloom Mts, DM Synnott (Warburg 1966: 192).

H(20) listed by Lett (1915: 102) without locality. H(20) listed by Blockeel & Long (1998: 76).

H(21) listed by Lett (1915: 102) without locality. H(21) listed by Blockeel & Long (1998: 76).

H22 1956: on bank, Rossan Bog, nr Kinnegad, ALK King (Warburg 1957: 329).

H23 1959: peat face, Lisclogher Bog, ALK

King (Warburg 1960: 772).
H(24) listed by Lett (1915: 102). H(24) listed by Blockeel & Long (1998: 76).
H(25) listed by Lett (1915: 102). H(25) listed by Blockeel & Long (1998: 76).
H26 1965: peat *ca* 700 ft alt., cliffs S of Glendaduff, [The] Ox Mts, RD Fitzgerald (Warburg 1966: 192).
[H27 1957: peat cutting, lower slopes of Maumtrasna, EM Lobley (BBS exc.) (Warburg 1958b: 474). H27 deleted because locality (E of Skeltia, Maumtrasna) is in H16 (Crundwell 1970: 198)].
H27 1987: side of drain, Salia, Achill I., E Rosen & DM Synnott (Blockeel 1988: 34).
H(28) 1937: Cliffony, no collector named (BBS exc.) (Armitage 1938: 11).
H(29) listed by Lett (1915: 102). H(29) listed by Blockeel & Long (1998: 76).
H30 1965: peat block in bog, Carricknacrannoge, nr Dowra, RD Fitzgerald & EM Lobley (Warburg 1966: 192).
H(31) listed by Blockeel & Long (1998: 76).
H(32) 1947: bank of bog hole, Black I., Lough Muckno, Hope Castle demesne, Castleblaney, JS Thomson (anon. 1948b: 119).
H(33) listed by Lett (1915: 102). H(33) listed by Blockeel & Long (1998: 76).
H(34) listed by Lett (1915: 102).
†H34 listed by Blockeel & Long (1998: 76).
H(35) listed by Lett (1915: 102).
†H35 listed by Blockeel & Long (1998: 76).
†H36 listed by Blockeel & Long (1998: 76).
H(37) listed by Lett (1915: 102).
†H37 listed by Blockeel & Long (1998: 76).
H(38) listed by Lett (1915: 102). H(38) listed by Blockeel & Long (1998: 76).
H(39) listed by Lett (1915: 102). H(39) listed by Blockeel & Long (1998: 76).
H(40) listed by Blockeel & Long (1998: 76).

25/10 ***Dicranella heteromalla*** (Hedw.) Schimp.
(syn. *Dicranella heteromalla* var. *sericea* Schimp., *D. heteromalla* var. *stricta* Schimp.)

H(1) listed by Lett (1915: 102) without details.
†H1 listed by Blockeel & Long (1998: 76).
H(2) listed by Lett (1915: 102) without details.
†H2 listed by Blockeel & Long (1998: 76).
H(3) listed by Lett (1915: 102) without details.
†H3 listed by Blockeel & Long (1998: 76).
H(4) listed by Lett (1915: 102) without details.
†H4 listed by Blockeel & Long (1998: 76).
H(5) listed by Lett (1915: 102) without details.
†H5 listed by Blockeel & Long (1998: 76).
H(6) listed by Lett (1915: 102) without details.
†H6 listed by Blockeel & Long (1998: 76).
H(7) listed by Lett (1915: 102) without details.
†H7 listed by Blockeel & Long (1998: 76).
H(8) listed by Lett (1915: 102) without details.
†H8 listed by Blockeel & Long (1998: 76).
H9 1957: Bohatch Wood, nr Mountshannon, ALK King (Warburg 1958b: 474).
H(10) listed by Lett (1915: 102) without details.
†H10 listed by Blockeel & Long (1998: 76).
H11 1954: bank in boreen on slope of Mt Brandon, ALK King (Warburg 1955: 583).
H(12) listed by Lett (1915: 102) without details.
†H12 listed by Blockeel & Long (1998: 76).
H(13) listed by Lett (1915: 102) without details.
†H13 listed by Blockeel & Long (1998: 76).
H(14) listed by Lett (1915: 102) without details.
†H14 listed by Blockeel & Long (1998: 76).
H15 1957: open drain, nr Chevy Chase Wood, Owendalulleegh, EM Lobley (BBS exc.) (Warburg 1958b: 474).
H(16) listed by Lett (1915: 102) without details.
†H16 listed by Blockeel & Long (1998: 76).
[H(18) listed by Lett (1915: 102) without details. H18 deleted because no valid record or voucher specimen traced (Blockeel 1999: 4)].
H(19) listed by Lett (1915: 102) without details.
†H19 listed by Blockeel & Long (1998: 76).
H(20) listed by Lett (1915: 102) without details.
†H20 listed by Blockeel & Long (1998: 76).
H(21) listed by Lett (1915: 102) without details.

†H21 listed by Blockeel & Long (1998: 76).
H22 1965: clay bank, woodland, Staleen, Donmore, DM Synnott (Warburg 1966: 192).
H(23) listed by Lett (1915: 102) without details.
†H23 listed by Blockeel & Long (1998: 76).
H24 1957: Carn Clonhugh Hill, ALK King (Warburg 1958b: 474).
H(25) listed by Lett (1915: 102) without details.
†H25 listed by Blockeel & Long (1998: 76).
H26 1957: W slope of [The] Ox Mts, ALK King (Warburg 1958b: 474).
H(27) listed by Lett (1915: 102) without details.
†H27 listed by Blockeel & Long (1998: 76).
H(28) 1937: Gleniff, no collector named (BBS exc.) (Armitage 1938: 11).
†H28 listed by Blockeel & Long (1998: 76).
H(29) listed by Lett (1915: 102) without details.
†H29 listed by Blockeel & Long (1998: 76).
H(30) listed by Lett (1915: 102) without details.
†H30 listed by Blockeel & Long (1998: 76).
H(31) listed by Lett (1915: 102). H(31) listed by Blockeel & Long (1998: 76).
H(32) listed by Lett (1915: 102) without details.
†H32 listed by Blockeel & Long (1998: 76).
H(33) listed by Lett (1915: 102) without details.
†H33 listed by Blockeel & Long (1998: 76).
H(34) listed by Lett (1915: 102) without details.
†H34 listed by Blockeel & Long (1998: 76).
H(35) listed by Lett (1915: 102) without details.
†H35 listed by Blockeel & Long (1998: 76).
H(36) listed by Lett (1915: 102) without details.
H36 1953: bog nr Sandholes, nr Cookstown, MPH Kertland & EM Lobley (Warburg 1955: 583).
H37 1951: Rough I., RD Fitzgerald (Warburg 1952: 99).
H(38) listed by Lett (1915: 102).
†H38 listed by Blockeel & Long (1998: 76).
H(39) listed by Lett (1915: 102) without details.
†H39 listed by Blockeel & Long (1998: 76).
H(40) listed by Lett (1915: 102) without details.
†H40 listed by Blockeel & Long (1998: 76).

26/1 ***Dicranoweisia cirrata*** (Hedw.) Lindb. ex Milde

H1 1951: rock, Cove Harbour, EF Warburg (BBS exc.) (Warburg 1952: 99).
H(3) listed by Lett (1915: 106).
†H3 listed by Blockeel & Long (1998: 77).
H(4) listed by Lett (1915: 106). H(4) listed by Blockeel & Long (1998: 77).
H4 2002: on roadside tree, nr Sullivan's Quay, Cork city centre, W67, TL Blockeel 31/300 (Rothero 2003: 49).
H(5) listed by Lett (1915: 107). H(5) listed by Blockeel & Long (1998: 77).
H(6) listed by Lett (1915: 107).
†H6 listed by Blockeel & Long (1998: 77).
H8 1966: rocks at 1400 ft alt., Slievereagh, nr Ballylanders, MFV Corley & Parker (Perry 1967: 410).
H12 1956: crevice of rock on summit of Tara Hill, ALK King (Warburg 1957: 329).
H13 1969: on stones in old quarry, Lackan, nr Oldleighlin, RD Fitzgerald (Crundwell 1970: 198).
[H(19) listed by Lett (1915: 107) without details. H19 deleted because no valid record or voucher specimen traced (Blockeel 1999: 4)].
H(20) listed by Lett (1915: 107).
†H20 listed by Blockeel & Long (1998: 77).
H(21) listed by Lett (1915: 107).
†H21 listed by Blockeel & Long (1998: 77).
H22 1978: W-facing Silurian rock, E of Carnbane, Oldcastle, DM Synnott (Hill 1980b: 36).
H25 1972: on Old Red Sandstone rock, Slieve Bawn, NW of Lanesborough, WV Rubers (U) (Crundwell 1974: 167).
H(31) listed by Lett (1915: 107). H(31) listed by Blockeel & Long (1998: 77).
H(34) listed by Lett (1915: 107).
†H34 listed by Blockeel & Long (1998: 77).
[H(35) listed by Lett (1915: 107) as: Slieve League, leg. HW Lett. H35 deleted: specimen (from Slieve League, 1902, leg. HW Lett, DBN), is a mixture of *Ptychomitrium polyphyllum* and *Ulota phyllantha*, comm. DM Synnott (Blockeel 1989: 26)].
H35 2001: on stone wall by lane, 20 m alt., Doonan, Teelin Bay, G57, NG Hodgetts 3767 (Rothero 2002: 44).
H(36) listed by Lett (1915: 107).
†H36 listed by Blockeel & Long (1998: 77).
[H(37) listed by Lett (1915: 107) as: Ardmore,

leg. HW Lett. H37 deleted: specimen from Ardmore, 1887, leg. HW Lett (DBN), is *Weissia controversa*, comm. DM Synnott (Blockeel 1989: 26)].

H37 1964: on trees in wood, 210 m, below Tower, Slieve Gullion, RD Fitzgerald (NMW), comm. AR Perry (Blockeel 1990: 30).

H(38) listed by Lett (1915: 107).

†H38 listed by Blockeel & Long (1998: 77).

H(39) listed by Lett (1915: 107).

†H39 listed by Blockeel & Long (1998: 77).

H(40) listed by Lett (1915: 107).

†H40 listed by Blockeel & Long (1998: 77).

[26/2 *Dicranoweisia crispula* (Hedw.) Milde]

[Old records from H20 and H21 treated as doubtful by Lett (1915: 107) are regarded as errors].

27/1 *Arctoa fulvella* (Dicks.) Bruch, Schimp. & W.Gümbel
(syn. *Dicranum fulvellum* (Dicks.) Sm.)

H(1) no date: MacGillicuddy's Reeks, Taylor (Lett 1915: 107).

†H1 listed by Blockeel & Long (1998: 77).

H35 1970: rocks in corrie above Lough Agh, Slieve League, MFV Corley (Hill 1978: 17).

28/2 *Kiaeria blyttii* (Bruch, Schimp. & W. Gümbel) Broth.

[H7 deleted because record not traced, comm. DM Synnott (Hill 1981: 24)].

H27 1987: top of boulder in scree on E slope of N corrie, Mweelrea, JA Paton (Blockeel 1988: 34).

H34 2002: in crevices of schist on low outcrops, 480 m alt., just SW of summit of Bulbin Mountain, C34, DT Holyoak 02-796 (Rothero 2003: 49).

H35 1962: rock ledge at 1330 ft [alt.], N side of Slieve Snaght, Derryveagh Mts, AC Crundwell (BBS exc.) (Warburg 1963b: 494).

[H38 deleted because specimen (DBN) is incorrectly named (Hill 1981: 24)].

H38 2002: on boulder on N-facing hillside near stream, 280 m alt., below Black Stairs, Thomas's Mountain, J32, DT Holyoak 02-1046 (Rothero 2003: 49).

H40 1965: cliffs, *ca* 1700 ft alt., Mullaghmore, nr Dungiven, RD Fitzgerald (Warburg 1966: 193).

[28/3 *Kiaeria starkei* (F.Weber & D.Mohr) I. Hagen]

[H(7) listed by Lett (1915: 107) as 1871: Galtee More, leg. Carroll. H7 deleted because specimen (DBN) is incorrectly named (Hill 1981: 24)].

[H(20) listed by Lett (1915: 107) as: Powerscourt Waterfall, leg. Orr. H20 deleted because specimen (DBN) is incorrectly named (Hill 1981: 24)].

29/2 *Dicranum bonjeanii* De Not.
(syn. *Dicranum bonjeanii* var. *rugifolium* (Bosw.) Dixon)

[H(1) listed by Lett (1915: 108) without details. H1 deleted because no valid record or voucher specimen traced (Blockeel 1999: 4)].

H(2) listed by Lett (1915: 108) without details.

†H2 listed by Blockeel & Long (1998: 77).

H(3) listed by Lett (1915: 108) without details.

†H3 listed by Blockeel & Long (1998: 77).

[H(4) listed by Lett (1915: 108) without details. H4 deleted because no valid record or voucher specimen traced (Blockeel 1999: 4)].

[H(6) listed by Lett (1915: 108) without details. H6 deleted because no valid record or voucher specimen traced (Blockeel 1999: 4)].

H(7) listed by Lett (1915: 108) without details.

†H7 listed by Blockeel & Long (1998: 77).

H(8) listed by Lett (1915: 108) without details.

†H8 listed by Blockeel & Long (1998: 77).

[H(9) listed by Lett (1915: 108) without details. H9 deleted because no valid record or voucher specimen traced (Blockeel 1999: 4)].

H(10) 1949: Loughnaminch, Balingarry, AP Fanning (Warburg 1951: 499).

H11 1966: bog, Derryfadda nr Johnstown, J Appleyard *et al.* (BBS exc.) (Perry 1967: 410).

H(12) listed by Lett (1915: 108) without details.

†H12 listed by Blockeel & Long (1998: 77).

[H(13) listed by Lett (1915: 108) without details. H13 deleted because no valid record or voucher specimen traced (Blockeel 1999: 4)].
H(15) listed by Lett (1915: 108) without details.
†H15 listed by Blockeel & Long (1998: 77).
H(16) listed by Lett (1915: 108) without details.
†H16 listed by Blockeel & Long (1998: 77).
[H(17) listed by Lett (1915: 108) without details. H17 deleted because no valid record or voucher specimen traced (Blockeel 1999: 4)].
H(18) listed by Lett (1915: 108) without details.
†H18 listed by Blockeel & Long (1998: 77).
[H(19) listed by Lett (1915: 108) without details. H19 deleted because no valid record or voucher specimen traced (Blockeel 1999: 4)].
H20 1962: Raven's Glen, Glencree, ALK King (Warburg 1963b: 495).
[H(21) listed by Lett (1915: 108) without details. H21 deleted because no valid record or voucher specimen traced (Blockeel 1999: 4)].
H22 1965: marsh by Royal Canal W of Ferrans Lock, ALK King (Warburg 1966: 193).
H(23) listed by Lett (1915: 108) without details.
†H23 listed by Blockeel & Long (1998: 77).
[H(24) listed by Lett (1915: 108) without details. H24 deleted because no valid record or voucher specimen traced (Blockeel 1999: 4)].
H(25) listed by Lett (1915: 108) without details.
†H25 listed by Blockeel & Long (1998: 77).
H(26) listed by Lett (1915: 108) without details.
†H26 listed by Blockeel & Long (1998: 77).
H(27) listed by Lett (1915: 108).
†H27 listed by Blockeel & Long (1998: 77).
H28 1970: Knocknarea, W of Sligo, J Appleyard (BBS exc.) (Crundwell 1971b: 375, Appleyard 1971: 387).
H(29) listed by Lett (1915: 108).
†H29 listed by Blockeel & Long (1998: 77).
[H(30) listed by Lett (1915: 108) without details. H30 deleted because no valid record or voucher specimen traced (Blockeel 1999: 4)].
[H(31) listed by Lett (1915: 108) without details. H31 deleted because no valid record or voucher specimen traced (Blockeel 1999: 4)].
H32 1980: forming tufts in small, slightly acidic drumlin marsh, Tld. [= Townland] Lisarrilly, N Lockhart (Hill 1983: 50).
H(33) listed by Lett (1915: 108) without details.
†H33 listed by Blockeel & Long (1998: 77).
H(34) 1937: Bundoran, no collector named (BBS exc.) (Armitage 1938: 11), as var. *rugifolium*.
1937: River Drouses, JB Duncan & EM Lobley (anon. 1938b: 24), as var. *rugifolium*.
H(34) listed by Lett (1915: 108) without details.
†H34 listed by Blockeel & Long (1998: 77).
H(35) listed by Lett (1915: 108) without details.
†H35 listed by Blockeel & Long (1998: 77).
H(36) listed by Lett (1915: 108) without details.
†H36 listed by Blockeel & Long (1998: 77).
H(37) listed by Lett (1915: 108) without details.
†H37 listed by Blockeel & Long (1998: 77).
H(38) listed by Lett (1915: 108) without details. H(38) listed by Blockeel & Long (1998: 77).
H(39) listed by Lett (1915: 108) without details.
†H39 listed by Blockeel & Long (1998: 77).
H(40) 1937: Kilrea, JD Houston (anon. 1938d: 39).
†H40 listed by Blockeel & Long (1998: 77).

29/4 ***Dicranum scoparium*** Hedw.
(syn. *Dicranum scoparium* var. *alpestre* Huebener, *D. scoparium* var. *orthophyllum* Brid., *D. scoparium* var. *spadiceum* (Zetterst.) Boulay, *D. scoparium* var. *turfosum* Milde)

H(1) listed by Lett (1915: 107) without details.
†H1 listed by Blockeel & Long (1998: 78).
H(2) listed by Lett (1915: 107).
†H2 listed by Blockeel & Long (1998: 78).
H(3) listed by Lett (1915: 107) without details.
H3 1953: hillside in pass of Keimaneigh, ALK King (Warburg 1954: 480).
H(4) listed by Lett (1915: 107) without details.

†H4 listed by Blockeel & Long (1998: 78).
H(5) listed by Lett (1915: 107) without details.
†H5 listed by Blockeel & Long (1998: 78).
H(6) listed by Lett (1915: 107, 108).
†H6 listed by Blockeel & Long (1998: 78).
H(7) listed by Lett (1915: 107, 108).
†H7 listed by Blockeel & Long (1998: 78).
H(8) listed by Lett (1915: 107) without details.
†H8 listed by Blockeel & Long (1998: 78).
H(9) listed by Lett (1915: 107) without details.
†H9 listed by Blockeel & Long (1998: 78).
H(10) listed by Lett (1915: 107).
†H10 listed by Blockeel & Long (1998: 78).
H(11) listed by Lett (1915: 107) without details.
†H11 listed by Blockeel & Long (1998: 78).
H(12) listed by Lett (1915: 107).
†H12 listed by Blockeel & Long (1998: 78).
H(13) listed by Lett (1915: 107) without details.
†H13 listed by Blockeel & Long (1998: 78).
H(14) listed by Lett (1915: 107) without details.
H14 1956: Magnesian limestone, E of Graigueadrisly, AA Cridland (Warburg 1958b: 475), as var. *spadiceum*.
H(15) listed by Lett (1915: 107) without details.
†H15 listed by Blockeel & Long (1998: 78).
H(16) listed by Lett (1915: 107) without details.
†H16 listed by Blockeel & Long (1998: 78).
H(17) listed by Lett (1915: 107) without details.
†H17 listed by Blockeel & Long (1998: 78).
H(18) listed by Lett (1915: 107) without details.
†H18 listed by Blockeel & Long (1998: 78).
H(19) listed by Lett (1915: 107) without details.
†H19 listed by Blockeel & Long (1998: 78).
H(20) listed by Lett (1915: 107, 108).
†H20 listed by Blockeel & Long (1998: 78).
H(21) listed by Lett (1915: 107) without details.
†H21 listed by Blockeel & Long (1998: 78).
H22 1950: marshy ground, Slane, JS Thomson (Warburg 1952: 99).
H(23) listed by Lett (1915: 108).
H23 1952: Derries Bog, Athlone, JP Brunker & ALK King (Warburg 1953: 308).
H(24) listed by Lett (1915: 107).
†H24 listed by Blockeel & Long (1998: 78).
H(25) listed by Lett (1915: 107) without details.
†H25 listed by Blockeel & Long (1998: 78).
H(26) listed by Lett (1915: 107) without details.
†H26 listed by Blockeel & Long (1998: 78).
H(27) listed by Lett (1915: 107, 108).
†H27 listed by Blockeel & Long (1998: 78).
H(28) listed by Lett (1915: 107) without details.
†H28 listed by Blockeel & Long (1998: 78).
H(29) listed by Lett (1915: 107) without details.
†H29 listed by Blockeel & Long (1998: 78).
H(30) listed by Lett (1915: 107, 108).
†H30 listed by Blockeel & Long (1998: 78)
H(31) listed by Lett (1915: 107, 108).
†H31 listed by Blockeel & Long (1998: 78).
H(32) listed by Lett (1915: 107).
†H32 listed by Blockeel & Long (1998: 78).
H(33) listed by Lett (1915: 107, 108).
†H33 listed by Blockeel & Long (1998: 78).
H(34) listed by Lett (1915: 107) without details.
†H34 listed by Blockeel & Long (1998: 78).
H(35) listed by Lett (1915: 107).
†H35 listed by Blockeel & Long (1998: 78).
H(36) listed by Lett (1915: 107) without details.
†H36 listed by Blockeel & Long (1998: 78).
H(37) listed by Lett (1915: 107, 108).
†H37 listed by Blockeel & Long (1998: 78).
H(38) listed by Lett (1915: 107, 108).
†H38 listed by Blockeel & Long (1998: 78).
H(39) listed by Lett (1915: 107, 108).
†H39 listed by Blockeel & Long (1998: 78).
H(40) listed by Lett (1915: 107).
H(40) no date: Kilrea, JD Houston (anon. 1937a: 366), as var. *orthophyllum*.
†H40 listed by Blockeel & Long (1998: 78).

29/5 ***Dicranum majus*** Sm.

H(1) listed by Lett (1915: 107) without details.
†H1 listed by Blockeel & Long (1998: 78).
H(2) listed by Lett (1915: 107).
†H2 listed by Blockeel & Long (1998: 78).
H(3) listed by Lett (1915: 107).
†H3 listed by Blockeel & Long (1998: 78).
H4 1966: ground in wood by Owenagearagh River, below Cloghroe, MFV Corley & JS Parker (Perry 1967: 410).
H(5) listed by Lett (1915: 107).

†H5 listed by Blockeel & Long (1998: 78).
H(6) listed by Lett (1915: 107).
†H6 listed by Blockeel & Long (1998: 78).
H(7) listed by Lett (1915: 107).
†H7 listed by Blockeel & Long (1998: 78).
H8 1966: bank in sheltered gully, stream on S side of Paradise Hill, Galtee Mts, MFV Corley & JS Parker (Perry 1967: 410).
H9 1973: on ground in dense ash-hazel wood, Poulavallan, PH Pitkin (Crundwell 1974: 167).
H(10) listed by Lett (1915: 107). H(10) listed by Blockeel & Long (1998: 78).
H(11) listed by Lett (1915: 107). H(11) listed by Blockeel & Long (1998: 78).
H(12) listed by Lett (1915: 107). H(12) listed by Blockeel & Long (1998: 78).
H(13) listed by Lett (1915: 107). H(13) listed by Blockeel & Long (1998: 78).
H14 1956: ground in conifer plantation, S of Abbeyleix, AA Cridland (Warburg 1958b: 475).
H16 1957: oakwoods, Ballynahinch, RE Parker (Warburg 1958b: 475).
H(20) listed by Lett (1915: 107).
†H20 listed by Blockeel & Long (1998: 78).
H(21) listed by Lett (1915: 107).
†H21 listed by Blockeel & Long (1998: 78).
H22 1978: fringe woodland, W of Moate Farm, Moynalty, DM Synnott (Hill 1979: 27).
†H25 listed by Blockeel & Long (1998: 78).
H(26) listed by Lett (1915: 107).
†H26 listed by Blockeel & Long (1998: 78).
H(27) listed by Lett (1915: 107).
†H27 listed by Blockeel & Long (1998: 78).
H(28) listed by Lett (1915: 107).
†H28 listed by Blockeel & Long (1998: 78).
H(29) listed by Lett (1915: 107).
†H29 listed by Blockeel & Long (1998: 78).
H(30) listed by Lett (1915: 107).
†H30 listed by Blockeel & Long (1998: 78).
H(31) listed by Lett (1915: 107). H(31) listed by Blockeel & Long (1998: 78).
H(33) listed by Lett (1915: 107).
†H33 listed by Blockeel & Long (1998: 78).
H(34) listed by Lett (1915: 107).
†H34 listed by Blockeel & Long (1998: 78).
H(35) listed by Lett (1915: 107).
†H35 listed by Blockeel & Long (1998: 78).
H(36) listed by Lett (1915: 107).
†H36 listed by Blockeel & Long (1998: 78).
H(38) listed by Lett (1915: 107). H(38) listed by Blockeel & Long (1998: 78).
H38 1999: on the ground in mixed woodland, 60 m alt., Tollymore Forest park, 4 km W of Newcastle, J33, TL Blockeel 28/344 (Rothero 2000: 48).
H(39) listed by Lett (1915: 107).
†H39 listed by Blockeel & Long (1998: 78).
H(40) listed by Lett (1915: 107).
†H40 listed by Blockeel & Long (1998: 78).

29/7 ***Dicranum bergeri*** Bland. ex Hoppe (syn. *Dicranum affine* Funck, *D. undulatum* Brid.)

H18 1957: hummocks of *Sphagnum*, Pollagh Bog, *ca* 8 miles W of Tullamore, CD Pigott (BBSUK) (Warburg 1958b: 475).

29/8 ***Dicranum fuscescens*** Sm. (syn. *Dicranum fuscescens* var. *falcifolium* Braithw.)

H1 1951: boulders, Gowlane, Glenbeigh (BBS exc.) (Warburg 1952: 99).
H(2) listed by Lett (1915: 108).
†H2 listed by Blockeel & Long (1998: 78).
H3 1953: hillside in pass of Keimaneigh, ALK King (Warburg 1954: 480).
H4 1967: on rocks, *ca* 1300 ft [alt.], Musherabeg, RD Fitzgerald (Crundwell 1968: 633).
H(6) listed by Lett (1915: 108).
†H6 listed by Blockeel & Long (1998: 78).
H(7) listed by Lett (1915: 108).
†H7 listed by Blockeel & Long (1998: 78).
H12 1969: rocks in scree, *ca* 1400 ft below Caher Roe's Den, Blackstairs Mts, RD Fitzgerald (Crundwell 1970: 198).
H13 1969: on rock, *ca* 1800 ft [alt.], Caher Roe's Den, Blackstairs Mts, RD Fitzgerald (Crundwell 1970: 198).
H(16) listed by Lett (1915: 108).
†H16 listed by Blockeel & Long (1998: 78).
H(20) listed by Lett (1915: 108).
†H20 listed by Blockeel & Long (1998: 78).
H(21) listed by Lett (1915: 108). H(21) listed by Blockeel & Long (1998: 78).
H25 2002: on NE-facing rock outcrop, 200 m alt., Kilronan Mt., Arigna, G91, NG Hodgetts 4145 (Rothero 2003: 49).
H(26) listed by Lett (1915: 108). H(26) listed by Blockeel & Long (1998: 78).
H(27) listed by Lett (1915: 108).
[H27 1962: peaty ground, top of Croaghpatrick, EF Warburg (Warburg 1963b: 495), as var. *congestum*. H27

record of var. *congestum* deleted because specimen (BBSUK) is incorrectly named (Hill 1981: 24)].
†H27 listed by Blockeel & Long (1998: 78).
H(29) listed by Lett (1915: 108).
†H29 listed by Blockeel & Long (1998: 78).
H(30) listed by Lett (1915: 108).
†H30 listed by Blockeel & Long (1998: 78).
H33 1957: exposed sandstone rocks, nr Meenameen Lough, L. Navar Forest, RE Parker (Warburg 1958b: 476).
H(34) listed by Lett (1915: 108).
†H34 listed by Blockeel & Long (1998: 78).
H(35) listed by Lett (1915: 108).
†H35 listed by Blockeel & Long (1998: 78).
H36 1952: sandstone outcrop, 600 ft [alt.], L. Bradan, RD Fitzgerald (Warburg 1953: 308).
H(38) listed by Lett (1915: 108). H(38) listed by Blockeel & Long (1998: 78).
H39 1952: schist, 600 ft [alt.], Loughan Bay, RD Fitzgerald (Warburg 1953: 308).
H(40) listed by Lett (1915: 108).
†H40 listed by Blockeel & Long (1998: 78).

[**29/9** ***Dicranum flexicaule*** Brid.
(syn. *Dicranum fuscescens* var. *congestum* (Brid.) Husn.)]

[A record from H27 was given by Smith (1978: 160) but omitted by Blockeel & Long (1998: 79).]

29/11 ***Dicranum scottianum*** Turner
(syn. *Dicranum scottii* Turner ex Gray, nom.illeg.)

H(1) listed by Lett (1915: 108).
†H1 listed by Blockeel & Long (1998: 78).
H(2) listed by Lett (1915: 108).
†H2 listed by Blockeel & Long (1998: 78).
H(3) listed by Lett (1915: 108).
†H3 listed by Blockeel & Long (1998: 78).
H4 1966: rocks at 1300 ft alt., E side of Musherabeg, Boggeragh Mts, MFV Corley & JS Parker (Perry 1967: 410).
H(5) listed by Lett (1915: 108). H(5) listed by Blockeel & Long (1998: 78).
H(6) listed by Lett (1915: 108).
†H6 listed by Blockeel & Long (1998: 78).
H(7) listed by Lett (1915: 108).
†H7 listed by Blockeel & Long (1998: 78).
H8 1966: rocks at 1400 ft alt., Slieveragh, nr Ballylanders, MFV Corley & JS Parker (Perry 1967: 410).
[H12 record dismissed because details not traced (Birks 1975, Crundwell 1976: 23)].
H(16) listed by Lett (1915: 108).
†H16 listed by Blockeel & Long (1998: 78).
H(20) listed by Lett (1915: 108).
†H20 listed by Blockeel & Long (1998: 78).
H(25) listed by Lett (1915: 108).
†H25 listed by Blockeel & Long (1998: 78).
H(26) listed by Lett (1915: 108). H(26) listed by Blockeel & Long (1998: 78).
H(27) listed by Lett (1915: 108).
†H27 listed by Blockeel & Long (1998: 78).
H28 1963: rocks, *ca* 900 ft [alt.], S of Knockachree, Slieve Gamph, RD Fitzgerald & AR Perry (Warburg 1964: 724).
H(29) listed by Lett (1915: 108).
†H29 listed by Blockeel & Long (1998: 78).
H(30) listed by Lett (1915: 108).
†H30 listed by Blockeel & Long (1998: 78).
H(33) listed by Lett (1915: 108).
†H33 listed by Blockeel & Long (1998: 78).
H(34) 1939: Glentocher Inishowen, JD Houston (anon. 1940a: 173).
†H34 listed by Blockeel & Long (1998: 78).
H(35) listed by Lett (1915: 108).
†H35 listed by Blockeel & Long (1998: 78).
H36 1952: sandstone outcrop, 600 ft [alt.], L. Bradan, RD Fitzgerald (Warburg 1953: 308).
H(38) listed by Lett (1915: 108). H(38) listed by Blockeel & Long (1998: 78).

[**29/13** ***Dicranum montanum*** Hedw.]

[Record from H26 given by Lett (1915: 108) rejected as error].

[**29/14** ***Dicranum flagellare*** Hedw.]

[H(2) listed by Lett (1915: 108) as Glen Fesk, leg. Taylor. H2 was listed by Smith (1978: 162), but based only on a dubious literature record, comm. MFV Corley (Hill 1980b: 36); H2 was omitted by Blockeel & Long (1998: 78).]
[H(3) listed by Lett (1915: 108) as: Glengarriff, leg. Wilson. H3 is omitted in all recent *CC*, e.g. by Blockeel & Long (1998: 78).]

30/1 ***Dicranodontium uncinatum*** (Harv.) A. Jaeger
(syn. *Dicranum uncinatum* (Harv.) Müll. Hal.)

H(2) 1935: Eagle's Nest, no collector named (BBS exc.) (Watson 1936: 264).
H16 1957: large tufts at base of large boulders, N slopes of Ben Gower, Twelve Pins, R Lewis (BBS exc.) (Warburg 1958b: 476).
[H20 record (Powerscourt, leg. Orr) regarded as dubious by Lett 1915: 108].
H(20) 1867: between Arklow and the Woodenbridge, D Moore (DBN), comm. DM Synnott (Blockeel 1989: 26).
H(27) 1901: Achill I., HW Lett (anon. 1902: 115).
1901: Nephin, HW Lett (Lett 1915: 108).
1909: Slievemore, Achill I., HW Lett (Lett 1915: 108).
†H27 listed by Blockeel & Long (1998: 79).

30/2 ***Dicranodontium asperulum*** (Mitt.) Broth.
(syn. *Dicranum asperulum* Mitt.)

H29 1970: among boulders, N-facing cliffs or slopes of Glenfarne, nr Belcoo, collector not recorded (seen by most members of BBS exc.) (Crundwell 1971b: 376, Appleyard 1971: 389).
H(30) 1909: Cuilcagh Mt., Tetley (Lett 1915: 108).
†H30 listed by Blockeel & Long (1998: 79).
†H33 listed by Blockeel & Long (1998: 79).

30/3 ***Dicranodontium denudatum*** (Brid.) E. Britton
(syn. *Dicranodontium denudatum* var. *alpinum* (Schimp.) I.Hagen, *Didymodon denudatus* (Brid.) Opiz, *Didymodon denudatus* var. *alpinus* (Schimp.) Braithw.)

H(1) listed by Lett (1915: 104).
†H1 listed by Blockeel & Long (1998: 79).
H(2) listed by Lett (1915: 104).
†H2 listed by Blockeel & Long (1998: 79).
H3 1967: on peat in flush, Glengarriff, RD Fitzgerald (Crundwell 1968: 633).
H(6) listed by Lett (1915: 104).
†H6 listed by Blockeel & Long (1998: 79).
[H12 deleted because no valid record or voucher specimen traced (Blockeel 1999: 4)].
H14 1956: dripping Old Red Sandstone rocks, The Cut, Slieve Bloom, AA Cridland (Warburg 1958b: 475).
H(16) listed by Lett (1915: 104).
H16 1957: NE side of Ben Baun at 1450 ft [alt.], Twelve Pins, AC Crundwell (BBS exc.) (Warburg 1958b: 475).
H(20) listed by Lett (1915: 104). H(20) listed by Blockeel & Long (1998: 79).
H(21) listed by Lett (1915: 104). H(21) listed by Blockeel & Long (1998: 79).
H(27) listed by Lett (1915: 104).
†H27 listed by Blockeel & Long (1998: 79).
H(28) listed by Lett (1915: 104).
†H28 listed by Blockeel & Long (1998: 79).
H30 1965: ground, *ca* 1750ft alt., S side of Cuilcagh, RD Fitzgerald & EM Lobley (Warburg 1966: 193).
H(33) listed by Lett (1915: 104).
†H33 listed by Blockeel & Long (1998: 79).
H34 1962: edge of Barnes Lough, EF Warburg (BBS exc.) (Warburg 1963b: 495).
H(35) listed by Lett (1915: 104).
[H35 1962: moorland above Dunlewy, EF Warburg (BBS exc.) (Warburg 1963b: 495), as var. *alpinum.* H35 record of var. *alpinum* deleted because the specimen is *Campylopus flexuosus* (Crundwell 1971b: 376)].
†H35 listed by Blockeel & Long (1998: 79).
H(36) listed by Lett (1915: 104).
†H36 listed by Blockeel & Long (1998: 79).
[H(38) listed by Lett (1915: 104) as: nr Holywood, leg. Hunter. H38 deleted: specimen from Hollywood Hill, 1903, leg. J Hunter (DBN), is *Campylopus paradoxus*, comm. DM Synnott (Blockeel 1989: 26)].
H(39) listed by Lett (1915: 104). H(39) listed by Blockeel & Long (1998: 79).
H40 1961: thin humus on boulder at *ca* 700 ft [alt.], Banagher Glen, nr Dungiven, RD Fitzgerald (Warburg 1962: 367).
1964: boggy ground, *ca* 1200 ft [alt.], Mullaghmore, Sperrin Mts, RD Fitzgerald (Warburg 1965: 862), as var. *alpinum*.

31/1 ***Campylopus subulatus*** Schimp.

[H1 deleted: specimen from Mt. near Sneem, 1878, leg. I Carroll (DBN), is *Campylopus shawii*, comm. DM Synnott (Blockeel 1989: 26)].
H(2) listed by Lett (1915: 105). H(2) listed by Blockeel & Long (1998: 79).
H(3) listed by Lett (1915: 105). H(3) listed by Blockeel & Long (1998: 79).
[H(16) listed by Lett (1915: 105) as 1907: L. Corrib shore nr Ballard, leg. McArdle. H16 deleted because specimen (DBN) is incorrectly named, comm. MFV Corley (Hill 1981: 24); H16 again deleted: specimen from Kylemore, leg. D Moore (DBN), is *Dicranum scottianum*, comm. DM Synnott (Blockeel 1989: 26)].
[H20 deleted: specimen from Powerscourt, 1860, leg. D Moore (DBN), is *Campylopus paradoxus*, comm. DM Synnott (Blockeel 1989: 26)].
[H(27) listed by Lett (1915: 105) as 1902: Achill I., leg. HW Lett. H27 deleted because specimen (DBN) is incorrectly named, comm. MFV Corley (Hill 1981: 24)].
H27 1987: gravelly ground in old quarry, roadside 4 km E of Keel, Achill I., DG Long (Blockeel 1988: 34).
[H28 deleted because no valid record or voucher specimen traced (Blockeel 1999: 4)].
H(29) listed by Lett (1915: 105). H(29) listed by Blockeel & Long (1998: 79).
H30 1952: gravel of small basalt fragments on ledges, etc., nr the base of rock outcrops, Cave Hill, Belfast, EW Jones (Warburg 1953: 307). Apparently omitted from the *CC* in error.
H(34) listed by Lett (1915: 105) without details. H(34) listed by Blockeel & Long (1998: 79).
H(35) 1890: among sand on rocks, Doochary Bridge, HN Dixon (K) (Crundwell 1970: 198).
†H35 listed by Blockeel & Long (1998: 79).
H(36) 1901: sandy detritus on boulder, Trillick River bed, J Hunter (CGE) (Crundwell 1970: 198).
H36 1999: on soil on gravel on road near cattle-grid, NW of Dart Mountain, H59, DT Holyoak 99-705A (BBSUK) (Rothero 2000: 48).
†H39 listed by Blockeel & Long (1998: 79).

31/2 ***Campylopus schimperi*** Milde

†H1 listed by Blockeel & Long (1998: 79).
H(2) listed by Lett (1915: 105). H(2) listed by Blockeel & Long (1998: 79).
H(20) listed by Lett (1915: 105). H(20) listed by Blockeel & Long (1998: 79).
H35 1969: rocky stream bank, valley on S slope of Muckish Mt., JA Paton (Crundwell 1971b: 376).
[H(39) listed by Lett (1915: 105)].

31/3 ***Campylopus gracilis*** (Mitt.) A.Jaeger (syn. *Campylopus schwarzii* Schimp., *C. symplectus* Stirt.)

H(1) listed by Lett (1915: 105).
†H1 listed by Blockeel & Long (1998: 79).
H(2) listed by Lett (1915: 105). H(2) listed by Blockeel & Long (1998: 79).
[H(3) listed by Lett (1915: 105) without details. H3 deleted because no valid record or voucher specimen traced (Blockeel 1999: 4)].
H(4) 1851: Ballinhassig Glen, I Carroll (BEL), comm. RD Fitzgerald (Perry 1967: 410).
H4 1966: boggy ground at 1200 ft alt., Musheramore, Boggeragh Mts, MFV Corley & JA Parker (Perry 1967: 410).
H(7) listed by Lett (1915: 105).
†H7 listed by Blockeel & Long (1998: 79).
H8 1966: wet rocks, *ca* 1600 ft [alt.], S side of Galtymore, Galtee Mts, RD Fitzgerald (BBS exc.) (Crundwell 1968: 633).
H(16) listed by Lett (1915: 105).
†H16 listed by Blockeel & Long (1998: 79).
H(20) 1949: North Prison, Lugnaquilia, 2000-2700 ft [alt.], AW Stelfox (per JS Thomson) (Warburg 1950: 383).
H(27) listed by Lett (1915: 105).
†H27 listed by Blockeel & Long (1998: 79).
H(28) listed by Lett (1915: 105).
†H28 listed by Blockeel & Long (1998: 79).
H30 1957: moorland on NW side of Tiltinbane, AC Crundwell (Warburg 1958b: 475).
H(34) listed by Lett (1915: 105). H(34) listed by Blockeel & Long (1998: 79).
H(35) listed by Lett (1915: 105).
†H35 listed by Blockeel & Long (1998: 79).
H(36) listed by Lett (1915: 105).
†H36 listed by Blockeel & Long (1998: 79).

31/4 ***Campylopus fragilis*** (Brid.) Bruch, Schimp. & W.Gümbel

H(1) listed by Lett (1915: 105) without details.
†H1 listed by Blockeel & Long (1998: 79).
H(2) listed by Lett (1915: 105) without details.
†H2 listed by Blockeel & Long (1998: 79).
H(3) listed by Lett (1915: 105) without details.
†H3 listed by Blockeel & Long (1998: 79).
H(4) listed by Lett (1915: 105) without details.
†H4 listed by Blockeel & Long (1998: 79).
†H5 listed by Blockeel & Long (1998: 79).
H(6) listed by Lett (1915: 105) without details.
†H6 listed by Blockeel & Long (1998: 79).
H(7) listed by Lett (1915: 105) without details.
†H7 listed by Blockeel & Long (1998: 79).
H8 1966: basalt rocks, Knockseefin, nr Pallas Grean, MFV Corley & JS Parker (Perry 1967: 410).
H9 1957: Slievecarron, 5 miles SW of Kinvarra, DH Dalby, conf. MFV Corley (K) (Crundwell 1970: 199). 1985: among rocks, near Slieve Elva, The Burren, AC Bouman (Blockeel 1987: 22).
H(10) listed by Lett (1915: 105) without details.
†H10 listed by Blockeel & Long (1998: 79).
[H(11) listed by Lett (1915: 105) without details. H11 deleted because no specimen traced, comm. MFV Corley (Crundwell 1970: 199)].
[H(12) listed by Lett (1915: 105) without details. H12 deleted because no specimen traced, comm. MFV Corley (Crundwell 1970: 199)].
[H(13) listed by Lett (1915: 105) without details. H13 deleted because no specimen traced, comm. MFV Corley (Crundwell 1970: 199)].
[H(14) listed by Lett (1915: 105) without details. H14 deleted because no specimen traced, comm. MFV Corley (Crundwell 1970: 199)].
H15 1994: steep bank beside Boleyneendorish River, Slieve Aughty, M50, JA Paton 2700 (Blockeel 1995c: 41).
H(16) listed by Lett (1915: 105) without details.
†H16 listed by Blockeel & Long (1998: 79).
[H(17) listed by Lett (1915: 105) without details. H17 deleted because no specimen traced, comm. MFV Corley (Crundwell 1970: 199)].
H(18) listed by Lett (1915: 105) without details.
†H18 listed by Blockeel & Long (1998: 79).
H(20) listed by Lett (1915: 105) without details.
†H20 listed by Blockeel & Long (1998: 79).
[H(21) listed by Lett (1915: 105) without details. H21 deleted because no valid record or voucher specimen traced (Blockeel 1999: 4)].
[H22 1952: bank, Clonycavan Bog, nr Ballivor, ALK King (Warburg 1953: 307). H22 deleted because specimen (Clonycavan Bog, nr Ballivor, King, BM) is *C. pyriformis*, redet. MFV Corley (Crundwell 1970: 199)].
[H23 1952: The Derries Bog, Athlone, JP Brunker & ALK King (Warburg 1953: 307). H23 deleted because specimen (Derries Bog, Athlone, JP Brunker & King, BM) is *C. flexuosus,* redet. MFV Corley (Crundwell 1970: 199)].
[H(24) listed by Lett (1915: 105) without details. H24 deleted because no valid record or voucher specimen traced (Blockeel 1999: 4)].
[H(25) listed by Lett (1915: 105) without details. H25 deleted because no specimen traced, comm. MFV Corley (Crundwell 1970: 199)].
H25 2002: amongst rocks by stream in crags, 150 m alt., Kilronan Mt., Arigna, G91, NG Hodgetts 4155 (Rothero 2003: 49).
[H(26) listed by Lett (1915: 105) without details. H26 deleted because no specimen traced, comm. MFV Corley (Crundwell 1970: 199)].
H(27) listed by Lett (1915: 105) without details.
†H27 listed by Blockeel & Long (1998: 79).
H(28) listed by Lett (1915: 105) without details.
†H28 listed by Blockeel & Long (1998: 79).
H(29) listed by Lett (1915: 105) without details.
†H29 listed by Blockeel & Long (1998: 79).
H(30) listed by Lett (1915: 105) without details.
†H30 listed by Blockeel & Long (1998: 79).

[H(31) listed by Lett (1915: 105) without details. H31 deleted because no specimen traced, comm. MFV Corley (Crundwell 1970: 199)].
H31 1999: in rock crevice on bouldery moorland slope, 300 m alt., Two Mile River, Carlingford, J11, TL Blockeel 28/164 (Rothero 2000: 48).
[H(32) listed by Lett (1915: 105) without details. H32 deleted because no specimen traced, comm. MFV Corley (Crundwell 1970: 199)].
H(33) listed by Lett (1915: 105) without details.
†H33 listed by Blockeel & Long (1998: 79).
H(34) listed by Lett (1915: 105) without details.
†H34 listed by Blockeel & Long (1998: 79).
H(35) listed by Lett (1915: 105) without details.
†H35 listed by Blockeel & Long (1998: 79).
[H(36) listed by Lett (1915: 105) without details. H36 deleted because no specimen traced, comm. MFV Corley (Crundwell 1970: 199)].
H36 2002: on thin soil over rock in old quarry, 185 m alt., Butterlope Glen, H49, DT Holyoak 02-1111 (Rothero 2003: 49).
H(37) listed by Lett (1915: 105) without details.
†H37 listed by Blockeel & Long (1998: 79).
H(38) listed by Lett (1915: 105) without details.
†H38 listed by Blockeel & Long (1998: 79).
H(39) listed by Lett (1915: 105) without details.
†H39 listed by Blockeel & Long (1998: 79).
H(40) listed by Lett (1915: 105) without details.
†H40 listed by Blockeel & Long (1998: 79).

31/5a *Campylopus pyriformis* (Schultz) Brid. **var. *pyriformis***

H(1) listed by Lett (1915: 104).
†H1 listed by Blockeel & Long (1998: 80).
H(2) listed by Lett (1915: 104).
†H2 listed by Blockeel & Long (1998: 80).
H(3) listed by Lett (1915: 104) without details.
†H3 listed by Blockeel & Long (1998: 80).
H(4) listed by Lett (1915: 104).
†H4 listed by Blockeel & Long (1998: 80).
H(5) listed by Lett (1915: 104).
†H5 listed by Blockeel & Long (1998: 80).
H(6) listed by Lett (1915: 104).
†H6 listed by Blockeel & Long (1998: 80).
H(7) listed by Lett (1915: 104).
†H7 listed by Blockeel & Long (1998: 80).
H(8) listed by Lett (1915: 104).
†H8 listed by Blockeel & Long (1998: 80).
H(9) 1945: near L. Inchiquin, JS Thomson (anon. 1946c: 280).
†H9 listed by Blockeel & Long (1998: 80).
H10 1967: on moor, Knockfine, Keeper Hill, RD Fitzgerald (Crundwell 1968: 633).
[H(11) listed by Lett (1915: 104) as 1913: Great Saltee I., leg. HW Lett. H(11) deleted because the locality (Great Saltee I., 1913, in Lett 1915) is in H12, *teste* ALK King (Warburg 1955: 583)].
H11 1966: rotting stump, young plantation nr Foulkscourt House, W of Johnstown, ERB Little (BBS exc.) (Perry 1967: 410).
H(12) 1913: Great Saltee I. (from Lett 1915), originally reported from H11, corrected to H12 *teste* ALK King (Warburg 1955: 583).
†H12 listed by Blockeel & Long (1998: 80).
H13 1969: on dryish peat in bog, Crannagh, foot of Mt Leinster, RD Fitzgerald (Crundwell 1970: 199).
H(14) listed by Lett (1915: 104).
†H14 listed by Blockeel & Long (1998: 80).
H15 1961: peat nr Cloon Bridge, nr Gort, EM Lobley (Warburg 1962: 367).
†H16 listed by Blockeel & Long (1998: 80).
H(17) listed by Lett (1915: 104). H(17) listed by Blockeel & Long (1998: 80).
H(18) listed by Lett (1915: 104).
†H18 listed by Blockeel & Long (1998: 80).
H19 1953: Cromwellstown Hill, ALK King (Warburg 1954: 479).
H(20) listed by Lett (1915: 104) without locality.
†H20 listed by Blockeel & Long (1998: 80).
H(21) listed by Lett (1915: 105).
†H21 listed by Blockeel & Long (1998: 80).
H22 1957: side of bog-hole, Rossan Bog, 1 mile SE of Kinnegad, ALK King (Warburg 1958b: 475).
H(23) listed by Lett (1915: 105).
†H23 listed by Blockeel & Long (1998: 80).
H(25) 1948: marsh, nr River Shannon, below Carrick-on-Shannon, ALK King (Warburg 1950: 383).
†H25 listed by Blockeel & Long (1998: 80).
H26 1970: on peaty ground, Glenaduff, NE

of Foxford, MFV Corley (Crundwell 1971b: 376).
H(27) listed by Lett (1915: 105).
†H27 listed by Blockeel & Long (1998: 80).
H(28) 1937: Ben Bulben, no collector named (BBS exc.) (Armitage 1938: 11).
†H28 listed by Blockeel & Long (1998: 80).
H(29) listed by Lett (1915: 105).
†H29 listed by Blockeel & Long (1998: 80).
H(30) listed by Lett (1915: 105).
†H30 listed by Blockeel & Long (1998: 80).
H(31) 1949: peat cutting, Essexford Bog, Inniskeen, JP Brunker (Warburg 1950: 383).
H(32) 1947: bog nr Castleblayney, ALK King (Crundwell 1972: 137).
H(33) listed by Lett (1915: 105).
†H33 listed by Blockeel & Long (1998: 80).
H(34) listed by Lett (1915: 105) without locality.
†H34 listed by Blockeel & Long (1998: 80).
H(35) listed by Lett (1915: 105).
†H35 listed by Blockeel & Long (1998: 80).
H(36) listed by Lett (1915: 105).
†H36 listed by Blockeel & Long (1998: 80).
H(37) listed by Lett (1915: 105).
†H37 listed by Blockeel & Long (1998: 80).
H(38) listed by Lett (1915: 105).
†H38 listed by Blockeel & Long (1998: 80).
H(39) listed by Lett (1915: 105).
†H39 listed by Blockeel & Long (1998: 80).
H(40) listed by Lett (1915: 105).
†H40 listed by Blockeel & Long (1998: 80).

Older records would not have distinguished var. *azoricus*, but as noted below recognition of that taxon may be of little value.

31/5b *Campylopus pyriformis* var. *azoricus* (Mitt.) M.F.V.Corley

H(20) 1868: Prince Edward's Seat, Enniskerry, collector unknown (DBN) (Corley 1976: 212, Hill 1978: 18).
H24 1986: bare peat on raised bog, Ballykenny, H Grogan & C Douglas (Blockeel 1987: 22).
H(27) 1910: Clare I., HW Lett (DBN) (Corley 1976: 212, Hill 1978: 18).
H(35) 1874: Trelleck, A Ley (LDS) (Corley 1976: 212, Hill 1978: 18).

Frahm (1999) regards this form as merely a modification from wet habitats, so that its nomenclatural recognition probably has little value.

31/6 *Campylopus flexuosus* (Hedw.) Brid. (syn. *Campylopus flexuosus* var. *paludosus* Schimp., *C. flexuosus* var. *zonatus* (Molendo) Anzi, *C. paradoxus* Wilson, *C. pyriformis* var. *fallaciosus* (Thér.) M.F.V.Corley)

H(1) listed by Lett (1915: 105) without details.
†H1 listed by Blockeel & Long (1998: 80).
H(2) listed by Lett (1915: 105).
†H2 listed by Blockeel & Long (1998: 80).
H(3) listed by Lett (1915: 105).
†H3 listed by Blockeel & Long (1998: 80).
H(4) listed by Lett (1915: 105) without details.
†H4 listed by Blockeel & Long (1998: 80).
H(5) listed by Lett (1915: 105) without details.
†H5 listed by Blockeel & Long (1998: 80).
H(6) listed by Lett (1915: 105) without details.
†H6 listed by Blockeel & Long (1998: 80).
H(7) listed by Lett (1915: 105) without details.
†H7 listed by Blockeel & Long (1998: 80).
H(8) listed by Lett (1915: 105) without details.
†H8 listed by Blockeel & Long (1998: 80).
H(9) listed by Lett (1915: 105) without details.
†H9 listed by Blockeel & Long (1998: 80).
H10 1951: Silvermines, AD Banwell, PJ Wanstall & EV Watson (Warburg 1953: 307).
H(11) listed by Lett (1915: 105) without details.
H11 1954: Mt Brandon, ALK King (Warburg 1955: 583).
H(12) listed by Lett (1915: 105).
†H12 listed by Blockeel & Long (1998: 80).
H(13) listed by Lett (1915: 105) without details.
†H13 listed by Blockeel & Long (1998: 80).
H(14) listed by Lett (1915: 105).
†H14 listed by Blockeel & Long (1998: 80).
H(16) listed by Lett (1915: 105).
H16 1957: Muckanaght, J Appleyard (BBS exc.) (Warburg 1960: 772), as var. *zonatus*.
H17 1966: rotten tree stump, Derreen, N of Monivea, MFV Corley & JS Parker

(Perry 1967: 410).
H(18) listed by Lett (1915: 105) without details.
†H18 listed by Blockeel & Long (1998: 80).
H(19) listed by Lett (1915: 105) without details.
†H19 listed by Blockeel & Long (1998: 80).
H(20) listed by Lett (1915: 105) without details.
†H20 listed by Blockeel & Long (1998: 80).
H(21) listed by Lett (1915: 105).
H21 1959: rock crevice, Slievenabawanoge Hill, ALK King (Warburg 1960: 772), as var. *zonatus*.
H22 1952: Clonycavan Bog, nr Ballivor, ALK King (Warburg 1953: 307).
H23 1952: The Derries Bog, nr Athlone, JP Brunker & ALK King (Warburg 1953: 307).
H24 1955: Derryad Bog, nr Killashee, TA Barry, comm. ALK King (Warburg 1956: 152).
H(25) listed by Lett (1915: 105) without details.
†H25 listed by Blockeel & Long (1998: 80).
H(26) listed by Lett (1915: 105) without details.
†H26 listed by Blockeel & Long (1998: 80).
H(27) listed by Lett (1915: 105).
†H27 listed by Blockeel & Long (1998: 80).
H(28) listed by Lett (1915: 105) without details.
H28 1965: rock at pathside by L. Gill, Slish Wood, AR Perry & EF Warburg (Warburg 1966: 193), as var. *zonatus*.
H(29) listed by Lett (1915: 105) without details.
†H29 listed by Blockeel & Long (1998: 80).
H(30) listed by Lett (1915: 105) without details.
†H30 listed by Blockeel & Long (1998: 80).
[H(31) listed by Lett (1915: 105) without details. H31 deleted because no valid record or voucher specimen traced (Blockeel 1999: 4)].
[H(32) listed by Lett (1915: 105) without locality. H32 deleted because no valid record or voucher specimen traced (Blockeel 1999: 4)].
H32 2002: in blanket bog, 340 m alt., NE of Lough Galluane, H54, N Lockhart (Rothero 2003: 49).
H(33) listed by Lett (1915: 105).
H33 1961: with *Dicranodontium asperulum* on wet ground, *ca* 1800 ft [alt.], Cuilcagh, RD Fitzgerald (Warburg 1962: 367), as var. *zonatus*.
H(34) listed by Lett (1915: 105) without details.
H34 1962: limestone scree *ca* 900 ft [alt.], Gap of Mamore, 6 miles N of Buncrana, RD Fitzgerald (Warburg 1963b: 495), as var. *zonatus*.
H(35) listed by Lett (1915: 105).
†H35 listed by Blockeel & Long (1998: 80).
H(36) listed by Lett (1915: 105) without details.
†H36 listed by Blockeel & Long (1998: 80).
H(37) listed by Lett (1915: 105) without details.
†H37 listed by Blockeel & Long (1998: 80).
H(38) listed by Lett (1915: 105).
†H38 listed by Blockeel & Long (1998: 80).
H(39) listed by Lett (1915: 105).
H(39) 1928: among boulders under the base of cliffs, Giant's Causeway, no collector named (BBS exc.) (Duncan 1928: 113, 116), as var. *zonatus*.
†H39 listed by Blockeel & Long (1998: 80).
H(40) listed by Lett (1915: 105) without details.
†H40 listed by Blockeel & Long (1998: 80).

31/7 ***Campylopus setifolius*** Wilson

H(1) listed by Lett (1915: 105).
†H1 listed by Blockeel & Long (1998: 80).
H(2) listed by Lett (1915: 105).
†H2 listed by Blockeel & Long (1998: 80).
H(3) listed by Lett (1915: 106) without details.
†H3 listed by Blockeel & Long (1998: 80).
[H(6) listed by Lett (1915: 106) as 1902: L. Coomshighaun [*sic* = Coumshingaun], leg. HW Lett. without details. H6 deleted because specimen (L. Coomsingaun [*sic* = Coumshingaun], Lett, DBN) is *C. flexuosus*, redet. MFV Corley (Crundwell 1970: 199)].
[H(7) listed by Lett (1915: 106) as 1902: L. Muskry, leg. HW Lett. H7 deleted because specimen (L. Muskry, Galtee Mts, Lett, DBN) is *Dicranodontium denudatum*, redet. MFV Corley (Crundwell 1970: 199)].
[H(9) listed by Lett (1915: 106) as: Carn Sefin, leg. McArdle. H9 deleted because specimen (Carn Seefin, D McArdle, BM) is *C. atrovirens*, redet. MFV Corley (Crundwell 1970: 199)].

H15 1957: bog above Chevy Chase Woods, Owendalulleegh, DG Catcheside & EM Lobley (BBS exc.) (Warburg 1958b: 475).
H(16) listed by Lett (1915: 106).
†H16 listed by Blockeel & Long (1998: 80).
[H(17) listed by Lett (1915: 106) without details. H17 deleted because no specimen traced, comm. MFV Corley (Crundwell 1970: 199)].
H(20) listed by Lett (1915: 106). H(20), record placed in parentheses, comm. AJE Smith (Hill 1980b: 36).
[H(21) listed by Lett (1915: 106). H21 deleted because no specimen traced, comm. MFV Corley (Crundwell 1970: 199)].
[H27 1957: wet ground, SE valley of Maumtrasna, AC Crundwell (BBS exc.) (Warburg 1958b: 475). H27 deleted because record (from Maumtrasna) is from locality in H16 (Crundwell 1970: 199)].
H27 1962: wet rocks in corrie, Slievemore, Achill I., EF Warburg (Warburg 1963c: 142, Crundwell 1970: 199).
H28 1967: amidst blocks and shaggy heather on N slopes of Knockachree, Slieve Gamph, HH Birks, HJB Birks & DA Ratcliffe (Crundwell 1968: 634).
[H(30) listed by Lett (1915: 106) as 1909: Cuilcagh, leg. Tetley. H30 deleted because specimen (Descent of Cuilcagh, WN Tetley, BBSUK) is *C. atrovirens*, redet. MFV Corley (Crundwell 1970: 199)].
H31 1999: with ericaceous shrubs among rocks on bank of stream, 300 m alt., Two Mile River, Carlingford, J11, TL Blockeel 28/167 (Rothero 2000: 48).
[H(32) listed by Lett (1915: 106) as 1910: Scotstown, leg. Bingham. H32 deleted because specimen (Scotstown, WR Bingham, DBN) is *C. flexuosus*, redet. MFV Corley (Crundwell 1970: 199)].
H(34) listed by Lett (1915: 106).
†H34 listed by Blockeel & Long (1998: 80).
H(35) listed by Lett (1915: 106).
†H35 listed by Blockeel & Long (1998: 80).
H(38) listed by Lett (1915: 106). H(38) record placed in parentheses, comm. AJE Smith (Hill 1980b: 36). H(38) listed by Blockeel & Long (1998: 80).
[H(40) 1936: Garvagh, JD Houston (anon. 1937a: 366). H40 deleted because specimen (marsh, Garvagh, Houston, BBSUK) is *C. flexuosus*, redet. MFV Corley (Crundwell 1970: 199)].

31/8 ***Campylopus shawii*** Wilson ex Hunt
(syn. *Campylopus shawii* var. *hamatus* Schimp.)

H1 1951: bog by L. Dreenaun, nr Waterville, no collector named (BBS exc.) (Warburg 1952: 99).
H2 1967: on wet moor, *ca* 900 ft [alt.], The Paps, RD Fitzgerald (Crundwell 1968: 634).
H(3) listed by Lett (1915: 105).
†H3 listed by Blockeel & Long (1998: 80).
H(27) no date: Nephin Mt., HW Lett (BM) (Crundwell 1969: 880).

31/9a ***Campylopus atrovirens*** De Not. **var.** ***atrovirens***
(syn. *Campylopus atrovirens* var. *muticus* Milde)

H(1) listed by Lett (1915: 106).
H(1) 1935: Brandon Mt., no collector named (BBS exc.) (Watson 1936: 264), as var. *muticus*.
1935: Connor Hill, no collector named (BBS exc.) (Watson 1936: 264), as var. *muticus*.
†H1 listed by Blockeel & Long (1998: 80).
H(2) listed by Lett (1915: 106).
†H2 listed by Blockeel & Long (1998: 80).
H(3) listed by Lett (1915: 106).
†H3 listed by Blockeel & Long (1998: 80).
H(4) listed by Lett (1915: 106).
†H4 listed by Blockeel & Long (1998: 80).
H(6) listed by Lett (1915: 106).
†H6 listed by Blockeel & Long (1998: 80).
H(7) listed by Lett (1915: 106).
†H7 listed by Blockeel & Long (1998: 80).
H8 1966: wet rocks *ca* 1600 ft [alt.], S side of Galtymore, Galtee Mts, RD Fitzgerald (Crundwell 1968: 634).
†H9 listed by Blockeel & Long (1998: 80).
H12 1975: around rocks on boggy hillside, Croghan, PH Pitkin (Hill 1979: 27).
H(14) listed by Lett (1915: 106).
†H14 listed by Blockeel & Long (1998: 80).
H15 1957: blanket bog, hills E of Gort, RE Parker (Warburg 1958b: 475).
H(16) listed by Lett (1915: 106).
†H16 listed by Blockeel & Long (1998: 80).
H17 1957: raised bog between mouths of R. Clare and R. Cregg, DH Dalby & EM

Lobley (BBS exc.) (Warburg 1958b: 475).
H(20) listed by Lett (1915: 106).
H(20) 1945: near Arts Lake, Wicklow, AW Stelfox, per JS Thomson (anon. 1946c: 280), as var. *muticus*.
†H20 listed by Blockeel & Long (1998: 80).
H(21) listed by Lett (1915: 106). H(21) listed by Blockeel & Long (1998: 80).
H24 1968: among *Sphagnum*, raised bog 1 mile SE of Cloondara, WV Rubers *et al.* (U) (Crundwell 1974: 167).
H25 2002: amongst *Sphagnum* in raised bog, 50 m alt., Corbo Bog, Clooncashel, W of Lanesborough, M96, NG Hodgetts 4081 (Rothero 2003: 49).
H(26) listed by Lett (1915: 106).
†H26 listed by Blockeel & Long (1998: 80).
H(27) listed by Lett (1915: 106).
†H27 listed by Blockeel & Long (1998: 80).
H(28) listed by Lett (1915: 106).
†H28 listed by Blockeel & Long (1998: 80).
H(29) listed by Lett (1915: 106).
†H29 listed by Blockeel & Long (1998: 80).
H(30) listed by Lett (1915: 106).
†H30 listed by Blockeel & Long (1998: 80).
H(31) listed by Lett (1915: 106).
†H31 listed by Blockeel & Long (1998: 80).
[H(32) listed by Lett (1915: 106) as 1910: Eskmore, leg. Bingham. H32 deleted because no valid record or voucher specimen traced (Blockeel 1999: 4)].
H(33) listed by Lett (1915: 106).
†H33 listed by Blockeel & Long (1998: 80).
H(34) listed by Lett (1915: 106) without locality.
†H34 listed by Blockeel & Long (1998: 80).
H(35) listed by Lett (1915: 106).
†H35 listed by Blockeel & Long (1998: 80).
H36 1951: moor, L. Lee, RD Fitzgerald (Warburg 1952: 99).
H(37) 1916: Camlough Mt., JD Houston (anon. 1917c: 9).
†H37 listed by Blockeel & Long (1998: 80).
H(38) listed by Lett (1915: 106).
H(38) 1928: Slieve Donard (BBS exc.) (Duncan 1928: 114, 117), as var. *muticus*.
†H38 listed by Blockeel & Long (1998: 80).
H(39) listed by Lett (1915: 106).
†H39 listed by Blockeel & Long (1998: 80).
H(40) listed by Lett (1915: 106) without details.
†H40 listed by Blockeel & Long (1998: 80).

31/9b *Campylopus atrovirens* var. *falcatus* Braithw.

H1 1951: steep rock face, Coomakista Pass, nr Waterville, RD Fitzgerald (BBS exc.) (Warburg 1952: 99).
H(3) listed by Lett (1915: 106). H(3) listed by Blockeel & Long (1998: 80).
H(16) listed by Lett (1915: 106).
†H16 listed by Blockeel & Long (1998: 80).
H27 1967: in wet soligenous blanket bog on steep N-facing slopes of Maumtrasna, HH Birks, HJB Birks & DA Ratcliffe (Crundwell 1968: 634).
H(35) listed by Lett (1915: 106) without details.
H(35) listed by Blockeel & Long (1998: 80).
H39 1988: on boulder with *Diplophyllum albicans*, Fair Head undercliff, D14, K Anderson, det. R Weyl (BBSUK) (Rothero 2001: 39).

31/9c *Campylopus atrovirens* var. *gracilis* Dixon

H(3) 1912: Glengarriff, HW Lett (Lett 1915: 106). H(3) listed by Blockeel & Long (1998: 80).

31/10 *Campylopus pilifer* Brid.
(syn. *Campylopus introflexus* sensu Lett 1915 non (Hedw.) Brid., *C. polytrichoides* De Not.)

H(1) listed by Lett (1915: 106).
H(1) 1905: Eagle's Nest, Killarney, DA Jones, SJ Owen & JB Duncan, *fide* U Duncan (Richards 1963: 414).
H1 1951: crevices of dry sunny rocks, Derrynane, PW Richards (Richards 1963: 414).
H(2) listed by Lett (1915: 106).
H(2) 1906: near Dinnis Bridge, Muckross, JC Wilson (GLA, *fide* AC Crundwell) (Richards 1963: 414).
H(3) listed by Lett (1915: 106).
H(3) 1829: near Glengarriff (BIRM 1232, ex Hb. W Wilson), conf. PW Richards (Richards 1963: 414).
1936: near Glengarriff, PW Richards (Richards 1963: 414).
†H3 listed by Blockeel & Long (1998: 80).
H16 listed in 1926 *CC*, cited by Richards (1963: 414).
†H16 listed by Blockeel & Long (1998: 80).

H27 listed in 1926 *CC*, cited by Richards (1963: 414). †H27 listed by Blockeel & Long (1998: 80).

31/11 ***Campylopus introflexus*** (Hedw.) Brid.

H1 1967: on bare peat, lower slopes of Brandon Mt., HH Bírks, HJB Birks & DA Ratcliffe (Crundwell 1968: 634).
H2 1953: wet peat flat, foot of Scragg Mt., Tralee, 500-600 ft [alt.], AP Fanning (BIRM), conf. PW Richards (Richards 1963: 416).
H3 1962: in small quantity on peat, fruiting freely, between Bantry and Glengarriff, AJE Smith, conf. PW Richards (Richards 1963: 416, Warburg 1964: 725).
H4 1966: peaty soil on rocks at 1200 ft alt., Musheramore, Boggeragh Mts, MFV Corley & JS Parker (Perry 1967: 411).
H5 1967: in bog, *ca* 700 ft [alt.], Lyrenamon, NW of Carrignavar, RD Fitzgerald (Crundwell 1968: 634).
H6 1961: shallow peat at 500 ft [alt.] below Coumshingaun, Comeragh Mts, DA Ratcliffe (Warburg 1962: 367).
H7 1966: peat cutting in bog between Seefin and Knockeenatoung, Galtee Mts, EM Lobley & RJ Murphy (BBS exc.) (Perry 1967: 411).
H8 1959: bog ½ mile E of Castleconnel [*sic* = Castleconnell], ALK King (Warburg 1960: 772).
1959: half mile E of Castleconnell, Limerick, AJE Smith (Richards 1963: 416).
H9 1958: top of Moneen Mt., Ballyvaghan, RB Ivimey-Cooke & MCF Proctor (Richards 1963: 416).
1959: bare wet peat cuttings on derelict raised bog nr Templebannagh Loughs, MCF Proctor & RB Ivimey-Cook (Warburg 1961: 161).
H10 1965: cut-away bog, L. Nahinch, Ballingarry, DM Synnott (Warburg 1966: 193).
H11 1966: stump in pine plantation, Foulkscourt House, nr Johnstown, J Appleyard *et al.* (BBS exc.) (Perry 1967: 411).
H12 1969: on peat *ca* 1400 ft [alt.], Caher Roe's Den, Blackstairs Mts, RD Fitzgerald (Crundwell 1970: 199).
H13 1969: in bog, Knockallard, nr Borris, RD Fitzgerald (Crundwell 1970: 199).
H14 1956: bog cuttings, Kylee, AA Cridland (Warburg 1958b: 475, Richards 1963: 416).
H15 1957: cut peat, hills E of Gort, RE Parker (Warburg 1958b: 475).
1957: well established patches, sphagnum above Chevy Chase woods, Owendalulleegh, EM Lobley (Richards 1963: 417).
H16 1953: Urrisbeg, Roundstone, B Salkeld *fide* ALK King (Richards 1963: 417).
H17 1957: bog between R. Clare and R. Cregg, RE Parker (Warburg 1958b: 475, Richards 1963: 417).
H(18) 1949: Ballywilliam Bog, Birr, AP Fanning, per EC Wallace (Warburg 1950: 383, Richards 1963: 417).
†H18 listed by Blockeel & Long (1998: 80).
H19 1968: cut-away edge of bog, Allenwood, ALK King (Crundwell 1969: 880).
H20 1961: peaty ground on burned heather moor at 1200 ft [alt.], Lugnaquilla, Glenmalure, DA Ratcliffe (Warburg 1962: 367).
H21 1942: turfy soil on top of Red Rock, Howth, JS Thomson (BIRM), conf. PW Richards (Duncan 1944: 209, Richards 1963: 417).
H22 1957: Rossan Bog, 1 mile SE of Kinnegad, ALK King (Warburg 1958b: 475, Richards 1963: 417).
H23 1952: bank in wet sphagnum bog, The Derries, Athlone, JP Brunker & ALK King (BIRM), conf. PW Richards (Warburg 1953: 307, Richards 1963: 417).
†H24 listed by Blockeel & Long (1998: 80).
H25 1967: in bog nr Derreenargan, ALK King (Crundwell 1968: 634).
H26 1957: W slope of [The] Ox Mts, below Loch Talt, ALK King (Warburg 1958b: 475, Richards 1963: 417).
H27 1953: Slievemore, Achill I., EC Wallace (Richards 1963: 417).
H28 1963: dry peat, *ca* 1100 ft [alt.], with *Pohlia nutans*, Lugnagall, Glencar, RD Fitzgerald & AR Perry (Warburg 1964: 725).
H29 1963: peat in bog E of Sriff Cottage, nr Dromahair, RD Fitzgerald & AR Perry (Warburg 1964: 725).
H30 1961: bare peat at *ca* 1800 ft [alt.], Cuilcagh, RD Fitzgerald (Warburg 1962: 367).

H31 1965: spruce plantation, Mullaghattin, Carlingford Peninsula, DM Synnott (Warburg 1966: 193).
H33 1959: bare dry peat hummocks, bog at Immeroo, RD Fitzgerald (Warburg 1960: 772, Richards 1963: 417).
H34 1962: Croaghconnellagh, Tawnawully Mts, J Appleyard & EC Wallace (BBS exc.) (Warburg 1963b: 495).
H35 1962: cut-away peat on north-facing slope on Downs peninsula, ALK King (Warburg 1963b: 495).
1962: cut-away peat above N-facing cliffs, near Rossbeg, ALK King (Richards 1963: 417).
H36 1958: peat, Mullanatoomog Bog, nr Drumquin, RD Fitzgerald (Warburg 1959: 632, Richards 1963: 417).
H37 1964: peat in bog, Derryadd townland, E of Lough Gullion, RD Fitzgerald (Warburg 1965: 862).
H38 1962: Pigeon Rock Mt., Mourne Mts, AW Stelfox, comm. RD Fitzgerald (Warburg 1965: 862).
H39 1969: heathy slope above Sallagh Braes, NW of Larne, JA Paton (Crundwell 1970: 199).
H40 1952: one tussock only, sphagnum bog, Benbradagh, *ca* 1200 ft [alt.], J Taylor & EM Lobley (Warburg 1953: 307, Richards 1963: 417).

31/12 *Campylopus brevipilus* Bruch, Schimp. & W.Gümbel
(syn. *Campylopus brevipilus* var. *auriculatus* Fergusson)

H(1) listed by Lett (1915: 106).
†H1 listed by Blockeel & Long (1998: 80).
H(2) listed by Lett (1915: 106).
†H2 listed by Blockeel & Long (1998: 80).
H(3) listed by Lett (1915: 106).
†H3 listed by Blockeel & Long (1998: 80).
H5 1967: in bog, *ca* 700 ft [alt.], Lyrenamon, NW of Carrignavar, RD Fitzgerald (Crundwell 1968: 634).
[H(6) listed by Lett (1915: 106) without details. H6 deleted because no valid record or voucher specimen traced (Blockeel 1999: 4)].
H(7) listed by Lett (1915: 106). H(7) listed by Blockeel & Long (1998: 80).
H(8) listed by Lett (1915: 106). H(8) listed by Blockeel & Long (1998: 80).
H9 1979: peat bog NE of L. Cullaunyheeda, nr Derrymore House, HMH van Melick (Hill 1981: 24).
H(10) 1949: Annagh Bog, Rathcabbin, AP Fanning (Warburg 1953: 307).
H12 1958: wet boggy ground, Forth Mt., 650 ft [alt.], ALK King (Warburg 1959: 632).
H15 1957: damp moor above Chevy Chase, nr Gort, DH Dalby (BBS exc.) (Warburg 1958b: 475).
H(16) listed by Lett (1915: 106).
†H16 listed by Blockeel & Long (1998: 80).
H17 1957: bog S of R. Clare to E of Galway to Headford Road, RE Parker (BBS exc.) (Warburg 1958b: 475).
H(20) listed by Lett (1915: 106).
†H20 listed by Blockeel & Long (1998: 80).
H(21) listed by Lett (1915: 106). H(21) listed by Blockeel & Long (1998: 80).
H25 2002: on drying-out raised bog, 110 m alt., Bellanagar Bog, Cornamucklagh and Falmore, M78 NG Hodgetts 4106 (Rothero 2003: 49).
H(26) listed by Lett (1915: 106).
†H26 listed by Blockeel & Long (1998: 80).
H(27) listed by Lett (1915: 106).
†H27 listed by Blockeel & Long (1998: 80).
H(28) 1914: Slishwood, WN Tetley (Lett 1915: 106, anon. 1924: 65).
†H28 listed by Blockeel & Long (1998: 80).
H(29) listed by Lett (1915: 106).
†H29 listed by Blockeel & Long (1998: 80).
H(31) listed by Lett (1915: 106). H(31) listed by Blockeel & Long (1998: 80).
H(33) listed by Lett (1915: 106). H(33) listed by Blockeel & Long (1998: 80).
H(34) listed by Lett (1915: 106).
†H34 listed by Blockeel & Long (1998: 80).
H(35) listed by Lett (1915: 106).
†H35 listed by Blockeel & Long (1998: 80).
H(38) listed by Lett (1915: 106).
†H38 listed by Blockeel & Long (1998: 80).
H(39) listed by Lett (1915: 106). H(39) listed by Blockeel & Long (1998: 80).

33/1 *Leucobryum glaucum* (Hedw.) Ångstr.

H(1) listed by Lett (1915: 100) without details.
†H1 listed by Blockeel & Long (1998: 81).
H(2) listed by Lett (1915: 100) without details.
†H2 listed by Blockeel & Long (1998: 81).
H(3) listed by Lett (1915: 100) without details.

†H3 listed by Blockeel & Long (1998: 81).
H(4) listed by Lett (1915: 100) without details.
†H4 listed by Blockeel & Long (1998: 81).
H(5) listed by Lett (1915: 100) without details.
†H5 listed by Blockeel & Long (1998: 81).
H(6) 1933: Knockmeàldowns [*sic* = Knockmealdown], E Armitage (anon. 1934b: 111).
1933: Poolvona, E Armitage (anon. 1934b: 111).
†H6 listed by Blockeel & Long (1998: 81).
H(7) listed by Lett (1915: 100) without details.
†H7 listed by Blockeel & Long (1998: 81).
H8 1959: raised bog E of Castleconnell, ALK King (Warburg 1960: 773).
H9 1971: moist peaty soil, Temple Bannagh, AG Side (Crundwell 1972: 137).
H10 1968: Monaincha Bog, nr Roscrea, G Drennan (Crundwell 1969: 880).
H11 1966: bog, Derryfadda, W of Johnstown, ERB Little (Perry 1967: 411).
H12 1958: Forth Mt., ALK King (Warburg 1959: 632).
H(13) listed by Lett (1915: 100) without details.
†H13 listed by Blockeel & Long (1998: 81).
H(14) listed by Lett (1915: 100) without details.
†H14 listed by Blockeel & Long (1998: 81).
H(15) listed by Lett (1915: 100) without details.
†H15 listed by Blockeel & Long (1998: 81).
H(16) listed by Lett (1915: 100) without details.
†H16 listed by Blockeel & Long (1998: 81).
H(17) listed by Lett (1915: 100) without details.
†H17 listed by Blockeel & Long (1998: 81).
H(18) listed by Lett (1915: 100) without details.
†H18 listed by Blockeel & Long (1998: 81).
†H19 listed by Blockeel & Long (1998: 81).
H(20) listed by Lett (1915: 100) without details.
†H20 listed by Blockeel & Long (1998: 81).
[H(21) listed by Lett (1915: 100) without details. H21 deleted because no valid record or voucher specimen traced (Blockeel 1999: 4)].
H22 1952: Clonycavan Bog, Ballivor, JP Brunker (Warburg 1953: 308).
H23 1952: Derries Bog, Athlone, JP Brunker & ALK King (Warburg 1953: 308).
†H24 listed by Blockeel & Long (1998: 81).
H(25) listed by Lett (1915: 100) without details.
†H25 listed by Blockeel & Long (1998: 81).
H(26) listed by Lett (1915: 100) without details.
†H26 listed by Blockeel & Long (1998: 81).
H(27) listed by Lett (1915: 100) without details.
†H27 listed by Blockeel & Long (1998: 81).
H(28) listed by Lett (1915: 100) without details.
†H28 listed by Blockeel & Long (1998: 81).
H(29) listed by Lett (1915: 100) without details.
†H29 listed by Blockeel & Long (1998: 81).
H(30) listed by Lett (1915: 100) without details.
†H30 listed by Blockeel & Long (1998: 81).
H(31) listed by Lett (1915: 100) without details.
†H31 listed by Blockeel & Long (1998: 81).
H(33) listed by Lett (1915: 100) without details.
†H33 listed by Blockeel & Long (1998: 81).
H(34) listed by Lett (1915: 100) without details.
†H34 listed by Blockeel & Long (1998: 81).
H(35) listed by Lett (1915: 100) without details.
†H35 listed by Blockeel & Long (1998: 81).
H36 1950: moor, Mary Gray (East), J Taylor (Warburg 1951: 499).
H(37) listed by Lett (1915: 100) without details.
†H37 listed by Blockeel & Long (1998: 81).
H(38) listed by Lett (1915: 100) without details.
†H38 listed by Blockeel & Long (1998: 81).
H(39) listed by Lett (1915: 100) without details.
†H39 listed by Blockeel & Long (1998: 81).
[H(40) listed by Lett (1915: 100) without details. H40 deleted because no valid record or voucher specimen traced (Blockeel 1999: 4)].
H40 1999: hummocks in short grassland below basalt crags, Binevenagh, C63, DT Holyoak 99-587 (BBSUK) (Rothero 2000: 48).

33/2 ***Leucobryum juniperoideum*** (Brid.) Müll.Hal.

[H1 record (Crundwell 1976: 23, see below) deleted because Torc Cascade is in H2, comm. DM Synnott (Hill 1979: 27)].
H1 1983: on banks in scrubby oak woodland, W bank of Blackwater River, above Blackwater Bridge, Kenmare River, DG Long (Hill 1984b: 26).
H2 1975: soil by path, Torc Cascade, WD Foster (Crundwell 1976: 23). Originally published as new to H1, but Torc Cascade locality is correctly placed in H2, comm. DM Synnott (Hill 1979: 27).
H3 1979: woodland floor, Glengarriff Wood, V95, N Lockhart, comm. NF Stewart, Hb. Forest & Wildlife Service [at Newtown Mount Kennedy] (Blockeel 1994: 36).
H6 1999: on bank under *Rhododendron* in N-facing oak woodland, 70 m alt., Lismore, by junction of Glenakeefe R and Owennashad R, S00, TL Blockeel 28/195 (Rothero 2000: 48).
H13 1999: on humus on bank, 20 m alt., path through copse, R Barrow, Saint Mullins, S73, TL Blockeel 28/330 (Rothero 2000: 48).
H16 1986: damp bank in ravine, woods at Kylemore Abbey, DG Long (Blockeel 1987: 22).
H38 2002: on old stump in woodland, 50 m alt., just N of Shimna River, J33, DT Holyoak 02-935 (Rothero 2003: 49).

This species rarely produces capsules. Non-fertile plants have often been overlooked as the commoner *L. glaucum*, from which they can be distinguished with some difficulty using characters described by AC Crundwell (in Corley & Hill 1981: 136). Identification based on leaf shape (e.g. Nyholm 1987: 65-66) is less reliable.

34/1 ***Fissidens exiguus*** Sull.

H10 1979: sandstone beside Clare River, Clare Glens, S of Newport, JA Paton (Hill 1980b: 34).

This taxon does not merit species rank: it is apparently a dwarfed form of *F. pusillus* which occurs in districts with base-poor sandstone rocks exposed in shaded oligotrophic streams (Holyoak 2001c).

34/2-6 ***Fissidens viridulus*** aggregate: identity of species uncertain

H(1) listed by Lett (1915: 100) as *F. pusillus*.
H(1) listed by Lett (1915: 100) as *F. minutulus*.
H(2) 1935: Torc Mt., etc., no collector named (BBS exc.) (Watson 1936: 264), as *F. pusillus*.
H2 1951: rocks below Torc Waterfall, JP Brunker (BBS exc.) (Warburg 1952: 100, amended by Warburg 1953: 308), as *F. viridulus*.
H(3) listed by Lett (1915: 99) as *F. incurvus* var. *tamarindifolius*.
H3 1955: rock of cliff above Glen Lough, H Milne-Redhead (Warburg 1956: 153), as *F. pusillus*.
H6 1966: rocks by stream, pass over the Punchbowl, Comeragh Mts, ERB Little (BBS exc.) (Perry 1967: 407), as *F. minutulus* var. *minutulus*.
H(7) listed by Lett (1915: 98) as *F. viridulus*, without details.
H9 1957: limestone rocks in hazel scrub on SE side of Slievecarron, J Appleyard, AC Crundwell & E Nyholm (BBS exc.) (Warburg 1958b: 476), as *F. minutulus*.
H10 1979: sandstone beside Clare River, Clare Glens, S of Newport, JA Paton (Hill 1980b: 34).
H(12) listed by Lett (1915: 98) as *F. viridulus*.
H(14) listed by Lett (1915: 98) as *F. viridulus*.
H15 1957: stones in stream-bed, The Punchbowl, nr Gort, AC Crundwell (BBS exc.) (Warburg 1958b: 476), as *F. pusillus*.
H(16) listed by Lett (1915: 98) as *F. viridulus*.
H17 1957: face of drainage ditch in field, Ballindooly, DH Dalby (BBS exc.) (Warburg 1958b: 476), as *F. viridulus*.
H(18) listed by Lett (1915: 98) as *F. viridulus*.
H19 1953: roadside bank, Cupidstown Hill, ALK King (Warburg 1954: 480), as *F. viridulus*.
H(20) listed by Lett (1915: 98) as *F. viridulus*.
H(21) listed by Lett (1915: 98) as *F. viridulus*.
H(21) listed by Lett (1915: 99) as *F. incurvus* var. *tamarindifolius*.
H(21) listed by Lett (1915: 99) as *F. bryoides* var. *intermedius*.

H(22) listed by Lett (1915: 98) as *F. viridulus*.

H23 1953: bank under tree roots, NE shore of L. Owel, JS Thomson (Warburg 1954: 480), as *F. viridulus*.

H28 1963: limestone boulder, Knocknarea Glen, nr Sligo, RD Fitzgerald & AR Perry (Warburg 1964: 723), as *F. minutulus* var. *minutulus*.

H(29) 1928: wooded glen, NE end of Glencar Lough (BBS exc.) (Duncan 1928: 118), as *F. pusillus*.

H29 1963: stones by streamlet above Glencar Waterfall, AR Perry & RD Fitzgerald (Warburg 1964: 723), as *F. minutulus* var. *minutulus*.

H30 1955: cleft by river, State Forest, Virginia, ALK King (Warburg 1956: 153), as *F. viridulus*.

H(31) listed by Lett (1915: 98) as *F. viridulus*, without locality.

H(33) listed by Lett (1915: 98) as *F. viridulus*.

H(33) listed by Lett (1915: 99) as *F. bryoides* var. *intermedius*.

H33 1957: stone in damp ride in wood below Hanging Rock, L. Macnean Lower, AC Crundwell (Warburg 1958b: 476), as *F. pusillus*.

H(34) 1937: Ballyshannon, no collector named (BBS exc.) (Armitage 1938: 11), as *F. viridulus* var. *Lylei*.

H(35) listed by Lett (1915: 99) as *F. incurvus* var. *tamarindifolius*.

H(37) listed by Lett (1915: 98) as *F. viridulus*.

H(38) listed by Lett (1915: 98) as *F. viridulus*.

H(38) listed by Lett (1915: 99) as *F. incurvus* var. *tamarindifolius*, without locality.

H(39) listed by Lett (1915: 98) as *F. viridulus*.

H(39) listed by Lett (1915: 100) as *F. pusillus*.

H(39) listed by Lett (1915: 100) as *F. minutulus*.

The present concept of species in the *F. viridulus* group dates from the study by Corley (1980b). Records listed above cannot be assigned to the species recognised in that revision without study of the specimens. They are not mentioned in the unpublished lists (MFV Corley MS) of material used in a revision for the *CC* (Corley & Hill 1981: 71).

34/2 ***Fissidens viridulus*** (Sw.) Wahlenb. *s.s.* (syn. *Fissidens bambergeri* auct., *F. viridulus* var. *bambergeri* auct., non (Schimp. ex Milde) Waldh., *F. viridulus* var. *viridulus*)

H1 1951: earthy overhanging bank, between Carrigasheen and Rineen Point, nr Waterville, EF Warburg (BBSUK), conf. MFV Corley (MFV Corley MS).

H7 1966: earthy ledge under limestone rock, Rock of Cashel, JA Paton (BBS exc.), conf. MFV Corley (Perry 1967: 407, as *F. bambergeri*; MFV Corley MS).

H9 1994: on humus on vertical bank of fluctuating stream by area of limestone pavement, Carran, The Burren, R29, TL Blockeel 23/161 (Blockeel 1995c: 41).

H11 1968: limestone quarry, N of Thomastown, JA Paton, conf. MFV Corley (MFV Corley MS).

H12 1966: cliff top, Cahore Point, J Appleyard, conf. MFV Corley (MFV Corley MS).

[H15 record (1968: bank above river, The Punchbowl, Gort, JA Paton, conf. MFV Corley, in MFV Corley MS and Corley & Hill 1981: 71) subsequently reidentified as *F. limbatus* (MO Hill unpublished note)].

H19 1967: in scrub by canal bank, near Louisa Bridge, Leixlip, ALK King (DBN), conf. MFV Corley (MFV Corley MS).

H22 1978: steep clay bank by the Boyne, Bective, DM Synnott (DBN), conf. MFV Corley (MFV Corley MS).

H23 1980: clay bank by stream, S side of Hill of Ushnagh, W of Mullingar, DM Synnott, conf. MFV Corley (Hill 1982: 25, MFV Corley MS).

H26 1987: E bank of Cloon River between Srah and Partry, DM Synnott (Blockeel 1988: 34).

H27 1965: earthy bank under hazels, W shore of L Conn, nr Errew, AMcG Stirling (BBSUK), conf. MFV Corley (Crundwell 1969: 877, as *F. bambergeri*; MFV Corley MS).

H28 1962: earthy bank at entrance to Bronze-Age cairn, Carrowkeel, EF Warburg (BBSUK), conf. MFV Corley (Warburg 1963b: 493, as *F. viridulus*; MFV Corley MS).

H29 2000: on soil and dead wood at edge of

Salix carr beside lough, Rinn Lough, N end, N09, DT Holyoak 00-767b (BBSUK) (Rothero 2001: 39).

H32 1952: on earth, Lisgall nr Carrickmacross, RD Fitzgerald det. AH Norkett (BBSUK), conf. MFV Corley (Warburg 1953: 308, as *F. viridulus*; MFV Corley MS).

H(33) 1919: Kinarla Lane, nr Enniskillen, WN Tetley, conf. MFV Corley (MFV Corley MS).

†H33 listed by Blockeel & Long (1998: 81).

H34 2002: in bryophyte mat on rocks beneath overhang on N-facing crags, 488 m alt., Bulbin Mt., just NW of summit, C43, DT Holyoak 02-514 (Rothero 2003: 50).

H35 2001: on rock at side of stream in woodland, 50 m alt., Lough Eske Castle, H98, NG Hodgetts 3889 (Rothero 2003: 50).

H36 1956: calcareous clay, Carrickaness Bridge, nr Drumquin, RD Fitzgerald (BBSUK), conf. MFV Corley (Warburg 1959: 632, as *F. viridulus*; MFV Corley MS).

H(37) 1882: under trees, Lurgan, CH Waddell (DBN), conf. MFV Corley (MFV Corley MS).

H(39) 1917: Portmore, J Glover, conf. MFV Corley (MFV Corley MS).

The present concept of this taxon dates from the study by Corley (1980b). Details of many specimens given above are based on an unpublished list (MFV Corley MS) of material used in a revision for the *CC* (Corley & Hill 1981: 71).

34/3 *Fissidens limbatus* Sull.
(syn. *Fissidens herzogii* Ruthe ex Herzog, *F. minutulus* auct. pro parte, *F. viridulus* auct. pro parte)

H1 1951: earthy overhanging bank, between Carrigasheen and Rineen Point, nr Waterville, EF Warburg (BBS exc.) (BBSUK, OXF), conf. MFV Corley (Warburg 1952: 100, as *F. viridulus*; Corley 1980b: 207).

H2 1983: on earth, Ross I., 3 km SW of Killarney, G Bloom (Hill 1984b: 26).

H3 1966: laneside bank, nr Eccles Hotel, Glengarriff, JPM Brenan (BBSUK), conf. MFV Corley (Crundwell 1969: 877, as *F. viridulus*; Corley 1980b: 207).

H15 1968: soil on S bank above river, the Punchbowl, Gort, JA Paton, conf. MFV Corley (Hill 1985: 23).

H21 1958: lane on slope of Kilmashogue Mt., ALK King (DBN), conf. MFV Corley (Corley 1980b: 207).

H27 1987: on bank of path in shady woodland, nr Rose Cottage, NW of Westport, DG Long (Blockeel 1988: 34).

The present concept of this taxon dates from the study by Corley (1980b). It was formerly included in *F. viridulus* by British authors and differs from that taxon only in the smaller bulging cells of the leaf lamina.

34/4 *Fissidens pusillus* (Wilson) Milde
(syn. *Fissidens minutulus* auct. pro parte)

H1 1979: on rock in Roughty River, G Bloom, conf. MFV Corley (MFV Corley MS).

H2 1965: on wet rocks at water level in stream, Torc Waterfall, Killarney, HJB Birks & HH Lees (BBSUK), conf. MFV Corley (Warburg 1966: 191, as *F. minutulus* var. *minutulus*; MFV Corley MS).

H3 1979: on rocks in stream, Gouganebarra, G Bloom, conf. MFV Corley (MFV Corley MS).

H4 1967: stones at water's edge, *ca* 1200 ft [alt.], Mushera, Boggeragh Mts, RD Fitzgerald (BBSUK), conf. MFV Corley (Crundwell 1968: 631, as *F. minutulus* var. *minutulus*; MFV Corley MS).

H5 1966: stones in R. Douglas, nr Kilworth, ERB Little (BBS exc.) (BBSUK), conf. MFV Corley (Perry 1967: 407, as *F. minutulus* var. *minutulus*; MFV Corley MS).

H6 1966: rock in stream, gorge, Barrarakeen, SE of Clonmel, no collector named (DBN), conf. MFV Corley (MFV Corley MS).

H7 1966: calcareous conglomerate beside L. Curra, Galtee Mts, JA Paton (BBS exc.) (BBSUK), conf. MFV Corley (Perry 1967: 407, as *F. minutulus* var. *minutulus*; MFV Corley MS).

H8 1966: rocks at waterfall, *ca* 1300 ft alt., S side of Galtymore, RD Fitzgerald

(BBS exc.) (BBSUK), conf. MFV Corley (Perry 1967: 407-408, as *F. minutulus* var. *minutulus*; MFV Corley MS).

H9 1957: Slieve Carran, J Appleyard (BBS exc.) (BBSUK), conf. MFV Corley (Warburg 1964: 723, as *F. minutulus* var. *minutulus*; MFV Corley MS).

H13 1999: on boulder at edge of stream, 30 m alt., Pollymounty River, N bank, Ballyknockcrumpin, S73, TL Blockeel 28/310 (Rothero 2000: 48).

H15 1957: calcareous rocks nr Punchbowl, nr Gort, EM Lobley (BBS exc.) (BBSUK), conf. MFV Corley (Warburg 1958b: 476, as *F. viridulus*; MFV Corley MS).

H16 1957: on stones in stream, Balinahinch [= Ballynahinch], Connemara, AC Crundwell (BBS exc.) (BBSUK), conf. MFV Corley (Warburg 1958b: 476, as *F. pusillus*; MFV Corley MS).

H20 1969: rocks in Aughrim River, between Aughrim and Woodenbridge, RD Fitzgerald (BBSUK), conf. MFV Corley (Crundwell 1970: 196, as *F. minutulus* var. *minutulus*; MFV Corley MS).

H22 2001: on skin of marl on limestone boulder on lough edge, 70 m alt., SE edge of Lough Sheelin, NW of Ross, N48, DT Holyoak 01-605 (Rothero 2002: 44).

H23 1987: on stone in ditch in dense shade from conifer trees and hedge by old ruined animal stalls in field *ca* ¼ mile up small road off N6 between Athlone and Moate, DA Newman (Blockeel 1988: 34).

H26 1987: boulder in scrub by limestone pavement, W of Keel Bridge, DM Synnott (Blockeel 1988: 34).

H27 1962: rock in stream, W side of Corraun Hill, EF Warburg (BBSUK), conf. MFV Corley (Warburg 1963b: 493, as *F. minutulus* var. *minutulus*; MFV Corley MS).

H(28) 1937: under rocks, Anacoona, Ben Bulben, HN Dixon (BBSUK), conf. MFV Corley (MFV Corley MS).

H29 1963: damp calcareous boulder, Peakadaw, Glenade, AR Perry, conf. MFV Corley (MFV Corley MS).

H30 1955: in cliff by river in state forest, Virginia, ALK King (BBSUK), conf. MFV Corley (MFV Corley MS).

H33 1957: on lump of stone in ash wood nr Hanging Rock, Lough Macnean Lower, AC Crundwell (BBSUK), conf. MFV Corley (Warburg 1958b: 476, as *F. minutulus*; MFV Corley MS).

[H34 was listed in error by Corley (1980b: 208) *fide* MFV Corley MS].

H35 1990: rock in stream, Rosbeg Peninsula, G69, P Martin (Blockeel 1991c: 41). 1990: basic stones in shaded gully, *ca* 20 m alt., N side of Sheskinmore Lough, NW of Ardara, G69, TL Blockeel 19/356 (Blockeel 1991c: 41).

H38 1952: rocks in stream, Tolleymore Park [*sic* = Tollymore], JW Fitzgerald, EW Jones & MPH Kertland (BBSUK), conf. MFV Corley (Warburg 1953: 309, as *F. pusillus*; MFV Corley MS).

H39 1963: wet rock face by water, Glenariff Glen, AR Perry, conf. MFV Corley (MFV Corley MS).

The present concept of this taxon dates from the study by Corley (1980b). Details of many specimens given above are based on an unpublished list (MFV Corley MS) of material used in a revision for the *CC* (Corley & Hill 1981: 71).

34/5 ***Fissidens gracilifolius*** Brugg.-Nan. & Nyholm
(syn. *Fissidens minutulus* Sull. var. *tenuifolius* (Boulay) Norkett, *F. pusillus* var. *tenuifolius* (Boulay) Podp., *F. viridulus* var. *tenuifolius* (Boulay) A.J.E. Sm.)

H2 1979: on rock in stream, Torc Waterfall, G Bloom (Hill 1980b: 34).

H7 1966: L. Curra, Galtee Mts, JA Paton (Crundwell 1970: 196).

H8 1966: limestone rocks by L. Gur, ERB Little (BBS exc.) (Perry 1967: 407-408).

†H9 listed by Blockeel & Long (1998: 81).

H23 1970: soft calcareous rock in woodland, W of Killinure Lough, S of Glassan, JA Paton (Crundwell 1971b: 374).

H24 1968: on limestone boulder in wood, Rathcline House, 2 miles SW of Lanesborough, WV Rubers *et al.* (U) (Crundwell 1975: 13).

H28 1962: damp Carboniferous limestone rock, Carrowkeel, EF Warburg (Warburg 1963b: 493).

†H29 listed by Blockeel & Long (1998: 81).

H30 2001: on steep limestone at base of crag, 230 m alt., Giant's Leap, S of Blacklion, H03, DT Holyoak 01-752 (Rothero 2002: 44).
†H33 listed by Blockeel & Long (1998: 81).

34/6 ***Fissidens incurvus*** Starke ex Röhl.
(syn. *Fissidens incurvus* var. *tamarindifolius* (Turner) Braithw.)

H5 1966: bank of R. Blackwater, 5 miles E of Fermoy, J Appleyard & JG Duckett (BBS exc.) (Perry 1967: 408).
H9 1959: soil in crevice in limestone pavement nr sea, Poulsallagh, MCF Proctor & RB Ivimey-Cook (Warburg 1963b: 493).
H11 1954: ground in shade of wood, R.[ight] bank of R. Barrow at Graiguenamanagh, ALK King, det. AH Norkett (Warburg 1955: 583), as *F. incurvus* var. *tamarindifolius*.
H(18) 1892: on mound of ice-house, Glashill Rectory, CD Russell (DBN), conf. MFV Corley (Hill 1982: 25).
H(21) listed by Lett (1915: 98).
†H21 listed by Blockeel & Long (1998: 82).
H24 1968: wood nr Elfleet Bay, L. Ree, WV Rubers *et al.* (U) (Crundwell 1975:13).
H25 2002: on shaded root-plate of fallen spruce, 50 m alt., Lough Keel, nr Rockingham Demesne, G80, NG Hodgetts 4137 (Rothero 2003: 50).
H26 1987: on limestone on W-facing hillside W of Partry, HLK Whitehouse & EJ Rosen (Hb. Rosen) (Blockeel 1989: 26).
H29 1963: dead stump in stream, Bawn, 1 mile S of Dromahair, AR Perry & RD Fitzgerald (Warburg 1964: 723).
H(31) listed by Lett (1915: 98).
†H31 listed by Blockeel & Long (1998: 82).
H(33) listed by Lett (1915: 98).
†H33 listed by Blockeel & Long (1998: 82).
H(37) listed by Lett (1915: 98). H(37) listed by Blockeel & Long (1998: 82).
H(38) listed by Lett (1915: 98). H(38) listed by Blockeel & Long (1998: 82).
H(39) listed by Lett (1915: 98). H(39) listed by Blockeel & Long (1998: 82).
H39 1999: on dry soil under chalk block on wooded slope, Murlough Bay, D14, DT Holyoak 99-766 (BBSUK) (Rothero 2000: 48).
H40 1999: on steep soil bank of small ditch partly shaded by woodland, Downhill Forest, C73, DT Holyoak 99-275 (BBSUK) (Rothero 2000: 48).

34/7 ***Fissidens bryoides*** Hedw.

H(1) listed by Lett (1915: 99).
†H1 listed by Blockeel & Long (1998: 82).
H(2) listed by Lett (1915: 99).
†H2 listed by Blockeel & Long (1998: 82).
H(3) listed by Lett (1915: 99).
†H3 listed by Blockeel & Long (1998: 82).
H(4) listed by Lett (1915: 99).
†H4 listed by Blockeel & Long (1998: 82).
H5 1956: by L. Arderry, W of Castlemartyr, EC Wallace (Warburg 1957: 329).
H6 1966: soil in ravine N of the Punchbowl, Comeragh Mts, ERB Little (BBS exc.) (Perry 1967: 408).
H(7) listed by Lett (1915: 99).
†H7 listed by Blockeel & Long (1998: 82).
H(8) listed by Lett (1915: 99), without details.
†H8 listed by Blockeel & Long (1998: 82).
H(9) listed by Lett (1915: 99), without details.
†H9 listed by Blockeel & Long (1998: 82).
H(10) listed by Lett (1915: 99).
†H10 listed by Blockeel & Long (1998: 82).
H11 1955: Woodstock Forest, Inistioge, ALK King (Warburg 1956: 153).
H(12) listed by Lett (1915: 99).
†H12 listed by Blockeel & Long (1998: 82).
[H(13) listed by Lett (1915: 99). H13 deleted because no valid record or voucher specimen traced (Blockeel 1999: 4)].
H13 1999: on bare vertical bank, 20 m alt., path through copse, R Barrow, Saint Mullins, S73, TL Blockeel 28/329 (Rothero 2000: 49).
H14 1956: calcareous hedgerow, Durrow, AA Cridland (Warburg 1958b: 476).
H15 1994: bank in Sitka Spruce plantation, nr Pollboy, Boleyneendorish River, Slieve Aughty, M50, RC Stern (Blockeel 1995c: 41).
H(16) listed by Lett (1915: 99).
†H16 listed by Blockeel & Long (1998: 82).
H(19) 1949: roadside bank, Calverstown, JS Thomson (Warburg 1950: 384).
H(20) listed by Lett (1915: 99).
†H20 listed by Blockeel & Long (1998: 82).
H(21) listed by Lett (1915: 99).
†H21 listed by Blockeel & Long (1998: 82).
H22 1965: clay bank by stream, woodland above R. Boyne, Donore, DM Synnott (Warburg 1966: 191).
†H23 listed by Blockeel & Long (1998: 82).

H24 1968: limestone pit, Lanesborough, WV Rubers *et al.* (U) (Crundwell 1975:13).
H25 1965: hedgeside, Kilronan, nr Ballyfarnan, EM Lobley & RD Fitzgerald (Warburg 1966: 191).
H(27) listed by Lett (1915: 99).
†H27 listed by Blockeel & Long (1998: 82).
†H28 listed by Blockeel & Long (1998: 82).
H29 1963: hollow in alder by stream, Bawn, 1 mile S of Dromahair, AR Perry & RD Fitzgerald (Warburg 1964: 723).
H(30) listed by Lett (1915: 99).
†H30 listed by Blockeel & Long (1998: 82).
[H(31) listed by Lett (1915: 99). H31 deleted because no valid record or voucher specimen traced (Blockeel 1999: 4)].
H32 1961: bank in old sandpit, Castleshane, nr Monaghan, RD Fitzgerald (Warburg 1962: 368).
H(33) listed by Lett (1915: 99).
†H33 listed by Blockeel & Long (1998: 82).
H(34) listed by Lett (1915: 99).
†H34 listed by Blockeel & Long (1998: 82).
H(35) listed by Lett (1915: 99).
†H35 listed by Blockeel & Long (1998: 82).
H(36) listed by Lett (1915: 99).
†H36 listed by Blockeel & Long (1998: 82).
H(37) listed by Lett (1915: 99).
†H37 listed by Blockeel & Long (1998: 82).
H(38) listed by Lett (1915: 99). H(38) listed by Blockeel & Long (1998: 82).
H38 1999: on shaded bank by path, 50 m alt., Tollymore Forest Park, 4 km W of Newcastle, TL Blockeel 28/353 (Rothero 2000: 48).
H(39) listed by Lett (1915: 99) without locality.
†H39 listed by Blockeel & Long (1998: 82).
H(40) listed by Lett (1915: 99) without details.
†H40 listed by Blockeel & Long (1998: 82).

34/8 ***Fissidens curnovii*** Mitt.

H(1) 1935: below O'Sullivan's Cascade, no collector named (BBS exc.) (Watson 1936: 264).
†H1 listed by Blockeel & Long (1998: 82).
H(2) listed by Lett (1915: 99).
†H2 listed by Blockeel & Long (1998: 82).
H3 1979: wet soil bank, Glengarriff Wood, N Lockhart (Hill 1980b: 34).
H5 1966: coarse clay by stream, R. Douglas, nr Kilworth, ERB Little (BBS exc.) (Perry 1967: 408).
H6 1962: rock cleft in Coumshingaun corrie, ALK King (Warburg 1963b: 493).
H7 1963: shaded rock crevices in small ravine, stream on N side of Galtymore Mt., DA Ratcliffe (Warburg 1964: 723).
H(12) 1913: Great Saltee I., HW Lett, conf. MFV Corley (Hill 1981: 22).
H(16) 1933: Muckanaght, Twelve Bens, PWM Richards (anon. 1938d: 39).
†H16 listed by Blockeel & Long (1998: 82).
H20 1975: rock beside Glencullin River, NW of Enniskerry, JA Paton (BBS exc.) (Crundwell 1976: 22).
H27 1962: vertical stream-bank nr the deserted village, Slievemore, Achill I., EF Warburg (Warburg 1963b: 493).
H(34) listed by Lett (1915: 99). H(34) listed by Blockeel & Long (1998: 82).
H38 1952: rocks in stream, Tolleymore [*sic* = Tollymore] Park, JW Fitzgerald, EW Jones & MPH Kertland (Warburg 1953: 309).

34/9 ***Fissidens rivularis*** (Spruce) Bruch, Schimp. & W.Gümbel

H2 1983: damp shady limestone rocks under trees on lake shore of Lough Leane, nr Ross Castle, V9588, DG Long 11774 (BBSUK, E) (Hill 1984b: 26, Long 1984a).
H6 1999: on boulders in stream at water level, 67 m alt., Ballymacart River at Ballymacart Bridge, 3 km W of Mine Head, X28, TL Blockeel & DH Wrench, 28/214 (Rothero 2000: 49).

34/10 ***Fissidens monguillonii*** Thér.

H29 2000: on damp, loamy soil on river bank at upper edge of reedswamp, R. Shannon at S edge of Carrick-on-Shannon, M99, DT Holyoak 00-753 (Rothero 2002: 44-45).
H30 2001: on damp soil on lough edge in carr, 45 m alt., Lough Oughter, nr Gartnanoul Point, hectad H30, DT Holyoak 01-835 (Rothero 2002: 44-45).
H33 1959: at roots of rushes, generally submerged, Kilturk Lough, RD Fitzgerald (Warburg 1960: 773, Fitzgerald & Fitzgerald 1960a).

34/11 ***Fissidens crassipes*** Wilson ex Bruch, Schimp. & W.Gümbel

H5 1966: damp stones in old quarry, Ballynalacken, nr Fermoy, J Appleyard & JG Duckett (BBS exc.) (Perry 1967: 408).
H6 1999: at water level at base of bridge pier, 8 m alt., R Bride, Tallowbridge, Tallow, W99, TL Blockeel 28/257 (Rothero 2000: 49).
H8 1979: on concrete by lake in grounds of Curragh Chase, G Bloom (Hill 1980b: 34).
H9 1957: limestone, Cather R., Murroogh, nr Black Head, AC Crundwell, EM Evans & E Nyholm (BBS exc.) (Warburg 1958b: 476).
H10 1979: submerged on rock, Lough Derg, nr Terryglass, G Bloom (Hill 1980b: 34).
H11 1966: rocks in R. Nore, nr Thomastown, J Appleyard *et al.* (BBS exc.) (Perry 1967: 408).
H13 1969: rocks by R. Slaney, Aghade Bridge, nr Tullow, RD Fitzgerald (Crundwell 1970: 196).
H14 1952: on pearl mussel, R. Nore, Attenagh, AW Stelfox, comm. JS Thomson (Warburg 1953: 309).
H16 1968: shaded boulder in stream, deciduous woodland NW of Ballynahinch Castle Hotel, AR Perry (Crundwell 1971b: 374).
H17 1966: stone in stream, Derreen, N of Monivea, MFV Corley & JS Parker (Perry 1967: 408).
H19 1968: on limestone wall of Grand Canal nr Naas, ALK King (Crundwell 1969: 878).
[H21 1952: on apron of salmon weir, R. Liffey, Lucan, ALK King (Warburg 1953: 309). H21 deleted because voucher specimen is *F. rufulus* (Smith 1972, Crundwell 1973: 507)].
H22 1967: rock in river flowing S into the Boyne between Slane and Beauparc, DM Synnott (Crundwell 1968: 631).
H25 1981: on stones in river from L. Nablahy, N of Stokestown, DM Synnott (Hill 1982: 25).
H28 1965: limestone at water's edge, stream, Dromore West, RD Fitzgerald & EM Lobley (Warburg 1966: 191).
H29 1963: wet rocks by stream above Glencar Waterfall, AR Perry & RD Fitzgerald (Warburg 1964: 723).
H30 2001: on limestone boulder at edge of lough, 70 m alt., SE shore of Lough Sheelin, NE of Ross, N48, DT Holyoak 01-653 (Rothero 2002: 45).
H31 1978: rock at high water mark R. Boyne ½ mile below Obelisk Bridge, DM Synnott (Hill 1980b: 34).
H(33) 1937: River Erne, Belleek, no collector named (BBS exc.) (Armitage 1938: 11).
†H33 listed by Blockeel & Long (1998: 82).
H36 1957: stone in river, English Ford, RD Fitzgerald (Warburg 1958b: 476).
H37 1964: stones by R. Blackwater, Carrickaness, nr Benburb, RD Fitzgerald (Warburg 1965: 860).
H(38) listed by Blockeel & Long (1998: 82).
H40 1968: rocks at waterfall, Ness Glen, NW of Claudy, JW Fitzgerald & HH Birks (Crundwell 1969: 878).

34/12 ***Fissidens rufulus*** Bruch, Schimp. & W. Gümbel

H6 1956: boulder in stream, Deelish, nr Dungarvan, EC Wallace (Warburg 1958b: 476).
H19 1969: bridge buttress at water level, Derryvullagh Bog, nr Athy, RD Fitzgerald (Crundwell 1970: 196).
H20 1975: rock beside Glencullin River, NW of Enniskerry, JA Paton (BBS exc.) (Crundwell 1976: 22).
H(33) 1937: River Erne, Belleek, no collector named (BBS exc.) (Armitage 1938: 11).
†H33 listed by Blockeel & Long (1998: 82).
H34 1967: on stones, Crana River, nr Buncrana, RD Fitzgerald (Crundwell 1968: 631).
H(38) listed by Lett (1915: 99). H(38) listed by Blockeel & Long (1998: 82).

34/13 ***Fissidens exilis*** Hedw.

H(1) listed by Lett (1915: 98) without details. H(1) listed by Blockeel & Long (1998: 82).
H8 1966: shady bank in wood on sea shore, nr Ballydonohoe House, E of Tarbert [*sic* = Tarbet], MFV Corley & JS Parker (Perry 1967: 408).
H(19) listed by Lett (1915: 98). H(19) listed by Blockeel & Long (1998: 82).
H(20) listed by Lett (1915: 98) without

locality. H(20) listed by Blockeel & Long (1998: 82).
H(21) listed by Lett (1915: 98).
†H21 listed by Blockeel & Long (1998: 82).
H22 1978: bank of stream in woodland, Somerville Slane, DM Synnott (Hill 1979: 26).
H32 1965: damp roadside nr Cavanagarvan, nr Monaghan, EM Lobley & RD Fitzgerald (Warburg 1966: 191).
H(38) listed by Lett (1915: 98). H(38) listed by Blockeel & Long (1998: 82).
H(39) listed by Lett (1915: 98). H(39) listed by Blockeel & Long (1998: 82).
H(40) 1912: Kilrea, JD Houston (anon. 1937a: 367).

34/14 ***Fissidens celticus*** Paton

H1 1978: damp clay bank, Laurach, DM Synnott (Hill 1980b: 34).
H2 1983: woodland bank above stream below Torc Cascade, Killarney, JA Paton (Hill 1984b: 26).
H3 1979: damp clay in *Corylus* scrub by Glengarriff River, DM Synnott (Hill 1981: 22).
H4 1983: rut in woodland ride, 9 km S of Cork Airport, G Bloom (Hill 1984b: 26).
H5 1966: coarse clay bank of stream, valley of R. Douglas, nr Kilworth, ERB Little *et al.* (BBS exc.) (Perry 1967: 408, Little 1967).
H7 1966: clay in wood, Tower, Slieveardagh Hills, ERB Little (BBS exc.) (Perry 1967: 408, Little 1967).
H8 1979: woodland bank, ravine of R. Daar, below Carrigkerry, JA Paton & AC Crundwell (Hill 1980b: 34).
H10 1979: bank in wood below conifer plantation, S slope of Keeper Hill, JA Paton (Hill 1980b: 34).
H16 1970: sides of ruts on shaded track E of Kylemore Castle, JA Paton (Crundwell 1971b: 374).
H25 1981: clay bank in ravine below waterfall, ESE of Kilronan Mt., Arigna, DM Synnott (Hill 1982: 25).
H27 1970: shaded bank nr stream above Delphi, N of Killary Harbour, JA Paton (Crundwell 1971b: 374).
H36 2002: on clay-loam bank by path near lake, 80 m alt., Drum Manor Forest Park, H77, DT Holyoak 02-1094 (Rothero 2003: 50).
H37 2002: on steep soil on shaded slope above stream, 65 m alt., Gosford Forest Park, H94, DT Holyoak 02-1084 (Rothero 2003: 50).
H38 2002: on vertical loamy soil on bank by river, 95 m alt., S bank of Shimna River W of Parnell's Bridge, Tollymore Forest Park, J33, DT Holyoak 02-1035 (Rothero 2003: 50).
H40 1990: on steep bank above stream, Ness Wood, L51, P Martin (Blockeel 1991c: 41).

34/15 ***Fissidens curvatus*** Hornsch.
(syn. *Fissidens algarvicus* Solms)

H1 1951: earthy roadside bank between Glenbeigh and Ross-Behy, V Allorge, EW Jones & EF Warburg (BBS exc.) (Warburg 1952: 100).

34/16 ***Fissidens osmundoides*** Hedw.

H(1) listed by Lett (1915: 99) without details.
†H1 listed by Blockeel & Long (1998: 82).
H(2) listed by Lett (1915: 99).
†H2 listed by Blockeel & Long (1998: 82).
H(3) listed by Lett (1915: 99).
†H3 listed by Blockeel & Long (1998: 82).
H4 1967: wet rocks, Dripsey Castle, nr Cork, RD Fitzgerald (Crundwell 1968: 631).
H(6) listed by Lett (1915: 99).
†H6 listed by Blockeel & Long (1998: 82).
H(7) listed by Lett (1915: 99).
†H7 listed by Blockeel & Long (1998: 82).
H9 1977: old peat cuttings, Lough Goller bog, S of Lisdoonvarna, PH Pitkin (Hill 1979: 26).
H(10) listed by Lett (1915: 99). H(10) listed by Blockeel & Long (1998: 82).
H(12) listed by Lett (1915: 99). H(12) listed by Blockeel & Long (1998: 82).
H(14) listed by Lett (1915: 99).
†H14 listed by Blockeel & Long (1998: 82).
H(16) listed by Lett (1915: 99).
†H16 listed by Blockeel & Long (1998: 82).
H(18) listed by Lett (1915: 99). H(18) listed by Blockeel & Long (1998: 82).
H(19) listed by Lett (1915: 99). H(19) listed by Blockeel & Long (1998: 82).
H(20) 1949: wet rocks above Lough Ouler, *ca* 2100 ft [alt.], Tonlegee, JP Brunker (Warburg 1950: 384).
†H20 listed by Blockeel & Long (1998: 82).

H(21) listed by Lett (1915: 99). H(21) listed by Blockeel & Long (1998: 82).
[H(23) listed by Lett (1915: 99) as 1909: L. Deravaragh, HW Lett. H23 discounted because based on dubious literature record (Hill 1981: 22)].
H(24) listed by Lett (1915: 99). H(24) listed by Blockeel & Long (1998: 82).
H(25) listed by Lett (1915: 99). H(25) listed by Blockeel & Long (1998: 82).
†H27 listed by Blockeel & Long (1998: 82).
H(28) listed by Lett (1915: 99).
†H28 listed by Blockeel & Long (1998: 82).
H29 1963: limestone rocks, *ca* 900 ft [alt.], Peakadaw, Glenade, RD Fitzgerald & AR Perry (Warburg 1964: 723).
H(30) listed by Lett (1915: 99).
†H30 listed by Blockeel & Long (1998: 82).
H(31) listed by Lett (1915: 99). H(31) listed by Blockeel & Long (1998: 82).
H31 1999: in stony, weakly base-rich flush on moorland slope by stream, 300 m alt., Two Mile River, Carlingford, J11, TL Blockeel 28/165 (Rothero 2000: 49).
H(32) listed by Lett (1915: 99).
†H32 listed by Blockeel & Long (1998: 82).
H(33) listed by Lett (1915: 99).
†H33 listed by Blockeel & Long (1998: 82).
H(34) listed by Lett (1915: 99).
†H34 listed by Blockeel & Long (1998: 82).
H(35) listed by Lett (1915: 99).
†H35 listed by Blockeel & Long (1998: 82).
H(36) listed by Lett (1915: 99).
†H36 listed by Blockeel & Long (1998: 82).
H(37) listed by Lett (1915: 99) without details.
†H37 listed by Blockeel & Long (1998: 82).
H(38) listed by Lett (1915: 99).
†H38 listed by Blockeel & Long (1998: 82).
H(39) listed by Lett (1915: 99).
†H39 listed by Blockeel & Long (1998: 82).
H(40) 1913: Granaghan, JD Houston (anon. 1937a: 367).
†H40 listed by Blockeel & Long (1998: 82).

34/17a *Fissidens taxifolius* Hedw. var. *taxifolius*
(syn. *Fissidens taxifolius* subsp. *taxifolius*)

H(1) listed by Lett (1915: 100) without details.
†H1 listed by Blockeel & Long (1998: 83).
H(2) listed by Lett (1915: 100) without details.
†H2 listed by Blockeel & Long (1998: 83).
H(3) listed by Lett (1915: 100) without details.
†H3 listed by Blockeel & Long (1998: 83).
H(4) listed by Lett (1915: 100) without details.
†H4 listed by Blockeel & Long (1998: 83).
†H5 listed by Blockeel & Long (1998: 83).
H(6) listed by Lett (1915: 100) without details.
†H6 listed by Blockeel & Long (1998: 83).
†H7 listed by Blockeel & Long (1998: 83).
H(8) listed by Lett (1915: 100) without details.
†H8 listed by Blockeel & Long (1998: 83).
H(9) listed by Lett (1915: 100) without details.
†H9 listed by Blockeel & Long (1998: 83).
H(10) listed by Lett (1915: 100) without details.
†H10 listed by Blockeel & Long (1998: 83).
H(11) listed by Lett (1915: 100) without details.
†H11 listed by Blockeel & Long (1998: 83).
H(12) listed by Lett (1915: 100) without details.
†H12 listed by Blockeel & Long (1998: 83).
H(13) listed by Lett (1915: 100) without details.
†H13 listed by Blockeel & Long (1998: 83).
H(14) listed by Lett (1915: 100) without details.
†H14 listed by Blockeel & Long (1998: 83).
H(15) listed by Lett (1915: 100) without details.
†H15 listed by Blockeel & Long (1998: 83).
H16 1957: rock ledges, wooded slopes above Kylemore Abbey, EV Watson (BBS exc.) (Warburg 1958b: 477).
H(17) listed by Lett (1915: 100) without details.
†H17 listed by Blockeel & Long (1998: 83).
H(18) listed by Lett (1915: 100) without details.
†H18 listed by Blockeel & Long (1998: 83).
H(19) listed by Lett (1915: 100) without details.
†H19 listed by Blockeel & Long (1998: 83).
H(20) listed by Lett (1915: 100) without details.
†H20 listed by Blockeel & Long (1998: 83).
H(21) listed by Lett (1915: 100) without details.
†H21 listed by Blockeel & Long (1998: 83).
†H22 listed by Blockeel & Long (1998: 83).
H(23) listed by Lett (1915: 100) without

details.
†H23 listed by Blockeel & Long (1998: 83).
H(24) listed by Lett (1915: 100) without details.
†H24 listed by Blockeel & Long (1998: 83).
H(25) listed by Lett (1915: 100) without details.
†H25 listed by Blockeel & Long (1998: 83).
H(26) listed by Lett (1915: 100) without details.
†H26 listed by Blockeel & Long (1998: 83).
H(27) listed by Lett (1915: 100) without details.
†H27 listed by Blockeel & Long (1998: 83).
H(28) listed by Lett (1915: 100) without details.
†H28 listed by Blockeel & Long (1998: 83).
H(29) listed by Lett (1915: 100) without details.
†H29 listed by Blockeel & Long (1998: 83).
H(30) listed by Lett (1915: 100) without details.
†H30 listed by Blockeel & Long (1998: 83).
H(31) listed by Lett (1915: 100) without details.
†H31 listed by Blockeel & Long (1998: 83).
H(32) listed by Lett (1915: 100) without details.
†H32 listed by Blockeel & Long (1998: 83).
H(33) listed by Lett (1915: 100) without details.
†H33 listed by Blockeel & Long (1998: 83).
H(34) listed by Lett (1915: 100) without details.
†H34 listed by Blockeel & Long (1998: 83).
H(35) listed by Lett (1915: 100) without details.
†H35 listed by Blockeel & Long (1998: 83).
H(36) listed by Lett (1915: 100) without details.
†H36 listed by Blockeel & Long (1998: 83).
H(37) listed by Lett (1915: 100) without details.
†H37 listed by Blockeel & Long (1998: 83).
H(38) listed by Lett (1915: 100) without details.
†H38 listed by Blockeel & Long (1998: 83).
H(39) listed by Lett (1915: 100) without details.
†H39 listed by Blockeel & Long (1998: 83).
H(40) listed by Lett (1915: 100) without details.
†H40 listed by Blockeel & Long (1998: 83).

34/17b ***Fissidens taxifolius* var. *pallidicaulis*** (Mitt.) Corb.
(syn. *Fissidens taxifolius* subsp. *pallidicaulis* (Mitt.) Mönk.)

H1 1951: by Lough Currane, Waterville, EC Wallace (Wallace 1976: 162, Hill 1978: 17).
H7 1975: Galtee Mountains, A Eddy (Wallace 1976: 162, Hill 1978: 17).
H16 1957: on rocks by stream, Kylemore, J Appleyard, conf. MFV Corley or EC Wallace (Hill 1980b: 34).
H27 1987: on wet rocks by stream, ravine on S side of Ben Gorm, Killary Harbour, DG Long 14600 (Blockeel 1989: 26).
H40 1990: on wet rock ledge in Big Cleft, Binevenagh, DM Synnott (Blockeel 1991c: 41).

34/18 ***Fissidens dubius*** P.Beauv.
(syn. *Fissidens cristatus* Wilson ex Mitt., *F. cristatus* var. *brevifolius* Lindb., *F. decipiens* De Not.)

H(1) listed by Lett (1915: 100) without details.
†H1 listed by Blockeel & Long (1998: 83).
H(2) listed by Lett (1915: 100).
†H2 listed by Blockeel & Long (1998: 83).
H(3) listed by Lett (1915: 100).
†H3 listed by Blockeel & Long (1998: 83).
H4 1967: wall of bridge, Mushera, RD Fitzgerald (Crundwell 1968: 631).
†H5 listed by Blockeel & Long (1998: 83).
H(6) listed by Lett (1915: 100).
†H6 listed by Blockeel & Long (1998: 83).
H(7) 1943: cliffs at L. Diheen, AW Stelfox, per JS Thomson (Duncan 1944: 209).
†H7 listed by Blockeel & Long (1998: 83).
H8 1966: on limestone, L. Gur, RD Fitzgerald (BBS exc) (Crundwell 1968: 631).
†H9 listed by Blockeel & Long (1998: 83).
H10 1965: stony ground by lake, Kilbarron Quay, L. Derg, ALK King (Warburg 1966: 191).
H(11) listed by Lett (1915: 100).
†H11 listed by Blockeel & Long (1998: 83).
H(12) listed by Lett (1915: 100).
†H12 listed by Blockeel & Long (1998: 83).
H13 1958: ruins, St Mullin's, ALK King (Warburg 1959: 633).
H(14) listed by Lett (1915: 100).
†H14 listed by Blockeel & Long (1998: 83).

H15 1957: mortar in wall, Kilreekill, RE Parker (Warburg 1958b: 476).
H(16) listed by Lett (1915: 100).
†H16 listed by Blockeel & Long (1998: 83).
H(17) listed by Lett (1915: 100).
†H17 listed by Blockeel & Long (1998: 83).
H18 1965: wall by R. Camcor above Kinnity, ALK King (Warburg 1966: 191).
H19 1952: sandy bank of canal, Leixlip, AW Stelfox, comm. JS Thomson (Warburg 1953: 309).
H(20) 1939: Devil's Glen, JS Thomson (anon. 1940a: 173).
H(21) 1949: calcareous tufa, Glenasmole, JP Brunker (Warburg 1951: 499).
†H21 listed by Blockeel & Long (1998: 83).
H22 1962: in grass in fixed dune, Laytown, ALK King (Warburg 1963b: 493).
H23 1952: roadside bank, Carrigybreen, Athlone, ALK King (Warburg 1953: 309).
H(25) listed by Lett (1915: 100).
†H25 listed by Blockeel & Long (1998: 83).
H(26) listed by Lett (1915: 100).
†H26 listed by Blockeel & Long (1998: 83).
H27 1962: dunes, Keel Bay, Achill I., EF Warburg (Warburg 1963b: 493).
H(28) listed by Lett (1915: 100).
†H28 listed by Blockeel & Long (1998: 83).
H(29) listed by Lett (1915: 100).
†H29 listed by Blockeel & Long (1998: 83).
H(30) listed by Lett (1915: 100). H(30) listed by Blockeel & Long (1998: 83).
H30 2001: on open limestone blocks on bank of stream, 320 m alt., W of Bellavally Gap, H12, DT Holyoak 01-628 (Rothero 2002: 45).
H(31) 1943: Ravensdale, JS Thomson (Duncan 1944: 209).
H31 1999: in crevices of rocky bank of stream, 150 m alt., Two Mile River, Carlingford, J11, TL Blockeel 28/150 (Rothero 2000: 49).
H32 1952: limestone, Lisgall, nr Carrickmacross, RD Fitzgerald (Warburg 1953: 309).
H(33) listed by Lett (1915: 100).
†H33 listed by Blockeel & Long (1998: 83).
H(34) 1948: crevices of dry stone wall nr sea, Clonmany, AM Irwin (anon. 1949c: 218).
†H34 listed by Blockeel & Long (1998: 83).
H(35) 1911: Killybegs, CA Cheetham (anon. 1915a: 126, Lett 1915: 100).
†H35 listed by Blockeel & Long (1998: 83).
H36 1957: mortar of bridge, Slaghtfreedan Lodge, L. Fea, RD Fitzgerald (Warburg 1958b: 476).
H37 1964: rocks by canal tow path, Carrickaness, nr Benburb, RD Fitzgerald (Warburg 1965: 860).
H(38) listed by Lett (1915: 100).
†H38 listed by Blockeel & Long (1998: 83).
H(39) 1928: Glenariff (BBS exc.) (Duncan 1928: 114, 117).
†H39 listed by Blockeel & Long (1998: 83).
H40 1952: limestone, waterfall, Umbra, RD Fitzgerald (Warburg 1953: 309).

34/19 ***Fissidens adianthoides*** Hedw.

H(1) listed by Lett (1915: 100) without details.
†H1 listed by Blockeel & Long (1998: 83).
H(2) listed by Lett (1915: 100) without details.
†H2 listed by Blockeel & Long (1998: 83).
H(3) listed by Lett (1915: 100) without details.
†H3 listed by Blockeel & Long (1998: 83).
H(4) listed by Lett (1915: 100) without details.
†H4 listed by Blockeel & Long (1998: 83).
H(5) listed by Lett (1915: 100) without details.
†H5 listed by Blockeel & Long (1998: 83).
H(6) listed by Lett (1915: 100) without details.
†H6 listed by Blockeel & Long (1998: 83).
H(7) listed by Lett (1915: 100) without details.
†H7 listed by Blockeel & Long (1998: 83).
H(8) listed by Lett (1915: 100) without details.
†H8 listed by Blockeel & Long (1998: 83).
H(9) listed by Lett (1915: 100) without details.
†H9 listed by Blockeel & Long (1998: 83).
H(10) listed by Lett (1915: 100) without details.
†H10 listed by Blockeel & Long (1998: 83).
H11 1954: heavily shaded bank by Ballycogan Road, Graiguenamanagh, ALK King (Warburg 1955: 583).
H12 1969: in marsh, Pallis Bridge, Wicklow Gap, RD Fitzgerald (Crundwell 1970: 197).
H(13) listed by Lett (1915: 100) without details.
†H13 listed by Blockeel & Long (1998: 83).

H(14) listed by Lett (1915: 100) without details.
†H14 listed by Blockeel & Long (1998: 83).
H15 1952: marsh by L. Derg, nr Ross Quay, ALK King (Warburg 1953: 309).
H(16) listed by Lett (1915: 100) without details.
†H16 listed by Blockeel & Long (1998: 83).
H(17) listed by Lett (1915: 100) without details.
†H17 listed by Blockeel & Long (1998: 83).
H(18) listed by Lett (1915: 100) without details.
†H18 listed by Blockeel & Long (1998: 83).
H(19) 1938: Rye Water, JS Thomson (anon. 1939b: 108).
†H19 listed by Blockeel & Long (1998: 83).
H(20) listed by Lett (1915: 100) without details.
†H20 listed by Blockeel & Long (1998: 83).
[H(21) listed by Lett (1915: 100) without details. H21 deleted because no valid record or voucher specimen traced (Blockeel 1999: 4)].
H22 1952: demesne wall, Carton, Maynooth, JP Brunker (Warburg 1953: 309).
H(23) listed by Lett (1915: 100) without details.
†H23 listed by Blockeel & Long (1998: 83).
H24 1965: raised bog S of Roosky, RD Fitzgerald & EM Lobley (Warburg 1966: 191).
H(25) listed by Lett (1915: 100) without details.
†H25 listed by Blockeel & Long (1998: 83).
H(26) listed by Lett (1915: 100) without details.
†H26 listed by Blockeel & Long (1998: 83).
H(27) listed by Lett (1915: 100) without details.
†H27 listed by Blockeel & Long (1998: 83).
H(28) listed by Lett (1915: 100) without details.
†H28 listed by Blockeel & Long (1998: 83).
H(29) listed by Lett (1915: 100) without details.
†H29 listed by Blockeel & Long (1998: 83).
H(30) listed by Lett (1915: 100) without details.
†H30 listed by Blockeel & Long (1998: 83).
[H(31) listed by Lett (1915: 100) without details. H31 deleted because no valid record or voucher specimen traced (Blockeel 1999: 4)].
[H(32) listed by Lett (1915: 100) without details. H32 deleted because no valid record or voucher specimen traced (Blockeel 1999: 4)].
H(33) listed by Lett (1915: 100) without details.
†H33 listed by Blockeel & Long (1998: 83).
H(34) listed by Lett (1915: 100) without details.
†H34 listed by Blockeel & Long (1998: 83).
H(35) listed by Lett (1915: 100) without details.
†H35 listed by Blockeel & Long (1998: 83).
H(36) listed by Lett (1915: 100) without details.
†H36 listed by Blockeel & Long (1998: 83).
H(37) listed by Lett (1915: 100) without details.
†H37 listed by Blockeel & Long (1998: 83).
H(38) listed by Lett (1915: 100) without details.
†H38 listed by Blockeel & Long (1998: 83).
H(39) listed by Lett (1915: 100) without details.
†H39 listed by Blockeel & Long (1998: 83).
H(40) listed by Lett (1915: 100) without details.
†H40 listed by Blockeel & Long (1998: 83).

34/20 ***Fissidens serrulatus*** Brid.

H1 1992: bouldery wooded river bank, on soil bank, 5 m alt., Glantrasna River, Lauragh Bridge, V75, DG Long 23185 (Blockeel 1994: 37).
H27 1970: ravine on S slope of Ben Gorm, N of Killary Harbour, JA Paton (Crundwell 1971b: 375).

34/21 ***Fissidens polyphyllus*** Wilson ex Bruch, Schimp. & W.Gümbel

H(1) listed by Lett (1915: 100). H(1) listed by Blockeel & Long (1998: 83).
H(2) listed by Lett (1915: 100).
†H2 listed by Blockeel & Long (1998: 83).
H(3) listed by Lett (1915: 100).
†H3 listed by Blockeel & Long (1998: 83).
H(4) listed by Lett (1915: 100). H(4) listed by Blockeel & Long (1998: 83).
H6 1967: in small rivulet by wooded glen N of Lismore, DA Ratcliffe, HH Birks & HJB Birks (Crundwell: 1969: 878).
H(20) 1942: Drumgoff Brook, Glenmalure, AW Stelfox, per JS Thomson (Duncan 1944: 209).

†H20 listed by Blockeel & Long (1998: 83).
H(28) listed by Lett (1915: 100).
†H28 listed by Blockeel & Long (1998: 83).

35/1 ***Octodiceras fontanum*** (Bach.Pyl.) Lindb.
(syn. *Fissidens fontanus* (Bach.Pyl.) Steud.)

H16 2000: on rocky SE shore close to lough margin, 8 m alt., Lough Donaghmeave, L64, J Ryan, det. N Lockhart (Rothero 2001: 39).
H29 1978: on rocks in shallow water of reed-swamp, Lough Carrickaport, JB Ryan, comm. N Lockhart (Hill 1981: 23).
[H(38) listed by Lett (1915: 99)].

36/1 ***Encalypta streptocarpa*** Hedw.
(syn. *Leersia contorta* Lindb.)

H(1) listed by Lett (1915: 121) without details.
†H1 listed by Blockeel & Long (1998: 83).
H(2) listed by Lett (1915: 121) without details.
†H2 listed by Blockeel & Long (1998: 83).
H3 1951: hillside in Pass of Keimaneigh, ALK King (Warburg 1952: 102).
H(4) listed by Lett (1915: 121) without details.
†H4 listed by Blockeel & Long (1998: 83).
H(5) listed by Lett (1915: 121) without details.
†H5 listed by Blockeel & Long (1998: 83).
H(6) listed by Lett (1915: 121) without details.
†H6 listed by Blockeel & Long (1998: 83).
H(7) listed by Lett (1915: 121) without details.
H7 1956: limestone wall in lane nr Knocklofty, EC Wallace (Warburg 1957: 332).
H(8) listed by Lett (1915: 121) without details.
†H8 listed by Blockeel & Long (1998: 83).
H(9) listed by Lett (1915: 121) without details.
†H9 listed by Blockeel & Long (1998: 83).
H(10) listed by Lett (1915: 121) without details.
†H10 listed by Blockeel & Long (1998: 83).
H(11) listed by Lett (1915: 121) without details.
†H11 listed by Blockeel & Long (1998: 83).
H(12) listed by Lett (1915: 121) without details.
†H12 listed by Blockeel & Long (1998: 83).
H(13) listed by Lett (1915: 121) without details.
†H13 listed by Blockeel & Long (1998: 83).
H(14) listed by Lett (1915: 121) without details.
†H14 listed by Blockeel & Long (1998: 83).
H15 1957: mortar in stone walls, nr Owendalulleegh R., RE Parker (Warburg 1958b: 480).
H(16) listed by Lett (1915: 121) without details.
†H16 listed by Blockeel & Long (1998: 83).
H(17) listed by Lett (1915: 121) without details.
†H17 listed by Blockeel & Long (1998: 83).
[H(18) listed by Lett (1915: 121) without details. H18 deleted because no valid record or voucher specimen traced (Blockeel 1999: 4)].
H(19) 1949: wall, nr Calverstown, JS Thomson (Warburg 1950: 385).
†H19 listed by Blockeel & Long (1998: 83).
H(20) listed by Lett (1915: 121) without details.
†H20 listed by Blockeel & Long (1998: 83).
H(21) listed by Lett (1915: 121) without details.
†H21 listed by Blockeel & Long (1998: 83).
H(22) listed by Lett (1915: 121) without details.
†H22 listed by Blockeel & Long (1998: 83).
H(23) listed by Lett (1915: 121) without details.
†H23 listed by Blockeel & Long (1998: 83).
H24 1957: wall, nr Lanesborough, ALK King (Warburg 1958b: 480).
H(25) listed by Lett (1915: 121) without details.
†H25 listed by Blockeel & Long (1998: 83).
H(26) listed by Lett (1915: 121) without details.
†H26 listed by Blockeel & Long (1998: 83).
H(27) listed by Lett (1915: 121) without details.
†H27 listed by Blockeel & Long (1998: 83).
H(28) listed by Lett (1915: 121) without details.
†H28 listed by Blockeel & Long (1998: 83).
H(29) listed by Lett (1915: 121) without details.
†H29 listed by Blockeel & Long (1998: 83).
[H(30) listed by Lett (1915: 121) without

details. H30 deleted because no valid record or voucher specimen traced (Blockeel 1999: 4)].
H30 2001: on mortared wall of bridge, 95 m alt., Deerpark, W of Virginia, N58, DT Holyoak 01-662 (Rothero 2002: 45).
H(31) listed by Lett (1915: 121) without details.
†H31 listed by Blockeel & Long (1998: 83).
[H(32) listed by Lett (1915: 121) without details. H32 deleted because no valid record or voucher specimen traced (Blockeel 1999: 4)].
H(33) listed by Lett (1915: 121) without details.
†H33 listed by Blockeel & Long (1998: 83).
H(34) listed by Lett (1915: 121) without details.
†H34 listed by Blockeel & Long (1998: 83).
H(35) listed by Lett (1915: 121) without details.
†H35 listed by Blockeel & Long (1998: 83).
H(36) listed by Lett (1915: 121) without details.
†H36 listed by Blockeel & Long (1998: 83).
H(37) listed by Lett (1915: 121) without details.
†H37 listed by Blockeel & Long (1998: 83).
H(38) listed by Lett (1915: 121) without details.
†H38 listed by Blockeel & Long (1998: 83).
H(39) listed by Lett (1915: 121) without details.
†H39 listed by Blockeel & Long (1998: 83).
H(40) listed by Lett (1915: 121) without details.
†H40 listed by Blockeel & Long (1998: 83).

36/2 ***Encalypta alpina*** Sm.
(syn. *Encalypta commutata* Nees & Hornsch.)

H(28) 1928: Gleniff, Ben Bulben (BBS exc.) (Duncan 1928: 114-115, 118).
†H28 listed by Blockeel & Long (1998: 83).

36/3 ***Encalypta rhaptocarpa*** Schwägr.
(syn. *Leersia rhabdocarpa* (Schwägr.) Lindb.)

H(9) listed by Lett (1915: 121). H(9) listed by Blockeel & Long (1998: 83).
H(27) listed by Lett (1915: 121). H(27) listed by Blockeel & Long (1998: 83).
H(28) listed by Lett (1915: 121).
†H28 listed by Blockeel & Long (1998: 83).
H(29) listed by Lett (1915: 121). H(29) listed by Blockeel & Long (1998: 83).
H40 1999: on crumbling basalt rock on open slope, 450 m alt., Benbradagh, just N of summit, C71, DT Holyoak 99-671 (BBSUK) (Rothero 2000: 49).

36/4 ***Encalypta vulgaris*** Hedw.
(syn. *Leersia extinctoria* Leyss. ex Broekm.)

H(1) listed by Lett (1915: 121). H(1) listed by Blockeel & Long (1998: 83).
H(2) listed by Lett (1915: 121).
†H2 listed by Blockeel & Long (1998: 83).
H(4) listed by Lett (1915: 121). H(4) listed by Blockeel & Long (1998: 83).
H(5) listed by Lett (1915: 121). H(5) listed by Blockeel & Long (1998: 83).
H6 1956: wall-top, Kilwinnin, Dungarvan, EC Wallace (Warburg 1957: 332).
H7 1956: earthy limestone wall, between Marlfield and Knocklofty, EC Wallace (Warburg 1957: 332).
H(9) 1945: top of wall, Fergus River, JS Thomson (anon. 1946c: 282).
†H9 listed by Blockeel & Long (1998: 83).
H(11) listed by Lett (1915: 121).
†H11 listed by Blockeel & Long (1998: 83).
H(13) listed by Lett (1915: 121).
†H13 listed by Blockeel & Long (1998: 83).
H14 1955: wall near Ballydine Bridge, nr Abbeyleix, JS Thomson (Warburg 1956: 154).
H15 1957: limestone wall, Kilreekill, RE Parker (Warburg 1958b: 480).
[H(16) listed by Lett (1915: 121) without locality. H16 deleted because no valid record or voucher specimen traced (Blockeel 1999: 4)].
H(18) listed by Lett (1915: 121). H(18) listed by Blockeel & Long (1998: 83).
H(19) 1949: sand pit on railway, N of Sallins, AW Stelfox (per JS Thomson) (Warburg 1950: 385).
[H(20) listed by Lett (1915: 121) without details. H20 deleted because no valid record or voucher specimen traced (Blockeel 1999: 4)].
H(21) listed by Lett (1915: 121). H(21) listed by Blockeel & Long (1998: 83).
H22 1978: clay soil on wall-top, Mount Nugent Road, 1 km N of Oldcastle, DM Synnott (Hill 1980b: 36).

H(23) listed by Lett (1915: 121). H(23) listed by Blockeel & Long (1998: 83).
†H24 listed by Blockeel & Long (1998: 83).
H25 1985: soil on limestone wall-top, roadside between Lecarrow and L. Ree, DL Kelly & G O'Donovan (Hill 1986: 20).
H(27) listed by Lett (1915: 121). H(27) listed by Blockeel & Long (1998: 83).
H32 1952: limestone, Lisgall, nr Carrickmacross, RD Fitzgerald (Warburg 1953: 311).
H(33) listed by Lett (1915: 121). H(33) listed by Blockeel & Long (1998: 83).
H(35) listed by Lett (1915: 121). H(35) listed by Blockeel & Long (1998: 83).
H37 1964: limestone in old quarry, Loughgall, RD Fitzgerald (Warburg 1965: 862).
H(39) listed by Lett (1915: 121). H(39) listed by Blockeel & Long (1998: 83).
H(40) listed by Lett (1915: 121).
†H40 listed by Blockeel & Long (1998: 83).

36/6 ***Encalypta ciliata*** Hedw.
(syn. *Leersia laciniata* Hedw. ex Lindb. nom. illeg.)

H(8) 1945: below Corrignabinnia, Galtees, RD Meikle (anon. 1947: 31).
†H8 listed by Blockeel & Long (1998: 84).
H(27) listed by Lett (1915: 121) without details. H(27) listed by Blockeel & Long (1998: 84).
[H28 listed by Lett (1915: 121) as: Benbulben, leg. Mackay. H28 deleted because record (Hooker & Taylor 1818) is based on *E. rhabdocarpa* (Crundwell 1970: 199)].
H(39) no date: Cave Hill, Templeton (Lett 1915: 121).
no date: no locality, Moore (Lett 1915: 121). H(39) listed by Blockeel & Long (1998: 84).
H(40) no date: Benbradagh, Moore (Lett 1915: 121).
†H40 listed by Blockeel & Long (1998: 84).

37/1 ***Eucladium verticillatum*** (Brid.) Bruch, Schimp. & W.Gümbel
(syn. *Mollia verticillata* (Brid.) Lindb., *Weisia verticillata* auct., *Weissia verticillata* Brid.)

H(1) listed by Lett (1915: 115) without details.
†H1 listed by Blockeel & Long (1998: 84).
H(2) listed by Lett (1915: 115). H(2) listed by Blockeel & Long (1998: 84).
H3 1998: seeps on walls of sea cave at head of rocky inlet, 10 m alt., Foilareal Bay, 7 km S of Timoleague, W43, JW Bates 3921 (Rothero 1999b: 41).
H(4) listed by Lett (1915: 115).
†H4 listed by Blockeel & Long (1998: 84).
H(5) listed by Lett (1915: 115). H(5) listed by Blockeel & Long (1998: 84).
H6 1956: spring on sea-cliff, W of Ardmore, EC Wallace (Warburg 1957: 332).
H7 1966: rock crevice, Cashel Park, J Appleyard & JG Duckett (BBS exc.) (Perry 1967: 413).
H8 1979: old mortar, crevices in wall of refectory undercroft, Askeaton Friary, EW Jones & G Bloom (Hill 1980b: 38).
†H9 listed by Blockeel & Long (1998: 84).
H10 1979: shaded rock above Clare River, Clare Glens, S of Newport, JA Paton (Hill 1980b: 38).
H11 1966: limestone face by R. Nore, Dysart Castle, nr Thomastown, RD Fitzgerald (BBS exc.) (Crundwell 1968: 636).
H12 1953: sandy cliff, Duncannon, ALK King (Warburg 1955: 585).
H(13) listed by Lett (1915: 115).
†H13 listed by Blockeel & Long (1998: 84).
H(14) listed by Lett (1915: 115).
†H14 listed by Blockeel & Long (1998: 84).
[H15 deleted because no valid record or voucher specimen traced (Blockeel 1999: 4)].
H16 1957: rock in wood, Derryclare Lough, AC Crundwell (BBS exc.) (Warburg 1958b: 479).
H17 1950: limestone swallowhole, Castlegar, JP Brunker (Warburg 1951: 500).
H(18) listed by Lett (1915: 115).
†H18 listed by Blockeel & Long (1998: 84).
H(19) 1938: Rye Water, JS Thomson (anon. 1939b: 109).
H(20) listed by Lett (1915: 115).
†H20 listed by Blockeel & Long (1998: 84).
H(21) listed by Lett (1915: 115). H(21) listed by Blockeel & Long (1998: 84).
H22 1963: wet limy soil nr sea, Gormanstown Camp, DM Synnott (Warburg 1964: 726).
H23 1953: bank, NE shore of L. Owel, JS Thomson (Warburg 1954: 482).
H24 1980: lock of Royal Canal at Drapers

Bridge, DM Synnott (Hill 1981: 26).
H25 1981: underside of bridge, S of L. O'Donra, N of Strokestown, DM Synnott (Hill 1982: 26).
H(26) listed by Lett (1915: 115). H(26) listed by Blockeel & Long (1998: 84).
H27 1962: vertical bank on low cliff, Coraun [*sic* = Caraun] Point, Achill I., EF Warburg (Warburg 1963b: 496).
H(28) listed by Lett (1915: 115).
†H28 listed by Blockeel & Long (1998: 84).
H(29) listed by Lett (1915: 115) without locality.
†H29 listed by Blockeel & Long (1998: 84).
H30 2001: on damp limestone in cave, 220 m alt., Giant's Leap, S of Blacklion, H03, DT Holyoak 01-757 (Rothero 2002: 45).
H31 1973: ruined masonry, Mellifont Abbey, MO Hill (Crundwell 1974: 168).
[H32 deleted because no valid record or voucher specimen traced (Blockeel 1999: 4)].
H(33) listed by Lett (1915: 115).
†H33 listed by Blockeel & Long (1998: 84).
H(34) listed by Lett (1915: 115).
†H34 listed by Blockeel & Long (1998: 84).
H(35) listed by Lett (1915: 115) as '34' but with localities Dunfanaghy and Slieve League so 35 was evidently intended.
†H35 listed by Blockeel & Long (1998: 84).
H36 1957: wet limestone cliff, Carrickaness Bridge, nr Drumquin, RD Fitzgerald (Warburg 1958b: 479).
H(37) listed by Lett (1915: 116).
†H37 listed by Blockeel & Long (1998: 84).
H(38) listed by Lett (1915: 116). H(38) listed by Blockeel & Long (1998: 84).
H38 2002: on damp mortar of wall of bridge, S bank of Shimna River W of Parnell's Bridge, Tollymore Forest Park, J33, DT Holyoak 02-1033 (Rothero 2003: 50).
H(39) listed by Lett (1915: 116).
†H39 listed by Blockeel & Long (1998: 84).
H40 1954: moist basalt outcrop, roadside, Portstewart, RD Fitzgerald (Warburg 1955: 585).

38/1a *Weissia controversa* Hedw. **var. *controversa***
(syn. *Mollia viridula* Lindb., *M. viridula* var. *amblyodon* (Brid.) Braithw.)

H(1) listed by Lett (1915: 115) without details.
†H1 listed by Blockeel & Long (1998: 84).
H(2) listed by Lett (1915: 115) without details.
†H2 listed by Blockeel & Long (1998: 84).
H(3) listed by Lett (1915: 115) without details.
†H3 listed by Blockeel & Long (1998: 84).
H(4) listed by Lett (1915: 115) without details.
†H4 listed by Blockeel & Long (1998: 84).
H(5) listed by Lett (1915: 115) without details.
†H5 listed by Blockeel & Long (1998: 84).
H(6) listed by Lett (1915: 115) without details.
†H6 listed by Blockeel & Long (1998: 84).
H(7) listed by Lett (1915: 115) without details.
†H7 listed by Blockeel & Long (1998: 84).
H(8) listed by Lett (1915: 115) without details.
†H8 listed by Blockeel & Long (1998: 84).
H(9) listed by Lett (1915: 115) without details.
†H9 listed by Blockeel & Long (1998: 84).
H(11) listed by Lett (1915: 115) without details.
†H11 listed by Blockeel & Long (1998: 84).
H(12) listed by Lett (1915: 115) without details.
†H12 listed by Blockeel & Long (1998: 84).
H(13) listed by Lett (1915: 115) without details.
†H13 listed by Blockeel & Long (1998: 84).
H(14) listed by Lett (1915: 115) without details.
†H14 listed by Blockeel & Long (1998: 84).
H15 1957: earth bank, Owendalulleegh, RE Parker (Warburg 1958b: 479).
H(16) listed by Lett (1915: 115) without details.
†H16 listed by Blockeel & Long (1998: 84).
H17 1966: on soil on wall, Derreen, N of Monivea, MFV Corley & JS Parker (Crundwell 1972: 139).
[H(18) listed by Lett (1915: 115) without details. H18 deleted because no valid record or voucher specimen traced (Blockeel 1999: 4)].
H(19) listed by Lett (1915: 115) without details.
†H19 listed by Blockeel & Long (1998: 84).
H(20) listed by Lett (1915: 115) without details.
†H20 listed by Blockeel & Long (1998: 84).
H(21) listed by Lett (1915: 115) without

details.
†H21 listed by Blockeel & Long (1998: 84).
H22 1956: bank in lane by Rossan Bog, ALK King (Warburg 1957: 331).
H23 1957: dry limestone rock on spur of Knock Eyon, ALK King (Warburg 1958b: 479).
H(24) listed by Lett (1915: 115) without details.
†H24 listed by Blockeel & Long (1998: 84).
H25 1965: clay bank, 1 mile N of Ballyfarnan, RD Fitzgerald & EM Lobley (Warburg 1966: 195).
H(26) listed by Lett (1915: 115) without details.
†H26 listed by Blockeel & Long (1998: 84).
H(27) listed by Lett (1915: 115) without details.
†H27 listed by Blockeel & Long (1998: 84).
H(28) listed by Lett (1915: 115) without details.
†H28 listed by Blockeel & Long (1998: 84).
H(29) listed by Lett (1915: 115) without details.
†H29 listed by Blockeel & Long (1998: 84).
H(30) listed by Lett (1915: 115) without details.
†H30 listed by Blockeel & Long (1998: 84).
H(31) listed by Lett (1915: 115) without details.
†H31 listed by Blockeel & Long (1998: 84).
H(32) listed by Lett (1915: 115) without details.
†H32 listed by Blockeel & Long (1998: 84).
H(33) listed by Lett (1915: 115) without details.
†H33 listed by Blockeel & Long (1998: 84).
H(34) listed by Lett (1915: 115) without details.
†H34 listed by Blockeel & Long (1998: 84).
H(35) 1946: clay bank, Naran, JS Thomson (anon. 1947: 30).
†H35 listed by Blockeel & Long (1998: 84).
H(36) listed by Lett (1915: 115) without details.
†H36 listed by Blockeel & Long (1998: 84).
H(37) listed by Lett (1915: 115) without details.
†H37 listed by Blockeel & Long (1998: 84).
H(38) listed by Lett (1915: 115) without details.
†H38 listed by Blockeel & Long (1998: 84).
H(39) listed by Lett (1915: 115).
†H39 listed by Blockeel & Long (1998: 84).
H(40) listed by Lett (1915: 115) without details.
†H40 listed by Blockeel & Long (1998: 84).

[38/1b *Weissia controversa* Hedw. **var. *crispata*** (Nees & Hornsch.) Nyholm (syn. *Mollia crispata* (Nees & Hornsch.) Braithw., *Weissia crispata* (Nees & Hornsch.) Müll.Hal.)]

[H6 1956: sea-cliffs W of Ardmore, EC Wallace (Warburg 1957: 331). Not listed for H6 by Corley & Hill (1981: 82) following revision of specimens by MO Hill].
[H15 1951: stones of bridge over Grand Canal, E of Clonfert, AP Fanning (Warburg 1953: 310). Not listed for H15 by Corley & Hill (1981: 82) following revision of specimens by MO Hill].
[H33 1957: earth-capped limestone rock on E side of Belmore Mt., AC Crundwell (Warburg 1958b: 479). Not listed for H33 by Corley & Hill (1981: 82) following revision of specimens by MO Hill].
[H(34) listed by Lett (1915: 118)].
[H(38) listed by Lett (1915: 118)].

[This taxon was listed for six Irish vice-counties by Smith (1978: 277) but none of these were accepted by MO Hill (MS) following a revision of specimens for the *CC* (Corley & Hill 1981: 82)].

38/1c *Weissia controversa* var. *densifolia* (Bruch, Schimp. & W.Gümbel) Wilson

H(1) 1854: Kenmare, Wilson (Lett 1915: 115). H(1) listed by Blockeel & Long (1998: 84).
H10 1951: mine workings, Silvermines, EV Watson (Perry 1967: 413).
H33 2000: in crevices at base of wall of old building below galvanised-iron roof, Drumcrow West, H05, DT Holyoak 00-402 (BBSUK) (Rothero 2001: 39).
H34 2002: on soil at base of concrete wall of building, 50 m alt., Dunree Head, C23, DT Holyoak 02-784 (Rothero 2003: 50).

38/2 *Weissia perssonii* Kindb.
(syn. *Weissia occidentalis* nomen nudum)

H3 1968: rocky cliffs, Garnish Point, W of

Allihies, JA Paton (BBS exc.) (Crundwell 1971a: 222, 1972: 139).
H6 1956: sea cliffs W of Ardmore, EC Wallace (BBS exc.) (Crundwell 1971a: 222, 1972: 139).
H27 1962: on peat under overhanging rock nr the harbour, Keel, Achill I., EF Warburg (OXF) (Crundwell 1971a: 222, 1972: 139).
H(34) 1909: rocks by sea, Finner, Bundoran, WN Tetley (BBSUK) (Crundwell 1971a: 222, 1972: 139).
H35 1962: rock crevice by sea, Ards Peninsula, nr Dunfanaghy, AC Crundwell (Crundwell 1971a: 222, 1972: 139).
H39 1963: chalky hillside ½ mile from sea, Murlough Bay, AR Perry (Crundwell 1971, 1972: 139).

This species was generally overlooked in Ireland and Britain as the commoner *W. controversa* until the late EF Warburg recognised it as different during the 1960s. Following the death of Dr Warburg, Crundwell (1971a) extended research on the species and found that it had already been named as *W. perssonii* by Kindberg in 1898 based on a Swedish specimen.

38/3 ***Weissia rutilans*** (Hedw.) Lindb.
(syn. *Mollia rutilans* (Hedw.) Lindb.)

H8 1993: old pasture nr estuary shore, ploughed for forestry in 1991, 5 m alt., Foynes I., R25, E Wiltshire (Blockeel 1994: 37).
H(35) listed by Lett (1915: 115). H(35) listed by Blockeel & Long (1998: 84).
H(38) listed by Lett (1915: 115). H(38) listed by Blockeel & Long (1998: 84).
H39 1952: basalt, 900 ft [alt.], Lurigethan, RD Fitzgerald (Warburg 1953: 311).
H40 1952: bare clay slip in valley-side, Downhill, EW Jones (Warburg 1953: 311).

[**38/4** ***Weissia condensa*** (Voit) Lindb.
(syn. *Mollia tortilis* (Schwägr.) Braithw., *Weissia tortilis* (Schwägr.) Müll.Hal.)]

[H(2) listed by Lett (1915: 115)].
[H(5) listed by Lett (1915: 115)].
[H(15) listed by Lett (1915: 115)].
[H(18) 1949: wall, Wood of Birr, AP Fanning (Warburg 1953: 310). H(18) was rejected for *CC* after study of specimen by MO Hill (Corley & Hill 1981: 82, MO Hill MS)].
[H(35) listed by Lett (1915: 115) without locality].
[H(39) listed by Lett (1915: 115) without locality].

38/5a ***Weissia brachycarpa*** (Nees & Hornsch.) Jur. **var.** ***brachycarpa***
(syn. *Weissia microstoma* (Hedw.) Müll. Hal. var. *brachycarpa* (Nees & Hornsch.) Müll.Hal.)

H33 2000: on steep soil at edge of path in scrub, Upper Lough Erne, S of Carragh, H32, DT Holyoak 00-322, conf. TL Blockeel (BBSUK) (Rothero 2001: 39).

38/5b ***Weissia brachycarpa*** **var.** ***obliqua*** (Nees & Hornsch.) M.O.Hill
(syn. *Mollia microstoma* (Hedw.) Lindb., *Weisia microstoma* auct., *Weissia microstoma* (Hedw.) Müll.Hal. var. *microstoma*)

H(1) 1935: Dingle, no collector named (BBS exc.) (Watson 1936: 265).
H(4) listed by Lett (1915: 114). H(4) listed by Blockeel & Long (1998: 85).
[H5 deleted because no valid record or voucher specimen traced (Blockeel 1999: 4)].
H15 1952: bank by marsh nr Ross Quay, L. Derg, MPH Kertland & ALK King (Warburg 1953: 310).
H16 1985: among rocks, W slope of Lissoughter, Connemara, AC Bouman (Blockeel 1987: 23).
[H(20) listed by Lett (1915: 114) without locality. H20 deleted because no valid record or voucher specimen traced (Blockeel 1999: 4)].
H(21) listed by Lett (1915: 114). H(21) listed by Blockeel & Long (1998: 85).
H22 1968: gravel pit, Gormanstown, ALK King (Crundwell 1969: 882).
H23 1952: roadside wall, nr Coosan, Athlone, ALK King (Warburg 1953: 310).
H24 1968: clay-covered limestone in pit 1 mile S of Lanesborough, WV Rubers *et al.* (U) (Crundwell 1975: 15).
H25 2002: on skeletal soil in limestone

grassland, 90 m alt., Killeglan grassland, Lugboy, M84, NG Hodgetts 4056 (Rothero 2003: 50).

H26 1962: soil in limestone pavement by Keel Bridge between Partry and Ballinrobe, AJE Smith (Warburg 1963b: 497).

H28 1963: limestone, *ca* 900 ft [alt.], NE side of Carrowkeel, Bricklieve Mts, RD Fitzgerald & AR Perry (Warburg 1964: 727).

H(31) listed by Lett (1915: 114). H(31) listed by Blockeel & Long (1998: 85).

H(34) listed by Lett (1915: 114). H(34) listed by Blockeel & Long (1998: 85).

H35 1962: bank above cliffs, Black Burrow, nr Dunfanaghy, EF Warburg (BBS exc.) (Warburg 1963b: 497).

H(37) listed by Lett (1915: 114).

†H37 listed by Blockeel & Long (1998: 85).

H(38) listed by Lett (1915: 114). H(38) listed by Blockeel & Long (1998: 85).

H(39) listed by Lett (1915: 114).

†H39 listed by Blockeel & Long (1998: 85).

H(40) 1946: Portstewart, WR Megaw (anon. 1947: 30).

†H40 listed by Blockeel & Long (1998: 85).

38/7 ***Weissia rostellata*** (Brid.) Lindb.
(syn. *Mollia rostellata* (Brid.) Lindb.)

H26 1987: on damp soil on wooded river bank, E bank of Cloon River, near Partry, DG Long (Blockeel 1988: 35).

H29 2000: on mud in ditch by lough, Carrickaport Lough, SE edge, H00, DT Holyoak 00-747 (BBSUK) (Rothero 2001: 39).

H30 2001: on open silty clay on bank, 45 m alt., River Erne, S of Baker's Bridge, H31, DT Holyoak 01-824 (Rothero 2002: 45).

H(39) no date: nr Knockmore Junction, Davies (Lett 1915: 114).
1906: Ballinderry, collector not named (Lett 1915: 114). H(39) listed by Blockeel & Long (1998: 85).

H39 1999: on exposed mud at edge of reservoir, North Woodburn Reservoir, J39, DT Holyoak 99-866 (BBSUK) (Rothero 2000: 49).

38/12b ***Weissia longifolia*** Mitt. **var. *angustifolia*** (Baumgartner) Crundw. & Nyholm
(syn. *Mollia crispa* auct., *Weissia crispa* auct. angl., non *Phascum crispum* Hedw.)

H11 1966: old sandpit, Dysart Castle, nr Inistioge, JG Duckett *et al.* (Perry 1967: 413).

H(19) listed by Lett (1915: 114). H(19) listed by Blockeel & Long (1998: 86).

H(21) listed by Lett (1915: 114). H(21) listed by Blockeel & Long (1998: 86).

H23 1980: limestone wall, crevice in shade, roadside W of Killavally Torque, NE of Kilbeggan, DM Synnott (Hill 1981: 27).

[H(28) listed by Lett (1915: 114)].

[H(29) listed by Lett (1915: 114)].

H(35) listed by Lett (1915: 114). H(35) listed by Blockeel & Long (1998: 86).

H(38) listed by Lett (1915: 114). H(38) listed by Blockeel & Long (1998: 86).

H(39) listed by Lett (1915: 114). H(39) listed by Blockeel & Long (1998: 86).

39/1 ***Tortella tortuosa*** (Hedw.) Limpr.
(syn. *Mollia tortuosa* (Hedw.) Schrank, *M. tortuosa* var. *angustifolia* (Jur.) Braithw., *Trichostomum tortuosum* (Hedw.) Dixon, *Trichostomum tortuosum* var. *fragilifolium* (Jur.) Dixon)

H(1) listed by Lett (1915: 118) without details.

†H1 listed by Blockeel & Long (1998: 86).

H(2) listed by Lett (1915: 118) without details.

H(2) 1935: near Eagle's Nest, no collector named (BBS exc.) (Watson 1936: 265), as var. *fragilifolium*.

†H2 listed by Blockeel & Long (1998: 86).

H(3) listed by Lett (1915: 118) without details.

†H3 listed by Blockeel & Long (1998: 86).

H(4) listed by Lett (1915: 118) without details.

†H4 listed by Blockeel & Long (1998: 86).

[H(5) listed by Lett (1915: 118) without details. H5 deleted because no valid record or voucher specimen traced (Blockeel 1999: 4)].

H(6) listed by Lett (1915: 118) without details.

†H6 listed by Blockeel & Long (1998: 86).
H(7) listed by Lett (1915: 118) without details.
†H7 listed by Blockeel & Long (1998: 86).
H(8) listed by Lett (1915: 118) without details.
†H8 listed by Blockeel & Long (1998: 86).
H(9) listed by Lett (1915: 118) without details.
†H9 listed by Blockeel & Long (1998: 86).
H(10) listed by Lett (1915: 118) without details.
†H10 listed by Blockeel & Long (1998: 86).
H(11) listed by Lett (1915: 118) without details.
†H11 listed by Blockeel & Long (1998: 86).
H12 1954: rocks by sea, Ballymoney, JS Thomson (Warburg 1955: 585).
H13 1969: mortar of wall, Aghade Bridge, nr Tullow, RD Fitzgerald (Crundwell 1970: 201).
H(14) listed by Lett (1915: 118) without details.
†H14 listed by Blockeel & Long (1998: 86).
H(15) listed by Lett (1915: 118) without details.
†H15 listed by Blockeel & Long (1998: 86).
H(16) listed by Lett (1915: 118) without details.
†H16 listed by Blockeel & Long (1998: 86).
H17 1950: limestone rocks nr Menlo, ALK King (Warburg 1951: 500).
H(18) listed by Lett (1915: 118) without details.
†H18 listed by Blockeel & Long (1998: 86).
H(19) 1949: on aqueduct, Rye Water, Leixlip, JP Brunker (Warburg 1950: 385).
†H19 listed by Blockeel & Long (1998: 86).
H(20) 1939: Devil's Glen, JS Thomson (anon. 1940a: 173).
†H20 listed by Blockeel & Long (1998: 86).
[H(21) listed by Lett (1915: 118) without details. H21 deleted because no valid record or voucher specimen traced (Blockeel 1999: 4)].
H22 1952: demesne wall, Carton, Maynooth, JP Brunker (Warburg 1953: 311).
H(23) listed by Lett (1915: 118) without details.
†H23 listed by Blockeel & Long (1998: 86).
H24 1966: limestone by shore of L. Ree, below Cashel Lodge, ALK King (Perry 1967: 413).
H(25) listed by Lett (1915: 118) without details.
†H25 listed by Blockeel & Long (1998: 86).
H(26) listed by Lett (1915: 118) without details.
†H26 listed by Blockeel & Long (1998: 86).
H(27) listed by Lett (1915: 118) without details.
†H27 listed by Blockeel & Long (1998: 86).
H(28) listed by Lett (1915: 118) without details.
†H28 listed by Blockeel & Long (1998: 86).
H(29) listed by Lett (1915: 118) without details.
H(29) 1937: Truskmore, no collector named (BBS exc.) (Armitage 1938: 12), as var. *fragilifolium*.
†H29 listed by Blockeel & Long (1998: 86).
[H(30) listed by Lett (1915: 118) without details. H30 deleted because no valid record or voucher specimen traced (Blockeel 1999: 4)].
H30 2001: on open limestone blocks on bank of stream, 320 m alt., W of Bellavally Gap, H12, DT Holyoak 01-627 (Rothero 2002: 45).
[H(31) listed by Lett (1915: 118) without details. H31 deleted because no valid record or voucher specimen traced (Blockeel 1999: 4)].
H31 1999: in crevices of rocky bank of stream, 150 m alt., Two Mile River, Carlingford, J11, TL Blockeel 28/151 (Rothero 2000: 49).
H32 1952: limestone, Lisgall, nr Carrickmacross, RD Fitzgerald (Warburg 1953: 311).
H(33) listed by Lett (1915: 118) without details.
†H33 listed by Blockeel & Long (1998: 86).
H(34) 1937: Bundoran, no collector named (BBS exc.) (Armitage 1938: 12), as var. *fragilifolium*.
H(34) listed by Lett (1915: 118) without details.
†H34 listed by Blockeel & Long (1998: 86).
H(35) listed by Lett (1915: 118) without details.
†H35 listed by Blockeel & Long (1998: 86).
H(36) listed by Lett (1915: 118) without details.
†H36 listed by Blockeel & Long (1998: 86).
H37 1962: old wall, Gosford Castle nr Markethill, EM Lobley & MPH Kertland (Warburg 1963b: 496).
H(38) listed by Lett (1915: 118).
†H38 listed by Blockeel & Long (1998: 86).

H(39) listed by Lett (1915: 118) without details.
†H39 listed by Blockeel & Long (1998: 86).
H(40) listed by Lett (1915: 118) without details.
†H40 listed by Blockeel & Long (1998: 86).

39/2 ***Tortella densa*** (Lor. & Molendo) Crundw. & Nyholm

†H9 listed by Blockeel & Long (1998: 86).
H26 1962: limestone pavement by Keel Bridge between Ballinrobe and Partry, AJE Smith (Warburg 1963b: 497).
H27 1965: stony shore of L. Conn, nr Errew, A McG Stirling (Perry 1967: 413).
H28 1965: limestone cliff facing *ca* NE above Gleniff, MCF Proctor (Warburg 1966: 195).
H33 1993: on calcareous cliffs, Crossmurrin NNR, SE part, H13, T Hallingbäck, comm. NG Hodgetts (Blockeel 1994: 38).

[**39/3** ***Tortella fragilis*** (Drumm.) Limpr. (syn. *Mollia fragilis* (Drumm.) Lindb.)]

[Records listed for seven vice-counties in Lett (1915: 118) are all erroneous; these have not been listed in recent *CC*].

[H33 should be deleted because the voucher specimen (1993: thin soil over limestone on exposed hilltop grassland, Crossmurrin, H13, T Hallingbäck, comm. NG Hodgetts (BBSUK): Blockeel 1994: 38, Hodgetts & Hallingbäck 1994) is a form of *T. tortuosa*, redet. DT Holyoak. Information on the record has been communicated to the BBS Recorder for Mosses].

39/4 ***Tortella nitida*** (Lindb.) Broth. (syn. *Mollia nitida* (Lindb.) Lindb.)

[H(1) listed by Lett (1915: 117) without details].
†H1 listed by Blockeel & Long (1998: 86).
[H(2) listed by Lett (1915: 117)].
H2 1966: limestone rock on N shore of Muckross Lake, Killarney, JA Paton (Perry 1967: 413).
H3 1968: rocks on coast, N side of Knocknagalloun, N of Allihies, JA Paton (Crundwell 1969: 882).
H5 1956: limestone, Carrigshane, nr Middleton, EC Wallace (Warburg 1957: 332).
[H(6) listed by Lett (1915: 117)].
[H(7) listed by Lett (1915: 117)].
H7 1966: limestone rocks, Ardfinnan, JA Paton (BBS exc.) (Perry 1967: 413).
H8 1993: limestone crag, Creeves, R24, E Wiltshire & MV O'Brien (Blockeel 1994: 38).
[H(9) listed by Lett (1915: 117)].
†H9 listed by Blockeel & Long (1998: 86).
H10 1968: Bellvue, L. Derg, MJP Scannell (Crundwell 1969: 882).
H15 1956: wall, Kilmacduagh, ALK King (Warburg 1957: 332).
[H(16) listed by Lett (1915: 117) without details].
H16 1968: limestone wall of roadside *ca* 1 mile NW of Cong, AR Perry (Crundwell 1969: 882).
[H(17) listed by Lett (1915: 117) as 1910: leg. Tetley (without locality). H(17) deleted because specimen (1910: railway bridge E of Galway City, leg. WN Tetley, BBSUK) is *T. tortuosa*, det. & comm. AC Crundwell (Warburg 1961: 166)].
H17 1968: degenerate limestone pavement S of Kilroghter, *ca* 4 miles N of Galway City, AR Perry (Crundwell 1969: 882).
[H(21) listed by Lett (1915: 117)].
H22 1962: limestone on the tumulus, Newgrange, EF Warburg (Warburg 1963b: 497).
H23 1979: limestone wall, Clare Hill, Moate, DM Synnott (Hill 1980b: 38).
H24 1966: limestone, E shore of L. Ree, below Cashel Lodge, ALK King (Perry 1967: 413).
[H(26) listed by Lett (1915: 117) as 1910: L. Cloon, leg. Tetley. H(26) deleted because specimen (1910: Cloon Lough, leg. WN Tetley, BBSUK) is *T. tortuosa*, det. & comm. AC Crundwell (Warburg 1961: 166)].
[†H26 listed by Blockeel & Long (1998: 86), but apparently in error since the preceding record has been deleted].
[H(27) listed by Lett (1915: 117)].
[H(28) listed by Lett (1915: 118)].
†H28 listed by Blockeel & Long (1998: 86).
[H(29) listed by Lett (1915: 118)].
[H(34) listed by Lett (1915: 118)].
[H(35) listed by Lett (1915: 118)].

H35 2001: in clints in limestone pavement, 20 m alt., St John's Point, Dunkineely, G76, NG Hodgetts 3735 (Rothero 2002: 45).
[H(40) listed by Lett (1915: 118)].

39/6 ***Tortella inclinata*** (R.Hedw.) Limpr.
(syn. *Mollia inclinata* (R.Hedw.) Lindb.)

H27 1962: bank above Achill Sound, Cloghmore, Achill I., EF Warburg (Warburg 1963b: 497).
H38 1952: amongst stones and sand, Sudderyford [*sic* = Slidderyford], RD Fitzgerald, det. AC Crundwell (Warburg 1961: 166).

All records in Lett (1915: 118) appear to be errors.

39/8a ***Tortella flavovirens*** (Bruch) Broth. **var. *flavovirens***
(syn. *Mollia flavovirens* (Bruch) Lindb.)

H(1) listed by Lett (1915: 117).
†H1 listed by Blockeel & Long (1998: 86).
H(2) listed by Lett (1915: 117).
H2 1952: dunes at Banna Strand, ALK King (Warburg 1964: 726).
H3 1964: above shore, Allihies, ERB Little (Perry 1967: 413).
[H5 deleted because no valid record or voucher specimen traced (Blockeel 1999: 4)].
H(6) listed by Lett (1915: 117).
†H6 listed by Blockeel & Long (1998: 86).
H8 1966: bank at edge of wood on sea shore, by Ballydonohoe House, E of Tarbet, MFV Corley & JS Parker (Perry 1967: 413).
†H9 listed by Blockeel & Long (1998: 86).
H(12) listed by Lett (1915: 117).
H12 1950: sand-dunes at Curracloe, ALK King (Warburg 1964: 726).
H(16) listed by Lett (1915: 117).
H16 1964: clay just above High Water Mark, Renvyle Point, ERB Little (Perry 1967: 413).
H17 1957: saltmarsh on E side of Galway City, AC Crundwell & E Nyholm (BBS exc.) (Warburg 1958b: 480).
H(20) listed by Lett (1915: 117).
H20 1990: on soil bank on low cliffs by sea, 10 m alt., Ardmore Point near Blainroe, T38, Long 18129 (Blockeel 1991c: 42).
H(21) listed by Lett (1915: 117).
H21 1954: railway embankment by sea, Sutton, ALK King (Warburg 1964: 726).
H(27) 1909: Mallarany, HW Lett & CH Waddell (BFT), comm. RD Fitzgerald (Warburg 1963b: 497).
†H27 listed by Blockeel & Long (1998: 86).
[H28 deleted because no valid record or voucher specimen traced (Blockeel 1999: 4)].
H(34) listed by Lett (1915: 117).
†H34 listed by Blockeel & Long (1998: 86).
†H35 listed by Blockeel & Long (1998: 86).
H37 1950: by tidal estuary, Rough I., RD Fitzgerald (Warburg 1951: 500).
H(38) listed by Lett (1915: 117). H(38) listed by Blockeel & Long (1998: 86).
H38 2002: in crevice of rocks on low coastal headland, 10 m alt., S of Killough, J53, DT Holyoak 02-1011 (Rothero 2003: 50).
†H39 listed by Blockeel & Long (1998: 86).
H(40) listed by Lett (1915: 117).
H40 1999: on soil in crevices of basalt rock on exposed grassy headland, Portstewart, C83, DT Holyoak 99-176 (BBSUK) (Rothero 2000: 49).

Records from before about 1975 would not have distinguished var. *glareicola* from var. *flavovirens*, but taxonomic recognition of these varieties apparently has little value (see note under var. *glareicola* below).

39/8b ***Tortella flavovirens*** **var. *glareicola*** (T. A.Chr.) Crundw. & Nyholm

H9 1972: dunes at Fanore, WV Rubers (U) (Crundwell 1975: 15).
H20 1972: dunes, Arklow, WV Rubers (U) (Crundwell 1975: 15).
H31 1965: Silurian rocks E of pier, Clogher Head, DM Synnott (Warburg 1966: 195).
H35 1962: dunes nr Mullaghderg Lough, The Rosses, AC Crundwell (BBS exc.) (Warburg 1963b: 497).

Study of numerous specimens from Cornwall has disclosed that plants intermediate between var. *flavovirens* and var. *glareicola* are common, and there is no difference in the habitats of the two forms. Hence there is apparently little value in taxonomic recognition of var. *glareicola* (DT Holyoak, unpublished).

40/1 ***Trichostomum brachydontium*** Bruch (syn. *Mollia brachydontia* (Bruch) Lindb., *M. brachydontia* var. *cophocarpa* (Schimp.) Braithw., *M. littoralis* (Mitt.) Braithw., *M. littoralis* var. *angustifolia* Lindb., *M. lutescens* Lindb., *Trichostomum mutabile* Bruch, *T. mutabile* var. *cophocarpum* Schimp.)

H(1) listed by Lett (1915: 116, 117).
†H1 listed by Blockeel & Long (1998: 87).
H(2) listed by Lett (1915: 116).
†H2 listed by Blockeel & Long (1998: 87).
H(3) listed by Lett (1915: 116).
†H3 listed by Blockeel & Long (1998: 87).
H4 2002: in seepage in recess among coastal rocks, 2 m alt., Charles Fort, Summer Cove, Kinsale, W64, TL Blockeel 31/275 (Rothero 2003: 50).
H5 1956: bank in lane nr Park House, Tourig, Youghal, EC Wallace (Warburg 1957: 332).
H(6) listed by Lett (1915: 116).
†H6 listed by Blockeel & Long (1998: 87).
H(8) listed by Lett (1915: 116).
†H8 listed by Blockeel & Long (1998: 87).
H(9) listed by Lett (1915: 116) without details.
†H9 listed by Blockeel & Long (1998: 87).
H10 1979: rocks on river-bank, N side of Clare Glens, nr Newport, AC Crundwell (Hill 1980b: 39).
[H(11) listed by Lett (1915: 116)].
H(12) listed by Lett (1915: 116).
H12 1975: hedgebank on coast, Duffcarrick Rocks, N of Courtown, JA Paton (Hill 1977a: 19).
H(14) listed by Lett (1915: 116). H(14) listed by Blockeel & Long (1998: 87).
[H15 deleted because no valid record or voucher specimen traced (Blockeel 1999: 4)].
H(16) listed by Lett (1915: 116, 117).
†H16 listed by Blockeel & Long (1998: 87).
[H17 deleted because no valid record or voucher specimen traced (Blockeel 1999: 4)].
H(21) listed by Lett (1915: 116, 117). H(21) listed by Blockeel & Long (1998: 87).
[H(22) listed by Lett (1915: 116)].
H23 1978: limestone bluff, L. Bane, S of Oldcastle, DM Synnott (Hill 1980b: 39).
H(25) listed by Lett (1915: 117). H(25) listed by Blockeel & Long (1998: 87).
H25 2002: on soil in limestone grassland, 80 m alt., Killeglan grassland, Lugboy, M84, NG Hodgetts 4054 (Rothero 2003: 50).
H(26) listed by Lett (1915: 116, 117).
†H26 listed by Blockeel & Long (1998: 87).
H(27) listed by Lett (1915: 116, 117).
†H27 listed by Blockeel & Long (1998: 87).
H(28) listed by Lett (1915: 116, 117).
H(28) 1928: Gleniff, Ben Bulben (BBS exc.) (Duncan 1928: 118), as *Trichostomum mutabile* var. *cophocarpum*.
1937: Ben Bulben, EM Lobley (anon. 1938b: 26), as *Trichostomum mutabile* var. *cophocarpum*.
†H28 listed by Blockeel & Long (1998: 87).
H(29) listed by Lett (1915: 117).
†H29 listed by Blockeel & Long (1998: 87).
H(30) listed by Lett (1915: 117). H(30) listed by Blockeel & Long (1998: 87).
H30 2001: on soil in crevice in limestone outcrop, 265 m alt., Legnaveagh, S of Blacklion, H03, DT Holyoak 01-744 (Rothero 2002: 45).
H(31) listed by Lett (1915: 116, 117). H(31) listed by Blockeel & Long (1998: 87).
H31 1999: in stony flush on moorland slope, 300 m alt., Two Mile River, Carlingford, J11, TL Blockeel 28/170 (Rothero 2000: 49).
[H(32) listed by Lett (1915: 116)].
H(33) listed by Lett (1915: 116, 117).
†H33 listed by Blockeel & Long (1998: 87).
H(34) listed by Lett (1915: 116, 117).
†H34 listed by Blockeel & Long (1998: 87).
H(35) listed by Lett (1915: 116, 117).
†H35 listed by Blockeel & Long (1998: 87).
H36 2002: on thin soil in crevice of rocks in old quarry, 185 m alt., Butterlope Glen, H49, DT Holyoak 02-1112 (Rothero 2003: 50).
H(38) listed by Lett (1915: 116, 117). H(38) listed by Blockeel & Long (1998: 87).
H38 2002: on soil in crevices of rocks by river, 45 m alt., by Shimna River in Tollymore Forest Park, J33, DT Holyoak 02-934 (Rothero 2003: 50).
H(39) listed by Lett (1915: 116, 117).
†H39 listed by Blockeel & Long (1998: 87).
H(40) listed by Lett (1915: 116).
†H40 listed by Blockeel & Long (1998: 87).

Plate 1. BBS Excursion at Belfast, 1928. Left to right, front row: Mrs Sherrin, Miss IM Roper, Mrs Milsom, Miss KE Smith, Rev. CH Binstead, Miss D Hilary, Mrs AS Bacon, Miss CA Cooper; back row: Miss AM Saunders, HH Knight, Rev. WR Megaw, WR Sherrin, JB Duncan, I Helsby, A Sutton, DA Jones, DB Bradshaw, unknown, FE Milsom. Photo by DB Bradshaw ©BBS.

Plate 2. BBS Excursion at Muckross, Killarney, Co. Kerry, 1935.
Left to right: JB Duncan, WCR Watson, DA Jones, Dr Walter Watson, FE Milsom, Miss AJ Cottis, Mrs AS Bacon. © BBS.

Plate 3. BBS Excursion at Bundoran, Co. Donegal, 1937.
Left to right, front row: Miss Jackson, Miss M Weightman, JB Duncan, Rev. CH Binstead, Miss G Wigglesworth; back row: Miss EM Lobley, Miss AM Irwin, Miss E Armitage, Mrs Watson, Dr Walter Watson, HN Dixon, Miss AM Saunders, CVB Marquand, Miss M Knox. © BBS.

Plate 4A.
Rev. CH Waddell,
from Wear
(1923, Plate facing p. 1).

Plate 4B.
Canon HW Lett,
from Wear
(1923, Plate facing p. 1).

Plate 4C. Rev. WR Megaw. © BBS.

Plate 4D. Miss JS Thomson,
photographed in 1943. © BBS.

Plate 4E. BBS Excursion at Torc, Co. Kerry, 1951.
Left to right: Mme V Allorge, EF Warburg, PW Richards. © BBS.

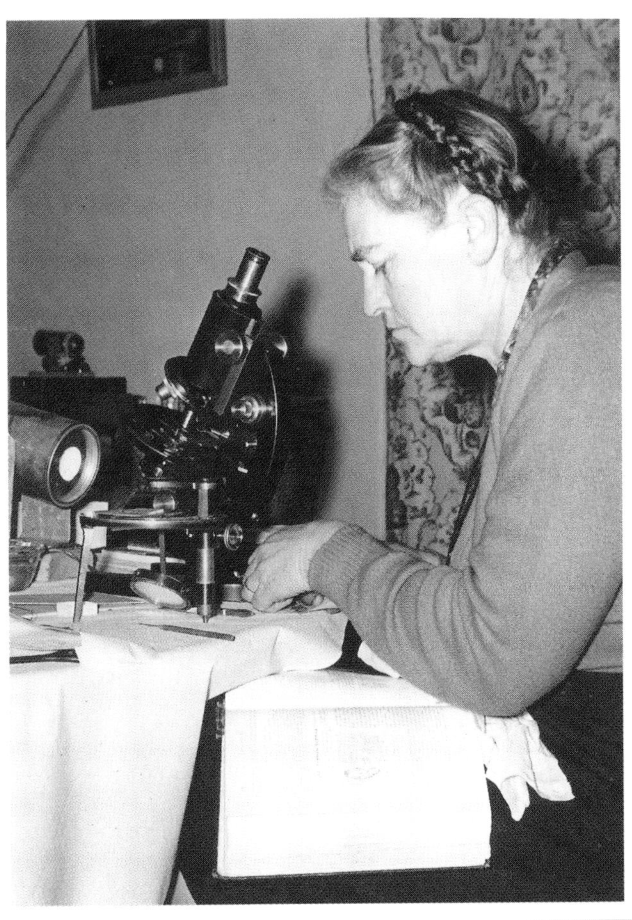

Plate 5A.
Mrs JW Fitzgerald.
Photographed by AR Perry,
Christmas 1963. © BBS.

Plate 5B.
RD Fitzgerald.
Photographed by AR Perry,
Easter 1962. © BBS.

Plate 6A. Miss EM Lobley, photographed in 1942. © BBS.

Plate 6B. RE Parker, with EF Warburg behind, photographed in 1956. © BBS.

Plate 6C. Mrs JA Paton, photographed at Box Hill, Surrey in 1972. © BBS.

Plate 6D. AR Perry, with Mrs JA Paton, photographed by Mrs J Proctor during BBS Excursion at Chudleigh Rocks, Devon on 20 October 1974. © BBS.

Plate 7A. BBS Excursion at Glengarriff Wood, Co. Kerry on 26 August 1979. Left to right: N Kirby, MV Fletcher, AC Crundwell (behind), Fletcher junior, ND Lockhart (in front), AJE Smith, Mrs R Fletcher, Mrs JA Paton (behind), Fletcher junior, Fletcher junior, unknown (behind), unknown (removing sweater), DM Synnott, EC Wallace (behind), P Goyvaerts (in front), G Bloom, F Bentley. Photographed by RC Stern. © BBS.

Plate 7B. BBS Excursion on boat to Clare Island, Co. Mayo, 24 July 1994. Left to right: S Dransgard, Miss K Long, DG Long, DM Synnott, DL Kelly. Photographed by GP Rothero ©.

Plate 8. BBS Excursion at Mullaghmore, The Burren, Co. Clare, 15 July 1994.
Left to right: ER Hurr, DM Synnott, CD Preston, PE Stanley, HLK Whitehouse, Mrs JA Paton, Ms S Hochstenbach, NG Hodgetts, RD Porley, Dr E Mooney, J Blackburn, GM Dirkse. © BBS.

40/2 ***Trichostomum crispulum*** Bruch (syn. *Mollia crispula* (Bruch) Lindb., *M. crispula* var. *elata* (Schimp.) Braithw., *M. crispula* var. *nigro-viride* Braithw., *Trichostomum crispulum* var. *brevifolium* (Müll.Hal.) Bruch, Schimp. & W.Gümbel, *T. crispulum* var. *elatum* Schimp.)

H(1) listed by Lett (1915: 116).
†H1 listed by Blockeel & Long (1998: 87).
H(2) listed by Lett (1915: 116).
†H2 listed by Blockeel & Long (1998: 87).
H(3) listed by Lett (1915: 116).
†H3 listed by Blockeel & Long (1998: 87).
H(4) listed by Lett (1915: 116).
†H4 listed by Blockeel & Long (1998: 87).
H5 1951: limestone walls, Mallow, EW Jones (Warburg 1952: 102).
1956: limestone wall, Ballyvergan East, Youghal, EC Wallace (Warburg 1957: 332), as var. *elatum.*
H(6) 1933: Ballymona, E Armitage (anon. 1934b: 119).
†H6 listed by Blockeel & Long (1998: 87).
H7 1956: wall in lane, nr Knocklofty, EC Wallace (Warburg 1957: 332).
H(8) listed by Lett (1915: 116).
†H8 listed by Blockeel & Long (1998: 87).
H(9) listed by Lett (1915: 116).
†H9 listed by Blockeel & Long (1998: 87).
H(10) listed by Lett (1915: 116).
†H10 listed by Blockeel & Long (1998: 87).
H11 1966: rocks by R. Nore, nr Thomastown, J Appleyard & RD Fitzgerald (BBS exc.) (Crundwell 1968: 636).
H(12) listed by Lett (1915: 116). H(12) listed by Blockeel & Long (1998: 87).
H(14) listed by Lett (1915: 116).
†H14 listed by Blockeel & Long (1998: 87).
H15 1994: on small limestone boulder at edge of lough, 25 m alt., near L. Briskeen, *ca* 5 km W of Gort, M40, TL Blockeel 23/156 (Blockeel 1995c: 43).
H(16) listed by Lett (1915: 116).
†H16 listed by Blockeel & Long (1998: 87).
H(17) listed by Lett (1915: 116).
†H17 listed by Blockeel & Long (1998: 87).
H18 1951: dry wall, hill to Kennedy's Cross, Birr, AP Fanning (Warburg 1953: 311).
H(19) 1949: wet side of aqueduct, Rye Water, Leixlip, JP Brunker (Warburg 1950: 384).
H(20) listed by Lett (1915: 116) without locality.
H20 1975: rocks above Glencullin River, NW of Enniskerry, JA Paton (BBS exc.) (Crundwell 1976: 25), as var. *elatum.*
H(21) listed by Lett (1915: 116). H(21) listed by Blockeel & Long (1998: 87).
H(22) listed by Lett (1915: 116).
†H22 listed by Blockeel & Long (1998: 87).
H(23) listed by Lett (1915: 116).
†H23 listed by Blockeel & Long (1998: 87).
H24 1965: old mortar, Cloonart Bridge, S of Roosky, EM Lobley & RD Fitzgerald (Warburg 1966: 195).
H25 1960: limestone wall at Rockingham, Boyle, ALK King (Warburg 1961: 166).
H(26) listed by Lett (1915: 116).
†H26 listed by Blockeel & Long (1998: 87).
H27 1962: Keel Bay, Achill I., EF Warburg (Warburg 1963b: 497).
H(28) listed by Lett (1915: 116).
H(28) 1937: Ben Bulben, no collector named (BBS exc.) (Armitage 1938: 12), as var. *elatum.*
1937: Ben Bulben, EM Lobley [separated from gathering of *Trichostomum mutabile* var. *cophocarpum*] (anon. 1938b: 26).
†H28 listed by Blockeel & Long (1998: 87).
H29 1963: limestone face at 800 ft [alt.], Peakadaw, Glenade, AR Perry & RD Fitzgerald (Warburg 1964: 727), as var. *elatum.*
H(30) listed by Lett (1915: 116). H(30) listed by Blockeel & Long (1998: 87).
H30 2001: on open soil at edge of track, 220 m alt., N of Legeelan, H03, DT Holyoak 01-740 (Rothero 2002: 45).
H31 1965: Silurian rock, E of pier, Clogher Head, DM Synnott (Warburg 1966: 195).
H(32) listed by Lett (1915: 116).
†H32 listed by Blockeel & Long (1998: 87).
H(33) listed by Lett (1915: 116).
†H33 listed by Blockeel & Long (1998: 87).
H(34) 1937: Bundoran, sand-dunes, no collector named (BBS exc.) (Armitage 1938: 12), as var. *brevifolium.*
H(34) listed by Lett (1915: 116).
†H34 listed by Blockeel & Long (1998: 87).
H(35) 1910: NW Donegal, J Glover (anon. 1915b: 9), det. as var. *elatum* by GB Savery.
H(35) listed by Lett (1915: 116).
†H35 listed by Blockeel & Long (1998: 87).
H36 1950: base of wooden fence, Washing Bay, J Taylor (Warburg 1954: 482).

H(37) listed by Lett (1915: 116).
†H37 listed by Blockeel & Long (1998: 87).
H(38) listed by Lett (1915: 116) without details.
†H38 listed by Blockeel & Long (1998: 87).
H(39) listed by Lett (1915: 116).
†H39 listed by Blockeel & Long (1998: 87).
H(40) listed by Lett (1915: 116).
†H40 listed by Blockeel & Long (1998: 87).

40/3a ***Trichostomum tenuirostre*** (Hook. & Taylor) Lindb. **var. *tenuirostre***
(syn. *Mollia tenuirostris* (Hook. & Taylor) Lindb., *Oxystegus tenuirostris* (Hook. & Taylor) A.J.E.Sm. var. *tenuirostris*)

H(1) listed by Lett (1915: 117).
†H1 listed by Blockeel & Long (1998: 87).
H(2) listed by Lett (1915: 117).
†H2 listed by Blockeel & Long (1998: 87).
H3 1953: corrie above Coomroe, Gougane Barra, ALK King (Warburg 1954: 482).
H(6) listed by Lett (1915: 117).
†H6 listed by Blockeel & Long (1998: 87).
H(7) listed by Lett (1915: 117).
†H7 listed by Blockeel & Long (1998: 87).
H(16) listed by Lett (1915: 117).
†H16 listed by Blockeel & Long (1998: 87).
H(20) listed by Lett (1915: 117).
†H20 listed by Blockeel & Long (1998: 87).
H(21) listed by Lett (1915: 117).
†H21 listed by Blockeel & Long (1998: 87).
H(22) listed by Lett (1915: 117).
†H22 listed by Blockeel & Long (1998: 87).
H26 1970: base of tree by pool W of Pollagh River, NE of Balla, JA Paton (Crundwell 1971b: 377).
H(27) listed by Lett (1915: 117).
†H27 listed by Blockeel & Long (1998: 87).
H(28) listed by Lett (1915: 117).
†H28 listed by Blockeel & Long (1998: 87).
H(31) listed by Lett (1915: 117). H(31) listed by Blockeel & Long (1998: 87).
H31 1999: on wet rock at edge of stream, 200 m alt., Two Mile River, Carlingford, J11, TL Blockeel 28/156 (Rothero 2000: 49).
H(33) listed by Lett (1915: 117).
†H33 listed by Blockeel & Long (1998: 87).
H(34) listed by Lett (1915: 117).
†H34 listed by Blockeel & Long (1998: 87).
H(35) listed by Lett (1915: 117).
†H35 listed by Blockeel & Long (1998: 87).
H36 1957: wet rocks, Corrick Bridge, nr Plumbridge, RD Fitzgerald (Warburg 1958b: 480).
H(38) listed by Lett (1915: 117). H(38) listed by Blockeel & Long (1998: 87).
H38 2002: in crevices of rocks above river, 45 m alt., by Shimna River in Tollymore Forest Park, J33, DT Holyoak 02-931 (Rothero 2003: 50).
H(39) listed by Lett (1915: 117).
†H39 listed by Blockeel & Long (1998: 87).
H40 1968: wet rocks by stream, Ness Glen, NW of Claudy, HH Birks & RD Fitzgerald (Crundwell 1969: 882).

40/3b ***Trichostomum tenuirostre*** **var. *holtii*** (Braithw.) Dixon
(syn. *Mollia tenuirostris* var. *holtii* Braithw., *Oxystegus tenuirostris* var. *holtii* (Braithw.) A.J.E.Sm.)

H(1) 1885: O'Sullivan's Cascade, Holt & Stewart (Lett 1915: 117). H(1) listed by Blockeel & Long (1998: 87).
H(2) 1885: Cromagloun, Holt & Stewart (Lett 1915: 117).
1911: Horse's Glen, Jones (Lett 1915: 117). H(2) listed by Blockeel & Long (1998: 87).

40/4 ***Trichostomum hibernicum*** (Mitt.) Dixon
(syn. *Mollia hibernica* (Mitt.) Lindb., *Oxystegus hibernicus* (Mitt.) Hilpert)

H(1) listed by Lett (1915: 117).
†H1 listed by Blockeel & Long (1998: 87).
H(2) listed by Lett (1915: 117).
†H2 listed by Blockeel & Long (1998: 87).
H(5) listed by Lett (1915: 117). H(5) placed in brackets, comm. HJB Birks (Hill 1981: 27). H(5) listed by Blockeel & Long (1998: 87).
H16 1957: damp rocks, SE valley of Maumtrasna, AC Crundwell (BBS exc.), originally published as record from H27 [see next entry] (Warburg 1958b: 480, Crundwell 1970: 201). †H16 listed by Blockeel & Long (1998: 87).
[H27 1957: damp rocks, SE valley of Maumtrasna, AC Crundwell (BBS exc.) (Warburg 1958b: 480). H27 deleted because locality (Maumtrasna) is in H16 (Crundwell 1970: 201)].
H27 1965: Sheffrey Hills, AMcG Stirling (Crundwell 1970: 201).

H(35) 1910: gully, Poisoned Glen, J Hunter (NMW) (Crundwell 1972: 139).

42/1 ***Pleurochaete squarrosa*** (Brid.) Lindb.

†H9 listed by Blockeel & Long (1998: 88).
H(20) no date: Arklow, Moore (Lett 1915: 114). H(20) listed by Blockeel & Long (1998: 88).
H(21) no date: Portmarnock, Taylor (Lett 1915: 114).
1852: no locality, leg. Orr (Lett 1915: 114).
†H21 listed by Blockeel & Long (1998: 88).
H22 1978: sand dunes, Mornington, DM Synnott (Hill 1980b: 38).

43/1 ***Paraleptodontium recurvifolium*** (Taylor) D.G.Long
(syn. *Leptodontium recurvifolium* (Taylor) Lindb.)

H(1) listed by Lett (1915: 118).
†H1 listed by Blockeel & Long (1998: 88).
H(2) 1911: Torc Cascade, Killarney, Kerry, DA Jones (anon. 1912a: 47).
†H2 listed by Blockeel & Long (1998: 88).
H3 1979: mildly base-rich turfy slope near stream, Lackawee, Slieve Miskish Mts, JA Paton (Hill 1980b: 39).
H16 1957: damp rocks on NE side of Benchoona, nr Killary Harbour, AC Crundwell (BBS exc.) (Warburg 1958b: 479).
H27 1965: among *Trichostomum hibernicum*, Sheffrey Hills, AMcG Stirling (Crundwell 1975: 16).
H35 1967: turf in wet crevice on calcareous schistose rocks at 1300 ft [alt.], N-facing corrie of Slieve League, nr Carrick, HH Birks, HJB Birks & DA Ratcliffe (Crundwell 1968: 637, HJB Birks, HH Birks & Ratcliffe 1969).

45/1 ***Pseudocrossidium hornschuchianum*** (Schultz) R.H.Zander
(syn. *Barbula hornschuchiana* Schultz, *B. hornschuchii* auct.)

H1 1951: wall top below Bunavalla, nr Darrynane, EF Warburg (BBS exc.) (Warburg 1952: 102).
H2 1951: ground, nr shore of L. Leane, Ross I., Killarney, JS Thomson (Warburg 1952: 102).
H(3) listed by Lett (1915: 120).
†H3 listed by Blockeel & Long (1998: 88).
H4 2002: on bare soil at foot of limestone wall, 40 m alt., Blarney, W67, TL Blockeel 31/289 (Rothero 2003: 50).
H(5) listed by Lett (1915: 120). H(5) listed by Blockeel & Long (1998: 88).
H5 2002: on gravelly ground in car park, 20 m alt., NW of Knockadoon Head, X07, TL Blockeel 31/313 (Rothero 2003: 50).
H7 1966: floor of limestone quarry, Ardfinnan, JA Paton (BBS exc.) (Perry 1967: 412).
H(8) listed by Lett (1915: 120).
†H8 listed by Blockeel & Long (1998: 88).
H9 1959: mossy calcareous dune turf, Fanore, S of Black Head, MCF Proctor & RB Ivimey-Cook (Warburg 1963b: 496).
H12 1954: road nr Curragh Wood, Inch, JS Thomson (Warburg 1955: 584).
H13 2002: on open thin soil on track in plantation, 310 m alt., S slope of Croaghaun, S85, DT Holyoak 02-361 (Rothero 2003: 50).
H15 1957: earth-covered rock, Killafeen, nr Gort, J Appleyard, AC Crundwell & RE Parker (BBS exc.) (Warburg 1958b: 478-479).
H16 1957: among gravel at roadside, Ballynahinch, AC Crundwell (BBS exc.) (Warburg 1958b: 478-479).
H19 1953: old wall by lane, Cupidstown Hill, ALK King (Warburg 1954: 482).
H20 1975: waste ground, Arklow, JA Paton (BBS Exc.) (Crundwell 1976: 25).
[H(21) listed by Lett (1915: 120) as 1855: Killiney, leg. Orr. H21 deleted: the record (from Killiney, 1855, leg. D Orr) is suspect and no specimen exists in DBN, comm. DM Synnot (Blockeel 1989: 27)].
H22 1973: wayside by archaeological site, Newgrange, MO Hill (Crundwell 1974: 168).
H23 1970: track E of Killinure Lough, S of Glassan, JA Paton (Crundwell 1971b: 377).
H25 1981: limestone quarry, Maddysrulla, W of Portrunny Bay, L. Ree, DM Synnott (Hill 1982: 26).
H26 1970: track-side, Glendaduff, NE of Foxford, MFV Corley (Crundwell 1971b: 377).
H27 1965: flat ground below cliffs, E end of

Keel Bay, Achill, EF Warburg (Warburg 1966: 194).

H28 1965: side of track nr Percy Mount, nr L. Gill, EF Warburg (Warburg 1966: 194).

H29 2000: on tarmac at edge of minor road, County Bridge, S of Garrison, G95, DT Holyoak 00-582 (BBSUK) (Rothero 2001: 40).

H30 1957: wall between Tiltinbane and Black Lion [*sic* = Blacklion], AC Crundwell (Warburg 1958b: 478-479).

H33 1957: earth-covered rock N of Cuileagh [*sic* = Cuilcagh], AC Crundwell (Warburg 1958b: 478-479).

H34 2001: on sandy track through dry coastal dunes, 10 m alt., Murvagh Upper, G87, NG Hodgetts 3904 (Rothero 2003: 50-51).

H35 1962: dunes, Murroe Strand, nr Dunfanaghy, EF Warburg & RE Longton (BBS exc.) (Warburg 1963b: 496).

†H36 listed by Blockeel & Long (1998: 88).

H(37) listed by Lett (1915: 120). H(37) listed by Blockeel & Long (1998: 88).

H(38) listed by Lett (1915: 120). H(38) listed by Blockeel & Long (1998: 88).

[H(39) listed by Lett (1915: 120). H39 deleted: specimens from Carrickfergus, leg. HW Lett, D Orr & SA Stewart (DBN), are *Barbula* cf. *trifaria*, comm. DM Synnott (Blockeel 1989: 27)].

H39 1999: among grasses on partly bare slope beside path in dunes, E of Portrush, C84, DT Holyoak 99-237 (BBSUK) (Rothero 2000: 50).

H(40) listed by Blockeel & Long (1998: 88).

H40 1999: on disturbed sandy ground at edge of track in dunes, Magilligan Point, C63, DT Holyoak 99-134 (BBSUK) (Rothero 2000: 50).

45/2 ***Pseudocrossidium revolutum*** (Brid.) R. H.Zander
(syn. *Barbula revoluta* Brid.)

H(1) listed by Lett (1915: 120) without details.

†H1 listed by Blockeel & Long (1998: 88).

H(2) listed by Lett (1915: 120) without details.

†H2 listed by Blockeel & Long (1998: 88).

H3 1966: wall of bridge, Sandy Cove, S of Kinsale, MFV Corley & JS Parker (Perry 1967: 412).

H(4) listed by Lett (1915: 120) without details.

†H4 listed by Blockeel & Long (1998: 88).

†H5 listed by Blockeel & Long (1998: 88).

H(6) 1933: nr Cappagh, E Armitage (anon. 1934b: 118).

†H6 listed by Blockeel & Long (1998: 88).

H(7) listed by Lett (1915: 120) without details.

†H7 listed by Blockeel & Long (1998: 88).

H(8) listed by Lett (1915: 120) without details.

†H8 listed by Blockeel & Long (1998: 88).

H(9) listed by Lett (1915: 120) without details.

†H9 listed by Blockeel & Long (1998: 88).

H(10) listed by Lett (1915: 120) without details.

†H10 listed by Blockeel & Long (1998: 88).

H(11) listed by Lett (1915: 120) without details.

†H11 listed by Blockeel & Long (1998: 88).

H(12) listed by Lett (1915: 120) without details.

†H12 listed by Blockeel & Long (1998: 88).

H(13) listed by Lett (1915: 120) without details.

†H13 listed by Blockeel & Long (1998: 88).

H(14) listed by Lett (1915: 120) without details.

†H14 listed by Blockeel & Long (1998: 88).

H15 1987: mortared walls, Portumna Abbey, HLK Whitehouse (Blockeel 1988: 35).

H(16) listed by Lett (1915: 120) without details.

†H16 listed by Blockeel & Long (1998: 88).

H(17) listed by Lett (1915: 120) without details.

†H17 listed by Blockeel & Long (1998: 88).

[H(18) listed by Lett (1915: 120) without details. H18 deleted because no valid record or voucher specimen traced (Blockeel 1999: 5)].

[H(19) listed by Lett (1915: 120) without details. H19 deleted because no valid record or voucher specimen traced (Blockeel 1999: 5)].

H(20) listed by Lett (1915: 120) without details.

†H20 listed by Blockeel & Long (1998: 88).

H(21) listed by Lett (1915: 120) without details.

†H21 listed by Blockeel & Long (1998: 88).

H(22) listed by Lett (1915: 120) without details.

†H22 listed by Blockeel & Long (1998: 88).
H(23) listed by Lett (1915: 120) without details.
†H23 listed by Blockeel & Long (1998: 88).
H(24) listed by Lett (1915: 120) without details.
†H24 listed by Blockeel & Long (1998: 88).
H(25) listed by Lett (1915: 120) without details.
†H25 listed by Blockeel & Long (1998: 88).
H26 1970: side of track, Keel Bridge, 3 miles N of Ballinrobe, J Appleyard (BBS exc.) (Crundwell 1971b: 377, Appleyard 1971: 388).
H(27) listed by Lett (1915: 120) without details.
†H27 listed by Blockeel & Long (1998: 88).
H(28) listed by Lett (1915: 120) without details.
†H28 listed by Blockeel & Long (1998: 88).
H(29) listed by Lett (1915: 120) without details.
†H29 listed by Blockeel & Long (1998: 88).
[H(30) listed by Lett (1915: 120) without details. H30 deleted because no valid record or voucher specimen traced (Blockeel 1999: 5)].
H30 2001: on open mortared wall of ruined house, 305 m alt., W of Bellavally Gap, H12, DT Holyoak 01-633 (Rothero 2002: 45).
H(31) listed by Lett (1915: 120) without details.
†H31 listed by Blockeel & Long (1998: 88).
H(32) listed by Lett (1915: 120) without details.
†H32 listed by Blockeel & Long (1998: 88).
H(33) listed by Lett (1915: 120) without details.
†H33 listed by Blockeel & Long (1998: 88).
H(34) listed by Lett (1915: 120) without details.
†H34 listed by Blockeel & Long (1998: 88).
H(35) listed by Lett (1915: 120) without details.
†H35 listed by Blockeel & Long (1998: 88).
H(36) listed by Lett (1915: 120) without details.
†H36 listed by Blockeel & Long (1998: 88).
H(37) listed by Lett (1915: 120) without details.
†H37 listed by Blockeel & Long (1998: 88).
H(38) listed by Lett (1915: 120) without details. H(38) listed by Blockeel & Long (1998: 88).
H38 1999: on mortar of stone bridge, 50 m alt., Tollymore Forest park, 4 km W of Newcastle, J33, TL Blockeel 28/352 (Rothero 2000: 50).
H(39) listed by Lett (1915: 120) without details.
†H39 listed by Blockeel & Long (1998: 88).
H(40) listed by Lett (1915: 120) without details.
†H40 listed by Blockeel & Long (1998: 88).

46/1 ***Bryoerythrophyllum recurvirostrum*** (Hedw.) P.C.Chen
(syn. *Barbula recurvirostra* (Hedw.) Dixon, *B. rubella* (Huebener) Mitt. hom. illeg., *B. rubella* var. *dentata* (Schimp.) Braithw.)

H(1) listed by Lett (1915: 118) without details.
†H1 listed by Blockeel & Long (1998: 88).
H(2) listed by Lett (1915: 118).
†H2 listed by Blockeel & Long (1998: 88).
H(3) listed by Lett (1915: 118) without details.
†H3 listed by Blockeel & Long (1998: 88).
H(4) listed by Lett (1915: 118) without details.
†H4 listed by Blockeel & Long (1998: 88).
H(5) listed by Lett (1915: 118) without details.
†H5 listed by Blockeel & Long (1998: 88).
H(6) listed by Lett (1915: 118) without details.
†H6 listed by Blockeel & Long (1998: 88).
H7 1966: conglomerate rocks, above L. Curra, Galtee Mts, ERB Little (BBS exc.) (Perry 1967: 413).
H(8) listed by Lett (1915: 118) without details.
†H8 listed by Blockeel & Long (1998: 88).
H(9) listed by Lett (1915: 118) without details.
†H9 listed by Blockeel & Long (1998: 88).
H(10) listed by Lett (1915: 118) without details.
†H10 listed by Blockeel & Long (1998: 88).
H(11) listed by Lett (1915: 118) without details.
†H11 listed by Blockeel & Long (1998: 88).
H(12) listed by Lett (1915: 118) without details.
†H12 listed by Blockeel & Long (1998: 88).
H(13) listed by Lett (1915: 118) without details.

†H13 listed by Blockeel & Long (1998: 88).
H(14) listed by Lett (1915: 118) without details.
†H14 listed by Blockeel & Long (1998: 88).
H(16) listed by Lett (1915: 118) without details.
†H16 listed by Blockeel & Long (1998: 88).
H17 1966: old limestone wall, Derreen, N of Monivea, MFV Corley & JS Parker (Perry 1967: 413).
[H(18) listed by Lett (1915: 118) without details. H18 deleted because no valid record or voucher specimen traced (Blockeel 1999: 5)].
[H(19) listed by Lett (1915: 118) without details. H19 deleted because no valid record or voucher specimen traced (Blockeel 1999: 5)].
H(20) listed by Lett (1915: 118) without details.
†H20 listed by Blockeel & Long (1998: 88).
H(21) listed by Lett (1915: 118) without details.
†H21 listed by Blockeel & Long (1998: 88).
H(22) listed by Lett (1915: 118) without details.
†H22 listed by Blockeel & Long (1998: 88).
H(23) listed by Lett (1915: 118) without details.
†H23 listed by Blockeel & Long (1998: 88).
H(24) listed by Lett (1915: 118) without details.
†H24 listed by Blockeel & Long (1998: 88).
H(25) listed by Lett (1915: 118) without details.
†H25 listed by Blockeel & Long (1998: 88).
H26 1970: bank by track, Glendaduff, NE of Foxford, MFV Corley (Crundwell 1971b: 377).
H(27) listed by Lett (1915: 118) without details.
†H27 listed by Blockeel & Long (1998: 88).
H(28) listed by Lett (1915: 118) without details.
†H28 listed by Blockeel & Long (1998: 88).
H(29) listed by Lett (1915: 118) without details.
†H29 listed by Blockeel & Long (1998: 88).
H(30) listed by Lett (1915: 118) without details.
†H30 listed by Blockeel & Long (1998: 88).
[H(31) listed by Lett (1915: 118) without details. H31 deleted because no valid record or voucher specimen traced (Blockeel 1999: 5)].
H(32) listed by Lett (1915: 118) without details.
†H32 listed by Blockeel & Long (1998: 88).
H(33) listed by Lett (1915: 118) without details.
†H33 listed by Blockeel & Long (1998: 88).
H(34) listed by Lett (1915: 118) without details.
†H34 listed by Blockeel & Long (1998: 88).
H(35) listed by Lett (1915: 118) without details.
†H35 listed by Blockeel & Long (1998: 88).
H(36) listed by Lett (1915: 118) without details.
†H36 listed by Blockeel & Long (1998: 88).
H(37) listed by Lett (1915: 118) without details.
†H37 listed by Blockeel & Long (1998: 88).
H(38) listed by Lett (1915: 118) without details.
†H38 listed by Blockeel & Long (1998: 88).
H(39) listed by Lett (1915: 118) without details.
†H39 listed by Blockeel & Long (1998: 88).
H(40) listed by Lett (1915: 118) without details.
†H40 listed by Blockeel & Long (1998: 88).

46/2 ***Bryoerythrophyllum ferruginascens*** (Stirt.) Giacom.
(syn. *Barbula ferruginascens* Stirt., *B. rubella* var. *ruberrima* Fergusson)

H(1) 1935: L. Cruttia, no collector named (BBS exc.) (Watson 1936: 265).
†H1 listed by Blockeel & Long (1998: 88).
H(7) listed by Lett (1915: 119).
†H7 listed by Blockeel & Long (1998: 88).
H9 1961: calcareous ground of old road, L. Ballycullinan, nr Corrofin, EM Lobley (Warburg 1966: 194).
H10 1979: bare ground by waste tip, Silvermines, RC Stern (Hill 1980b: 38).
H(14) 1912: stone by stream, Glencoura, Slieve Bloom, WN Tetley (as *B. spadicea*) (BBSUK), comm. AA Cridland (Warburg 1958b: 478).
H16 1957: Benchoona, J Appleyard (BBS exc.) (Warburg 1958b: 478).
†H27 listed by Blockeel & Long (1998: 88).
H(28) 1937: Ben Bulben, no collector named (BBS exc.) (Armitage 1938: 12).
†H28 listed by Blockeel & Long (1998: 88).
H29 1963: limestone, *ca* 1000 ft [alt.], Ballinlig, Glenade, RD Fitzgerald & AR

Perry (Warburg 1964: 726).
H34 1962: cement base of summit stone, Bulbin[Mt.] (BBS exc.) (Warburg 1963b: 496).
H(35) listed by Lett (1915: 119).
†H35 listed by Blockeel & Long (1998: 88).
H(39) 1928: Parkmore (BBS exc.) (Duncan 1928: 117), as *Barbula rubella* var. *ruberrima*. H(39) listed by Blockeel & Long (1998: 88).
H40 1964: decomposed basalt, *ca* 1400 ft Benbradagh, RD Fitzgerald (Warburg 1965: 864).

47/1 ***Leptodontium flexifolium*** (Dicks.) Hampe

H(1) listed by Lett (1915: 118).
H1 1951: burnt ground, Coomasaharn, nr Glenbeigh, EF Warburg (BBS exc.) (Warburg 1952: 102).
H3 1979: soil on rocks by shore, Adrigole, EC Wallace (Hill 1980b: 39).
H(6) listed by Lett (1915: 118).
†H6 listed by Blockeel & Long (1998: 89).
H10 1979: Clare Glens, G Bloom (Hill 1980b: 39).
H(12) 1911: Mt Blackstairs, WN Tetley (anon. 1912c: 9).
H(12) listed by Lett (1915: 118).
†H12 listed by Blockeel & Long (1998: 89).
H13 1969: on peat, *ca* 1000 ft [alt.], below Caher Roe's Den, Blackstairs Mts, RD Fitzgerald (Crundwell 1970: 202).
[H(14) listed by Lett (1915: 118)].
H20 1951: Seefin, AW Stelfox, comm. JS Thomson (Warburg 1952: 102).
H(21) listed by Lett (1915: 118). H(21) listed by Blockeel & Long (1998: 89).
[H(26) listed by Lett (1915: 118)].
H(27) listed by Lett (1915: 118).
†H27 listed by Blockeel & Long (1998: 89).
H(28) listed by Lett (1915: 118).
†H28 listed by Blockeel & Long (1998: 89).
H(29) 1937: Glenade, no collector named (BBS exc.) (Armitage 1938: 12).
H29 2001: with *Hypnum* on open ledge at base of sandstone crags, 418 m alt., Coal Pit, E slope of Bencroy, H01, DT Holyoak 01-795 (Rothero 2002: 46).
H30 1957: peaty bank on SW side of Tiltinbane, AC Crundwell (Warburg 1958b: 479).
H33 1960: thin dry peat on steep boulder slope, *ca* 600 ft [alt.], Doagh Lough, RD Fitzgerald (Warburg 1961: 165).
[H35 deleted because no valid record or voucher specimen traced (Blockeel 1999: 5)].
H37 1970: on peaty bank at 1800 ft [alt.], Slieve Gullion, MFV Corley (Crundwell 1971b: 378).
H(39) listed by Lett (1915: 118). H(39) listed by Blockeel & Long (1998: 89).
[H(40) listed by Lett (1915: 118)].

48/1 ***Hymenostylium recurvirostrum*** (Hedw.) Dixon
(syn. *Barbula curvirostris* Lindb., *Gymnostomum recurvirostrum* Hedw., *Weisia curvirostris* auct., *Weissia curvirostris* (Ehrh.) Müll.Hal., *Weissia curvirostris* var. *commutata* (Mitt.) Dixon)

H(1) apparently [number for vice-county is missing] listed by Lett (1915: 118) without details.
[H1 deleted because no valid record or voucher specimen traced (Blockeel 1999: 5)].
H(2) listed by Lett (1915: 118).
†H2 listed by Blockeel & Long (1998: 89).
H3 1998: rocks in freshwater streamlet on upper shore, 10 m alt., Simon's Cove, 5.5 km SE of Clonakilty, W43, JW Bates 3929 (Rothero 1999b: 42).
H(4) listed by Lett (1915: 118).
†H4 listed by Blockeel & Long (1998: 89).
H9 1957: limestone rocks, Blackhead [*sic* = Black Head], EM Lobley (BBS exc.) (Warburg 1958b: 479).
[H(10) listed by Lett (1915: 118). H10 deleted because no valid record or voucher specimen traced (Blockeel 1999: 5)].
H15 1994: on limestone slab in rough grassland at edge of *Cladium* marsh, 25 m alt., near L. Briskeen, *ca* 5 km W of Gort, M40, TL Blockeel 23/160 (Blockeel 1995c: 42).
H16 1953: basic rocks, W face of Lissoughter Hill, Recess, EC Wallace (Warburg 1954: 482).
[H(18) listed by Lett (1915: 118). H18 deleted because no valid record or voucher specimen traced (Blockeel 1999: 5)].
H20 1975: walls of ruined buildings, old lead works, Vale of Glendasan, WNW of Laragh, AR Perry (Hill 1977a: 19).
[H(21) listed by Lett (1915: 118). H21 deleted

because no valid record or voucher specimen traced (Blockeel 1999: 5)].
[H(22) listed by Lett (1915: 118). H22 deleted because specimen is *Barbula trifaria* (Synnott 1982, Hill 1983: 52)].
[H(23) listed by Lett (1915: 118). H23 deleted because specimen not traced (Synnott 1982, Hill 1983: 52)].
H26 1962: limestone pavement by Keel Bridge between Ballinrobe and Partry, AJE Smith (Warburg 1963b: 496).
H(27) listed by Lett (1915: 118).
†H27 listed by Blockeel & Long (1998: 89).
H(28) listed by Lett (1915: 118).
†H28 listed by Blockeel & Long (1998: 89).
H(29) 1937: Glenade, no collector named (BBS exc.) (Armitage 1938: 12).
†H29 listed by Blockeel & Long (1998: 89).
[H(30) listed by Lett (1915: 118). H30 deleted because no valid record or voucher specimen traced (Blockeel 1999: 5)].
[H(31) listed by Lett (1915: 118). H31 deleted because no valid record or voucher specimen traced (Blockeel 1999: 5)].
[H(33) listed by Lett (1915: 118). H33 deleted because no valid record or voucher specimen traced (Blockeel 1999: 5)].
H33 1999: on N-facing sandstone escarpment, 300 m alt., Letter Scarp, Lough Navar Forest, H05, RD Porley (Rothero 2000: 50).
H(34) 1937: Bundoran, no collector named (BBS exc.) (Armitage 1938: 12), as *Weisia curvirostris* var. *commutata*.
1937: Bundoran, EM Lobley (anon. 1938b: 26), as *Weisia curvirostris* var. *commutata*.
H34 2002: on thin damp soil over shale rocks, 10 m alt., Doagh Isle NE of Ballyliffin, C45, DT Holyoak 02-483 (Rothero 2003: 51).
[H(35) listed by Lett (1915: 118). H35 deleted because no valid record or voucher specimen traced (Blockeel 1999: 5)].
H35 2001: in rock crevice on N-facing crag in coire, 350 m alt., Slieve League above Lough Agh, G57, NG Hodgetts 3795 (Rothero 2003: 51).
H36 1951: damp limestone above Binawoods Spring, nr L. Lee, RD Fitzgerald (Warburg 1952: 102).
H(38) listed by Lett (1915: 118). H(38) listed by Blockeel & Long (1998: 89).
H(39) listed by Lett (1915: 118). H(39) listed by Blockeel & Long (1998: 89).
[H(40) listed by Lett (1915: 118). H40 deleted because no valid record or voucher specimen traced (Blockeel 1999: 5)].

48/2 ***Hymenostylium insigne*** (Dixon) Podp. (syn. *Gymnostomum insigne* (Dixon) A. J.E.Sm., *Weisia curvirostris* var. *insignis* auct., *Weissia curvirostris* var. *insignis* (Dixon) H.Schmidt)

H(28) 1928: Gleniff, Ben Bulben, CH Binstead, D Hilary & W Young, conf. HN Dixon & WE Nicholson (anon. 1929: 99).
†H28 listed by Blockeel & Long (1998: 89).
H(29) 1937: Glenade, no collector named (BBS exc.) (Armitage 1938: 12).
†H29 listed by Blockeel & Long (1998: 89).

49/1 ***Anoectangium aestivum*** (Hedw.) Mitt. (syn. *Anoectangium compactum* Schwägr., *Pleurozygodon aestivus* (Hedw.) Lindb.)

H(1) listed by Lett (1915: 126).
†H1 listed by Blockeel & Long (1998: 89).
H(2) listed by Lett (1915: 126).
†H2 listed by Blockeel & Long (1998: 89).
H(3) listed by Lett (1915: 126). H(3) listed by Blockeel & Long (1998: 89).
H(6) listed by Lett (1915: 126). H(6) listed by Blockeel & Long (1998: 89).
H6 1999: on wet, weakly base-rich rocks in gully on crags, 570 m alt., Lough Coumfea, Comeragh Mts, S20, TL Blockeel 28/238 (Rothero 2000: 50).
H(7) listed by Lett (1915: 126).
†H7 listed by Blockeel & Long (1998: 89).
H(8) listed by Lett (1915: 126). H(8) listed by Blockeel & Long (1998: 89).
H9 1979: rock by Fin Lough nr Newmarket on Fergus, EC Wallace (Hill 1980b: 38).
H(16) listed by Lett (1915: 126).
†H16 listed by Blockeel & Long (1998: 89).
H(20) listed by Lett (1915: 126). H(20) listed by Blockeel & Long (1998: 89).
H(27) listed by Lett (1915: 126).
†H27 listed by Blockeel & Long (1998: 89).
H(28) listed by Lett (1915: 126).
†H28 listed by Blockeel & Long (1998: 89).
H29 2000: on thin soil over limestone rocks on N-facing slope, 400 m alt., S of Glencar Lough, G74, DT Holyoak 00-632 (BBSUK) (Rothero 2001: 40).
H(31) listed by Lett (1915: 126). H(31) listed

by Blockeel & Long (1998: 89).
H33 1959: limestone cliffs, Buggan, RD Fitzgerald (Warburg 1960: 776).
H(34) listed by Lett (1915: 126).
†H34 listed by Blockeel & Long (1998: 89).
H(35) listed by Lett (1915: 126).
†H35 listed by Blockeel & Long (1998: 89).
H(38) listed by Lett (1915: 126). H(38) listed by Blockeel & Long (1998: 89).
H(39) listed by Lett (1915: 126).
†H39 listed by Blockeel & Long (1998: 89).

50/1 ***Gyroweisia tenuis*** (Hedw.) Schimp.
(syn. *Mollia tenuis* (Hedw.) Lindb.)

H(1) listed by Lett (1915: 115). H(1) listed by Blockeel & Long (1998: 89).
H3 1968: fallen masonry, Dunboy Castle, Castletown Bearhaven, JA Paton (Crundwell 1969: 882).
H(5) listed by Lett (1915: 115).
†H5 listed by Blockeel & Long (1998: 89).
H6 1966: cracks in bridge, Belleville Park, nr Cappoquin, JG Duckett & J Appleyard (Perry 1967: 413).
H8 1979: old mortar, crevices of wall in refectory undercroft, Askeaton Friary, EW Jones *et al.* (Hill 1980b: 38).
H10 1987: NE face at ground level of 1 m high mortared wall at entrance to drive, nr Leserragh House, NW of Coolbawn, HLK Whitehouse (Blockeel 1988: 35).
H11 1968: rock ledge in old limestone quarry N of Thomastown, JA Paton (Crundwell 1969: 882).
H14 1987: with *Rhynchostegiella tenella* and *Barbula cylindrica* at base of mortared wall under trees, HLK Whitehouse (Blockeel 1988: 35).
H15 1968: shaded river bank, The Punchbowl, nr Gort, JA Paton (Crundwell 1969: 882). This record apparently accounts for the H15 entry in Corley & Hill (1981: 81) so that the following was not new for this vice-county.
1987: crumbling mortar near base of WSW facing wall, shaded by yew, stable block, Portumna Abbey, HLK Whitehouse (Blockeel 1988: 35).
H16 1970: ledge in old marble quarry S of Lissoughter, AR Perry & HJ Perry (Crundwell 1974: 168).
H19 1987: near base of mortared SW-facing wall, shaded by trees, of mill on River Liffey at Victoria Bridge, W of Naas, HLK Whitehouse (Blockeel 1988: 35).
H20 1969: mortar of wall beside Aughrim River between Aughrim and Woodenbridge, RD Fitzgerald (Crundwell 1970: 201).
H(21) listed by Lett (1915: 115). H(21) listed by Blockeel & Long (1998: 89).
H25 2002: on mortar in wall of derelict gatehouse, 50 m alt., Lough Keel, nr Rockingham Demesne, G80, NG Hodgetts 4136 (Rothero 2003: 51).
H26 1987: on soft limestone boulder on lake shore, NE side of Cooley Lough, nr Ballyhean, DG Long (Blockeel 1988: 35).
H27 1987: on mortar of gatepost, lane below Slievemore, Dugort, Achill I., DG Long (Blockeel 1988: 35).
H(28) listed by Lett (1915: 115). H(28) listed by Blockeel & Long (1998: 89).
H29 1963: calcareous rock below crag, 800 ft [alt.], Peakadaw, Glenade, AR Perry & RD Fitzgerald (Warburg 1964: 726).
H30 2001: on mortared wall nr bridge, 60 m alt., Dermaferst Bridge, nr Lough Gowna, N28, DT Holyoak 01-695 (Rothero 2002: 46).
H31 1973: on mortar of wall, Mellifont Abbey, MO Hill (Crundwell 1974: 168).
H33 1951: damp bank, Poulaphouca, H Milne-Redhead (Warburg 1952: 102).
H(34) listed by Lett (1915: 115). H(34) listed by Blockeel & Long (1998: 89).
H35 1962: rocks between L. Naboll and L. Agher, below Muckish [Mt.], EF Warburg *et al.* (BBS exc.) (Warburg 1963b: 496).
H36 1953: sandstone rocks, Adairs Quarry, Cookstown, MPH Kertland & EM Lobley (Warburg 1955: 585).
H37 2002: in crevices of mortared wall, 65 m alt., Gosford Forest Park, H94, DT Holyoak 02-1076 (Rothero 2003: 51).
H(38) listed by Lett (1915: 115). H(38) listed by Blockeel & Long (1998: 89).
H38 2002: on sandstone in old quarry, 100 m alt., Scrabo Quarry, J47, DT Holyoak 02-1025 (Rothero 2003: 51).
H(39) listed by Lett (1915: 115). H(39) listed by Blockeel & Long (1998: 89).
†H40 listed by Blockeel & Long (1998: 89).

See note under *Leptobarbula berica*.

51/1 ***Gymnostomum viridulum*** Brid.
(syn. *Mollia calcarea* var. *mutica* sensu Lett 1915)

H1 1979: on old mortar in wall of Roughty Bridge, nr Kenmare, MT2, G Bloom, EW Jones & EC Wallace, Hb. G Bloom & Hb. EW Jones (Whitehouse & Crundwell 1991: 572, 1992: 50, Blockeel 1992: 26).
H2 1951: on wall by railway station, Tralee, MT1, AC Crundwell (GL) (Whitehouse & Crundwell 1991: 572, 1992: 50, Blockeel 1992: 26).
1979: on wall by railway station, Tralee, MT1, AC Crundwell (Hb. G Bloom, GL, NMW) (Whitehouse & Crundwell 1991: 572, 1992: 50, Blockeel 1992: 26).
H3 1984: on stonework of ruined mine building, copper mines above Allihies, MT2, DG Long (E) (Whitehouse & Crundwell 1991: 573, 1992: 50, Blockeel 1992: 26).
H4 1967: mortar of wall of bridge over Shournagh River nr Blarney, NT1, RD Fitzgerald (NMW) (Whitehouse & Crundwell 1991: 573, 1992: 50, Blockeel 1992: 26).
H5 1850: Lota, nr Cork, I Carroll (DBN) (Lett 1915: 115 as *Mollia calcarea* var. *mutica*; Whitehouse & Crundwell 1991: 573, 1992: 50, Blockeel 1992: 26).
1966: wall by roadside N of Kilworth, NT1, DM Synnott (DBN) (Whitehouse & Crundwell 1991: 573, 1992: 50, Blockeel 1992: 26).
H6 1956: on old walls, Dungarvan Harbour [= NT3], EC Wallace (BBSUK, NMW, RNG) (Warburg 1957: 332 as *G. calcareum*; Whitehouse & Crundwell 1991: 573, 1992: 50, Blockeel 1992: 26).
H7 1988: on mortar of old wall, Rock of Cashel, *ca* 120 m alt., NU4, DG Long 15445 (E) (Whitehouse & Crundwell 1991: 573, 1992: 50, Blockeel 1992: 26).
H11 1968: shaded rock ledge, limestone quarry, N of Thomastown, PU3, JA Paton (BBSUK, NMW) (Crundwell 1969: 882, Whitehouse & Crundwell 1991: 573, 1992: 50, Blockeel 1992: 26).
H14 1956: Roundwood Bridge over Mountrath River, NU3, AA Cridland (BBSUK) (Warburg 1958b: 479, Whitehouse & Crundwell 1991: 573, 1992: 50, Blockeel 1992: 26).
1987: mortar on underside of Cathole Bridge over Owenass River, 5 km SW of Rosenallis, NU3, HLK Whitehouse (Hb. HLK Whitehouse) (Whitehouse & Crundwell 1991: 573, 1992: 50, Blockeel 1992: 26).
H25 2002: damp mortar on retaining wall by river, 50 m alt., Cortober, S bank of R Shannon, M99, NG Hodgetts 4138 (Rothero 2003: 51).
H35 1990: on stony ground among sand-hills S of Anloge Hill, Horn Head, nr Dunfanaghy, NB4, TL Blockeel (BBSUK) (Whitehouse & Crundwell 1991: 573, 1992: 50, Blockeel 1992: 26).

This species and the next were not separated in Ireland until the revision by Whitehouse & Crundwell (1991, 1992).

51/2 ***Gymnostomum calcareum*** Nees & Hornsch.
(syn. *Mollia calcarea* (Nees & Hornsch.) Lindb., *Weisia calcarea* auct., *Weissia calcarea* (Nees & Hornsch.) Müll.Hal.)

H2 1951: on mortar of wall, foot of Torc Cascade, Killarney, PR Bell & EW Jones (Hb. EW Jones), conf. HLK Whitehouse & AC Crundwell (Hill 1985: 24, Whitehouse & Crundwell 1991: 569, 1992: 43).
[H(4) listed by Lett (1915: 115)].
[H4 deleted because specimen is *G. luisieri* (= *G. viridulum*), det. AC Crundwell & HLK Whitehouse (Hill 1985: 24)].
[H5 deleted because specimen is *G. luisieri* (= *G. viridulum*), det. AC Crundwell & HLK Whitehouse (Hill 1985: 24)].
[H6 deleted because specimen is *G. luisieri* (= *G. viridulum*), det. AC Crundwell & HLK Whitehouse (Hill 1985: 24)].
[H8 record (1979, mortar of wall, ruined abbey, Askeaton, EW Jones & G Bloom: Hill 1980b: 38) deleted because specimen has recurved leaf margins and is not *G. calcareum*, det. AC Crundwell & HLK Whitehouse (Hill 1985: 24)].
[H(9) listed by Lett (1915: 115)].
H9 1957: Slieve Carran, J Appleyard (NMW) (Hill 1985: 24, Whitehouse & Crundwell 1991: 569, 1992: 43).
1965: damp crevice of limestone rock, Black Head, AMcG Stirling (NMW) (Whitehouse & Crundwell 1991: 569,

1992: 43).
[H11 deleted because specimen is *G. luisieri* (= *G. viridulum*), det. AC Crundwell & HLK Whitehouse (Hill 1985: 24)].
H11 2000: on damp tufa in quarry, 50 m alt., 1 km N of Thomastown, S54, N Lockhart (Rothero 2001: 40).
[H14 deleted because specimen is *G. luisieri* (= *G. viridulum*), det. AC Crundwell & HLK Whitehouse (Hill 1985: 24)].
H15 1968: shaded river bank, the Punchbowl near Gort, JA Paton (BBSUK) (Whitehouse & Crundwell 1991: 569, 1992: 43, Blockeel 1992: 26).
H16 1957: retaining wall, Tullywee Bridge, Kylemore, Connemara, AC Crundwell (BBS exc.) (BBSUK) (Warburg 1958b: 479, Hill 1985: 24, Whitehouse & Crundwell 1991: 569, 1992: 43).
H26 1987: crevice under overhanging limestone rock, on W-facing slope W of Partry, HLK Whitehouse (BBSUK, Hb. HLK Whitehouse) (Blockeel 1988: 35, Whitehouse & Crundwell 1991: 569, 1992: 43).
H27 1987: on sides of large base-rich boulders, large gully at W foot of Croghaun, Achill I., TL Blockeel (BBSUK) (Blockeel 1988: 35, Whitehouse & Crundwell 1991: 569, 1992: 43).
H28 1871: shady crevices in moist rocks, Ben Bulben, D Moore (DBN) (Hill 1985: 24, Whitehouse & Crundwell 1991: 569, 1992: 43).
[1937: Ben Bulben, no collector named (BBS exc.) (Armitage 1938: 12). Specimen apparently not revised by Whitehouse & Crundwell (1991, 1992)].
1970: Knocknarea, DM Synnott (DBN) (Whitehouse & Crundwell 1991: 569, 1992: 43).
H29 1928: wooded glen, NE end of Glencar Lough, JB Duncan (BBS exc.) (E) (Duncan 1928: 118, Hill 1985: 24, Whitehouse & Crundwell 1991: 569, 1992: 43).
1970: Glenade, DM Synnott (DBN) (Whitehouse & Crundwell 1991: 569, 1992: 43).
H33 1957: limestone rocks on E side of Belmore Mt., AC Crundwell (BBSUK) (Warburg 1958b: 479, Hill 1985: 24, Whitehouse & Crundwell 1991: 569, 1992: 43).
H(34) 1907: on limestone, Ballyliffin, J Hunter (E) (Hill 1985: 24, Whitehouse & Crundwell 1991: 569, 1992: 44).
1911: on red sandstone, Finner Camp, Bundoran, WN Tetley (BBSUK) (Whitehouse & Crundwell 1991: 569, 1992: 44).
H34 2002: in crevice under overhang on crag in dunes, 15 m alt., Doagh Isle NE of Ballyliffin, C45, DT Holyoak 02-494 (Rothero 2003: 51).
H(35) 1909: limestone nr Dunfanaghy, N Donegal, J Hunter (LIV, NMW) (anon. 1910: 341, Lett 1915: 115, Hill 1985: 24, Whitehouse & Crundwell 1991: 569, 1992: 44).
H35 1970: on soil in crevices of limestone rocks W of Portnoo, N of Ardara, MFV Corley (Hb. MFV Corley) (Whitehouse & Crundwell 1991: 569, 1992: 44).
H36 1957: rock crevice, Burn Dennet, RD Fitzgerald (BBSUK) (Warburg 1958b: 479, Hill 1985: 24, Whitehouse & Crundwell 1991: 569, 1992: 44).
[H(38) listed by Lett (1915: 115)].
[H38 deleted because specimen (BM, Dixon) is *Gyroweisia tenuis*, det. HLK Whitehouse (Hill 1985: 24)].

51/3 ***Gymnostomum aeruginosum*** Sm.
(syn. *Mollia aeruginosa* (Sm.) Lindb., *M. aeruginosa* var. *ramosissima* (Bruch, Schimp. & W.Gümbel) Braithw., *Weisia rupestris* auct., *Weissia rupestris* (Schwägr.) Müll.Hal.)

H(1) listed by Lett (1915: 115) without details.
†H1 listed by Blockeel & Long (1998: 90).
H(2) listed by Lett (1915: 115).
†H2 listed by Blockeel & Long (1998: 90).
H(3) listed by Lett (1915: 115) without details.
†H3 listed by Blockeel & Long (1998: 90).
H(6) listed by Lett (1915: 115).
†H6 listed by Blockeel & Long (1998: 90).
H(7) listed by Lett (1915: 115).
†H7 listed by Blockeel & Long (1998: 90).
H8 1966: on rocks above L. Curra, Galtee Mts, J Appleyard (Crundwell 1968: 636).
H9 1957: rocks by roadside, The Burren, J Appleyard (BBS exc.) (Warburg 1958b: 479).
H(16) listed by Lett (1915: 115).

†H16 listed by Blockeel & Long (1998: 90).
H(20) listed by Lett (1915: 115). H(20) listed by Blockeel & Long (1998: 90).
H(21) listed by Lett (1915: 115). H(21) listed by Blockeel & Long (1998: 90).
H22 1978: wet, lime-encrusted stones, shore of L. Sheelin, Ross, DM Synnott (Hill 1980b: 38).
H23 1970: limestone wall nr Killinure Lough, S of Glassan, JA Paton (Crundwell 1971b: 377).
H(25) listed by Lett (1915: 115).
†H25 listed by Blockeel & Long (1998: 90).
H(26) listed by Lett (1915: 115).
†H26 listed by Blockeel & Long (1998: 90).
H(27) listed by Lett (1915: 115).
†H27 listed by Blockeel & Long (1998: 90).
H(28) 1928: Gleniff, Ben Bulben (BBS exc.) (Duncan 1928: 118).
†H28 listed by Blockeel & Long (1998: 90).
H(29) listed by Lett (1915: 115) without locality.
†H29 listed by Blockeel & Long (1998: 90).
H30 2001: on limestone boulders at edge of lough, 70 m alt., NW shore of Lough Sheelin, nr Kilnahard, N48, DT Holyoak 01-678 (Rothero 2002: 46).
[H(31) listed by Lett (1915: 115) without details. H31 deleted because no valid record or voucher specimen traced (Blockeel 1999: 5)].
H(33) listed by Lett (1915: 115). H(33) listed by Blockeel & Long (1998: 90).
H33 1999: on ± basic sandstone escarpment, 300 m alt., Bolusty Beg Scarp, Lough Navar Forest, H05, RD Porley (Rothero 2000: 50).
H(34) listed by Lett (1915: 115).
†H34 listed by Blockeel & Long (1998: 90).
H(35) listed by Lett (1915: 115).
†H35 listed by Blockeel & Long (1998: 90).
H36 1957: rocks, Binnawooda Springs, RD Fitzgerald (Warburg 1958b: 479).
H(37) 1885: in loose tufts on L. Neagh shore at Ardmore Glebe, HW Lett (DBN), comm. DM Synnott (Blockeel 1989: 27).
H(38) listed by Lett (1915: 115). H(38) listed by Blockeel & Long (1998: 90).
H38 2002: on steep old concrete by river, 170 m alt., W of Glen River in Donards Wood nr Newcastle, J32, DT Holyoak 02-1043 (Rothero 2003: 51).
H(39) listed by Lett (1915: 115).
†H39 listed by Blockeel & Long (1998: 90).
H(40) 1937: Ness Glen, JD Houston (anon. 1938d: 40).
†H40 listed by Blockeel & Long (1998: 90).

52/1 ***Molendoa warburgii*** (Crundw. & M.O. Hill) R.H.Zander
(syn. *Anoectangium warburgii* Crundw. & M.O.Hill)

H27 1982: on soft damp N-facing schist, 370 m alt., above L. Knockacorraun, on E side of Corraun Hill, Corraun Peninsula, L7696, DM Synnott (Hill 1983: 52, Synnott 1983a).

53/1 ***Barbula convoluta*** Hedw.
(syn. *Barbula convoluta* var. *commutata* (Jur.) Husn., *B. convoluta* var. *sardoa* Bruch, Schimp. & W.Gümbel)

H(1) listed by Lett (1915: 120) without details.
H(1) 1935: Dingle, no collector named (BBS exc.) (Watson 1936: 265), as var. *Sardoa*.
†H1 listed by Blockeel & Long (1998: 90).
H(2) listed by Lett (1915: 120).
†H2 listed by Blockeel & Long (1998: 90).
H(3) listed by Lett (1915: 120) without details.
H3 1953: bank, Foulastookeen Mt., ALK King (Warburg 1954: 482), as var. *commutata*.
H(4) listed by Lett (1915: 120) without details.
H4 1966: wall at edge of road above R. Lee, Innishcarra Bridge, MFV Corley & JS Parker (Perry 1967: 412), as var. *commutata*.
H(5) listed by Lett (1915: 120).
†H5 listed by Blockeel & Long (1998: 90).
H6 1953: Carrickbeg Wood, nr Carrick-on-Suir, ALK King (Warburg 1954: 482). 1956: wall-top, nr Kilmanahan Bridge, Clonmel, EC Wallace (Warburg 1957: 331), as var. *commutata*.
H(7) listed by Lett (1915: 120) without details.
†H7 listed by Blockeel & Long (1998: 90).
H(8) listed by Lett (1915: 120) without details.
H8 1979: quay wall on S side of River Shannon, Limerick, HMH van Melick (Hill 1981: 26); as var. *commutata*.
H(9) 1945: wall by Fergus River, JS Thomson (anon. 1946c: 282).

H9 1966: limestone wall by road nr Killinaboy, MFV Corley & JS Parker (Perry 1967: 412), as var. *commutata*.
H10 1967: wall of bridge, Rossaguile Bridge, Keeper Hill, RD Fitzgerald (Crundwell 1968: 635), as var. *commutata*.
1968: path in garden, Loughtea House, E side of L. Derg, 4½ miles N of Killaloe, AR Perry (Crundwell 1969: 881).
H(11) listed by Lett (1915: 120) without details.
H11 1966: roadside, Foulkscourt Hourse, nr Johnstown, J Appleyard (BBS exc.) (Perry 1967: 412)), as var. *commutata*.
H(12) listed by Lett (1915: 120) without details.
†H12 listed by Blockeel & Long (1998: 90).
H(13) listed by Lett (1915: 120) without details.
H13 1969: mortar of wall, Cranagh, foot of Mt Leinster, RD Fitzgerald (Crundwell 1970: 200), as var. *commutata*.
H(14) listed by Lett (1915: 120) without details.
†H14 listed by Blockeel & Long (1998: 90).
H(15) listed by Lett (1915: 120) without details.
†H15 listed by Blockeel & Long (1998: 90).
H(16) listed by Lett (1915: 120) without details.
H16 1957: old wall, Clifden, EM Lobley (BBS exc.) (Warburg 1958b: 479), as var. *commutata*.
H(17) listed by Lett (1915: 120) without details.
H17 1966: limestone wall, Derreen, N of Monivea, MFV Corley & JS Parker (Perry 1967: 412)), as var. *commutata*.
H(18) listed by Lett (1915: 120) without details.
†H18 listed by Blockeel & Long (1998: 90).
H(19) 1949: nr Calverstown, JS Thomson (Warburg 1950: 384).
†H19 listed by Blockeel & Long (1998: 90).
H(20) listed by Lett (1915: 120).
†H20 listed by Blockeel & Long (1998: 90).
H(21) listed by Lett (1915: 120).
†H21 listed by Blockeel & Long (1998: 90).
H22 1951: garden path, Slane, JS Thomson (Warburg 1952: 102).
H(23) listed by Lett (1915: 120) without details.
†H23 listed by Blockeel & Long (1998: 90).
H24 1968: limestone pit 1 mile S of Lanesborough, WV Rubers *et al.* (U) (Crundwell 1974: 168).
1965: wall, Cloonart Bridge, RD Fitzgerald & EM Lobley (Warburg 1966: 194), as var. *commutata*.
H(25) listed by Lett (1915: 120) without details.
H25 1966: wall, Kilronan Mt., nr Ballyfarnan, RD Fitzgerald & EM Lobley (Warburg 1966: 194), as var. *commutata*.
H(26) listed by Lett (1915: 120) without details.
†H26 listed by Blockeel & Long (1998: 90).
H(27) listed by Lett (1915: 120) without details.
†H27 listed by Blockeel & Long (1998: 90).
H(28) 1928: walls, nr Sligo (BBS exc.) (Duncan 1928: 119), as var. *sardoa*.
†H28 listed by Blockeel & Long (1998: 90).
H(29) listed by Lett (1915: 120) without details.
H29 1963: stone wall, *ca* 200 ft [alt.], Glencar Waterfall, RD Fitzgerald & AR Perry (Warburg 1964: 726), as var. *commutata*.
H(30) listed by Lett (1915: 120) without details.
†H30 listed by Blockeel & Long (1998: 90).
H(31) listed by Lett (1915: 120) without details.
H31 1964: stone wall, Mellifont Abbey, nr Collon, JW Fitzgerald & MPH Kertland (Warburg 1965: 863), as var. *commutata*.
H(32) 1947: top of wall, Hope Castle demesne, Castleblaney, JS Thomson (anon. 1948b: 120).
†H32 listed by Blockeel & Long (1998: 90).
H(33) listed by Lett (1915: 120) without details.
H33 1957: earth-capped limestone wall, nr Belcoo, AC Crundwell (Warburg 1958b: 479), as var. *commutata*.
H(34) listed by Lett (1915: 120) without details.
H34 1967: on mortar of bridge, Crana R. nr Buncrana, RD Fitzgerald (Crundwell 1968: 635), as var. *commutata*.
H(35) listed by Lett (1915: 120) without details.
H35 1962: stone wall in grounds of Glenveagh Castle, RE Longton (BBS exc.) (Warburg 1963b: 496), as var. *commutata*.
H(36) listed by Lett (1915: 120) without

details.
H36 1950: brick and mortar rubble heap, Seskinore, J Taylor (Warburg 1954: 482), as var. *commutata*.
H(37) listed by Lett (1915: 120) without details.
H37 1962: old calcareous wall nr Keady, EM Lobley & MPH Kertland (Warburg 1963b: 496).
H(38) listed by Lett (1915: 120) without details.
†H38 listed by Blockeel & Long (1998: 90).
H(39) listed by Lett (1915: 120).
†H39 listed by Blockeel & Long (1998: 90).
H(40) listed by Lett (1915: 120) without details.
†H40 listed by Blockeel & Long (1998: 90).

53/2 *Barbula unguiculata* Hedw.
(syn. *Barbula unguiculata* var. *apiculata* (Hedw.) Bruch, Schimp. & W.Gümbel, *B. unguiculata* var. *cuspidata* (Schultz) Brid., *B. unguiculata* var. *fastigiata* (Schultz) Huebener)

H(1) listed by Lett (1915: 120) without details.
†H1 listed by Blockeel & Long (1998: 90).
H(2) listed by Lett (1915: 120) without details.
†H2 listed by Blockeel & Long (1998: 90).
H(3) listed by Lett (1915: 120) without details.
†H3 listed by Blockeel & Long (1998: 90).
H(4) listed by Lett (1915: 120) without details.
†H4 listed by Blockeel & Long (1998: 90).
H5 1951: wall, Mallow, EC Wallace & EF Warburg (Warburg 1952: 102).
H6 1962: right bank of R. Suir above Clonmel, ALK King (Warburg 1963b: 494).
†H7 listed by Blockeel & Long (1998: 90).
H(8) listed by Lett (1915: 120) without details.
†H8 listed by Blockeel & Long (1998: 90).
H(9) listed by Lett (1915: 120) without details.
†H9 listed by Blockeel & Long (1998: 90).
H(10) listed by Lett (1915: 120) without details.
†H10 listed by Blockeel & Long (1998: 90).
H(11) listed by Lett (1915: 120) without details.
†H11 listed by Blockeel & Long (1998: 90).
H(12) listed by Lett (1915: 120) without details.
H12 1975: roadside wall, NE side of Tara Hill, S of Coolgreany, AR Perry (Hill 1977a: 18), as var. *commutata*.
H(13) listed by Lett (1915: 120) without details.
†H13 listed by Blockeel & Long (1998: 90).
H(14) listed by Lett (1915: 120) without details.
†H14 listed by Blockeel & Long (1998: 90).
H(15) listed by Lett (1915: 120) without details.
†H15 listed by Blockeel & Long (1998: 90).
H(16) listed by Lett (1915: 120) without details.
†H16 listed by Blockeel & Long (1998: 90).
H(17) listed by Lett (1915: 120) without details.
†H17 listed by Blockeel & Long (1998: 90).
[H(18) listed by Lett (1915: 120) without details. H18 deleted because no valid record or voucher specimen traced (Blockeel 1999: 5)].
H(19) listed by Lett (1915: 120) without details.
†H19 listed by Blockeel & Long (1998: 90).
H(20) listed by Lett (1915: 120) without details.
†H20 listed by Blockeel & Long (1998: 90).
H(21) listed by Lett (1915: 120, 121) without locality.
†H21 listed by Blockeel & Long (1998: 90).
H(22) listed by Lett (1915: 120) without details.
H22 1950: gravel quarry, Slane, JS Thomson (Warburg 1952: 102), as var. *cuspidata*.
H(23) listed by Lett (1915: 120).
†H23 listed by Blockeel & Long (1998: 90).
H(24) listed by Lett (1915: 120) without details.
†H24 listed by Blockeel & Long (1998: 90).
H(25) listed by Lett (1915: 120) without details.
†H25 listed by Blockeel & Long (1998: 90).
H(26) listed by Lett (1915: 120) without details.
†H26 listed by Blockeel & Long (1998: 90).
H(27) listed by Lett (1915: 120) without details.
†H27 listed by Blockeel & Long (1998: 90).
†H28 listed by Blockeel & Long (1998: 90).
H(29) listed by Lett (1915: 120) without details.
†H29 listed by Blockeel & Long (1998: 90).

[H(30) listed by Lett (1915: 120) without details. H30 deleted because no valid record or voucher specimen traced (Blockeel 1999: 5)].
H30 2001: on mortared wall, 305 m alt., W of Bellavally Gap, H12, DT Holyoak 01-630A (Rothero 2002: 46).
H(31) listed by Lett (1915: 120).
†H31 listed by Blockeel & Long (1998: 90).
H(32) listed by Lett (1915: 120) without details.
†H32 listed by Blockeel & Long (1998: 90).
H(33) listed by Lett (1915: 120) without details.
†H33 listed by Blockeel & Long (1998: 90).
H(34) listed by Lett (1915: 120) without details.
†H34 listed by Blockeel & Long (1998: 90).
H(35) listed by Lett (1915: 120) without details.
†H35 listed by Blockeel & Long (1998: 90).
H36 1953: boulders, Adairs Quarry, Cookstown, MPH Kertland & EM Lobley (Warburg 1955: 584).
H(37) listed by Lett (1915: 120, 121).
†H37 listed by Blockeel & Long (1998: 90).
H(38) listed by Lett (1915: 120, 121). H(38) listed by Blockeel & Long (1998: 90).
H38 2002: on wall of bridge, 50 m alt., by Shimna River in Tollymore Forest Park, J33, DT Holyoak 02-923 (Rothero 2003: 51).
H(39) listed by Lett (1915: 120, 121).
†H39 listed by Blockeel & Long (1998: 90).
H(40) listed by Lett (1915: 120) without details.
†H40 listed by Blockeel & Long (1998: 90).

54/1 ***Didymodon acutus*** (Brid.) K.Saito **var. *acutus***
(syn. *Barbula acuta* (Brid.) Brid., *B. gracilis* (Schleich.) Schwägr.)

[H(4) listed by Lett (1915: 120)].
H6 1966: sand dunes, Bunmahon, ERB Little (BBS exc.) (Perry 1967: 412).
H(8) listed by Lett (1915: 120). H(8) listed by Blockeel & Long (1998: 90).
H9 1960: open mossy fixed-dune turf, Fanore, MCF Proctor & RB Ivimey-Cook (Warburg 1961: 165).
H18 1957: calcareous soil beside R. Toberlin, Ballycollis, JS Thomson (Warburg 1958b: 478).
[H26 deleted because no valid record or voucher specimen traced (Blockeel 1999: 5)].
H(27) listed by Blockeel & Long (1998: 90).
H(28) 1928: rocks above Glencar Lough, N side (BBS exc.) (Duncan 1928: 119).
H(28) listed by Blockeel & Long (1998: 90).
H31 1968: quarry at Castlecoo Hill, Clogher Head, DM Synnott (Crundwell 1969: 881).
H(38) listed by Lett (1915: 120). H(38) listed by Blockeel & Long (1998: 90).
[H(39) listed by Lett (1915: 120) without locality].

54/2 ***Didymodon acutus*** **var. *icmadophilus*** (Schimp. ex Müll.Hal.) R.H.Zander
(syn. *Barbula icmadophila* Schimp. ex Müll.Hal., *Didymodon icmadophilus* (Schimp. ex Müll.Hal.) K.Saito)

H(28) 1880: mixed with *Schistidium apocarpum*, Benbulbin [*sic* = Ben Bulben], D McArdle (DBN), comm. DM Synnott, conf. AC Crundwell (Hill 1984b: 27, Synnott 1983b).

This taxon was treated at species rank by Blockeel & Long (1998: 90), but is regarded as a variety of *D. acutus* here following Kučera (2000: 8).

54/3 ***Didymodon rigidulus*** Hedw.
(syn. *Barbula rigidula* (Hedw.) Mitt.)

H(1) listed by Lett (1915: 119).
†H1 listed by Blockeel & Long (1998: 91).
H(2) listed by Lett (1915: 119). H(2) listed by Blockeel & Long (1998: 91).
H3 1953: wall, Pass of Keimaneigh, ALK King (Warburg 1955: 584).
H(4) listed by Lett (1915: 119). H(4) listed by Blockeel & Long (1998: 91).
H4 2002: on concrete wall top, Compass Hill, Kinsale, W64, TL Blockeel 31/301 (Rothero 2003: 51).
H(5) listed by Lett (1915: 119). H(5) listed by Blockeel & Long (1998: 91).
H5 2002: on top of old wall, River Bride, Ardarou Wood, Glenville, W78, Blockeel TL 31/370 (Rothero 2003: 51).
H(6) 1933: nr Cappagh, E Armitage (anon. 1934b: 117).
†H6 listed by Blockeel & Long (1998: 91).
H(8) listed by Lett (1915: 119).
†H8 listed by Blockeel & Long (1998: 91).

H(9) 1945: rocks, Roughan Ho.[use], Kilnaboy, JS Thomson (anon. 1946c: 282).
†H9 listed by Blockeel & Long (1998: 91).
H(10) listed by Lett (1915: 119).
†H10 listed by Blockeel & Long (1998: 91).
H(11) listed by Lett (1915: 119).
†H11 listed by Blockeel & Long (1998: 91).
H(12) listed by Lett (1915: 119).
†H12 listed by Blockeel & Long (1998: 91).
H13 1971: wall nr Carlow, AG Side (Crundwell 1972: 138).
H(14) listed by Lett (1915: 119).
†H14 listed by Blockeel & Long (1998: 91).
H15 1952: wall of pier, Ross Quay, L. Derg, MPH Kertland & ALK King (Warburg 1953: 310).
H16 1957: old wall, Roundstone, EM Lobley (BBS exc.) (Warburg 1958b: 478).
H(17) listed by Lett (1915: 119).
†H17 listed by Blockeel & Long (1998: 91).
H18 1957: beside R. Toberlin, Ballycollis, JS Thomson (Warburg 1958b: 478).
[H19 deleted because no valid record or voucher specimen traced (Blockeel 1999: 5)].
H(20) listed by Lett (1915: 120).
†H20 listed by Blockeel & Long (1998: 91).
H(21) listed by Lett (1915: 120).
†H21 listed by Blockeel & Long (1998: 91).
H22 1966: limestone wall, Staholmog, E of Kells, RD Fitzgerald & EM Lobley (Perry 1967: 412).
H(23) listed by Lett (1915: 120).
†H23 listed by Blockeel & Long (1998: 91).
H24 1957: wall of bridge at Glen Ballinalee, ALK King (Warburg 1958b: 478).
H(25) listed by Lett (1915: 120).
†H25 listed by Blockeel & Long (1998: 91).
H(26) listed by Lett (1915: 120).
†H26 listed by Blockeel & Long (1998: 91).
H(27) listed by Lett (1915: 120).
†H27 listed by Blockeel & Long (1998: 91).
H(28) listed by Lett (1915: 120).
†H28 listed by Blockeel & Long (1998: 91).
H(29) listed by Lett (1915: 120).
†H29 listed by Blockeel & Long (1998: 91).
H30 1957: limestone wall, Cornahaw, SW of Black Lion [*sic* = Blacklion], AC Crundwell (Warburg 1958b: 478).
H(32) listed by Lett (1915: 120). H(32) listed by Blockeel & Long (1998: 91).
H(33) listed by Blockeel & Long (1998: 91).
H33 2000: on mortared wall of bridge, Cladagh River below Marble Arch, H13, DT Holyoak 00-90 (BBSUK) (Rothero 2001: 40).
H(34) listed by Lett (1915: 120).
†H34 listed by Blockeel & Long (1998: 91).
H(35) listed by Lett (1915: 120).
†H35 listed by Blockeel & Long (1998: 91).
H36 1953: bridge wall, Cookstown, MPH Kertland & EM Lobley (Warburg 1955: 584).
H(37) listed by Lett (1915: 120).
†H37 listed by Blockeel & Long (1998: 91).
H(38) listed by Lett (1915: 120). H(38) listed by Blockeel & Long (1998: 91).
H38 1999: on mortared wall of the Hermitage, 55 m alt., Tollymore Forest park, 4 km W of Newcastle, J33, TL Blockeel 28/341 (Rothero 2000: 50).
H(39) listed by Lett (1915: 120).
†H39 listed by Blockeel & Long (1998: 91).
H(40) listed by Lett (1915: 120).
†H40 listed by Blockeel & Long (1998: 91).

54/4 ***Didymodon nicholsonii*** **Culm.**
(syn. *Barbula nicholsonii* Culm.)

H2 1951: ground, nr shore of L. Leane, Ross I., Killarney, JS Thomson (Warburg 1952: 101).
H4 2002: on broken wall top, 3 m alt., Kinsale, W65, TL Blockeel 31/272 (Rothero 2003: 51).
H5 1951: Fermoy Station platform, EF Warburg (Warburg 1952: 101).
1951: by the River, Mallow, EW Jones (Warburg 1952: 101).
H8 1992: on rocks by River Maigue 60 m alt., Bruree, R53, E Wiltshire (Blockeel 1993: 50).
H12 1954: near waterspout, road to Curragh Wood, Inch, JS Thomson (Warburg 1955: 584).
H13 2002: on thin soil over vertical damp concrete of bridge, 65 m alt., just W of Bunclody, S95, DT Holyoak 02-363 (Rothero 2003: 51).
H29 2000: on damp tarmac at edge of road, Glencar Waterfalls, G74, DT Holyoak 00-504 (BBSUK) (Rothero 2001: 40).
H30 2001: in crevices of damp tarmac, 245 m alt., Slieve Glah, E slope, H40, DT Holyoak 01-687 (Rothero 2002: 46).
H33 2000: on tarmac at edge of parking area by lough, NW edge of Lough Macnean Lower, H03, DT Holyoak 00-296 (BBSUK) (Rothero 2001: 40).

54/7 ***Didymodon australasiae*** (Hook. & Grev.) R.H.Zander, **var.** ***umbrosus*** (Müll.Hal.) R.H.Zander
(syn. *Didymodon umbrosus* (Müll.Hal.) R.H.Zander, *Trichostomopsis umbrosa* (Müll.Hal.) H.Rob.)

H21 1988: on garden path, Howth, DW Robinson, comm. DM Synnott (Blockeel 1989: 28, Synnott & Robinson 1989, 1990).

This taxon was treated at species rank by Blockeel & Long (1998: 91), but is regarded as a variety of *D. australasiae* here following Kučera (2000: 12).

54/8 ***Didymodon vinealis*** (Brid.) R.H.Zander
(syn. *Barbula cylindrica* var. *vinealis* (Brid.) Lindb., *B. vinealis* Brid.)

H3 1999: on bare sandy flats contaminated by outflow from old copper mine, 2 m alt., Ballydonegan Strand, Allihies, V54, DG Long 28513 (Rothero 2000: 50).
H(4) listed by Lett (1915: 120) without locality.
†H4 listed by Blockeel & Long (1998: 91).
H(5) listed by Lett (1915: 120) without details. H(5) listed by Blockeel & Long (1998: 91).
H6 1956: wall-top, Kilmanahan Park, nr Knocklofty, EC Wallace (Warburg 1957: 331).
H(11) listed by Lett (1915: 120) as 1 [*sic* = H11] Thomastown 1909 leg. Phillips, and Duninga 1911 leg. Tetley. H(11) listed by Blockeel & Long (1998: 91).
H12 1954: road nr Curragh Wood, Inch, JS Thomson (Warburg 1955: 584).
H(14) listed by Lett (1915: 120).
†H14 listed by Blockeel & Long (1998: 91).
H(18) listed by Lett (1915: 120). H(18) listed by Blockeel & Long (1998: 91).
H(19) listed by Lett (1915: 120). H(19) listed by Blockeel & Long (1998: 91).
H(20) listed by Lett (1915: 120). H(20) listed by Blockeel & Long (1998: 91).
H20 1997: on wall by lagoon, E side of Broad Lough, N of Wicklow, T39, DG Long 27346, E (Rothero 2000: 50).
H(21) listed by Lett (1915: 120).
†H21 listed by Blockeel & Long (1998: 91).
H23 1979: limestone bluff, Fore, DM Synnott (DBN) (Blockeel 1989: 27).
H24 1966: limestone on E shore of L. Ree, ALK King (Perry 1967: 412).
†H27 listed by Blockeel & Long (1998: 91).
H(28) listed by Lett (1915: 120). H(28) listed by Blockeel & Long (1998: 91).
H(33) listed by Lett (1915: 120) without details. H(33) listed by Blockeel & Long (1998: 91).
[H(34) listed by Lett (1915: 120) without details. H34 deleted because no valid record or voucher specimen traced (Blockeel 1999: 5)].
H35 2002: on sand of path in dune grassland, 8 m alt., Drumnatinny N of Falcarragh, B93, DT Holyoak 02-454 (Rothero 2003: 51).
H(36) listed by Lett (1915: 120).
†H36 listed by Blockeel & Long (1998: 91).
H(37) listed by Lett (1915: 120).
†H37 listed by Blockeel & Long (1998: 91).
H(38) listed by Lett (1915: 120). H(38) listed by Blockeel & Long (1998: 91).
H(39) listed by Lett (1915: 120). H(39) listed by Blockeel & Long (1998: 91).
H40 1999: on sandy gravel of path at base of building, Magilligan Point, Martello Tower, C63, DT Holyoak 99-137 (BBSUK) (Rothero 2000: 50).

54/9 ***Didymodon insulanus*** (De Not.) M.O. Hill
(syn. *Barbula cylindrica* (Taylor) Schimp.)

H(1) listed by Lett (1915: 120) without details.
†H1 listed by Blockeel & Long (1998: 91).
H(2) listed by Lett (1915: 120) without details.
†H2 listed by Blockeel & Long (1998: 91).
H3 1951: roadside by tunnel at Turner's Rock, ALK King (Warburg 1952: 101).
H(4) listed by Lett (1915: 120) without details.
H4 1951: roadside bank NW of Mallow, AC Crundwell (Warburg 1952: 101).
H(5) listed by Lett (1915: 120) without details.
†H5 listed by Blockeel & Long (1998: 91).
H(6) listed by Lett (1915: 120) without details.
†H6 listed by Blockeel & Long (1998: 91).
H7 1956: wall, Knocklofty, EC Wallace (Warburg 1957: 331).
H(8) listed by Lett (1915: 120) without

details.
†H8 listed by Blockeel & Long (1998: 91).
H(9) 1945: nr Kilnaboy, JS Thomson (anon. 1946c: 282).
†H9 listed by Blockeel & Long (1998: 91).
H10 1952: limestone rocks, Terryglass Bay, L. Derg, MPH Kertland & ALK King (Warburg 1953: 310).
H(11) listed by Lett (1915: 120) without details.
†H11 listed by Blockeel & Long (1998: 91).
H(12) listed by Lett (1915: 120) without details.
†H12 listed by Blockeel & Long (1998: 91).
H(13) listed by Lett (1915: 120) without details.
†H13 listed by Blockeel & Long (1998: 91).
H14 1956: calcareous bank in beechwood, Emo Estate, AA Cridland (Warburg 1958b: 478).
H15 1987: mortared walls, Portumna Abbey, HLK Whitehouse (Blockeel 1988: 35).
H(16) listed by Lett (1915: 120) without details.
†H16 listed by Blockeel & Long (1998: 91).
[H(17) listed by Lett (1915: 120) without details. H17 deleted because no valid record or voucher specimen traced (Blockeel 1999: 5)].
H18 1957: bank by roadside, nr Ballinacarr, JS Thomson (Warburg 1958b: 478).
H(19) 1946: Cupidstown Hill, AW Stelfox (per JS Thomson) (anon. 1947: 30).
†H19 listed by Blockeel & Long (1998: 91).
H(20) listed by Lett (1915: 120) without details.
†H20 listed by Blockeel & Long (1998: 91).
H(21) listed by Lett (1915: 120) without details.
†H21 listed by Blockeel & Long (1998: 91).
H(22) listed by Lett (1915: 120) without details.
†H22 listed by Blockeel & Long (1998: 91).
H(23) listed by Lett (1915: 120) without details.
†H23 listed by Blockeel & Long (1998: 91).
H24 1957: boulder by R. Inny, Ballymacarrow Bridge, ALK King (Warburg 1958b: 478).
H(25) listed by Lett (1915: 120) without details.
†H25 listed by Blockeel & Long (1998: 91).
H(26) listed by Lett (1915: 120) without details.
†H26 listed by Blockeel & Long (1998: 91).
H(27) listed by Lett (1915: 120) without details.
†H27 listed by Blockeel & Long (1998: 91).
H(28) listed by Lett (1915: 120) without details.
†H28 listed by Blockeel & Long (1998: 91).
H(29) listed by Lett (1915: 120) without details.
†H29 listed by Blockeel & Long (1998: 91).
H(30) listed by Lett (1915: 120) without details.
†H30 listed by Blockeel & Long (1998: 91).
[H(31) listed by Lett (1915: 120) without details. H31 deleted because no valid record or voucher specimen traced (Blockeel 1999: 5)].
[H(32) listed by Lett (1915: 120) without details. H32 deleted because no valid record or voucher specimen traced (Blockeel 1999: 5)].
H(33) listed by Lett (1915: 120) without details.
†H33 listed by Blockeel & Long (1998: 91).
H(34) listed by Lett (1915: 120) without details.
†H34 listed by Blockeel & Long (1998: 91).
H(35) listed by Lett (1915: 120) without details.
†H35 listed by Blockeel & Long (1998: 91).
H(36) listed by Lett (1915: 120) without details.
†H36 listed by Blockeel & Long (1998: 91).
H(37) listed by Lett (1915: 120) without details.
†H37 listed by Blockeel & Long (1998: 91).
H(38) listed by Lett (1915: 120) without details.
†H38 listed by Blockeel & Long (1998: 91).
H(39) listed by Lett (1915: 120) without details.
†H39 listed by Blockeel & Long (1998: 91).
H(40) 1936: Kilrea, JD Houston (anon. 1937a: 367).
†H40 listed by Blockeel & Long (1998: 91).

54/10 ***Didymodon luridus*** Hornsch. ex Spreng. (syn. *Barbula lurida* (Hornsch.) Lindb., *B. trifaria* auct. non (Hedw.) Mitt.)

H(1) listed by Lett (1915: 119). H(1) listed by Blockeel & Long (1998: 91).
H(2) listed by Lett (1915: 119).
†H2 listed by Blockeel & Long (1998: 91).
H3 1998: on soil at roadside amid exposed coastal pastures, 50 m alt.,

Ballymacredmond, 8 km SSE of Timoleague, W43, JW Bates 3915 (Rothero 1999b: 42).
H(4) listed by Lett (1915: 119) without locality. H(4) listed by Blockeel & Long (1998: 91).
H4 2002: on broken wall top, 25 m alt., Kinsale, W65, TL Blockeel 31/271 (Rothero 2003: 51).
H(5) listed by Lett (1915: 119). H(5) listed by Blockeel & Long (1998: 91).
H5 2002: in concrete water channel in garden, 10 m alt., Fota House, Foaty I., W77, TL Blockeel 31/345 (Rothero 2003: 51).
[H(6) listed by Lett (1915: 119) as 1902: Tramore, leg. HW Lett. H6 deleted: specimen from Tramore, 1902, leg. HW Lett (DBN), is *Barbula tophacea*, comm. DM Synnott (Blockeel 1989: 27)].
H7 1999: in silt on embankment wall by river, 10 m alt., River Suir, N bank, Kilsheelan, S22, TL Blockeel 28/187 (Rothero 2000: 50).
H8 1959: rocks by R. Shannon, Castleconnell, ALK King (Warburg 1960: 775).
[H12 1950: The Rocks, Wexford, ALK King (Warburg 1951: 500). H12 deleted: specimen from The Rocks, Wexford, 1950, leg. ALK King (DBN), is *Barbula* cf. *fallax*, comm. DM Synnott (Blockeel 1989: 27)].
H13 1954: wall by towpath, L.[eft] bank of R. Barrow below Graiguenamanagh, ALK King (Warburg 1955: 584).
H16 1994: on soil among calcareous rubble in small shrubbery, 20 m alt., Clifden, L66, TL Blockeel 23/242 (Blockeel 1995c: 42).
H(17) listed by Lett (1915: 119) without locality. H(17) listed by Blockeel & Long (1998: 91).
[H(18) listed by Lett (1915: 119) as 1907: Geashill, leg. HW Lett. H18 deleted: specimen from Geashill, 1907, leg. HW Lett (DBN), is a mixture of *Barbula rigidula* and *B. recurvirostris*, comm. DM Synnott (Blockeel 1989: 27)].
†H21 listed by Blockeel & Long (1998: 91).
H22 1980: large stone by drain, N of Newtown Lough, Clonmellon, DM Synnott (Hill 1981: 26).
H23 1980: limestone boulder by road, N of Castletown, DM Synnott (Hill 1981: 26).
H25 2002: on limestone at edge of turlough, 60 m alt., Four Roads Turlough, M85, NG Hodgetts 4078 (Rothero 2003: 51).
H(26) listed by Lett (1915: 119).
†H26 listed by Blockeel & Long (1998: 91).
H29 1961: concrete path, Glencar, RD Fitzgerald & MPH Kertland (Warburg 1962: 370).
H31 1973: base of wall, Mellifont Abbey, MO Hill (Crundwell 1974: 168).
H(33) listed by Lett (1915: 119). H(33) listed by Blockeel & Long (1998: 91).
H(34) 1937: Bundoran, no collector named (BBS exc.) (Armitage 1938: 12).
H(35) listed by Lett (1915: 119). H(35) listed by Blockeel & Long (1998: 91).
H(38) listed by Lett (1915: 119). H(38) listed by Blockeel & Long (1998: 91).
H(39) listed by Blockeel & Long (1998: 91).

54/12 ***Didymodon sinuosus*** (Mitt.) Delogne (syn. *Barbula sinuosa* (Mitt.) Garov., *Oxystegus sinuosus* (Mitt.) Hilpert, *Trichostomum sinuosum* (Mitt.) Müll. Hal.)

H1 1951: Darrynane, J Appleyard (BBS exc.) (Warburg 1952: 102).
H2 1951: rock, shore of Ross I., JS Thomson (Warburg 1952: 102).
H3 1979: rocks, S slope of Sugarloaf Mt., nr Lackavane, HMH van Melick (Hill 1981: 27).
H4 2002: on shaded limestone boulder, 40 m alt., Blarney in the Castle grounds, W67, TL Blockeel 31/294 (Rothero 2003: 51).
H6 1956: wall of park, Kilmanahan, nr Knocklofty, EC Wallace (Warburg 1957: 331).
†H7 listed by Blockeel & Long (1998: 91).
H(8) listed by Lett (1915: 120).
†H8 listed by Blockeel & Long (1998: 91).
H9 1979: on wall at roadside, 6 km SW of Ennis, AC Crundwell & JA Paton (Hill 1980b: 39).
H10 1987: mortar at base of wall of old graveyard with *Rhynchostegiella tenella*, SW of Coolbawn, HLK Whitehouse (Blockeel 1988: 35-36).
H11 1973: on stone on slope down to cave, Dunmore Cave, DL Kelly (Crundwell 1974: 168).
H15 1957: rocks nr Punchbowl, nr Gort, EM

Lobley (BBS exc.) (Warburg 1958b: 478).

H(16) listed by Lett (1915: 120). H(16) listed by Blockeel & Long (1998: 91).

[H17 deleted because no valid record or voucher specimen traced (Blockeel 1999: 5)].

H(19) 1949: root of tree on damp bank, nr Calverstown, JS Thomson (Warburg 1950: 384).

H(21) listed by Lett (1915: 120).

†H21 listed by Blockeel & Long (1998: 91).

H22 1950: stone, garden of Glebe House, Slane, JS Thomson (Warburg 1952: 102).

H23 1952: stone on garden path, Woodlands, nr Multyfarnham, JS Thomson (Warburg 1954: 482).

H25 1972: on limestone wall, shore of L. Ree, Lanesborough, WV Rubers (U) (Crundwell 1974: 168).

H27 1987: on tree roots on wooded lake shore, by lake, Westport House, DG Long (Blockeel 1988: 35-36).

H(28) 1928: rocks above Glencar Lough, N side (BBS exc.) (Duncan 1928: 119).

†H28 listed by Blockeel & Long (1998: 91).

H29 2000: on limestone boulder, W of Glencar waterfalls, G74, DT Holyoak 00-505 (Rothero 2002: 46).

H(30) 1911: on lake shore, Farnham Wood, J Glover (anon. 1915b: 9), labelled as *Barbula cylindrica* but redet. as *B. sinuosa* Braithw. by GB Savery.

†H30 listed by Blockeel & Long (1998: 91).

H31 1968: limestone outcrop, Castle Roche, DM Synnott (DBN) (Blockeel 1989: 27).

H32 1950: limestone, L. Aphuca, RD Fitzgerald (Warburg 1951: 500).

H(33) listed by Blockeel & Long (1998: 91).

H33 2000: on soil over limestone by river in wooded ravine, nr Pollreagh, H13, DT Holyoak 00-420 (Rothero 2002: 46).

H35 1962: rocks, Tranarossan Bay, nr Rosapenna, Mulroy Bay, EM Lobley & MPH Kertland (BBS exc.) (Warburg 1963b: 497).

H36 1956: base of trees on bank of R. Blackwater, Aratrea Bridge, RD Fitzgerald (Warburg 1959: 634).

H37 1962: mortar of old wall nr Keady, EM Lobley & MPH Kertland (Warburg 1963b: 497).

H(38) listed by Blockeel & Long (1998: 91).

H(39) listed by Blockeel & Long (1998: 91).

54/13 ***Didymodon tophaceus*** (Brid.) Lisa (syn. *Barbula brevifolia* Lindb., *B. brevifolia* var. *acutifolia* (Schimp.) Braithw., *B. tophacea* (Brid.) Mitt.)

H(1) listed by Lett (1915: 119) without details.

†H1 listed by Blockeel & Long (1998: 92).

H2 1951: wall nr entrance to Torc Waterfall, JS Thomson (Warburg 1952: 101).

H3 1951: rocks in stream in intertidal zone, Cape Clear, IS Rorison (Warburg 1952: 101).

H(4) listed by Lett (1915: 119) without details. H(4) listed by Blockeel & Long (1998: 92).

H4 2002: seepage in earthy recess in coastal bank, 2 m alt., Charles Fort, Summer Cove, Kinsale, W64, TL Blockeel 31/274 (Rothero 2003: 51).

H(5) listed by Lett (1915: 119) without details.

†H5 listed by Blockeel & Long (1998: 92).

H(6) listed by Lett (1915: 119) without details.

†H6 listed by Blockeel & Long (1998: 92).

H(8) listed by Lett (1915: 119) without details.

†H8 listed by Blockeel & Long (1998: 92).

H(9) listed by Lett (1915: 119) without details.

†H9 listed by Blockeel & Long (1998: 92).

H(10) listed by Lett (1915: 119) without details.

†H10 listed by Blockeel & Long (1998: 92).

H(12) listed by Lett (1915: 119) without details.

†H12 listed by Blockeel & Long (1998: 92).

H(14) listed by Lett (1915: 119) without details.

†H14 listed by Blockeel & Long (1998: 92).

[H(15) listed by Lett (1915: 119) without details. H15 deleted because no valid record or voucher specimen traced (Blockeel 1999: 5)].

H(16) listed by Lett (1915: 119) without details.

†H16 listed by Blockeel & Long (1998: 92).

[H(17) listed by Lett (1915: 119) without details. H17 deleted because no valid record or voucher specimen traced (Blockeel 1999: 5)].

[H(18) listed by Lett (1915: 119) without

details. H18 deleted because no valid record or voucher specimen traced (Blockeel 1999: 5)].
H(19) 1938: Rye Water, JS Thomson (anon. 1939b: 109).
H(20) listed by Lett (1915: 119) without details.
†H20 listed by Blockeel & Long (1998: 92).
H(21) listed by Lett (1915: 119) without details.
†H21 listed by Blockeel & Long (1998: 92).
H22 1978: tufa by road, SE of Stackallan Bridge, Slane, DM Synnott (Hill 1979: 27).
H(23) listed by Lett (1915: 119) without details.
†H23 listed by Blockeel & Long (1998: 92).
H(25) listed by Lett (1915: 119) without details.
†H25 listed by Blockeel & Long (1998: 92).
H(26) listed by Lett (1915: 119) without details.
†H26 listed by Blockeel & Long (1998: 92).
H(27) listed by Lett (1915: 119) without details.
†H27 listed by Blockeel & Long (1998: 92).
H(28) listed by Lett (1915: 119) without details.
†H28 listed by Blockeel & Long (1998: 92).
H(29) listed by Lett (1915: 119) without details.
†H29 listed by Blockeel & Long (1998: 92).
H30 2001: on thin tufa on wet clay bank above stream, 320 m alt., W of Bellavally Gap, H12, DT Holyoak, 01-626A (Rothero 2002: 46).
[H(31) listed by Lett (1915: 119) without details. H31 deleted because no valid record or voucher specimen traced (Blockeel 1999: 5)].
[H32 deleted because no valid record or voucher specimen traced (Blockeel 1999: 5)].
[H33) listed by Lett (1915: 119) without details. H33 deleted because no valid record or voucher specimen traced (Blockeel 1999: 5)].
H33 1999: on ± base-rich ledge on N-facing sandstone escarpment, 280 m alt., Braade ASSI, Lough Navar Forest, H05, RD Porley 2037 (Rothero 2000: 50).
H(34) listed by Lett (1915: 119) without details.
†H34 listed by Blockeel & Long (1998: 92).
H(35) listed by Lett (1915: 119) without details.
†H35 listed by Blockeel & Long (1998: 92).
H36 1953: calcareous sandstone, Adairs Quarry, Cookstown, MPH Kertland & EM Lobley (Warburg 1955: 584).
[H(37) listed by Lett (1915: 119) without details. H37 deleted because no valid record or voucher specimen traced (Blockeel 1999: 5)].
H37 2002: in crevices of mortared wall, 65 m alt., Gosford Forest Park, H94, DT Holyoak 02-1078 (Rothero 2003: 51).
H(38) listed by Lett (1915: 119) without details. H(38) listed by Blockeel & Long (1998: 92).
H38 2002: on wall of bridge, 50 m alt., by Shimna River in Tollymore Forest Park, J33, DT Holyoak 02-927 (Rothero 2003: 51).
H(39) listed by Lett (1915: 119) as var. *acutifolia*.
†H39 listed by Blockeel & Long (1998: 92).
†H40 listed by Blockeel & Long (1998: 92).

54/14 ***Didymodon spadiceus*** (Mitt.) Limpr. (syn. *Barbula spadicea* (Mitt.) Braithw.)

H(1) listed by Lett (1915: 119). H(1) listed by Blockeel & Long (1998: 92).
H(4) listed by Lett (1915: 119). H(4) listed by Blockeel & Long (1998: 92).
H(5) listed by Lett (1915: 119). H(5) listed by Blockeel & Long (1998: 92).
H6 1966: silt on rocks, R. Owenashad, nr Lismore, EM Lobley & RD Fitzgerald (BBS exc.) (Perry 1967: 412).
H(7) listed by Lett (1915: 119). H(7) listed by Blockeel & Long (1998: 92).
H9 1957: limestone rocks in hazel scrub on SE side of Slievecarran, J Appleyard & AC Crundwell (BBS exc.) (Warburg 1958b: 478).
H(10) listed by Lett (1915: 119).
†H10 listed by Blockeel & Long (1998: 92).
H(11) listed by Lett (1915: 119). H(11) listed by Blockeel & Long (1998: 92).
H(14) listed by Lett (1915: 119).
†H14 listed by Blockeel & Long (1998: 92).
H(19) 1939: Golden Falls, Ballymore-Eustace, JF Thomson, comm. ALK King (Warburg 1966: 194).
[H(20) listed by Lett (1915: 119) as 1848: leg. Moore (no locality). H20 deleted because specimen from Powerscourt, leg. D Moore (DBN), is *Barbula*

rigidula, comm. DM Synnott (Blockeel 1989: 27)].
H23 1957: quarry, NE end of L. Owel, JS Thomson (Warburg 1958b: 478).
H(25) listed by Lett (1915: 119). H(25) listed by Blockeel & Long (1998: 92).
H27 1972: old shaded wall, Rosturk Castle, W of Newport, WV Rubers, (U) (Crundwell 1975: 15).
H(28) listed by Lett (1915: 119).
†H28 listed by Blockeel & Long (1998: 92).
H(29) listed by Lett (1915: 119).
†H29 listed by Blockeel & Long (1998: 92).
[H(30) listed by Lett (1915: 119) as 1911: Killykeen, leg. HW Lett. H30 deleted because specimen from Killykeen, 1911, leg. HW Lett (DBN), is *Barbula recurvirostris*, comm. DM Synnott (Blockeel 1989: 27)].
H30 2001: on steep clay bank above stream, 320 m alt., W of Bellavally Gap, H12, DT Holyoak 01-625 (Rothero 2002: 46).
[H(31) listed by Lett (1915: 119). H31 deleted because no valid record or voucher specimen traced (Blockeel 1999: 5)].
[H(32) listed by Lett (1915: 119) without details. H32 deleted because no valid record or voucher specimen traced (Blockeel 1999: 5)].
H(33) listed by Lett (1915: 119).
†H33 listed by Blockeel & Long (1998: 92).
H(35) listed by Lett (1915: 119). H(35) listed by Blockeel & Long (1998: 92).
H(36) listed by Lett (1915: 119).
†H36 listed by Blockeel & Long (1998: 92).
H(38) listed by Lett (1915: 119). H(38) listed by Blockeel & Long (1998: 92).
H(39) listed by Lett (1915: 119). H(39) listed by Blockeel & Long (1998: 92).
H(40) listed by Blockeel & Long (1998: 92).

54/15 ***Didymodon fallax*** (Hedw.) R.H.Zander (syn. *Barbula fallax* Hedw., *B. fallax* var. *brevifolia* (With.) Kindb.)

H(1) listed by Lett (1915: 119) without details.
†H1 listed by Blockeel & Long (1998: 92).
H(2) listed by Lett (1915: 119) without details.
†H2 listed by Blockeel & Long (1998: 92).
H(3) listed by Lett (1915: 119) without details.
†H3 listed by Blockeel & Long (1998: 92).
H(4) listed by Lett (1915: 119) without details.
†H4 listed by Blockeel & Long (1998: 92).
H(5) listed by Lett (1915: 119) without details.
†H5 listed by Blockeel & Long (1998: 92).
H(6) listed by Lett (1915: 119) without details.
†H6 listed by Blockeel & Long (1998: 92).
†H7 listed by Blockeel & Long (1998: 92).
H(8) listed by Lett (1915: 119) without details.
†H8 listed by Blockeel & Long (1998: 92).
H(9) listed by Lett (1915: 119) without details.
†H9 listed by Blockeel & Long (1998: 92).
H(10) listed by Lett (1915: 119) without details.
†H10 listed by Blockeel & Long (1998: 92).
H(11) listed by Lett (1915: 119) without details.
†H11 listed by Blockeel & Long (1998: 92).
H(12) listed by Lett (1915: 119) without details.
†H12 listed by Blockeel & Long (1998: 92).
H(13) listed by Lett (1915: 119) without details.
†H13 listed by Blockeel & Long (1998: 92).
H(14) listed by Lett (1915: 119) without details.
†H14 listed by Blockeel & Long (1998: 92).
H15 1957: boulder in pasture, hills E of Gort, RE Parker (Warburg 1958b: 478).
H(16) listed by Lett (1915: 119) without details.
†H16 listed by Blockeel & Long (1998: 92).
H(17) listed by Lett (1915: 119) without details.
†H17 listed by Blockeel & Long (1998: 92).
H(18) listed by Lett (1915: 119) without details.
†H18 listed by Blockeel & Long (1998: 92).
H(19) listed by Lett (1915: 119) without details.
†H19 listed by Blockeel & Long (1998: 92).
H(20) listed by Lett (1915: 119) without details.
†H20 listed by Blockeel & Long (1998: 92).
H(21) listed by Lett (1915: 119) without details.
†H21 listed by Blockeel & Long (1998: 92).
H(22) listed by Lett (1915: 119) without details.
†H22 listed by Blockeel & Long (1998: 92).
H(23) listed by Lett (1915: 119) without details.

†H23 listed by Blockeel & Long (1998: 92).
H24 1957: side of lane to bog, Newtonforbes [*sic* = Newtown Forbes], ALK King (Warburg 1958b: 478).
H(25) listed by Lett (1915: 119) without details.
†H25 listed by Blockeel & Long (1998: 92).
H(26) listed by Lett (1915: 119) without details.
†H26 listed by Blockeel & Long (1998: 92).
H(27) listed by Lett (1915: 119) without details.
†H27 listed by Blockeel & Long (1998: 92).
H(28) listed by Lett (1915: 119) without details.
†H28 listed by Blockeel & Long (1998: 92).
H(29) listed by Lett (1915: 119) without details.
†H29 listed by Blockeel & Long (1998: 92).
H(30) listed by Lett (1915: 119) without details.
†H30 listed by Blockeel & Long (1998: 92).
[H(31) listed by Lett (1915: 119) without details. H31 deleted because no valid record or voucher specimen traced (Blockeel 1999: 5)].
H(32) listed by Lett (1915: 119) without details.
†H32 listed by Blockeel & Long (1998: 92).
H(33) listed by Lett (1915: 119) without details.
†H33 listed by Blockeel & Long (1998: 92).
H(34) listed by Lett (1915: 119) without details.
†H34 listed by Blockeel & Long (1998: 92).
H(35) listed by Lett (1915: 119) without details.
†H35 listed by Blockeel & Long (1998: 92).
H(36) listed by Lett (1915: 119) without details.
†H36 listed by Blockeel & Long (1998: 92).
H(37) listed by Lett (1915: 119) without details.
†H37 listed by Blockeel & Long (1998: 92).
H(38) listed by Lett (1915: 119).
†H38 listed by Blockeel & Long (1998: 92).
H(39) listed by Lett (1915: 119) without details.
†H39 listed by Blockeel & Long (1998: 92).
H(40) listed by Lett (1915: 119) without details.
†H40 listed by Blockeel & Long (1998: 92).

54/16 ***Didymodon tomaculosus*** (Blockeel) M. F.V.Corley
(syn. *Barbula tomaculosus* Blockeel)

H18 1987: barley stubble, Derrybrat, 5 km NW of Kilcormac, HLK Whitehouse (Blockeel 1988: 35).
H19 1987: barley field, 2.5 km E of Rathangan, HLK Whitehouse (Blockeel 1988: 35).
H21 2002: in stubble field (wheat) with *Bryum klinggraeffii*, *Dicranella schreberiana* and *D. staphylina*, 60 m alt., SE of Hazelhatch station, N93, CD Preston, conf. TL Blockeel (Rothero 2003: 51).

54/17 ***Didymodon ferrugineus*** (Schimp. ex Besch.) M.O.Hill
(syn. *Barbula recurvifolia* Schimp., *B. reflexa* (Brid.) Brid.)

[H(1) listed by Lett (1915: 119) without details. H1 deleted because no valid record or voucher specimen traced (Blockeel 1999: 5)].
H(2) listed by Lett (1915: 119). H(2) listed by Blockeel & Long (1998: 92).
H(3) listed by Lett (1915: 119). H(3) listed by Blockeel & Long (1998: 92).
†H9 listed by Blockeel & Long (1998: 92).
H(11) listed by Lett (1915: 119). H(11) listed by Blockeel & Long (1998: 92).
H12 1950: sand dunes, Curracloe, ALK King (Warburg 1951: 500).
H13 2002: on open thin soil on track in plantation, 310 m alt., slope of Croaghaun, S85 DT Holyoak 02-360 (Rothero 2003: 52).
H15 1957: on rock, limestone pavement, Garryland Wood, nr Gort, AC Crundwell (BBS exc.) (Warburg 1958b: 478).
H(16) listed by Lett (1915: 119).
†H16 listed by Blockeel & Long (1998: 92).
H19 1969: in disused sandpit nr Downings, ALK King (Crundwell 1970: 201).
H(21) listed by Lett (1915: 119). H(21) listed by Blockeel & Long (1998: 92).
H22 1978: foot of roadside bank, E of Roachtown Mill, Crossakeel, DM Synnott (Hill 1980b: 38).
H(23) listed by Lett (1915: 119) without locality.
†H23 listed by Blockeel & Long (1998: 92).

H25 1968: on limestone boulder, St John's Wood, 3 miles SE of Knockcroghery, WV Rubers *et al.* (U) (Crundwell 1974: 168).
H(26) listed by Lett (1915: 119).
†H26 listed by Blockeel & Long (1998: 92).
H(27) 1937: Dugort, Achill I., no collector named (BBS exc.) (Armitage 1938: 13).
†H27 listed by Blockeel & Long (1998: 92).
H(28) listed by Lett (1915: 119).
†H28 listed by Blockeel & Long (1998: 92).
H(29) listed by Lett (1915: 119).
†H29 listed by Blockeel & Long (1998: 92).
H30 2001: on thin soil between limestone fragments on track, 100 m alt., Deerpark, W of Virginia, N58, DT Holyoak 01-665 (Rothero 2002: 46).
H(32) listed by Lett (1915: 119) without locality. H(32) listed by Blockeel & Long (1998: 92).
H(33) listed by Lett (1915: 119).
H33 1957: earth-capped limestone wall, nr Belcoo, AC Crundwell (Warburg 1958b: 478).
H(34) 1937: Bundoran, no collector named (BBS exc.) (Armitage 1938: 12).
†H34 listed by Blockeel & Long (1998: 92).
H(35) listed by Lett (1915: 119).
†H35 listed by Blockeel & Long (1998: 92).
H(38) listed by Lett (1915: 119). H(38) listed by Blockeel & Long (1998: 92).
H39 1952: hollow in dunes, Portrush, EW Jones (Warburg 1953: 310).
H(40) listed by Lett (1915: 119).
†H40 listed by Blockeel & Long (1998: 92).

54/18 ***Didymodon giganteus*** (Funck) Jur.
(syn. *B. maxima* Syed & Crundw., *Barbula recurvifolia* var. *robusta* (Braithw.) Paris, *B. reflexa* var. *maxima* Braithw., *B. reflexa* var. *robusta* Braithw., *Didymodon maximus* (Syed & Crundw.) M.O.Hill)

H(28) no date (probably 1858): Benbulben, D Moore (Lett 1915: 119, Synnott 1981).
†H28 listed by Blockeel & Long (1998: 92).
H(29) 1937: Glenade, no collector named (BBS exc.) (Armitage 1938: 12).
1937: Glenade, HN Dixon, JB Duncan & EM Lobley (anon. 1938b: 24) [erroneously listed as vc 29].
†H29 listed by Blockeel & Long (1998: 92).

Syed & Crundwell (1973) raised *Barbula reflexa* var. *maxima* Braithw. to species rank as *B. maxima* Syed & Crundw., regarding it as an endemic Irish species. This species was later reported from Northwest Territories, Canada, implying a remarkable range disjunction (Synnott 1981). However, Kučera (2000: 20, 48) is apparently correct in treating it as a synonym of *D. giganteus* (Funck) Jur., a species known from the Pyrenees, Alps and Carpathians but not from Great Britain.

57/1 ***Pterygoneurum ovatum*** (Hedw.) Dixon
(syn. *Tortula pusilla* Mitt.)

H(4) no date: nr Cork, Taylor (Lett 1915: 111)
no date: nr Passage, Murray (Lett 1915: 111). H(4) listed by Blockeel & Long (1998: 93).
H(21) 1804: no locality, Stokes (Lett 1915: 111).
no date: nr Dublin, GA Hunt (K) (Lett 1915: 111). H(21) listed by Blockeel & Long (1998: 93).

57/2 ***Pterygoneurum lamellatum*** (Lindb.) Jur.
(syn. *Tortula lamellata* Lindb.)

H(21) no date: no locality, Moore (Lett 1915: 111). H(21) placed in brackets, comm. PD Coker (Hill 1981: 25). H(21) listed by Blockeel & Long (1998: 93).
H(38) 1870: nr Donaghdee, SA Stewart (Lett 1915: 111). H(38) placed in brackets, comm. PD Coker (Hill 1981: 25). H(38) listed by Blockeel & Long (1998: 93).

58/2 ***Aloina rigida*** (Hedw.) Limpr.
(syn. *Tortula stellata* Lindb.)

[H(4) listed by Lett (1915: 111)].
H19 1969: sand pit, Geraldine House, nr Athy, RD Fitzgerald (BBSUK), conf. MO Hill (Crundwell 1970: 200, MO Hill MS).
[H(21) listed by Lett (1915: 111)].
H(21) *ca* 1833: wall tops, Balgriffin, D Moore (GL), conf. MO Hill (MO Hill MS).
1855: Cardiff's Bridge nr Dublin, Wilson (BM), conf. MO Hill (MO Hill MS).
H(38) 1877: damp debris of slate rocks,

Cregagh Glen, SA Stewart (DBN), conf. MO Hill (Lett 1915: 111; MO Hill MS).
[H(39) listed by Lett (1915: 111)].
H(39) 1928: nr Larne, W Young (NMW, Hb. EC Wallace), conf. MO Hill (MO Hill MS).
1928: earth-capped wall, coast road, Glenarm, JB Duncan (Hb. UK Duncan), conf. MO Hill (MO Hill MS).

Specimens from Ireland and Britain were revised by MO Hill for the *CC* (Corley & Hill 1981). The details given above are from an unpublished list by MO Hill (MS).

58/3 ***Aloina aloides*** (Schultz) Kindb.
(syn. *Aloina aloides* var. *aloides* (Schultz) Kindb., *Tortula aloides* (Schultz) De Not.)

H(1) listed by Lett (1915: 112).
†H1 listed by Blockeel & Long (1998: 93).
[H(2) listed by Lett (1915: 112) without details. H2 deleted because no valid record or voucher specimen traced (Blockeel 1999: 5)].
H3 1984: on stonework of ruined mine building, copper mines above Allihies, DG Long (Hill 1985: 23).
H5 1951: wall top, nr Mallow, EC Wallace & EF Warburg (Warburg 1952: 101).
H(6) listed by Lett (1915: 112).
†H6 listed by Blockeel & Long (1998: 93).
H7 1966: soil, limestone rocks, Ardfinnan, ERB Little & JA Paton (BBS exc.) (Perry 1967: 411).
H(8) listed by Lett (1915: 112).
†H8 listed by Blockeel & Long (1998: 93).
H(9) 1945: by bridge over Fergus [River], Kilnaboy, JS Thomson (anon. 1946c: 282).
†H9 listed by Blockeel & Long (1998: 93).
H(11) listed by Lett (1915: 112).
†H11 listed by Blockeel & Long (1998: 93).
[H(12) listed by Lett (1915: 112). H12 deleted because no valid record or voucher specimen traced (Blockeel 1999: 5)].
H(13) listed by Lett (1915: 112).
†H13 listed by Blockeel & Long (1998: 93).
H14 1956: limestone wall, Mountmellick, nr Owenass River, A Cridland (BBSUK) (Hill 1978: 18).
H(15) listed by Lett (1915: 112).
†H15 listed by Blockeel & Long (1998: 93).
[H(16) listed by Lett (1915: 112) without locality. H16 deleted because no valid record or voucher specimen traced (Blockeel 1999: 5)].
[H(17) listed by Lett (1915: 112) without details. H17 deleted because no valid record or voucher specimen traced (Blockeel 1999: 5)].
H18 1957: bare ground in field, nr Geashill, JS Thomson (Warburg 1958b: 477).
H19 1952: sandy bank of canal, Leixlip, AW Stelfox, comm. JS Thomson (Warburg 1953: 310).
[H(20) listed by Lett (1915: 112) without locality. H20 deleted because no valid record or voucher specimen traced (Blockeel 1999: 5)].
[H(21) listed by Lett (1915: 112). H21 deleted because no valid record or voucher specimen traced (Blockeel 1999: 5)].
H22 1950: on ground, Slane, JS Thomson (Warburg 1952: 101).
H23 1954: wall, nr Multyfarnham, JS Thomson (Warburg 1955: 584).
H24 1980: limestone wall, Draper Bridge, Royal Canal, DM Synnott (Hill 1981: 25).
H25 2002: on skeletal soil in limestone grassland, 80 m alt., Killeglan grassland, Lugboy, M84, NG Hodgetts 4053 (Rothero 2003: 52).
[H(27) listed by Lett (1915: 112) without locality. H27 deleted because no valid record or voucher specimen traced (Blockeel 1999: 5)].
H(28) listed by Lett (1915: 112) without locality
†H28 listed by Blockeel & Long (1998: 93).
H(29) listed by Lett (1915: 112) without details.
†H29 listed by Blockeel & Long (1998: 93).
[H(30) listed by Lett (1915: 112) as 1909: Blacklion, Tetley. H30 deleted because no valid record or voucher specimen traced (Blockeel 1999: 5)].
H31 1973: ruined masonry, Mellifont Abbey, MO Hill (Crundwell 1974: 167).
H(32) 1947: ruins of old cottage, nr Castleblaney, JS Thomson (anon. 1948b: 120).
H33 1957: earth-capped limestone wall, nr Belcoo, AC Crundwell (Warburg 1958b: 477).
H35 2002: on heavily grazed soil terraces above beach, 10 m alt., Trabane, Malin

Beg, G57, NG Hodgetts 3786 (Rothero 2003: 52).
H(36) listed by Lett (1915: 112).
†H36 listed by Blockeel & Long (1998: 93).
H(37) listed by Lett (1915: 112) without details.
†H37 listed by Blockeel & Long (1998: 93).
H(38) listed by Lett (1915: 112). H(38) listed by Blockeel & Long (1998: 93).
H38 2002: on thin soil over sandstone in old quarry, 100 m alt., Scrabo Quarry, J47, DT Holyoak, 02-1027 (Rothero 2003: 52).
H(39) listed by Lett (1915: 112).
†H39 listed by Blockeel & Long (1998: 93).
H(40) 1937: Benbradach [*sic* = Benbradagh], JD Houston (anon. 1938d: 39).
†H40 listed by Blockeel & Long (1998: 93).

58/4 ***Aloina ambigua*** (Bruch & Schimp.) Limpr.
(syn. *Aloina aloides* var. *ambigua* (Bruch & Schimp.) E.J.Craig, *Tortula ericaefolia* Lindb.)

H(2) 1873: Cromaglawn, Killarney, D Moore (DBN), conf. MO Hill (Lett 1915: 111; MO Hill MS).
[H(4) listed by Lett (1915: 111) without locality].
H5 1956: earthy bank, lane nr shore, S of Youghal Strand, EC Wallace (BBSUK), conf. MO Hill (Warburg 1957: 330, MO Hill MS).
H6 1956: wall tops, Dungarvan Harbour, EC Wallace (BBSUK), conf. MO Hill (Warburg 1957: 330, MO Hill MS).
[H(8) listed by Lett (1915: 111)].
H9 1961: on limestone rocks, Black Head, EM Lobley (Hb. RD Fitzgerald), conf. MO Hill (MO Hill MS).
[H12 1958: sandy roadside bank by R. Barrow estuary, Whitechurch, ALK King (Warburg 1959: 634). Not accepted for H12 by Corley & Hill (1981: 76) following revision of specimens by MO Hill].
[H14 1956: Carboniferous Limestone wall, Mountmellick, AA Cridland (Warburg 1958b: 477). Not accepted for H14 by Corley & Hill (1981: 76) following revision of specimens by MO Hill].
[H16 1957: old wall, Clifden, DH Dalby, EM Lobley & JH Tallis (BBS exc.) (Warburg 1958b: 477). Not accepted for H16 by Corley & Hill (1981: 76) following revision of specimens by MO Hill].
[H(19) listed by Lett (1915: 112)].
[H(21) listed by Lett (1915: 112)].
H(21) 1848: wall tops nr College botanic garden, Southside of Dublin, D Moore (BM), conf. MO Hill (MO Hill MS). 1860: mud walls nr Glasnevin, D McArdle (BM), conf. MO Hill (MO Hill MS).
[H(23) listed by Lett (1915: 112)].
[H(28) 1928: nr Rosses Point, Sligo (BBS exc.) (Duncan 1928: 119). Not accepted for H28 by Corley & Hill (1981: 76) following revision of specimens by MO Hill].
H(31) 1883: Carlingford quarry, CH Waddell (DBN), conf. MO Hill (Lett 1915: 112; MO Hill MS).
[H(33) listed by Lett (1915: 112)].
[H(34) listed by Lett (1915: 112)].
[H(37) listed by Lett (1915: 112)].
[H(38) listed by Lett (1915: 112)].
[H(39) listed by Lett (1915: 112)].
H(39) 1877: clay banks, Carrickfergus, SA Stewart (CRK), conf. MO Hill (MO Hill MS).

Specimens from Ireland and Britain were revised by MO Hill for the *CC* (Corley & Hill 1981). The details given above are from an unpublished list by (MO Hill MS).

59/1 ***Leptobarbula berica*** (De Not.) Schimp.

H16 1986: on moist wall of the house, Letterdife House, Roundstone, T Arts, comm. HLK Whitehouse (Blockeel 1988: 35).

This species was overlooked as *Gyroweisia tenuis* by bryologists in Britain and Ireland until Appleyard *et al.* (1985) and Whitehouse & During (1987) clarified the identification characters of plants lacking sporophytes.

60/1a ***Tortula subulata*** Hedw. **var.** ***subulata***

H1 1951: stone wall, Glenbeigh, AC Crundwell & PW Richards (BBS exc.) (Warburg 1952: 101).
[H(3) listed by Lett (1915: 113). H3 deleted

because no valid record or voucher specimen traced (Blockeel 1999: 5)].
H(4) listed by Lett (1915: 113) without details.
†H4 listed by Blockeel & Long (1998: 94).
H(5) listed by Lett (1915: 113). H(5) listed by Blockeel & Long (1998: 94).
H(8) listed by Lett (1915: 113).
†H8 listed by Blockeel & Long (1998: 94).
H(9) listed by Lett (1915: 113). H(9) listed by Blockeel & Long (1998: 94).
H(11) listed by Lett (1915: 113). H(11) listed by Blockeel & Long (1998: 94).
H(12) listed by Lett (1915: 113). H(12) listed by Blockeel & Long (1998: 94).
H(13) listed by Lett (1915: 113). H(13) listed by Blockeel & Long (1998: 94).
H(14) listed by Lett (1915: 113). H(14) listed by Blockeel & Long (1998: 94).
H(16) listed by Lett (1915: 113). H(16) listed by Blockeel & Long (1998: 94).
H(20) listed by Lett (1915: 113).
†H20 listed by Blockeel & Long (1998: 94).
H(21) listed by Lett (1915: 113).
†H21 listed by Blockeel & Long (1998: 94).
H22 1978: soil on wall top, Bellewstown, DM Synnott (Hill 1979: 27).
H(25) 1940: nr Boyle, JS Thomson (Duncan 1944: 210).
H(27) listed by Lett (1915: 113). H(27) listed by Blockeel & Long (1998: 94).
H28 1963: limestone, *ca* 1100 ft [alt.], Lugnagall, Glencar, RD Fitzgerald & AR Perry (Warburg 1964: 725).
H(29) listed by Lett (1915: 113) without details.
†H29 listed by Blockeel & Long (1998: 94).
H(30) listed by Lett (1915: 113).
†H30 listed by Blockeel & Long (1998: 94).
[H(31) listed by Lett (1915: 113) without details. H31 deleted because no valid record or voucher specimen traced (Blockeel 1999: 5)].
[H(32) listed by Lett (1915: 113) without locality. H32 deleted because no valid record or voucher specimen traced (Blockeel 1999: 5)].
†H33 listed by Blockeel & Long (1998: 94).
[H(34) listed by Lett (1915: 113) without locality. H34 deleted because no valid record or voucher specimen traced (Blockeel 1999: 5)].
†H35 listed by Blockeel & Long (1998: 94).
H(36) 1946: bank, road to Loch Doon, nr Naran, JS Thomson (anon. 1947: 30).
H36 1957: Bin Rocks, Bin Mt., RD Fitzgerald (Warburg 1958b: 478).
H(37) listed by Lett (1915: 113). H(37) listed by Blockeel & Long (1998: 94).
H(38) listed by Lett (1915: 113). H(38) listed by Blockeel & Long (1998: 94).
H(39) listed by Lett (1915: 113).
†H39 listed by Blockeel & Long (1998: 94).
H(40) listed by Lett (1915: 113).
†H40 listed by Blockeel & Long (1998: 94).

60/1b *Tortula subulata* var. *angustata* (Schimp.) Limpr.

H(38) listed by Blockeel & Long (1998: 94).

60/1c *Tortula subulata* var. *subinermis* (Bruch & Schimp.) Wilson

H29 1963: base of tree by stream, Bawn, 1 mile S of Dromahair, AR Perry & RD Fitzgerald (Warburg 1964: 725).

60/1d *Tortula subulata* var. *graeffii* Warnst.

H23 1980: stone-faced roadside bank, N of Castletown, DM Synnott (Hill 1981: 25).
H30 1957: limestone wall, SW of Black Lion [*sic* = Blacklion], AC Crundwell (Warburg 1958b: 478).

60/2 *Tortula cuneifolia* (Dicks.) Turner

H(1) listed by Lett (1915: 112). H(1) listed by Blockeel & Long (1998: 94).
H(3) listed by Lett (1915: 112).
†H3 listed by Blockeel & Long (1998: 94).
[H(4) listed by Lett (1915: 112) without details. H4 deleted because all records traced are from Cork and are in H5 or are inadequately localised, comm. NF Stewart (Blockeel 1995c: 42)].
H(5) listed by Lett (1915: 112). H(5) listed by Blockeel & Long (1998: 94).
H(8) listed by Lett (1915: 112).
†H8 listed by Blockeel & Long (1998: 94).
H12 1954: mud bank, 1 mile from sea, Inch, JS Thomson (Warburg 1955: 584).
H(14) listed by Lett (1915: 112). H(14) listed by Blockeel & Long (1998: 94).
H(21) listed by Lett (1915: 112). H(21) listed by Blockeel & Long (1998: 94).
H(38) listed by Blockeel & Long (1998: 94).

60/5 ***Tortula marginata*** (Bruch & Schimp.) Spruce

H13 1999: on decomposing mortar of derelict building, 10 m alt., Saint Mullins, banks of R Barrow, S73, TL Blockeel 28/315 (Rothero 2000: 50).
H15 1957: rocks, Punchbowl, nr Gort, EM Lobley (BBS exc.) (Warburg 1958b: 478).
H16 1994: with *Barbula rigidula* on crumbling mortar at base of wall at rear of Letterdife House, Roundstone, L74, JA Paton & HLK Whitehouse (Blockeel 1995c: 41).
H(17) listed by Lett (1915: 112). H(17) listed by Blockeel & Long (1998: 94).
H23 1970: soft calcareous rock in woodland W of Killinure Lough, S of Glassan, JA Paton (Crundwell 1971b: 376).
H26 1987: on stone on wall top sheltered by bushes, E side of L. Carra opposite Otter Point, HLK Whitehouse (Blockeel 1988: 34).
H27 1987: on decaying plaster of ruined cottage, Keem, Achill I., HLK Whitehouse (Blockeel 1988: 34-35).
H29 1965: boulder above Glencar Lough, nr Glencar Waterfall, EM Lobley & RD Fitzgerald (Warburg 1966: 194).
H36 1958: limestone, Carrickaness Bridge, nr Drumquin, RD Fitzgerald (Warburg 1959: 634).
H(38) listed by Lett (1915: 112). H(38) listed by Blockeel & Long (1998: 94).
H(39) listed by Lett (1915: 112). H(39) listed by Blockeel & Long (1998: 94).

60/6 ***Tortula vahliana*** (Schultz) Mont.
(syn. *Tortula vahliana* var. *subflaccida* (Lindb.) Braithw., *T. vahlii* Lindb. nom. illeg.)

[H(20) listed by Lett (1915: 112) as 1851 and 1856: nr Bray, leg. Orr, and 1860: Bray, leg. Moore. H20 record discounted as doubtful (Birks 1974, Crundwell 1975: 15)].
H(21) 1829: nr Dublin, no collector named (Lett 1915: 112).
1829: Dublin, T Drummond (Lett 1915: 112), as var. *subflaccida*.
1860: Glasnevin, no collector named (Lett 1915: 112), as var. *subflaccida*.
no date: Blanchardstown, no collector named (Lett 1915: 112). H(21) listed by Blockeel & Long (1998: 94).
[H(29) listed by Lett (1915: 112) without details. H29 record discounted because details not traced (Birks 1974, Crundwell 1975: 15)].
[H39 1950: calcareous alumina beds, Larne, RD Fitzgerald (Warburg 1951: 499). H39 deleted because specimen (BBSUK) is *Barbula unguiculata*, comm. CD Preston, conf. MO Hill (Hill 1986: 20)].

60/8a ***Tortula muralis*** Hedw. **var.** ***muralis***
(syn. *Tortula muralis* var. *rupestris* Chevall.)

H(1) listed by Lett (1915: 112) without details.
†H1 listed by Blockeel & Long (1998: 94).
H(2) listed by Lett (1915: 112) without details.
†H2 listed by Blockeel & Long (1998: 94).
H(3) listed by Lett (1915: 112) without details.
†H3 listed by Blockeel & Long (1998: 94).
H(4) listed by Lett (1915: 112) without details.
†H4 listed by Blockeel & Long (1998: 94).
†H5 listed by Blockeel & Long (1998: 94).
H(6) listed by Lett (1915: 112) without details.
H6 1956: limestone park wall, Knocklofty, EC Wallace (Warburg 1959: 634), as var. *rupestris*.
H(7) listed by Lett (1915: 112) without details.
†H7 listed by Blockeel & Long (1998: 94).
H(8) listed by Lett (1915: 112) without locality.
†H8 listed by Blockeel & Long (1998: 94).
H(9) listed by Lett (1915: 112) without details.
†H9 listed by Blockeel & Long (1998: 94).
H(10) listed by Lett (1915: 112) without details.
†H10 listed by Blockeel & Long (1998: 94).
H(11) listed by Lett (1915: 112) without details.
†H11 listed by Blockeel & Long (1998: 94).
H12 1954: wall, Inch, JS Thomson (Warburg 1955: 584).
H(13) listed by Lett (1915: 112) without details.
†H13 listed by Blockeel & Long (1998: 94).

H(14) listed by Lett (1915: 112) without details.
†H14 listed by Blockeel & Long (1998: 94).
H(15) listed by Lett (1915: 112) without details.
†H15 listed by Blockeel & Long (1998: 94).
H(16) listed by Lett (1915: 112) without locality.
†H16 listed by Blockeel & Long (1998: 94).
H(17) listed by Lett (1915: 112) without details.
†H17 listed by Blockeel & Long (1998: 94).
H(18) listed by Lett (1915: 112) without details.
†H18 listed by Blockeel & Long (1998: 94).
H(19) listed by Lett (1915: 112) without details.
†H19 listed by Blockeel & Long (1998: 94).
H(20) listed by Lett (1915: 112) without details.
†H20 listed by Blockeel & Long (1998: 94).
H(21) listed by Lett (1915: 112).
†H21 listed by Blockeel & Long (1998: 94).
H(22) listed by Lett (1915: 112) without details.
†H22 listed by Blockeel & Long (1998: 94).
H(23) listed by Lett (1915: 112) without details.
†H23 listed by Blockeel & Long (1998: 94).
†H24 listed by Blockeel & Long (1998: 94).
H(25) listed by Lett (1915: 112) without details.
†H25 listed by Blockeel & Long (1998: 94).
H(26) listed by Lett (1915: 112) without details.
H26 1953: on limestone rock, E shore of L. Carra, opposite Otter Point, EC Wallace (Warburg 1961: 164).
H(27) listed by Lett (1915: 112) without details.
†H27 listed by Blockeel & Long (1998: 94).
H(28) listed by Lett (1915: 112) without details.
†H28 listed by Blockeel & Long (1998: 94).
H(29) listed by Lett (1915: 112).
†H29 listed by Blockeel & Long (1998: 94).
H(30) listed by Lett (1915: 112) without details.
†H30 listed by Blockeel & Long (1998: 94).
H(31) listed by Lett (1915: 112) without details.
†H31 listed by Blockeel & Long (1998: 94).
H(32) listed by Lett (1915: 112) without details.
†H32 listed by Blockeel & Long (1998: 94).
H(33) listed by Lett (1915: 112) without details.
†H33 listed by Blockeel & Long (1998: 94).
H(34) listed by Lett (1915: 112) without details.
†H34 listed by Blockeel & Long (1998: 94).
H(35) listed by Lett (1915: 112) without details.
†H35 listed by Blockeel & Long (1998: 94).
H(36) listed by Lett (1915: 112) without details.
†H36 listed by Blockeel & Long (1998: 94).
H(37) listed by Lett (1915: 112) without details.
†H37 listed by Blockeel & Long (1998: 94).
H(38) listed by Lett (1915: 112).
†H38 listed by Blockeel & Long (1998: 94).
H(39) listed by Lett (1915: 112).
†H39 listed by Blockeel & Long (1998: 94).
H(40) 1934: Moneycarrie, AM Irwin, det. as var. *rupestris* by W Watson (anon. 1936: 274).
H(40) listed by Lett (1915: 112) without details.
†H40 listed by Blockeel & Long (1998: 94).

[60/8b ***Tortula muralis*** **Hedw. var.** ***aestiva*** **Brid. ex Hedw.]**

[H21 was given by Smith (1978: 218), apparently on the basis of the record regarded as doubtful in Lett (1915: 112) given as 1858: Glasnevin, leg. Orr].
[H38 deleted because no valid record or voucher specimen traced (Blockeel 1999: 5)].

[All Irish records are omitted by Blockeel & Long (1998: 95).]

60/11 ***Tortula atrovirens*** **(Sm.) Lindb.**
(syn. *Desmatodon convolutus* (Brid.) Grout)

H(1) 1935: Slea Head, no collector named (BBS exc.) (Watson 1936: 264-265).
[H(3) listed by Lett (1915: 112) as: Connemara, leg. Taylor. H3 deleted because the only record traced (Connemara, leg. T Taylor, in Lett 1915) is from H16, comm. NF Stewart (Blockeel 1995c: 42)].
H(4) listed by Lett (1915: 112) without locality. H(4) listed by Blockeel & Long (1998: 95).

H(5) listed by Lett (1915: 112). H(5) listed by Blockeel & Long (1998: 95).
H5 2002: on earth on vertical sea-cliff, 10 m alt., Ballycotton, W96, TL Blockeel 31/286 (Rothero 2003: 52).
H8 1993: SW-facing low shale cliff by estuary shore, 5 m alt., Foynes I., R25, E Wiltshire (Blockeel 1994: 37).
H12 1953: sandy bank by sea, Clone, WR Megaw (Warburg 1954: 481).
H(16) listed by Lett (1915: 112) without details. H(16) listed by Blockeel & Long (1998: 95).
H(20) listed by Lett (1915: 112). H(20) listed by Blockeel & Long (1998: 95).
H(21) listed by Lett (1915: 112).
†H21 listed by Blockeel & Long (1998: 95).
H35 2001: on earth and stone hedge-bank at top of cliff, 10 m alt., Trabane, Malin Beg, G47, NG Hodgetts 3772 (Rothero 2003: 52).
H(38) listed by Blockeel & Long (1998: 95).
H(39) listed by Lett (1915: 112). H(39) listed by Blockeel & Long (1998: 95).

60/12 ***Tortula lanceola*** R.H.Zander
(syn. *Pottia lanceolata* (Hedw.) Müll. Hal.)

H(4) listed by Lett (1915: 111). H(4) listed by Blockeel & Long (1998: 95).
H(5) listed by Lett (1915: 111). H(5) listed by Blockeel & Long (1998: 95).
H6 1956: wall top, Kilmanahan Bridge, nr Clonmel, EC Wallace (Warburg 1957: 330).
H19 1952: sandy bank of canal, Leixlip, AW Stelfox, comm. JS Thomson (Warburg 1954: 481).
H(21) listed by Lett (1915: 111).
†H21 listed by Blockeel & Long (1998: 95).
H22 1978: path by R. Boyne below Navan, DM Synnott (Hill 1979: 27).

60/13 ***Tortula wilsonii*** (Hook.) R.H.Zander
(syn. *Pottia asperula* Mitt., *P. wilsonii* (Hook.) Bruch & Schimp.)

[H3 deleted because no valid record or voucher specimen traced (Blockeel 1999: 5)].
H(5) no date: Great I., Carroll (Lett 1915: 111).
no date: Youghal, Carroll (Lett 1915: 111). H(5) listed by Blockeel & Long (1998: 95).
H(20) no date: Bray Head, no collector named (Lett 1915: 111). H(20) listed by Blockeel & Long (1998: 95).
H(21) 1856: Howth, Moore (Lett 1915: 111) as *P. asperula*.
no date: Howth, Moore (Lett 1915: 111) as *P. wilsoni*.
†H21 listed by Blockeel & Long (1998: 95).

60/14 ***Tortula viridifolia*** (Mitt.) Blockeel & A. J.E.Sm.
(syn. *Pottia crinita* Wilson ex Bruch, Schimp. & W.Gümbel, *P. viridifolia* Mitt.)

H(1) listed by Lett (1915: 111) without details. H(1) listed by Blockeel & Long (1998: 95).
H(2) listed by Lett (1915: 111). H(2) listed by Blockeel & Long (1998: 95).
H(3) 1934: wall tops, Baltimore, EW Jones (BBSUK) (Hill 1978: 19).
†H3 listed by Blockeel & Long (1998: 95).
H(4) listed by Lett (1915: 111). H(4) listed by Blockeel & Long (1998: 95).
H(5) listed by Lett (1915: 111). H(5) listed by Blockeel & Long (1998: 95).
H6 1966: spoil heaps from old mine, cliff-top, Bunmahon, J Appleyard (Hill 1983: 51).
H(12) listed by Lett (1915: 111).
H12 1975: roadside wall by sea, Clones Strand, SE of Coolgreany, AR Perry (Hill 1977a: 18).
H(21) listed by Lett (1915: 111). H(21) listed by Blockeel & Long (1998: 95).
H35 1963: soily crevice in boulder on shore in bay N of Rossarrell Point, nr Malin Beg, AR Perry & RD Fitzgerald (Warburg 1964: 725).
H(38) listed by Blockeel & Long (1998: 95).
H(39) listed by Lett (1915: 111).
†H39 listed by Blockeel & Long (1998: 95).
H(40) 1930: Portstewart, WR Megaw (anon. 1931a: 252).
1937: Portstewart, WR Megaw (anon. 1938d: 39).

60/15 ***Tortula modica*** R.H.Zander
(syn. *Pottia intermedia* (Turner) Fürnr.)

H1 1951: earth-capped wall, Glenbeigh, EW Jones (BBS exc.) (Warburg 1952: 101).
[H(3) 1934: wall-tops, Baltimore, EW Jones

(Warburg 1960: 774). H3 deleted because specimen (BBSUK) is incorrectly named (Hill 1978: 19)].

H(4) listed by Lett (1915: 111) without locality. H(4) listed by Blockeel & Long (1998: 95).

H10 1987: walled garden, Luska, HLK Whitehouse (Blockeel 1988: 35).

H(13) listed by Lett (1915: 111). H(13) listed by Blockeel & Long (1998: 95).

H(15) listed by Lett (1915: 111).

†H15 listed by Blockeel & Long (1998: 95).

H16 1969: among siliceous boulders, roadside nr Maumeen Lough, Callow, AR Perry & HJ Perry (Crundwell 1974: 168).

H18 1957: garden path, Charleville Castle, Tullamore, JS Thomson (Warburg 1958b: 477).

H20 1950: wall between Valleymount and Ballyknockan, ALK King (Warburg 1951: 499).

H(21) listed by Lett (1915: 111) without locality.

†H21 listed by Blockeel & Long (1998: 95).

H(26) listed by Lett (1915: 111). H(26) listed by Blockeel & Long (1998: 95).

H(27) listed by Lett (1915: 111). H(27) listed by Blockeel & Long (1998: 95).

H31 1965: crevice in Silurian rock E of pier, Clogher Head, DM Synnott (Warburg 1966: 194).

H(33) listed by Blockeel & Long (1998: 95).

H(37) listed by Lett (1915: 111). H(37) listed by Blockeel & Long (1998: 95).

H(38) listed by Lett (1915: 111). H(38) listed by Blockeel & Long (1998: 95).

H(39) listed by Lett (1915: 111). H(39) listed by Blockeel & Long (1998: 95).

60/16 ***Tortula truncata*** (Hedw.) Mitt. (syn. *Pottia truncata* (Hedw.) Bruch & Schimp., *P. truncatula* (With.) Büse)

†H1 listed by Blockeel & Long (1998: 96).

H3 1951: dry wall cracks, Cape Clear, IA Rorison (Warburg 1952: 101).

H(4) listed by Lett (1915: 110).

†H4 listed by Blockeel & Long (1998: 96).

H(5) listed by Lett (1915: 110).

†H5 listed by Blockeel & Long (1998: 96).

H6 1966: cart tracks in field N of the Punchbowl, Comeragh Mts, EM Lobley (BBS exc.) (Perry 1967: 412).

H7 1966: arable field nr Ardfinnan, J Appleyard & JG Duckett (BBS exc.) (Perry 1967: 412).

H(8) listed by Lett (1915: 110) without details.

†H8 listed by Blockeel & Long (1998: 96).

H(9) listed by Lett (1915: 110) without details.

†H9 listed by Blockeel & Long (1998: 96).

H10 1967: bare ground in pasture, Devils Bit Mt., RD Fitzgerald (Crundwell 1968: 635).

H12 1963: cart-track in lane S of Inch, ALK King (Warburg 1964: 725).

H13 1969: stubble field, Ballykeenan, nr Myshall, RD Fitzgerald (Crundwell 1970: 200).

H(14) listed by Lett (1915: 110).

†H14 listed by Blockeel & Long (1998: 96).

H15 1957: woodland ride, Chevy Chase, nr Gort, AC Crundwell (BBS exc.) (Warburg 1958b: 477).

H(16) listed by Lett (1915: 110) without details.

†H16 listed by Blockeel & Long (1998: 96).

H(19) listed by Lett (1915: 110). H(19) listed by Blockeel & Long (1998: 96).

H19 2002: in stubble field (winter wheat) 70 m alt., Furry Field, Courttown East townland, Athy, S69, HF Fox & CD Preston (Rothero 2003: 52).

H(20) listed by Lett (1915: 110) without locality.

†H20 listed by Blockeel & Long (1998: 96).

H(21) listed by Lett (1915: 110).

†H21 listed by Blockeel & Long (1998: 96).

H22 1951: damp ground, Slane, JS Thomson (Warburg 1952: 101).

H23 1952: old cart track, Clonhugh Demesne, JS Thomson (Warburg 1953: 309).

H24 1968: in limestone pit 1 mile S of Lanesborough, WV Rubers *et al.* (U) (Crundwell 1974: 168).

H25 1970: track in field nr L. Ree, Portrunny Bay, JA Paton (Crundwell 1971b: 377).

H26 1962: edge of farm track nr Keel Bridge between Ballinrobe and Partry, AJE Smith (Warburg 1963b: 496).

H(27) listed by Lett (1915: 110).

†H27 listed by Blockeel & Long (1998: 96).

†H28 listed by Blockeel & Long (1998: 96).

H(29) 1928: wooded glen, NE end of Glencar Lough (BBS exc.) (Duncan 1928: 118).

†H29 listed by Blockeel & Long (1998: 96).

H(30) listed by Lett (1915: 110). H(30) listed by Blockeel & Long (1998: 96).

H30 2001: on open damp soil at edge of track, 315 m alt., W of Bellavally Gap, H12, DT Holyoak 01-638 (Rothero 2002: 47).
H(31) listed by Lett (1915: 110). H(31) listed by Blockeel & Long (1998: 96).
[H32 deleted because no valid record or voucher specimen traced (Blockeel 1999: 5)].
H(33) listed by Lett (1915: 111).
†H33 listed by Blockeel & Long (1998: 96).
H(34) listed by Lett (1915: 111).
†H34 listed by Blockeel & Long (1998: 96).
H35 1962: edge of track, Corcreagan, W of Dunfanaghy, AC Crundwell (BBS exc.) (Warburg 1963b: 496).
H(36) listed by Lett (1915: 111) without details.
†H36 listed by Blockeel & Long (1998: 96).
H(37) listed by Lett (1915: 111).
†H37 listed by Blockeel & Long (1998: 96).
H(38) listed by Lett (1915: 111).
†H38 listed by Blockeel & Long (1998: 96).
H(39) listed by Lett (1915: 111). H(39) listed by Blockeel & Long (1998: 96).
H39 1999: on damp mud of drained reservoir, Copeland Reservoir, J49, DT Holyoak 99-845 (BBSUK) (Rothero 2000: 50).
H(40) listed by Lett (1915: 111) without details.
†H40 listed by Blockeel & Long (1998: 96).

60/17 ***Tortula protobryoides*** R.H.Zander
(syn. *Pottia bryoides* (Dicks.) Mitt.)

H(21) no date: Howth, Orr (Lett 1915: 110). H(21) listed by Blockeel & Long (1998: 96).
H(39) no date: nr Lisburn, Davies (Lett 1915: 110). H(39) listed by Blockeel & Long (1998: 96).

60/18a ***Tortula acaulon*** (With.) R.H.Zander **var.** ***acaulon***
(syn. *Phascum cuspidatum* Hedw. var. *cuspidatum*)

H1 1951: earthy wall-top, nr Darrynane, EF Warburg (BBS exc.) (Warburg 1952: 101).
[H3 deleted because no valid record or voucher specimen traced (Blockeel 1999: 5)].
H(4) listed by Lett (1915: 110).
†H4 listed by Blockeel & Long (1998: 96).
H(5) listed by Lett (1915: 110).
†H5 listed by Blockeel & Long (1998: 96).
H6 1966: field nr Clogheen, nr Ballymacarbry, Clonmel, JA Paton *et al.* (BBS exc.) (Perry 1967: 412).
H7 1966: cultivated field nr Ardfinnan, J Appleyard & JG Duckett (BBS exc.) (Perry 1967: 412).
H8 1966: on clay, Knockseefin, nr Nicker, RD Fitzgerald (BBS exc.) (Crundwell 1968: 635).
H9 hedgebank, lane S of Rosroe Lough E of Newmarket of Fergus, JA Paton (Hill 1980b: 38).
H10 1987: walled garden, Luska, HLK Whitehouse (Blockeel 1988: 35).
H11 1966: road verge nr Foulkscourt House, nr Johnstown, ERB Little (BBS exc.) (Perry 1967: 412).
H12 1964: old tree stumps, Fethard-on-Sea, ALK King (Warburg 1965: 863).
H13 1999: on bare soil at edge of path, 8 m alt., R Barrow nr canal, 1 km NW of Saint Mullins, S73, TL Blockeel 28/326 (Rothero 2000: 51).
H14 1956: disturbed calcareous ground by roadside, nr Castletown, AA Cridland (Warburg 1958b: 477).
H15 1963: mud in marsh nr lead deposit, Tynagh, MJP Scannell, comm. DM Synnott (Warburg 1965: 863).
H16 1957: earth bank, Clifden, AC Crundwell (BBS exc.) (Warburg 1958b: 477).
H17 1970: edge of track, side of L. Corrib, SW of Keekill, AR Perry & HJ Perry (Crundwell 1974: 168).
H(18) listed by Lett (1915: 110). H(18) listed by Blockeel & Long (1998: 96).
H19 1987: barley field, 2.5 km E of Rathangan, HLK Whitehouse (Blockeel 1988: 35).
H(20) listed by Lett (1915: 110). H(20) listed by Blockeel & Long (1998: 96).
H(21) listed by Lett (1915: 110).
†H21 listed by Blockeel & Long (1998: 96).
H22 1978: damp clay by the Boyne, Bective Bridge, DM Synnott (Hill 1979: 27).
H23 1970: roadside, Butler's Bridge, S of Mullingar, JA Paton (Crundwell 1971b: 377).
H24 1957: bank, Ballymacarrow Bridge, ALK King (Warburg 1958b: 477).
H26 1970: shore of L. Carra, nr Partry House, J Appleyard (BBS exc.) (Crundwell

1971b: 377, Appleyard 1971: 388).
†H28 listed by Blockeel & Long (1998: 96).
H29 1970: track S of Kinlough, J Appleyard (BBS exc.) (Crundwell 1971b: 377, Appleyard 1971: 388).
H31 1967: railway cutting, Braganstown, Dunleer, DM Synnott (Crundwell 1968: 635).
H32 1952: Lisgall, Carrickmacross, RD Fitzgerald (Warburg 1953: 309).
H33 1957: roadside bank, Enniskillen, AC Crundwell (Warburg 1958b: 477).
H(34) listed by Lett (1915: 110) without locality.
†H34 listed by Blockeel & Long (1998: 96).
H35 1962: oat field, Ards Peninsula, nr Dunfanaghy, AC Crundwell *et al.* (BBS exc.) (Warburg 1963b: 496).
H(37) listed by Lett (1915: 110).
†H37 listed by Blockeel & Long (1998: 96).
H(38) listed by Lett (1915: 110). H(38) listed by Blockeel & Long (1998: 96).
H(39) listed by Lett (1915: 110). H(39) listed by Blockeel & Long (1998: 96).
H39 1999: on thin soil on top of wall, White Park Bay, D04, DT Holyoak 99-604 (BBSUK) (Rothero 2000: 51).
H(40) listed by Blockeel & Long (1998: 96).

Blockeel (1995b) checked voucher specimens in BBSUK and NMW and established that only one Irish specimen represented var. *papillosa* (see below). However, voucher material for at least some of the records listed above will be in other herbaria and hence have remained unchecked.

[60/18b *Tortula acaulon* var. *pilifera* (Hedw.) R.H.Zander
(syn. *Phascum acaulon* var. *piliferum* (Hedw.) Brockm., *Phascum cuspidatum* var. *piliferum* (Hedw.) Hook. & Taylor)]

[Records from H21 and H39 given by Lett (1915: 110) are dismissed as errors].

60/18d *Tortula acaulon* var. *papillosa* (Lindb.) R.H.Zander
(syn. *Phascum cuspidatum* subsp. *papillosum* (Lindb.) J.Guerra & Ros)

H38 2002: on disturbed ground by estuarine bay, 5 m alt., W of Dundrum, J33, DT Holyoak 02-954 (Rothero 2003: 52).
H(39) pre-1950: Belfast, Stewart (H) (Guerra *et al.* 1991, Blockeel 1995b: 60, 1996: 45).

This form was first reported from Ireland and Britain by Guerra *et al.* (1991). Revision of herbarium material by Blockeel (1995b) did not reveal any other Irish specimens. Although rare in most of Britain, var. *papillosa* is frequent in W Cornwall where it occupies similar habitats to var. *acaulon* and is frequently connected to that form by intermediate plants.

61/1 *Microbryum starckeanum* (Hedw.) R.H. Zander
(syn. *Pottia starckeana* (Hedw.) Müll. Hal. subsp. *starckeana*, *Pottia starckeana* (Hedw.) Müll.Hal. var. *starckeana*, *P. starckeana* var. *brachyodus* (Bruch, Schimp. & W. Gümbel) Müll.Hal., *P. starckei* Lindb. nom. illeg., *P. starckei* var. *affinis* (Hook. & Taylor) Braithw.)

H(4) listed by Lett (1915: 111). H(4) listed by Blockeel & Long (1998: 96).
H(5) 1851: Youghal, anon. (BM), det. DF Chamberlain (MS) as '*P. starkeana* subsp. *starkeana* var. *brachyodus*' (Hill 1980a, Chamberlain in Hill 1980b, Hill 1981: 37).
H(5) listed by Lett (1915: 111) without details.
H21 1830: Killiney Hill, Dublin, Jany (BM), det. DF Chamberlain (MS) as '*P. starkeana* subsp. *starkeana* var. *brachyodus*' (Hill 1980a, Chamberlain in Hill 1980b, Hill 1981: 37).
H(21) listed by Lett (1915: 111).
†H21 listed by Blockeel & Long (1998: 96).
H(33) listed by Lett (1915: 111). H(33) listed by Blockeel & Long (1998: 96).
H(38) listed by Lett (1915: 111). H(38) listed by Blockeel & Long (1998: 96).
H(39) listed by Lett (1915: 111). H(39) listed by Blockeel & Long (1998: 96).

Records of *Pottia starckeana* var. *starckeana* and of *P. starckeana* var. *brachyodus* were revised by DF Chamberlain (MS) for the *CC* (Corley & Hill 1981: 77).

61/2 ***Microbryum davallianum*** (Sm.) R.H. Zander
(syn. *Pottia starckeana* subsp. *conica* (Schleich. ex Schwägr.) D.F.Chamb., *P. starckeana* subsp. *minutula* (Schleich. ex Schwägr.) Bouvet, *P. commutata* Limpr., *P. davalliana* (Sm.) C.E.O. Jensen, *P. minutula* (Schleich. ex Schwägr.) Fürnr., *P. starckei* var. *davallii* Lindb.)

H(1) listed by Lett (1915: 111).
H1 1951: bare places in pasture, Castlegregory, AC Crundwell, conf. as *P. starkeana* subsp. *conica* by MO Hill (Warburg 1952: 101, MO Hill MS).
H2 1951: earth-covered wall, Tralee, AC Crundwell, conf. as *P. starkeana* subsp. *conica* by MO Hill (Warburg 1952: 101; MO Hill MS).
[H(4) listed by Lett (1915: 111)].
H(5) listed by Lett (1915: 111).
H5 1978: on soil in arboretum, Fota I., N Kirby (BBSUK), conf. as *P. starkeana* subsp. *conica* by MO Hill (Hill 1980b: 37; MO Hill MS).
H11 1966: soil by roadside, Foulkscourt House, nr Johnstown, JG Duckett *et al.* (BBS exc.) (BBSUK), conf. as *P. starkeana* subsp. *conica* by MO Hill (Perry 1967: 412; MO Hill MS).
H14 2002: in stubble field, 80 m alt., Garrans Crossroads NE of Stradbally, S59, HF Fox & CD Preston (Rothero 2003: 52).
H(15) 1865: Lough Derg, D Moore (BM), det. DF Chamberlain as *P. starkeana* ssp. *minutula* (DF Chamberlain MS). Pre-1950 record of '*P. starkeana* ssp. *minutula*' listed (Chamberlain in Hill 1980b, Hill 1981: 37).
H(15) listed by Lett (1915: 111).
H15 1994: flower bed, Coole, 3 km N of Gort, M40, NG Hodgetts, RD Porley & HLK Whitehouse (Blockeel 1995c: 42).
H19 1969: in sand pit, Geraldine House, nr Athy, RD Fitzgerald (BBSUK), conf. as *P. starkeana* subsp. *conica* by MO Hill (Crundwell 1970: 200; MO Hill MS).
H(21) *ca* 1850: nr Dublin, B Carrington (BM), det. DF Chamberlain as *P. starkeana* ssp. *minutula* (DF Chamberlain MS). Pre-1950 record of '*P. starkeana* ssp. *minutula*' listed (Chamberlain in Hill 1980b, Hill 1981: 37). H(21) listed by Lett (1915: 111).
H21 1973: lawn of housing estate, Bayside, Dublin, MO Hill (BBSUK), conf. as *P. starkeana* subsp. *conica* by MO Hill (Crundwell 1974: 168; MO Hill MS).
H22 1965: bare ground, Newtown Commons, Duleek, DM Synnott (Warburg 1966: 194), as *P. davalliana*. Post-1950 record of '*P. starkeana* ssp. *minutula*' accepted, but record of '*P. starkeana* ssp. *conica*' deleted (Chamberlain in Hill 1980b, Hill 1981: 37).
H23 1965: Newtown Commons, Duleek, DM Synnott (BBSUK); originally listed in *CC* as '*P. starkeana* subsp. *conica*' but redet. by DF Chamberlain (MS) as '*P. starkeana* subsp. *Minutula*' (Hill 1980a). Apparently omitted from *CC* in error.
H(28) 1928: roadside, nr Lough, nr Sligo, W Young (BBSUK), conf. as *P. starkeana* subsp. *conica* by MO Hill (MO Hill MS).
[1928: nr Rosses Point, Sligo (BBS exc.) (Duncan 1928: 119), as *Pottia minutula*. Specimen apparently not revised for *CC* by DF Chamberlain (MS)].
H31 1967: railway cutting, Braganstown, Dunleer, DM Synnott (BBSUK), conf. as *P. starkeana* subsp. *conica* by MO Hill (Crundwell 1968: 635; MO Hill MS).
H33 1957: soil on E side of Belmone [*sic* = Belmore] Mt., AC Crundwell, conf. as *P. starkeana* subsp. *conica* by MO Hill (MO Hill MS).
H34 2002: on loamy soil nr gateway into field, 5 m alt., Inch Level, C32, DT Holyoak 02-838 (Rothero 2003: 52).
[H(38) listed by Lett (1915: 111)].
H(39) listed by Lett (1915: 111).
H(39) 1928: in chalk pit, Glenarm, A Sutton (BBSUK), conf. as *P. starkeana* subsp. *conica* by MO Hill (MO Hill MS).
H39 1999: on disturbed soil on bank by track, White Park Bay, D04, DT Holyoak 99-607 (BBSUK) (Rothero 2000: 50).
H(40) 1923: Port Stewart, AE Richards [*sic*], det. DF Chamberlain as '*P. starkeana* subsp. *Minutula*' (Hill 1980a, Chamberlain in Hill 1980b, Hill 1981: 37, DF Chamberlain MS).
1923: Port Stewart, EA Richards [*sic*], det. as *P. starkeana* subsp. *conica* by MO Hill (MO Hill MS).

Records of *Pottia starckeana* subsp.

conica were revised by MO Hill (MS) for the *CC* (Corley & Hill 1981: 77); those of *P. starckeana* subsp. *minutula* were revised by DF Chamberlain (MS).

61/3 ***Microbryum rectum*** (With.) R.H.Zander (syn. *Pottia recta* (With.) Mitt.)

H1 1951: wall, nr Darrynane, AC Crundwell, etc. (BBS exc.) (Warburg 1952: 101).
[H(4) listed by Lett (1915: 110) as 1829: nr Cork, leg. Wilson. H4 deleted because all records traced are from Cork and are in H5 or are inadequately localised, comm NF Stewart (Blockeel 1995c: 42)].
H(5) listed by Lett (1915: 110). H(5) listed by Blockeel & Long (1998: 97).
H7 1966: on ground, Rock of Cashel, RD Fitzgerald (Crundwell 1968: 635).
H8 1979: roadside by sea, Beagh Castle nr Askeaton, G Bloom (Hill 1980b: 37).
H11 1966: fallow field by R. Nore, Dysart Castle, nr Thomastown, RD Fitzgerald (BBS exc.) (Crundwell 1968: 635).
H14 2002: in stubble field, 80 m alt., Garrans Crossroads NE of Stradbally, HF Fox & CD Preston (Rothero 2003: 52).
H15 1994: on compacted soil of flower bed, with Phascum *cuspidatum*, Coole Park, M40, RD Porley (Blockeel 1995c: 42).
H16 1969: compacted calcareous soil in gateway to field, Ballydotia, ½ mile NE of Moycullen, AR Perry & HJ Perry (Crundwell 1970: 200).
H19 2002: in stubble field, 65 m alt., Coursetown House, W of Athy, S69, HF Fox & CD Preston (Rothero 2003: 52).
[H20 deleted because no valid record or voucher specimen traced (Blockeel 1999: 5)].
H(21) listed by Lett (1915: 110). H(21) listed by Blockeel & Long (1998: 97).
H22 1980: on drainage spoil N of Newtown Lough, Clonmellon, DM Synnott (Hill 1981: 26).
H23 1952: old cart track, Clonhugh Demesne, NE end of L. Owel, JS Thomson (Warburg 1953: 309).
H(28) 1928: nr Rosses Point, Sligo (BBS exc.) (Duncan 1928: 119). H(28) listed by Blockeel & Long (1998: 97).
H31 1967: roadside, Mullinscross, Dunleer, DM Synnott (Crundwell 1968: 635).
H(34) 1898: on bare clay of tennis ground by the sea, Fahan Point, J Hunter (see *Irish Naturalist*, July 1898, p. 157) (anon. 1899: 16, Lett 1915: 110).

61/4 ***Microbryum curvicolle*** (Hedw.) R.H. Zander
(syn. *Phascum curvicolle* Hedw.)

H(16) no date: Benlettery, Wade (Lett 1915: 110). H(16) listed by Blockeel & Long (1998: 97).
H(21) no date: no locality, Taylor (Lett 1915: 110).
†H21 listed by Blockeel & Long (1998: 97).

62/1 ***Hennediella stanfordensis*** (Steere) Blockeel
(syn. *Hyophila stanfordensis* (Steere) A. J.E.Sm. & H.Whitehouse, *Tortula stanfordensis* Steere)

H21 1978: shady soil banks beside paths, St Stephen's Green, Dublin, PH Pitkin (Hill 1979: 27, Whitehouse & Newton 1988: 93, Blockeel 1989: 27).

62/3 ***Hennediella heimii*** (Hedw.) R.H.Zander
(syn. *Pottia heimii* (Hedw.) Fürnr.)

H2 1952: clay on wall top, Blennerville, AP Fanning (Warburg 1953: 309).
[H3 deleted because no valid record or voucher specimen traced (Blockeel 1999: 5)].
H(4) listed by Lett (1915: 110).
†H4 listed by Blockeel & Long (1998: 98).
H(5) listed by Lett (1915: 110). H(5) listed by Blockeel & Long (1998: 98).
H6 1964: crevice on iron spar, muddy estuary of R. Blackwater, nr Templemichael, DM Synnott (Warburg 1965: 863).
H8 1992: on shaded shale cliff with freshwater seepage, NE shore of Foynes I., Shannon Estuary, R25, JD Reynolds & S Reynolds, comm. E Wiltshire (Blockeel 1993: 50).
H(9) listed by Lett (1915: 110).
H9 1994: under rocks on cliffs, Poulsallagh, SW of Fanore, M00, JM Blackburn (Blockeel 1999: 15).
H12 1961: rough pasture by Lady's Island Lake, ALK King (Warburg 1962: 369).
H(16) listed by Lett (1915: 110) without

details.
†H16 listed by Blockeel & Long (1998: 98).
H(20) 1946: dunes S of Mizen Head, Brittas Bay, AW Stelfox (per JS Thomson) (anon. 1947: 30).
H(21) listed by Lett (1915: 110). H(21) listed by Blockeel & Long (1998: 98).
H(27) listed by Lett (1915: 110). H(27) listed by Blockeel & Long (1998: 98).
H(28) listed by Blockeel & Long (1998: 98).
H29 1970: bank, cliffs W of Tullaghan, J Appleyard (BBS exc.) (Crundwell 1971b: 376, Appleyard 1971: 389).
[H31 deleted because no valid record or voucher specimen traced (Blockeel 1999: 5)].
H(34) listed by Lett (1915: 110).
†H34 listed by Blockeel & Long (1998: 98).
†H35 listed by Blockeel & Long (1998: 98).
H(38) listed by Lett (1915: 110). H(38) listed by Blockeel & Long (1998: 98).
H38 2000: on wet bank by shore with *Amblystegium serpens*, Pickie, Bangor, J48, R Weyl (Rothero 2001: 41).
H(39) listed by Lett (1915: 110).
†H39 listed by Blockeel & Long (1998: 98).
H(40) listed by Lett (1915: 110). H(40) listed by Blockeel & Long (1998: 98).

63/1 ***Acaulon muticum*** (Hedw.) Müll.Hal. (syn. *Acaulon minus* (Hook. & Taylor) A.Jaeger)

H(1) listed by Lett (1915: 110).
†H1 listed by Blockeel & Long (1998: 98).
H(4) listed by Lett (1915: 110). H(4) listed by Blockeel & Long (1998: 98).
H(21) listed by Lett (1915: 110). H(21) listed by Blockeel & Long (1998: 98).
H(34) listed by Lett (1915: 110). H(34) listed by Blockeel & Long (1998: 98).
H(35) listed by Lett (1915: 110) without locality. H(35) listed by Blockeel & Long (1998: 98).
H(39) listed by Lett (1915: 110). H(39) listed by Blockeel & Long (1998: 98).
H(40) listed by Blockeel & Long (1998: 98).

65/1 ***Syntrichia ruralis*** (Hedw.) F.Weber & D.Mohr
(syn. *Tortula calcicolens* W.Kramer, *T. ruralis* (Hedw.) P.Gaertn., B.Mey. & Scherb. subsp. *ruralis*)

H1 1951: rocks in dunes, Darrynane, EF Warburg (BBS exc.) (Warburg 1952: 101).
H(4) listed by Lett (1915: 114) without locality.
†H4 listed by Blockeel & Long (1998: 98).
H5 1956: hedgebank in lane to Youghal Strand, EC Wallace (Warburg 1957: 331).
H6 1962: sand dunes, Bunmahon, AJE Smith (Warburg 1963b: 495).
H7 1966: roof, Ardfinnan, J Appleyard & JG Duckett (BBS exc.) (Perry 1967: 411).
H(8) listed by Lett (1915: 114) without details.
†H8 listed by Blockeel & Long (1998: 98).
H(9) listed by Lett (1915: 114).
†H9 listed by Blockeel & Long (1998: 98).
H(10) listed by Lett (1915: 114).
†H10 listed by Blockeel & Long (1998: 98).
H(11) listed by Lett (1915: 114). H(11) listed by Blockeel & Long (1998: 98).
H(13) listed by Lett (1915: 114).
†H13 listed by Blockeel & Long (1998: 98).
H(14) listed by Lett (1915: 114).
†H14 listed by Blockeel & Long (1998: 98).
H15 1957: old wall, Garryland Woods, nr Gort, EM Lobley (BBS exc.) (Warburg 1958b: 478).
[H(16) listed by Lett (1915: 114). H16 deleted because no valid record or voucher specimen traced (Blockeel 1999: 5)].
H(17) listed by Lett (1915: 114).
†H17 listed by Blockeel & Long (1998: 98).
H(18) listed by Lett (1915: 114). H(18) listed by Blockeel & Long (1998: 98).
H(19) listed by Lett (1915: 114). H(19) listed by Blockeel & Long (1998: 98).
H(20) listed by Lett (1915: 114) without locality.
†H20 listed by Blockeel & Long (1998: 98).
H(21) listed by Lett (1915: 114).
†H21 listed by Blockeel & Long (1998: 98).
H22 1950: stone by R. Boyne, Slane, JS Thomson (Warburg 1952: 101).
H23 1980: limestone rocks, Hill of Ushnagh, DM Synnott (Hill 1982: 25).
H24 1957: wall by R. Inny (right bank), Ballymacarrow Bridge, ALK King (Warburg 1958b: 478).
H25 1957: limestone quarry, nr Boyle, ALK King (Warburg 1958b: 478).
H(27) listed by Lett (1915: 114).
†H27 listed by Blockeel & Long (1998: 98).
H(28) listed by Lett (1915: 114). H(28) listed

by Blockeel & Long (1998: 98).
H29 1970: roof of derelict dwelling, Glenaniff valley, J Appleyard (BBS exc.) (Crundwell 1971b: 376, Appleyard 1971: 388).
H(30) listed by Lett (1915: 114). H(30) listed by Blockeel & Long (1998: 98).
H30 2001: on soil amongst limestone gravel of car park, 80 m alt., N shore of Lough Sheelin, nr Kilnahard, N48, DT Holyoak 01-671 (Rothero 2002: 47).
H(31) listed by Lett (1915: 114). H(31) listed by Blockeel & Long (1998: 98).
H(33) listed by Lett (1915: 114).
†H33 listed by Blockeel & Long (1998: 98).
H(34) listed by Lett (1915: 114).
†H34 listed by Blockeel & Long (1998: 98).
H(35) listed by Lett (1915: 114).
H35 1962: basic rocks, Tranarossan Bay, nr Rosapenna, EM Lobley & MPH Kertland (BBS exc.) (Warburg 1963b: 495).
H(37) listed by Lett (1915: 114).
†H37 listed by Blockeel & Long (1998: 98).
H(38) listed by Lett (1915: 114). H(38) listed by Blockeel & Long (1998: 98).
H(39) listed by Lett (1915: 114) without locality.
†H39 listed by Blockeel & Long (1998: 98).
H(40) listed by Lett (1915: 114).
†H40 listed by Blockeel & Long (1998: 98).

65/2 ***Syntrichia ruraliformis*** (Besch.) Cardot (syn. *Tortula ruraliformis* (Besch.) Grout, *T. ruralis* var. *arenicola* Braithw. nom. illeg., *T. ruralis* subsp. *ruraliformis* (Besch.) Dixon)

H(1) listed by Lett (1915: 114).
†H1 listed by Blockeel & Long (1998: 98).
H(2) 1949: sandy spit, W Barrow Harbour, Tralee, AP Fanning (Warburg 1951: 500).
H3 1986: Trebawn Strand, Sherkin I., W02, JR Akeroyd, CJ Hora & SL Jury (Blockeel 1990: 30).
H5 1956: sandy ground, Youghal Strand, EC Wallace (Warburg 1957: 331).
H(6) listed by Lett (1915: 114).
†H6 listed by Blockeel & Long (1998: 98).
H(9) listed by Lett (1915: 114).
†H9 listed by Blockeel & Long (1998: 98).
†H12 listed by Blockeel & Long (1998: 98).
H(16) listed by Lett (1915: 114).
†H16 listed by Blockeel & Long (1998: 98).
H19 1957: sandy flat by R. Liffey below Ballymore-Eustace, ALK King (Warburg 1958b: 478).
†H20 listed by Blockeel & Long (1998: 98).
H(21) listed by Lett (1915: 114).
†H21 listed by Blockeel & Long (1998: 98).
†H22 listed by Blockeel & Long (1998: 98).
H(27) listed by Lett (1915: 114).
†H27 listed by Blockeel & Long (1998: 98).
H(28) listed by Lett (1915: 114).
†H28 listed by Blockeel & Long (1998: 98).
[H(31) listed by Lett (1915: 114) without details. H31 deleted because no valid record or voucher specimen traced (Blockeel 1999: 5)].
H33 1959: rock in old quarry, Roscorr Viaduct, RD Fitzgerald (Warburg 1960: 775).
H(34) listed by Lett (1915: 114) without details.
†H34 listed by Blockeel & Long (1998: 98).
H(35) listed by Lett (1915: 114).
†H35 listed by Blockeel & Long (1998: 98).
[H(37) listed by Lett (1915: 114) without details. H37 deleted because no valid record or voucher specimen traced (Blockeel 1999: 5)].
H(38) listed by Lett (1915: 114).
†H38 listed by Blockeel & Long (1998: 98).
H(39) listed by Lett (1915: 114).
†H39 listed by Blockeel & Long (1998: 98).
H(40) listed by Lett (1915: 114).
†H40 listed by Blockeel & Long (1998: 98).

65/4 ***Syntrichia intermedia*** Brid. (syn. *Tortula intermedia* (Brid.) Berk., *T. montana* (Nees) Lindb. hom.illeg.)

H3 1967: roof of kitchen, Castle Hotel, Macroom, RD Fitzgerald (Crundwell 1968: 634).
H4 1950: mud-capped wall, Bishopstown, JS Thomson (Warburg 1952: 101).
H5 1956: limestone rock, Carrigshane Hill, Midleton, EC Wallace (Warburg 1957: 331).
H(6) 1933: Knock Maun, E Armitage (anon. 1934b: 116).
H7 1956: wall-top, Clonmel, EC Wallace (Warburg 1957: 331).
H(8) listed by Lett (1915: 113).
†H8 listed by Blockeel & Long (1998: 99).
H(9) listed by Lett (1915: 113).
†H9 listed by Blockeel & Long (1998: 99).
H(12) listed by Lett (1915: 113). H(12) listed

by Blockeel & Long (1998: 99).
H(13) listed by Lett (1915: 113) without details.
†H13 listed by Blockeel & Long (1998: 99).
†H14 listed by Blockeel & Long (1998: 99).
H(15) listed by Lett (1915: 113).
†H15 listed by Blockeel & Long (1998: 99).
H(16) listed by Lett (1915: 113).
†H16 listed by Blockeel & Long (1998: 99).
H(17) listed by Lett (1915: 113).
†H17 listed by Blockeel & Long (1998: 99).
H(18) listed by Lett (1915: 113). H(18) listed by Blockeel & Long (1998: 99).
H19 1950: churchyard wall, Donoughmore, Maynooth, JP Brunker (Warburg 1951: 500).
H(21) listed by Lett (1915: 113).
†H21 listed by Blockeel & Long (1998: 99).
H22 1950: stone, Slane, JS Thomson (Warburg 1952: 101).
H(23) listed by Lett (1915: 113).
†H23 listed by Blockeel & Long (1998: 99).
H(24) listed by Lett (1915: 113). H(24) listed by Blockeel & Long (1998: 99).
H(25) 1949: walls of old castle ruins, Roscommon Town, ALK King (Warburg 1951: 500).
†H25 listed by Blockeel & Long (1998: 99).
H(26) 1945: Cong, W Mayo [*sic*], ML Anderson, per JS Thomson (anon. 1946c: 282).
†H26 listed by Blockeel & Long (1998: 99).
H27 1987: on cottage wall, Murrisk, P Martin (Blockeel 1988: 34).
H(28) listed by Lett (1915: 114).
†H28 listed by Blockeel & Long (1998: 99).
H29 1965: limestone wall, Dromahair, EF Warburg (Warburg 1966: 193).
H30 2001: on open vertical concrete wall nr lough, 75 m alt., N shore of Lough Sheelin, NW of Mount Nugent, N48, DT Holyoak 01-667A (Rothero 2002: 47).
H(31) listed by Lett (1915: 114). H(31) listed by Blockeel & Long (1998: 99).
H32 1950: limestone, L. Aphuca, RD Fitzgerald (Warburg 1951: 500).
H(33) listed by Lett (1915: 114).
†H33 listed by Blockeel & Long (1998: 99).
H(34) 1937: Ballyshannon, no collector named (BBS exc.) (Armitage 1938: 12).
H34 2001: on S-facing limestone rocks above fen, 30 m alt., nr Lough Naharash, Ballyshannon Turloughs, G86, NG Hodgetts 3728 (Rothero 2002: 47).
H(35) 1908: Killybegs, CA Cheetham (anon. 1915: 128).
H(38) listed by Lett (1915: 114). H(38) listed by Blockeel & Long (1998: 99).
H38 2002: on mortar on top of old wall, 7 m alt., SE of Castle I., Strangford Lough, J54, DT Holyoak 02-999 (Rothero 2003: 52).
H(39) listed by Lett (1915: 114).
†H39 listed by Blockeel & Long (1998: 99).
H40 1999: on S-facing basalt crags, 140 m alt., Windy Hill, C73, DT Holyoak 99-539 (BBSUK) (Rothero 2000: 51).

65/5 ***Syntrichia princeps*** (De Not.) Mitt. (syn. *Tortula princeps* De Not.)

H(28) no date: Benbulben, Moore (Lett 1915: 114).
†H28 listed by Blockeel & Long (1998: 99).
H(39) 1866: Glenarm deerpark, Moore (Lett 1915: 114).
†H39 listed by Blockeel & Long (1998: 99).
H(40) 1885: Benevenagh, SA Stewart (Lett 1915: 114).
†H40 listed by Blockeel & Long (1998: 99).

65/7a ***Syntrichia laevipila*** Brid. **var.** ***laevipila*** (syn. *Tortula laevipila* (Brid.) Schwägr. var. *laevipila*)

H1 1951: elder between Glenbeigh and Caragh Bridge, PW Richards (BBS exc.) (Warburg 1952: 101).
H(2) listed by Lett (1915: 113). H(2) listed by Blockeel & Long (1998: 99).
H3 1967: trees by roadside S of Macroom, RD Fitzgerald (Crundwell 1968: 634).
H(4) listed by Lett (1915: 113) without locality.
†H4 listed by Blockeel & Long (1998: 99).
[H5 deleted because no valid record or voucher specimen traced (Blockeel 1999: 5)].
H(6) listed by Lett (1915: 113) without locality.
†H6 listed by Blockeel & Long (1998: 99).
†H7 listed by Blockeel & Long (1998: 99).
H(8) listed by Lett (1915: 113).
†H8 listed by Blockeel & Long (1998: 99).
H(9) listed by Lett (1915: 113). H(9) listed by Blockeel & Long (1998: 99).
H10 1951: elders in wooded gully above Silvermines, AD Banwell, PJ Wanstall & EV Watson (Warburg 1953: 310).
H(11) listed by Lett (1915: 113). H(11) listed

by Blockeel & Long (1998: 99).
H(12) listed by Lett (1915: 113).
†H12 listed by Blockeel & Long (1998: 99).
H(14) listed by Lett (1915: 113). H(14) listed by Blockeel & Long (1998: 99).
†H15 listed by Blockeel & Long (1998: 99).
H18 1957: bank nr Ballycolllis, JS Thomson (Warburg 1958b: 478).
H(19) 1937: Straffan, JS Thomson (anon. 1938d: 39).
H(20) listed by Lett (1915: 113).
†H20 listed by Blockeel & Long (1998: 99).
H(21) listed by Lett (1915: 113).
†H21 listed by Blockeel & Long (1998: 99).
H22 1951: base of beech, Julianstown, RD Fitzgerald (Warburg 1952: 101).
H23 1980: on elder, Hill of Ushnagh, DM Synnott (Hill 1981: 25).
†H25 listed by Blockeel & Long (1998: 99).
H27 1987: on *Fraxinus* in open parkland, nr Rose Cottage, NW of Westport, DG Long (Blockeel 1988: 34).
H28 1953: sycamore, Grange, EC Wallace (Warburg 1954: 481).
H29 1963: alders beside stream, Bawn, 1 mile S of Dromahair, RD Fitzgerald & AR Perry (Warburg 1964: 725).
H(30) listed by Lett (1915: 113). H(30) listed by Blockeel & Long (1998: 99).
H30 2001: on concrete wall nr lough, 75 m alt., Lough Sheelin, N shore, NW of Mount Nugent, N48, DT Holyoak 01-667B (Rothero 2002: 47).
H(31) listed by Lett (1915: 113). H(31) listed by Blockeel & Long (1998: 99).
[H(32) listed by Lett (1915: 113) without locality. H32 deleted because no valid record or voucher specimen traced (Blockeel 1999: 5)].
H(33) listed by Lett (1915: 113).
†H33 listed by Blockeel & Long (1998: 99).
H34 1968: on tree, Red Castle Glen, nr Moville, HH Birks (Crundwell 1969: 880).
H(35) listed by Lett (1915: 113).
†H35 listed by Blockeel & Long (1998: 99).
H(36) listed by Lett (1915: 113).
†H36 listed by Blockeel & Long (1998: 99).
H(37) listed by Lett (1915: 113).
†H37 listed by Blockeel & Long (1998: 99).
H(38) listed by Lett (1915: 113). H(38) listed by Blockeel & Long (1998: 99).
H(39) listed by Lett (1915: 113) without details.
†H39 listed by Blockeel & Long (1998: 99).
H(40) listed by Lett (1915: 113). H(40) listed by Blockeel & Long (1998: 99).
H40 1999: on bark of *Salix cinerea* in open *Salix* scrub at landward edge of sand dunes, Umbra, C73, DT Holyoak 99-149 (BBSUK) (Rothero 2000: 51).

Old records listed above apparently did not separate var. *laevipilaeformis* from var. *laevipila*. However, there is evidence that separation of these taxa may have little value (MM Yeo in Hill *et al.* 1992: 218).

65/7b ***Syntrichia laevipila* var. *laevipilaeformis*** (De Not.) Amann (syn. *Tortula laevipila* var. *laevipilaeformis* (De Not.) Limpr.)

H12 1954: tree, road nr Curragh Wood, Inch, JS Thomson (Warburg 1955: 584).
†H14 listed by Blockeel & Long (1998: 99).
[H18 deleted because no valid record or voucher specimen traced (Blockeel 1999: 5)].
H22 1978: ash trunk by R. Nanny, E of Cooper Hill Bridge, Julianstown, DM Synnott (Hill 1980b: 37).
H25 1952: tree trunk in lane to Carrigynachten Bog, nr Athlone, ALK King (Warburg 1953: 310).
H30 1956: tree, Virginia, JS Thomson (Warburg 1957: 331).
H(33) listed by Blockeel & Long (1998: 99).
H35 1962: trees nr the Priory, Ards Peninsula, J Appleyard (BBS exc.) (Warburg 1963b: 495).

65/8 ***Syntrichia papillosa*** (Wilson) Jur. (syn. *Tortula papillosa* Wilson)

H1 1951: rocks in dunes, Darrynane, EF Warburg (BBS exc.) (Warburg 1952: 101).
H4 2002: on roadside tree, South Mall, Cork city centre, W67, TL Blockeel 31/299 (Rothero 2003: 52).
H5 2002: on bole of deciduous tree, 10 m alt., Fota House, Foaty I., W77, TL Blockeel 31/342 (Rothero 2003: 52).
H6 1999: on *Salix* on river bank, 8 m alt., R Bride, just W of Tallowbridge, Tallow, W99, TL Blockeel 28/267 (Rothero 2000: 51).
H8 1966: ash nr L. Gur, nr Herbertstown, J

Appleyard (BBS exc.) (Perry 1967: 411).

H(9) listed by Lett (1915: 113). H(9) listed by Blockeel & Long (1998: 99).

H10 1979: on old poplar at the harbour, Terryglass, Lough Derg, EW Jones *et al.* (Hill 1980b: 37).

H11 1979: on elm, Carrigeen, W of Waterford, nr River Suir, HMH van Melick (Hill 1981: 25).

H12 1953: elm, Inch, WR Megaw (Warburg 1954: 481).

H(15) listed by Lett (1915: 113).

†H15 listed by Blockeel & Long (1998: 99).

H18 1990: on old apple tree, 55 m alt., grounds of Birr Castle, N00, DG Long 18140 (Blockeel 1991c: 42).

H(20) listed by Lett (1915: 113). H(20) listed by Blockeel & Long (1998: 99).

H(21) listed by Lett (1915: 113).

†H21 listed by Blockeel & Long (1998: 99).

H22 1966: ash tree 6 miles E of Kells, RD Fitzgerald & EM Lobley (Crundwell 1968: 634).

H25 2002: on old ash tree with *Zygodon viridissimus,* 35 m alt., Galey Bay caravan site, Lough Ree, M95, NG Hodgetts 4067 (Rothero 2003: 52).

H27 1999: on *Salix* by river, 5 m alt., Westport, L98, DG Long 28437 (Rothero 2000: 51).

H29 1963: alders beside stream, Bawn, 1 mile S of Dromahair, RD Fitzgerald & AR Perry (Warburg 1964: 725).

H(31) listed by Lett (1915: 113). H(31) listed by Blockeel & Long (1998: 99).

H(34) listed by Lett (1915: 113).

†H34 listed by Blockeel & Long (1998: 99).

H36 1956: old ash overhanging river, Ardtrea Bridge, RD Fitzgerald (Warburg 1957: 331).

H(38) listed by Lett (1915: 113). H(38) listed by Blockeel & Long (1998: 99).

H(39) listed by Lett (1915: 113). H(39) listed by Blockeel & Long (1998: 99).

H(40) listed by Lett (1915: 113). H(40) listed by Blockeel & Long (1998: 99).

65/9 ***Syntrichia latifolia*** (Bruch ex Hartm.) Huebener
(syn. *Tortula latifolia* Bruch ex Hartm., *T. mutica* Lindb.)

H(4) listed by Lett (1915: 113). H(4) listed by Blockeel & Long (1998: 100).

H5 1999: on alder by river, Tallow, W99, DH Wrench (Rothero 2000: 51).

H(6) listed by Lett (1915: 113). H(6) listed by Blockeel & Long (1998: 100).

H6 1999: at base of ash tree on river bank, 8 m alt., R Bride, just W of Tallowbridge, Tallow, W99, TL Blockeel 28/266 (Rothero 2000: 51).

H7 1966: riverside wall, Clonmel, JA Paton (BBS exc.) (Perry 1967: 411).

H8 1979: quay wall, S side of River Shannon at Limerick, HMH van Melick (Hill 1981: 25).

H12 1975: pier of bridge W of Courtown, JA Paton (BBS exc.) (Crundwell 1976: 24).

H14 1956: wall by R. Barrow below Barranagh's Bridge, Mountmellick, AA Cridland (Warburg 1958b: 478).

H(20) listed by Lett (1915: 113). H(20) listed by Blockeel & Long (1998: 100).

H(21) listed by Lett (1915: 113).

†H21 listed by Blockeel & Long (1998: 100).

H22 1967: on whitethorn covered with mud, R. Nanny, Athcarne Castle, Duleek, DM Synnott (Crundwell 1968: 634).

H29 2000: on ash and alder at edge of water, Bonet River, 2 km SW of Manorhamilton, G83, DT Holyoak 00-579 (BBSUK) (Rothero 2001: 41).

H36 1956: trees by river, Ardtrea Bridge, RD Fitzgerald (Warburg 1957: 331).

H(38) listed by Lett (1915: 113). H(38) listed by Blockeel & Long (1998: 100).

H38 1999: on alder by river, River Lagan, Drum, J36, DT Holyoak 1999-870 (BBSUK) (Rothero 2000: 51).

H(39) listed by Lett (1915: 113). H(39) listed by Blockeel & Long (1998: 100).

H(40) 1937: Castledawson, WR Megaw (anon. 1938d: 39).

66/1 ***Cinclidotus fontinaloides*** (Hedw.) P. Beauv.

H(1) listed by Lett (1915: 121) without details.

†H1 listed by Blockeel & Long (1998: 100).

H(2) listed by Lett (1915: 121) without details.

†H2 listed by Blockeel & Long (1998: 100).

H3 1967: rocks at water edge, hydro-electric reservoir S of Macroom, RD Fitzgerald (Crundwell 1968: 635).

H(4) listed by Lett (1915: 121) without details.

†H4 listed by Blockeel & Long (1998: 100).
H(5) listed by Lett (1915: 121) without details.
†H5 listed by Blockeel & Long (1998: 100).
H(6) listed by Lett (1915: 121) without details.
†H6 listed by Blockeel & Long (1998: 100).
[H(7) listed by Lett (1915: 121) without details. H7 deleted because no valid record or voucher specimen traced (Blockeel 1999: 6)].
H(8) listed by Lett (1915: 121) without details.
†H8 listed by Blockeel & Long (1998: 100).
H(9) listed by Lett (1915: 121) without details.
†H9 listed by Blockeel & Long (1998: 100).
H(10) listed by Lett (1915: 121) without details.
†H10 listed by Blockeel & Long (1998: 100).
H11 1968: concrete on bank of Dinin River, Dysart Bridge, S of Castlecomber, JA Paton (Crundwell 1969: 881).
H(12) listed by Lett (1915: 121) without details.
†H12 listed by Blockeel & Long (1998: 100).
H(13) listed by Lett (1915: 121) without details.
†H13 listed by Blockeel & Long (1998: 100).
H14 1955: concrete wall, Ballydine Bridge, nr Abbeyleix, JS Thomson (Warburg 1956: 154).
H(15) listed by Lett (1915: 121) without details.
†H15 listed by Blockeel & Long (1998: 100).
H(16) listed by Lett (1915: 121) without details.
†H16 listed by Blockeel & Long (1998: 100).
H(17) listed by Lett (1915: 121) without details.
†H17 listed by Blockeel & Long (1998: 100).
H(20) listed by Lett (1915: 121) without details.
†H20 listed by Blockeel & Long (1998: 100).
[H(21) listed by Lett (1915: 121) without details. H21 deleted because no valid record or voucher specimen traced (Blockeel 1999: 6)].
H(22) listed by Lett (1915: 121) without details.
†H22 listed by Blockeel & Long (1998: 100).
H(23) listed by Lett (1915: 121) without details.
†H23 listed by Blockeel & Long (1998: 100).
H(24) listed by Lett (1915: 121) without details.
†H24 listed by Blockeel & Long (1998: 100).
H(25) listed by Lett (1915: 121) without details.
†H25 listed by Blockeel & Long (1998: 100).
H(26) listed by Lett (1915: 121) without details.
†H26 listed by Blockeel & Long (1998: 100).
H(27) listed by Lett (1915: 121) without details.
†H27 listed by Blockeel & Long (1998: 100).
H(28) listed by Lett (1915: 121) without details.
†H28 listed by Blockeel & Long (1998: 100).
H(29) listed by Lett (1915: 121) without details.
†H29 listed by Blockeel & Long (1998: 100).
H(30) listed by Lett (1915: 121) without details.
†H30 listed by Blockeel & Long (1998: 100).
H31 1952: rock by stream, Little Ash, nr Dundalk, RD Fitzgerald (Warburg 1953: 311).
[H(32) listed by Lett (1915: 121) without details. H32 deleted because no valid record or voucher specimen traced (Blockeel 1999: 6)].
H(33) listed by Lett (1915: 121) without details.
†H33 listed by Blockeel & Long (1998: 100).
H(34) listed by Lett (1915: 121) without details.
†H34 listed by Blockeel & Long (1998: 100).
H(35) listed by Lett (1915: 121) without details.
†H35 listed by Blockeel & Long (1998: 100).
H(36) listed by Lett (1915: 121) without details.
†H36 listed by Blockeel & Long (1998: 100).
H(37) listed by Lett (1915: 121) without details.
†H37 listed by Blockeel & Long (1998: 100).
[H(38) listed by Lett (1915: 121) without details. H38 deleted because no valid record or voucher specimen traced (Blockeel 1999: 6)].
H38 2002: on rock at edge of lake, 5 m alt., E side of Quoile Pondage Basin NNR, Downpatrick, J44, DT Holyoak 02-992 (Rothero 2003: 52).
[H(39) listed by Lett (1915: 121) without details. H39 deleted because no valid record or voucher specimen traced (Blockeel 1999: 6)].
H39 1999: on sloping concrete at end of dam,

South Woodburn Reservoirs, J38, DT Holyoak 99-893 (BBSUK) (Rothero 2000: 51).
H(40) listed by Lett (1915: 121) without details.
†H40 listed by Blockeel & Long (1998: 100).

66/2 ***Cinclidotus riparius*** (Brid.) Arnott

H(9) 1884: nr Ennis in river, SA Stewart (DBN, Hb. Lett & CGE), conf. TL Blockeel (Blockeel 1998: 188).
1884: on stones, River Fergus at Ennis, SA S[tewart] (DBN), conf. TL Blockeel (Blockeel 1998: 188).

Although Stewart (1890) claimed *C. riparius* as an addition to the Irish flora, the records were discounted for many years as misidentified *C. fontinaloides* (e.g. in Lett 1915: 121) until Blockeel (1998) confirmed that the specimens had been correctly identified.

68/1 ***Schistidium maritimum*** (Turner) Bruch & Schimp.
(syn. *Grimmia maritima* Turner)

H(1) listed by Lett (1915: 122).
†H1 listed by Blockeel & Long (1998: 100).
H(3) listed by Lett (1915: 122).
†H3 listed by Blockeel & Long (1998: 100).
H(4) listed by Lett (1915: 122) without details.
†H4 listed by Blockeel & Long (1998: 100).
H(5) listed by Lett (1915: 122).
†H5 listed by Blockeel & Long (1998: 100).
H6 1956: sea cliffs, Ardmore, EC Wallace (Warburg 1957: 330).
H(8) listed by Lett (1915: 122). H(8) listed by Blockeel & Long (1998: 100).
H8 1992: on shale rocks on shore, Foynes I., Shannon Estuary, R25, E Wiltshire (Rothero 2000: 51).
H(9) listed by Lett (1915: 122). H(9) listed by Blockeel & Long (1998: 100).
H12 1953: rocks, Ballymoney, WR Megaw (Warburg 1954: 480).
H13 1954: wall by towpath, left bank of R. Barrow, below Graiguenamanagh, ALK King (Warburg 1956: 153).
†H16 listed by Blockeel & Long (1998: 100).
H17 1966: boulders by estuary E of Galway railway station, G Halliday (Perry 1967: 413).
[H(20) listed by Lett (1915: 122) without locality. H20 deleted because no valid record or voucher specimen traced (Blockeel 1999: 6)].
H(21) listed by Lett (1915: 122).
†H21 listed by Blockeel & Long (1998: 100).
H(27) listed by Lett (1915: 122).
†H27 listed by Blockeel & Long (1998: 100).
H(28) listed by Lett (1915: 122).
†H28 listed by Blockeel & Long (1998: 100).
H(29) listed by Lett (1915: 122).
†H29 listed by Blockeel & Long (1998: 100).
H(31) listed by Lett (1915: 122). H(31) listed by Blockeel & Long (1998: 100).
H(34) listed by Lett (1915: 122).
†H34 listed by Blockeel & Long (1998: 100).
H(35) listed by Lett (1915: 122) without details.
†H35 listed by Blockeel & Long (1998: 100).
H(38) listed by Lett (1915: 122). H(38) listed by Blockeel & Long (1998: 100).
H38 2002: on top of wall above beach, 10 m alt., S of Kilough, J53, DT Holyoak 02-1010 (Rothero 2003: 52).
H(39) listed by Lett (1915: 122).
†H39 listed by Blockeel & Long (1998: 100).
H(40) listed by Lett (1915: 122). H(40) listed by Blockeel & Long (1998: 100).
H40 1999: on basalt rock on grassy slope of low coastal headland, Portstewart, C83, DT Holyoak 99-175 (BBSUK) (Rothero 2000: 51).

68/2 ***Schistidium rivulare*** (Brid.) Podp.
(syn. *Grimmia alpicola* var. *rivularis* (Brid.) Wahlenb., *G. apocarpa* var. *rivularis* F.Weber & D.Mohr, *Schistidium alpicola* (Hedw.) Limpr. var. *rivulare* (Brid.) Limpr.)

H(1) listed by Lett (1915: 122).
†H1 listed by Blockeel & Long (1998: 100).
[H2 1966: wet rocks in stream, Torc Cascade, nr Killarney, MFV Corley & JS Parker (Perry 1967: 414). H2 not listed by Blockeel & Long 1998: 100, apparently because voucher specimen not revised by A Orange].
[H3 deleted because voucher (1967: on rocks in stream, Aghacunna, W of Macroom, RD Fitzgerald, Crundwell 1968: 637) is *S. apocarpum,* redet. A Orange (Blockeel 1996: 46)].
H3 2002: on rocks in river, 5 m alt., S bank of River Bandon, NE of Bandon, W55,

TL Blockeel 31/372 (Rothero 2003: 52).
H4 1967: on rocks, R. Laney, Carrigagulla Bridge, RD Fitzgerald (Crundwell 1968: 637).
H(5) listed by Lett (1915: 122). H(5) listed by Blockeel & Long (1998: 100).
H(6) listed by Lett (1915: 122). H(6) listed by Blockeel & Long (1998: 100).
H7 1966: rocks in river from L. Muskrey, Galtee Mts, ERB Little (BBS exc.) (Perry 1967: 414).
[H8 deleted because voucher (1992: on stonework of bridge, at water level, 100 m alt., bridge over Glencorbry River, 1.5 km S of Glin, R14, E Wiltshire (Blockeel 1994: 38) is *S. platyphyllum*, det. A Orange (Blockeel 1996: 46))].
H8 1999: under bridge over Caher River, Mountcollins, SE of Abbefeale, R11, J Reynolds, det. A Orange (Rothero 2000: 51).
[H(13) listed by Lett (1915: 122)].
†H16 listed by Blockeel & Long (1998: 100).
H20 1969: boulder in Aughrim River between Aughrim and Woodenbridge, RD Fitzgerald (Crundwell 1970: 202).
H(21) listed by Lett (1915: 122). H(21) listed by Blockeel & Long (1998: 100).
H25 2002: on limestone rock by loch, 45 m alt., Drummans I., Lough Key Forest Park, G80 NG Hodgetts 4114 (Rothero 2003: 52).
[H28 deleted because voucher (1965: limestone pavement *ca* 100 ft alt., stream edge, Dromore West, RD Fitzgerald & EM Lobley, Warburg 1966: 195) is *S. platyphyllum*, redet. A Orange (Blockeel 1996: 46)].
H(29) listed by Lett (1915: 122) without details.
†H29 listed by Blockeel & Long (1998: 100).
H(30) listed by Lett (1915: 122).
†H30 listed by Blockeel & Long (1998: 100).
†H33 listed by Blockeel & Long (1998: 100).
H(34) listed by Lett (1915: 122).
†H34 listed by Blockeel & Long (1998: 100).
H35 1969: rocks in stream, Glen River, below Carrick, JA Paton (NMW), det. A Orange (Blockeel 1996: 46).
H(38) listed by Lett (1915: 122). H(38) listed by Blockeel & Long (1998: 100).
H(39) listed by Lett (1915: 122).
†H39 listed by Blockeel & Long (1998: 100).
H(40) 1937: Stradreagh, JD Houston (anon. 1938d: 39).
†H40 listed by Blockeel & Long (1998: 100).

68/3 ***Schistidium platyphyllum*** (Mitt.) H. Perss.
(syn. *Schistidium alpicola* var. *alpicola* auct. non (Hedw.) Limpr., *S. rivulare* subsp. *latifolium* (J.E.Zetterst.) B. Bremer)

H1 1979: Roughty River above Kenmore, V97, EC Wallace (NMW) (Orange 1995: 57, Blockeel 1996: 46).
H8 1991: on boulders, 100 m alt., in Bilboa River, R835535, N Lockhart & A O'Suillivan (BBSUK) (Orange 1995: 57, Blockeel 1992: 26, 1996: 46).
H19 1957: rocks by River Liffey below Ballymore Eustace, [= N90 or 91], ALK King (BBSUK) (Warburg 1958b: 477, Orange 1995: 57, Blockeel 1966: 46).
H28 no date: Dromore West, G43, RD Fitzgerald & EM Lobley (BBSUK) (Orange 1995: 57, Blockeel 1996: 46).
H33 1960: Correl Glen, H05, RD Fitzgerald (NMW) (Orange 1995: 57, Blockeel 1997a: 43).
H36 2002: on sloping rock at edge of river, 95 m alt., just below Carrickaness Bridge W of Drumquin, H27, DT Holyoak 02-1121 (Rothero 2003: 52).
H(39) 1887: nr Broughshane [= D10], HW Lett (BBSUK) (Orange 1995: 57, Blockeel 1997a: 43).
H(40) 1939: Downhill [= C73], JS Thompson (NMW) (Orange 1995: 57, Blockeel 1996: 46).

68/4 ***Schistidium agassizii*** Sull. & Lesq.

H35 1998: on rocks in unshaded river with *Racomitrium aciculare, Ephebe lanata, Dermatocarpon intestiniforme*, 25 m alt., Lackagh River, Glen Lough, 9 km W of Millford, B12, A Orange 11740 (Rothero 1999b: 42).

68/5 ***Schistidium apocarpum*** (Hedw.) Bruch & Schimp. aggregate

†H1 listed by Blockeel & Long (1998: 101).
†H2 listed by Blockeel & Long (1998: 101).
†H3 listed by Blockeel & Long (1998: 101).
†H4 listed by Blockeel & Long (1998: 101).
H5 1951: wall, Mallow, EC Wallace & EF Warburg (Warburg 1952: 100).

†H6 listed by Blockeel & Long (1998: 101).
†H7 listed by Blockeel & Long (1998: 101).
†H8 listed by Blockeel & Long (1998: 101).
†H9 listed by Blockeel & Long (1998: 101).
†H10 listed by Blockeel & Long (1998: 101).
†H11 listed by Blockeel & Long (1998: 101).
†H12 listed by Blockeel & Long (1998: 101).
†H13 listed by Blockeel & Long (1998: 101).
†H14 listed by Blockeel & Long (1998: 101).
†H15 listed by Blockeel & Long (1998: 101).
†H16 listed by Blockeel & Long (1998: 101).
†H17 listed by Blockeel & Long (1998: 101).
†H18 listed by Blockeel & Long (1998: 101).
†H19 listed by Blockeel & Long (1998: 101).
†H20 listed by Blockeel & Long (1998: 101).
†H21 listed by Blockeel & Long (1998: 101).
†H22 listed by Blockeel & Long (1998: 101).
†H23 listed by Blockeel & Long (1998: 101).
H24 1957: wall of Ballymacarrow Bridge, ALK King (Warburg 1958b: 477).
†H25 listed by Blockeel & Long (1998: 101).
†H26 listed by Blockeel & Long (1998: 101).
†H27 listed by Blockeel & Long (1998: 101).
†H28 listed by Blockeel & Long (1998: 101).
†H29 listed by Blockeel & Long (1998: 101).
†H30 listed by Blockeel & Long (1998: 101).
†H31 listed by Blockeel & Long (1998: 101).
†H32 listed by Blockeel & Long (1998: 101).
†H33 listed by Blockeel & Long (1998: 101).
†H34 listed by Blockeel & Long (1998: 101).
†H35 listed by Blockeel & Long (1998: 101).
†H36 listed by Blockeel & Long (1998: 101).
†H37 listed by Blockeel & Long (1998: 101).
†H38 listed by Blockeel & Long (1998: 101).
†H39 listed by Blockeel & Long (1998: 101).
†H40 listed by Blockeel & Long (1998: 101).

The present treatment of 68/5 to 68/17 dates from the publication by Blom (1996), who showed that several similar species had been widely confused under the name *Schistidium apocarpum*. In Ireland these included the common *S. apocarpum s.s.* and *S. crassipilum*, the rare *S. elegantulum*, and possibly others as yet unrecorded from Ireland. Lett (1915: 122) listed *Grimmia apocarpa* from all Irish vice-counties except H5 and H24, but he undoubtedly listed several species together under this name. The preceding list summarises more recent records that can only be assigned to an aggregate of closely similar species resembling *S. apocarpum*. Material recently identified or reidentified as the segregate species recognised by Blom (1996) is listed below.

68/5 ***Schistidium apocarpum*** (Hedw.) Bruch & Schimp. *s.s.*
(syn. *Grimmia apocarpa* Hedw.)

H3 1979: rocks on shore, Glenbeg Lough, AJE Smith, det. AJE Smith (Rothero 2004).
H9 1968: Poulsallagh, Lisdoonvarna, M Price-Jones, det. AJE Smith (Rothero 2004).
H16 1962: on rock, Lissoughter, nr Recess, AJE Smith, det. AJE Smith (Rothero 2004).
H25 2002: on boulder at entrance to campsite, 30 m alt., Hodson's Bay, Lough Ree, N04, NG Hodgetts 4051 (Rothero 2003: 52).
H28 2001: on limestone of tomb, 35 m alt., Creevykeel megalithic tomb, G75, NG Hodgetts 3723 (Rothero 2002: 47).
H33 2002: on open limestone rock, NE slope of Cuilcagh, H13, DT Holyoak 02-895B (Rothero 2003: 52).
H34 2001: on limestone cliffs in railway cutting, 30 m alt., nr Lough Naharash, Ballyshannon Turloughs, G86, NG Hodgetts 3729 (Rothero 2002: 47).
H35 2002: on open limestone on N-facing slope, 250 m alt., just NE of Lough Salt, C12, DT Holyoak 02-682 (Rothero 2003: 52).
H36 2002: on concrete, 180 m alt., in old quarry W of Brackagh South, H57, DT Holyoak 02-1104 (Rothero 2003: 53).
H37 2002: on mortar on top of wall of bridge, 65 m alt., Gosford Forest Park, H94, DT Holyoak 02-1086 (Rothero 2003: 53).
H38 2002: on mortar on top of old wall, 7 m alt., SE of Castle I., Strangford Lough, J54, DT Holyoak 02-998 (Rothero 2003: 53).
H39 2002: on open basalt crag in gully, 355 m alt., McArt's Fort, Cave Hill, J37, DT Holyoak 02-1063 (Rothero 2003: 53).

See notes above under *S. apocarpum* aggregate. The present treatment of 68/5 to 68/17 dates from the publication by Blom (1996).

68/8 ***Schistidium pruinosum*** (Wilson ex Schimp.) Roth
(syn. *Grimmia conferta* var. *pruinosa* (Wilson) Braithw.)

H(39) 1890: Cave Hill, Belfast, CH Waddell (BM, E), conf. HH Blom (Blom 1996: 111).
1928: Bellevue Gardens, Belfast, HH Knight (NMW), det. AJE Smith (Rothero 2004).
H(39) listed by Blockeel & Long (1998: 101).

Recognition of *S. pruinosum* as a distinct species is based on the taxonomic revision by Blom (1996). Although *Grimmia conferta* var. *pruinosa* is listed for H9, H38, H39 and H40 by Lett (1915: 122), the original specimens need to be reidentified before any but those from H39 (Cave Hill) can safely be assigned to *S. pruinosum*. The original specimen also needs to be reidentified in order to allocate Lett's (*loc. cit.*) H32 record of *Grimmia apocarpa* var. *pumila* Schimp. (1907: Drumreaske, leg. Kane) in the current classification.

68/9 ***Schistidium strictum*** (Turner) Loeske ex Martensson
(syn. *Grimmia stricta* Turner)

†H1 listed by Blockeel & Long (1998: 101).
H1 1983: on exposed rocks by stream, 420 m alt., below Eagle's Nest, Coomcallee, Macgillicuddy's Reeks, V88, DG Long (E), det. HH Blom (Rothero 2004).
H(2) listed by Blockeel & Long (1998: 101).
H3 1967: on boulder in flush, Aghacunna, RD Fitzgerald (Crundwell 1968: 637).
H(4) listed by Blockeel & Long (1998: 101).
†H6 listed by Blockeel & Long (1998: 101).
H(8) listed by Blockeel & Long (1998: 101).
H13 1972: on wall nr the Black Banks, Blackstairs Mts, WV Rubers (U) (Crundwell 1974: 169).
H(18) listed by Blockeel & Long (1998: 101).
H25 1968: on limestone boulder, Annaghmore Lough, 3 miles NW of Strokestown, WV Rubers *et al.* (U) (Crundwell 1974: 169).
H27 1972: on lakeside boulder, Pontoon Bridge, WV Rubers (U) (Crundwell 1974: 169).
1987: on large basic blocks on hillside, 270 m alt., Caheraspic, Sheefry Hills, L97, DG Long (E), det. AJE Smith (Rothero 2004).
H28 1962: limestone rocks, Gleniff, AC Crundwell (BBS exc.) (Warburg 1963b: 497).
H29 1963: limestone boulders, Peakadaw, Glenade, RD Fitzgerald & AR Perry (Warburg 1964: 727).
H(30) listed by Blockeel & Long (1998: 101).
H35 1950: rocks *ca* 1200 ft alt., Muckish Mt., RD Fitzgerald (Warburg 1966: 195).
H(39) listed by Blockeel & Long (1998: 101).

Although the distribution of *S. strictum* given in the *CC* by Blockeel & Long (1998: 101) probably remains 'reasonably accurate' (Rothero 2004) it is desirable that all records of the species are reassessed following the taxonomic revision by Blom (1996). As yet, only the records from H1 and H27 have been confirmed (Rothero 2004).

68/12 ***Schistidium confertum*** (Funck) Bruch & Schimp.
(syn. *Grimmia conferta* Funck, *Schistidium apocarpum* var. *confertum* (Funck) Bruch & Schimp.)

H(26) listed by Lett (1915: 121). H(26) listed by Blockeel & Long (1998: 101).
H(31) listed by Lett (1915: 121). H(31) listed by Blockeel & Long (1998: 101).
H(32) listed by Lett (1915: 121). H(32) listed by Blockeel & Long (1998: 101).
H(38) listed by Blockeel & Long (1998: 101).
H(38) 1910: on basalt rocks, Bellam Hill, Carnlough, CH Waddell (E), det. HH Blom (Rothero 2004).
H(39) listed by Blockeel & Long (1998: 101).
H(39) 1928: on limestone, Cave (?) Hill, Belfast, WR Megaw & J McAndrew (E), det. HH Blom (Rothero 2004).
H(40) listed by Blockeel & Long (1998: 101).

See notes above under *S. apocarpum* aggregate. Treatment of *S. confertum* at species rank dates from the publication by Blom (1996). Although the distribution of *S. confertum* given in the *CC* by Blockeel & Long (1998: 101) probably remains 'reasonably accurate' (Rothero 2004) it is desirable that all records of the species are reassessed following the taxonomic revision by Blom (1996). As yet, only the records from H(38) and H(39) have been confirmed (Rothero 2004).

68/16 ***Schistidium crassipilum*** H.H.Blom

H13 2002: on concrete at base of old fence post, 335 m alt., S slope of Croaghaun, nr car park, S85, DT Holyoak 02-355 (Rothero 2003: 53).
H18 1978: on limey soil in quarry, Millpark, NW of Roscrea, DT Holyoak, conf. AJE Smith (BBSUK) (Rothero 2001: 42).
H25 2002: on limestone rock, 90 m alt., Killeglan grassland, Lugboy, M84, NG Hodgetts 4055 (Rothero 2003: 53).
H26 1962: on limestone pavement, by Keel Bridge between Ballinrobe and Partry, AJE Smith, det. AJE Smith (Rothero 2004).
H28 1987: on limestone boulder at foot of cliffs, 400 m alt., Gleniff above Clogh, G74, DG Long, det. HH Blom (Rothero 2004).
H29 2000: on limestone boulder on grassy slope, Glenade Lough, NW side, G84, DT Holyoak 00-502 (BBSUK) (Rothero 2001: 41).
H30 2001: on open mortared wall of ruined house, 305 m alt., W of Bellavally Gap, H12, DT Holyoak 01-634 (Rothero 2002: 48).
H33 2000: on concrete fence post nr roadside, Owenbrean River, H13, DT Holyoak 00-251 (BBSUK) (Rothero 2001: 41).
H35 2001: on calcareous rock nr stream, 300 m alt., Slieve League above Lough Agh, G57, NG Hodgetts 3803 (Rothero 2003: 53).
H36 2002: on mortar on top of wall, 175 m alt., Gortin Glen Forest Park camping ground, H48, DT Holyoak 02-1119 (Rothero 2003: 53).
H(39) 1928: on limestone rocks, Belfast Mt., WR Megaw (NMW), det. AJE Smith (Rothero 2003a).
H(40) 1946: on top of stone wall, Ballinallan, AM Irwin (E), det. AJE Smith (Rothero 2003a).

See notes above under *S. apocarpum* aggregate. Recognition of *S. crassipilum* as a species distinct from *S. apocarpum* dates from the publication by Blom (1996).

68/17a ***Schistidium elegantulum*** H.H.Blom **subsp.** ***elegantulum***

H(5) no date: Little I., Cork, collector not named (BM), conf. HH Blom (Blom 1996: 237). H(5) listed by Blockeel & Long (1998: 102) and Rothero (2004).

See notes above under *S. apocarpum* aggregate. Recognition of *S. elegantulum* as a species distinct from *S. apocarpum* and recognition of its subspecies dates from the publication by Blom (1996).

68/17b ***Schistidium elegantulum*** **subsp.** ***wilsonii*** H.H.Blom

H9 1962: on limestone rock, summit of Corkscrew Hill, M30, AJE Smith, det. AJE Smith (Rothero 2004).
H(16) 1831: Connemara, Cum Vari prope Renvyle, collector not named (BM - Shuttlewood), conf. HH Blom (Blom 1996: 243). H(16) listed by Blockeel & Long (1998: 102).
H(26) 1906: Cony, Co Mayo, D McArdle (BM), conf. HH Blom (Blom 1996: 243). H(26) listed by Blockeel & Long (1998: 102).

See notes above under *S. apocarpum* aggregate. Recognition of *S. elegantulum* as a species distinct from *S. apocarpum* and recognition of its subspecies dates from the publication by Blom (1996).

69/2 ***Grimmia crinita*** Brid.

H21 1950: Dublin, city wall, SW Greene (TCD), det. J Muñoz, conf. TL Blockeel (Muñoz & Pando 2000, Blockeel in Blockeel *et al.* 2002: 89).

69/3 ***Grimmia laevigata*** (Brid.) Brid.
(syn. *Grimmia campestris* Burchell ex Hook.)

H(3) listed by Lett (1915: 124) without details. H(3) record placed in parentheses, comm. AJE Smith (Hill 1980b: 39). H(3) listed by Blockeel &

Long (1998: 102).
H5 1956: stone parapet of bridge, Youghal, EC Wallace (Warburg 1957: 330).
H(39) 1837: Giant's Causeway, Moore (Lett 1915: 124). H(39) record placed in parentheses, comm. AJE Smith (Hill 1980b: 39). H(39) listed by Blockeel & Long (1998: 102).

69/7 ***Grimmia donniana*** **Sm.**
(syn. *Grimmia doniana* auct., *G. donii* Sm. ex Lindb. nom. illeg., *G. donii* var. *sudetica* Huebener, *G. donniana* Sm. var. *donniana*)

H(1) listed by Lett (1915: 123).
H(1) 1935: nr L. Cruttia, no collector named (BBS exc.) (Watson 1936: 264).
H(2) listed by Lett (1915: 123). H(2) listed by Blockeel & Long (1998: 102).
[H(3) listed by Lett (1915: 123)].
H(6) listed by Lett (1915: 123).
H6 1966: boulder scree above the lake, Coumshingaun, J Appleyard (BBS exc.) (Perry 1967: 414).
H7 1966: limestone scree, *ca* 1300 ft alt., Knockeenatoung, Galtee Mts, EM Lobley & RJ Murphy (BBS exc.) (Perry 1967: 414).
H16 1994: on dry boulder, 70 m alt., nr E margin of L. Bollard, Errisbeg, L64, TL Blockeel 23/195 (Blockeel 1995c: 43).
H19 1954: wall by lane from Glending to Newtown, ALK King (Warburg 1955: 584).
H(20) 1941: Glendalough, JS Thomson (Duncan 1944: 210).
†H20 listed by Blockeel & Long (1998: 102).
H21 1953: granite on NE slope of Three Rock Mt., above Barnacullia, ALK King (Warburg 1954: 481).
H27 1951: Mweelrea, H Milne-Redhead (Warburg 1952: 100).
H31 1968: on boulder by stream, Tullaghomeath, Carlingford Pen., DM Synnott (Crundwell 1969: 883).
H(34) listed by Lett (1915: 123). H(34) listed by Blockeel & Long (1998: 102).
[H(35) listed by Lett (1915: 123) without details].
H(37) listed by Lett (1915: 123). H(37) listed by Blockeel & Long (1998: 102).
H(38) listed by Lett (1915: 123).
†H38 listed by Blockeel & Long (1998: 102).
H(39) listed by Lett (1915: 123).
†H39 listed by Blockeel & Long (1998: 102).

69/10 ***Grimmia longirostris*** **Hook.**
(syn. *Grimmia affinis* Hornsch., *G. ovalis* auct. non (Hedw.) Lindb.)

H1 1951: boulders by L. Cruthia, Brandon Mt., AC Crundwell (Warburg 1952: 100).
H(4) listed by Lett (1915: 123). H (4) record placed in parentheses, comm. AJE Smith (Hill 1980b: 39). H(4) listed by Blockeel & Long (1998: 102).
[H6 deleted (Smith 1971, Crundwell 1972: 139)].
[H(16) listed by Lett (1915: 123)].
[H(21) listed by Lett (1915: 123). H21 record dismissed as dubious literature record, comm. AJE Smith (Hill 1980b: 39).
H(38) listed by Lett (1915: 123). H(38) record placed in parentheses, comm. AJE Smith (Hill 1980b: 39). H(38) listed by Blockeel & Long (1998: 102).
H(39) record placed in parentheses, comm. AJE Smith (Hill 1980b: 39). H(39) listed by Blockeel & Long (1998: 102).

69/13 ***Grimmia atrata*** **Miel. ex Hoppe & Hornsch.**

H35 1990: on boulder at edge of lough, 460 m alt., L. Feeane, Aghla More, B92, Blockeel 19/466 (Hb. TL Blockeel) (Blockeel 1991c: 43).
1990: in dense robust tufts on crumbling flaky rock on the SW of the saddle between Aghla More and Aghla Beg, B92, DM Synnott (Blockeel 1991c: 43).

69/15a ***Grimmia pulvinata*** **(Hedw.) Sm. var. *pulvinata***

H(1) listed by Lett (1915: 122).
†H1 listed by Blockeel & Long (1998: 103).
H(2) listed by Lett (1915: 122).
†H2 listed by Blockeel & Long (1998: 103).
H(3) listed by Lett (1915: 122).
†H3 listed by Blockeel & Long (1998: 103).
H(4) listed by Lett (1915: 122).
†H4 listed by Blockeel & Long (1998: 103).
H5 1951: walls, Mallow, EC Wallace & EF Warburg (Warburg 1952: 100).
H(6) listed by Lett (1915: 122).
†H6 listed by Blockeel & Long (1998: 103).
H(7) 1947: stones, Two-mile-bridge,

Clonmel, KC Harris (anon. 1948b: 120).
†H7 listed by Blockeel & Long (1998: 103).
H(8) listed by Lett (1915: 122).
†H8 listed by Blockeel & Long (1998: 103).
H(9) listed by Lett (1915: 122).
†H9 listed by Blockeel & Long (1998: 103).
H(10) listed by Lett (1915: 122).
†H10 listed by Blockeel & Long (1998: 103).
H(11) listed by Lett (1915: 122).
†H11 listed by Blockeel & Long (1998: 103).
H(12) listed by Lett (1915: 122).
†H12 listed by Blockeel & Long (1998: 103).
H(13) listed by Lett (1915: 122).
†H13 listed by Blockeel & Long (1998: 103).
H(14) listed by Lett (1915: 122).
†H14 listed by Blockeel & Long (1998: 103).
H(15) listed by Lett (1915: 122).
†H15 listed by Blockeel & Long (1998: 103).
H(16) listed by Lett (1915: 122).
†H16 listed by Blockeel & Long (1998: 103).
H(17) listed by Lett (1915: 122).
†H17 listed by Blockeel & Long (1998: 103).
H(18) listed by Lett (1915: 122).
†H18 listed by Blockeel & Long (1998: 103).
H(19) listed by Lett (1915: 122).
†H19 listed by Blockeel & Long (1998: 103).
H(20) listed by Lett (1915: 122).
†H20 listed by Blockeel & Long (1998: 103).
H(21) listed by Lett (1915: 122).
†H21 listed by Blockeel & Long (1998: 103).
†H22 listed by Blockeel & Long (1998: 103).
H(23) listed by Lett (1915: 122).
†H23 listed by Blockeel & Long (1998: 103).
†H24 listed by Blockeel & Long (1998: 103).
H(25) listed by Lett (1915: 122).
†H25 listed by Blockeel & Long (1998: 103).
H26 1953: limestone rocks by shore of L. Carra, E of Otter Point, EC Wallace (Warburg 1955: 584).
H(27) listed by Lett (1915: 122).
†H27 listed by Blockeel & Long (1998: 103).
H(28) listed by Lett (1915: 122).
†H28 listed by Blockeel & Long (1998: 103).
H(29) listed by Lett (1915: 122).
†H29 listed by Blockeel & Long (1998: 103).
H(30) listed by Lett (1915: 122).
†H30 listed by Blockeel & Long (1998: 103).
H(31) listed by Lett (1915: 122).
†H31 listed by Blockeel & Long (1998: 103).
†H32 listed by Blockeel & Long (1998: 103).
H(33) listed by Lett (1915: 122).
†H33 listed by Blockeel & Long (1998: 103).
H(34) listed by Lett (1915: 122).
†H34 listed by Blockeel & Long (1998: 103).
H(35) listed by Lett (1915: 122).
†H35 listed by Blockeel & Long (1998: 103).
H(36) listed by Lett (1915: 122).
†H36 listed by Blockeel & Long (1998: 103).
H(37) listed by Lett (1915: 122).
†H37 listed by Blockeel & Long (1998: 103).
H(38) listed by Lett (1915: 122).
†H38 listed by Blockeel & Long (1998: 103).
H(39) listed by Lett (1915: 122).
†H39 listed by Blockeel & Long (1998: 103).
H(40) listed by Lett (1915: 122).
†H40 listed by Blockeel & Long (1998: 103).

69/16 ***Grimmia orbicularis*** Bruch ex Wilson

H(4) listed by Lett (1915: 122). H(4) listed by Blockeel & Long (1998: 103).
H(5) listed by Lett (1915: 122). H(5) listed by Blockeel & Long (1998: 103).
H(21) listed by Lett (1915: 122). H(21) placed in parentheses, comm. AJE Smith (Hill 1980b: 39).
[H(38) listed by Lett (1915: 122) as: Spelga Mt., leg. HW Lett. H38 record placed in parentheses, comm. AJE Smith (Hill 1980b: 39); record later deleted because the only specimen traced (1886: Spelga Mt., HW Lett, DBN) is *G. trichophylla*, det. DM Synnott, comm. NF Stewart (Blockeel 1995c: 43)].

69/17 ***Grimmia torquata*** Hornsch. ex Grev.

H(1) listed by Lett (1915: 122).
†H1 listed by Blockeel & Long (1998: 103).
H(2) listed by Lett (1915: 122). H(2) listed by Blockeel & Long (1998: 103).
H6 1963: calcareous sandstone cliffs at 1600 ft [alt.], N corrie of Fauscoum, Comeragh Mts, DA Ratcliffe (Warburg 1964: 727).
H(7) listed by Lett (1915: 122).
†H7 listed by Blockeel & Long (1998: 103).
H(20) listed by Lett (1915: 122). H(20) listed by Blockeel & Long (1998: 103).
H27 1965: basic rocks, 1400 ft alt., nr Lugnacolliwee Lough, Sheeffrey Hills, A McG Stirling (Warburg 1966: 196).

69/18 ***Grimmia funalis*** (Schwägr.) Bruch & Schimp.

H(1) listed by Lett (1915: 122).
†H1 listed by Blockeel & Long (1998: 103).
H(4) listed by Lett (1915: 122). H(4) listed by Blockeel & Long (1998: 103).

H(7) 1945: cliffs 2100 ft [alt.], Galtees, RD Meikle (anon. 1947: 29).
H(16) listed by Lett (1915: 122).
†H16 listed by Blockeel & Long (1998: 103).
H(20) listed by Lett (1915: 122). H(20) listed by Blockeel & Long (1998: 103).
H27 1968: small limestone outcrops at edge of dune system nr coast 4 miles S of Killadoon, AR Perry (Crundwell 1969: 883).
H34 1962: rocks nr the summit, Bulbin [Mt.], J Appleyard (BBS exc.) (Warburg 1963b: 497).
H(35) listed by Lett (1915: 122) without details. H(35) listed by Blockeel & Long (1998: 103).
H(38) listed by Lett (1915: 122). H(38) listed by Blockeel & Long (1998: 103).
H(39) listed by Lett (1915: 122). H(39) listed by Blockeel & Long (1998: 103).
H(40) listed by Lett (1915: 122).
†H40 listed by Blockeel & Long (1998: 103).

69/19 ***Grimmia trichophylla*** **Grev.**
(syn. *Grimmia subsquarrosa* Wilson, *G. stirtonii* Schimp., *G. trichophylla* var. *stirtonii* (Schimp.) Moell., *G. trichophylla* var. *subsquarrosa* (Wilson) A.J.E.Sm., *G. trichophylla* var. *trichophylla*)

H(1) listed by Lett (1915: 122).
H1 1951: rocks in dunes, Darrynane, J Appleyard & EF Warburg (BBS exc.) (Warburg 1952: 100), as *G. subsquarrosa*.
H(2) listed by Lett (1915: 123). H(2) listed by Blockeel & Long (1998: 103).
H(3) listed by Lett (1915: 123).
†H3 listed by Blockeel & Long (1998: 103).
H(4) listed by Lett (1915: 123).
†H4 listed by Blockeel & Long (1998: 103).
H(6) listed by Lett (1915: 123).
†H6 listed by Blockeel & Long (1998: 103).
H8 1966: rocks, Knockseefin, nr Nicker, J Appleyard *et al.* (BBS exc.) (Crundwell 1968: 637).
1966: basalt boulders, Knockroe, nr Caherconlish, MFV Corley & JS Parker (Perry 1967: 414), as *G. subsquarrosa*.
H(9) no date: wall nr Roughan Ho.[use], Kilnaboy, JS Thomson (anon. 1946c: 281).
†H9 listed by Blockeel & Long (1998: 103).
[H(11) listed by Lett (1915: 123) as *G. subsquarrosa*].
H12 1975: granite boulders, wall of old building, Cloroge, Mt Leinster, AR Perry (Hill 1977a: 19) (as *G. stirtonii*). H12 apparently omitted in error from *CC*.
H(13) listed by Lett (1915: 123).
†H13 listed by Blockeel & Long (1998: 103).
H14 1956: flagstone wall, E of Garrintaggart, AC Cridland (Warburg 1958b: 477).
H(16) listed by Lett (1915: 123).
H(16) 1912: Connemara, CA Cheetham (anon. 1915: 126).
†H16 listed by Blockeel & Long (1998: 103).
H18 1962: basalt on Croghan Hill, ALK King (Warburg 1963b: 498).
H19 1953: granite boulder, Cupidstown Hill, ALK King (Warburg 1954: 480).
1953: Cupidstown Hill, AW Stelfox, comm. JS Thomson (Warburg 1954: 480), as *G. stirtonii*.
H(20) listed by Lett (1915: 123).
†H20 listed by Blockeel & Long (1998: 103).
H(21) listed by Lett (1915: 123).
H(21) 1942: Carrickmines, JS Thomson (Duncan 1944: 210), as *G. Stirtoni*.
H22 1978: Lower Palaeozoic rocks, N side of Bellewstown, DM Synnott (Hill 1979: 28).
[H(23) listed by Lett (1915: 123) as 1909: Mullingar, leg. HW Lett. H23 discounted because based on dubious literature record (Hill 1981: 27)].
H(26) 1910: Slieve Gamph, WN Tetley (anon. 1911c: 8).
H(26) listed by Lett (1915: 123). H(26) listed by Blockeel & Long (1998: 103).
H(27) 1908: Westport, CA Cheetham (anon. 1911a: 13).
H(27) listed by Lett (1915: 123).
†H27 listed by Blockeel & Long (1998: 103).
H(28) 1928: nr Rosses Point, Sligo (BBS exc.) (Duncan 1928: 119).
†H28 listed by Blockeel & Long (1998: 103).
H29 1970: on bridge, Largydonnell, E Hegewald (BBS exc.) (Crundwell 1971b: 378, Appleyard 1971: 389).
H(30) listed by Lett (1915: 123). H(30) listed by Blockeel & Long (1998: 103).
H(31) listed by Lett (1915: 123). H(31) listed by Blockeel & Long (1998: 103).
H31 1999: on top of boulder on bank of stream, 350 m alt., Two Mile River, Carlingford, J11, TL Blockeel 28/185 (Rothero 2000: 52).

[H(32) listed by Lett (1915: 123) without locality. H32 deleted because no valid record or voucher specimen traced (Blockeel 1999: 6)].
H33 2000: on sandstone boulder in wall, S of Crossmurrin Nature Reserve, H13, DT Holyoak 00-140 (BBSUK) (Rothero 2001: 42).
H(34) listed by Lett (1915: 123).
†H34 listed by Blockeel & Long (1998: 103).
H(35) 1911: Killybegs, CA Cheetham (anon.1915: 126).
H(35) listed by Lett (1915: 123).
†H35 listed by Blockeel & Long (1998: 103).
H(36) listed by Lett (1915: 123).
†H36 listed by Blockeel & Long (1998: 103).
H(37) listed by Lett (1915: 123). H(37) listed by Blockeel & Long (1998: 103).
H(38) listed by Lett (1915: 123). H(38) listed by Blockeel & Long (1998: 103).
H38 2002: on rock outcrop above river, 150 m alt., W of Glen River in Donards Wood nr Newcastle, J32, DT Holyoak 02-1040 (Rothero 2003: 53).
H(39) 1928: on boulders and exposed glaciated rocks on moorland, Fair Head (BBS exc.) (Duncan 1928: 113, 116), as *G. Stirtoni*.
H(39) listed by Lett (1915: 123).
†H39 listed by Blockeel & Long (1998: 103).
H40 1950: basalt rock, Middle Taghmore, nr Limavady, J Taylor (Warburg 1951: 499).

Grimmia lisae De Not. is treated as a distinct species by Greven (1995: 90-93) and Muñoz & Pando (2000: 41-43), that apparently corresponds at least partly to *G. trichophylla* var. *subsquarrosa* of Smith (1978, 1992). Greven (1995: 92) gives three records of *G. lisae* from Ireland (Kerry, Glenbeigh, leg. Wallace; Killarney, Muckross Lake, leg. HC Greven 2223 and 2224; Killarney, Gap of Dunloe, leg. HC Greven 2222). More research is needed to establish that material from Ireland and Britain that is referred to *G. lisae* differs consistently from *G. trichophylla*, and to check the distribution of each form.

69/20 ***Grimmia retracta*** Stirt.

H(1) 1935: below O'Sullivan's Cascade, no collector named (BBS exc.) (Watson 1936: 264).
†H1 listed by Blockeel & Long (1998: 104).
H(2) listed by Lett (1915: 125). H(2) listed by Blockeel & Long (1998: 104).
†H3 listed by Blockeel & Long (1998: 104).
H16 1957: boulders on shore of L. Muck, nr Killary Harbour, AC Crundwell (BBS exc.) (Warburg 1958b: 477).
H(33) listed by Blockeel & Long (1998: 104).
H35 1972: granite boulder, Glen Lough, WV Rubers (U) (Crundwell 1975: 16).

The taxonomic status of *G. retracta* is uncertain. It was treated as a synonym of *G. lisae* (see above) by Greven (1995: 19, 90), but not assigned to any species recognised by Muñoz & Pando (2000: 110) because no type material was seen.

69/21 ***Grimmia hartmanii*** Schimp.

H(2) listed by Lett (1915: 123). H(2) listed by Blockeel & Long (1998: 104).
H(3) listed by Lett (1915: 123).
†H3 listed by Blockeel & Long (1998: 104).
H(7) 1945: by Loch Curra, Galtees, RD Meikle (anon. 1947: 29).
†H16 listed by Blockeel & Long (1998: 104).
H(20) 1939: Devil's Glen, Ashford, DB Bradshaw (anon. 1940a: 173).
H(26) listed by Lett (1915: 123). H(26) listed by Blockeel & Long (1998: 104).
H29 1972: on siliceous outcrop, E end of L. Gill, N of Dromahair, WV Rubers (U) (Crundwell 1974: 169).
H(31) 1943: Ravensdale, JS Thomson (Duncan 1944: 210).
H(34) listed by Lett (1915: 123). H(34) listed by Blockeel & Long (1998: 104).
H35 1972: granite boulder in *Alnus* wood, Glen Lough, WV Rubers (U) (Crundwell 1974: 169).
H(38) listed by Lett (1915: 123). H(38) listed by Blockeel & Long (1998: 104).
H(39) listed by Lett (1915: 123).
†H39 listed by Blockeel & Long (1998: 104).
H(40) listed by Blockeel & Long (1998: 104).
H40 1999: on basalt rocks of low wall by river, Garvagh Forest, C81, DT Holyoak 99-308 (BBSUK) (Rothero 2000: 52).

69/22 ***Grimmia britannica*** A.J.E.Sm..
(syn. *Grimmia austrofunalis* auct. non Müll.Hal. *G. decipiens* var. *robusta* (Fergusson) Braithw., *G. robusta* Fergusson, *G. trichophylla* var. *robusta* (Fergusson) A.J.E.Sm.)

H(1) 1935: nr L. Cruttia, no collector named (BBS exc.) (Watson 1936: 264).
†H1 listed by Blockeel & Long (1998: 104).
H(2) 1935: Brickeen Bridge, no collector named (BBS exc.) (Watson 1936: 264).
H3 1979: on rocks by the sea, Adrigole, EC Wallace (Hill 1980b: 39), as *G. decipiens* var. *robusta*.
H(16) listed by Lett (1915: 123).
H16 no date: Connemara, Killadoon, alt. 150 m, HMH van Melick 871349 (Greven 1997: 830).
†H16 listed by Blockeel & Long (1998: 104).
H(21) listed by Lett (1915: 123). H(21) listed by Blockeel & Long (1998: 104).
H35 1962: rocks above cliffs, Black Burrow, nr Dunfanaghy, EF Warburg & AC Crundwell (BBS exc.) (Warburg 1963b: 498).
H(38) listed by Lett (1915: 123). H(38) listed by Blockeel & Long (1998: 104).
H(39) listed by Lett (1915: 123). H(39) listed by Blockeel & Long (1998: 104).
H40 1968: on boulders in block litter below basalt cliffs, Benbradagh, HH Birks & RD Fitzgerald (Crundwell 1969: 883), as *G. decipiens* var. *robusta*.

Greven (1997) referred this taxon to *G. austrofunalis* (the name adopted by Blockeel & Long 1998: 104), but Muñoz & Pando (2000: 20-21) regard *G. austrofunalis* as being restricted to the Southern Hemisphere. Hence the name *G. britannica* is used here following Smith (1992) and Greven (1995: 49-52). There has been some doubt about the validity at species rank of *G. britannica* since some material referred to it appears to be *G. longirostris* or *G. trichophylla*, but further research is needed.

69/23 ***Grimmia decipiens*** (Schultz) Lindb.

H(6) listed by Lett (1915: 123). H(6) listed by Blockeel & Long (1998: 104).
H(16) listed by Lett (1915: 123).
†H16 listed by Blockeel & Long (1998: 104).
H(20) listed by Lett (1915: 123). H(20) listed by Blockeel & Long (1998: 104).
H(21) listed by Lett (1915: 123). H(21) listed by Blockeel & Long (1998: 104).
H27 1987: on exposed basic boulder, basic outcrop below N coire of Croagh Patrick, GP Rothero (Blockeel 1988: 36).
H(31) listed by Lett (1915: 123) without locality. H(31) listed by Blockeel & Long (1998: 104).
H(38) listed by Lett (1915: 123). H(38) listed by Blockeel & Long (1998: 104).
H38 2002: on boulder on N-facing hillside, 280 m alt., below Black Stairs, Thomas's Mt., J32, DT Holyoak, 02-1052 (Rothero 2003: 53).
H(39) listed by Lett (1915: 123). H(39) listed by Blockeel & Long (1998: 104).
H39 1990: on boulder in woodland, Murlough Bay, D14, P Martin (Rothero 1999b: 43).
1999: on dolerite rock on exposed cliff top, E of Lough Fadden, D14, DT Holyoak 99-793 (BBSUK) (Rothero 2000: 52).

69/25 ***Grimmia ramondii*** (Lam. & DC.) Margad.
(syn. *Dryptodon patens* (Hedw.) Brid., *Grimmia curvata* (Brid.) De Sloover, *G. patens* (Hedw.) Bruch, Schimp. & W. Gümbel)

H(1) listed by Lett (1915: 124).
†H1 listed by Blockeel & Long (1998: 104).
[H(2) listed by Lett (1915: 124). H2 deleted (Smith 1971, Crundwell 1972: 139)].
H2 1983: boulders on lake shore, N end of Lough Managh, Mangerton Mt., DG Long (Hill 1984b: 28).
H(3) listed by Lett (1915: 124). H(3) listed by Blockeel & Long (1998: 104).
H(6) listed by Lett (1915: 124).
†H6 listed by Blockeel & Long (1998: 104).
H(7) listed by Lett (1915: 124). H(7) listed by Blockeel & Long (1998: 104).
H(16) listed by Lett (1915: 124).
†H16 listed by Blockeel & Long (1998: 104).
H(20) listed by Lett (1915: 124).
†H20 listed by Blockeel & Long (1998: 104).
H(21) listed by Lett (1915: 124). H(21) listed by Blockeel & Long (1998: 104).
H(27) listed by Lett (1915: 124). H(27) listed by Blockeel & Long (1998: 104).

[H(31) listed by Lett (1915: 124) as 1899: Carlingford Mt., leg. HW Lett. H31 deleted: specimen from Golden River, Carlingford Mt., 1899, leg. HW Lett (DBN), is *Racomitrium heterostichum*, comm. DM Synnott (Blockeel 1989: 28)].
[H(33) listed by Lett (1915: 124) as 1905: Castlecaldwell, leg. HW Lett. H33 deleted: specimen from Castlecaldwell, 1905, leg. HW Lett (DBN), is *Cinclidotus fontinaloides*, comm. DM Synnott (Blockeel 1989: 28)].
H34 1962: rocks by Barnes Lough, EF Warburg (BBS exc.) (Warburg 1963b: 498).
H(35) listed by Lett (1915: 124).
†H35 listed by Blockeel & Long (1998: 104).
H(38) listed by Lett (1915: 124). H(38) listed by Blockeel & Long (1998: 104).
H38 2002: on boulder on N-facing hillside, 280 m alt., below Black Stairs, Thomas's Mt., J32, DT Holyoak 02-1050 (Rothero 2003: 53).
H(39) listed by Lett (1915: 124). H(39) listed by Blockeel & Long (1998: 104).
H(40) listed by Lett (1915: 124).
†H40 listed by Blockeel & Long (1998: 104).

Listed as *Grimmia curvata* by Blockeel & Long (1998: 104); adoption of the name *G. ramondii* follows Muñoz & Pando (2000: 71).

70/1 ***Racomitrium ellipticum*** (Turner) Bruch & Schimp.
(syn. *Grimmia elliptica* (Turner) Arnott, *Rhacomitrium ellipticum* auct.)

H(1) listed by Lett (1915: 124).
†H1 listed by Blockeel & Long (1998: 104).
H2 1983: rock on N shore of L. Managh, Horse's Glen, Mangerton Mt., JA Paton (Hill 1984b: 28).
H(3) listed by Lett (1915: 124).
†H3 listed by Blockeel & Long (1998: 104).
H(4) listed by Lett (1915: 124). H(4) listed by Blockeel & Long (1998: 104).
H(16) listed by Lett (1915: 124).
†H16 listed by Blockeel & Long (1998: 104).
H(20) listed by Lett (1915: 124). H(20) listed by Blockeel & Long (1998: 104).
[H(21) listed by Lett (1915: 124). H21 record deleted (Smith 1973a, Crundwell 1974: 169)].
H(27) listed by Lett (1915: 124) without locality.
†H27 listed by Blockeel & Long (1998: 104).
[H(28) listed by Lett (1915: 124) as Benbulben, leg. R Brown. H28 deleted because record is based on Bulbein Mt. [*sic* = Bulbin Mt.] which is in H34 (Crundwell 1970: 202)].
†H31 listed by Blockeel & Long (1998: 104).
H(34) listed by Lett (1915: 124). H(34) listed by Blockeel & Long (1998: 104).
H34 2002: on schist rocks on N-facing slope, 490 m alt., Bulbin Mt. just NW of summit, C34, DT Holyoak 02-512B (Rothero 2003: 53).
H(35) listed by Lett (1915: 124).
†H35 listed by Blockeel & Long (1998: 104).
[H(37) listed by Lett (1915: 124) without details. H37 record deleted (Smith 1973a, Crundwell 1974: 169)].
H(38) listed by Lett (1915: 124).
†H38 listed by Blockeel & Long (1998: 104).
H(39) listed by Lett (1915: 124).
†H39 listed by Blockeel & Long (1998: 104).
H(40) listed by Lett (1915: 124).
†H40 listed by Blockeel & Long (1998: 104).

70/2 ***Racomitrium aciculare*** (Hedw.) Brid.
(syn. *Grimmia acicularis* (Hedw.) Müll. Hal., *G. acicularis* var. *denticulata* (Bruch, Schimp. & W.Gümbel) Braithw., *Rhacomitrium aciculare* auct.)

H(1) listed by Lett (1915: 124) without details.
†H1 listed by Blockeel & Long (1998: 104).
H(2) listed by Lett (1915: 124) without details.
†H2 listed by Blockeel & Long (1998: 104).
H(3) listed by Lett (1915: 124) without details.
†H3 listed by Blockeel & Long (1998: 104).
H(4) listed by Lett (1915: 124) without details.
†H4 listed by Blockeel & Long (1998: 104).
H(6) listed by Lett (1915: 124) without details.
†H6 listed by Blockeel & Long (1998: 104).
H(7) listed by Lett (1915: 124) without details.
†H7 listed by Blockeel & Long (1998: 104).
H(8) no date: S Tipperary and Limerick boundary, AW Stelfox, per JS Thomson (anon. 1946c: 281).
†H8 listed by Blockeel & Long (1998: 104).

H(9) listed by Lett (1915: 124) without details.
†H9 listed by Blockeel & Long (1998: 104).
H10 1979: stream, W side of Keeper Hill, S of Silvermine Mts, HMH van Melick (Hill 1981: 28).
[H(11) listed by Lett (1915: 124) without details. H11 deleted because no valid record or voucher specimen traced (Blockeel 1999: 6)].
H(12) listed by Lett (1915: 124) without details.
†H12 listed by Blockeel & Long (1998: 104).
H(13) listed by Lett (1915: 124) without details.
†H13 listed by Blockeel & Long (1998: 104).
H(14) listed by Lett (1915: 124) without details.
†H14 listed by Blockeel & Long (1998: 104).
[H(15) listed by Lett (1915: 124) without details. H15 deleted because no valid record or voucher specimen traced (Blockeel 1999: 6)].
H(16) listed by Lett (1915: 124) without details.
†H16 listed by Blockeel & Long (1998: 104).
[H(18) listed by Lett (1915: 124) without details. H18 deleted because no valid record or voucher specimen traced (Blockeel 1999: 6)].
H(20) listed by Lett (1915: 124) without details.
†H20 listed by Blockeel & Long (1998: 104).
H(21) listed by Lett (1915: 124) without details.
†H21 listed by Blockeel & Long (1998: 104).
H22 1950: Slane, JS Thomson (Warburg 1952: 100).
H(25) listed by Lett (1915: 124) without details.
†H25 listed by Blockeel & Long (1998: 104).
H(26) listed by Lett (1915: 124) without details.
†H26 listed by Blockeel & Long (1998: 104).
H(27) listed by Lett (1915: 124) without details.
†H27 listed by Blockeel & Long (1998: 104).
H(28) listed by Lett (1915: 124) without details.
†H28 listed by Blockeel & Long (1998: 104).
H(29) listed by Lett (1915: 124) without details.
†H29 listed by Blockeel & Long (1998: 104).
H(30) listed by Lett (1915: 124) without details.
†H30 listed by Blockeel & Long (1998: 104).
[H(31) listed by Lett (1915: 124) without details. H31 deleted because no valid record or voucher specimen traced (Blockeel 1999: 6)].
H31 1999: on boulder in stream, 350 m alt., Two Mile River, Carlingford, J11, TL Blockeel 28/184 (Rothero 2000: 52).
[H(32) listed by Lett (1915: 124) without details. H32 deleted because no valid record or voucher specimen traced (Blockeel 1999: 6)].
H(33) listed by Lett (1915: 124) without details.
†H33 listed by Blockeel & Long (1998: 104).
H(34) listed by Lett (1915: 124) without details.
†H34 listed by Blockeel & Long (1998: 104).
H(35) listed by Lett (1915: 124) without details.
†H35 listed by Blockeel & Long (1998: 104).
H(36) listed by Lett (1915: 124) without details.
†H36 listed by Blockeel & Long (1998: 104).
H(37) listed by Lett (1915: 124) without details.
†H37 listed by Blockeel & Long (1998: 104).
H(38) listed by Lett (1915: 124) without details.
†H38 listed by Blockeel & Long (1998: 104).
H(39) listed by Lett (1915: 124).
†H39 listed by Blockeel & Long (1998: 104).
H(40) listed by Lett (1915: 124) without details.
†H40 listed by Blockeel & Long (1998: 104).

70/3 ***Racomitrium aquaticum*** (Schrad.) Brid. (syn. *Grimmia aquatica* (Schrad.) Müll. Hal., *Rhacomitrium aquaticum* auct.)

H(1) listed by Lett (1915: 124).
†H1 listed by Blockeel & Long (1998: 105).
H(2) listed by Lett (1915: 124).
†H2 listed by Blockeel & Long (1998: 105).
H(3) listed by Lett (1915: 124).
†H3 listed by Blockeel & Long (1998: 105).
H4 1967: wet rocks, *ca* 1300 ft [alt.], Musherabeg, RD Fitzgerald (Crundwell 1968: 637).
H5 1967: stones nr stream, Coolgreen Glen, SW of Watergrasshill, RD Fitzgerald (Crundwell 1968: 637).
†H6 listed by Blockeel & Long (1998: 105).
H(7) listed by Lett (1915: 124).
†H7 listed by Blockeel & Long (1998: 105).

H8 1966: damp rock at 1600 ft alt., Temple Hill, Galtee Mts, MFV Corley & JS Parker (Perry 1967: 414).
H(11) listed by Lett (1915: 124). H(11) listed by Blockeel & Long (1998: 105).
H(12) listed by Lett (1915: 124).
†H12 listed by Blockeel & Long (1998: 105).
H(13) listed by Lett (1915: 124).
†H13 listed by Blockeel & Long (1998: 105).
H(16) listed by Lett (1915: 124).
†H16 listed by Blockeel & Long (1998: 105).
H(18) listed by Lett (1915: 124). H(18) listed by Blockeel & Long (1998: 105).
H(20) listed by Lett (1915: 124).
†H20 listed by Blockeel & Long (1998: 105).
H21 1950: boulder by stream, Larch Hill, Whitechurch, JP Brunker (Warburg 1951: 499).
H24 1965: boulders on Corn Hill, nr Drumlish, EM Lobley & RD Fitzgerald (Warburg 1966: 196).
H(25) listed by Lett (1915: 124). H(25) listed by Blockeel & Long (1998: 105).
H25 2002: on rocks by stream, 150 m alt., Kilronan Mt., Arigna, G91, NG Hodgetts 4151 (Rothero 2003: 53).
H(26) listed by Lett (1915: 124).
†H26 listed by Blockeel & Long (1998: 105).
H(27) listed by Lett (1915: 124).
†H27 listed by Blockeel & Long (1998: 105).
H(28) listed by Lett (1915: 124).
†H28 listed by Blockeel & Long (1998: 105).
H(29) listed by Lett (1915: 124).
†H29 listed by Blockeel & Long (1998: 105).
H(30) listed by Lett (1915: 124).
†H30 listed by Blockeel & Long (1998: 105).
H(31) listed by Lett (1915: 124).
†H31 listed by Blockeel & Long (1998: 105).
H(32) listed by Lett (1915: 124). H(32) listed by Blockeel & Long (1998: 105).
H33 1965: wet rocks in deep cleft, *ca* 2000 ft alt., Cuilcagh, nr Belcoo, RD Fitzgerald (Warburg 1966: 196).
H34 1962: boulder by stream above Barnes Bridge, EF Warburg (BBS exc.) (Warburg 1963b: 498).
H(35) listed by Lett (1915: 124).
†H35 listed by Blockeel & Long (1998: 105).
H36 1958: wet rocks, 950 ft [alt.], Eagle Rocks, Beleevanmore Mt., RD Fitzgerald (Warburg 1959: 633).
†H37 listed by Blockeel & Long (1998: 105).
H(38) listed by Lett (1915: 124).
†H38 listed by Blockeel & Long (1998: 105).
H(39) listed by Lett (1915: 124) without locality.
†H39 listed by Blockeel & Long (1998: 105).
H40 1965: rocks *ca* 1600 ft alt., Mullaghmore, nr Dungiven, RD Fitzgerald (Warburg 1966: 196).

70/4 ***Racomitrium fasciculare*** (Hedw.) Brid. (syn. *Grimmia fascicularis* (Hedw.) Müll.Hal., *Rhacomitrium fasciculare* auct.)

H(1) listed by Lett (1915: 125) without details.
†H1 listed by Blockeel & Long (1998: 105).
H(2) listed by Lett (1915: 125) without details.
†H2 listed by Blockeel & Long (1998: 105).
H(3) listed by Lett (1915: 125) without details.
†H3 listed by Blockeel & Long (1998: 105).
H(4) listed by Lett (1915: 125) without details.
†H4 listed by Blockeel & Long (1998: 105).
H(6) listed by Lett (1915: 125) without details.
†H6 listed by Blockeel & Long (1998: 105).
H(7) listed by Lett (1915: 125) without details.
†H7 listed by Blockeel & Long (1998: 105).
H(8) no date: S Tipperary and Limerick boundary, AW Stelfox, per JS Thomson (anon. 1946c: 281).
†H8 listed by Blockeel & Long (1998: 105).
H10 1965: cut-away bog, L. Nahinch, ALK King (Warburg 1966: 196).
H(11) listed by Lett (1915: 125) without details.
†H11 listed by Blockeel & Long (1998: 105).
H(12) listed by Lett (1915: 125) without details.
†H12 listed by Blockeel & Long (1998: 105).
H(13) listed by Lett (1915: 125) without details.
†H13 listed by Blockeel & Long (1998: 105).
H(14) listed by Lett (1915: 125) without details.
†H14 listed by Blockeel & Long (1998: 105).
[H(15) listed by Lett (1915: 125) without details. H15 deleted because no valid record or voucher specimen traced (Blockeel 1999: 6)].
H(16) listed by Lett (1915: 125) without details.
†H16 listed by Blockeel & Long (1998: 105).
H19 1954: wall of lane between Glending

and Newtown, ALK King (Warburg 1955: 584).
H(20) listed by Lett (1915: 125) without details.
†H20 listed by Blockeel & Long (1998: 105).
H(21) listed by Lett (1915: 125) without details.
†H21 listed by Blockeel & Long (1998: 105).
H22 1978: quarry, Teevurcher, N of Moynalty, DM Synnott (Hill 1979: 28).
H24 1966: boulders, Corn Hill, nr Drumlish, RD Fitzgerald & EM Lobley (Perry 1967: 414).
H(25) listed by Lett (1915: 125) without details.
†H25 listed by Blockeel & Long (1998: 105).
H(26) listed by Lett (1915: 125) without details.
†H26 listed by Blockeel & Long (1998: 105).
H(27) listed by Lett (1915: 125) without details.
†H27 listed by Blockeel & Long (1998: 105).
H(28) listed by Lett (1915: 125) without details.
†H28 listed by Blockeel & Long (1998: 105).
H(29) listed by Lett (1915: 125) without details.
†H29 listed by Blockeel & Long (1998: 105).
H(30) listed by Lett (1915: 125) without details.
†H30 listed by Blockeel & Long (1998: 105).
[H(31) listed by Lett (1915: 125) without details. H31 deleted because no valid record or voucher specimen traced (Blockeel 1999: 6)].
H31 1999: on boulder on slope above stream, 300 m alt., Two Mile River, Carlingford, J11, TL Blockeel 28/172 (Rothero 2000: 52).
[H(32) listed by Lett (1915: 125) without details. H32 deleted because no valid record or voucher specimen traced (Blockeel 1999: 6)].
H(33) listed by Lett (1915: 125) without details.
†H33 listed by Blockeel & Long (1998: 105).
H(34) listed by Lett (1915: 125) without details.
†H34 listed by Blockeel & Long (1998: 105).
H(35) listed by Lett (1915: 125) without details.
†H35 listed by Blockeel & Long (1998: 105).
H(36) listed by Lett (1915: 125) without details.
†H36 listed by Blockeel & Long (1998: 105).
H(37) listed by Lett (1915: 125) without details.
†H37 listed by Blockeel & Long (1998: 105).
H(38) listed by Lett (1915: 125) without details.
†H38 listed by Blockeel & Long (1998: 105).
H(39) listed by Lett (1915: 125) without details.
†H39 listed by Blockeel & Long (1998: 105).
H(40) listed by Lett (1915: 125) without details.
†H40 listed by Blockeel & Long (1998: 105).

70/5-8 ***Racomitrium heterostichum*** aggregate

H(1) 1935: L. Naluchan, no collector named (BBS exc.) (Watson 1936: 264), as *Rhacomitrium ramulosum.*
H(6) 1933: Coumshingaun, E Armitage (anon. 1934b: 114), as *Rhacomitrium protensum.*
H30 1910: Tents Mt., WN Tetley (anon. 1915b: 9), as *Rhacomitrium protensum.*
H36 1957: rocks, 1750 ft [alt.], Dart Mt., Sperrin Mts, RD Fitzgerald (Warburg 1958b: 477), as *Rhacomitrium heterostichum* var. gracilescens.
H(39) 1923: Slemish Mt., WR Megaw (anon. 1924: 68), as *Rhacomitrium heterostichum* var. *gracilescens.*

Specimens supporting the records listed above have apparently not been reidentified as any of the segregate species covered in the review by Blockeel (1991b). Many old records (e.g. of *Grimmia microcarpa*, *G. obtusa*, *G. obtusa* var. *subsimplex*, *G. affinis*, *G. affinis* var. *gracilescens* and *G. heterosticha* from Lett 1915: 123-125) are not listed here because they can also be placed only as the aggregate of species unless specimens have been revised.

70/5 ***Racomitrium macounii*** Kindb. **subsp.** ***alpinum*** (E.Lawton) Frisvoll

H1 1998: unshaded rocks by river with *Racomitrium aciculare, Brachythecium plumosum, Parmelia conspersa*, 40 m alt., Dromanassig Waterfall, Sheen River SE of Kenmare, V96, A Orange 11904 (Rothero 1999b: 43).

The present treatment of 70/5 to 70/8 in Britain and Ireland dates from the review by Blockeel (1991b).

70/6 ***Racomitrium sudeticum*** (Funck) Bruch & Schimp.
(syn. *Racomitrium affine* sensu A.J.E. Sm., *Rhacomitrium sudeticum* auct.)

H1 1983: rock in NW corrie, Mullaghanattin, NW of Kenmare, JA Paton (Hill 1984b: 28 as *R. affine*; Blockeel 1991b: 34, 1992: 27).
H3 1979: Shehy Mts, JA Paton (Blockeel 1991b: 34, 1992: 27).
H6 1999: on top of boulder by corrie lake, 530 m alt., Lough Coumfea, Comeragh Mts, S20, TL Blockeel 28/231 (Rothero 2000: 52).
H12 1969: Blackstairs Mts, RD Fitzgerald (Blockeel 1991b: 34, 1992: 27).
H16 1985: Lissoughter, AC Bouman (Blockeel 1991b: 34, 1992: 27).
H20 1969: Lough Ouler, RD Fitzgerald (Blockeel 1991b: 34, 1992: 27).
H(27) 1917: Achill, WR Tetley (Blockeel 1991b: 34, 1992: 27).
†H27 listed by Blockeel & Long (1998: 105).
H28 1963: Knockachree, AR Perry & RD Fitzgerald (Blockeel 1991b: 34, 1992: 27).
H(30) 1909: Cuilcagh, WR Tetley (Blockeel 1991b: 34, 1992: 27).
H30 2001: in shallow crevices of open gritstone rocks, 650 m alt., Cuilcagh, SW of summit, H12, DT Holyoak 01-769 (Rothero 2002: 48).
H31 1999: on boulder on moorland slope, 300 m alt., Two Mile River, Carlingford, J11, TL Blockeel 28/161 (Rothero 2000: 52).
H33 1959: Quilcagh [*sic* = Cuilcagh], RD Fitzgerald (Blockeel 1991b: 34, 1992: 27).
H34 2002: on schist crags, 485 m alt., Bulbin Mt. just NW of summit, C34, DT Holyoak 02-502 (Rothero 2003: 54).
H(35) 1890: Errigal, HN Dixon (Blockeel 1991b: 34 , 1992: 27).
†H35 listed by Blockeel & Long (1998: 105).
H(38) 1917: Thomas Mt., J Glover (Blockeel 1991b: 34, 1992: 27).
†H38 listed by Blockeel & Long (1998: 105).
H(39) 1809: Slemish, J Templeton (Blockeel 1991b: 34, 1992: 27).

Records from Ireland and Britain were revised by Blockeel (1991b).

70/7 ***Racomitrium affine*** (Schleich. ex F. Weber & D.Mohr) Lindb.
(syn. *Rhacomitrium affine* auct.)

H16 1985: on rock, W slope of Lissoughter, Connemara, AC Bouman (Blockeel 1987: 23).
1994: on wall top, 100 m alt., Glencoaghan, below SW slopes of Derryclare, L85, TL Blockeel 23/180 (Blockeel 1995c: 43).
H(27) 1933: Mallarany, PW Richards (Blockeel 1991b: 34, 1992: 27).
H33 2000: on sandstone boulder on moorland slope, SE of Carricknagower Lough, H05, DT Holyoak 00-320 (BBSUK) (Rothero 2001: 42).
H34 1967: Red Castle, RD Fitzgerald (Blockeel 1991b: 34, 1992: 27).
H36 2002: on granite boulder, 210 m alt., in old quarry SW of Cam Lough, H67, DT Holyoak 02-1101 (Rothero 2003: 54).
H38 1960: Commedagh, AW Stelfox (Blockeel 1991b: 34, 1992: 27).
H39 1950: Crow Glen, RD Fitzgerald (Blockeel 1991b: 34, 1992: 27).

Records from Ireland and Britain were revised by Blockeel (1991b), using characters elucidated in the taxonomic review by Frisvoll (1988). Earlier records (e.g. in Corley & Hill 1981: 89) should be discounted because identification was based on different characters to those used by Frisvoll (most of earlier Irish and British records placed as *R. affine* are now referred to *R. sudeticum*).

70/8 ***Racomitrium heterostichum*** (Hedw.) Brid.
(syn. *Racomitrium heterostichum* var. gracilescens auct. pro parte, *R..obtusum* (Brid.) Brid., *Rhacomitrium heterostichum* auct.)

H(1) 1935: Brandon Mt., HN Dixon (Blockeel 1991b: 35, 1992: 26).
†H1 listed by Blockeel & Long (1998: 105).
H2 1979: Torc, EC Wallace (Blockeel 1991b: 35, 1992: 26).

H3 2002: on large boulder, 530 m alt., Gougane Barra, Lough Fadda, W06, TL Blockeel 31/323 (Rothero 2003: 54).
H4 1967: Blarney, RD Fitzgerald (Blockeel 1991b: 35, 1992: 26).
H6 1966: Clonmel, RD Fitzgerald (Blockeel 1991b: 35, 1992: 26).
H7 1966: Knockastakeen, RD Fitzgerald (Blockeel 1991b: 35, 1992: 26).
H11 1954: Mt Brandon, ALK King (Warburg 1955: 584, Blockeel 1991b: 35, 1992: 26).
H14 1956: siliceous rock above Johnsborough, Slieve Bloom, AA Cridland (Warburg 1958b: 477, Blockeel 1991b: 35, 1992: 26).
H15 1957: sandstone boulder, hills E of Gort, RE Parker (Warburg 1958b: 477, Blockeel 1991b: 35, 1992: 26).
H16 1996: E side of NE corrie of Muckanaght, Twelve Bens, L75, DG Long 26252 (Blockeel 1997a: 43).
H19 1953: dry exposed boulder, Cupidstown Hill, ALK King (Warburg 1954: 481, Blockeel 1991b: 35, 1992: 26).
H(20) 1873: Lough Bray, Lindberg (Blockeel 1991b: 53, 1992: 26).
†H20 listed by Blockeel & Long (1998: 105).
[H21 uncertain record given by Blockeel 1991b: 35 as: 1855: Dublin Mts, Orr)].
H22 1978: roadside quarry, Teevurcher, N of Moynalty, DM Synnott (Hill 1979: 28, Blockeel 1991b: 35, 1992: 26).
H24 1965: boulder, *ca* 750 ft alt., Corn Hill, nr Drumlish, RD Fitzgerald & EM Lobley (Warburg 1966: 196, Blockeel 1991b: 35, 1992: 26).
H(25) 1910: Sheegorey, WR Tetley (Blockeel 1991b: 35, 1992: 26).
†H25 listed by Blockeel & Long (1998: 105).
H27 1966: Knappagh, M Barnes (Blockeel 1991b: 35, 1992: 26).
H(28) 1903: L. Gill, WR Tetley (Blockeel 1991b: 35, 1992: 26).
†H28 listed by Blockeel & Long (1998: 105).
H29 2001: on steep, E-facing sandstone crag, 420 m alt., Coal Pit, E slope of Bencroy, H01, DT Holyoak 01-793 (Rothero 2002: 48).
H30 2001: on open horizontal rock on heathy hillside, 285 m alt., Slieve Glah, E slope, H40, DT Holyoak 01-691 (Rothero 2002: 48).
H31 1951: Flurry Bridge [correction of Fluny? Bridge], RD Fitzgerald (Blockeel 1991b: 35, 1992: 26-27).
H33 2000: on sandstone boulder in limestone grassland, S of Crossmurrin Nature Reserve, H13, DT Holyoak 00-136 (BBSUK) (Rothero 2001: 42).
H34 2001: on siliceous rocks on NW-facing slope above disused railway, 100 m alt., Barnesmore Gap, SE of Ardinawark, H08, NG Hodgetts 3884 (Rothero 2003: 54).
H35 1950: Poisoned Glen, RD Fitzgerald (Blockeel 1991b: 35, 1992: 26).
H37 1964: Slieve Gullion, RD Fitzgerald (Blockeel 1991b: 35, 1992: 26).
H38 1950: Ards, RD Fitzgerald (Blockeel 1991b: 35, 1992: 26).
H39 1963: Fair Head, AR Perry (Blockeel 1991b: 35, 1992: 26).
H40 1999: on unshaded boulders and basalt outcrop on SW- to W-facing slope, 370 m alt., E of Binevenagh Lake, C63, DT Holyoak 99-250 (BBSUK) (Rothero 2000: 52-53).

Records from Britain and Ireland were revised by Blockeel (1991b).

70/10 ***Racomitrium lanuginosum*** (Hedw.) Brid.
(syn. *Grimmia hypnoides* Lindb., *Rhacomitrium lanuginosum* auct.)

H(1) listed by Lett (1915: 125) without details.
†H1 listed by Blockeel & Long (1998: 105).
H(2) listed by Lett (1915: 125) without details.
†H2 listed by Blockeel & Long (1998: 105).
H(3) listed by Lett (1915: 125) without details.
†H3 listed by Blockeel & Long (1998: 105).
H(4) listed by Lett (1915: 125) without details.
†H4 listed by Blockeel & Long (1998: 105).
H(5) listed by Lett (1915: 125) without details.
†H5 listed by Blockeel & Long (1998: 105).
H(6) listed by Lett (1915: 125) without details.
†H6 listed by Blockeel & Long (1998: 105).
H(7) listed by Lett (1915: 125) without details.
†H7 listed by Blockeel & Long (1998: 105).
H8 1966: ground on moor, Slievereagh, nr Ballylanders, MFV Corley & JS Parker

(Perry 1967: 414).
H(9) listed by Lett (1915: 125) without details.
†H9 listed by Blockeel & Long (1998: 105).
H10 1979: heath on S slope of Keeper Hill, JA Paton (Hill 1980b: 40).
H(11) listed by Lett (1915: 125) without details.
†H11 listed by Blockeel & Long (1998: 105).
H(12) listed by Lett (1915: 125) without details.
†H12 listed by Blockeel & Long (1998: 105).
H(13) listed by Lett (1915: 125) without details.
†H13 listed by Blockeel & Long (1998: 105).
H(14) listed by Lett (1915: 125) without details.
†H14 listed by Blockeel & Long (1998: 105).
H15 1961: among hummock-forming Sphagna in bog nr Cloon Bridge, nr Gort, EM Lobley (Warburg 1962: 369).
H(16) 1911: Arrishay, CA Cheetham (anon.1915: 127).
H(16) listed by Lett (1915: 125) without details.
†H16 listed by Blockeel & Long (1998: 105).
H(17) listed by Lett (1915: 125) without details.
†H17 listed by Blockeel & Long (1998: 105).
H18 1990: amongst *Calluna* on raised bog, 60 m alt., Woodfield Bog nr Clara, N23, DG Long 18137 (Blockeel 1991c: 43).
[H(19) listed by Lett (1915: 125) without details. H19 deleted because no valid record or voucher specimen traced (Blockeel 1999: 6)].
H(20) listed by Lett (1915: 125) without details.
†H20 listed by Blockeel & Long (1998: 105).
H(21) listed by Lett (1915: 125) without details.
†H21 listed by Blockeel & Long (1998: 105).
H22 1978: quarry, Teevurcher, N of Moynalty, DM Synnott (Hill 1979: 28).
H23 1980: raised bog E of Lissmacaffry, DM Synnott (Hill 1981: 28).
H24 1965: raised bog S of Roosky, RD Fitzgerald & EM Lobley (Warburg 1966: 196).
H(25) listed by Lett (1915: 125) without details.
†H25 listed by Blockeel & Long (1998: 105).
†H26 listed by Blockeel & Long (1998: 105).
H(27) listed by Lett (1915: 125) without details.
†H27 listed by Blockeel & Long (1998: 105).
H(28) listed by Lett (1915: 125) without details.
†H28 listed by Blockeel & Long (1998: 105).
H(29) listed by Lett (1915: 125) without details.
†H29 listed by Blockeel & Long (1998: 105).
H(30) listed by Lett (1915: 125) without details.
†H30 listed by Blockeel & Long (1998: 105).
H(31) listed by Lett (1915: 125) without details.
†H31 listed by Blockeel & Long (1998: 105).
H(32) listed by Lett (1915: 125) without details.
†H32 listed by Blockeel & Long (1998: 105).
H(33) listed by Lett (1915: 125) without details.
†H33 listed by Blockeel & Long (1998: 105).
H(34) listed by Lett (1915: 125) without details.
†H34 listed by Blockeel & Long (1998: 105).
H(35) listed by Lett (1915: 125) without details.
†H35 listed by Blockeel & Long (1998: 105).
H(36) listed by Lett (1915: 125) without details.
†H36 listed by Blockeel & Long (1998: 105).
H(37) listed by Lett (1915: 125) without details.
†H37 listed by Blockeel & Long (1998: 105).
H(38) listed by Lett (1915: 125) without details.
†H38 listed by Blockeel & Long (1998: 105).
H(39) listed by Lett (1915: 125) without details.
†H39 listed by Blockeel & Long (1998: 105).
H(40) listed by Lett (1915: 125) without details.
†H40 listed by Blockeel & Long (1998: 105).

70/11 ***Racomitrium ericoides*** (Brid.) Brid.
(syn. *Racomitrium canescens* auct. non (Hedw.) Brid., *R.. canescens* (Hedw.) Brid. var. *ericoides* (Brid.) Hampe, *Rhacomitrium ericoides* auct.)

H1 1951: roadside, Windy Gap, between Caragh Lake and Glenbeigh, PW Richards (BBS exc.) (BBSUK) (Warburg 1952: 100, Hill 1984a: 25, 1984b: 28).
H2 1983: roadside nr Galway's Bridge, J Appleyard (Hill 1984a: 25, 1984b: 28).
H3 1953: bank of road below Coomataggert

Mt., nr Gougane Barra, ALK King (BBSUK) (Warburg 1954: 481, Hill 1984a: 25, 1984b: 28).

H5 1967: track in bog, *ca* 800 ft [alt.], Lyrenamon, NW of Garrignavar, RD Fitzgerald (BBSUK) (Crundwell 1968: 637, Hill 1984a: 25, 1984b: 28).

H12 1975: roadside quarry, Cummer Vale, NW of Gorey, DM Synnott (DBN) (Hill 1984a: 25, 1984b: 28).

H13 1969: track in old quarry, Lackan, nr Oldleighlin, RD Fitzgerald (BBSUK) (Crundwell 1970: 202; Hill 1984a: 25, 1984b: 28).

H15 1957: rocky place by the roadside nr Lough Cutra, J Appleyard (BBS exc.) (BBSUK) (Warburg 1958b: 477, Hill 1984a: 25, 1984b: 28).

H16 1955: on granite in Cloosh Valley, Connemara, ALK King (DBN) (Hill 1984a: 25, 1984b: 28).

H18 1965: moorland at Letter Cross, Slieve Bloom Mts, ALK King (BBSUK) (Perry 1967: 414, Hill 1984a: 25, 1984b: 28).

H(19) 1946: Cupidstown Hill, AW Stelfox (per JS Thomson) (BBSUK) (anon. 1947: 30, Hill 1984a: 25, 1984b: 28).

H20 1956: hillslope above Rocky Valley, ALK King (DBN) (Hill 1984a: 25, 1984b: 28).

H(21) 1850: Kilakee, D Orr (DBN) (Hill 1984a: 25, 1984b: 28).

H25 1981: shore of Boyle R., W of Boyle, DM Synnott (DBN) (Hill 1984a: 25, 1984b: 28).

[H(26) 1945: Cong, W Mayo [*sic*], ML Anderson, per JS Thomson (anon. 1946c: 281), as *R. canescens*. H(26) not listed for any species of *R. canescens* group following revision of specimens by Hill (1984a)].

H(27) 1910: nr Louisburgh, HW Lett (DBN) (Hill 1984a: 25, 1984b: 28).

†H27 listed by Blockeel & Long (1998: 106).

H(28) 1911: Ben Weeskin, WN Tetley (BBSUK) (Hill 1984a: 25, 1984b: 28).

H29 1963: on ground, *ca* 900 ft [alt.], Boggaun, nr Manorhamilton, RD Fitzgerald & AR Perry (BBSUK) (Warburg 1964: 727, Hill 1984a: 25, 1984b: 28).

H(30) 1909: by river, Lower Quilcagh [*sic* = Cuilcagh], WN Tetley (BBSUK) (Hill 1984a: 25, 1984b: 28).

H(31) 1883: Anglesey Mt., HW Lett (DBN) (Hill 1984a: 25, 1984b: 28).

H(32) 1947: beside railway sleepers, Castleblaney, JS Thomson (BBSUK) (anon. 1948b: 120, Hill 1984a: 25, 1984b: 28).

H(33) 1907: stone slope nr the bridge, Correll Glen, WN Tetley (BBSUK) (Hill 1984a: 25, 1984b: 28).

H34 2002: on soil amongst rocks in old quarry, 197 m alt., NE slope of Damph, SW of Glentogher, C43, DT Holyoak 02-585 (Rothero 2003: 54).

H(35) 1907: Killybegs, CA Cheetham, (DBN) (anon. 1915a: 127, Hill 1984a: 25, 1984b: 28).

H35 2001: on broken tarmac in lane, 20 m alt., Doonan, Teelin Bay, G57, NG Hodgetts 3756 (Rothero 2002: 48).

H36 1999: on soil on gravel on road nr cattle-grid, NW of Dart Mt., H59, DT Holyoak 99-705B (BBSUK) (Rothero 2000: 53).

H(38) 1883: sandhills, Newcastle, CH Waddell (DBN) (Hill 1984a: 25, 1984b: 28).

H38 2002: on open sandy shingle in dune heathland, 5 m alt., Murlough NNR, J33, DT Holyoak 02-949 (Rothero 2003: 54).

H(39) 1928: Portrush sand-hills, A Sutton (BBSUK) (Hill 1984a: 25, 1984b: 28).

H39 1999: in low vegetation on damp sand of bank by dune slack, E of Portrush, C84, DT Holyoak 99-238 (BBSUK) (Rothero 2000: 53).

H40 1999: on tarmac at edge of minor road, Windy Hill, C73, DT Holyoak 99-552 (BBSUK) (Rothero 2000: 53).

Although Hill (1978: 20) noted that older records of '*R. canescens*' from Ireland (except H22) 'may be presumed to be var. *ericoides*', the present treatment of 70/11 to 70/13 dates from the taxonomic revision by Frisvoll (1983) and review of specimens from Britain and Ireland by Hill (1984a). Older records (e.g. those listed as *Grimmia canescens* and *G. canescens* var. *ericoides* in Lett 1915: 125) can only be safely assigned to the species currently recognised when specimens have been re-examined.

70/12 ***Racomitrium elongatum*** Frisvoll
(syn. *Rhacomitrium elongatum* auct.)

H20 1975: road by Upper Lake, Glendalough, DM Synnott (DBN) (Hill 1984a: 25, 1984b: 28).
H(39) 1910: Sallagh Braes, J Glover (NMW) (Hill 1984a: 25, 1984b: 28).
See note under 70/11.

70/13 ***Racomitrium canescens*** (Hedw.) Brid.
(syn. *Racomitrium canescens* var. *canescens*, *Rhacomitrium canescens* auct.)

H21 1979: on sand dunes, golf course nr Donabate, EC Wallace (Hill 1980b: 39-40).
H22 1968: calcareous sand dunes nr Mayden Tower, Mornington, DM Synnott (BBSUK) (Crundwell 1969: 883, Hill 1978: 20).
H38 1961: Dundrum sandhills, SAG Caldwell (NMW) (Hill 1979: 28).

See note under 70/11.

71/1 ***Ptychomitrium polyphyllum*** (Sw.) Bruch & Schimp.
(syn. *Glyphomitrium polyphyllum* (Sm.) Mitt.)

H(1) listed by Lett (1915: 126) without details.
†H1 listed by Blockeel & Long (1998: 106).
H(2) listed by Lett (1915: 126) without details.
†H2 listed by Blockeel & Long (1998: 106).
H(3) listed by Lett (1915: 126) without details.
†H3 listed by Blockeel & Long (1998: 106).
H(4) listed by Lett (1915: 126) without details.
†H4 listed by Blockeel & Long (1998: 106).
H5 1956: old quarry, Youghal, EC Wallace (Warburg 1957: 330).
H(6) listed by Lett (1915: 126) without details.
†H6 listed by Blockeel & Long (1998: 106).
H(7) listed by Lett (1915: 126) without details.
†H7 listed by Blockeel & Long (1998: 106).
H(8) listed by Lett (1915: 126) without details.
†H8 listed by Blockeel & Long (1998: 106).
H(9) listed by Lett (1915: 126) without details.
†H9 listed by Blockeel & Long (1998: 106).
H(10) listed by Lett (1915: 126) without details.
†H10 listed by Blockeel & Long (1998: 106).
H(11) listed by Lett (1915: 126) without details.
†H11 listed by Blockeel & Long (1998: 106).
H(12) listed by Lett (1915: 126) without details.
†H12 listed by Blockeel & Long (1998: 106).
H(13) listed by Lett (1915: 126) without details.
†H13 listed by Blockeel & Long (1998: 106).
H(14) listed by Lett (1915: 126) without details.
†H14 listed by Blockeel & Long (1998: 106).
H15 1957: sandstone walls, nr Owendalulleegh R., RE Parker (Warburg 1958b: 477).
H(16) listed by Lett (1915: 126) without details.
†H16 listed by Blockeel & Long (1998: 106).
[H(17) listed by Lett (1915: 126) without details. H17 deleted because no valid record or voucher specimen traced (Blockeel 1999: 6)].
[H(18) listed by Lett (1915: 126) without details. H18 deleted because no valid record or voucher specimen traced (Blockeel 1999: 6)].
H19 1954: wall in lane from Glending to Newtown, ALK King (Warburg 1955: 584).
H(20) listed by Lett (1915: 126) without details.
†H20 listed by Blockeel & Long (1998: 106).
[H(21) listed by Lett (1915: 126) without details. H21 deleted because no valid record or voucher specimen traced (Blockeel 1999: 6)].
H22 1978: roadside wall, Petersville Cross Roads, N of Moynalty, DM Synnott (Hill 1979: 31).
[H(23) listed by Lett (1915: 126) without details. H23 discounted because no localised record traced (Hill 1981: 32)].
H(25) 1940: nr Boyle, JS Thomson (Duncan 1944: 210).
†H25 listed by Blockeel & Long (1998: 106).
H(26) listed by Lett (1915: 126) without details.
†H26 listed by Blockeel & Long (1998: 106).
H(27) listed by Lett (1915: 126) without

details.
†H27 listed by Blockeel & Long (1998: 106).
H(28) listed by Lett (1915: 126) without details.
†H28 listed by Blockeel & Long (1998: 106).
H(29) listed by Lett (1915: 126) without details.
†H29 listed by Blockeel & Long (1998: 106).
H(30) listed by Lett (1915: 126) without details.
†H30 listed by Blockeel & Long (1998: 106).
H(31) listed by Lett (1915: 126) without details.
†H31 listed by Blockeel & Long (1998: 106).
H(32) listed by Lett (1915: 126) without details.
†H32 listed by Blockeel & Long (1998: 106).
H(33) listed by Lett (1915: 126) without details.
†H33 listed by Blockeel & Long (1998: 106).
H(34) listed by Lett (1915: 126) without details.
†H34 listed by Blockeel & Long (1998: 106).
H(35) listed by Lett (1915: 126) without details.
†H35 listed by Blockeel & Long (1998: 106).
H(36) listed by Lett (1915: 126) without details.
†H36 listed by Blockeel & Long (1998: 106).
H(37) listed by Lett (1915: 126) without details.
†H37 listed by Blockeel & Long (1998: 106).
H(38) listed by Lett (1915: 126) without details. H(38) listed by Blockeel & Long (1998: 106).
H38 2002: on parapet of bridge, 50 m alt., by Shimna River in Tollymore Forest Park, J33, DT Holyoak 02-925 (Rothero 2003: 54).
H(39) listed by Lett (1915: 126) without details.
†H39 listed by Blockeel & Long (1998: 106).
H(40) listed by Lett (1915: 126) without details. H(40) listed by Blockeel & Long (1998: 106).

72/1 ***Glyphomitrium daviesii*** (Dicks.) Brid.

H(1) listed by Lett (1915: 125).
†H1 listed by Blockeel & Long (1998: 106).
H(2) listed by Lett (1915: 125) without details.
†H2 listed by Blockeel & Long (1998: 106).
H(3) listed by Lett (1915: 125). H(3) listed by Blockeel & Long (1998: 106).
[H15 record dismissed as doubtful (Birks 1976, Hill 1977a: 22)].
H(16) listed by Lett (1915: 125).
†H16 listed by Blockeel & Long (1998: 106).
H27 1987: on rocks in opened out area of gorge *ca* 500 ft above sea level mixed with *Ptychomitrium*, W slopes of Mweelrea, DA Newman (Blockeel 1988: 36).
[H(34) listed by Lett (1915: 125) as 1875: Urrisbeg, leg. Stewart. H34 record deleted because the locality is in H16 (Birks 1976, Hill 1977a: 22)].
H(35) listed by Lett (1915: 125). H(35) listed by Blockeel & Long (1998: 106).
H35 2002: in crevice beneath overhang on W-facing granite crag, 498 m alt., SW slope of Slieve Snaght, B91, DT Holyoak 02-463 (Rothero 2003: 54).
H(38) listed by Lett (1915: 126).
†H38 listed by Blockeel & Long (1998: 106).
H(39) listed by Lett (1915: 126).
†H39 listed by Blockeel & Long (1998: 106).
H(40) listed by Lett (1915: 126).
†H40 listed by Blockeel & Long (1998: 106).

73/1 ***Campylostelium saxicola*** (F.Weber & D.Mohr) Bruch, Schimp. & W.Gümbel (syn. *Glyphomitrium saxicola* (F.Weber & D.Mohr) Mitt.)

H(1) listed by Lett (1915: 126).
†H1 listed by Blockeel & Long (1998: 106).
H(2) listed by Lett (1915: 126). H(2) listed by Blockeel & Long (1998: 106).
H(20) listed by Lett (1915: 126). H(20) listed by Blockeel & Long (1998: 106).
H(21) listed by Lett (1915: 126). H(21) listed by Blockeel & Long (1998: 106).
H(28) 1937: Ben Bulbin, no collector named (BBS exc.) (Armitage 1938: 11).
H(29) listed by Lett (1915: 126).
†H29 listed by Blockeel & Long (1998: 106).
H(40) 1937: Inishgore, WR Megaw (anon. 1938d: 39).
†H40 listed by Blockeel & Long (1998: 106).

74/1 ***Blindia acuta*** (Hedw.) Bruch, Schimp. & W.Gümbel (syn. *Blindia acuta* var. *arenacea* Molendo, *B. acuta* var. *trichodes* Braithw.)

H(1) listed by Lett (1915: 104).
H(1) 1935: Brandon Mt., no collector named

(BBS exc.) (Watson 1936: 264), as var. *trichodes*.
†H1 listed by Blockeel & Long (1998: 107).
H(2) listed by Lett (1915: 104).
†H2 listed by Blockeel & Long (1998: 107).
H(3) listed by Lett (1915: 104).
†H3 listed by Blockeel & Long (1998: 107).
H4 1967: wet rocks, *ca* 1300 ft [alt.], Musherabeg, RD Fitzgerald (Crundwell 1968: 632).
H(6) listed by Lett (1915: 104).
†H6 listed by Blockeel & Long (1998: 107).
H(7) listed by Lett (1915: 104).
†H7 listed by Blockeel & Long (1998: 107).
H8 1966: wet rock face at *ca* 1600 ft alt., S side of Galtymore, RD Fitzgerald (BBS exc.) (Perry 1967: 409).
H(13) listed by Lett (1915: 104).
†H13 listed by Blockeel & Long (1998: 107).
H(16) listed by Lett (1915: 104) without locality.
H16 1969: crevices in wet rocks by stream, hillside E of Carn Seefin, Glann, Oughterard, AR Perry & HJ Perry (Crundwell 1970: 197), as var. *arenacea*.
H(20) listed by Lett (1915: 104).
†H20 listed by Blockeel & Long (1998: 107).
H(21) listed by Lett (1915: 104). H(21) listed by Blockeel & Long (1998: 107).
H(26) listed by Lett (1915: 104).
†H26 listed by Blockeel & Long (1998: 107).
H(27) listed by Lett (1915: 104).
†H27 listed by Blockeel & Long (1998: 107).
H(28) listed by Lett (1915: 104).
†H28 listed by Blockeel & Long (1998: 107).
H29 2000: on intermittently flushed sandstone rock, County Bridge, S of Garrison, G95, DT Holyoak 00-583 (BBSUK) (Rothero 2001: 42).
H(31) listed by Lett (1915: 104). H(31) listed by Blockeel & Long (1998: 107).
H31 1999: on sloping surface of irrigated rock on steep bank of stream, 300 m alt., Two Mile River, Carlingford, J11, TL Blockeel 28/159 (Rothero 2000: 53).
H(33) listed by Lett (1915: 104). H(33) listed by Blockeel & Long (1998: 107).
H33 2000: on damp boulder by river in ravine woodland, just below Marble Arch, H13, DT Holyoak 00-149 (BBSUK) (Rothero 2001: 42).
H(34) listed by Lett (1915: 104).
†H34 listed by Blockeel & Long (1998: 107).
H(35) listed by Lett (1915: 104).
H35 1963: schistose rocks, *ca* 20 ft [alt.], Silver Strand, Malin Beg, RD Fitzgerald & AR Perry (Warburg 1964: 724), as var. *arenacea*.
H36 1951: wet sandstone at edge of L. Lee, RD Fitzgerald (Warburg 1952: 99).
H(37) listed by Lett (1915: 104).
†H37 listed by Blockeel & Long (1998: 107).
H(38) listed by Lett (1915: 104).
†H38 listed by Blockeel & Long (1998: 107).
H(39) listed by Lett (1915: 104).
†H39 listed by Blockeel & Long (1998: 107).
H(40) 1937: Inishgore, JD Houston (anon. 1938d: 39), as var. *trichodes*.
H40 1958: rocks, 1800 ft [alt.], Dart Mt., RD Fitzgerald (Warburg 1959: 632).

75/1 ***Seligeria pusilla*** (Hedw.) Bruch, Schimp. & W.Gümbel

[H(18) listed by Lett (1915: 104)].
H(28) 1937: Annacoona, no collector named (BBS exc.) (Armitage 1938: 11).
†H28 listed by Blockeel & Long (1998: 107).
H29 1963: damp limestone, *ca* 900 ft [alt.], Peakadaw, Glenade, RD Fitzgerald & AR Perry (Warburg 1964: 723).
H30 2001: on damp limestone at base of crag, 230 m alt., Giant's Leap, S of Blacklion, H03, DT Holyoak 01-753 (Rothero 2002: 49).
H33 1959: limestone scarp, Magho, Lower Lough Erne, RD Fitzgerald (Warburg 1960: 771).
H(39) listed by Lett (1915: 104).
†H39 listed by Blockeel & Long (1998: 107).

75/2 ***Seligeria acutifolia*** Lindb.
(syn. *Seligeria acutifolia* var. *longiseta* (Lindb.) Schimp.)

H9 1994: on damp shaded limestone at base of crag, 180 m alt., Glen of Clab, M20, TL Blockeel 23/171 (Blockeel 1995c: 41).
H(28) 1937: wet limestone cliff, with *S. pusilla*, Anacoona, Ben Bulben, HN Dixon (BBSUK), det. L Gos (Blockeel 1993: 48).
H28 1970: upper cliffs, Gleniff, DM Synnott (DBN), det. L Gos (Blockeel 1993: 48).
H29 2000: on damp limestone beneath overhang at base of crag in woodland above lough, Lough Gill, E shore, W of Moneyduff, G73, DT Holyoak 00-549

(BBSUK) (Rothero 2001: 42).

H30 2001: on damp limestone in entrance to small cave at base of crag, 205 m alt., Giant's Leap, S of Blacklion, H03, DT Holyoak 01-748 (Rothero 2002: 49).

H33 1993: dry vertical limestone face in gorge, Marble Arch, H13, NG Hodgetts 2769 (Blockeel 1994: 36).

[H(39) 1936: Whitepark Bay, WR Megaw (anon. 1937a: 366), as var. *longiseta*. H39 deleted because specimen is *S. paucifolia* (Blockeel 1987: 21)].

H(39) 1870: with *S. pusilla*, Crow Glen, SA Stewart (DBN), det. L Gos (Blockeel 1993: 48).

H40 1999: on base of chalk block on grassy hillside, 300 m alt., Benbradagh, SW slope, C71, DT Holyoak 99-672 (BBSUK) (Rothero 2000: 53).

75/6 ***Seligeria recurvata*** (Hedw.) Bruch, Schimp. & W.Gümbel
(syn. *Seligeria setacea* Lindb. nom. illeg.)

H(1) listed by Lett (1915: 104).

†H1 listed by Blockeel & Long (1998: 107).

H3 1955: steeply inclined rock-faces above Glen Lough, E Milne-Redhead (Warburg 1956: 152).

H16 1968: mica schist face, E-facing cliffs at 1400 ft [alt.], Muckanaght, AR Perry (Crundwell 1969: 879).

H27 1965: basic rocks, 1500 ft alt., E end of Sheeffry Hills, nr Gortmore, A McG Stirling (Warburg 1966: 192).

H28 1970: limestones cliffs, Gleniff, S of Clogh, *ca* 3 miles E of Benbulbin [*sic* = Ben Bulben], E Hegewald (BBS exc.) (Crundwell 1971b: 375, Appleyard 1971: 387-388).

†H29 listed by Blockeel & Long (1998: 107).

[H30 deleted because no valid record or voucher specimen traced (Blockeel 1999: 6)].

H31 1966: vertical rock by Two-mile River, Carlingford Mt., DM Synnott (Perry 1967: 409).

H33 1957: moist shaded rocks of cliff, nr Glencreawan Lough, L. Navar Forest, RE Parker (Warburg 1958b: 474).

H(34) listed by Lett (1915: 104). H(34) listed by Blockeel & Long (1998: 107).

H34 2002: on damp schist rock under overhang on N facing crag, 490 m alt., NW of summit of Bulbin Mt., C34, DT Holyoak 02-524 (Rothero 2003: 54).

H35 1965: vertical calcareous sandstone outcrop on E side of Banagher Hill, L. Eske, EW Jones (Warburg 1966: 192).

H36 1957: altered mica-schist, Butterlope Glen, nr Plumbridge, RD Fitzgerald (Warburg 1958b: 474).

75/7 ***Seligeria calycina*** Mitt. ex Lindb.
(syn. *Seligeria paucifolia* auct. non (Dicks.) Carruth.)

H(39) 1936: on chips of limestone among grass, Whitepark Bay, WR Megaw (E) [as *S. acutifolia*] (Blockeel 1987: 21).

H40 1964: chalk blocks, *ca* 1000 ft [alt.], Benbradagh, RD Fitzgerald (Warburg 1965: 861, Fitzgerald & Fitzgerald 1966a).

75/8 ***Seligeria calcarea*** (Hedw.) Bruch, Schimp. & W.Gümbel

H(39) no date: no locality, Templeton (Lett 1915: 104).
no date: Black Mt., SA Stewart (Lett 1915: 104). H(39) listed by Blockeel & Long (1998: 107).

H39 1999: on vertical side of chalk boulder nr base of cliffs, White Park Bay, D04, DT Holyoak 99-616 (BBSUK) (Rothero 2000: 53).

H(40) 1937: Benbradach [*sic* = Benbradagh], JD Houston (anon. 1938d: 38).

†H40 listed by Blockeel & Long (1998: 107).

75/9 ***Seligeria donniana*** (Sm.) Müll.Hal.
(syn. *Seligeria doniana* auct., *S. donnii* Lindb. nom. illeg.)

H9 1957: Slieve Carran, J Appleyard (BBS exc.) (Warburg 1958b: 474).

H29 1963: damp limestone, *ca* 900 ft [alt.], Peakadaw, Glenade, RD Fitzgerald & AR Perry (Warburg 1964: 723).

H30 2001: on damp limestone at base of crag, 230 m alt., Giant's Leap, S of Blacklion, H03, DT Holyoak 01-751 (Rothero 2002: 49).

H33 1959: damp limestone, Middle Claddagh Glen, RD Fitzgerald (Warburg 1960: 771).

H35 2002: in crevices of limestone crag, 270 m alt., SW of Lough Salt, C12, DT

Holyoak 02-641 (Rothero 2003: 54).

H(39) 1876: Colin Glen, Stewart (Lett 1915: 104). H(39) listed by Blockeel & Long (1998: 108).

H39 1999: on damp chalk below overhang by stream, N of Red Hall, J49, DT Holyoak 99-842 (BBSUK) (Rothero 2000: 53).

75/10 *Seligeria trifaria* (Brid.) Lindb. aggregate
(syn. *Seligeria tristicha* (Brid.) Bruch, Schimp. & W.Gümbel)

H(28) 1937: Annacoona, no collector named (BBS exc.) (Armitage 1938: 11), as *S. tristicha*.
1937: Gleniff, HN Dixon, CVB Marquand, EM Lobley, comm. HN Dixon (anon. 1938b: 23) as *S. tristicha*.

†H28 listed by Blockeel & Long (1998: 108).

H(29) 1937: Glenade, no collector named (BBS exc.) (Armitage 1938: 11).

†H29 listed by Blockeel & Long (1998: 108).

H33 1960: damp limestone, *ca* 500 ft [alt.], Upper Buggan, RD Fitzgerald (Warburg 1961: 160).

Blockeel, Ochyra & Gos (2000: 32) point out that both *S. patula* and *S. trifaria* occur in the British Isles. Voucher specimens for the records listed above need to be re-examined to check whether they can be assigned to either of these species, although mature capsules or ripe spores appear to be necessary for reliable identification and these are lacking in most herbarium specimens. Recent gatherings from Ireland c.fr. (one from H28, five from H29, two from H33) are all of *S. patula* with no *S. trifaria s.s.* (DT Holyoak, unpublished).

75/10A *Seligeria patula* (Lindb.) Broth.
(syn. *Seligeria trifaria* auct., non (Brid.) Lindb.)

H33 2000: on thin tufa film over wet limestone at base of N-facing crag, N of Glencreawan Lough, H05, DT Holyoak 00-279 (Rothero 2002: 49).

See note under the preceding species.

75/11 *Seligeria oelandica* C.E.O.Jensen & Medelius

H28 1962: wet limestone outcrops, on the steep slope, facing NE of an open corrie, *ca* 1000 ft [alt.], Gleniff, Dartry Mts, AC Crundwell & EF Warburg (BBS exc.) (Crundwell & Warburg 1963, Warburg 1964: 724).

H29 1963: with *S. trifaria* on wet limestone outcrops, Ballinlig, Glenade, AR Perry & RD Fitzgerald (Warburg 1964: 724).

H33 2000: on thin tufaceous film on limestone pebbles in open flush on N-facing slope, N of Glencreawan Lough, H05, DT Holyoak 00-264 (BBSUK) (Rothero 2001: 43).

76/1 *Brachydontium trichodes* (F.Weber) Milde
(syn. *Brachyodus trichodes* (F.Weber) Nees & Hornsch.)

H(20) no date: Lough Bray, Taylor (Lett 1915: 104). H(20) listed by Blockeel & Long (1998: 108).

H(21) no date: nr Dublin (Lett 1915: 104).
1863: Kelly's Glen, Moore (Lett 1915: 104). H(21) listed by Blockeel & Long (1998: 108).

H(28) 1937: Ben Bulben, no collector named (BBS exc.) (Armitage 1938: 11).

H35 2002: on underside of quartzite overhang on crag, 590 m alt., N slope of Muckish, C02, DT Holyoak 02-729 (Rothero 2003: 54).

†H38 listed by Blockeel & Long (1998: 108).

H(40) 1937: Inishgore, WR Megaw (anon. 1938d: 38).

77/1 *Discelium nudum* (Dicks.) Brid.
(syn. *Grimmia nuda* (Dicks.) Turner)

H29 2001: on open damp clay on bank above roadside ditch, 265 m alt., SE of Slievenakilla, N of Bencroy, H02, DT Holyoak 01-798A (Rothero 2002: 49).

H30 1961: bare shaley earth beside stream, *ca* 1100 ft [alt.], Bellavally, RD Fitzgerald (Warburg 1962: 371, Fitzgerald & Fitzgerald 1966a).

H33 2002: on steep clay bank above stream, 395 m alt., Altscraghy NE slope of Cuilcagh, H12, DT Holyoak 02-902 (Rothero 2003: 54).

[H39 record from nr Belfast, leg. R Brown (as *Grimmia nuda* in *Engl. Bot.* 1421) regarded as dubious by Lett (1915: 132)].

78/1 ***Funaria hygrometrica*** Hedw.
(syn. *F. hygrometrica* var. *calvescens* (Schwägr.) Mont.)

H(1) listed by Lett (1915: 133) without details.
†H1 listed by Blockeel & Long (1998: 108).
H(2) listed by Lett (1915: 133) without details.
†H2 listed by Blockeel & Long (1998: 108).
H3 1951: Cape Clear, IA Rorison (Warburg 1952: 103).
H(4) listed by Lett (1915: 133) without details.
†H4 listed by Blockeel & Long (1998: 108).
H5 1956: old wall, Glenally, Youghal, EC Wallace (Warburg 1957: 333).
†H6 listed by Blockeel & Long (1998: 108).
H(7) listed by Lett (1915: 133) without details.
†H7 listed by Blockeel & Long (1998: 108).
H(8) listed by Lett (1915: 133) without details.
†H8 listed by Blockeel & Long (1998: 108).
H(9) listed by Lett (1915: 133) without details.
†H9 listed by Blockeel & Long (1998: 108).
H10 1965: burnt ground, cut-away bog, L. Nahinch, Balingarry, DM Synnott (Warburg 1966: 196).
H(11) listed by Lett (1915: 133) without details.
†H11 listed by Blockeel & Long (1998: 108).
H12 1961: floor of roofless ruin, Coolstuff Cross Roads, ALK King (Warburg 1962: 372).
†H13 listed by Blockeel & Long (1998: 108).
H(13) listed by Lett (1915: 133) without details.
H(14) listed by Lett (1915: 133) without details.
†H14 listed by Blockeel & Long (1998: 108).
H15 1952: bank by marsh, nr Ross Quay, MPH Kertland & ALK King (Warburg 1953: 312).
H16 1957: bare earth face, L. Muck, nr Killary Harbour, AC Crundwell (BBS exc.) (Warburg 1958b: 481).
H(17) listed by Lett (1915: 133) without details.
†H17 listed by Blockeel & Long (1998: 108).
H(18) listed by Lett (1915: 133) without details.
†H18 listed by Blockeel & Long (1998: 108).
[H(19) listed by Lett (1915: 133) without details. H19 deleted because no valid record or voucher specimen traced (Blockeel 1999: 6)].
H(20) 1941: Ballinaclash, JS Thomson (Duncan 1944: 212).
†H20 listed by Blockeel & Long (1998: 108).
H(21) listed by Lett (1915: 133) without details.
†H21 listed by Blockeel & Long (1998: 108).
H22 1950: Slane, JS Thomson (Warburg 1952: 103).
H23 1952: The Derries Bog, nr Athlone, JP Brunker & ALK King (Warburg 1953: 312).
H24 1954: bank, Cloonfin Bog, nr Ballinalee, ALK King (Warburg 1955: 585).
H25 1962: yard, Boyle, PW Warburg (Warburg 1963b: 498).
H(26) listed by Lett (1915: 133) without details.
†H26 listed by Blockeel & Long (1998: 108).
H(27) listed by Lett (1915: 133) without details.
†H27 listed by Blockeel & Long (1998: 108).
H(28) listed by Lett (1915: 133) without details.
†H28 listed by Blockeel & Long (1998: 108).
H(29) listed by Lett (1915: 133) without details.
†H29 listed by Blockeel & Long (1998: 108).
H(30) listed by Lett (1915: 133) without details.
†H30 listed by Blockeel & Long (1998: 108).
H(31) listed by Lett (1915: 133) without details.
†H31 listed by Blockeel & Long (1998: 108).
H(32) listed by Lett (1915: 133) without details.
†H32 listed by Blockeel & Long (1998: 108).
H(33) listed by Lett (1915: 133) without details.
†H33 listed by Blockeel & Long (1998: 108).
H(34) listed by Lett (1915: 133) without details.
†H34 listed by Blockeel & Long (1998: 108).
H(35) listed by Lett (1915: 133) without details.
†H35 listed by Blockeel & Long (1998: 108).
H(36) listed by Lett (1915: 133) without details.

†H36 listed by Blockeel & Long (1998: 108).
H(37) listed by Lett (1915: 133).
†H37 listed by Blockeel & Long (1998: 108).
H(38) listed by Lett (1915: 133).
†H38 listed by Blockeel & Long (1998: 108).
H(39) listed by Lett (1915: 133) without details.
†H39 listed by Blockeel & Long (1998: 108).
H(40) listed by Lett (1915: 133) without details.
†H40 listed by Blockeel & Long (1998: 108).

Lett (1915: 133) lists a record of the closely related *F. microstoma* Bruch & Schimp. from H(5) Fermoy based on a specimen in (BM). However, Dixon (1924: 303) regarded occurrence of 'the true *F. microstoma*' in Britain as 'exceedingly doubtful' and it has been omitted from all modern lists of Irish and British mosses.

78/2 ***Funaria muhlenbergii*** Turner (syn. *Funaria calcarea* Wahlenb., *F. hibernica* Hook.)

[H3 record dismissed (no specimen seen by Crundwell & Nyholm 1974, Crundwell 1975: 16)].
H(4) pre-1836: on chalky soil at Blarney nr Cork, T. Drummond (type of *F. hibernica*), (GL) (Lett 1915: 133, Crundwell & Nyholm 1974: 223, Crundwell 1975: 16).
H(5) no date: nr Fermoy, J Carroll (E) (Crundwell & Nyholm 1974: 223, Crundwell 1975: 16). Same record probably listed by Lett (1915: 133) as 1852: Glanworth, leg. Carroll.
[H33 record dismissed (no specimen seen by Crundwell & Nyholm 1974, Crundwell 1975: 16)].
[H(39) listed by Lett (1915: 133) as 1847: Cave Hill, leg. Orr and undated: Carrick-a-rede, leg. Dixon. H39 record dismissed (no specimen seen by Crundwell & Nyholm 1974, Crundwell 1975: 16)].
[H(40) listed by Lett (1915: 133) as 1904: Magilligan, leg. HW Lett. H40 record dismissed (no specimen seen by Crundwell & Nyholm 1974, Crundwell 1975: 16)].

Crundwell & Nyholm (1974) revised British and Irish records of *F. muhlenbergii* and separated *F. pulchella* H.Philib. from it, the latter species being unknown in Ireland.

79/1 ***Entosthodon attenuatus*** (Dicks.) Bryhn (syn. *Funaria attenuata* (Dicks.) Lindb., *F. templetonii* Sm.)

H(1) listed by Lett (1915: 133).
†H1 listed by Blockeel & Long (1998: 108).
H(2) listed by Lett (1915: 133).
†H2 listed by Blockeel & Long (1998: 108).
H(3) listed by Lett (1915: 133).
†H3 listed by Blockeel & Long (1998: 108).
H(4) listed by Lett (1915: 133). H(4) listed by Blockeel & Long (1998: 108).
H(5) listed by Lett (1915: 133). H(5) listed by Blockeel & Long (1998: 108).
H6 1966: boulders in stream, E of the Punchbowl, Clonmel, JA Paton & ERB Little (BBS exc.) (Perry 1967: 414).
H(7) listed by Lett (1915: 133).
†H7 listed by Blockeel & Long (1998: 108).
H8 1979: wet rocky bank by road, E side of Sugar Hill, nr Newcastle West, EW Jones (Hill 1980b: 40).
H(9) listed by Lett (1915: 133). H(9) listed by Blockeel & Long (1998: 108).
H12 1975: bank nr R. Bann, Camolin, JA Paton (BBS exc.) (Crundwell 1976: 26).
H(16) listed by Lett (1915: 133).
†H16 listed by Blockeel & Long (1998: 108).
H(20) listed by Lett (1915: 133). H(20) listed by Blockeel & Long (1998: 108).
H(21) listed by Lett (1915: 133). H(21) listed by Blockeel & Long (1998: 108).
H25 1968: on peaty soil, Slieve Bawn, 4 miles NW of Lanesborough, WV Rubers *et al.* (U) (Crundwell 1974: 169).
H(27) listed by Lett (1915: 133).
†H27 listed by Blockeel & Long (1998: 108).
H(28) 1928: Gleniff, Ben Bulben (BBS exc.) (Duncan 1928: 118).
†H28 listed by Blockeel & Long (1998: 108).
H(29) 1928: wooded glen, NE end of Glencar Lough (BBS exc.) (Duncan 1928: 118).
†H29 listed by Blockeel & Long (1998: 108).
H(31) listed by Lett (1915: 133). H(31) listed by Blockeel & Long (1998: 108).
H31 1999: in earthy crevice on rocky bank by stream, 150 m alt., Two Mile River, Carlingford, J11, TL Blockeel 28/149 (Rothero 2000: 53).
H(33) listed by Lett (1915: 133). H(33) listed by Blockeel & Long (1998: 108).

H33 1999: on ledges of N-facing sandstone scarp, 280 m alt., Braade ASSI, Lough Navar Forest, H05, RD Porley 2038 (Rothero 2000: 53).
H(34) listed by Lett (1915: 133).
†H34 listed by Blockeel & Long (1998: 108).
H(35) listed by Lett (1915: 133).
†H35 listed by Blockeel & Long (1998: 108).
†H36 listed by Blockeel & Long (1998: 108).
H(38) listed by Lett (1915: 133). H(38) listed by Blockeel & Long (1998: 108).
H(39) listed by Lett (1915: 133).
†H39 listed by Blockeel & Long (1998: 108).
H(40) listed by Lett (1915: 133).
†H40 listed by Blockeel & Long (1998: 108).

79/2 ***Entosthodon fascicularis*** (Hedw.) Müll. Hal.
(syn. *Funaria fascicularis* (Hedw.) Lindb.)

H(1) listed by Lett (1915: 133). H(1) listed by Blockeel & Long (1998: 109).
H(2) listed by Lett (1915: 133). H(2) listed by Blockeel & Long (1998: 109).
H(3) 1934: fallow field Barloge Farm, Baltimore, EW Jones (Warburg 1960: 777).
†H3 listed by Blockeel & Long (1998: 109).
[H(4) listed by Lett (1915: 133). H4 deleted because the only specimen traced (1907: Douglas, O Peyton (DBN)) is *F. hygrometrica*, det DM Synnott, comm. NF Stewart (Blockeel 1995c: 44)].
H(5) listed by Lett (1915: 133). H(5) listed by Blockeel & Long (1998: 109).
H(8) listed by Lett (1915: 133). H(8) listed by Blockeel & Long (1998: 109).
[H(14) listed by Lett (1915: 133) as 1912: Slieve Bloom, leg. Tetley. H14 deleted because specimen on which record is based (Slieve Bloom, WN Tetley (BBSUK), see Lett 1915) is *F. obtusa* (Warburg 1958b: 481)].
[H(16) listed by Lett (1915: 133) as 1895: Carn Seafin, leg. McArdle. H16 deleted because no valid record or voucher specimen traced (Blockeel 1999: 6)].
H(19) 1949: waste ground, Blackhall Castle, nr Calverston, JS Thomson (Warburg 1950: 385).
†H19 listed by Blockeel & Long (1998: 109).
H20 1975: bank of ditch in field, Pennycomequick Bridge, NE of Arklow, JA Paton (BBS exc.) (Crundwell 1976: 26).
H(21) listed by Lett (1915: 133). H(21) listed by Blockeel & Long (1998: 109).
H(27) listed by Lett (1915: 133). H(27) listed by Blockeel & Long (1998: 109).
[H31) listed by Lett (1915: 133) as 1900: Carlingford Mt., leg. HW Lett. H31 deleted: specimen from Carlingford, leg. HW Lett & CH Waddell (DBN), is *F. obtusa*, comm. DM Synnott (Blockeel 1989: 28)].
H(36) listed by Lett (1915: 133). H(36) listed by Blockeel & Long (1998: 109).
H(38) listed by Lett (1915: 133). H(38) listed by Blockeel & Long (1998: 109).
H(39) listed by Lett (1915: 133). H(39) listed by Blockeel & Long (1998: 109).
H(40) listed by Lett (1915: 133). H(40) listed by Blockeel & Long (1998: 109).

79/3 ***Entosthodon obtusus*** (Hedw.) Lindb.
(syn. *Funaria ericetorum* (Bals.-Criv. & De Not.) Dixon, *F. obtusa* (Hedw.) Lindb.)

H(1) listed by Lett (1915: 132).
†H1 listed by Blockeel & Long (1998: 109).
H(2) listed by Lett (1915: 132).
†H2 listed by Blockeel & Long (1998: 109).
†H3 listed by Blockeel & Long (1998: 109).
H(4) listed by Lett (1915: 132) without details.
†H4 listed by Blockeel & Long (1998: 109).
[H(5) listed by Lett (1915: 132) without details. H5 deleted because no valid record or voucher specimen traced (Blockeel 1999: 6)].
H6 1966: boulder in stream E of the Punchbowl, Clonmel, JA Paton & ERB Little (BBS exc.) (Perry 1967: 414).
H(7) listed by Lett (1915: 133).
†H7 listed by Blockeel & Long (1998: 109).
H(9) listed by Lett (1915: 133).
†H9 listed by Blockeel & Long (1998: 109).
H10 1951: vertical soil bank beside gorge, Silvermines, AD Banwell, PJ Wanstall & EV Watson (Warburg 1953: 312).
H12 1954: damp bank, Inch, JS Thomson (Warburg 1955: 585).
H13 1975: bank by stream, The Black Banks, Mt Leinster, JA Paton (BBS exc.) (Crundwell 1976: 26).
H(14) 1912: Slieve Bloom (part N of Capanarrow), WN Tetley (BBSUK), comm. AA Cridland (Warburg 1958b:

481).

H15 1957: vertical face of roadside ditch, moor above Chevy Chase, nr Gort, DH Dalby (BBS exc.) (Warburg 1958b: 481).

H(16) listed by Lett (1915: 133).

†H16 listed by Blockeel & Long (1998: 109).

H(20) listed by Lett (1915: 133).

†H20 listed by Blockeel & Long (1998: 109).

H(21) listed by Lett (1915: 133). H(21) listed by Blockeel & Long (1998: 109).

H25 1968: on loamy banks, Slieve Bawn, 4 miles NW of Lanesborough, WV Rubers *et al.* (U) (Crundwell 1974: 169).

H26 1965: ground *ca* 600 ft alt., cliffs S of Glendaduff, [The] Ox Mts, RD Fitzgerald (Warburg 1966: 196).

H(27) listed by Lett (1915: 133).

†H27 listed by Blockeel & Long (1998: 109).

H28 1963: clay at *ca* 700 ft [alt.], Lugnagall, Glencar, RD Fitzgerald & AR Perry (Warburg 1964: 728).

H29 1963: ground, *ca* 500 ft [alt.], Peakadaw, Glenade, RD Fitzgerald & AR Perry (Warburg 1964: 728).

H30 1961: wet clay, *ca* 1500 ft [alt.], Bellavally, Cuilcagh, RD Fitzgerald (Warburg 1962: 372).

H(31) listed by Lett (1915: 133). H(31) listed by Blockeel & Long (1998: 109).

H33 1959: calcareous clay, Lough Scolban, RD Fitzgerald (Warburg 1960: 778).

H(34) listed by Lett (1915: 133).

†H34 listed by Blockeel & Long (1998: 109).

H(35) 1907: Killybegs, Donegal, CA Cheetham (anon. 1909a: 309).

H(35) listed by Lett (1915: 133).

†H35 listed by Blockeel & Long (1998: 109).

H36 1951: sandy bank of stream in shade, L. Bradan, RD Fitzgerald (Warburg 1952: 103).

H(37) listed by Lett (1915: 133).

†H37 listed by Blockeel & Long (1998: 109).

H(38) listed by Lett (1915: 133).

†H38 listed by Blockeel & Long (1998: 109).

H(39) listed by Lett (1915: 133).

†H39 listed by Blockeel & Long (1998: 109).

H(40) 1937: Kilrea, JD Houston (anon. 1938d: 40).

†H40 listed by Blockeel & Long (1998: 109).

80/1 ***Physcomitrium pyriforme*** (Hedw.) Brid.

H1 1951: roadside bank, nr Caragh Bridge, nr Glenbeigh, EF Warburg (BBS exc.) (Warburg 1952: 103).

H2 1952: clay of river bank, Ballyseedy, Tralee, AP Fanning (Warburg 1953: 312).

[H(3) listed by Lett (1915: 132) without details. H3 deleted because no valid record or voucher specimen traced (Blockeel 1999: 6)].

H(4) listed by Lett (1915: 132).

†H4 listed by Blockeel & Long (1998: 109).

H(5) listed by Lett (1915: 132). H(5) listed by Blockeel & Long (1998: 109).

H6 1999: on soil in cattle pasture on flood plain, Tallow, X09, DH Wrench (Rothero 2000: 53).

H(8) listed by Lett (1915: 132) without details.

†H8 listed by Blockeel & Long (1998: 109).

H9 1974: small marsh in discontinuity of limestone pavement, Poulnabrown, E of Ballyvaughan, PH Pitkin (Crundwell 1975: 16).

H10 1990: on damp soil on river bank, 55 m alt., Brick Bridge, grounds of Birr Castle, N00, DG Long 18145 (Blockeel 1991c: 43).

H(11) listed by Lett (1915: 132). H(11) listed by Blockeel & Long (1998: 109).

H13 1967: bank of R. Slaney, Kilcarry, E Booth (Crundwell 1968: 638).

H(18) listed by Lett (1915: 132). H(18) listed by Blockeel & Long (1998: 109).

H19 1957: mud thrown out of Rye Water, Louisa Bridge, Leixlip, ALK King (Warburg 1958b: 481).

H(20) listed by Lett (1915: 132). H(20) listed by Blockeel & Long (1998: 109).

H(21) listed by Lett (1915: 132).

†H21 listed by Blockeel & Long (1998: 109).

H22 1953: bank of ditch, Curragha Bog, ALK King (Warburg 1954: 483).

H23 1952: side of old cart track, NE end of L. Owel, JS Thomson (Warburg 1953: 312).

H24 1980: clay bank of drain, shore of Glen Lough, DM Synnott (Hill 1981: 28).

H25 2002: on muddy ground by lough, 85 m alt., Shad Lough, M87, NG Hodgetts 4095 (Rothero 2003: 54).

H(28) listed by Lett (1915: 132). H(28) listed by Blockeel & Long (1998: 109).

H29 2001: on open sandy mud at edge of lough, 60 m alt., E shore of Lough Allen, nr Gubarusheen, G91, DT Holyoak 01-783 (Rothero 2002: 49).

H(30) 1941: Cavan, JS Thomson (Duncan 1944: 212).
H(33) listed by Blockeel & Long (1998: 109).
H33 2000: in disturbed sandy area in grassland, Marble Arch, by visitor centre, H13, DT Holyoak 00-169 (BBSUK) (Rothero 2001: 43).
H(34) listed by Lett (1915: 132).
†H34 listed by Blockeel & Long (1998: 109).
H35 2002: on open damp sand on bank of small stream in dunes, 20 m alt., just E of Chapel Lough, Mullaghdoo, B72, DT Holyoak 02-389 (Rothero 2003: 54).
H(36) listed by Lett (1915: 132).
†H36 listed by Blockeel & Long (1998: 109).
H(37) listed by Lett (1915: 132). H(37) listed by Blockeel & Long (1998: 109).
H(38) listed by Lett (1915: 132).
†H38 listed by Blockeel & Long (1998: 109).
H(39) listed by Lett (1915: 132).
†H39 listed by Blockeel & Long (1998: 109).
H(40) listed by Lett (1915: 132). H(40) listed by Blockeel & Long (1998: 109).
H40 1999: on bare silty mud on bank of large ditch, Umbra, C73, DT Holyoak 99-108 (BBSUK) (Rothero 2000: 53).

80/3 ***Physcomitrium sphaericum*** (Ludw.) Brid.

H39 1999: on damp mud of drained reservoir in sparse herbaceous vegetation, Copeland Reservoir, J49, DT Holyoak 99-846 (BBSUK) (Rothero 2000: 53, Holyoak in Blockeel *et al.* 2000a: 69).

81/1 ***Aphanorhegma patens*** (Hedw.) Lindb. (syn. *Physcomitrella patens* (Hedw.) Bruch, Schimp. & W.Gümbel)

H(4) listed by Lett (1915: 132). H(4) listed by Blockeel & Long (1998: 109).
H6 1999: on bare mud in marshy field, 8 m alt., R. Bride, 1 km E of Tallowbridge, Tallow, X09, TL Blockeel 28/253 (Rothero 2000: 53).
H8 1979: meadow nr ruin of Carrygogunnell Castle, Corcamore, W of Limerick, HMH van Melick (Hill 1981: 28).
H9 1957: mud at side of path in pasture, SE side of Slievecarron, J Appleyard & AC Crundwell (BBS exc.) (Warburg 1958b: 481).
H12 2000: on mud between rocks at base of dam, Coolree Reservoir, W of Newbay, T02, DT Holyoak 00-775 (BBSUK) (Rothero 2001: 43).
H14 1966: marshy field by Owenbeg River, E of Abbeyleix, JA Paton & GCG Argent (Perry 1967: 414).
H15 1957: damp soil in pasture liable to flood, Garryland Wood, nr Gort, J Appleyard & AC Crundwell (BBS exc.) (Warburg 1958b: 481).
H17 1962: turlough about 4 miles W of Tuam, PW Warburg (Warburg 1963b: 498).
H(21) listed by Lett (1915: 132). H(21) listed by Blockeel & Long (1998: 109).
H22 1964: bare mud, bank of R. Boyne, Donore, Drogheda, DM Synnott (Warburg 1965: 865).
H24 1968: shore of small lake, Fort William, 4 miles S of Lanesborough, WV Rubers *et al.* (U) (Crundwell 1974: 169).
H26 1987: on mud under *Salix* by river, E bank of Cloon River nr Partry, DG Long (Blockeel 1988: 36).
H29 2000: on soil nr edge of river, R. Shannon, E bank at Drumsna, M99, DT Holyoak 00-760 (BBSUK) (Rothero 2001: 43).
H30 2001: on open silty clay on bank, 45 m alt., River Erne, S of Baker's Bridge, H31, DT Holyoak 01-823 (Rothero 2002: 49).
H34 2002: on loamy soil nr gateway into field, 5 m alt., Inch Level, C32, DT Holyoak 02-836 (Rothero 2003: 54).
H37 2002: on soil heap at edge of woodland, 65 m alt., Gosford Forest Park, H94, DT Holyoak 02-1087 (Rothero 2003: 54).
H(39) listed by Lett (1915: 132). H(39) listed by Blockeel & Long (1998: 109).
H39 1999: on damp mud of drained reservoir, Copeland Reservoir, J49, DT Holyoak 99-844 (BBSUK) (Rothero 2000: 53).

83/2 ***Ephemerum sessile*** (Bruch) Müll.Hal.

H12 2000: on drying mud at edge of reservoir, Coolree Reservoir, W of Newbay, T02, DT Holyoak 00-773a (BBSUK) (Rothero 2001: 43).
H16 1965: cart rut in field N of Oughterhard, nr L. Corrib, DF Chamberlain (Warburg 1966: 196).
H24 2001: on open mud on lough shore, 60 m alt., Lough Gowna, S shore, W of Dring, N28, DT Holyoak 01-864 (Rothero

2002: 49).

[H29 2000: on mud at edge of lough amongst sedges, Rinn Lough, NW end, N09, DT Holyoak 00-761 (BBSUK) (Rothero 2001: 43). This record is apparently based on a related taxon rather than on *E. sessile* (VS Bryan & DT Holyoak, in preparation)].

H35 1962: path to Mevagh Church, Rossguill Peninsula, EF Warburg (BBS exc.) (Warburg 1963b: 498).

H39 1999: on nearly dry mud at edge of reservoir, South Woodburn Reservoirs, J38, DT Holyoak 99-875 (BBSUK) (Rothero 2000: 53).

A similar taxon with longer leaves and stronger teeth at the leaf margins is known from the inundation zones beside several Irish lakes (VS Bryan & DT Holyoak, in preparation).

83/3 ***Ephemerum cohaerens*** (Hedw.) Hampe

H(15) 1865: Portumna, Moore (Lett 1915: 110). H(15) listed by Blockeel & Long (1998: 110).

H24 2001: on open mud on lough shore, 60 m alt., Lough Gowna, S shore, W of Dring, N28, DT Holyoak 01-868 (Rothero 2002: 49).

H29 2000: on soil of low bank beside river, R. Shannon, N of Jamestown, M99, DT Holyoak 00-758 (BBSUK) (Rothero 2001: 43).

83/4 ***Ephemerum stellatum*** H.Philib.

H1 1951: cliff path, Darrynane, AC Crundwell (BBS exc.) (Warburg 1952: 103).

This taxon should probably not be recognised as a species. Irish and British specimens placed as *E. stellatum* appear to consist only of variants of *E. serratum* or *E. minutissimum* having untoothed or weakly toothed leaves (Holyoak 2001a).

83/5a ***Ephemerum serratum***
or
83/5b ***E. minutissimum***

H(4) listed by Lett (1915: 110) as *E. serratum*.

H(18) listed by Lett (1915: 110) as *E. serratum*, without locality.

H29 1963: wet clayey pasture below limestone scarp, Boggaun, nr Manorhamilton, AR Perry & RD Fitzgerald (Warburg 1964: 728).

H(34) listed by Lett (1915: 110) as *E. serratum*.

H(38) listed by Lett (1915: 110) as *E. serratum*.

H(38) listed by Lett (1915: 110) as *E. minutissimum*, without locality.

H(39) listed by Lett (1915: 110) as *E. serratum*.

H(39) listed by Lett (1915: 110) as *E. minutissimum*.

H(40) listed by Lett (1915: 110) as *E. serratum*.

Old specimens of these taxa need to be reidentified because the original identifications may have been based on unreliable leaf characters (see note under the next species).

83/5a ***Ephemerum serratum*** (Hedw.) Hampe *s.s.*
(syn. *Ephemerum serratum* var. *serratum*)

H1 1951: bare soil in pasture, nr L. Dreenaun, nr Waterville, AC Crundwell & EC Wallace (BBS exc.) (Warburg 1952: 103).

H3 1979: damp soil in flush, N-facing sloping moorland nr Sheep's Head, AC Crundwell *et al.* (Hill 1980b: 40).

H12 1969: bare patch in marshy ground, Pallis Bridge, nr Wicklow Gap, RD Fitzgerald (Crundwell 1970: 203).

H13 1969: bare ground in field nr Ballintemple House, Tullow, RD Fitzgerald (Crundwell 1970: 203).

H20 1969: stubble field, Ballygahan House, nr Avoca, RD Fitzgerald (Crundwell 1970: 203).

H24 2001: on mud in open carr on lough shore, 60 m alt., Lough Gowna, S shore, W of Dring, N28, DT Holyoak 01-870 (Rothero 2002: 49-50).

H26 1987: raised mud bank, nr Cloon River, nr Partry, MAS Burton (Blockeel 1988: 36).

H27 1987: amongst *Fossombronia pusilla* var. *maritima*, flat sandy area behind strand, Trawmore sand, nr Dookinelly, Achill I., JA Paton (Blockeel 1988: 36).

H29 2000: on mud in ditch by lough, Carrickaport Lough, SE edge, H00, DT Holyoak 00-748 (BBSUK) (Rothero 2001: 43).

H30 2001: on soil over sand on lough margin, 60 m alt., Lough Gowna, NW of Dermaferst Bridge, N29, DT Holyoak 01-701 (Rothero 2002: 49-50).

H34 1962: stubble field nr Castleforward, nr Newtown Cunningham, EF Warburg *et al.* (BBS exc.) (Warburg 1963b: 498).

H35 1962: garden soil, Glan Alla, nr Rathmullan, Lough Swilly, EM Lobley & MPH Kertland (BBS exc.) (Warburg 1963b: 498).

H38 2002: on open gravelly sediment in inundation zone of reservoir, 125 m alt., NW end of Lough Island Reavy Reservoir, J23, DT Holyoak 02-962 (Rothero 2003: 54-55).

Some records of *E. serratum s.s.* and *E. minutissimum* may have been based on unreliable leaf characters (given in key by Smith 1978: 350) rather than the reliable characters of mature spores. These suspicions are strengthened because *E. serratum s.s.* never occurs in arable fields in Cornwall (cf. records from H20, H34 and H35 above), whereas *E. minutissimum* is plentiful in that habitat. Numerous recent Irish finds of *E. serratum s.s.* have been made mainly from inundation zones beside loughs and reservoirs.

83/5b *Ephemerum minutissimum* Lindb.
(syn. *Ephemerum serratum* var. *minutissimum* (Lindb.) Grout)

H4 1979: edge of marshy ground, E of Ballygarvan, JA Paton (Hill 1980b: 40).

H5 1966: arable field, Kilworth, JG Duckett *et al.* (BBS exc.) (Perry 1967: 414-415).

H6 1966: soil in field, Clogheen, S of Clonmel, ERB Little (BBS exc.) (Perry 1967: 414-415).

H7 1966: arable field, Ardfinnan, JG Duckett & J Appleyard (BBS exc.) (Perry 1967: 414-415).

H10 1967: bare ground in pasture, Devils Bit Mt., RD Fitzgerald (Crundwell 1968: 638).

H11 1966: arable field, Inistioge, JG Duckett *et al.* (Perry 1967: 414-415).

H14 1966: marshy field beside Owenbeg River, E of Abbeyleix, JA Paton & GCG Argent (Perry 1967: 414-415).

H19 2002: in stubble field, 80 m alt., N of R445 W of Newhall Crossroads, W of Naas, N81, HF Fox & CD Preston (Rothero 2003: 55).

H21 2002: in stubble field, 60 m alt., SE of Hazelhatch Station, N93, CD Preston (Rothero 2003: 55).

H22 1978: hayfield, Caraguban, Duleek, DM Synnott (Hill 1980b: 40).

H27 1987: marshy area on edge of wood, nr Rose Cottage, NW of Westport House, JA Paton (Blockeel 1988: 36).

H31 1966: wheat stubble, S of Dromiskin, DM Synnott (Perry 1967: 414-415).

H33 1960: potato field, Killybreed, RD Fitzgerald (Warburg 1961: 168).

H34 1962: stubble field nr Castleforward, nr Newtown Cunningham, EF Warburg *et al.* (BBS exc.) (Warburg 1963b: 498).

H36 1957: ground in quarry, Carrickaness Bridge, nr Drumquin, RD Fitzgerald (Warburg 1958b: 481).

H37 1964: fallow field, SE corner of Lough Gullion, RD Fitzgerald (Warburg 1965: 865).

[H38 deleted because no valid record or voucher specimen traced (Blockeel 1999: 6)].

[H39 deleted because no valid record or voucher specimen traced (Blockeel 1999: 6)].

H40 1952: stubble field, Coleraine, EW Jones (Warburg 1953: 312).

This taxon was treated as a variety of *E. serratum* by Smith (1978: 350) and Blockeel & Long (1998: 110), but Risse (1996, 1997) and Holyoak (2001a: 16, and in prep.) prefer to treat them as separate species because intermediate plants do not occur and they often occupy distinct habitats. Some records listed above of *E. minutissimum* and *E. serratum* may have been confused because identification was formerly sometimes based on unreliable leaf characters rather than the characters of mature spores.

83/6 ***Ephemerum spinulosum*** Bruch & Schimp.

H39 1999: on mud exposed at edge of reservoir, North Woodburn Reservoir, J39, DT Holyoak 99-852, conf. VS Bryan (BBSUK, BEL, DUKE) (Rothero 2000: 53, Holyoak 2001c). This remains the only record of the species in Europe.

84/1 ***Oedipodium griffithianum*** (Dicks.) Schwägr.

H(1) no date: Brandon, Taylor (Lett 1951: 132). H(1) listed by Blockeel & Long (1998: 110).
H(35) no date: Errigal, Dixon (Lett 1915: 132). H(35) listed by Blockeel & Long (1998: 110).

85/2 ***Tayloria tenuis*** (Dicks.) Schimp.
(syn. *Tayloria longicollis* (Dicks.) Dixon)

H(40) 1868: Benbradagh, SA Stewart (Lett 1915: 132)
1884: Benbradagh, SA Stewart (Lett 1915: 132). H(40) listed by Blockeel & Long (1998: 110).

86/1 ***Tetraplodon angustatus*** (Hedw.) Bruch & Schimp.

H18 1988: on dung amongst *Sphagnum magellanicum* on raised bog, Clara Bog Nature Reserve, N Lockhart (Blockeel 1989: 28).

86/2 ***Tetraplodon mnioides*** (Hedw.) Bruch & Schimp.
(syn. *Tetraplodon bryoides* Lindb.)

H(1) listed by Lett (1915: 132).
†H1 listed by Blockeel & Long (1998: 111).
H(2) listed by Lett (1915: 132). H(2) listed by Blockeel & Long (1998: 111).
H(3) listed by Lett (1915: 132).
†H3 listed by Blockeel & Long (1998: 111).
H7 1954: Lilleton [*sic* = Littleton] Bog, MJP Scannell, comm. JS Thomson (Warburg 1955: 585).
H(14) listed by Lett (1915: 132). H(14) listed by Blockeel & Long (1998: 111).
H(16) listed by Lett (1915: 132).
†H16 listed by Blockeel & Long (1998: 111).
H17 1985: raised bog, Leaha, H Grogan & C Douglas (Blockeel 1987: 24).
H19 1955: bank of drain in bog, Baronstown East, nr Newbridge, ALK King (Warburg 1956: 155).
H(20) listed by Lett (1915: 132).
†H20 listed by Blockeel & Long (1998: 111).
H23 1982: on dung, bog nr Street, Rathowen, V Gordon (Hill 1986: 22).
H24 1972: raised bog, Killashee, WV Rubers (U) (Crundwell: 1975: 16).
H25 1968: on bone 2 miles NW of Lanesborough, WV Rubers *et al.* (U) (Crundwell 1975: 16).
H(27) listed by Lett (1915: 132).
†H27 listed by Blockeel & Long (1998: 111).
H28 1957: *ca* 1400 ft [alt.], Ben Bulben, E Johnson, comm. ALK King (Warburg 1959: 635).
H29 1970: N-facing cliffs or hillslopes, Glenfarne, nr Belcoo, E Hegewald (BBS exc.) (Crundwell 1971b: 378, Appleyard 1971: 389).
H(30) 1910: Cuilcagh, WN Tetley (anon. 1915b: 10).
H(30) listed by Lett (1915: 132). H(30) listed by Blockeel & Long (1998: 111).
H33 1950: scarp by the gap, Cuilcagh, J Taylor (Warburg 1954: 483).
H(35) listed by Lett (1915: 132).
†H35 listed by Blockeel & Long (1998: 111).
H36 1958: Altatavan Burn, 1250 ft [alt.], N side of Mullaghcarn, RD Fitzgerald (Warburg 1959: 635).
H(38) listed by Lett (1915: 132). H(38) listed by Blockeel & Long (1998: 111).
H(39) listed by Lett (1915: 132). H(39) listed by Blockeel & Long (1998: 111).
H40 1958: droppings on rock, 1800 ft [alt.], Dart Mt., RD Fitzgerald (Warburg 1959: 635).

88/1 ***Splachnum sphaericum*** Hedw.
(syn. *Splachnum ovatum* Hedw., *S. pedunculatum* Lindb. nom. illeg., *S. pedunculatum* var. *sphaericum* (Hedw.) Braithw.)

H(1) listed by Lett (1915: 132).
†H1 listed by Blockeel & Long (1998: 111).
H3 1967: sheep droppings, *ca* 1200 ft [alt.], Foilanumera, RD Fitzgerald (Crundwell 1968: 638).
H7 1966: old sheep dung, L. Muskry, Galtee Mts, JG Duckett *et al.* (BBS exc.) (Perry

1967: 415).
H9 1963: blanket bog, *ca* 950 ft [alt.], N side of Slieve Elva, Lisdoonvarna, G Halliday (Warburg 1964: 728).
H11 1966: old cow dung, Derryfadda Bog, nr Urlingford, JG Duckett *et al.* (BBS exc.) (Perry 1967: 415).
H16 1957: Muckanaght, J Appleyard (BBS exc.) (Warburg 1958b: 481).
H(20) listed by Lett (1915: 132) without locality.
†H20 listed by Blockeel & Long (1998: 111).
H(21) listed by Lett (1915: 132). H(21) listed by Blockeel & Long (1998: 111).
H(26) listed by Lett (1915: 132). H(26) listed by Blockeel & Long (1998: 111).
†H27 listed by Blockeel & Long (1998: 111).
H(28) listed by Lett (1915: 131).
†H28 listed by Blockeel & Long (1998: 111).
H(29) listed by Lett (1915: 132). H(29) listed by Blockeel & Long (1998: 111).
H29 2000: on sheep dung in open blanket bog, NW of Crockauns, G74, DT Holyoak 00-650 (BBSUK) (Rothero 2001: 43).
H(30) listed by Lett (1915: 132).
†H30 listed by Blockeel & Long (1998: 111).
H33 1951: Florence Court Moors, J McK Moon, det. & comm. J Taylor (Warburg 1953: 312).
H34 1962: dung on moorland, N side of Croaghconnellagh, EF Warburg *et al.* (BBS exc.) (Warburg 1963b: 498).
H(35) listed by Lett (1915: 132).
†H35 listed by Blockeel & Long (1998: 111).
H36 1952: cow dung, L. Bradan, RD Fitzgerald (Warburg 1953: 312).
H(38) [erroneously as H39] listed by Lett (1915: 132) from 1979: Donaghadee Bog, leg. Templeton, and Slieve Bingian, leg. HW Lett.
†H38 listed by Blockeel & Long (1998: 111).
H(39) listed by Lett (1915: 132).
†H39 listed by Blockeel & Long (1998: 111).
H(40) listed by Lett (1915: 132).
†H40 listed by Blockeel & Long (1998: 111).

88/2 ***Splachnum ampullaceum*** Hedw.

H(1) listed by Lett (1915: 131) without details.
†H1 listed by Blockeel & Long (1998: 111).
H(2) listed by Lett (1915: 131).
†H2 listed by Blockeel & Long (1998: 111).
†H3 listed by Blockeel & Long (1998: 111).
H7 1966: dung, cut-over bog, Urlingford, DM Synnott *et al.* (BBS exc.) (Perry 1967: 415).
H8 1991: on cutaway bog, 60 m alt., 3 km NW of Cappamore, R75, N Lockhart & A O'Suillivan (Blockeel 1992: 27).
H(9) listed by Lett (1915: 131).
†H9 listed by Blockeel & Long (1998: 111).
H12 1969: on cow dung, marshy ground, Pallis Bridge, Wicklow Gap, RD Fitzgerald (Crundwell 1970: 203).
H14 1965: marsh at Derry Hills, ALK King (Warburg 1966: 196).
H(15) listed by Blockeel & Long (1998: 111).
H(16) listed by Lett (1915: 131).
†H16 listed by Blockeel & Long (1998: 111).
[H(17) listed by Lett (1915: 131) without details. H17 deleted because no valid record or voucher specimen traced (Blockeel 1999: 6)].
H(19) listed by Lett (1915: 131). H(19) listed by Blockeel & Long (1998: 111).
H(20) listed by Lett (1915: 131).
†H20 listed by Blockeel & Long (1998: 111).
H(21) listed by Lett (1915: 131). H(21) listed by Blockeel & Long (1998: 111).
H(22) listed by Lett (1915: 131) without locality.
†H22 listed by Blockeel & Long (1998: 111).
H23 1971: lake above Ben Loughs, L Grubb (Crundwell 1974: 170).
H24 1965: raised bog S of Roosky, RD Fitzgerald & EM Lobley (Warburg 1966: 196).
H25 1966: bog on W side of R. Shannon, SW of Termonbarry, G Halliday & GCG Argent (Perry 1967: 415).
H26 1981: on dung, cutaway bog, Kilskeagh Townland, nr L. Carra, N Lockhart (Hill 1983: 53).
†H27 listed by Blockeel & Long (1998: 111).
H(28) listed by Lett (1915: 131).
†H28 listed by Blockeel & Long (1998: 111).
H29 1965: droppings *ca* 500 ft alt., Aghadunvane, L. Melvin, RD Fitzgerald & EM Lobley (Warburg 1966: 196).
H(33) listed by Lett (1915: 131).
†H33 listed by Blockeel & Long (1998: 111).
H(34) listed by Lett (1915: 131). H(34) listed by Blockeel & Long (1998: 111).
H(35) listed by Lett (1915: 131).
H35 1962: cut-away bog nr Dowros Head, ALK King (Warburg 1963b: 498).
H36 1957: cow dung, Evishbrack, nr Cookstown, RD Fitzgerald (Warburg

1958b: 481).
H(37) 1916: Camlough Mt., JD Houston (anon. 1917c: 10).
†H37 listed by Blockeel & Long (1998: 111).
H(38) listed by Lett (1915: 131). H(38) listed by Blockeel & Long (1998: 111).
†H39 listed by Blockeel & Long (1998: 111).
H(40) 1912: marsh by lake, Kilrea, JD Houston (anon. 1914a: 102).
†H40 listed by Blockeel & Long (1998: 111).

91/1 ***Orthodontium lineare*** Schwägr. (syn. *Orthodontium gracile* var. *heterocarpum* W.Watson)

H5 1978: on rotting stump in woodland, Fota I., N Kirby (Hill 1980b: 40).
H6 1999: on rotting stump in pine plantation, 60 m alt., Fennor, *ca* 5 km W of Tramore, S50, TL Blockeel 28/297 (Rothero 2000: 54).
H20 1992: in crevice of damp ?granitic rock on steep cliff slopes above lake, Upper Lough Bray, FJ Rumsey (Blockeel 1994: 38).
H(21) no date: Howth Demesne, H Hudson & JS Thomson, per JS Thomson (Duncan 1944: 212).
†H21 listed by Blockeel & Long (1998: 112).
H27 1987: shaded peaty bank under shrubs, valley above Sraheens Lough, Achill I., DG Long (Blockeel 1988: 36).
H29 2001: on rotting wood of stump in woodland, 60 m alt., N shore of Garadice Lough, E of Killaphort, H11, DT Holyoak 01-818 (Rothero 2002: 50).
H30 2001: on tree stump, 95 m alt., Deerpark, W of Virginia, N58, DT Holyoak 01-655 (Rothero 2002: 50).
H33 1999: in small quantity on N-facing sandstone scarp, 280 m alt., Braade ASSI, Lough Navar Forest, H05, RD Porley 2036 (Rothero 2000: 54).
H36 1958: bark of tree, Drumlea Wood, 4 miles E of Gortin, RD Fitzgerald (Warburg 1959: 636).
H37 1964: vertical peat faces in raised bog S of Derrycrow, nr Lough Gullion, RD Fitzgerald (Warburg 1965: 865).
H38 1999: on old conifer stump, 50 m alt., Tollymore Forest park, 4 km W of Newcastle, J33, TL Blockeel 28/346 (Rothero 2000: 54).
H39 1973: rotten tree trunk in wood, Cavehill, Belfast, P Hackney (Hackney 1973, Crundwell 1974: 170).
H40 1999: on rotting wood of fallen trunk at edge of ornamental woodland, Downhill, C73, DT Holyoak 99-215 (BBSUK) (Rothero 2000: 54).

91/2 ***Orthodontium gracile*** Schwägr. ex Bruch, Schimp. & W.Gümbel

H33 1993: sandstone cliff face, Lough Navar Forest, H05, C Sérgio, comm. NG Hodgetts (Blockeel 1994: 38, Hodgetts & Hallingbäck 1994). Not refound during thorough searches in 1999 (Porley & Matcham 2003: 64).

92/1 ***Leptobryum pyriforme*** (Hedw.) Wilson

[H(3) listed by Lett (1915: 133) as: Blarney Castle, leg. Carroll. H3 deleted because the only record traced (Blarney Castle, I Carroll, in Lett 1915) is from H4, comm. NF Stewart (Blockeel 1995c: 44)].
H(4) listed by Lett (1915: 133). H(4) listed by Blockeel & Long (1998: 112).
H4 2002: on ledge at entrance to limestone cave, 40 m alt., Blarney in the Castle grounds, W67, TL Blockeel 31/196 (Rothero 2003: 55).
H6 1999: on bare mud in marshy field, 8 m alt., R. Bride, 1 km E of Tallowbridge, Tallow, X09, TL Blockeel 28/254 (Rothero 2000: 54).
H(7) listed by Lett (1915: 133). H(7) listed by Blockeel & Long (1998: 112).
H8 1979: sandy-loamy soil of meadow, Mungret, W of Limerick, HMH van Melick (Hill 1981: 29).
H9 1956: damp rock-face in glen below the Spa, Lisdoonvarna, ALK King (Warburg 1957: 333).
H14 1956: disturbed calcareous soil, roadside, Castletown, AA Cridland (Warburg 1958b: 482).
H17 1985: bare peat on raised bog, Lisnagerragh, H Grogan & C Douglas (Blockeel 1987: 24).
H18 1987: barley stubble, Derrybrat, 5 km NW of Kilcormac, HLK Whitehouse (Blockeel 1988: 36).
H(21) listed by Lett (1915: 134). H(21) listed by Blockeel & Long (1998: 112).
H22 1980: on side of tussock by lake edge, Lough Shesk, Clonmellon, DM Synnott (Hill 1981: 29).

H23 1957: forestry plantation, NE end of L. Owel, JS Thomson (Warburg 1958b: 482).
H25 1981: ledge in limestone quarry, Croghan, N of Elphin, DM Synnott (Hill 1982: 27).
H26 1965: rock clefts, *ca* 750 ft alt., cliffs S of Glendaduff, [The] Ox Mts, RD Fitzgerald (Warburg 1966: 197).
H27 1962: peaty ground by roadside nr Sraheens Lough, Achill I., EF Warburg (Warburg 1963b: 498).
H29 1963: clay bank at stream side below Glencar Waterfall, AR Perry & RD Fitzgerald (Warburg 1964: 728).
H(31) listed by Lett (1915: 134). H(31) listed by Blockeel & Long (1998: 112).
H(33) listed by Lett (1915: 134). H(33) listed by Blockeel & Long (1998: 112).
H33 1999: on ledge on N-facing sandstone escarpment, 280 m alt., Braade ASSI, Lough Navar Forest, H05, RD Porley 2042 (Rothero 2000: 54).
H(34) listed by Lett (1915: 134). H(34) listed by Blockeel & Long (1998: 112).
H34 2002: on loamy soil nr gateway into field, 5 m alt., Inch Level, C32, DT Holyoak 02-837 (Rothero 2003: 55).
H35 2002: on loamy soil in flowerpot at camping ground, 20 m alt., SE of Portsalon, C23, DT Holyoak 02-878 (Rothero 2003: 55).
H36 2002: on open damp soil in ditch, 185 m alt., Barnes Gap, H58, DT Holyoak 02-1141 (Rothero 2003: 55).
H(38) listed by Lett (1915: 134). H(38) listed by Blockeel & Long (1998: 112).
H38 2002: on thin soil on floor of old quarry, 100 m alt., Scrabo Quarry, J47, DT Holyoak 02-1031 (Rothero 2003: 55).
H(39) listed by Lett (1915: 134). H(39) listed by Blockeel & Long (1998: 112).
H39 2002: on mud by reservoir, 95 m alt., NE edge of Bonner's Reservoir, Lisburn, J26, DT Holyoak 02-1007 (Rothero 2003: 55).
H(40) listed by Lett (1915: 134). H(40) listed by Blockeel & Long (1998: 112).

93/1a ***Pohlia elongata*** **Hedw. subsp.** ***elongata*** **var.** ***elongata***
(syn. *Webera elongata* (Hedw.) Schwägr.)

H(1) listed by Lett (1915: 134). H(1) listed by Blockeel & Long (1998: 112).
[H2 deleted because no valid record or voucher specimen traced (Blockeel 1999: 6)].
H3 1979: rocky stream gully, above Glenbeg Lough, Ardgroom, RC Stern (Hill 1980b: 40).
H6 1966: bank of stream N of Coumshingaun Lough, Comeragh Mts, JA Paton (BBS exc.) (Perry 1967: 415).
[H(7) listed by Lett (1915: 134)].
H7 1966: turfy bank, moorland N of Muskry, J Appleyard (BBS exc.) (Perry 1967: 415).
H8 1966: bank in gully, Monabrack, J Appleyard (BBS exc.) (Perry 1967: 415).
[H(12) listed by Lett (1915: 134)].
H16 1965: wet silty bank by stream, SW side of Devilsmother, G Halliday & GCG Argent (Warburg 1966: 197).
H(20) listed by Lett (1915: 134). H(20) listed by Blockeel & Long (1998: 112).
H(27) 1937: Croaghaun, Achill I., no collector named (BBS exc.) (Armitage 1938: 13).
H27 1987: sandy soil below scree, E slope of N corrie, Mweelrea, JA Paton (Blockeel 1988: 36).
H29 2001: on steep, E-facing sandstone crag, 420 m alt., Coal Pit, E slope of Bencroy, H01, DT Holyoak 01-791 (Rothero 2002: 50).
[H(31) listed by Lett (1915: 134)].
H(34) no date: Bulbein [= Bulbin Mt.], R Brown (Lett 1915: 134).
H34 2002: on thin soil on ledges of steep NW-facing crag, 420 m alt., NW slope of Bulbin Mt., C34, DT Holyoak 02-807 (Rothero 2003: 55).
H35 1970: in crevices of rocks in gully, N corrie, above L. Agh, Slieve League, MFV Corley (Crundwell 1971b: 379).
[H(36) listed by Lett (1915: 134) without data].
H(38) listed by Lett (1915: 134). H(38) listed by Blockeel & Long (1998: 112).
[H(39) listed by Lett (1915: 134) without data].
[H(40) listed by Lett (1915: 134)].
H40 1968: Glenfomna Water, Sperrin Mts, RD Fitzgerald (Crundwell 1969: 884).

93/1b ***Pohlia elongata*** **subsp.** ***elongata*** **var.** ***acuminata*** (Hoppe & Hornsch.) Huebener (syn. *Pohlia acuminata* Hoppe & Hornsch., *Webera acuminata* (Hoppe & Hornsch.) Schimp.)

H(1) 1828: Brandon, Wilson (Lett 1915: 134). H(1) listed by Blockeel & Long (1998: 112).
[H2 deleted because no valid record or voucher specimen traced (Blockeel 1999: 6)].
[H7 treated as dubious record in *CC* by Warburg (1963a: 54)].
H7 1966: ledge on rocks above L. Curra, Galtee Mts, JA Paton (BBS exc.) (Perry 1967: 415).
[H(16) 1933: Muckanaght, Twelve Bens, PWM Richards (anon. 1938d: 40). H16 treated as dubious record in *CC* by Warburg (1963a: 54)].
[H(20) listed by Lett (1915: 134) as: Toole's Rocks, leg. Moore. H20 treated as dubious record in *CC* by Warburg (1963a: 54)].
[H31 treated as dubious record in *CC* by Warburg (1963a: 54)].
[H(38) listed by Lett (1915: 134) as: Slieve Donard, leg. HW Lett. H38 treated as dubious record in *CC* by Warburg (1963a: 54)].

93/1c ***Pohlia elongata*** **subsp.** ***polymorpha*** (Hoppe & Hornsch.) Nyholm (syn. *Pohlia polymorpha* Hoppe & Hornsch.)

H(1) 1873: Connor Hill, Moore (Lett 1915: 134). H(1) listed by Blockeel & Long (1998: 112).
H(7) 1855: Galteemore, Moore (Lett 1915: 134).
1943: cliffs at L. Diheen, AW Stelfox, per JS Thomson (Duncan 1944: 212).
H7 1966: earthy cliff ledges, L. Curra, Galtee Mts, JG Duckett (BBS exc.) (Perry 1967: 415).
H16 1970: rock ledge, NE slope of Muckanaght, Twelve Pins, JA Paton (Crundwell 1971b: 379).
[H(21) listed by Lett (1915: 134) as 1853: Templeogue, leg. Orr].

93/3 ***Pohlia cruda*** (Hedw.) Lindb. (syn. *Webera cruda* (Hedw.) Bruch)

H(1) listed by Lett (1915: 134).
†H1 listed by Blockeel & Long (1998: 113).
H(7) 1943: cliffs at L. Diheen, AW Stelfox, per JS Thomson (Duncan 1944: 212).
†H7 listed by Blockeel & Long (1998: 113).
H(8) 1945: Galtees, RD Meikle (anon. 1947: 32).
H10 1979: rock crevice nr waterfall, W side of Keeper Hill, S of Silvermine Mts, HMH van Melick (Hill 1981: 29).
H16 1957: rock crevice, 1600 ft [alt.], N side of Muckanaght, AC Crundwell (BBS exc.) (Warburg 1958b: 482).
H(20) listed by Lett (1915: 134). H(20) listed by Blockeel & Long (1998: 113).
H(21) listed by Lett (1915: 134). H(21) listed by Blockeel & Long (1998: 113).
H27 1987: under boulder in block scree, Caheraspic corrie, Sheeffry Mts, DM Synnott (Blockeel 1988: 36).
H29 1965: clefts of rock, *ca* 1000 ft alt., Aghadunvane, L. Melvin, RD Fitzgerald & EM Lobley (Warburg 1966: 197).
H33 1999: on N-facing sandstone scarp, 300 m alt., Letter Scarp, Lough Navar Forest, H05, RD Porley 2039 (Rothero 2000: 54).
H(34) listed by Lett (1915: 134).
†H34 listed by Blockeel & Long (1998: 113).
H35 2002: on soil beneath overhang on limestone crag, 270 m alt., just SW of Lough Salt, C12, DT Holyoak 02-697 (Rothero 2003: 55).
H(38) listed by Lett (1915: 134). H(38) listed by Blockeel & Long (1998: 113).
H(39) listed by Lett (1915: 134).
†H39 listed by Blockeel & Long (1998: 113).
H40 1964: clefts of basalt *ca* 1200 ft [alt.], Benbradagh, RD Fitzgerald & MPH Kertland (Warburg 1965: 865).

93/4 ***Pohlia nutans*** (Hedw.) Lindb. (syn. *Pohlia nutans* 'var. *alpina* Ldbg.' of Lett 1915: 134, *P. nutans* var. *longiseta* (Huebener) Delogne, *Webera nutans* Hedw., *Webera nutans* var. *longiseta* Huebener)

H(1) listed by Lett (1915: 134) without details.
†H1 listed by Blockeel & Long (1998: 113).
H(2) listed by Lett (1915: 134) without

details.
†H2 listed by Blockeel & Long (1998: 113).
H(3) listed by Lett (1915: 134) without details.
†H3 listed by Blockeel & Long (1998: 113).
H4 1966: peaty bank, Seefin, Boggeragh Mts, MFV Corley & JS Parker (Perry 1967: 415).
H(5) listed by Lett (1915: 134) without details.
†H5 listed by Blockeel & Long (1998: 113).
H(6) listed by Lett (1915: 134) without details.
†H6 listed by Blockeel & Long (1998: 113).
H7 1954: Littleton Bog, MJP Scannell, comm. JS Thomson (Warburg 1955: 585).
H(8) listed by Lett (1915: 134) without details.
†H8 listed by Blockeel & Long (1998: 113).
H(9) listed by Lett (1915: 134) without details.
†H9 listed by Blockeel & Long (1998: 113).
H(10) listed by Lett (1915: 134) without details.
†H10 listed by Blockeel & Long (1998: 113).
H(11) listed by Lett (1915: 134) without details.
†H11 listed by Blockeel & Long (1998: 113).
H(12) listed by Lett (1915: 134) without details.
†H12 listed by Blockeel & Long (1998: 113).
[H(13) listed by Lett (1915: 134) as 'var. *alpina* Ldbg.'].
H13 1969: on peat, *ca* 1100 ft [alt.], below Caher Roe's Den, Blackstairs Mts, RD Fitzgerald (Crundwell 1970: 203).
H(14) listed by Lett (1915: 134) without details.
†H14 listed by Blockeel & Long (1998: 113).
H15 1962: amongst birches, raised bog nr Woodford, AJE Smith (Warburg 1963b: 498).
H(16) listed by Lett (1915: 134) without details.
†H16 listed by Blockeel & Long (1998: 113).
H17 1965: peat on blanket bog by T.40 road between Cregg R. and R. Clare, AJE Smith (Warburg 1966: 197).
H(18) listed by Lett (1915: 134) without details.
†H18 listed by Blockeel & Long (1998: 113).
H(19) 1949: Ballymount Bog, nr Calverstown, JS Thomson (Warburg 1950: 385).
1949: Ballymount Bog, nr Calverstown, JS Thomson (Warburg 1950: 385), as var. *longiseta*.
H(20) listed by Lett (1915: 134) without details.
†H20 listed by Blockeel & Long (1998: 113).
H(21) listed by Lett (1915: 134) without details.
†H21 listed by Blockeel & Long (1998: 113).
H22 1952: bank in Clonycavan Bog, nr Ballivor, ALK King (Warburg 1953: 313).
H23 1952: The Derries Bog, nr Athlone, ALK King (Warburg 1953: 313).
H24 1957: raised bog, Newtownforbes [*sic* = Newtown Forbes], MPH Kertland & ALK King (Warburg 1958b: 482).
H(25) listed by Lett (1915: 134) without details.
†H25 listed by Blockeel & Long (1998: 113).
[H27 1957: soil under boulder, SE valley of Maumtrasna, AC Crundwell (BBS exc.) (Warburg 1958b: 482). H27 deleted because locality (E of Skeltia, Maumtrasna) is in H16 (Crundwell 1970: 203)].
H27 1970: boggy slope nr Erriff Bridge, N of Maumtrasna, JA Paton (Crundwell 1971b: 379).
H28 1963: peat overlying limestone, *ca* 1100 ft [alt.], Lugnagall, Glencar, AR Perry & RD Fitzgerald (Warburg 1964: 728).
H(29) listed by Lett (1915: 134) without details.
†H29 listed by Blockeel & Long (1998: 113).
H(30) listed by Lett (1915: 134).
†H30 listed by Blockeel & Long (1998: 113).
[H(31) listed by Lett (1915: 134) without details. H31 deleted because no valid record or voucher specimen traced (Blockeel 1999: 6)].
H(32) listed by Lett (1915: 134) without details.
†H32 listed by Blockeel & Long (1998: 113).
H(33) listed by Lett (1915: 134) without details.
†H33 listed by Blockeel & Long (1998: 113).
H(34) listed by Lett (1915: 134).
†H34 listed by Blockeel & Long (1998: 113).
H(35) listed by Lett (1915: 134) without details.
†H35 listed by Blockeel & Long (1998: 113).
H(36) listed by Lett (1915: 134) without details.
†H36 listed by Blockeel & Long (1998: 113).
H(37) listed by Lett (1915: 134).

†H37 listed by Blockeel & Long (1998: 113).
H(38) listed by Lett (1915: 134).
†H38 listed by Blockeel & Long (1998: 113).
H(39) listed by Lett (1915: 134) without details.
†H39 listed by Blockeel & Long (1998: 113).
H(40) listed by Lett (1915: 134).
†H40 listed by Blockeel & Long (1998: 113).

93/6 ***Pohlia drummondii*** (Müll.Hal.) A.L. Andrews

H1 1983: damp mud by lake, W shore of Coomasaharn Lake, below Coomreagh, DG Long (Hill 1984b: 28).
[H2 record 1951: bare ground in short turf, nr Keeper's Cottage, Derrycunihy Woods, nr Killarney, EF Warburg (BBS exc.) (BBSUK), redet. MO Hill (Warburg 1952: 104, as *P. rothii*; MO Hill MS) should be deleted because the locality is in H1 (see Kelly 1984b)].
[H3 apparently listed in error by Lewis & Smith (1978: 24)].
[H5 apparently listed in error by Lewis & Smith (1978: 24)].
H5 2002: sparsely on bare ground by gravelly path, 55 m alt., Glenbower Wood nr Killeagh, W97, TL Blockeel 31/305 (Rothero 2003: 55).
[H6 apparently listed in error by Lewis & Smith (1978: 24)].
[H12 apparently listed in error by Lewis & Smith (1978: 24)].
H16 1957: Muckanaght, J Appleyard (BBS exc.) (BBSUK), redet. MO Hill (Warburg 1958b: 482, as *P. rothii*; MO Hill MS).
[H20 apparently listed in error by Lewis & Smith (1978: 24)].
[H25 apparently listed in error by Lewis & Smith (1978: 24)].
H27 1970: layby on N side of Killary Harbour, JA Paton (BBSUK), redet. MO Hill (Crundwell 1971b: 379, as *P. rothii*; MO Hill MS).
H28 1970: floor of quarry, roadside nr Masshill, W of Cloonacool, J Appleyard (BBS exc.) (BBSUK), redet. MO Hill (Crundwell 1971b: 379, Appleyard 1971: 389, as *P. rothii*; MO Hill MS).
[H33 apparently listed in error by Lewis & Smith (1978: 24)].
H34 1968: on ground, *ca* 1600 ft [alt.], Bulbin Mt., Inishowen, RD Fitzgerald & HH Birks (BBSUK), redet. MO Hill (Crundwell 1969: 884, as *P. rothii*; MO Hill MS).
1969: stream bank S of Lough Inn, W of Moville, Inishowen, JA Paton (Hill 1977a: 20).
H35 1969: margin of roadside lake, E of Errigal Mt., JA Paton, conf. MO Hill (MO Hill MS).
1970: track, Slieve League, MFV Corley (Hill 1977a: 20).
[H36 apparently listed in error by Lewis & Smith (1978: 24)].
H36 2002: on thin soil over quarried schist, 180 m alt., Barnes Gap, H58, DT Holyoak, 02-1143 (Rothero 2003: 55).
[H39 apparently listed in error by Lewis & Smith (1978: 24)].

Irish and British specimens were revised by MO Hill (MS) for the *CC* (Corley & Hill 1981: 94).

93/8 ***Pohlia filum*** (Schimp.) Mårtensson (syn. *Pohlia gracilis* (Bruch, Schimp. & W.Gümbel) Lindb.)

H6 1966: wet sandy track by River Glenshelane, 2 miles N of Cappoquin, EM Lobley (BBSUK), labelled as *Pohlia rothii* (Hill 1981: 29).
H27 1987: disused sand pit, E of L. Doo, E of Dugort, Achill I., JA Paton (Blockeel 1988: 37).
H35 1991: on gravel in old quarry, 60 m alt., SE end of Lough Nacung Upper, B91, DG Long 20275 (Blockeel 1993: 51).
H36 1957: side of stony path, Baronscourt, RD Fitzgerald (BBSUK), labelled as *Pohlia rothii* (Hill 1981: 29).
H40 2002: on open sandy soil by track in old quarry, 285 m alt., above Whitewater Bridge, NE of Lough Fea, H78, DT Holyoak 02-1150 (Rothero 2003: 55).

93/9 ***Pohlia andalusica*** (Höhn.) Broth. (syn. *Pohlia rothii* (Correns ex Limpr.) Broth.)

[H1 1951: side of path nr Cummergorm Glen, Glenbeigh, AC Crundwell, det. AC Crundwell (BBS exc.) listed as *P. rothii* (Warburg 1952: 104, Lewis & Smith 1978: 26, Hill 1979: 29). Same H1 record of *P. rothii* deleted because specimen belongs to another taxon, comm. AC Crundwell (Hill 1981: 29)].

[H2 record of *P. rothii* (1951: bare ground in short turf, nr Keeper's Cottage, Derricunihy [*sic* = Derrycunihy] Woods, nr Killarney, EF Warburg , BBS exc., Warburg 1952: 104) reidentified as *P. drummondii* by MO Hill (MS). This locality is in H1].

[H3 record of *P. rothii* (1966: damp ground by path, Few Heads Point, Glengarriff, JPM Brenan, Crundwell 1969: 884) has not been reidentified as any of the segregate species recognised by Lewis & Smith 1978].

H3 1968: mine-waste, old copper mines, Allihies, JA Paton (Hb. MO Hill), listed as *P. rothii* (Lewis & Smith 1978: 26, Hill 1979: 29, MO Hill MS).

[H5 record of *P. rothii* (1966: on track, Castlecooke, nr Kilworth, RD Fitzgerald, BBS exc., Crundwell 1968: 638) has not been reidentified as any of the segregate species recognised by Lewis & Smith 1978].

H6 1966: mine waste, old copper mine, Bunmahon, JA Paton 1277, listed as *P. rothii* (Lewis & Smith 1978: 26, Hill 1979: 29, MO Hill MS). [Another record from H6 (1966: sandy track by R. Glenshelane, N of Cappoquin, EM Lobley *et al.*, BBS exc., Perry 1967: 415, listed as *P. rothii*) has not been reidentified as any of the segregate species recognised by Lewis & Smith 1978].

[H12 record of *P. rothii* (1969: on path, Wicklow Gap, RD Fitzgerald, Crundwell 1971b: 379) has not been reidentified as any of the segregate species recognised by Lewis & Smith 1978].

[H16 record of *P. rothii* (1957: Muckanaght, J Appleyard (BBS exc.), Warburg 1958b: 482) reidentified as *P. drummondii* by MO Hill (MS)].

[H20 record of *P. rothii* (1964: in clump of *Nardia scalaris*, nr Aughavannagh, at 1400 ft [alt.], ALK King, Warburg 1965: 865) has not been reidentified as any of the segregate species recognised by Lewis & Smith 1978].

[H25 record of *P. rothii* (1948: marshy ground on right bank of river Shannon below Carrick-on-Shannon, ALK King, Warburg 1952: 104, erroneously published as H45) has not been reidentified as any of the segregate species recognised by Lewis & Smith 1978].

[H27 record of *P. rothii* (1970: layby on N side of Killary Harbour, JA Paton, Crundwell 1971b: 379) redet. by MO Hill (MS) as *P. drummondii*].

[H28 record of *P. rothii* (1970: roadside quarry, nr Masshill, J Appleyard (BBS exc.), Crundwell 1971b: 379, Appleyard 1971: 389) redet. by MO Hill (MS) as *P. drummondii*].

[H33 record of *P. rothii* (1960: on sand at edge of lake, Lough Scolban, RD Fitzgerald, Warburg 1961: 169) has not been reidentified as any of the segregate species recognised by Lewis & Smith 1978].

[H34 record of *P. rothii* (1968: on ground, *ca* 1600 ft [alt.], Bulbin Mt., Inishowen, RD Fitzgerald, Crundwell 1969: 884) redet. by MO Hill (MS) as *P. drummondii*].

[H35 record of *P. rothii* (1963: quarry by Losset Beg, nr Creeslough, ALK King, Warburg 1964: 728) has not been reidentified as any of the segregate species recognised by Lewis & Smith 1978].

[H36 record of *P. rothii* (1957: side of stony path, Baronscourt, RD Fitzgerald, Warburg 1958b: 482) has not been reidentified as any of the segregate species recognised by Lewis & Smith 1978].

[H40 record of *P. rothii* (1953: sandy N shore of L. Fea, MPH Kertland & EM Lobley, Warburg 1955: 585) has not been reidentified as any of the segregate species recognised by Lewis & Smith 1978].

93/10 ***Pohlia bulbifera*** (Warnst.) Warnst.

H1 1951: damp ground nr waterfall in Finglas River, nr Waterville, JS Thomson (BBS exc.) (Warburg 1952: 104). H1 listed by Lewis & Smith (1978: 24).

H3 1979: marshy soil beside track, NE end of Glen Lough, Adrigole, JA Paton (Hill 1980b: 40).

H4 1967: on path, Carrigagulla Bridge, Bogeragh Mts, RD Fitzgerald

(Crundwell 1968: 638-639). H4 listed by Lewis & Smith (1978: 24).

H6 1999: on bare peaty soil on dried-out bed of overspill lake, 500 m alt., Coumalocha, Comeragh Mts, S20, TL Blockeel 28/240 (Rothero 2000: 54).

H11 2000: on thin soil over limestone in disused quarry, 50 m alt., 1 km N of Thomastown, S54, N Lockhart (Rothero 2001: 43).

H16 1968: shore of L. Muck, NE of Letterfrack, JA Paton (Crundwell 1969: 884). Listed for H16 by Lewis & Smith (1978: 24).

H27 1970: roadside on N side of Killary Harbour, JA Paton (Crundwell 1971b: 379). Listed for H27 by Lewis & Smith (1978: 24).

H28 1970: bank of Owenaher R., SW of Cloonacool, JA Paton (BBS exc.) (Crundwell 1971b: 379, Appleyard 1971: 389). Listed for H28 by Lewis & Smith (1978: 24).

H30 2001: on damp shale by stream, 455 m alt., W slope of Cuilcagh, H12, DT Holyoak 01-785 (Rothero 2002: 50).

H33 1960: sandy side of drain, Lough Achork, RD Fitzgerald (Warburg 1961: 169). H33 listed by Lewis & Smith (1978: 24).

H34 1969: S margin of L. Inn, W of Moville, JA Paton (Crundwell 1970: 203). H34 also listed by Lewis & Smith (1978: 24).

H35 1969: margin of pool below road E of Errigal, JA Paton (Crundwell 1970: 203). H35 also listed by Lewis & Smith (1978: 24).

H36 1957: detritus at edge of stream, Sheskinawaddy, RD Fitzgerald (Warburg 1958b: 482). H36 listed by Lewis & Smith (1978: 24).

H38 2002: on peaty soil at edge of reservoir, 280 m alt., N end of Spelga Dam, J22, DT Holyoak 02-917 (Rothero 2003: 55).

H39 1967: on bare earth in crevices, Glen Rock, Cushybracken, nr Glaryford, RD Fitzgerald (Crundwell 1968: 638-639). H39 listed by Lewis & Smith (1978: 24).

93/11 ***Pohlia annotina*** (Hedw.) Lindb.
(syn. *Pohlia proligera* sensu A.J.E.Sm. non (Lindb. ex Breidl.) Lindb. Ex Arnell, *Webera annotina* (Hedw.) Bruch, *W. proligera* Lindb. ex Limpr.)

H1 1951: earthy bank of R. Dehy, Glenbeigh, EF Warburg (BBS exc.) (Warburg 1952: 104). H1 listed by Lewis & Smith (1978: 24) as *P. proligera*.

H2 1967: on old road, *ca* 900 ft [alt.], The Paps, RD Fitzgerald (Crundwell 1968: 639). H2 listed by Lewis & Smith (1978: 24) as *P. proligera*.

H3 1967: ground by stream, *ca* 1100 ft [alt.], Foilanumera, RD Fitzgerald (Crundwell 1968: 639). H3 listed by Lewis & Smith (1978: 24) as *P. proligera*.

H4 1966: earthy bank in disused quarry above R. Lee, Innishcarra Bridge, MFV Corley & JS Parker (Perry 1967: 415), as *P. proligera*. Also, 1967: on track, Carrigagulla Bridge, Bogeragh Mts, RD Fitzgerald (Crundwell 1968: 639), as *P. annotina*. H4 listed by Lewis & Smith (1978: 24) as *P. proligera*.

H5 1967 on track in bog, *ca* 700 ft [alt.], Lyrenamon, RD Fitzgerald (Crundwell 1968: 639). H5 listed by Lewis & Smith (1978: 24) as *P. proligera*.

H6 1966: earthy bank above Sgillage [*sic* = Sgilloge] Loughs, Comeragh Mts, JA Paton (Crundwell 1968: 639). H6 listed by Lewis & Smith (1978: 24) as *P. proligera*.

H7 1966: mound of earth by L. Curra, J Appleyard (BBS exc.) (Perry 1967: 415). H7 listed by Lewis & Smith (1978: 24) as *P. proligera*.

H8 1979: gravelly soil in roadside quarry, Sugar Hill, S of Knockanimpaha, JA Paton (Hill 1980b: 40).

H9 1979: side of ditch, W side of Slievebernagh, AC Crundwell (Hill 1980b: 40).

H10 1967: bare ground in pasture, Devils Bit Mt., RD Fitzgerald (Crundwell 1968: 639). H10 listed by Lewis & Smith (1978: 24) as *P. proligera*.

[H(11) listed by Lett (1915: 134)].

[H(12) listed by Lett (1915: 134)].

H12 1972: on timber road, Mountfin House, 2 km W of Ferns, WV Rubers (U)

(Crundwell 1975: 17). H12 listed by Lewis & Smith (1978: 24) as *P. proligera*.

H13 1967: bank of R. Slaney, Kilcarry, E Booth (Crundwell 1968: 639). H13 listed by Lewis & Smith (1978: 24) as *P. proligera*.

H14 1975: ledge of quarry nr Spink, AG Side (Crundwell 1976: 27). H14 listed by Lewis & Smith (1978: 24) as *P. proligera*.

H16 1955: bank of roadside drain, Ballinahinch, ALK King (Warburg 1956: 155). H16 listed by Lewis & Smith (1978: 24) as *P. proligera*.

H19 1954: sandy bank by pond in townland of Redbog, nr Blessington, ALK King (Warburg 1955: 585). H19 listed by Lewis & Smith (1978: 24) as *P. proligera*.

[H(20) listed by Lett (1915: 134)].

H20 listed by Lewis & Smith (1978: 24) as *P. proligera*. †H20 listed by Blockeel & Long (1998: 113).

[H(21) listed by Lett (1915: 134)].

H(21) listed by Lewis & Smith (1978: 24) as *P. proligera*. H(21) listed by Blockeel & Long (1998: 113).

H25 1965: damp bankside, Kilronan, nr Ballyfarnan, EM Lobley & RD Fitzgerald (Warburg 1966: 197). H25 listed by Lewis & Smith (1978: 24) as *P. proligera*.

[H27 1957: bare soil, SE valley of Maumtrasna, AC Crundwell (BBS exc.) (Warburg 1958b: 482). H27 deleted because locality (E of Skeltia, Maumtrasna) is in H16 (Crundwell 1970: 203)].

H27 1970: layby on N side of Killary Harbour, JA Paton (Crundwell 1971b: 379). Listed for H27 by Lewis & Smith (1978: 24) as *P. proligera*.

[H(28) 1928: nr Rosses Point, Sligo (BBS exc.) (Duncan 1928: 119), as *Webera annotina*].

H28 listed by Lewis & Smith (1978: 24) as *P. proligera*. †H28 listed by Blockeel & Long (1998: 113).

H29 1970: N-facing cliffs or hill slopes of Glenfarne, nr Belcoo, JA Paton (BBS exc.) (Crundwell 1971b: 379, Appleyard 1971: 389). Listed for H29 by Lewis & Smith (1978: 24) as *P. proligera*.

H30 2001: on damp shale by stream, 455 m alt., W slope of Cuilcagh, H12, DT Holyoak 01-779 (Rothero 2002: 50).

H31 1968: by stream E of Clermont Carn, DM Synnott (Crundwell 1969: 884). Listed for H31 by Lewis & Smith (1978: 24) as *P. proligera*.

H33 listed by Lewis & Smith (1978: 24) as *P. proligera*. †H33 listed by Blockeel & Long (1998: 113).

H34 1962: rock crevices by stream, E side of Bulbin [Mt.], EF Warburg (BBS exc.) (Warburg 1963b: 499). Listed for H34 by Lewis & Smith (1978: 24) as *P. proligera*.

H35 1962: side of track nr workings, Muckish [Mt.], EF Warburg *et al.* (BBS exc.) (Warburg 1963b: 499). Listed for H35 by Lewis & Smith (1978: 24) as *P. proligera*.

H36 listed by Lewis & Smith (1978: 24) as *P. proligera*. †H36 listed by Blockeel & Long (1998: 113).

H37 listed by Lewis & Smith (1978: 24) as *P. proligera*. †H37 listed by Blockeel & Long (1998: 113).

[H(38) 1908: Bryansford, CH Waddell, det. as *W.*[*ebera*] *proligera* by JA Wheldon (anon. 1909a: 310). H(38) listed by Lett (1915: 134)].

H38 listed by Lewis & Smith (1978: 24) as *P. proligera*. †H38 listed by Blockeel & Long (1998: 113).

[H(39) 1928: Glenariff (BBS exc.) (Duncan 1928: 114, 117), as *Webera proligera*. [H(39) listed by Lett (1915: 134)].

H39 listed by Lewis & Smith (1978: 24) as *P. proligera*. †H39 listed by Blockeel & Long (1998: 113).

H40 listed by Lewis & Smith (1978: 24) as *P. proligera*. †H40 listed by Blockeel & Long (1998: 113).

Records from before the taxonomic revision by Lewis & Smith (1978: 24) cannot be assigned to this or any of the related species with complete confidence unless specimens have been reidentified, although most records from the 1950s and 1960s are probably correct.

93/12 ***Pohlia proligera*** (Lindb. ex Breidl.) Lindb. ex Arnell

H40 1965: crumbling schist, Altalacky River, Mullaghmore, nr Dungiven [C70], RD Fitzgerald, det. as *P. proligera ca* 1993 by AC Crundwell (Warburg 1966: 197, Fitzgerald & Fitzgerald 1966a, Blockeel 1994: 39).

Irish and British specimens were revised and separated from those of *P. annotina* by AC Crundwell (in Blockeel 1994: 39). The name *P. proligera* had formerly been much used for an aggregate comprising the commoner *P. annotina* and the much rarer *P. proligera s.s.* (e.g. by Lewis & Smith 1978, Smith 1978).

93/13 ***Pohlia camptotrachela*** (Renauld & Cardot) Broth.

H1 1983: damp ruts in old pasture, W bank of Blackwater River, above Blackwater Bridge, Kenmare River, DG Long (Hill 1984b: 28).
H3 1968: Glenbeag Lough, Slieve Miskish Mts, JA Paton (Lewis & Smith 1978: 27, Hill 1979: 29).
H9 1979: hedgebank bordering lane, W side of Slieve Bernagh, G Bloom (Hill 1981: 29).
H10 1979: field beside Clare River, S of Derrygareen, E of Newport, JA Paton (Hill 1980b: 40).
H12 1975: Pallis Bridge, SE of Wicklow Gap, JA Paton (Lewis & Smith 1978: 27, Hill 1979: 29).
H16 1986: soil in marshy field, nr Courhoor Lough, Cleggan, DG Long (Blockeel 1987: 24).
H20 1975: S of Aghavannagh, JA Paton (Lewis & Smith 1978: 27, Hill 1979: 29).
H27 1987: on gravelly roadside, lane below Slievemore, Dugort, Achill I., DG Long (Blockeel 1988: 37).
H30 2001: on open damp soil on track in plantation, 315 m alt., W of Bellavally Gap, H12, DT Holyoak 01-642 (Rothero 2002: 50).
H33 2002: on soil below crag, 566 m alt., NE slope of Cuilcagh, H12, DT Holyoak 02-910 (Rothero 2003: 55).
H34 2002: on sandy soil among pebbles by river, 15 m alt., by Clonmany River SE of Clonmany, C34, DT Holyoak, 02-545 (Rothero 2003b: 55).
H35 1969: Doe Castle, Creeslough, JA Paton (Lewis & Smith 1978: 27, Hill 1979: 29).
H36 2002: on damp soil on track, 185 m alt., Butterlope Glen, H49, DT Holyoak 02-1100 (Rothero 2003: 55).
H39 1969: Drumfreshky, Cushendun, JA Paton (Lewis & Smith 1978: 27, Hill 1979: 29).
H40 1999: on damp soil by tarmac track, Banagher Glen, C60, DT Holyoak 99-638 (BBSUK) (Rothero 2000: 54).

93/14 ***Pohlia flexuosa*** Harv
(syn. *Pohlia muyldermansii* R.Wilczek & Demaret, *P. muyldermansii* var. *pseudomuyldermansii* Arts, Nordhorn-Richter & A.J.E.Sm.)

H1 1966: woodland nr O'Sullivan's Cascade, JA Paton (Lewis & Smith 1978: 27, Hill 1979: 29).
H2 1983: earthy slope on S side of Lough Erhogh, Horse's Glen, Mangerton Mt., JA Paton (Hill 1984b: 28).
H3 1968: Glenbeag Lough, Ardgroom, JA Paton (Lewis & Smith 1978: 27, Hill 1979: 29).
H6 1966: Sgilloge Loughs, Comeragh Mts, JA Paton (Lewis & Smith 1978: 27, Hill 1979: 29).
H7 1966: Lough Cultra, Galtee Mts, JG Duckett & JA Paton (Lewis & Smith 1978: 27, Hill 1979: 29).
H9 1979: hedgebank bordering lane, W side of Slieve Bernagh, G Bloom (Hill 1981: 29).
H16 1957: damp soil on NE side of Benchoona, nr Killary Harbour, AC Crundwell (Lewis & Smith 1978: 27, Hill 1979: 29).
H27 1987: on wet soil at base of gully in N corrie, Slievemore, TL Blockeel (Blockeel 1988: 37).
H29 2000: on steep soil at base of N-facing sandstone crag, ESE of Bronagh, G93, DT Holyoak 00-465 (BBSUK) (Rothero 2001: 43).
H34 2002: on vertical soil of bank above river, 35 m alt., by Crana River NE of Buncrana, C33, DT Holyoak 02-580 (Rothero 2003: 55).

H36 2002: on open damp soil in ditch, 185 m alt., Barnes Gap, H58, DT Holyoak 02-1142 (Rothero 2003: 55).
H39 1999: on steep sandstone bank, Murlough Bay, D14, DT Holyoak 99-771 (BBSUK) (Rothero 2000: 54).
H40 2002: on gravelly soil at edge of quarry, 280 m alt., above Whitewater Bridge, NE of Lough Fea, H78, DT Holyoak, 02-1149 (Rothero 2003: 55).

93/16 ***Pohlia lutescens*** (Limpr.) H.Lindb.

H2 1966: bank beside lane, woodland below Torc Cascade, Killarney, JA Paton, conf. HLK Whitehouse (Watson 1968: 443, Crundwell 1969: 884, HLK Whitehouse MS).
H8 1979: stream-bank in field above road, E side of Sugar Hill, S of Knockanimpaha, JA Paton (Hill 1980b: 41).
H10 1979: rock crevices on W side of Keeper Hill, HMH van Melick (Hill 1981: 29).
H12 1974: bare soil nr stream 3 miles N of Enniscorthy, AG Side (Crundwell 1975: 17).
H27 1987: on soil on crumbling slope by stream, Ooghnadirka, Achill I., DG Long (Blockeel 1988: 37).
H33 2000: on vertical soil bank by track, N of Benaughlin, H13, DT Holyoak 00-348 (BBSUK) (Rothero 2001: 43).
H36 2002: on thin soil over rotting bough of *Quercus* nr lake, 80 m alt., Drum Manor Forest Park, H77, DT Holyoak 02-1093 (Rothero 2003: 55).
H37 2002: on steep soil on bank above stream, 65 m alt., Gosford Forest Park, H94, DT Holyoak 02-1083 (Rothero 2003: 55).

93/17 ***Pohlia lescuriana*** (Sull.) Grout
(syn. *Pohlia pulchella* (Hedw.) Lindb.)

H3 1979: top of garden wall, house by Glenbeg Lake, G Bloom (Hill 1980b: 41).
H4 1983: ride in woodland, 9 km S of Cork Airport, G Bloom (Hill 1985: 25).
H8 1979: nr road by stream, E of Knockanimpaha, G Bloom (Hill 1980b: 41).

93/18 ***Pohlia melanodon*** (Brid.) A.J.Shaw
(syn. *Pohlia carnea* (Schimp.) Lindb., *P. delicatula* (Hedw.) Grout, *Webera carnea* Schimp.)

H1 1951: earthy bank, Garrough, below Coad Mt., EF Warburg (BBS exc.) (Warburg 1952: 104).
H2 1983: shady soil over limestone in woodland, E of Doo Lough, Muckross Park, Killarney, DG Long (Hill 1984b: 28).
H(4) listed by Lett (1915: 134).
†H4 listed by Blockeel & Long (1998: 114).
H(5) listed by Lett (1915: 134). H(5) listed by Blockeel & Long (1998: 114).
H6 1966: ditch by road below Coumshingaun, J Appleyard & JG Duckett (BBS exc.) (Perry 1967: 416).
H7 1966: on soil in field W of Longfordpass South, nr Orlingford (*sic* = Urlingord), ERB Little & JA Paton (BBS exc.) (Crundwell 1968: 639).
H(8) listed by Lett (1915: 134) without locality.
†H8 listed by Blockeel & Long (1998: 114).
H(9) listed by Lett (1915: 134) without locality.
†H9 listed by Blockeel & Long (1998: 114).
H11 1966: boggy depression in field, Foulkscourt House, nr Johnstown, J Appleyard (BBS exc.) (Perry 1967: 416).
H12 1974: bank of stream 3 miles N of Enniscorthy, AG Side (Crundwell 1975: 17).
H13 1975: ditch bank on edge of fen SW of Yellowford Cross Roads, S of Baltinglass, JA Paton (BBS exc.) (Crundwell 1976: 27).
H14 1956: calcareous Old Red Sandstone beside waterfall, nr Clonaslee, Slieve Bloom, AA Cridland (Warburg 1958b: 482).
H15 1957: turlough, Garrylands, J Appleyard (BBS exc.) (Warburg 1958b: 482).
H16 1957: side of ditch, Clifden, AC Crundwell (BBS exc.) (Warburg 1958b: 482-483).
H17 1957: turlough, Killower, nr Tuam, AC Crundwell (BBS exc.) (Warburg 1958b: 482-483).
H(18) 1949: pits of sandstone boulders, Cancor Rivers at Comber, Kinitty, AP Fanning (Warburg 1951: 501).

H(19) 1949: muddy bank, nr Calverstown, JS Thomson (Warburg 1950: 385).
H19 2002: in stubble field, 65 m alt., Coursetown House, W of Athy, S69, HF Fox & CD Preston (Rothero 2003: 55).
H(20) listed by Lett (1915: 134).
†H20 listed by Blockeel & Long (1998: 114).
H(21) listed by Lett (1915: 134).
†H21 listed by Blockeel & Long (1998: 114).
H22 1967: calcareous mud by side of stream, Ardmulchan, Navan, DM Synnott (Crundwell 1968: 639).
H23 1987: disturbed soil between graves, Heathstown churchyard, NW of Kinnegad, HLK Whitehouse (Blockeel 1988: 37).
H25 2002: on muddy bank by channel into harbour, 35 m alt., Lecarrow Harbour, M95, NG Hodgetts 4071 (Rothero 2003: 55).
H26 1970: W bank of Pollagh River, NE of Balla, JA Paton (Crundwell 1971b: 379).
H(27) listed by Lett (1915: 134) without locality.
†H27 listed by Blockeel & Long (1998: 114).
H28 1962: among *Dicranella varia* on wet bare talus below cliffs, Gleniff, EF Warburg (BBS exc.) (Warburg 1963b: 499).
H29 1963: clay bank at stream side below Glencar Waterfall, AR Perry & RD Fitzgerald (Warburg 1964: 729).
H(30) 1941: Killykeen, JG Finlay (Duncan 1944: 213).
†H30 listed by Blockeel & Long (1998: 114).
H31 1967: steep clay bank by stream, Townley Hall, Drogheda, DL Kelly (Crundwell 1968: 639).
H(32) 1947: garden path, Hope Castle, Castleblaney, JS Thomson (anon. 1948b: 122).
†H32 listed by Blockeel & Long (1998: 114).
H(33) listed by Lett (1915: 134).
†H33 listed by Blockeel & Long (1998: 114).
H34 1969: wet clay roadside bank, Kinnagoe Bay, W of Inishowen Head, JA Paton (Crundwell 1970: 204).
H35 1962: garden soil, Glen Alla nr Rathmullen, Lough Swilly, EM Lobley & MPH Kertland (BBS exc.) (Warburg 1963b: 499).
1962: clayey bank by sea, Dunfanaghy, AC Crundwell (BBS exc.) (Warburg 1963b: 499).
H36 2002: on steep soil on bank on limestone, 95 m alt., nr Carrickaness Bridge W of Drumquin, H27, DT Holyoak, 02-1124 (Rothero 2003: 55).
H37 2002: on gritty sediment between stones by reservoir, 155 m alt., NE edge of Seagahan Reservoir, H93, DT Holyoak 02-1070 (Rothero 2003: 55).
H(38) listed by Lett (1915: 134).
†H38 listed by Blockeel & Long (1998: 114).
H(39) listed by Lett (1915: 134).
†H39 listed by Blockeel & Long (1998: 114).
H(40) listed by Lett (1915: 134) without locality.
†H40 listed by Blockeel & Long (1998: 114).

93/19a ***Pohlia wahlenbergii*** (F.Weber & D. Mohr) A.L.Andrews **var.** ***wahlenbergii*** (syn. *Pohlia albicans* (Wahlenb.) Lindb., *Webera albicans* (Wahlenb.) Schimp.)

H(1) listed by Lett (1915: 135).
†H1 listed by Blockeel & Long (1998: 114).
H2 1966: damp ground on edge of stream by Torc Cascade, Killarney, MFV Corley & JS Parker (Perry 1967: 416).
H3 1967: on roadside at 900 ft [alt.], Cahernacaha, RD Fitzgerald (Crundwell: 639).
H4 1951: roadside bank NW of Mallow, AC Crundwell (Warburg 1952: 104).
H5 1951: lane, nr Mallow, EC Wallace & EF Warburg (Warburg 1952: 104).
H(6) 1947: walls in woods, Bagwell's Wood, SW of Clonmel, KC Harris (anon. 1948b: 122).
†H6 listed by Blockeel & Long (1998: 114).
H7 1966: on soil in field W of Longfordpass South, nr Orlingford (*sic* = Urlingford), ERB Little & JA Paton (BBS exc.) (Crundwell 1968: 639).
H(8) listed by Lett (1915: 135).
†H8 listed by Blockeel & Long (1998: 114).
H9 1957: path in pasture on SE side of Slievecarran, J Appleyard & AC Crundwell (BBS exc.) (Warburg 1958b: 483).
H10 1951: clay bank of ditch, Silvermines, AD Banwell, PJ Wanstall & EV Watson (Warburg 1953: 313).
H11 1966: roadside, Foulkscourt House, nr Johnstown, JG Duckett *et al.* (BBS exc.) (Perry 1967: 416).
H(12) listed by Lett (1915: 135).
†H12 listed by Blockeel & Long (1998: 114).
H13 1969: sandy groud at roadside, Corrabut

Gap, nr Mt Leinster, RD Fitzgerald (Crundwell 1970: 204).
H(14) listed by Lett (1915: 135).
†H14 listed by Blockeel & Long (1998: 114).
H15 1957: ride, Garryland Wood, nr Gort, AC Crundwell (BBS exc.) (Warburg 1958b: 483).
†H16 listed by Blockeel & Long (1998: 114).
†H17 listed by Blockeel & Long (1998: 114).
H(18) listed by Lett (1915: 135). H(18) listed by Blockeel & Long (1998: 114).
H19 1952: path in wood, Lyons House, nr Newcastle, ALK King (Warburg 1955: 586).
H(20) listed by Lett (1915: 135).
†H20 listed by Blockeel & Long (1998: 114).
H(21) listed by Lett (1915: 135).
†H21 listed by Blockeel & Long (1998: 114).
H22 1950: marshy ground, Slane, JS Thomson (Warburg 1952: 104).
H23 1952: old cart track, Clonhugh Demesne, NE end of L. Owel, JS Thomson (Warburg 1953: 313).
H24 1957: Ardagh Hill, MPH Kertland & ALK King (Warburg 1958b: 483).
H25 1962: yard, Boyle, PW Warburg (Warburg 1963b: 499).
H26 1970: shore of L. Carra, nr Partry House, J Appleyard (BBS exc.) (Crundwell 1971b: 379, Appleyard 1971: 388).
†H27 listed by Blockeel & Long (1998: 114).
†H28 listed by Blockeel & Long (1998: 114).
H29 1961: damp rock clefts at top waterfall, Glencar, RD Fitzgerald & MPH Kertland (Warburg 1962: 373).
H(30) 1949: lake shore at Lanesborough Lodge, Quivvy Lough, JP Brunker (Warburg 1950: 385).
†H30 listed by Blockeel & Long (1998: 114).
H(31) listed by Lett (1915: 135). H(31) listed by Blockeel & Long (1998: 114).
H(32) listed by Lett (1915: 135).
†H32 listed by Blockeel & Long (1998: 114).
†H33 listed by Blockeel & Long (1998: 114).
H(34) listed by Lett (1915: 135) without locality.
†H34 listed by Blockeel & Long (1998: 114).
H(35) listed by Lett (1915: 135).
†H35 listed by Blockeel & Long (1998: 114).
H36 1952: shaded bank, Glen Curry, nr Omagh, RD Fitzgerald (Warburg 1953: 313).
H(37) listed by Lett (1915: 135).
†H37 listed by Blockeel & Long (1998: 114).
H(38) listed by Lett (1915: 135). H(38) listed by Blockeel & Long (1998: 114).
H38 2002: on bare wet sand by pool in old quarry, 20 m alt., SW of Kilkeel, J21, DT Holyoak 02-1061 (Rothero 2003: 56).
H(39) listed by Lett (1915: 135).
†H39 listed by Blockeel & Long (1998: 114).
H(40) listed by Lett (1915: 135).
†H40 listed by Blockeel & Long (1998: 114).

93/19b *Pohlia wahlenbergii* var. *glacialis* (Schleich. ex Brid.) E.F.Warb.

H28 1963: dripping hollow in limestone face at 1000 ft [alt.], Gleniff, Dartry Mts, AR Perry & RD Fitzgerald (Warburg 1964: 728-729).

93/19c *Pohlia wahlenbergii* var. *calcarea* (Warnst.) E.F.Warb.
(syn. *Webera calcarea* Warnst.)

H(16) 1945: Cornamona, Galway, KC Harris (anon. 1946c: 283).
H34 2002: on thin calcareous sand on ledges in shallow ravine, 35 m alt., S of Soldiers Hill, NW of Malin, C45, DT Holyoak 02-566 (Rothero 2003: 56).
H35 1963: soil over gneiss rocks nr sea in bay N of Rossarrell Point, nr Malin Beg, AR Perry & RD Fitzgerald (Warburg 1964: 729).
[H39 deleted because no valid record or voucher specimen traced (Blockeel 1999: 6)].

94/1 *Epipterygium tozeri* (Grev.) Lindb.

H(2) listed by Lett (1915: 135). H(2) listed by Blockeel & Long (1998: 115).
H3 1968: shaded bank behind Dumboy Castle, Castletown Bearhaven, JA Paton (Crundwell 1969: 884).
H(4) listed by Lett (1915: 135).
†H4 listed by Blockeel & Long (1998: 115).
H9 1979: bank of R. Inagh, 11 km W of Ennis, AC Crundwell (Hill 1980b: 41).
H12 1975: bank of stream S of Clonough Bridge, E of Inch, JA Paton (BBS exc.) (Crundwell 1976: 27).
H20 1975: bank of ditch in field, Pennycomequick Bridge, NE of Arklow, JA Paton (BBS exc.) (Crundwell 1976: 27).
H34 1969: wet clay roadside bank, Kinnagoe

Bay, W of Inishowen Head, JA Paton (Crundwell 1970: 204).
H38 1950: earth bank of stream, Gransha Church, RD Fitzgerald (Warburg 1951: 501).
H(39) listed by Lett (1915: 135).
†H39 listed by Blockeel & Long (1998: 115).

95/1 ***Plagiobryum zieri*** (Hedw.) Lindb.

H(1) listed by Lett (1915: 135). H(1) listed by Blockeel & Long (1998: 115).
H16 1953: earthy crevices, basic rocks, W side of Lissoughter Hill, Recess, EC Wallace (Warburg 1954: 483).
H27 1965: E end of Sheeffry Hills, nr Gortmore, AMcG Stirling (Warburg 1966: 198).
H(28) 1928: Gleniff, Ben Bulben (BBS exc.) (Duncan 1928: 118).
†H28 listed by Blockeel & Long (1998: 115).
H29 1965: clefts of rock, *ca* 1150 ft alt., Aghadunvane, L. Melvin, RD Fitzgerald & EM Lobley (Warburg 1966: 198).
H(34) listed by Lett (1915: 135).
†H34 listed by Blockeel & Long (1998: 115).
†H35 listed by Blockeel & Long (1998: 115).
H(39) listed by Lett (1915: 135). H(39) listed by Blockeel & Long (1998: 115).
H(40) listed by Lett (1915: 135).
†H40 listed by Blockeel & Long (1998: 115).

96/1a ***Anomobryum julaceum*** (P.Gaertn., B. Mey. & Scherb.) Schimp. **var. *julaceum***
(syn. *Anomobryum filiforme* (Dicks.) Husn. var. *filiforme*, *Bryum filiforme* Dicks.)

H(1) listed by Lett (1915: 135).
†H1 listed by Blockeel & Long (1998: 115).
H(2) listed by Lett (1915: 135).
†H2 listed by Blockeel & Long (1998: 115).
H(3) listed by Lett (1915: 135).
†H3 listed by Blockeel & Long (1998: 115).
H(6) listed by Lett (1915: 135).
†H6 listed by Blockeel & Long (1998: 115).
H(7) listed by Lett (1915: 135).
†H7 listed by Blockeel & Long (1998: 115).
H15 1957: Chevy Chase, nr Gort, J Appleyard (BBS exc.) (Warburg 1958b: 483).
H(16) listed by Lett (1915: 135) without locality.
†H16 listed by Blockeel & Long (1998: 115).
H(20) listed by Lett (1915: 135). H(20) listed by Blockeel & Long (1998: 115).
[H21 deleted because no valid record or voucher specimen traced (Blockeel 1999: 6)].
H(27) listed by Lett (1915: 135).
†H27 listed by Blockeel & Long (1998: 115).
H(28) listed by Lett (1915: 135).
†H28 listed by Blockeel & Long (1998: 115).
H29 1963: stone in path, *ca* 850 ft [alt.], Glencar Waterfall, RD Fitzgerald & AR Perry (Warburg 1964: 729).
H(30) listed by Lett (1915: 135). H(30) listed by Blockeel & Long (1998: 115).
H(31) listed by Lett (1915: 135). H(31) listed by Blockeel & Long (1998: 115).
H33 1959: rock in stream, Marble Arch, RD Fitzgerald (Warburg 1960: 778).
H(34) listed by Lett (1915: 135) without locality.
†H34 listed by Blockeel & Long (1998: 115).
H(35) listed by Lett (1915: 135).
H35 1972: Muckish Mt., 500 ft [alt.], WV Rubers (U) (Crundwell 1975: 17).
H36 1951: drain, Leagh's Bridge, RD Fitzgerald (Warburg 1952: 104).
H(37) listed by Lett (1915: 135). H(37) listed by Blockeel & Long (1998: 115).
H(38) listed by Lett (1915: 135). H(38) listed by Blockeel & Long (1998: 115).
H(39) listed by Lett (1915: 135).
†H39 listed by Blockeel & Long (1998: 115).
H(40) listed by Lett (1915: 135).
†H40 listed by Blockeel & Long (1998: 115).

96/1b ***Anomobryum julaceum* var. *concinnatum*** (Spruce) J.E.Zetterst.
(syn. *Anomobryum concinnatum* Spruce, *A. filiforme* var. *concinnatum* (Spruce) Loeske, *Bryum concinnatum* Spruce)

[H(1) listed by Lett (1915: 135)].
H8 1966: damp rocks at 2300 ft alt., Temple Hill, Galtee Mts, MFV Corley & JS Parker (Perry 1967: 416).
H9 1957: Slievecarran, J Appleyard (Warburg 1958b: 483).
H16 1968: wet crevice in SE-facing rocks nr St Patrick's Bed and Holy Well, Maumeen, Maamturk Mts, AR Perry (Crundwell 1970: 204).
H26 1987: in peaty crevice on limestone pavement, Keel Bridge, Lough Carra, DG Long (Blockeel 1988: 37).
[H(28) listed by Lett (1915: 135)].

H28 1965: tops of sandy hillocks behind dunes, coast W of Strandhill, AR Perry & EF Warburg (Warburg 1966: 198).
H(29) 1928: wooded glen, NE end of Glencar Lough (BBS exc.) (Duncan 1928: 118).
†H29 listed by Blockeel & Long (1998: 115).
[H(34) listed by Lett (1915: 135) without locality].
H34 2001: in dune grassland, 10 m alt., Finner Camp, Ballyshannon, G86, NG Hodgetts 3726 (Rothero 2002: 50).
H35 1970: on soil in crevices of limestone rocks nr Portnoo, N of Ardara, MFV Corley (Crundwell 1971b: 379).
[H(39) listed by Lett (1915: 135)].
H40 1964: decomposed basalt at *ca* 1200 ft [alt.], Benbradagh, RD Fitzgerald & MPH Kertland (Warburg 1965: 866).

97/1 ***Bryum marratii*** Hook.f. & Wilson

H1 1983: damp hollow on fixed dunes, W side of Rossbehy Creek, Glenbeigh, DG Long, conf. AC Crundwell (BBSUK) (Hill 1984b: 28).
H(21) 1873: on the North Bull, nr Dublin, D Moore (DBN), conf. ALK King (Lett 1915: 136, Warburg 1963c: 142-143). H (21) record transferred from square brackets to round brackets [signifying change from uncertain record to old record] (Warburg 1964: 729).
H27 1962: bare ground in slack, Keel Bay, Achill I., EF Warburg (Warburg 1963b: 499).
H34 1969: ditch beside road nr estuary of Clonmany River, Tullagh Bay, JA Paton (Crundwell 1970: 204), voucher specimens (BBSUK, E) redet. as *B. marratii* by DT Holyoak 2002 (Rothero 2003: 56).
H35 1962: dunes nr Dunfanaghy, AC Crundwell (BBS exc.) (Warburg 1963b: 499, 1963c: 143).
H(40) 1906: nr Portstewart, WR Megaw (anon. 1937a: 368).
1936: by the [River] Bann nr Portstewart, WR Megaw (BFT), conf. EF Warburg (Megaw 1938, Warburg 1963c: 143).

97/2 ***Bryum warneum*** (Röhl.) Blandow ex Brid.

H(21) 1857: North Bull, D Moore (DBN) (MO Hill *et al.* MS notes).
1857: North Bull, Orr (Lett 1915: 136).
1860: Malahide Sands, D Moore (DBN) (MO Hill *et al.* MS notes). Old record(s) for H(21) placed in parentheses by Hill (1980b: 41), based on distribution map (Seaward 1973: 451).
no date: Portmarnock, *fide* McArdle (Lett 1915: 136).
[H29 deleted because no record traced (Seaward 1973: 451, Crundwell 1974: 170)].
H34 2002: on damp sand in dune slack, 5 m alt., N of Fahan, C32, DT Holyoak 02-774 (Rothero 2003: 56).
H35 2002: on open damp sand on disturbed ground at edge of dune-slack, Catherine's Isle, ENE of Dunfanaghy, C03, DT Holyoak 02-859 (Rothero 2003: 56).
[H(39) listed by Lett (1915: 136)].

97/4 ***Bryum calophyllum*** R.Br.

H16 1986: in damp hollow on sandy flats, 5 m alt., W of Doon Hill, nr Ballyconeely, L54, DG Long (E), det. DT Holyoak (Rothero 2003: 56).
[H21 records (1860: North Bull, D Orr, in Lett 1915: 136, with very scanty and inadequate specimen in DBN; 1860: Malahide, D Moore, in Lett 1915: 136, no specimen) appear doubtful (Warburg 1963c: 143)].
H27 1962: bare ground in slacks, Keel Bay, Achill I., EF Warburg, conf. AC Crundwell (Warburg 1963b: 499, 1963c: 143).
[H40 record (1936: Magilligan, WR Megaw, in Megaw 1938) doubtful (Warburg 1963c: 143). H40 deleted because the voucher specimen is *B. neodamense* (Crundwell 1973: 511)].

97/7 ***Bryum uliginosum*** (Brid.) Bruch & Schimp.
(syn. *B. cernuum* (Hedw.) Bruch, Schimp. & W.Gümbel)

[H1 dismissed because record not traced (Smith 1973b: 454, Crundwell 1974: 170)].
[H(2) listed by Lett (1915: 136)]
H(7) listed by Lett (1915: 136).
H(7) placed in parentheses as pre-1950

record, based on distribution map (Smith 1973, Hill 1980b: 41). H(7) listed by Blockeel & Long (1998: 116).

H(18) listed by Lett (1915: 136).

H(18) placed in parentheses as pre-1950 record, based on distribution map (Smith 1973, Hill 1980b: 41). H(18) listed by Blockeel & Long (1998: 116).

H(19) listed by Lett (1915: 136) without details.

H(19) placed in parentheses as pre-1950 record, based on distribution map (Smith 1973, Hill 1980b: 41). H(19) listed by Blockeel & Long (1998: 116).

H(21) listed by Lett (1915: 136).

H(21) placed in parentheses as pre-1950 record, based on distribution map (Smith 1973, Hill 1980b: 41). H(21) listed by Blockeel & Long (1998: 116).

H25 1968: among *Schoenus* on peat-covered limestone, Annaghmore L., 3 miles NW of Strokestown, WV Rubers *et al.* (U) (Crundwell 1975: 17, Hill 1980b: 41).

[H(32) listed by Lett (1915: 136) without locality. H32 record dismissed because not localised (Smith 1973b: 454, Crundwell 1974: 170)].

H(33) listed by Lett (1915: 136).

H(33) placed in parentheses as pre-1950 record, based on distribution map (Smith 1973, Hill 1980b: 41). H(33) listed by Blockeel & Long (1998: 116).

H34 2002: on vertical damp sand on N-facing bank in shallow ravine, 30 m alt., S of Soldiers Hill, NW of Malin, C45, DT Holyoak 02-561 (Rothero 2003: 56).

H(35) listed by Lett (1915: 136).

H(35) placed in parentheses as pre-1950 record, based on distribution map (Smith 1973, Hill 1980b: 41). H(35) listed by Blockeel & Long (1998: 116).

H(39) placed in parentheses as pre-1950 record, based on distribution map (Smith 1973, Hill 1980b: 41). H(39) listed by Blockeel & Long (1998: 116).

H(40) listed by Lett (1915: 136).

H(40) placed in parentheses as pre-1950 record, based on distribution map (Smith 1973, Hill 1980b: 41). H(40) listed by Blockeel & Long (1998: 116).

97/8 ***Bryum pallens*** Sw.
(syn. *Bryum fallax* Milde, *B. pallens* var. *fallax* Jur.)

H(1) listed by Lett (1915: 138) without details.

†H1 listed by Blockeel & Long (1998: 116).

H(4) listed by Lett (1915: 138).

†H4 listed by Blockeel & Long (1998: 116).

H5 1966: gravelly detritus by river, Araglin, J Appleyard *et al.* (BBS exc.) (Perry 1967: 416).

H(6) listed by Lett (1915: 138).

†H6 listed by Blockeel & Long (1998: 116).

H(7) listed by Lett (1915: 138).

†H7 listed by Blockeel & Long (1998: 116).

H8 1957: rocks by left bank of R. Shannon, nr Castleconnell, ALK King (Warburg 1958b: 483).

H(9) listed by Lett (1915: 138).

†H9 listed by Blockeel & Long (1998: 116).

H10 1951: ground, nr mine workings, Silvermines, AD Banwell, PJ Wanstall & EV Watson (Warburg 1953: 313).

H(11) listed by Lett (1915: 138).

†H11 listed by Blockeel & Long (1998: 116).

H12 1975: gravelly track, Croghan, Croghan Mt., JA Paton (BBS exc.) (Crundwell 1976: 27).

H(13) listed by Lett (1915: 138).

†H13 listed by Blockeel & Long (1998: 116).

H15 1957: marshy turf over limestone, Loughrea, RE Parker (Warburg 1958b: 483).

H(16) listed by Lett (1915: 138).

†H16 listed by Blockeel & Long (1998: 116).

†H17 listed by Blockeel & Long (1998: 116).

H(18) listed by Lett (1915: 138).

†H18 listed by Blockeel & Long (1998: 116).

[H(19) listed by Lett (1915: 138). H19 deleted because no valid record or voucher specimen traced (Blockeel 1999: 6)].

H(20) listed by Lett (1915: 138). H(20) listed by Lett (1915: 136).

†H20 listed by Blockeel & Long (1998: 116).

H(21) listed by Lett (1915: 138).

†H21 listed by Blockeel & Long (1998: 116).

H22 1978: side of wet ditch, Petersville cross roads, N of Moynalty, DM Synnott (sterile, presumed to be var. *pallens*) (Hill 1982: 27).

H(23) listed by Lett (1915: 138).

†H23 listed by Blockeel & Long (1998: 116).

H24 1980: drained shore of Glen Lough, S of Mostrim, DM Synnott (Hill 1981: 30).

H(25) listed by Lett (1915: 138).
†H25 listed by Blockeel & Long (1998: 116).
H26 1957: depressions in limestone rocks, nr L. Carra, RE Parker (Warburg 1958b: 483).
H(27) listed by Lett (1915: 138).
†H27 listed by Blockeel & Long (1998: 116).
†H28 listed by Blockeel & Long (1998: 116).
H(29) listed by Lett (1915: 138).
H29 1965: wall nr waterfall, Glencar, RD Fitzgerald & EM Lobley (Warburg 1966: 198).
H(30) listed by Lett (1915: 139).
†H30 listed by Blockeel & Long (1998: 116).
[H(31) listed by Lett (1915: 139). H31 deleted because no valid record or voucher specimen traced (Blockeel 1999: 6)].
H(32) listed by Lett (1915: 139) without locality.
†H32 listed by Blockeel & Long (1998: 116).
H(33) listed by Lett (1915: 139).
†H33 listed by Blockeel & Long (1998: 116).
H(34) listed by Lett (1915: 139).
†H34 listed by Blockeel & Long (1998: 116).
H(35) listed by Lett (1915: 139).
†H35 listed by Blockeel & Long (1998: 116).
H(36) listed by Lett (1915: 139).
†H36 listed by Blockeel & Long (1998: 116).
H(37) listed by Lett (1915: 139) without details.
†H37 listed by Blockeel & Long (1998: 116).
H(38) listed by Lett (1915: 139). H(38) listed by Blockeel & Long (1998: 116).
H(39) listed by Lett (1915: 139).
†H39 listed by Blockeel & Long (1998: 116).
H(40) listed by Lett (1915: 139).
†H40 listed by Blockeel & Long (1998: 116).

97/9 ***Bryum turbinatum*** (Hedw.) Turner

[H(21) listed by Lett (1915: 139)].
H(27) 1937: The Valley, Achill I., no collector named (BBS exc.) (Armitage 1938: 13). Smith (1973c) shows this record as post-1930, so that Hill (1980b: 42) left H27 without brackets. Blockeel & Long (1998: 116) correctly add brackets to H (27), on the basis that the record was by then over fifty years old. It remains the most recent confirmed record of the species in Ireland or Britain.
[H(39) listed by Lett (1915: 139)].

97/11 ***Bryum weigelii*** Spreng.
(syn. *Bryum duvalii* Voit)

[H(6) listed by Lett (1915: 139) as: nr Waterford, leg. Madden. H6 deleted because record dubious and almost certainly erroneous, comm. AJE Smith (Hill 1981: 30)]. Record later reinstated as:
H(6) 1852: nr Waterford, E Madden (DBN), comm. DM Synnott (Blockeel 1988: 37).

97/13 ***Bryum algovicum*** Sendtn. ex Müll.Hal. **var. *rutheanum*** (Warnst.) Crundw.
(syn. *Bryum pendulum* (Hornsch.) Schimp.)

H(1) listed by Lett (1915: 136) without details.
†H1 listed by Blockeel & Long (1998: 116).
H(2) listed by Lett (1915: 136). H(2) listed by Blockeel & Long (1998: 116).
H(4) listed by Lett (1915: 136) without details. H(4) listed by Blockeel & Long (1998: 116).
H(5) listed by Lett (1915: 136). H(5) listed by Blockeel & Long (1998: 116).
H6 1963: sandy flat, Tramore, ALK King (Warburg 1964: 729).
H(7) listed by Lett (1915: 136). H(7) listed by Blockeel & Long (1998: 116).
H(9) 1945: rocks above Roughan Ho.[use], Kilnaboy, JS Thomson (anon. 1946c: 283).
†H9 listed by Blockeel & Long (1998: 116).
H11 1968: wall nr Kilfane, N of Thomastown, JA Paton (Crundwell 1969: 884).
H(12) listed by Lett (1915: 136). H(12) listed by Blockeel & Long (1998: 116).
H12 2001: on open sand/shingle bar between lagoon and sea, 2 m alt., Lady's Island Lake, SE edge, T00, DT Holyoak 01-594 (Rothero 2002: 50-51).
H13 1961: bridge over Douglas River nr Aghade, ALK King (Warburg 1962: 373).
H14 1955: wall, Abbeyleix, JS Thomson (Warburg 1956: 155).
H16 1957: sandy ground by sea, Bunowen Bay, AC Crundwell (BBS exc.) (Warburg 1958b: 483).
H(18) listed by Lett (1915: 136). H(18) listed by Blockeel & Long (1998: 116).
[H(19) listed by Lett (1915: 136) without

details].
H(20) 1948: bank, Shelton Abbey Woods, Arklow, ALK King (Warburg 1950: 385).
†H20 listed by Blockeel & Long (1998: 116).
H(21) listed by Lett (1915: 136).
†H21 listed by Blockeel & Long (1998: 116).
H22 1952: demesne wall, Carton, Maynooth, JP Brunker (Warburg 1953: 313).
H23 1957: wall in Mullingar, ALK King (Warburg 1958b: 483).
H(25) 1940: nr Boyle, JS Thomson (Duncan 1944: 213).
H25 2002: on small hummock in limestone grassland on river bank, 45 m alt., Suck River Callows, N of Athleague Bridge, M85, NG Hodgetts 4161 (Rothero 2003: 56).
H(27) 1937: Achill I., no collector named (BBS exc.) (Armitage 1938: 13).
†H27 listed by Blockeel & Long (1998: 116).
†H28 listed by Blockeel & Long (1998: 116).
H(29) listed by Lett (1915: 136). H(29) listed by Blockeel & Long (1998: 116).
H29 2001: on soil and sandstone boulders on lough margin, 45 m alt., N shore of Lough Erril, N09, DT Holyoak 01-855 (Rothero 2002: 50-51).
H30 1956: wall, Virginia, JS Thomson (Warburg 1957: 333).
[H31 deleted because no valid record or voucher specimen traced (Blockeel 1999: 7)].
H(33) listed by Lett (1915: 136). H(33) listed by Blockeel & Long (1998: 116).
H(34) 1937: Bundoran, E Armitage (anon. 1938b: 28).
†H34 listed by Blockeel & Long (1998: 116).
H35 1962: dunes, Dunfanaghy, AC Crundwell (BBS exc.) (Warburg 1963b: 499).
H37 2002: in crevices of mortared wall, 65 m alt., Gosford Forest Park, H94, DT Holyoak, 02-1075 (Rothero 2003: 56).
H(38) listed by Lett (1915: 136). H(38) listed by Blockeel & Long (1998: 116).
H(39) listed by Lett (1915: 136). H(39) listed by Blockeel & Long (1998: 116).
H(40) listed by Lett (1915: 136). H(40) listed by Blockeel & Long (1998: 116).
H40 1999: on sandy slope at edge of dunes, W of Portstewart, C83, DT Holyoak 99-601 (BBSUK) (Rothero 2000: 54).

97/14 ***Bryum salinum*** I.Hagen ex Limpr.

H17 1957: on tussocks in drainage channel in field by the sea on E side of Galway city, E Nyholm & AC Crundwell (Nyholm & Crundwell 1958: 376). †H17 listed by Blockeel & Long (1998: 116).

97/17 ***Bryum amblyodon*** Müll.Hal.
(syn. *Bryum imbricatum* auct. non (Schwägr.) Bruch & Schimp., *B. inclinatum* "(Brid.) Blandow" hom. illeg., *B. stenotrichum* Müll.Hal.)

[H(2) listed by Lett (1915: 135). H2 deleted because no valid record or voucher specimen traced (Blockeel 1999: 7)].
[H(3) listed by Lett (1915: 135). H3 deleted because no valid record or voucher specimen traced (Blockeel 1999: 7)].
H(4) listed by Lett (1915: 135) without details. H(4) listed by Blockeel & Long (1998: 117).
H(5) listed by Lett (1915: 135). H(5) listed by Blockeel & Long (1998: 117).
H(6) listed by Lett (1915: 135).
†H6 listed by Blockeel & Long (1998: 117).
[H(8) listed by Lett (1915: 135) without details. H8 deleted because no valid record or voucher specimen traced (Blockeel 1999: 7)].
H(9) listed by Lett (1915: 135) without details.
†H9 listed by Blockeel & Long (1998: 117).
H(11) listed by Lett (1915: 135). H(11) listed by Blockeel & Long (1998: 117).
[H(15) listed by Lett (1915: 135) without details. H15 deleted because no valid record or voucher specimen traced (Blockeel 1999: 7)].
H(16) listed by Lett (1915: 135).
†H16 listed by Blockeel & Long (1998: 117).
H(19) listed by Lett (1915: 135). H(19) listed by Blockeel & Long (1998: 117).
H20 1955: bank of Annanwe River nr Sally Gap, ALK King (Warburg 1956: 155).
H(21) listed by Lett (1915: 135). H(21) listed by Blockeel & Long (1998: 117).
H22 2001: on thin limey soil at edge of track by lough, 70 m alt., SE edge of Lough Sheelin, NW of Ross, N48, DT Holyoak 01-602 (Rothero 2002: 51).
H23 1957: bank in marsh by N end of L. Ennell, nr Mullingar, ALK King (Warburg 1958b: 483).

H24 1966: lock gate of disused canal, Aghnaskea Bridge, ALK King (Perry 1967: 416).
H(25) listed by Lett (1915: 135). H(25) listed by Blockeel & Long (1998: 117).
H(26) listed by Lett (1915: 135). H(26) listed by Blockeel & Long (1998: 117).
H(27) listed by Lett (1915: 135).
†H27 listed by Blockeel & Long (1998: 117).
H(28) 1937: Annacoona, no collector named (BBS exc.) (Armitage 1938: 12).
†H28 listed by Blockeel & Long (1998: 117).
H(29) 1937: Kinlough, no collector named (BBS exc.) (Armitage 1938: 12).
†H29 listed by Blockeel & Long (1998: 117).
H(30) listed by Lett (1915: 135).
†H30 listed by Blockeel & Long (1998: 117).
H(33) listed by Lett (1915: 135). H(33) listed by Blockeel & Long (1998: 117).
H33 2000: on thin soil at edge of track, S of Crossmurrin Nature Reserve, H13, DT Holyoak 00-135 (BBSUK) (Rothero 2001: 43).
H(35) listed by Lett (1915: 135). H(35) listed by Blockeel & Long (1998: 117).
H35 2002: in crevice in boulder at edge of lough, 233 m alt., SW edge of Lough Reelan, C12, DT Holyoak 02-685 (Rothero 2003: 56).
H36 2002: on gravelly soil on bank between ditch and road, 210 m alt., nr Kelly's Bridge, Ardnamona, H07, DT Holyoak 02-1132 (Rothero 2003: 56).
H(37) listed by Lett (1915: 135). H(37) listed by Blockeel & Long (1998: 117).
H(38) listed by Lett (1915: 135). H(38) listed by Blockeel & Long (1998: 117).
H39 1990: basalt outcrop at Denny's Lough, Garron Plateau above Carnlough, DM Synnott (Blockeel 1991c: 43).
H(40) listed by Lett (1915: 135).
†H40 listed by Blockeel & Long (1998: 117).

The name *B. inclinatum* (Brid.) Blandow [1809] (basionym *Pohlia inclinata* Sw. ex Brid. [1803]) has been widely used for this species (the correct authorship of this combination is *B. inclinatum* (Brid.) Turton [1806], as pointed out by Margadant & During 1982: 367, Demaret & Geissler 1990). Nevertheless, these combinations are illegitimate homonyms, as shown by Ochi (1980: 144), who proposed that *B. amblyodon* Müll.Hal. [1879] based on a type-specimen from South America should be used as a replacement name, since it has priority over the name *B. stenotrichum* Müll.Hal. [1887] which had been adopted by some authors (including Ochi 1972: 90). Subsequently, Geissler (1984) proposed that *B. imbricatum* (Schwägr.) Bruch & Schimp. should be used and this was followed e.g. by Blockeel & Long (1998). However, Demaret & Geissler (1990) have corrected Geissler (1984) by showing that the type of *B. imbricatum* is dioicous with an indistinct leaf border so it may represent a different taxon to *B. inclinatum* and therefore should not be used as a replacement name. Hence, it seems clear that *B. amblyodon* Müll.Hal. [1879] is the earliest valid name that can be unambiguously referred to the species previously known as *B. inclinatum*.

97/18 ***Bryum intermedium*** (Brid.) Blandow

H(4) listed by Lett (1915: 136). H(4) listed by Blockeel & Long (1998: 117).
H(12) listed by Lett (1915: 136). H(12) listed by Blockeel & Long (1998: 117).
H(21) listed by Lett (1915: 136). H(21) listed by Blockeel & Long (1998: 117).
[H31 deleted because no valid record or voucher specimen traced (Blockeel 1999: 7)].
H(34) listed by Lett (1915: 136). H(34) listed by Blockeel & Long (1998: 117).
H(37) listed by Lett (1915: 136). H(37) listed by Blockeel & Long (1998: 117).
H(38) listed by Lett (1915: 136). H(38) listed by Blockeel & Long (1998: 117).
H(39) listed by Lett (1915: 136). H(39) listed by Blockeel & Long (1998: 117).
H(40) listed by Blockeel & Long (1998: 117).

97/19 ***Bryum donianum*** Grev.
(syn. *Bryum donii* Grev. ex Kindb. orthogr. pro *B. donianum*)

†H1 listed by Blockeel & Long (1998: 117).
[H(3) listed by Lett (1915: 139) as: by River Lee above the Jail, Carroll. H3 deleted because the only record traced (R. Lee above Cork Jail, in Lett 1915) is from H4, comm. NF Stewart (Blockeel 1995c: 44)].

H(4) listed by Blockeel & Long (1998: 117).
H5 1966: bank nr river 5 miles E of Fermoy, J Appleyard & JG Duckett (BBS exc.) (Perry 1967: 417).
H7 1966: among limestone outcrops, Cashel Rock, Cashel, J Appleyard (BBS exc.) (Perry 1967: 417).
†H7 listed by Blockeel & Long (1998: 117).
H19 1958: stony roadside bank, nr Elverstown, ALK King (Warburg 1959: 636).
H(20) listed by Lett (1915: 139).
†H20 listed by Blockeel & Long (1998: 117).
H(21) listed by Lett (1915: 139). H(21) listed by Blockeel & Long (1998: 117).
H22 1962: earthy wall nr Clonard, EF Warburg (Warburg 1963b: 499).
H28 1970: on a wall by the road, nr Bunduff Strand, S of Mullaghmore, J Appleyard (BBS exc.) (Crundwell 1971b: 381, Appleyard 1971: 388-389).

97/20a ***Bryum capillare*** **Hedw. var.** ***capillare*** (syn. *Bryum capillare* var. *macrocarpum* Huebener)

H(1) listed by Lett (1915: 139) without details.
H1 record placed as var. *capillare* by Crundwell (1974: 171) following taxonomic revision by Syed (1973). †H1 listed by Blockeel & Long (1998: 117).
H(2) listed by Lett (1915: 139).
H2 record placed as var. *capillare* by Crundwell (1974: 171) following taxonomic revision by Syed (1973). †H2 listed by Blockeel & Long (1998: 117).
H(3) listed by Lett (1915: 139) without details.
H3 record placed as var. *capillare* by Crundwell (1974: 171) following taxonomic revision by Syed (1973). †H3 listed by Blockeel & Long (1998: 117).
H(4) listed by Lett (1915: 139) without details.
H4 record placed as var. *capillare* by Crundwell (1974: 171) following taxonomic revision by Syed (1973). †H4 listed by Blockeel & Long (1998: 117).
H(5) listed by Lett (1915: 139) without details.
H5 record placed as var. *capillare* by Crundwell (1974: 171) following taxonomic revision by Syed (1973). †H5 listed by Blockeel & Long (1998: 117).
H(6) listed by Lett (1915: 139) without details.
H6 record placed as var. *capillare* by Crundwell (1974: 171) following taxonomic revision by Syed (1973). †H6 listed by Blockeel & Long (1998: 117).
H(7) listed by Lett (1915: 139) without details.
H7 record placed as var. *capillare* by Crundwell (1974: 171) following taxonomic revision by Syed (1973). †H7 listed by Blockeel & Long (1998: 117).
H(8) listed by Lett (1915: 139) without details.
H8 record placed as var. *capillare* by Crundwell (1974: 171) following taxonomic revision by Syed (1973). †H8 listed by Blockeel & Long (1998: 117).
H(9) listed by Lett (1915: 139) without details.
H9 record placed as var. *capillare* by Crundwell (1974: 171) following taxonomic revision by Syed (1973). †H9 listed by Blockeel & Long (1998: 117).
H(10) listed by Lett (1915: 139) without details.
H10 record placed as var. *capillare* by Crundwell (1974: 171) following taxonomic revision by Syed (1973). †H10 listed by Blockeel & Long (1998: 117).
H(11) listed by Lett (1915: 139) without details.
H11 record placed as var. *capillare* by Crundwell (1974: 171) following taxonomic revision by Syed (1973). †H11 listed by Blockeel & Long (1998: 117).
H(12) listed by Lett (1915: 139) without details.
H12 record placed as var. *capillare* by Crundwell (1974: 171) following taxonomic revision by Syed (1973). †H12 listed by Blockeel & Long (1998: 117).
H(13) listed by Lett (1915: 139) without details.
H13 record placed as var. *capillare* by Crundwell (1974: 171) following taxonomic revision by Syed (1973). †H13 listed by Blockeel & Long (1998: 117).
H(14) listed by Lett (1915: 139) without details.
H14 record placed as var. *capillare* by

Crundwell (1974: 171) following taxonomic revision by Syed (1973). †H14 listed by Blockeel & Long (1998: 117).

H(15) listed by Lett (1915: 139) without details.

H15 record placed as var. *capillare* by Crundwell (1974: 171) following taxonomic revision by Syed (1973). †H15 listed by Blockeel & Long (1998: 117).

H(16) listed by Lett (1915: 139) without details.

H16 record placed as var. *capillare* by Crundwell (1974: 171) following taxonomic revision by Syed (1973). †H16 listed by Blockeel & Long (1998: 117).

H17 1950: limestone nr Menlo, ALK King (Warburg 1954: 484).

H(18) listed by Lett (1915: 139) without details.

H18 record placed as var. *capillare* by Crundwell (1974: 171) following taxonomic revision by Syed (1973). †H18 listed by Blockeel & Long (1998: 117).

H(19) listed by Lett (1915: 139).

H19 record placed as var. *capillare* by Crundwell (1974: 171) following taxonomic revision by Syed (1973). †H19 listed by Blockeel & Long (1998: 117).

H(20) listed by Lett (1915: 139) without details.

H20 record placed as var. *capillare* by Crundwell (1974: 171) following taxonomic revision by Syed (1973). †H20 listed by Blockeel & Long (1998: 117).

H(21) listed by Lett (1915: 139) without details.

H21 record placed as var. *capillare* by Crundwell (1974: 171) following taxonomic revision by Syed (1973). †H21 listed by Blockeel & Long (1998: 117).

H(22) listed by Lett (1915: 139) without details.

H22 record placed as var. *capillare* by Crundwell (1974: 171) following taxonomic revision by Syed (1973). †H22 listed by Blockeel & Long (1998: 117).

H(23) listed by Lett (1915: 139) without details.

H23 record placed as var. *capillare* by Crundwell (1974: 171) following taxonomic revision by Syed (1973). †H23 listed by Blockeel & Long (1998: 117).

H(24) listed by Lett (1915: 139) without details.

H24 record placed as var. *capillare* by Crundwell (1974: 171) following taxonomic revision by Syed (1973). †H24 listed by Blockeel & Long (1998: 117).

H(25) listed by Lett (1915: 139) without details.

H25 record placed as var. *capillare* by Crundwell (1974: 171) following taxonomic revision by Syed (1973). †H25 listed by Blockeel & Long (1998: 117).

H(26) listed by Lett (1915: 139) without details.

H26 record placed as var. *capillare* by Crundwell (1974: 171) following taxonomic revision by Syed (1973). †H26 listed by Blockeel & Long (1998: 117).

H(27) listed by Lett (1915: 139) without details.

H27 record placed as var. *capillare* by Crundwell (1974: 171) following taxonomic revision by Syed (1973). †H27 listed by Blockeel & Long (1998: 117).

H(28) listed by Lett (1915: 139) without details.

H28 record placed as var. *capillare* by Crundwell (1974: 171) following taxonomic revision by Syed (1973). †H28 listed by Blockeel & Long (1998: 117).

H(29) listed by Lett (1915: 139) without details.

H29 record placed as var. *capillare* by Crundwell (1974: 171) following taxonomic revision by Syed (1973). †H29 listed by Blockeel & Long (1998: 117).

H(30) listed by Lett (1915: 139) without details.

H30 record placed as var. *capillare* by Crundwell (1974: 171) following taxonomic revision by Syed (1973). †H30 listed by Blockeel & Long (1998: 117).

H(31) listed by Lett (1915: 139) without details.
H31 record placed as var. *capillare* by Crundwell (1974: 171) following taxonomic revision by Syed (1973). †H31 listed by Blockeel & Long (1998: 117).
H(32) listed by Lett (1915: 139) without details.
H32 record placed as var. *capillare* by Crundwell (1974: 171) following taxonomic revision by Syed (1973). †H32 listed by Blockeel & Long (1998: 117).
H(33) listed by Lett (1915: 139) without details.
H33 record placed as var. *capillare* by Crundwell (1974: 171) following taxonomic revision by Syed (1973). †H33 listed by Blockeel & Long (1998: 117).
H(34) listed by Lett (1915: 139) without details.
H34 record placed as var. *capillare* by Crundwell (1974: 171) following taxonomic revision by Syed (1973). †H34 listed by Blockeel & Long (1998: 117).
H(35) listed by Lett (1915: 139) without details.
H35 record placed as var. *capillare* by Crundwell (1974: 171) following taxonomic revision by Syed (1973). †H35 listed by Blockeel & Long (1998: 117).
H(36) listed by Lett (1915: 139) without details.
H36 record placed as var. *capillare* by Crundwell (1974: 171) following taxonomic revision by Syed (1973). †H36 listed by Blockeel & Long (1998: 117).
H(37) listed by Lett (1915: 139) without details.
H37 record placed as var. *capillare* by Crundwell (1974: 171) following taxonomic revision by Syed (1973). †H37 listed by Blockeel & Long (1998: 117).
H(38) listed by Lett (1915: 139) without details.
H(38) record placed as var. *capillare* by Crundwell (1974: 171) following taxonomic revision by Syed (1973). H (38) listed by Blockeel & Long (1998: 117).
H38 1999: on old stump in amenity woodland, 55 m alt., Tollymore Forest Park, 4 km W of Newcastle, J33, TL Blockeel 28/331 (Rothero 2000: 54).
H(39) listed by Lett (1915: 139) without details.
H39 record placed as var. *capillare* by Crundwell (1974: 171) following taxonomic revision by Syed (1973). †H39 listed by Blockeel & Long (1998: 117).
H(40) listed by Lett (1915: 139) without details.
H40 record placed as var. *capillare* by Crundwell (1974: 171) following taxonomic revision by Syed (1973). †H40 listed by Blockeel & Long (1998: 117).

97/20b *Bryum capillare* var. *rufifolium* (Dixon) Podp.
(syn. *Bryum rufifolium* Dixon)

H9 1953: limestone rocks, Black Head, MCF Proctor (GL) (Warburg 1954: 484, Syed 1973: 275, Crundwell 1974: 171).
H25 2001: on mortar of wall by road, 45 m alt., Boyle River, W bank, nr Cootehall, G80, DT Holyoak 01-830 (Rothero 2002: 51).
H29 2000: Peakadaw, on thin soil over limestone on S-facing crag, G84, DT Holyoak 00-462 (BBSUK) (Rothero 2001: 44).
H33 2000: in crevices at base of wall of old building below galvanised-iron roof, Drumcrow West, H05, DT Holyoak 00-403 (BBSUK) (Rothero 2001: 44).

97/21 *Bryum elegans* Nees ex Brid.
(syn. *Bryum capillare* var. *elegans* (Brid.) Husn.)

H28 1970: on limestone boulders below Cormac Keagh's Hole, Eagle Rock, E of Benbulbin [*sic* = Ben Bulben], JA Paton (BBS exc.) (Crundwell 1971b: 380, Appleyard 1971: 390, Syed 1973: 280, Crundwell 1974: 172).
1970: in mossy turf among limestone rocks, Gleniff, S of Cliffony, J Appleyard (Syed 1973: 280, Crundwell 1974: 172).

97/23 ***Bryum laevifilum*** Syed
(syn. *Bryum flaccidum* auct. non Brid., *B. subelegans* auct. non Kindb.)

H1 1979: tree trunk in native oak woodland, Uragh Wood, SW shore of Inchiquin Lough, Cloonee Lakes area, HMH van Melick (Hill 1981: 31).

The name *B. laevifilum* is adopted for this species following Hodgetts (2001).

97/24 ***Bryum torquescens*** Bruch & Schimp.
(syn. *Bryum capillare* var. *obconicum* auct., *B. obconicum* auct.)

[H(2) listed by Lett (1915: 136, 139)].
H(2) 1885: on wall above Muckross on Mangerton road, SA Stewart (GL) (Syed 1973: 311, Crundwell 1974: 172).
[H(5) listed by Lett (1915: 136). H5 deleted by Crundwell 1974: 172 following revision by Syed 1973].
[H(8) listed by Lett (1915: 137). H8 deleted by Crundwell 1974: 172 following revision by Syed 1973].
[H(16) listed by Lett (1915: 137)].
[H16 1957: bare earth face, L. Muck, nr Killary Harbour, AC Crundwell (BBS exc.) (Warburg 1958b: 483), as *B. obconicum*. H16 deleted by Crundwell 1974: 172 following revision by Syed 1973].
[H(20) listed by Lett (1915: 139) without details].
[H(21) listed by Lett (1915: 137, 139). H21 deleted by Crundwell 1974: 172 following revision by Syed 1973].
[H24 1957: wall nr Lanesborough, ALK King (Warburg 1958b: 483), as *B. obconicum*].
[H(33) listed by Lett (1915: 139)].
H(34) 1937: Bundoran, no collector named (BBS exc.) (Armitage 1938: 12), as *B. obconicum*; apparently the same specimen redet. as *B. torquescens* by Syed (1973: 311), see next entry.
1937: on rock at small old quarry by road nr town, Bundoran, CH Binstead (BBSUK) (Syed 1973: 311, Crundwell 1974: 172).
H34 2002: on loose sand on foredune slope above beach, 10 m alt., Kinnoge Bay, C64, DT Holyoak 02-533 (Rothero 2003: 56).
[H(39) listed by Lett (1915: 139)].

All records of *B. capillare* var. *obconicum* and *B. obconicum* (e.g. from Lett 1915: 139) were deleted by Crundwell (1974: 172) following the taxonomic review by Syed (1973). Some of the records were probably based on *B. torquescens*.

97/26 ***Bryum creberrimum*** Taylor
(syn. *Bryum affine* Lindb. hom. illeg.)

[H2 record rejected as doubtful by AJE Smith (Crundwell 1974: 171), although no voucher specimen was seen (AJE Smith MS notes)].
[H(3) listed by Lett (1915: 136)].
H21 1988: on unshaded rotten log, close to the Quarry Lake, Phoenix Park, O13, DL Kelly, conf. AJE Smith (Blockeel 1990: 31).

97/27 ***Bryum pallescens*** Schleich. ex Schwägr.

[H(1) listed by Lett (1915: 137). H1 record rejected by AJE Smith (Crundwell 1974: 171)].
H1 1979: rock crevices, SW shore of Inchiquin Lough, Cloonee Lakes area, HMH van Melick (Hill 1981: 30).
H3 1998: on mortared stone wall of farm outbuilding, receiving runoff from roof, 60 m alt., Ballymacredmond, 8 km SSE of Timoleague, W43, JW Bates 3913 (Rothero 1999b: 44).
H(7) no date: Clonmel, collector not named (BM, Hb. Braithwaite), conf. AJE Smith (AJE Smith MS). Same record apparently listed by Lett (1915: 137) as: nr Clonmel, leg. Sidebotham.
H9 1979: wall of derelict farm house, W slope of Slieve Bernagh, in valley of Killuran River, EW Jones (Hill 1980b: 42).
H15 2002: on old mine tailings, nr Tynagh, J Good, det. DT Holyoak 02-1162 (Rothero 2003: 56).
H(16) 1831: below Ben Coona & L. Fee [= L76], RJ Shuttleworth (BM), det. AJE Smith, comm. RA Finch (Blockeel 1990: 32).
[H(21) listed by Lett (1915: 137). H21 record rejected by AJE Smith (Crundwell 1974: 171)].

H22 1978: crumbling shale by road, SE of Stackallen Bridge, Slane, DM Synnott (Hill 1979: 29).

[H(28) listed by Lett (1915: 137) without data].

H28 2002: in gutter below galvanised iron roof, 115 m alt., SW of Doonbeakin, S of Dromore West, G42, DT Holyoak 02-662 (Rothero 2003: 56).

H29 2001: on concrete below galvanised fence, 415 m alt., E slope of Bencroy, H01, DT Holyoak 01-797 (Rothero 2002: 51).

H30 2001: on open damp mortared wall, 50 m alt., River Erne, W bank, W of Belturbet, H31, DT Holyoak 01-702 (Rothero 2002: 51).

H33 1957: limestone rocks, nr Marble Arch, L. Macnean Lower, AC Crundwell (BBSUK), conf. AJE Smith (Warburg 1958b: 483, AJE Smith MS).

H34 2002: on shaded rock at entrance to old mine, 116 m alt., S of Glentogher, C43, DT Holyoak 02-592 (Rothero 2003: 56).

[H(35) listed by Lett (1915: 137). H35 record rejected by AJE Smith (Crundwell 1974: 171)].

H35 2002: on thin detritus over rusted remains of car (Opel Kadett), 90 m alt., NE edge of Lough Barra, B91, DT Holyoak 02-408 (Rothero 2003: 56).

H36 2002: on damp mud among debris of ruined building, 180 m alt., in old quarry W of Brackagh South, H57, DT Holyoak 02-1109 (Rothero 2003: 56-57).

H(38) 1908: Scrabo Hill, HW Lett (DBN), conf. AJE Smith (Lett 1915: 137, AJE Smith MS).

[H(39) listed by Lett (1915: 137)].

H40 2002: on ground of old fire-site in old quarry, 280 m alt., above Whitewater Bridge, NE of Lough Fea, H78, DT Holyoak 02-1153 (Rothero 2003: 57).

AJE Smith revised Irish and British specimens for the *CC* (Corley & Hill 1981: 99). Details of three of the specimens given above are from unpublished notes made during this revision (AJE Smith MS).

97/28a *Bryum pseudotriquetrum* (Hedw.) P. Gaertn., B.Mey. & Scherb. **var. *pseudotriquetrum*** (syn. *Bryum ventricosum* Relhan nom. illeg.)

H(1) listed by Lett (1915: 139) without details.

†H1 listed by Blockeel & Long (1998: 118).

H(2) listed by Lett (1915: 139) without details.

†H2 listed by Blockeel & Long (1998: 118).

†H3 listed by Blockeel & Long (1998: 118).

H(4) listed by Lett (1915: 139) without details.

†H4 listed by Blockeel & Long (1998: 118).

H(5) listed by Lett (1915: 139) without details.

†H5 listed by Blockeel & Long (1998: 118).

H(6) listed by Lett (1915: 139) without details.

†H6 listed by Blockeel & Long (1998: 118).

H(7) listed by Lett (1915: 139) without details.

†H7 listed by Blockeel & Long (1998: 118).

H(8) listed by Lett (1915: 139) without details.

†H8 listed by Blockeel & Long (1998: 118).

H(9) listed by Lett (1915: 139) without details.

†H9 listed by Blockeel & Long (1998: 118).

H(10) listed by Lett (1915: 139) without details.

†H10 listed by Blockeel & Long (1998: 118).

H11 1954: shaded dripping bank by the Ballyeogan road, Graiguenamanagh, ALK King (Warburg 1955: 586).

H12 1966: flush by stream nr Kiltealy, Blackstairs Mts, JG Duckett *et al.* (Perry 1967: 416).

H(14) listed by Lett (1915: 139) without details.

†H14 listed by Blockeel & Long (1998: 118).

H15 1956: rock on lake-shore at Loughrea, ALK King (Warburg 1957: 334).

H(16) listed by Lett (1915: 139) without details.

†H16 listed by Blockeel & Long (1998: 118).

H17 1970: boggy field at edge of L. Corrib, SW of Keekill, AR Perry & HJ Perry (Crundwell 1974: 170).

H(18) listed by Lett (1915: 139) without details.

†H18 listed by Blockeel & Long (1998: 118).

H(19) listed by Lett (1915: 139) without details.

†H19 listed by Blockeel & Long (1998: 118).
H(20) listed by Lett (1915: 139) without details.
†H20 listed by Blockeel & Long (1998: 118).
H(21) listed by Lett (1915: 139) without details.
†H21 listed by Blockeel & Long (1998: 118).
H22 1956: side of drain by lane to Rossan Bog, nr Kinnegad, ALK King (Warburg 1957: 334).
H23 1966: Scraw Bog, Portnashangar, ALK King (Perry 1967: 416).
H24 1965: bottom of ditch, *ca* 800 ft alt., Corn Hill, nr Drumlish, RD Fitzgerald & EM Lobley (Warburg 1966: 198).
H25 1960: limy shore of L. Ree, Hodson's Bay, AW Stelfox (Crundwell 1970: 204).
H26 1960: marshy ground by lane at Downhill, Ballina, ALK King (Warburg 1961: 170).
H(27) listed by Lett (1915: 139) without details.
†H27 listed by Blockeel & Long (1998: 118).
H(28) listed by Lett (1915: 139) without details.
†H28 listed by Blockeel & Long (1998: 118).
H(29) 1948: marsh, nr R. Shannon, below Carrick-on-Shannon, ALK King (Warburg 1950: 385).
†H29 listed by Blockeel & Long (1998: 118).
H(30) listed by Lett (1915: 139) without details.
†H30 listed by Blockeel & Long (1998: 118).
[H(31) listed by Lett (1915: 139) without details. H31 deleted because no valid record or voucher specimen traced (Blockeel 1999: 7)].
H31 1999: on wet rock ledge by stream, 300 m alt., Two Mile River, Carlingford, J11, TL Blockeel 28/175 (Rothero 2000: 55).
H(32) listed by Lett (1915: 139) without details.
†H32 listed by Blockeel & Long (1998: 118).
H(33) listed by Lett (1915: 139) without details.
†H33 listed by Blockeel & Long (1998: 118).
H(34) listed by Lett (1915: 139) without details.
†H34 listed by Blockeel & Long (1998: 118).
H(35) listed by Lett (1915: 139) without details.
†H35 listed by Blockeel & Long (1998: 118).
H(36) listed by Lett (1915: 139) without details.
†H36 listed by Blockeel & Long (1998: 118).
H(37) listed by Lett (1915: 139) without details.
†H37 listed by Blockeel & Long (1998: 118).
H(38) listed by Lett (1915: 139) without details. H(38) listed by Blockeel & Long (1998: 118).
H38 2002: on rock at edge of stream, 225 m alt., Spinkwee River, W of Slievenabrock, J33, DT Holyoak 02-1021 (Rothero 2003: 57).
H(39) listed by Lett (1915: 139) without details.
†H39 listed by Blockeel & Long (1998: 118).
H(40) listed by Lett (1915: 139) without details.
†H40 listed by Blockeel & Long (1998: 118).

The records listed above probably include dioicous plants carefully determined as var. *pseudotriquetrum* along with plants lacking gametangia that might represent either variety.

97/28b *Bryum pseudotriquetrum* var. *bimum* (Schreb.) Lilj.
(syn. *Bryum bimum* (Schreb.) Turner)

[H(1) listed by Lett (1915: 136). H1 deleted because no valid record or voucher specimen traced (Blockeel 1999: 7)].
[H(2) listed by Lett (1915: 136). H2 deleted because no valid record or voucher specimen traced (Blockeel 1999: 7)].
[H(4) listed by Lett (1915: 136). H4 deleted because no valid record or voucher specimen traced (Blockeel 1999: 7)].
[H(5) listed by Lett (1915: 136) without details. H5 deleted because no valid record or voucher specimen traced (Blockeel 1999: 7)].
[H(8) listed by Lett (1915: 136). H8 deleted because no valid record or voucher specimen traced (Blockeel 1999: 7)].
H9 1968: bare peat in cutting on bog NW of Rinroe House, 4 miles E of Killinaboy, AR Perry (Crundwell 1970: 204).
H11 1968: damp floor of old limestone quarry N of Thomastown, JA Paton (Crundwell 1969: 885).
H12 1958: among *Brachythecium*, Forth Mt., ALK King (Warburg 1959: 636).
[H(13) listed by Lett (1915: 136) without details. H13 deleted because no valid

record or voucher specimen traced (Blockeel 1999: 7)].

[H(14) listed by Lett (1915: 136) as 1867: Slieve Margy, leg. RC Browne. H14 deleted because specimen on which the record is based (see Lett 1915) is var. *pseudotriquetrum*, det. EV Watson, comm. AA Cridland (Warburg 1958b: 483)].

[H(18) listed by Lett (1915: 136). H18 deleted because no valid record or voucher specimen traced (Blockeel 1999: 7)].

H(20) listed by Lett (1915: 136). H(20) listed by Blockeel & Long (1998: 118).

[H(21) listed by Lett (1915: 136). H21 deleted because no valid record or voucher specimen traced (Blockeel 1999: 7)].

H23 1957: wet gravel flat by L. Ennell, nr Lilliput House, ALK King (Warburg 1958b: 483).

H25 1968: in *Schoenus* vegetation, John's Wood, 3 miles SE of Knockcroghery, WV Rubers *et al.* (U) (Crundwell 1975: 17).

[H(27) listed by Lett (1915: 136). H27 deleted because no valid record or voucher specimen traced (Blockeel 1999: 7)].

H(28) listed by Lett (1915: 136).

†H28 listed by Blockeel & Long (1998: 118).

[H(30) listed by Lett (1915: 136) without locality. H30 deleted because no valid record or voucher specimen traced (Blockeel 1999: 7)].

[H(31) listed by Lett (1915: 136). H31 deleted because no valid record or voucher specimen traced (Blockeel 1999: 7)].

H(32) 1947: wet ground beside old railway cutting, Castleblaney, JS Thomson (anon. 1948b: 122).

[H(33) listed by Lett (1915: 136) without locality. H33 deleted because no valid record or voucher specimen traced (Blockeel 1999: 7)].

H33 2000: in calcareous flush at edge of road, NE of Lough Achork, H05, DT Holyoak 00-211 (BBSUK) (Rothero 2001: 44).

[H(34) listed by Lett (1915: 136) without locality. H34 deleted because no valid record or voucher specimen traced (Blockeel 1999: 7)].

H(35) listed by Lett (1915: 136).

H35 2002: on wet path, 90 m alt., Meenanall NW of Lough Anna, G89, NG Hodgetts 3852 (Rothero 2003: 57).

[H(37) listed by Lett (1915: 136) without locality. H37 deleted because no valid record or voucher specimen traced (Blockeel 1999: 7)].

H(38) listed by Lett (1915: 136). H(38) listed by Blockeel & Long (1998: 118).

[H(39) listed by Lett (1915: 136). H39 deleted because no valid record or voucher specimen traced (Blockeel 1999: 7)].

H(40) listed by Lett (1915: 136) without locality. H(40) listed by Blockeel & Long (1998: 118).

97/29 ***Bryum neodamense*** Itzigs. ex Müll.Hal.

H9 1957: *Schoenus* fen, L. Bunny, RE Parker (Warburg 1958b: 483).

H17 1957: fens, Cloonboo, RE Parker (Warburg 1958b: 483).

H22 1978: on wet lime-encrusted stones, E shore of L. Sheelin, DM Synnott (Hill 1980b: 42).

H23 1979: E shore of L. Lene, Fore, DM Synnott (Hill 1980b: 42).

H25 1970: calcareous shore of L. Ree, Portrunny Bay, JA Paton (Crundwell 1971b: 379).

H26 1962: wet ground on limestone pavement by Keel Bridge between Ballinrobe and Partry, AJE Smith (Warburg 1963b: 499).

H30 2001: on thin marl on almost unshaded limestone boulder about 50 cm above lough shore, 75 m alt., NW shore of Lough Sheelin, nr Kilnahard, N48, DT Holyoak 01-672 (Rothero 2002: 51).

[H34 1969: ditch beside road nr estuary of Clonmany River, Tullagh Bay, JA Paton (Crundwell 1970: 204), voucher specimens (BBSUK, E) redet. as *B. marratii* by DT Holyoak, 2002 (Rothero 2003: 57)].

H(37) 1886: marshy shore of Lough Neagh, Carter's Bay, CH Waddell (DBN), comm. DM Synnott (Blockeel 1989: 29).

H(40) 1937: Magilligan, WR Megaw (anon. 1938d: 40), as *B. neodamense*.
1937: edge of swamp, Magilligan, W Megaw (Hb. JB Duncan), specimen formerly misidentified as *B. calophyllum* (Crundwell 1973: 511).

97/30 ***Bryum caespiticium*** Hedw.
(syn. *Bryum caespiticium* var. *caespiticium*)

H(1) 1935: Dingle, no collector named (BBS exc.) (Watson 1936: 265).
†H1 listed by Blockeel & Long (1998: 118).
[H(2) listed by Lett (1915: 137) without details. H2 deleted because no valid record or voucher specimen traced (Blockeel 1999: 7)].
H(4) listed by Lett (1915: 137) without details.
†H4 listed by Blockeel & Long (1998: 118).
[H(5) listed by Lett (1915: 137) without details. H5 deleted because no valid record or voucher specimen traced (Blockeel 1999: 7)].
[H(6) listed by Lett (1915: 137) without details. H6 deleted because no valid record or voucher specimen traced (Blockeel 1999: 7)].
H(7) listed by Lett (1915: 137) without details. H(7) listed by Blockeel & Long (1998: 118).
H(8) listed by Lett (1915: 137) without details.
†H8 listed by Blockeel & Long (1998: 118).
[H(9) listed by Lett (1915: 137) without details. H9 deleted because no valid record or voucher specimen traced (Blockeel 1999: 7)].
[H(12) listed by Lett (1915: 137) without details. H12 deleted because no valid record or voucher specimen traced (Blockeel 1999: 7)].
[H(13) listed by Lett (1915: 137) without details. H13 deleted because no valid record or voucher specimen traced (Blockeel 1999: 7)].
[H(15) listed by Lett (1915: 137) without details. H15 deleted because no valid record or voucher specimen traced (Blockeel 1999: 7)].
[H(18) listed by Lett (1915: 137) without details. H18 deleted because no valid record or voucher specimen traced (Blockeel 1999: 7)].
[H(19) listed by Lett (1915: 137) without details. H19 deleted because no valid record or voucher specimen traced (Blockeel 1999: 7)].
[H(20) listed by Lett (1915: 137) without details. H20 deleted because no valid record or voucher specimen traced (Blockeel 1999: 7)].
[H(21) listed by Lett (1915: 137) without details. H21 deleted because no valid record or voucher specimen traced (Blockeel 1999: 7)].
[H(23) listed by Lett (1915: 137) without details. H23 deleted because record not traced (Synnott 1982, Hill 1983: 54)].
H(25) 1940: nr Boyle, JS Thomson (Crundwell 1968: 639).
H25 2002: in crevices of rocks in limestone wall, 80 m alt., Cloonchambers, M68, NG Hodgetts 4121 (Rothero 2003: 57).
H(27) listed by Lett (1915: 137) without details.
†H27 listed by Blockeel & Long (1998: 118).
[H(28) listed by Lett (1915: 137) without details. H28 deleted because no valid record or voucher specimen traced (Blockeel 1999: 7)].
[H(30) listed by Lett (1915: 137) without details. H30 deleted because no valid record or voucher specimen traced (Blockeel 1999: 7)].
[H(31) listed by Lett (1915: 137) without details. H31 deleted because no valid record or voucher specimen traced (Blockeel 1999: 7)].
[H(32) listed by Lett (1915: 137) without details. H32 deleted because no valid record or voucher specimen traced (Blockeel 1999: 7)].
H(33) listed by Lett (1915: 137) without details. H(33) listed by Blockeel & Long (1998: 118).
[H(34) listed by Lett (1915: 137) without details. H34 deleted because no valid record or voucher specimen traced (Blockeel 1999: 7)].
[H(35) listed by Lett (1915: 137) without details. H35 deleted because no valid record or voucher specimen traced (Blockeel 1999: 7)].
H(36) listed by Lett (1915: 137) without details.
†H36 listed by Blockeel & Long (1998: 118).
[H(37) listed by Lett (1915: 137) without details. H37 deleted because no valid record or voucher specimen traced (Blockeel 1999: 7)].
[H(38) listed by Lett (1915: 137) without details. H38 deleted because no valid record or voucher specimen traced (Blockeel 1999: 7)].
[H(39) listed by Lett (1915: 137) without

details. H39 deleted because no valid record or voucher specimen traced (Blockeel 1999: 7)].
[H(40) listed by Lett (1915: 137) without details. H40 deleted because no valid record or voucher specimen traced (Blockeel 1999: 7)].

97/32 ***Bryum argenteum*** **Hedw.**
(syn. *Bryum argenteum* var. *lanatum* (P. Beauv.) Hampe, *B. argenteum* var. *majus* Schwägr.)

H(1) listed by Lett (1915: 137).
H(1) 1935: Dingle, no collector named (BBS exc.) (Watson 1936: 265).
†H1 listed by Blockeel & Long (1998: 119).
H(2) listed by Lett (1915: 137).
†H2 listed by Blockeel & Long (1998: 119).
H(3) listed by Lett (1915: 137) without locality.
†H3 listed by Blockeel & Long (1998: 119).
H(4) listed by Lett (1915: 137).
†H4 listed by Blockeel & Long (1998: 119).
H(5) listed by Lett (1915: 137).
H5 1966: old quarry, Ballynalacken, nr Fermoy, J Appleyard & JG Duckett (BBS exc.) (Perry 1967: 416), as var. *lanatum*.
H(6) listed by Lett (1915: 137).
H6 1966: quarry N of Lismore, J Appleyard & JG Duckett (BBS exc.) (Perry 1967: 416), as var. *lanatum*.
H7 1962: wall by left bank of R. Suir, Clonmel, ALK King (Warburg 1963b: 499).
H(8) listed by Lett (1915: 137).
†H8 listed by Blockeel & Long (1998: 119).
H(9) listed by Lett (1915: 137) without locality.
H9 1969: amongst grass, dunes, Murroogh, SW of Black Head, AR Perry & HJ Perry (Crundwell 1970: 204), as var. *lanatum*.
H(10) listed by Lett (1915: 137).
†H10 listed by Blockeel & Long (1998: 119).
H(11) listed by Lett (1915: 137).
H11 1966: old quarry, Dysart Castle, Inistioge, JG Duckett *et al* (Perry 1967: 416), as var. *lanatum*.
H(12) listed by Lett (1915: 137).
†H12 listed by Blockeel & Long (1998: 119).
H(13) listed by Lett (1915: 137).
†H13 listed by Blockeel & Long (1998: 119).
H(14) listed by Lett (1915: 137).
†H14 listed by Blockeel & Long (1998: 119).
H15 1957: roadside above Chevy Chase Woods, Owendallulleegh [*sic* = Owendalulleegh], EM Lobley (BBS exc.) (Warburg 1958b: 484).
H(16) listed by Lett (1915: 137).
H16 1969: roadside boulder in lay-by 2 miles NE of Spiddle, AR Perry & HJ Perry (Crundwell 1970: 204), as var. *lanatum*.
H17 1973: side of track, edge of L. Corrib, SW of Keekill, AR Perry & HJ Perry (Crundwell 1974: 171).
H(18) listed by Lett (1915: 137).
†H18 listed by Blockeel & Long (1998: 119).
H(19) listed by Lett (1915: 137) without details.
†H19 listed by Blockeel & Long (1998: 119).
H(20) listed by Lett (1915: 137).
H20 1975: on stone bridge, Avonbeg River, N Kirby (BBS exc.) (Crundwell 1976: 28), as var. *lanatum*.
H(21) listed by Lett (1915: 137).
H21 1967: Kilmainham Hospital grounds, Dublin, JS Jackson (Crundwell 1968: 639), as var. *lanatum*.
H22 1950: ground beside Mill, Slane, JS Thomson (Warburg 1952: 105).
H23 1952: old cart track, Clonhugh Demesne, NE end of L. Owel, JS Thomson (Warburg 1953: 314).
H24 1965: roadside S of Roosky, RD Fitzgerald & EM Lobley (Warburg 1966: 198).
H25 1962: slate roof, Boyle, EF Warburg (Warburg 1963b: 499).
H26 1953: roof of hotel, Ballinrobe, EC Wallace (Warburg 1954: 484).
H(27) listed by Lett (1915: 137).
†H27 listed by Blockeel & Long (1998: 119).
H28 1970: gravel at roadside by Bellannagraugh Bridge, SW of Cloonacool, [The] Ox Mts, AR Perry & HJ Perry (Crundwell 1974: 171), as var. *lanatum*.
H29 1963: roadside at Dromahair, AR Perry & RD Fitzgerald (Warburg 1964: 729).
H(30) 1941: Cavan, JS Thomson (Duncan 1944: 213).
†H30 listed by Blockeel & Long (1998: 119).
H(31) listed by Lett (1915: 137).
H31 1963: tiled roof of dwelling house, Grangebellew, Drogheda, DM Synnott (Warburg 1965: 866), as var. *lanatum*. H31 was erroneously listed in parentheses by Blockeel & Long (1998:

118).
†H32 listed by Blockeel & Long (1998: 119).
†H33 listed by Blockeel & Long (1998: 119).
H(34) listed by Lett (1915: 137) without locality.
†H34 listed by Blockeel & Long (1998: 119).
H(35) listed by Lett (1915: 137).
†H35 listed by Blockeel & Long (1998: 119).
H(36) listed by Lett (1915: 137).
†H36 listed by Blockeel & Long (1998: 119).
H(37) listed by Lett (1915: 137).
H37 1964: limestone in old quarry, Loughgall, RD Fitzgerald (Warburg 1965: 866), as var. *lanatum*.
H(38) listed by Lett (1915: 137).
†H38 listed by Blockeel & Long (1998: 119).
H(39) listed by Lett (1915: 137).
†H39 listed by Blockeel & Long (1998: 119).
H(40) listed by Lett (1915: 137) without details.
†H40 listed by Blockeel & Long (1998: 119).

97/34 ***Bryum gemmiferum*** R.Wilczek & Demaret

H4 1979: field nr Longfield's Bridge, W of Mallow, JA Paton (Hill 1980b: 42).
H8 1979: bank of R. Maigue, S of Croom, JA Paton (Hill 1980b: 42).
H12 1975: forestry track, Killinierin, JA Paton (Smith & Whitehouse 1978: 39, Hill 1979: 29).
H19 2002: wet area in barley stubble on clay, 95 m alt., 1.5 km W of Kildare railway station, M71, HE Fox & CD Preston (Rothero 2003: 57).
H21 1975: damp sand in ditch, Royal Dublin Golf Course, Bull I., PH Pitkin (Smith & Whitehouse 1978: 39, Hill 1979: 29).
H22 1980: on shell-marl beside drainage ditch, N of Newtown Lough, Clonmellon, DM Synnott (Hill 1981: 30).
H25 2002: on thin soil on limestone boulder on lake shore, 47 m alt., N shore of Annaghmore Lough, M98, DT Holyoak 02-890 (Rothero 2003: 57).
H29 2000: on steep sand bank by river, Duff River, E bank, W of Tullaghan, G75, DT Holyoak 00-500 (BBSUK) (Rothero 2001: 44).
H30 2001: on limestone boulders at edge of lough, 70 m alt., NW shore of Lough Sheelin, nr Kilnahard, N48, DT Holyoak 01-677 (Rothero 2002: 51).
H36 2002: on sandy soil in damp hollow in old quarry, 177 m alt., Killucan, H67, DT Holyoak 02-1095 (Rothero 2003: 57).
H38 2002: on bank of sandy gravel in old quarry, 20 m alt., SW of Kilkeel, J21, DT Holyoak 02-1057 (Rothero 2003: 57).
H39 1999: on mud of dried reservoir, Copeland Reservoir, J49, DT Holyoak 99-891 (BBSUK) (Rothero 2000: 55).

97/36 ***Bryum bicolor*** Dicks.
(syn. *Bryum atropurpureum* Bruch, Schimp. & W.Gümbel, *B. atropurpureum* var. *gracilentum* (Braithw.) Dixon)

H(1) listed by Lett (1915: 137).
†H1 listed by Blockeel & Long (1998: 119).
H(2) listed by Lett (1915: 137).
†H2 listed by Blockeel & Long (1998: 119).
†H3 listed by Blockeel & Long (1998: 119).
H(4) listed by Lett (1915: 137) without locality.
†H4 listed by Blockeel & Long (1998: 119).
H(5) listed by Lett (1915: 137) without locality.
†H5 listed by Blockeel & Long (1998: 119).
H6 1966: concrete wall in quarry N of Lismore, J Appleyard & JG Duckett (BBS exc.) (Perry 1967: 416).
H7 1966: roadside, Ardfinnan, J Appleyard & JG Duckett (BBS exc.) (Perry 1967: 416).
H(8) listed by Lett (1915: 137) without locality.
†H8 listed by Blockeel & Long (1998: 119).
H(9) listed by Lett (1915: 137).
†H9 listed by Blockeel & Long (1998: 119).
H10 1967: roadside, Devils Bit Mt., RD Fitzgerald (Crundwell 1968: 639).
H11 1968: masonry, Jerpoint Abbey, SW of Thomastown, VS Paton (Crundwell 1969: 885).
H12 1966: roadside verge nr Kiltealy, Blackstairs Mts, JG Duckett *et al.* (Perry 1967: 416).
H13 1969: roadside, the Nine Stones, N of Mt Leinster, RD Fitzgerald (Crundwell 1970: 205).
H14 1956: heap of flagstone rubble, W of Garrintaggart, AA Cridland (Warburg 1958b: 483).
H15 1961: roadside nr Cloon Bridge, nr Gort,

EM Lobley (Warburg 1962: 373).
†H16 listed by Blockeel & Long (1998: 119).
H18 1987: barley stubble, Derrybrat, 5 km NW of Kilcormac, HLK Whitehouse (Blockeel 1988: 37).
H(19) listed by Lett (1915: 137).
H19 1954: rock in stream below waterfall, Rye Water aqueduct, nr Leixlip, ALK King (Warburg 1955: 586), as var. *gracilentum*.
H(20) listed by Lett (1915: 137).
†H20 listed by Blockeel & Long (1998: 119).
H(21) listed by Lett (1915: 137).
H21 1952: salmon weir in R. Liffey, Lucan demesne, ALK King (Warburg 1953: 313).
H22 1960: sandy floor of quarry at Grangegeeth, ALK King (Warburg 1961: 170).
H23 1954: path in wood, NE of L. Owel, JS Thomson (Warburg 1955: 586).
H25 1962: yard, Boyle, PW Warburg (Warburg 1963b: 499).
H27 1965: damp place on low earthy cliff, Keel, Achill [I.], EF Warburg (Warburg 1966: 198).
H28 1963: roadside at Carney, Drumcliff Bay, AR Perry & RD Fitzgerald (Warburg 1964: 729).
H29 1963: concrete path below Glencar Waterfall, AR Perry & RD Fitzgerald (Warburg 1964: 729).
H30 1961: roadside, *ca* 1000 ft [alt.], Bellavally, Cuilcagh, RD Fitzgerald (Warburg 1962: 373).
H(31) 1945: Ravensdale, JS Thomson (anon. 1946c: 283), as *B. atropurpureum*.
†H32 listed by Blockeel & Long (1998: 119).
H33 1959: edge of road, Magho, Lower Lough Erne, RD Fitzgerald (Warburg 1960: 778).
H(34) listed by Lett (1915: 137).
†H34 listed by Blockeel & Long (1998: 119).
H35 1970: on soil in disused quarry nr Portnoo, N of Ardara, MFV Corley (Crundwell 1971b: 379).
†H36 listed by Blockeel & Long (1998: 119).
†H37 listed by Blockeel & Long (1998: 119).
H(38) listed by Lett (1915: 137).
H(38) 1915: Mountstewart, CH Waddell (anon. 1916a: 160), as *B. atropurpureum* var. *gracilentum*.
†H38 listed by Blockeel & Long (1998: 119).
H(39) listed by Lett (1915: 137).
†H39 listed by Blockeel & Long (1998: 119).
†H40 listed by Blockeel & Long (1998: 119).

See notes under the next species.

97/37 ***Bryum dunense*** A.J.E.Sm. & H. Whitehouse

H12 2001: on open sandy mud above brackish lagoon, 1 m alt., SW of Tacumshin Lake, T00, DT Holyoak 01-875 (Rothero 2002: 51).
H28 1969: roadside verge nr Bunduff Lough, N of Cliffony nr Bundoran, JA Paton (Smith & Whitehouse 1978: 44, Hill 1979: 30).
H34 1969: bank of Clonmany River, SE of Clonmany, JA Paton (Smith & Whitehouse 1978: 44, Hill 1979: 30).
H35 1969: bank by road nr Sessiagh Loch, Dunfanaghy, JA Paton (Smith & Whitehouse 1978: 44-45, Hill 1979: 30).
H39 1999: on mainly bare sandy slope in fixed dunes, E of Portrush, C84, DT Holyoak 99-239 (BBSUK) (Rothero 2000: 55).
H40 1999: on bare sandy slope of semi-fixed dune, Magilligan Point, C63, DT Holyoak 99-139 (BBSUK) (Rothero 2000: 55).

The frequent occurrence of plants intermediate between *B. bicolor* and *B. dunense* suggests that they should not be treated as distinct species; the oldest name for the species is *B. dichotomum* Hedw. (Holyoak 2003).

97/38 ***Bryum radiculosum*** Brid.
(syn. *Bryum murale* Wilson ex Hunt)

H1 1983: on old wall by road, nr bridge leading to Rossmore I., Kenmare River, DG Long (Hill 1984b: 29).
H(2) listed by Lett (1915: 138). H(2) listed by Blockeel & Long (1998: 119).
H(3) listed by Lett (1915: 138). H(3) listed by Blockeel & Long (1998: 119).
H5 2002: on stonework of bridge, 10 m alt., Fota House, Foaty I., W77, TL Blockeel 31/343 (Rothero 2003: 57).
H7 1988: on mortar of old wall, 120 m, Rock of Cashel, S04, DG Long 15444 (Blockeel 1990: 32).
H(8) listed by Lett (1915: 138). H(8) listed by Blockeel & Long (1998: 119).

H9 1979: pocket of soil on limestone rock, N end of L. Cullaunyheeda, S of Tulla, AC Crundwell (Hill 1980b: 42).
H(10) listed by Lett (1915: 138). H(10) listed by Blockeel & Long (1998: 119).
H11 1968: masonry, Jerpoint Abbey, SW of Thomastown, JA Paton (Crundwell 1969: 885).
H(12) listed by Lett (1915: 138).
†H12 listed by Blockeel & Long (1998: 119).
H14 1957: Carboniferous Limestone wall, Strahard, NE of Mountmellick, AA Cridland (Warburg 1958b: 484).
H15 1987: mortared walls, Portumna Abbey, HLK Whitehouse (Blockeel 1988: 37).
H16 1986: mortar of old wall, Cleggan Farm, DG Long (Blockeel 1987: 24).
H18 1987: lime kiln at roadside, Slieve Bloom Mts, 5 km E of Kinnitty, HLK Whitehouse (Blockeel 1988: 37).
H20 1958: concrete post, nr Woodend Brook, Blessington, ALK King (Warburg 1959: 636).
H(21) listed by Lett (1915: 138). H(21) listed by Blockeel & Long (1998: 119).
H(23) listed by Lett (1915: 138).
†H23 listed by Blockeel & Long (1998: 119).
H27 1987: on shady wall, lane below Slievemore, Dugort, Achill I., DG Long (Blockeel 1988: 37).
H(29) listed by Lett (1915: 138). H(29) listed by Blockeel & Long (1998: 119).
H29 2001: on mortared wall of ruined house, 190 m alt., S of Crumpaun, G74, DT Holyoak 01-725 (Rothero 2002: 51).
H(30) listed by Lett (1915: 138). H(30) listed by Blockeel & Long (1998: 119).
H30 2001: on open mortared wall of ruined house, 305 m alt., W of Bellavally Gap, H12, DT Holyoak 01-632 (Rothero 2002: 51).
H(31) listed by Lett (1915: 138).
†H31 listed by Blockeel & Long (1998: 119).
H(32) listed by Lett (1915: 138). H(32) listed by Blockeel & Long (1998: 119).
H(33) listed by Lett (1915: 138). H(33) listed by Blockeel & Long (1998: 119).
H33 2000: on crumbling concrete by road bridge, Lady Craigavon Bridge, H32, DT Holyoak 00-164 (BBSUK) (Rothero 2001: 44).
H(35) listed by Lett (1915: 138). H(35) listed by Blockeel & Long (1998: 119).
H35 2002: on wall at edge of lake, 5 m alt., E edge of New Lake, SW of Dunfanaghy, C03, DT Holyoak 02-648 (Rothero 2003: 57).
†H36 listed by Blockeel & Long (1998: 119).
H37 2002: in crevices of mortared wall, 65 m alt., Gosford Forest Park, H94, DT Holyoak 02-1077 (Rothero 2003: 57).
H(38) listed by Lett (1915: 138). H(38) listed by Blockeel & Long (1998: 119).
H38 2002: on wall of bridge, 50 m alt., by Shimna River in Tollymore Forest Park, J33, DT Holyoak 02-928 (Rothero 2003: 57).
H(39) listed by Lett (1915: 138). H(39) listed by Blockeel & Long (1998: 119).
H39 1999: top of concrete wall by reservoir, Dungonnell Dam, D11, DT Holyoak 99-822 (BBSUK) (Rothero 2000: 55).
H40 1999: in crevice of mortared stone wall, old burial ground, Downhill, C73, DT Holyoak 99-207 (BBSUK) (Rothero 2000: 55).

97/39 ***Bryum ruderale*** Crundw. & Nyholm

H1 1962: stony ground amongst shingle, Ross Behy nr Glenbeigh, HLK Whitehouse (Crundwell & Nyholm 1964: 607, Warburg 1965: 867).
H2 1951: earth-covered wall, Tralee, AC Crundwell, comm. DF Chamberlain (Warburg 1965: 867).
†H3 listed by Blockeel & Long (1998: 119), but there appears to be no published record to justify this.
H6 1966: arable field nr Clogheen, nr Ballymacarbry, Clonmel, JA Paton & ERB Little (BBS exc.) (Perry 1967: 417).
H7 1962: roadside at Seskin, E of Clonmel, HLK Whitehouse (Crundwell & Nyholm 1964: 607, Warburg 1965: 867).
H8 1962: path, Askeaton Friary, HLK Whitehouse (Crundwell & Nyholm 1964: 607, Warburg 1965: 867).
H9 1962: earth on stone nr Bunratty Castle, HLK Whitehouse (Crundwell & Nyholm 1964: 607, Warburg 1965: 867).
H10 1987: barley field, 2 km SW of Ballinderry, HLK Whitehouse (Blockeel 1988: 37).
H11 1962: edge of path by stream, Monefelim Bridge, HLK Whitehouse (Crundwell & Nyholm 1964: 607, Warburg 1965: 867).
H13 1966: roadside verge nr Ballymurphy,

Blackstairs Mts, JG Duckett *et al.* (Perry 1967: 417).

H14 1987: barley field, 2 km W of Mountmellick, HLK Whitehouse (Blockeel 1988: 37).

H15 1962: roadside nr Aughrim, W of Ballinasloe, HLK Whitehouse (Crundwell & Nyholm 1964: 607, Warburg 1965: 867).

H16 1965: footpath on limestone by R. Oughterard, Oughterard, DF Chamberlain (Warburg 1966: 198).

H18 1987: barley stubble, Derrybrat, 5 km NW of Kilcormac, HLK Whitehouse (Blockeel 1988: 37).

H19 2002: in stubble field, 65 m alt., Coursetown House, W of Athy, S69, HF Fox & CD Preston (Rothero 2003: 57).

H20 1962: roadside nr Rathdangan, HLK Whitehouse (Crundwell & Nyholm 1964: 607, Warburg 1965: 867).

H21 2002: in stubble field, 60 m alt., SE of Hazelhatch Station, N93, CD Preston (Rothero 2003: 57).

H22 1978: track by L. Brackan, nr Drumconrath, DM Synnott (Hill 1980b: 42).

H23 1962: roadside Bunbrosna, EF Warburg (Crundwell & Nyholm 1964: 607, Warburg 1965: 867).

H24 1980: limestone wall, Draper Bridge, Royal Canal, DM Synnott (Hill 1981: 30).

H25 1962: earth by roadside, W end of bridge, Shannonbridge, HLK Whitehouse (Crundwell & Nyholm 1964: 607, Warburg 1965: 867).

H27 1987: side of roadside drain at Cloughmore Pier, Achill I., DM Synnott (Blockeel 1988: 37).

H29 2001: on limestone soil at edge of track, 55 m alt., N shore of Garadice Lough, E of Killaphort, H11, DT Holyoak 01-815 (Rothero 2002: 51).

H30 2001: on open soil amongst limestone gravel at edge of car park, 50 m alt., Town Lough, nr Killashandra, H30, DT Holyoak 01-833 (Rothero 2002: 51).

H33 2000: on disturbed stony soil, Marble Arch, by visitor centre, H13, DT Holyoak 00-148 (BBSUK) (Rothero 2001: 44).

H34 1962: roadside bank, Speenoge, S of Buncrana, AC Crundwell (Crundwell & Nyholm 1964: 607, Warburg 1965: 867).

H35 1962: hotel garden, Dunfanaghy, AC Crundwell (Crundwell & Nyholm 1964: 607, Warburg 1965: 867).

H37 2002: on disturbed soil at base of wall, 65 m alt., Gosford Forest Park, H94, DT Holyoak 02-1074 (Rothero 2003: 57).

H38 2002: on disturbed ground by estuarine bay, 5 m alt., W of Dundrum, J33, DT Holyoak 02-955 (Rothero 2003: 57).

H39 1969: bank of track above White Park Bay, JA Paton (Crundwell 1970: 205).

H40 1962: roadside bank, Feeny, AC Crundwell (Crundwell & Nyholm 1964: 607, Warburg 1965: 867).

97/40 ***Bryum violaceum*** Crundw. & Nyholm

H1 1962: oatfield nr Gallerus Oratory, Dingle Peninsula, HLK Whitehouse (Crundwell & Nyholm 1964: 609, Warburg 1965: 867).

H8 1979: roadside by sea, Beagh Castle, nr Askeaton, G Bloom (Hill 1980b: 42).

H9 1979: on soil, N end of Finn Lough, NW of Sixmilebridge, AC Crundwell (Hill 1980b: 42).

H13 1999: on bare soil at edge of path, 8 m alt., R Barrow nr canal, 1 km NW of Saint Mullins, S73, TL Blockeel 28/327 (Rothero 2000: 55).

H14 2002: in stubble field, 80 m alt., Garrans Crossroads NE of Stradbally, S59, HF Fox & CD Preston (Rothero 2003: 57).

H18 1987: barley stubble, Derrybrat, 5 km NW of Kilcormac, HLK Whitehouse (Blockeel 1988: 37).

H19 1987: barley field, 2.5 km E of Rathangan, HLK Whitehouse (Blockeel 1988: 37).

H21 2002: in stubble field, 60 m alt., SE of Hazelhatch Station, N93, CD Preston (Rothero 2003: 57).

H29 2001: on open soil in garden, 50 m alt., SE of Loughrinn, N09, DT Holyoak 01-858 (Rothero 2002: 52).

H34 1962: roadside bank nr Speenoge, Inishowen, EF Warburg (Crundwell & Nyholm 1964: 609-610, Warburg 1965: 867).

H35 1962: roadside, Ards Peninsula, nr Dunfanaghy, AC Crundwell (Crundwell & Nyholm 1964: 609-610, Warburg 1965: 867).

H(38) 1909: on spongy patches of *Conferva*, Lenaderg, JH Davies (DBN), comm.

DM Synnott (Blockeel 1989: 29).

H40 1962: roadside bank, Feeny, AC Crundwell (Crundwell & Nyholm 1964: 609-610, Warburg 1965: 867).

97/41 ***Bryum klinggraeffii*** **Schimp.**

H1 1962: oatfield nr Gallerus Oratory, Dingle Peninsula, HLK Whitehouse (Crundwell & Nyholm 1964: 614, Warburg 1965: 867).

H3 1979: grounds of Golf Links Hotel, Glengarriff, G Bloom (Hill 1980b: 42).

H5 1966: track, Castle Cooke, nr Kilworth, J Appleyard (Perry 1967: 417).

H6 1999: on soil in overgrown pasture, 60 m alt., Ballymacart R at Ballymacart Bridge, 3 km W of Mine Head, X28, TL Blockeel 28/211 (Rothero 2000: 55).

H7 1966: edge of fen carr, Bansha, J Appleyard (BBS exc.) (Perry 1967: 417).

H8 1966: on soil in marshy ground by L. Gur, ERB Little (BBS exc.) (Crundwell 1966: 640).

H9 1957: with *P.*[*hyscomitrella*] *patens*, mud at side of path in pasture on SE side of Slievecarran, J Appleyard & AC Crundwell (Crundwell & Nyholm 1964: 614, Warburg 1965: 867).

H10 1979: field beside Clare River, S of Derrygareen, JA Paton (Hill 1980b: 42).

H13 1975: bank at edge of fen SW of Yellowford Cross Roads, S of Baltinglass, JA Paton (BBS exc.) (Crundwell 1976: 28).

H14 1987: barley field, 2 km W of Mountmellick, HLK Whitehouse (Blockeel 1988: 37).

H15 1957: with *P.*[*hyscomitrella*] *patens*, damp soil in pasture liable to flood, Garryland Wood, nr Gort, J Appleyard & AC Crundwell (Crundwell & Nyholm 1964: 614, Warburg 1965: 867).

H16 1969: soil at edge of field, Farravaun, Glann, Oughterard, AR Perry & HJ Perry (Crundwell 1970: 205).

H18 1987: barley stubble, Derrybrat, 5 km NW of Kilcormac, HLK Whitehouse (Blockeel 1988: 37).

H19 1987: barley stubble, 2.5 km E of Rathangan, HLK Whitehouse (Blockeel 1988: 37).

H20 1975: waste ground by bridge over Avonbeg River, Greenan, WSW of Rathdrum, AR Perry (Hill 1981: 30-31).

H21 2002: in stubble field, 60 m alt., SE of Hazelhatch Station, N93, CD Preston (Rothero 2003: 57).

H22 1965: amongst *Pottia davalliana*, bare ground, Newtown Commons, Duleek, DM Synnott, comm. DF Chamberlain (Warburg 1966: 198).

H23 1962: roadside, Bunbrosna, EF Warburg (Crundwell & Nyholm 1964: 614, Warburg 1965: 867).

H24 1968: with *Physcomitrella patens* on shore of small lake, Fort William, 4 miles S of Lanesborough, WV Rubers *et al.* (U) (Crundwell 1974: 171).

H25 1970: track across marshy field, Barry Beg, N of Athlone, JA Paton (Crundwell 1971b: 380).

H27 1962: peaty ground by roadside nr Straheens Lough, Achill I., EF Warburg (Crundwell & Nyholm 1964: 614, Warburg 1965: 867).

H28 1965: side of track nr Percy Mount, nr L. Gill, EF Warburg (Warburg 1966: 198).

H29 2000: on soil of low bank by river, R. Shannon, N of Jamestown, M99, DT Holyoak 00-759 (BBSUK) (Rothero 2001: 44).

H30 2001: on open sandy soil on lough shore, 45 m alt., shore of Lough Oughter, W of Inishconnell, hectad H30, DT Holyoak 01-684 (Rothero 2002: 52).

H34 1962: roadside bank nr Speenoge, Inishowen, EF Warburg (Crundwell & Nyholm 1964: 614, Warburg 1965: 867).

H35 1990: on soil on roadside verge, 60 m alt., nr Ballyarr Wood, *ca* 5 km E of Kilmacrenan, C12, TL Blockeel 19/501 (Blockeel 1991c: 44).

H39 1999: on mud of dried reservoir, Copeland Reservoir, J49, DT Holyoak 99-886 (BBSUK) (Rothero 2000: 55).

97/42 ***Bryum sauteri*** **Bruch, Schimp. & W. Gümbel**

H3 1968: edge of pool nr Dunboy Castle, Castletown Bearhaven, JA Paton (Crundwell 1969: 885).

H4 1968: roadside, Shournagh River, nr Blarney, RD Fitzgerald (Crundwell 1969: 885).

H6 1966: bank of ditch of field, cliffs W of Bunmahon, JA Paton (BBS exc.) (Perry 1967: 417).

H8 1979: nr road by stream, E of Knockanimpaha, G Bloom (Hill 1980b: 42).

H13 1969: earth-topped wall, Crannagh, foot of Mt Leinster, RD Fitzgerald (Crundwell 1970: 205).

H16 1969: cart rut in track nr Farravaun, Glann, Oughterard, AR Perry & HJ Perry (Crundwell 1970: 205).

H20 1962: roadside nr Rathdangan, HLK Whitehouse (Crundwell & Nyholm 1964: 617, Warburg 1965: 867).

H27 1987: amongst *Anthoceros* and *Riccia* spp., damp trackside below Slievemore, N of Slievemore Hotel, Dugort, Achill I., JA Paton (Blockeel 1988: 37).

H30 2001: on thin soil between limestone fragments on track, 100 m alt., Deerpark, W of Virginia, N58, DT Holyoak 01-666 (Rothero 2002: 52).

H34 1962: stubble field nr Castleforward, nr Newtown Cunningham, EF Warburg (Crundwell & Nyholm 1964: 617, Warburg 1965: 867).

H35 1969: marshy field nr Doe Castle, N of Creeslough, JA Paton (Crundwell 1970: 205).

97/43 ***Bryum tenuisetum*** Limpr.

H3 1979: among rocks by the sea, coast nr League Pt, SW of Bantry, AC Crundwell (Hill 1980b: 42).

H29 2001: on damp sand on lough shore, 60 m alt., E shore of Lough Allen, W of Cleighran More, G91, DT Holyoak 01-784 (Rothero 2002: 52).

H35 2002: on thin soil on damp rock beside estuary, 5 m alt., E bank of Lackagh River nr Lackagh Bridge, C03, DT Holyoak 02-678 (Rothero 2003: 57).

97/44 ***Bryum subapiculatum*** Hampe
(syn. *Bryum microerythrocarpum* Müll. Hal. & Kindb.)

H1 1962: roadside at Brandon Creek, Dingle Peninsula, HLK Whitehouse (Crundwell & Nyholm 1964: 624, Warburg 1965: 867).

H3 1968: rocky slope on N side of Knocknagallaun, N of Allihies, JA Paton (Crundwell 1969: 885).

H5 1966: gravelly track, Castle Cooke, nr Kilworth, J Appleyard (BBS exc.) (Perry 1967: 416).

H6 1999: on soil in overgrown pasture, 60 m alt., Ballymacart R at Ballymacart Bridge, 3 km W of Mine Head, X28, TL Blockeel 28/211 (Rothero 2000: 55).

H12 2001: on soil in grassland at upper edge of saltmarsh, 2 m alt., Lady's Island Lake, SE edge, T10, DT Holyoak 01-597 (Rothero 2002: 52).

H13 1999: on bare soil at edge of path, 8 m alt., R Barrow, nr canal, 1 km NW of Saint Mullins, S73, TL Blockeel 28/327 (Rothero 2000: 55).

H15 1994: in *Lolium perenne* field, Cappaghmore, 5 km SW of Kinvarra, M30, PE Stanley, RC Stern & HLK Whitehouse (Blockeel 1995c: 44).

H16 1965: field by L. Corrib, *ca* 1½ m.[iles] NW of Oughterard, DF Chamberlain (Warburg 1966: 198).

H20 1975: soil beside river path, Arklow, JA Paton (BBS exc.) (Crundwell 1976: 28).

H22 1970: peaty cornfield W of An Uaimh, JA Paton (Crundwell 1971b: 380).

H23 1980: boggy ground at margin of Mount Dalton Lough, W of Mullingar, DM Synnott (Hill 1981: 30).

H27 1987: on peaty soil by track, Dooega, Achill I., TL Blockeel (Blockeel 1988: 38).

H29 1963: clay clod in field below limestone scarp, Boggaun, Manorhamilton, AR Perry & RD Fitzgerald (Crundwell & Nyholm 1964: 624, Warburg 1965: 867).

H30 2001: on open damp soil on bank by track, 315 m alt., W of Bellavally Gap, H12, DT Holyoak 01-639 (Rothero 2002: 52).

H34 2002: on exposed soil of flushed bank on N-facing low coastal headland, 7 m alt., Culoort NW of Malin, C45, DT Holyoak 02-574 (Rothero 2003: 57).

H36 2002: on gravelly sand in old quarry, 177 m alt., Killucan, H67, DT Holyoak 02-1097B (Rothero 2003: 57).

H37 1962: stubble field between Moy and Loughgall, AC Crundwell (Crundwell & Nyholm 1964: 624, Warburg 1965: 867).

H38 2002: on gravelly soil on verge beside road, 210 m alt., nr N end of Silent Valley Reservoir, J32, DT Holyoak 02-978 (Rothero 2003: 57).

H40 1999: on bare sandy slope of semi-fixed dune, Magilligan Point, C63, DT Holyoak 99-140 (BBSUK) (Rothero

2000: 55).

97/45 ***Bryum bornholmense*** Wink. & R.Ruthe

H1 1951: among rocks in pasture by the sea, Cloghane, Dingle Peninsula, AC Crundwell (Crundwell & Nyholm 1964: 628, Warburg 1965: 867). Accepted for H1 following revision of specimen(s) by Crundwell & Whitehouse (2001: 174).
H10 1965: cut-away bog, L. Nahinch, between Birr and Borrisokane, ALK King (Warburg 1966: 198). Accepted for H10 following revision of specimen(s) by Crundwell & Whitehouse (2001: 174).
[H11 1962: edge of path by stream, Monefelim Bridge, HLK Whitehouse (Crundwell & Nyholm 1964: 628, Warburg 1965: 867). Record from H11 rejected following revision of specimen (s) by Crundwell & Whitehouse (2001: 174)].
[H15 1994: bare patches in sown rye-grass field, Cappaghmore, SW of Kinvarra, M30, RC Stern, conf. AC Crundwell (Blockeel 1995c: 44). Record from H15 rejected following revision of specimen (s) by Crundwell & Whitehouse (2001: 174)].
[H21 1967: on shaded bank on golf links at Corballis, ALK King (Crundwell 1968: 640). Record from H21 rejected following revision of specimen(s) by Crundwell & Whitehouse (2001: 174)].
H22 1978: bare peat on burned bog, Dalystown, SW of Trim, DM Synnott (Hill 1979: 30). Accepted for H22 following revision of specimen(s) by Crundwell & Whitehouse (2001: 174).
[H23 1970: peat in cutover bog S of Doonis Lough, N of Glassan, JA Paton (Crundwell 1971b: 380). Record from H23 rejected following revision of specimen(s) by Crundwell & Whitehouse (2001: 174)].
[H28 1963: soil over limestone at 900 ft [alt.], Carrowkeel, NE end of Bricklieve Mts, AR Perry & RD Fitzgerald (Crundwell & Nyholm 1964: 628, Warburg 1965: 867). Record from H28 rejected following revision of specimen(s) by Crundwell & Whitehouse (2001: 174)].
[H29 1970: lower ground on slopes of Crockauns, S of Glencar Lake, J Appleyard (BBS exc.) (Crundwell 1971b: 380, Appleyard 1971: 390). Record from H29 rejected following revision of specimen(s) by Crundwell & Whitehouse (2001: 174)].
[H35 1962: sand on cliff between Maghery and Crohy Head, nr Dunglow, AC Crundwell (Crundwell & Nyholm 1964: 628, Warburg 1965: 867). Record from H35 rejected following revision of specimen(s) by Crundwell & Whitehouse (2001: 174)].
H35 2002: on gritty soil amongst granite rocks on hill top, 520 m alt., W summit of Edenadooish, B92, DT Holyoak 02-437 (Rothero 2003: 57).

B. bornholmense was overlooked in Ireland and Britain until the taxonomic revision of the '*Bryum erythrocarpum* complex' by Crundwell & Nyholm (1964). Crundwell & Whitehouse (2001) gave a revised account of the characters of the species and a revised list of vice-county records, showing that from about 1962 to 2001 it was still often misidentified.

97/46 ***Bryum rubens*** Mitt.

H1 1962: oatfield nr Gallerus Oratory, Dingle Peninsula, HLK Whitehouse (Crundwell & Nyholm 1964: 632, Warburg 1965: 867).
H2 1966: ride in woods below Torc Cascade, Killarney, JA Paton (Perry 1967: 416).
H3 1967: on path, old bridge by lake S of Macroom, RD Fitzgerald (Crundwell 1968: 640).
H4 1967: on bare ground, Carrigafroca, RD Fitzgerald (Crundwell 1968: 640).
H5 no date: nr Fermoy, J Chandler (NY) (Crundwell & Nyholm 1964: 632, Warburg 1965: 867).
H6 1966: arable field, Ballynamult, S of Clonmel, J Appleyard (BBS exc.) (Perry 1967: 416).
H7 1966: arable field, Ardfinnan, J Appleyard (BBS exc.) (Perry 1967: 416).
H8 1966: marsh, L. Gur, J Appleyard (BBS exc.) (Perry 1967: 416).
H9 1962: earth on stone nr Bunratty Castle, HLK Whitehouse (Crundwell & Nyholm

1964: 632, Warburg 1965: 867).

H10 1987: barley field, 2 km SW of Ballinderry, HLK Whitehouse (Blockeel 1988: 38).

H11 1968: arable field nr Summerhill House, N of Thomastown, JA Paton (Crundwell 1969: 885).

H12 1972: on timber road, wood at Mountfin House, 2 km W of Ferns, WV Rubers (U) (Crundwell 1974: 171).

H13 1969: stubble field, Ballykeenan, nr Myshall, RD Fitzgerald (Crundwell 1970: 205).

H14 1987: barley field, 2 km W of Mountmellick, N40, HLK Whitehouse (Blockeel 1995c: 44).

H15 1994: base of wall, Coole, 3 km N of Gort, M40, NG Hodgetts, RD Porley & HLK Whitehouse (Blockeel 1995c: 44).

H16 1969: on edge of field, Farravaun, Oughterard, SW of Black Head, AR Perry & HJ Perry (Crundwell 1970: 205).

H17 1970: soil by road, Baranny, *ca* 2 miles SW of Cloonboo, AR Perry & HJ Perry (Crundwell 1974: 171).

H18 1987: barley stubble, Derrybrat, 5 km NW of Kilcormac, HLK Whitehouse (Blockeel 1988: 38).

H19 1987: barley field, 2.5 km E of Rathdangan, HLK Whitehouse (Blockeel 1988: 38).

H20 1962: roadside nr Rathdangan, HLK Whitehouse (Crundwell & Nyholm 1964: 632, Warburg 1965: 867).

H21 1966: in cleft of stump of Spanish chestnut, Mt Mervion Wood, ALK King (Crundwell 1968: 640).

H22 1973: archeological site, Dowth, MO Hill (Crundwell 1974: 171).

H23 1962: roadside, Bunbrosna, EF Warburg (Crundwell & Nyholm 1964: 632, Warburg 1965: 867).

H25 1973: on path, shore of L. Ree, St John's Wood, WV Rubers (U) (Crundwell 1974: 171).

H27 1970: marshy trackside, Bundorragha, N of Killary Harbour, JA Paton (Crundwell 1971b: 380).

H28 1970: woodland, Lissadell House, N of Drumcliff, JA Paton (BBS exc.) (Crundwell 1971b: 380, Appleyard 1971: 389).

H29 1982: cindery path round cottage, Killanummery, Dromahair, RJ Fisk (Blockeel 1988: 38).

H31 1967: railway cutting, Braganstown, Dunbeer, DM Synnott (Crundwell 1968: 640).

H33 2000: on disturbed stony soil, Marble Arch, by visitor centre, H13, DT Holyoak 00-144 (BBSUK) (Rothero 2001: 44).

H34 1962: stubble field E of Newtown Cunningham, AC Crundwell (Crundwell & Nyholm 1964: 632, Warburg 1965: 867).

H35 1962: oatfield, Ards Peninsula nr Dunfanaghy, AC Crundwell (Crundwell & Nyholm 1964: 632, Warburg 1965: 867).

H36 1962: hayfield nr Donaghmore, AC Crundwell (Crundwell & Nyholm 1964: 632, Warburg 1965: 867).

H37 2002: on disturbed soil by path, 65 m alt., Gosford Forest Park, H94, DT Holyoak 02-1079 (Rothero 2003: 57).

H38 2002: on bank of sandy gravel in old quarry, 20 m alt., SW of Kilkeel, J21, DT Holyoak 02-1059 (Rothero 2003: 57).

H39 1999: on soil amongst gravel at edge of car park, White Park Bay, D04, DT Holyoak 99-606 (BBSUK) (Rothero 2000: 55).

H40 1953: sand quarry S of Lough Fea, MPH Kertland & EM Lobley (Crundwell & Nyholm 1964: 632, Warburg 1965: 867).

B. rubens was often confused with allied species until the taxonomic revision of the '*Bryum erythrocarpum* complex' by Crundwell & Nyholm (1964). Older records of *B. rubens* (e.g. in Lett 1915: 138) cannot be safely assigned to this species unless the specimens have been reidentified.

[97/38-46 *Bryum erythrocarpum* Schwaegr., nom illeg.]

[H1 1951: among rocks in pasture by the sea, Cloghane, Dingle Peninsula, AC Crundwell (Warburg 1952: 104)].

[H14 1956: disturbed calcareous roadside verge, Castletown, AA Cridland (Warburg 1958b: 483)].

[H(16) 1912: Cregduff, Galway, CA Cheetham (anon. 1913a: 75)].

[H(31) 1943: Feede wood, JS Thomson

(Duncan 1944: 213)].

[H(40) 1913: Granahan, JD Houston (anon. 1937a: 368)].

This name was formerly used for several small species of *Bryum* with red rhizoidal tubers. In addition to the records listed above, Lett (1915: 137-138) reported *B. erythrocarpum* for 14 Irish vice-counties. Unless specimens have been revised since about 1960 it is impracticable to identify any of these records with the species now recognised.

97/47 *Bryum riparium* I.Hagen

H1 1951: small ditch, S side of Lough Currane [= 82/44], EF Warburg (BBS exc.) (Whitehouse 1963: 399, Warburg 1964: 729).

H6 1966: damp rocks on cliffs above Sgilloge Loughs, Comeragh Mts, JA Paton (BBS exc.) (Perry 1967: 417).

H16 1957: by a stream on NE side of Benchoona [= 84/83], J Appleyard (BBS exc.) (Warburg 1958b: 484 as *B. mildeanum*; Whitehouse 1963: 400, Warburg 1964: 729).

[H27 1957: rocks in stream bed, SE valley of Maumtrasna [= 94/03], AC Crundwell & E Nyholm (BBS exc.) (Warburg 1958b: 484 as *B. mildeanum*; Whitehouse 1963: 400, Warburg 1964: 729). H27 deleted because locality (SE valley of Maumtrasna) is in H16 (Crundwell 1970: 205)]. Entry for H27 in Blockeel & Long (1998: 120) is thus apparently erroneous.

H(38) 1885: with *Dichodontium pellucidum*, Slievenabrock (2 miles W of Newcastle), Mourne Mts [= 14/48], HW Lett (DBN) (Whitehouse 1963: 399, Warburg 1964: 729).

[97/48 *Bryum mildeanum* Jur.]
(syn. *Bryum mildei* Jur. ex Arn. nom. illeg.)

[H1 listed in *CC* by Warburg 1963a: 58, but redet. as *B. riparium* (Whitehouse 1963: 399, Warburg 1964: 729)].

[H2 listed in *CC* by Warburg 1963a: 58, but not accepted in later revisions because no specimens traced to support record (1906: Horse's Glen, Mangerton Mt., Killarney, DA Jones) (Lett 1915: 138, Whitehouse 1963: 403, Warburg 1964: 729)].

[H16 1957: Benchoona, J Appleyard (BBS exc.) (Warburg 1958b: 484), as *B. mildeanum*. H16 listed in *CC* by Warburg 1963a: 58, but redet. as *B. riparium* (Whitehouse 1963: 400, Warburg 1964: 729)].

[H21 listed in *CC* by Warburg 1963a: 58, but not accepted in later revision because specimen (1856: Kilrock Quarry, Howth, D Orr, DBN, e.g. in Lett 1915: 138) is *B. caespiticium* (Whitehouse 1963: 402, Warburg 1964: 729)].

[H27 1957: rocks in stream, SE valley of Maumtrasna, AC Crundwell & E Nyholm (BBS exc.) (Warburg 1958b: 484), as *B. mildeanum*. H27 listed in *CC* by Warburg 1963a: 58, but redet. as *B. riparium* (Whitehouse 1963: 400, Warburg 1964: 729) and locality later shown to be in H16 (see above)].

[H39 listed in *CC* by Warburg 1963a: 58, but not accepted in later revision because specimens misidentified (Slemish Mt., D Moore, DBN, e.g. in Lett 1915: 138, is *B. alpinum* accompanied by *B. capillare*; 1889: ditch on Knockagh, Carrickfergus, CH Waddell, BFT, is '*B. erythrocarpum*') (Whitehouse 1963: 402-403, Warburg 1964: 729)].

97/51 *Bryum alpinum* With.
(syn. *Bryum alpinum* var. *viride* Husn.)

H(1) listed by Lett (1915: 138).

H(1) 1934: Brandon Mt., JB Duncan. (anon. 1936: 278-279), as var. *viride*.
1935: nr L. Cruttia, no collector named (BBS exc.) (Watson 1936: 265), as var. *viride*.

†H1 listed by Blockeel & Long (1998: 121).

H(2) listed by Lett (1915: 138).

†H2 listed by Blockeel & Long (1998: 121).

H(3) listed by Lett (1915: 138).

H3 1966: damp boggy ground on slope above low cliffs by the road from Bantry to Sheep's Head, W of Glanlough, JPM Brenan (Crundwell 1969: 886), as var. *viride*.

H(4) listed by Lett (1915: 138).

†H4 listed by Blockeel & Long (1998: 121).

H5 1967: path in bog, Lyreamon, NW of Carrignavar, RD Fitzgerald (Crundwell

1968: 641).
H(6) listed by Lett (1915: 138).
†H6 listed by Blockeel & Long (1998: 121).
H(7) listed by Lett (1915: 138).
†H7 listed by Blockeel & Long (1998: 121).
H8 1979: gravelly quarry, N side of Sugar Hill, S of Knockanimpaha, JA Paton (Hill 1980b: 43).
H(9) listed by Lett (1915: 138) without locality.
†H9 listed by Blockeel & Long (1998: 121).
H(13) listed by Lett (1915: 138). H(13) listed by Blockeel & Long (1998: 121).
H(14) listed by Lett (1915: 138). H(14) listed by Blockeel & Long (1998: 121).
H(16) listed by Lett (1915: 138).
H16 1970: NW shore of L. Fee, S of Killary Harbour, JA Paton (Crundwell 1971b: 380), as var. *viride*.
H(20) listed by Lett (1915: 138).
†H20 listed by Blockeel & Long (1998: 121).
H(21) listed by Lett (1915: 138). H(21) listed by Blockeel & Long (1998: 121).
H24 1957: Carn Clonhugh Hill, ALK King (Warburg 1958b: 484).
H(25) listed by Lett (1915: 138). H(25) listed by Blockeel & Long (1998: 121).
H(26) listed by Lett (1915: 138).
†H26 listed by Blockeel & Long (1998: 121).
H(27) listed by Lett (1915: 138).
†H27 listed by Blockeel & Long (1998: 121).
H28 1963: schistose rocks, *ca* 250 ft [alt.], Castleore, Slish Mt., RD Fitzgerald & AR Perry (Warburg 1964: 729).
1970: boulders, nr Owenaher R., SW of Cloonacool, J Appleyard (BBS exc.) (Crundwell 1971b: 380, Appleyard 1971: 389), as var. *viride*.
H(30) listed by Lett (1915: 138). H(30) listed by Blockeel & Long (1998: 121).
H(31) listed by Lett (1915: 138). H(31) listed by Blockeel & Long (1998: 121).
H33 1950: rock crevices on moor, nr Carricknagower Lake, Barr of Drumlead, J Taylor (Warburg 1952: 105).
H(34) listed by Lett (1915: 138).
H34 1968: floor of old quarry, Crockavishane, Inishowen, HH Birks and RD Fitzgerald (Crundwell 1969: 886), as var. *viride*.
H(35) listed by Lett (1915: 138).
H35 1963: schistose rocks, *ca* 20 ft [alt.], Silver Strand, Malin Beg, RD Fitzgerald & AR Perry (Warburg 1964: 729).
H36 1951: wet sandstone, edge of L. Lee, RD Fitzgerald (Warburg 1952: 105).
H(37) listed by Lett (1915: 138).
†H37 listed by Blockeel & Long (1998: 121).
H(38) listed by Lett (1915: 138).
H38 1950: rock in R. Bann, RD Fitzgerald (Warburg 1951: 501), as var. *viride*.
H(39) listed by Lett (1915: 138).
H(39) 1928: Fair Head (BBS exc.) (Duncan 1928: 113, 116), as var. *viride*.
†H39 listed by Blockeel & Long (1998: 121).
H(40) listed by Lett (1915: 138).
†H40 listed by Blockeel & Long (1998: 121).

98/1 ***Rhodobryum roseum*** (Hedw.) Limpr. (syn. *Bryum proliferum* Lindb. & Arn., *B. roseum* Hedw.)

[H(1) listed by Lett (1915: 139) without details. H1 deleted because no valid record or voucher specimen traced (Blockeel 1999: 7)].
H(2) listed by Lett (1915: 139).
†H2 listed by Blockeel & Long (1998: 121).
H(4) listed by Lett (1915: 139). H(4) listed by Blockeel & Long (1998: 121).
H(5) listed by Lett (1915: 139). H(5) listed by Blockeel & Long (1998: 121).
H6 1966: boulders by Owennashad River, N of Lismore, J Appleyard (BBS exc.) (Perry 1967: 417).
H8 1966: among turf on limestone rocks, nr Hospital, Knockainy, MFV Corley & JS Parker (Perry 1967: 417).
H(9) 1945: boulder in wood, Kilnaboy, nr Corofin, JS Thomson (anon.1946a: 261).
1945: Grove, Roughan House, Kilnaboy, JS Thomson (anon. 1946c: 284).
H(15) listed by Lett (1915: 139).
†H15 listed by Blockeel & Long (1998: 121).
H16 1973: soil in acid oakwood, Hill of Doon, L. Corrib, DL Kelly (Crundwell 1975: 18).
H(18) 1949: grassy bank, Comber Kinitty, AP Fanning (Warburg 1953: 314).
H(20) 1945: Glenmacnass, F Winder, per JS Thomson (anon. 1946c: 284).
H22 1966: W side of limestone outcrop, Caraguban, Duleek, DM Synnott (Perry 1967: 417).
H26 1953: mossy limestone rocks, shore of L. Carra, nr Clogher House, EC Wallace (Warburg 1954: 484).
H29 1968: *Corylus-Fraxinus* wood 1 mile NE of Roosky, WV Rubers *et al.* (U)

(Crundwell 1974: 172).

H31 1965: E of pier, Clogher Head, DM Synnott (Warburg 1966: 199).

H33 1959: grass above limestone boulders, Knockmore Cliffs, RD Fitzgerald (Warburg 1960: 779).

H(34) listed by Lett (1915: 139). H(34) listed by Blockeel & Long (1998: 121).

H35 1969: dunes nr Rinnalea Point, Inisfree Bay, JA Paton (Crundwell 1970: 206).

H36 1957: grass at foot of limestone rocks, Butterlope Glen, nr Plumbridge, RD Fitzgerald (Warburg 1958b: 484).

H(38) listed by Lett (1915: 139). H(38) listed by Blockeel & Long (1998: 121).

H(39) listed by Lett (1915: 139).

†H39 listed by Blockeel & Long (1998: 121).

H(40) listed by Lett (1915: 139).

†H40 listed by Blockeel & Long (1998: 121).

99/1 ***Mnium hornum*** Hedw.

H(1) listed by Lett (1915: 141) without details.

†H1 listed by Blockeel & Long (1998: 121).

H(2) listed by Lett (1915: 141) without details.

†H2 listed by Blockeel & Long (1998: 121).

H(3) listed by Lett (1915: 141) without details.

†H3 listed by Blockeel & Long (1998: 121).

H(4) listed by Lett (1915: 141) without details.

†H4 listed by Blockeel & Long (1998: 121).

†H5 listed by Blockeel & Long (1998: 121).

H(6) listed by Lett (1915: 141) without details.

†H6 listed by Blockeel & Long (1998: 121).

H(7) listed by Lett (1915: 141) without details.

†H7 listed by Blockeel & Long (1998: 121).

H(8) listed by Lett (1915: 141) without details.

†H8 listed by Blockeel & Long (1998: 121).

H(9) listed by Lett (1915: 141) without details.

†H9 listed by Blockeel & Long (1998: 121).

H(10) listed by Lett (1915: 141) without details.

†H10 listed by Blockeel & Long (1998: 121).

H(11) listed by Lett (1915: 141) without details.

†H11 listed by Blockeel & Long (1998: 121).

H(12) listed by Lett (1915: 141) without details.

†H12 listed by Blockeel & Long (1998: 121).

H(13) listed by Lett (1915: 141) without details.

†H13 listed by Blockeel & Long (1998: 121).

H(14) listed by Lett (1915: 141) without details.

†H14 listed by Blockeel & Long (1998: 121).

H(15) listed by Lett (1915: 141) without details.

†H15 listed by Blockeel & Long (1998: 121).

H(16) listed by Lett (1915: 141) without details.

†H16 listed by Blockeel & Long (1998: 121).

H(17) listed by Lett (1915: 141) without details.

†H17 listed by Blockeel & Long (1998: 121).

H(18) listed by Lett (1915: 141) without details.

†H18 listed by Blockeel & Long (1998: 121).

[H(19) listed by Lett (1915: 141) without details. H19 deleted because no valid record or voucher specimen traced (Blockeel 1999: 7)].

H(20) listed by Lett (1915: 141) without details.

†H20 listed by Blockeel & Long (1998: 121).

H(21) listed by Lett (1915: 141) without details.

†H21 listed by Blockeel & Long (1998: 121).

H22 1963: wood above R. Boyne, Staleen, Donore, DM Synnott, comm. ALK King (Warburg 1964: 730).

†H23 listed by Blockeel & Long (1998: 121).

H(24) listed by Lett (1915: 141) without details.

†H24 listed by Blockeel & Long (1998: 121).

H(25) listed by Lett (1915: 141) without details.

†H25 listed by Blockeel & Long (1998: 121).

H(26) listed by Lett (1915: 141) without details.

†H26 listed by Blockeel & Long (1998: 121).

H(27) listed by Lett (1915: 141) without details.

†H27 listed by Blockeel & Long (1998: 121).

H(28) listed by Lett (1915: 141) without details.

†H28 listed by Blockeel & Long (1998: 121).

H(29) listed by Lett (1915: 141) without details.

†H29 listed by Blockeel & Long (1998: 121).

†H30 listed by Blockeel & Long (1998: 121).

H(31) listed by Lett (1915: 141) without details.

†H31 listed by Blockeel & Long (1998: 121).

H(32) listed by Lett (1915: 141) without details.
†H32 listed by Blockeel & Long (1998: 121).
H(33) listed by Lett (1915: 141) without details.
†H33 listed by Blockeel & Long (1998: 121).
H(34) listed by Lett (1915: 141) without details.
†H34 listed by Blockeel & Long (1998: 121).
H(35) listed by Lett (1915: 141) without details.
†H35 listed by Blockeel & Long (1998: 121).
H(36) listed by Lett (1915: 141) without details.
†H36 listed by Blockeel & Long (1998: 121).
H(37) listed by Lett (1915: 141) without details.
†H37 listed by Blockeel & Long (1998: 121).
H(38) listed by Lett (1915: 141) without details.
†H38 listed by Blockeel & Long (1998: 121).
H(39) listed by Lett (1915: 141) without details.
†H39 listed by Blockeel & Long (1998: 121).
H(40) listed by Lett (1915: 141) without details.
†H40 listed by Blockeel & Long (1998: 121).

99/3 ***Mnium thomsonii*** Schimp.
(syn. *Mnium orthorhynchum* auct. non Brid.)

H9 1959: amongst limestone blocks on summit cairn of Slievecarran, SW of Kinvarra, MCF Proctor & RB Ivimey-Cook (Warburg 1963b: 499).
H16 1957: rocks above Glencorbet, 700 ft [alt.], Twelve Pins, AC Crundwell (BBS exc.) (Warburg 1958b: 484).
H(28) 1928: Gleniff, Ben Bulben (BBS exc.) (Duncan 1928: 114-115, 118).
†H28 listed by Blockeel & Long (1998: 121).
H(29) 1937: Truskmore, no collector named (BBS exc.) (Armitage 1938: 12).
†H29 listed by Blockeel & Long (1998: 121).
H33 1999: on ± base-rich ledge on N-facing sandstone escarpment, 290 m alt., Culcarrick Scarp, Lough Navar Forest, H05, RD Porley 2130, conf. NG Hodgetts (Rothero 2000: 55).
H35 2001: on N-facing crag just above lough, 250 m alt., Slieve League above Lough Agh, G57, NG Hodgetts 3812 (Rothero 2003: 58).

99/5a ***Mnium marginatum*** (Dicks.) P.Beauv. **var.** ***marginatum***
(syn. *Mnium riparium* Mitt., *M. serratum* Schrad. ex Brid.)

H(1) listed by Lett (1915: 141). H(1) listed by Blockeel & Long (1998: 121).
H6 1956: bank of R. Suir, under beeches, Knocklofty Bridge, EC Wallace (Warburg 1957: 334).
H16 1957: rocks above Glencorbet, 700 ft [alt.], Twelve Pins, AC Crundwell (BBS exc.) (Warburg 1958b: 484).
H(20) listed by Lett (1915: 141). H(20) listed by Blockeel & Long (1998: 121).
[H(26) listed by Lett (1915: 141)]
H(28) listed by Lett (1915: 141).
†H28 listed by Blockeel & Long (1998: 121).
H(29) 1937: Glenade, no collector named (BBS exc.) (Armitage 1938: 12).
†H29 listed by Blockeel & Long (1998: 121).
H(33) 1937: Belleek, no collector named (BBS exc.) (Armitage 1938: 12).
†H33 listed by Blockeel & Long (1998: 121).
H34 1962: rock crevice, E side of Bulbin [Mt.], EF Warburg (BBS exc.) (Warburg 1963b: 499).
H35 2001: in short turf on sandy bank above cliffs, 15 m alt., Maghera Strand nr caves, G69, NG Hodgetts 3834 (Rothero 2003: 58).
2002: on sand in low dunes, 15 m alt., Drumnatinny N of Falcarragh, B93, DT Holyoak 02-456 (Rothero 2003: 58).
[H(37) listed by Lett (1915: 141) without details].
H(39) listed by Lett (1915: 141).
†H39 listed by Blockeel & Long (1998: 121).
H(40) 1936: Gortin, JD Houston (anon. 1937a: 368).

The records listed above probably include those based on specimens demonstrated to be synoicous (var. *marginatum*) and material lacking gametangia that could not be determined as either variety.

[**99/5b** ***Mnium marginatum*** (Dicks.) P.Beauv. **var.** ***dioicum*** (H.Müll.) Crundw.]

[Listed for E Mayo, Armagh and Antrim by Smith (1978: 435), but not accepted for any Irish vice-county by MO Hill following revision of specimens for *CC* (Corley & Hill 1981: 102)].

99/6 ***Mnium stellare*** Hedw.

H(2) listed by Lett (1915: 142).
†H2 listed by Blockeel & Long (1998: 121).
H(6) listed by Lett (1915: 142).
†H6 listed by Blockeel & Long (1998: 121).
H9 1962: clay in mouth of cave above L. Inchiquin, ALK King (Warburg 1963b: 500).
H11 1973: cave mouth, Dunmore cave, DL Kelly (Crundwell 1974: 172).
H16 1994: humus on basic rock face under overhanging tree, 30 m alt., Derryclare Wood, L84, TL Blockeel 23/241 (Blockeel 1995c: 44).
H(20) listed by Lett (1915: 142). H(20) listed by Blockeel & Long (1998: 121).
H(21) 1938: Bohernabreena, JS Thomson (anon. 1939b: 110).
H23 1953: roadside bank nr NE end of L. Owel, JS Thomson (Warburg 1954: 484).
†H28 listed by Blockeel & Long (1998: 121).
H29 1959: growing through *Trichostomum brachydontium* in clefts of limestone rocks at Glenade, ALK King (Warburg 1964: 730).
1963: crevice of limestone, *ca* 900 ft [alt.], Boggaun, nr Manorhamilton, RD Fitzgerald & AR Perry (Warburg 1964: 730).
H30 2001: on ruined mortared wall, 305 m alt., W of Bellavally Gap, H12, DT Holyoak 01-630B (Rothero 2002: 52).
H(33) listed by Lett (1915: 142).
†H33 listed by Blockeel & Long (1998: 121).
H34 2002: in open damp grassland on flushed slope below dunes, 10 m alt., Doagh Isle NE of Ballyliffin, C45, DT Holyoak 02-486 (Rothero 2003: 58).
H(35) 1945: bank by road nr Loch Clooney, Naran, JS Thomson (anon. 1947: 32).
H(36) listed by Lett (1915: 142).
†H36 listed by Blockeel & Long (1998: 121).
H(39) listed by Lett (1915: 142).
†H39 listed by Blockeel & Long (1998: 121).
H40 1964: basalt, *ca* 1200 ft [alt.], Benbradagh, RD Fitzgerald & MPH Kertland (Warburg 1965: 868).

100/1 ***Cinclidium stygium*** Sw.

H23 1966: marsh nr Knockdrin [= Scraw Bog, nr Mullingar], ALK King (Perry 1967: 418, King 1967b).
H28 1963: fen at 800 ft [alt.], NE of Carrowkeel, Bricklieve Mts, AR Perry & RD Fitzgerald (Warburg 1964: 730).
H29 1965: calcareous flush *ca* 700 ft alt., hillside nr county boundary S of Glencar Lough, AR Perry & EF Warburg (Warburg 1966: 199).
H39 1999: in open area of wet calcareous flush, E of Crockravar, D21, DT Holyoak 99-779 (BBSUK) (Rothero 2000: 55).

101/1 ***Rhizomnium punctatum*** (Hedw.) T.J. Kop.
(syn. *Mnium punctatum* Hedw.)

H(1) listed by Lett (1915: 142) without details.
†H1 listed by Blockeel & Long (1998: 122).
H(2) listed by Lett (1915: 142) without details.
†H2 listed by Blockeel & Long (1998: 122).
H(3) listed by Lett (1915: 142) without details.
†H3 listed by Blockeel & Long (1998: 122).
H(4) listed by Lett (1915: 142) without details.
†H4 listed by Blockeel & Long (1998: 122).
H5 1956: old quarry, Youghal, EC Wallace (Warburg 1957: 334).
H(6) listed by Lett (1915: 142) without details.
†H6 listed by Blockeel & Long (1998: 122).
H(7) listed by Lett (1915: 142) without details.
†H7 listed by Blockeel & Long (1998: 122).
H(8) listed by Lett (1915: 142) without details.
†H8 listed by Blockeel & Long (1998: 122).
H(9) listed by Lett (1915: 142) without details.
†H9 listed by Blockeel & Long (1998: 122).
H10 1965: marsh by L. Nahinch, nr Borrisokane, ALK King (Perry 1967: 418).
H(11) listed by Lett (1915: 142) without

details.
†H11 listed by Blockeel & Long (1998: 122).
H(12) listed by Lett (1915: 142) without details.
†H12 listed by Blockeel & Long (1998: 122).
H(13) listed by Lett (1915: 142) without details.
†H13 listed by Blockeel & Long (1998: 122).
H(14) listed by Lett (1915: 142) without details.
†H14 listed by Blockeel & Long (1998: 122).
H(15) listed by Lett (1915: 142) without details.
†H15 listed by Blockeel & Long (1998: 122).
H(16) listed by Lett (1915: 142) without details.
†H16 listed by Blockeel & Long (1998: 122).
H17 1966: rotten log in wood by stream, Derreen, N of Monivea, MFV Corley & JS Parker (Perry 1967: 418).
H(18) listed by Lett (1915: 142) without details.
†H18 listed by Blockeel & Long (1998: 122).
H(20) listed by Lett (1915: 142) without details.
†H20 listed by Blockeel & Long (1998: 122).
H(21) listed by Lett (1915: 142) without details.
†H21 listed by Blockeel & Long (1998: 122).
[H(22) listed by Lett (1915: 142) without details. H22 deleted because record not traced (Synnott 1982, Hill 1983: 54)].
H23 1957: marshy ground, nr Ballinafid, JS Thomson (Warburg 1958b: 484).
H(24) 1941: Ardnacliff, JG Finlay (Duncan 1944: 213).
†H23 listed by Blockeel & Long (1998: 122).
H(25) 1940: nr Lough Key, JS Thomson (Duncan 1944: 213).
†H25 listed by Blockeel & Long (1998: 122).
H(26) listed by Lett (1915: 142) without details.
†H26 listed by Blockeel & Long (1998: 122).
H(27) listed by Lett (1915: 142) without details.
†H27 listed by Blockeel & Long (1998: 122).
H(28) listed by Lett (1915: 142) without details.
†H28 listed by Blockeel & Long (1998: 122).
H(29) listed by Lett (1915: 142) without details.
†H29 listed by Blockeel & Long (1998: 122).
H(30) listed by Lett (1915: 142) without details.
†H30 listed by Blockeel & Long (1998: 122).
[H(31) listed by Lett (1915: 142) without details. H31 deleted because no valid record or voucher specimen traced (Blockeel 1999: 7)].
H(32) listed by Lett (1915: 142) without details.
†H32 listed by Blockeel & Long (1998: 122).
H(33) listed by Lett (1915: 142) without details.
†H33 listed by Blockeel & Long (1998: 122).
H(34) listed by Lett (1915: 142) without details.
†H34 listed by Blockeel & Long (1998: 122).
H(35) listed by Lett (1915: 142) without details.
†H35 listed by Blockeel & Long (1998: 122).
H(36) listed by Lett (1915: 142) without details.
†H36 listed by Blockeel & Long (1998: 122).
H37 1964: flush at *ca* 700 ft [alt.], below tower, Slieve Gullion, RD Fitzgerald (Warburg 1965: 868).
H(38) listed by Lett (1915: 142) without details.
†H38 listed by Blockeel & Long (1998: 122).
H(39) listed by Lett (1915: 142) without details.
†H39 listed by Blockeel & Long (1998: 122).
H(40) listed by Lett (1915: 142) without details.
†H40 listed by Blockeel & Long (1998: 122).

101/3 ***Rhizomnium pseudopunctatum*** (Bruch & Schimp.) T.J.Kop.
(syn. *Mnium pseudopunctatum* Bruch & Schimp.)

H(2) listed by Lett (1915: 142). H(2) listed by Blockeel & Long (1998: 122).
H(6) listed by Lett (1915: 142).
†H6 listed by Blockeel & Long (1998: 122).
H(12) listed by Lett (1915: 142). H(12) listed by Blockeel & Long (1998: 122).
H13 1975: fen SW of Yellowford Cross Roads, S of Baltinglass, JA Paton (BBS exc.) (Crundwell 1976: 29).
H16 1988: iron-rich flush, Bunscannive, Connemara, N Lockhart (Blockeel 1989: 30).
H19 1998: on margin of calcareous, spring-fed fen with *Calliergonella cuspidata, Drepanocladus cossonii* and *Tomentypnum nitens*, 100 m alt., Pollardstown Fen, N71, N Lockhart (Rothero 2001: 44).

H(21) listed by Lett (1915: 142). H(21) listed by Blockeel & Long (1998: 122).
H22 1971: fen-bog transition, site of L. Frehaun, ½ mile S of L. Shesk, Clonmellon, DM Synnott (Crundwell 1974: 172).
H(27) listed by Lett (1915: 142).
†H27 listed by Blockeel & Long (1998: 122).
H28 1963: fen at 800 ft [alt.], NE of Carrowkeel, Bricklieve Mts, AR Perry & RD Fitzgerald (Warburg 1964: 730).
H29 2000: in moss carpet in open calcareous flush with *Equisetum palustre*, S of Glencar Lough, G74, DT Holyoak 00-636 (BBSUK) (Rothero 2001: 44).
H30 1970: flush below crags, below Englishman's House, Glenfarne, nr Belcoo, J Appleyard (BBS exc.) (Crundwell 1971b: 381, Appleyard 1971: 389-390).
H(31) listed by Lett (1915: 142). H(31) listed by Blockeel & Long (1998: 122).
H(32) listed by Lett (1915: 142). H(32) listed by Blockeel & Long (1998: 122).
H33 1957: *Schoenus* flush, L. Navar Forest, RE Parker (Warburg 1958b: 484).
H35 2001: in poor fen at margin of lough, 180 m alt., Croleavy Lough, Teelin, G57, NG Hodgetts 3763 (Rothero 2002: 52).
H(36) listed by Lett (1915: 142).
†H36 listed by Blockeel & Long (1998: 122).
H(37) listed by Lett (1915: 142). H(37) listed by Blockeel & Long (1998: 122).
H(38) listed by Lett (1915: 142). H(38) listed by Blockeel & Long (1998: 122).
H(39) listed by Lett (1915: 142). H(39) listed by Blockeel & Long (1998: 122).
H39 1999: in wet area of calcareous flush on moorland, E of Crockravar, D21, DT Holyoak 99-779A (Rothero 2000: 55).
H(40) listed by Blockeel & Long (1998: 122).

102/1 ***Plagiomnium cuspidatum*** (Hedw.) T.J. Kop.
(syn. *Mnium cuspidatum* Hedw., *M. silvaticum* auct., *M. sylvaticum* Lindb. nom. illeg.)

H1 1951: roadside between station and the sea, Glenbeigh, JS Thomson (BBS exc.) (Warburg 1952: 105).
H(2) listed by Lett (1915: 141).
†H2 listed by Blockeel & Long (1998: 122).
H(7) 1944: below Loch Diheen, AW Stelfox (per JS Thomson) (anon. 1947: 32).
[H(9) listed by Lett (1915: 141) without details. H9 deleted because no valid record or voucher specimen traced (Blockeel 1999: 7)].
[H11 deleted because record appears to be error in transcription by Duncan 1926 resulting from confusion of *M. cuspidatum* Hedw. and *M. cuspidatum* (L.) Neck. (= *M. affine*) (Warburg 1958b: 484)].
H(12) listed by Lett (1915: 141). H(12) listed by Blockeel & Long (1998: 122).
[H(13) listed by Lett (1915: 141) without details. H13 deleted because no valid record or voucher specimen traced (Blockeel 1999: 7)].
[H14 deleted because record appears to be error in transcription by Duncan 1926 resulting from confusion of *M. cuspidatum* Hedw. and *M. cuspidatum* (L.) Neck. (= *M. affine*) (Warburg 1958b: 484)].
H(15) listed by Lett (1915: 141). H(15) listed by Blockeel & Long (1998: 122).
H16 1957: short turf on calcareous sand, Dog's Bay, RE Parker (BBS exc.) (Warburg 1958b: 484).
H17 1957: grass turf on calcareous soil, Ballindooly Castle, RE Parker (Warburg 1958b: 484).
H(20) listed by Blockeel & Long (1998: 122).
H21 1950: sand dunes, Corballis, Donabate, JP Brunker (Warburg 1951: 502).
[H(23) listed by Lett (1915: 141). H23 deleted because record not traced (Synnott 1982, Hill 1983: 54)].
H24 1968: wood at shore of L. Forbes, W of Castle Forbes, WV Rubers *et al.* (U) (Crundwell 1974: 172).
[H25 deleted because record appears to be error in transcription by Duncan 1926 resulting from confusion of *M. cuspidatum* Hedw. and *M. cuspidatum* (L.) Neck. (= *M. affine*) (Warburg 1958b: 484)].
H25 2002: at base of *Juncus* tussock in muddy pasture, 35 m alt., Cullagh, Lough Ree, W of Lanesborough, M98, NG Hodgetts 4086 (Rothero 2003: 58).
H(26) listed by Lett (1915: 141). H(26) listed by Blockeel & Long (1998: 122).
H27 1962: grey dunes nr Caraun Point, Achill I., EF Warburg (Warburg 1963b: 500).
H(28) 1912: sandhills by the sea,

Mullaghmore, WN Tetley (anon. 1913b: 11).

H(28) listed by Lett (1915: 141). H(28) listed by Blockeel & Long (1998: 122).

H29 1969: boulder on shore of L. Gill, nr old castle NW of Sriff Cottag (*sic* = Cottage), JA Paton (Crundwell 1970: 206).

H(30) 1937: Lough Ramor, JS Thomson (anon. 1939b: 110).

H(32) 1947: shore of Lough Muckno, Castleblaney, JS Thomson (anon. 1948b: 122).

H35 1969: cliff top S of Ards House, Ballymore, JA Paton (Crundwell 1970: 206).

H36 1957: turf at limestone quarry, Carrickaness Bridge, RD Fitzgerald (Warburg 1958b: 484).

H(38) 1898: Sandhills, Ballykinler, CH Waddell, conf. HN Dixon (anon. 1899: 17, Lett 1915: 141).

H(39) listed by Blockeel & Long (1998: 122).

H(40) listed by Lett (1915: 141) without details

†H40 listed by Blockeel & Long (1998: 122).

102/2 *Plagiomnium affine* (Blandow) T.J. Kop.
(syn. *Mnium affine* Blandow, *M. cuspidatum* (L.) Neck.)

H3 1986: on grazed wall, 200 m N of the 'Jolly Roger' pub on road to N end of island, Sherkin I., W02, JR Akeroyd, CJ Hora & SL Jury 7908 (Blockeel 1990: 32).

[H9 deleted because record appears to be error in transcription by Duncan 1926 resulting from confusion of *M. cuspidatum* Hedw. and *M. cuspidatum* (L.) Neck. (= *M. affine*) (Warburg 1958b: 484)].

[H12 deleted because record appears to be error in transcription by Duncan 1926 resulting from confusion of *M. cuspidatum* Hedw. and *M. cuspidatum* (L.) Neck. (= *M. affine*) (Warburg 1958b: 484)].

H12 1969: in grass beside road, Killinierin, nr Inch, RD Fitzgerald (Crundwell 1970: 206). Listed following revision of specimens (Koponen 1971, Crundwell 1973: 512).

H14 1957: peaty ground by R. Erkina, Durrow, AA Cridland (Warburg 1958b: 484). H14 listed following revision of specimens (Koponen 1971, Crundwell 1973: 512).

H15 1994: in *Lolium perenne* field, Cappaghmore, 5 km NW of Kinvarra, M30, PE Stanley, RC Stern & HLK Whitehouse (Blockeel 1995c: 44).

H17 1966: stone in wood, Derreen, N of Monivea, MFV Corley & JS Parker (Perry 1967: 417). H17 listed following revision of specimens (Koponen 1971, Crundwell 1973: 512).

H20 1964: bog, Ballybetagh, just inside Wicklow border, ALK King (Warburg 1966: 199). H20 listed following revision of specimens (Koponen 1971, Crundwell 1973: 512).

[H(25) 1940: nr Boyle, JS Thomson (Duncan 1944: 213). H25 not listed (Koponen 1971, Crundwell 1973: 512), although it is unclear whether a specimen was revised].

H25 1981: with *Littorella*, shore of L. Ree, John's Wood, DM Synnott (Hill 1982: 28).

H33 2000: on soil at base of *Phragmites* and *Salix* on lough margin, Kilturk Lough, S shore, H32, DT Holyoak 00-163 (BBSUK) (Rothero 2001: 44).

H35 2001: in short turf in dune heath, 15 m alt., Maghera Strand, dune heath peninsula, G69, NG Hodgetts 3826 (Rothero 2003: 58).

H36 listed following revision of specimens (Koponen 1971, Crundwell 1973: 512). †H36 listed by Blockeel & Long (1998: 122).

H(38) listed following revision of specimens (Koponen 1971, Crundwell 1973: 512). H(38) listed by Blockeel & Long (1998: 122).

Old records of '*Mnium cuspidatum*' (L.) Neck. (e.g. in Lett 1915: 141-142) can be safely assigned to *M. affine* only if voucher specimens have been reidentified.

102/4 ***Plagiomnium elatum*** (Bruch & Schimp.) T.J.Kop.
(syn. *Mnium affine* var. *elatum* Bruch & Schimp., *M. cuspidatum* var. *elatum* (Bruch & Schimp.) Lindb., *M. seligeri* Jur. ex Lindb.)

H2 1967: flush, *ca* 900 ft [alt.], The Paps, RD Fitzgerald (Crundwell 1968: 641).
H5 1956: margin of lake, nr Churchtown, nr Midleton, EC Wallace (Warburg 1957: 334).
H8 1966: turf on hummocks at edge of lake, S side of L. Gur, MFV Corley & JS Parker (Perry 1967: 418).
H9 1959: wet rushy meadow by road E of Kilfenora, MCF Proctor & RB Ivimey-Cook (Warburg 1963b: 500).
H10 1965: marsh at Carrig, Birr, DM Synnott (Warburg 1966: 199).
H11 1985: wooded island in R. Suir, Fiddown, DL Kelly (Hill 1986: 22).
H13 1975: bog nr road, Yellowford Cross Roads, N of Rathvilly, AR Perry (Hill 1977a: 22).
H14 1965: marsh, Derry Hills, Clonaslee, ALK King & DM Synnott (Warburg 1966: 199).
H15 1994: basic flush, nr Pollboy, Boleyneendorish River, Slieve Aughty, M50, RC Stern (Blockeel 1995c: 44).
H16 1968: amongst *Phragmites* in swamp by vice-county boundary one mile NE of Clonbur, AR Perry (Crundwell 1970: 206).
H17 1966: turf on rocks at edge of river, Derreen, N of Monivea MVF Corley & JS Parker (Perry 1967: 418).
H18 1984: fen beside Fin Lough, nr Clonmacnoise, V Power (Hill 1986: 22).
H19 1961: Morristown fen, nr Newbridge, ALK King (Warburg 1962: 373).
H(21) 1937: marshy ground at Bohernabreena, JS Thomson, comm. ALK King (Warburg 1965: 868).
H22 1965: wet channel, Commons, Duleek, DM Synnott (Warburg 1966: 199).
[H23 deleted because record not traced (Synnott 1982, Hill 1983: 54)].
H24 1966: marsh on E shore of L. Ree, ALK King (Perry 1967: 418).
H25 1940: side of stream, Rockingham demesne, Boyle, JS Thomson, comm. ALK King (Warburg 1966: 199).
H26 1960: marsh by lane behind Downhill, Ballina, ALK King (Warburg 1962: 171).
H27 1960: marsh by N end of Termoncanagh Lake, The Mullet, ALK King (Warburg 1962: 171).
H(28) 1937: Ben Bulben, no collector named (BBS exc.) (Armitage 1938: 12).
†H28 listed by Blockeel & Long (1998: 122).
H29 1963: calcareous flush in field below limestone scarp, Boggaun, nr Manorhamilton, AR Perry & RD Fitzgerald (Warburg 1964: 730).
H30 1965: marsh, Carricknacrannoge, EM Lobley & RD Fitzgerald (Warburg 1966: 199).
[H(32) listed by Lett (1915: 141)].
H32 1980: tufts in calcareous marsh, L. Duff, N Lockhart (Hill 1983: 54).
H(33) listed by Lett (1915: 142).
†H33 listed by Blockeel & Long (1998: 122).
H34 2001: in fen with *Juncus articulatus* and *Carex* spp., 25 m alt., nr Lough Naharash, Ballyshannon Turloughs, G86, NG Hodgetts 3734 (Rothero 2002: 52).
H(35) listed by Lett (1915: 142).
†H35 listed by Blockeel & Long (1998: 122).
H36 1957: bog, Glengeen Lodge, RD Fitzgerald (Warburg 1959: 636).
H39 1990: flushed slope, Loughnatrose, Garron Plateau above Carnlough, DM Synnott (Blockeel 1991c: 44).
H40 1999: in short turf of dune slack with other bryophytes at edge of course, Benone, E of golf course, C73, DT Holyoak 99-80 (BBSUK) (Rothero 2000: 55).

102/5 ***Plagiomnium ellipticum*** (Brid.) T.J. Kop.
(syn. *Mnium rugicum* Laurer)

H6 1964: sand-dunes at Bunmahon, ALK King (Warburg 1965: 868).
H7 1966: in flush, *ca* 1000 ft [alt.], Knockastakeen, Galtee Mts, RD Fitzgerald (BBS exc.) (Crundwell 1968: 641).
H8 1966: marshy ground by L. Gur, ERB Little (BBS exc.) (Perry 1967: 417).
H9 1959: bottom of small turlough SW of Mullagh More, nr Corofin, MCF Proctor & RB Ivimey-Cook (Warburg 1962: 171).
H10 1979: marsh on shore of L. Derg, S of

Terryglass, EW Jones (Hill 1980b: 43).
H15 1957: damp soil in pasture liable to flood, Garryland Wood, nr Gort, J Appleyard & AC Crundwell (BBS exc.) (Warburg 1958b: 484).
H16 1970: marsh on edge of lough by Bunowen Castle, Ballyconneely, MFV Corley (Crundwell 1971b: 380).
H17 1957: wet grass turf of marshy meadow, nr Ballindooly Castle, RE Parker (Warburg 1958b: 484).
H19 1967: Newbridge Fen, ALK King (Crundwell 1968: 641).
H22 1978: marshy edge of bog, NW of Petersville Cross Roads, N of Moynalty, DM Synnott (Hill 1979: 30).
H23 1953: Scraw Bog, nr Portnashangan, JS Thomson (Warburg 1956: 156).
H25 2002: below carr and tall herbs at lough edge, 35 m alt., St John's Wood, Lough Ree, M95, NG Hodgetts 4060 (Rothero 2003: 58).
H27 1960: marsh by N end of Termoncarragh Lake, The Mullet, ALK King (Warburg 1962: 171).
H28 1970: marshy ground, W valley, Bricklieve Mts, J Appleyard (BBS exc.) (Crundwell 1971b: 380, Appleyard 1971: 389).
H29 1963: calcareous flush in field below limestone scarp, Boggaun, nr Manorhamilton, AR Perry & RD Fitzgerald (Warburg 1964: 730).
H30 1970: flush below crags, below Englishman's House, Glenfarne, nr Belcoo, J Appleyard (BBS exc.) (Crundwell 1971b: 380, Appleyard 1971: 389-390).
H33 1956: moorland flush, hills N of Belcoo, RE Parker (Warburg 1957: 334).
H35 1962: *Phragmites* fen by Mullaghderg Lough, The Rosses, EF Warburg *et al.* (BBS exc.) (Warburg 1963b: 500).
H37 1970: swamp S of Portadown, MFV Corley & JS Faulkner (Crundwell 1971b: 380).
H38 1956: fen carr at N side of L. Aghery between Ballynahinch and Dromore, BS Gunning & JS Pate, det. & comm. RE Parker (Warburg 1957: 334).
H39 1956: moorland flush, N side of Crockaneel, Ballypatrick Forest, RE Parker (Warburg 1957: 334).
H40 1956: fen carr, Downhill, BS Gunning & JS Pate, det. & comm. RE Parker (Warburg 1957: 334).

102/6 *Plagiomnium undulatum* (Hedw.) T.J. Kop.
(syn. *Mnium undulatum* Hedw.)

H(1) listed by Lett (1915: 142) without details.
†H1 listed by Blockeel & Long (1998: 123).
H(2) listed by Lett (1915: 142) without details.
†H2 listed by Blockeel & Long (1998: 123).
H3 1953: island in Gougane Barra Lake, ALK King (Warburg 1954: 484).
H(4) listed by Lett (1915: 142) without details.
†H4 listed by Blockeel & Long (1998: 123).
H(5) listed by Lett (1915: 142) without details.
†H5 listed by Blockeel & Long (1998: 123).
H(6) listed by Lett (1915: 142) without details.
†H6 listed by Blockeel & Long (1998: 123).
†H7 listed by Blockeel & Long (1998: 123).
H(8) listed by Lett (1915: 142) without details.
†H8 listed by Blockeel & Long (1998: 123).
H(9) listed by Lett (1915: 142) without details.
†H9 listed by Blockeel & Long (1998: 123).
H(10) listed by Lett (1915: 142) without details.
†H10 listed by Blockeel & Long (1998: 123).
H(11) listed by Lett (1915: 142) without details.
†H11 listed by Blockeel & Long (1998: 123).
H(12) listed by Lett (1915: 142) without details.
†H12 listed by Blockeel & Long (1998: 123).
H(13) listed by Lett (1915: 142) without details.
†H13 listed by Blockeel & Long (1998: 123).
H(14) listed by Lett (1915: 142) without details.
†H14 listed by Blockeel & Long (1998: 123).
H(15) listed by Lett (1915: 142) without details.
†H15 listed by Blockeel & Long (1998: 123).
H(16) listed by Lett (1915: 142) without details.
†H16 listed by Blockeel & Long (1998: 123).
H17 1957: at junction of grass turf and limestone wall, Ballindooly Castle, RE Parker (Warburg 1958b: 484).
H(18) listed by Lett (1915: 142) without

details.
†H18 listed by Blockeel & Long (1998: 123).
H(19) listed by Lett (1915: 142) without details.
†H19 listed by Blockeel & Long (1998: 123).
H(20) listed by Lett (1915: 142) without details.
†H20 listed by Blockeel & Long (1998: 123).
H(21) listed by Lett (1915: 142) without details.
†H21 listed by Blockeel & Long (1998: 123).
H(22) listed by Lett (1915: 142) without details.
†H22 listed by Blockeel & Long (1998: 123).
H(23) listed by Lett (1915: 142) without details.
†H23 listed by Blockeel & Long (1998: 123).
H(24) listed by Lett (1915: 142) without details.
†H24 listed by Blockeel & Long (1998: 123).
H(25) listed by Lett (1915: 142) without details.
†H25 listed by Blockeel & Long (1998: 123).
H(26) 1945: Cong, W Mayo [*sic*], ML Anderson, per JS Thomson (anon. 1946c: 284).
†H26 listed by Blockeel & Long (1998: 123).
H(27) listed by Lett (1915: 142) without details.
†H27 listed by Blockeel & Long (1998: 123).
H(28) listed by Lett (1915: 142) without details.
†H28 listed by Blockeel & Long (1998: 123).
H(29) listed by Lett (1915: 142) without details.
†H29 listed by Blockeel & Long (1998: 123).
H(30) listed by Lett (1915: 142) without details.
†H30 listed by Blockeel & Long (1998: 123).
H(31) listed by Lett (1915: 142) without details.
†H31 listed by Blockeel & Long (1998: 123).
H(32) listed by Lett (1915: 142) without details.
†H32 listed by Blockeel & Long (1998: 123).
H(33) listed by Lett (1915: 142) without details.
†H33 listed by Blockeel & Long (1998: 123).
H(34) listed by Lett (1915: 142) without details.
†H34 listed by Blockeel & Long (1998: 123).
H(35) listed by Lett (1915: 142) without details.
†H35 listed by Blockeel & Long (1998: 123).
H(36) listed by Lett (1915: 142) without details.
†H36 listed by Blockeel & Long (1998: 123).
H(37) listed by Lett (1915: 142) without details.
†H37 listed by Blockeel & Long (1998: 123).
H(38) listed by Lett (1915: 142) without details.
†H38 listed by Blockeel & Long (1998: 123).
H(39) listed by Lett (1915: 142) without details.
†H39 listed by Blockeel & Long (1998: 123).
H(40) listed by Lett (1915: 142) without details.
†H40 listed by Blockeel & Long (1998: 123).

102/7 ***Plagiomnium rostratum*** (Schrad.) T.J. Kop.
(syn. *Mnium longirostrum* Brid., *M. rostratum* Schrad.)

H1 1951: rock cleft, *ca* 1700 ft [alt.], Coomagrossaun, nr Glenbeigh, RD Fitzgerald (BBS exc.) (Warburg 1952: 105).
H(2) listed by Lett (1915: 142).
†H2 listed by Blockeel & Long (1998: 123).
H(3) listed by Lett (1915: 142).
†H3 listed by Blockeel & Long (1998: 123).
H(4) listed by Lett (1915: 142).
†H4 listed by Blockeel & Long (1998: 123).
H(5) listed by Lett (1915: 142).
†H5 listed by Blockeel & Long (1998: 123).
H6 1964: earth-topped wall by R. Glendine, ALK King (Warburg 1965: 868).
H7 1966: rocks above L. Curra, Galtee Mts, JA Paton (BBS exc.) (Perry 1967: 417).
H8 1966: turf on top of limestone rocks, S end of L. Gur, MFV Corley & JS Parker (Perry 1967: 417).
H9 1983: wall by Shannon estuary, just below Limerick bridge, SL Jury *et al.* (Hill 1986: 22).
H10 1951: clayey bank of ditch, Silvermines, AD Banwell, PJ Wanstall & EV Watson (Warburg 1953: 314).
H(11) listed by Lett (1915: 142).
†H11 listed by Blockeel & Long (1998: 123).
H(13) listed by Lett (1915: 142).
†H13 listed by Blockeel & Long (1998: 123).
H14 1952: roadside bank, Lacca crossroads, ALK King (Warburg 1953: 314).
H16 1968: shaded crevice in damp N-facing calcareous rock outcrop at 1600 ft [alt.], Muckanaght, Twelve Pins, AR Perry (Crundwell 1970: 206).

H17 1966: damp limestone wall by road, Ryehill, N of Monivea, MFV Corley & JS Parker (Perry 1967: 417).
H18 1954: path in wood, Gloster House, Brosna, ALK King (Warburg 1955: 586).
H(19) 1938: Rye Water, JS Thomson (anon. 1939b: 110).
H(20) listed by Lett (1915: 142).
†H20 listed by Blockeel & Long (1998: 123).
H(21) listed by Lett (1915: 142).
†H21 listed by Blockeel & Long (1998: 123).
H22 1956: grassy patch on Rossan Bog, nr Kinnegad, ALK King (Warburg 1957: 334).
H23 1952: Clonhugh Wood, NE end of L. Owel, JS Thomson (Warburg 1953: 314).
H24 1972: on sheltered limestone boulder, Rathcline House, S of Lanesborough, WV Rubers (U) (Crundwell 1974: 172).
H(25) 1940: nr Boyle, JS Thomson (Duncan 1944: 213).
†H25 listed by Blockeel & Long (1998: 123).
H(26) listed by Lett (1915: 142).
†H26 listed by Blockeel & Long (1998: 123).
H27 1987: stone beside path on edge of wood, nr Rose Cottage, NW of Westport, JA Paton (Blockeel 1988: 38).
†H28 listed by Blockeel & Long (1998: 123).
H(29) listed by Lett (1915: 142).
†H29 listed by Blockeel & Long (1998: 123).
H(30) listed by Lett (1915: 142).
†H30 listed by Blockeel & Long (1998: 123).
H31 1952: rock by stream, Little Ash, nr Dundalk, RD Fitzgerald (Warburg 1953: 314).
H(32) listed by Lett (1915: 142).
†H32 listed by Blockeel & Long (1998: 123).
H(33) listed by Lett (1915: 142).
†H33 listed by Blockeel & Long (1998: 123).
H(34) listed by Lett (1915: 142).
†H34 listed by Blockeel & Long (1998: 123).
H(35) listed by Lett (1915: 142).
†H35 listed by Blockeel & Long (1998: 123).
H(36) listed by Lett (1915: 142).
†H36 listed by Blockeel & Long (1998: 123).
H(37) listed by Lett (1915: 142).
†H37 listed by Blockeel & Long (1998: 123).
H(38) listed by Lett (1915: 142). H(38) listed by Blockeel & Long (1998: 123).
H(39) listed by Lett (1915: 142).
†H39 listed by Blockeel & Long (1998: 123).
H(40) listed by Lett (1915: 142).
†H40 listed by Blockeel & Long (1998: 123).

104/1 ***Aulacomnium palustre*** (Hedw.) Schwägr.
(syn. *Gymnocybe palustris* (Hedw.) Fries)

H(1) listed by Lett (1915: 141) without details.
†H1 listed by Blockeel & Long (1998: 123).
H(2) listed by Lett (1915: 141) without details.
†H2 listed by Blockeel & Long (1998: 123).
†H3 listed by Blockeel & Long (1998: 123).
H(4) listed by Lett (1915: 141) without details.
†H4 listed by Blockeel & Long (1998: 123).
H(5) listed by Lett (1915: 141) without details.
†H5 listed by Blockeel & Long (1998: 123).
H(6) listed by Lett (1915: 141) without details.
†H6 listed by Blockeel & Long (1998: 123).
H7 1966: among *Sphagnum* in bog between Seefin and Knockeenatoung, Galtee Mts, EM Lobley & RJ Murphy (BBS exc.) (Perry 1967: 418).
H(8) listed by Lett (1915: 141) without details.
†H8 listed by Blockeel & Long (1998: 123).
H(9) listed by Lett (1915: 141) without details.
†H9 listed by Blockeel & Long (1998: 123).
[H(10) listed by Lett (1915: 141) without details. H10 deleted because no valid record or voucher specimen traced (Blockeel 1999: 7)].
H(11) listed by Lett (1915: 141) without details.
†H11 listed by Blockeel & Long (1998: 123).
H(12) listed by Lett (1915: 141) without details.
†H12 listed by Blockeel & Long (1998: 123).
H(13) listed by Lett (1915: 141) without details.
†H13 listed by Blockeel & Long (1998: 123).
H(14) listed by Lett (1915: 141) without details.
†H14 listed by Blockeel & Long (1998: 123).
H15 1957: blanket bog, hills E of Gort, RE Parker (Warburg 1958b: 481).
H(16) listed by Lett (1915: 141) without details.
†H16 listed by Blockeel & Long (1998: 123).
H(17) listed by Lett (1915: 141) without details.
†H17 listed by Blockeel & Long (1998: 123).

H(18) listed by Lett (1915: 141) without details.
†H18 listed by Blockeel & Long (1998: 123).
[H(19) listed by Lett (1915: 141) without details. H19 deleted because no valid record or voucher specimen traced (Blockeel 1999: 7)].
H(20) listed by Lett (1915: 141) without details.
†H20 listed by Blockeel & Long (1998: 123).
[H(21) listed by Lett (1915: 141) without details. H21 deleted because no valid record or voucher specimen traced (Blockeel 1999: 7)].
H22 1952: Clonycavan Bog, nr Ballivor, ALK King (Warburg 1953: 312).
H(23) 1946: Scraw Bog, Portnashangan, Mullingar, KC Harris (anon. 1947: 32).
†H23 listed by Blockeel & Long (1998: 123).
H(24) listed by Lett (1915: 141) without details.
†H24 listed by Blockeel & Long (1998: 123).
H(25) listed by Lett (1915: 141) without details.
†H25 listed by Blockeel & Long (1998: 123).
H(26) listed by Lett (1915: 141) without details.
†H26 listed by Blockeel & Long (1998: 123).
H(27) listed by Lett (1915: 141) without details.
†H27 listed by Blockeel & Long (1998: 123).
H(28) listed by Lett (1915: 141) without details.
†H28 listed by Blockeel & Long (1998: 123).
H(29) listed by Lett (1915: 141) without details.
†H29 listed by Blockeel & Long (1998: 123).
H(30) listed by Lett (1915: 141) without details.
†H30 listed by Blockeel & Long (1998: 123).
H(31) listed by Lett (1915: 141) without details.
†H31 listed by Blockeel & Long (1998: 123).
H(32) listed by Lett (1915: 141) without details.
†H32 listed by Blockeel & Long (1998: 123).
H(33) listed by Lett (1915: 141) without details.
†H33 listed by Blockeel & Long (1998: 123).
H(34) listed by Lett (1915: 141) without details.
†H34 listed by Blockeel & Long (1998: 123).
H(35) listed by Lett (1915: 141) without details.
†H35 listed by Blockeel & Long (1998: 123).
H(36) listed by Lett (1915: 141) without details.
†H36 listed by Blockeel & Long (1998: 123).
H(37) listed by Lett (1915: 141) without details.
†H37 listed by Blockeel & Long (1998: 123).
H(38) listed by Lett (1915: 141) without details.
†H38 listed by Blockeel & Long (1998: 123).
H(39) listed by Lett (1915: 141) without details.
†H39 listed by Blockeel & Long (1998: 123).
†H40 listed by Blockeel & Long (1998: 123).

104/3 ***Aulacomnium androgynum*** (Hedw.) Schwägr.
(syn. *Orthopyxis androgyna* (Hedw.) P. Beauv.)

H(18) listed by Lett (1915: 141) without details. H(18) listed by Blockeel & Long (1998: 123).
H(20) listed by Lett (1915: 141) without details. H(20) listed by Blockeel & Long (1998: 123).
†H30 listed by Blockeel & Long (1998: 123).
H31 1978: old peat bank with *Mnium hornum*, Ardee Bog, DM Synnott (Hill 1979: 31).
H33 1960: thin humus on boulder and in crevices of cliff, *ca* 700 ft [alt.], scarp N of Lough Navar, RD Fitzgerald (Warburg 1961: 168).
H(37) listed by Lett (1915: 141) without details. H(37) listed by Blockeel & Long (1998: 123).
H(38) listed by Lett (1915: 141) without details. H(38) listed by Blockeel & Long (1998: 123).
H(39) listed by Lett (1915: 141) without details. H(39) listed by Blockeel & Long (1998: 123).
H(40) listed by Lett (1915: 141) without details. H(40) listed by Blockeel & Long (1998: 123).

[- ***Calomnion complanatum*** (Hook.f. & Wils.) Lindb.]

[- ***Leptotheca gaudichaudii*** Schwaegr.]

[These two alien species were found at a single locality in Co. Kerry in 2000 by AR Perry and PE Stanley, established on the trunks of cultivated tree ferns. They were almost certainly introduced to Ireland from Australasia with the ferns (Fox, Blockeel & Perry 2001: 5, AR Perry pers. comm.)].

105/1 ***Paludella squarrosa*** (Hedw.) Brid.

H27 1998: scattered amongst *Homalothecium nitens, Aulacomnium palustre* and *Sphagnum* spp. with *Leiocolea rutheana* in quaking lawn beside pool system in rich fen, 70 m alt., Bellacorick Bog, G02, N Lockhart (Lockhart 1999, Rothero 1999b: 44).

P. squarrosa is also known as a Littletonian (Postglacial) fossil in Co. Kildare (Barry & Synnott 1970).

106/1 ***Meesia uliginosa*** Hedw.

H35 2002: on damp humic sand in dune slack, 5 m alt., SE of Rosepenna, C13, DT Holyoak 02-597 (BBSUK) (Rothero 2003: 58).

106/2 ***Meesia triquetra*** (Richter) Ångstr. (syn. *Meesia tristicha* Bruch & Schimp.)

H27 1957: iron flush in T.A.E. Bog stretching N of the road between Dooleeg and Bellacorrick, ALK King, conf. EF Warburg (King 1958b, Warburg 1958a, King & Scannell 1960). The habitat of this population was drained in the 1950s and despite repeated searches the population has not been re-found and the species is now thought to be extinct in Ireland (N Lockhart, pers. comm.).

M. triquetra is also known as a Littletonian (Postglacial) fossil in Co. Kildare (Barry & Synnott 1970).

[106/- ***Meesia longiseta*** Hedw.]

[Reported as a Littletonian (i.e. Postglacial) fossil from Littleton bog, Co. Tipperary by Barry & Synnott (1973)].

107/1 ***Amblyodon dealbatus*** (Hedw.) Bruch & Schimp.

H1 1953: wet clefts, cliffs S of L. Slat, AP Fanning (Warburg 1954: 483).

H9 1977: 'Roche's Marsh', at road-junction 2 miles E of Kilfenora, PH Pitkin (Hill 1979: 31).

H16 1957: E side of Skeltia, Maumtrasna, EM Lobley (BBS exc.) (Parker 1958: 494, Crundwell 1970: 206).

H17 1957: turlough, Killower, nr Tuam, AC Crundwell (BBS exc.) (Warburg 1958b: 481).

H(21) listed by Lett (1915: 132). H(21) listed by Blockeel & Long (1998: 124).

H26 1965: NE shore of L. Carra, nr Clogher House, AMcG Stirling (Warburg 1966: 199).

†H27 listed by Blockeel & Long (1998: 124).

H(28) 1928: Gleniff, Ben Bulben (BBS exc.) (Duncan 1928: 118).

†H28 listed by Blockeel & Long (1998: 124).

†H29 listed by Blockeel & Long (1998: 124).

H(31) listed by Lett (1915: 132). H(31) listed by Blockeel & Long (1998: 124).

H(32) listed by Lett (1915: 132). H(32) listed by Blockeel & Long (1998: 124).

H33 1960: wet humus at base of cliffs, *ca* 700 ft [alt.], scarp N of Lough Navar, RD Fitzgerald (Warburg 1961: 168).

H(34) listed by Lett (1915: 132). H(34) listed by Blockeel & Long (1998: 124).

H34 2002: on sand at base of slope by stream in shallow ravine, 30 m alt., S of Soldiers Hill, NW of Malin, C45, DT Holyoak 02-560 (Rothero 2003: 58).

H(35) listed by Lett (1915: 132). H(35) listed by Blockeel & Long (1998: 124).

H35 2002: in moss mat on damp sandy soil at base of slope, 7 m alt., N end of Rosses Strand, C14, DT Holyoak 02-599 (Rothero 2003: 58).

H(38) listed by Lett (1915: 132). H(38) listed by Blockeel & Long (1998: 124).

H(39) listed by Lett (1915: 132). H(39) listed by Blockeel & Long (1998: 124).

H(40) 1937: Magilligan Sandhills, WR Megaw

(anon. 1938d: 40).
†H40 listed by Blockeel & Long (1998: 124).

108/1 ***Catoscopium nigritum*** (Hedw.) Brid.

H27 1965: damp sandy flat nr L. Doo, Achill [I.], EF Warburg (Warburg 1966: 199).
H(34) 1937: slack in sand-dunes, Bundoran, no collector named (BBS exc.) (Armitage 1938: 12).
H35 1970: sandy flush by sea, Rossbeg, NW of Ardara, MFV Corley (Crundwell 1971b: 381).
H(39) 1925: Portrush Sandhills, WR Megaw (anon. 1926: 220).
H(40) 1900: Magilligan Sands, HW Lett & CH Waddell, comm. CH Waddell (anon. 1901: 83, Lett 1915: 141).
†H40 listed by Blockeel & Long (1998: 124).

109/1 ***Plagiopus oederianus*** (Sw.) H.A.Crum & L.E.Anderson
(syn. *Bartramia oederi* (Sw.) Brid., *Plagiopus oederi* (Sw.) Limpr.)

H(1) listed by Lett (1915: 139). H(1) listed by Blockeel & Long (1998: 124).
H(29) listed by Lett (1915: 139).
H29 1963: limestone, *ca* 800 ft [alt.], Peakadaw, Glenade, RD Fitzgerald & AR Perry (Warburg 1964: 730).
H(39) listed by Lett (1915: 139). H(39) listed by Blockeel & Long (1998: 124).

110/1 ***Bartramia halleriana*** Hedw.
(syn. *Bartramia norvegica* Lindb. nom. illeg.)

H(1) listed by Lett (1915: 140).
†H1 listed by Blockeel & Long (1998: 124).
H(2) listed by Lett (1915: 140). H(2) listed by Blockeel & Long (1998: 124).
H(4) listed by Lett (1915: 140). H(4) listed by Blockeel & Long (1998: 124).
H(6) listed by Lett (1915: 140). H(6) listed by Blockeel & Long (1998: 124).
H(7) listed by Lett (1915: 140). H(7) listed by Blockeel & Long (1998: 124).
H(20) listed by Lett (1915: 140). H(20) listed by Blockeel & Long (1998: 124).
H(27) listed by Lett (1915: 140) without locality. H(27) listed by Blockeel & Long (1998: 124).
H(36) listed by Lett (1915: 140). H(36) listed by Blockeel & Long (1998: 124).
H(39) listed by Lett (1915: 140). H(39) listed by Blockeel & Long (1998: 124).

110/2 ***Bartramia pomiformis*** Hedw.
(syn. *Bartramia pomiformis* var. *crispa* (Brid.) Bruch, Schimp. & W.Gümbel)

H(1) listed by Lett (1915: 139, 140). H(1) listed by Blockeel & Long (1998: 124).
H(2) listed by Lett (1915: 139, 140).
†H2 listed by Blockeel & Long (1998: 124).
†H3 listed by Blockeel & Long (1998: 124).
H(4) listed by Lett (1915: 139).
†H4 listed by Blockeel & Long (1998: 124).
H(5) listed by Lett (1915: 139). H(5) listed by Blockeel & Long (1998: 124).
H(6) listed by Lett (1915: 139).
†H6 listed by Blockeel & Long (1998: 124).
H(7) 1947: sandstone cliffs, wood nr Kilsheelan, KC Harris (anon. 1948b: 121).
†H7 listed by Blockeel & Long (1998: 124).
H8 1966: basalt rocks, Knockroe, nr Caherconlish, MFV Corley & JS Parker (Perry 1967: 418).
H9 1979: stone wall in lane on W side of Slieve Bernagh hills, 5 km N of Broadford, DM Synnott (Hill 1981: 32).
H(11) listed by Lett (1915: 139). H(11) listed by Blockeel & Long (1998: 124).
H(12) listed by Lett (1915: 139).
†H12 listed by Blockeel & Long (1998: 124).
H(13) listed by Lett (1915: 139). H(13) listed by Blockeel & Long (1998: 124).
H16 1968: siliceous rock crevices in deep ravine, moorland by roadside, Shinnanagh, *ca* 1½ miles SW of Ballynakill Lough, N of Clifden, AR Perry (Crundwell 1969: 886).
[H(19) listed by Lett (1915: 139) without details. H19 deleted because specimen from Hill of Castlewarden, 1864, leg. Douglas (DBN), is *Philonotis calcarea*, comm. DM Synnott (Blockeel 1989: 30); again deleted because no valid record or voucher specimen traced (Blockeel 1999: 7)].
H(20) listed by Lett (1915: 139).
†H20 listed by Blockeel & Long (1998: 124).
[H(21) listed by Lett (1915: 139). H21 deleted because no valid record or voucher specimen traced (Blockeel 1999: 7)].
H22 1978: roadside wall, SE side of Hill 689, 4 miles NE of Moynalty, DM Synnott (Hill 1979: 31).

H(26) listed by Lett (1915: 139) [as '6' but evidently a misprint]. H(26) listed by Blockeel & Long (1998: 124).
H(27) listed by Lett (1915: 139).
†H27 listed by Blockeel & Long (1998: 124).
H28 1963: clefts of rock, *ca* 900 ft [alt.], S of Knockachree, Slieve Gamph, RD Fitzgerald & AR Perry (Warburg 1964: 730).
H29 1970: dry rock face, N-facing cliffs or hill slopes of Glenfarne, nr Belcoo, J Appleyard (BBS exc.) (Crundwell 1971b: 381, Appleyard 1971: 389-390).
H(30) listed by Lett (1915: 139).
†H30 listed by Blockeel & Long (1998: 124).
H(31) listed by Lett (1915: 140). H(31) listed by Blockeel & Long (1998: 124).
H(33) listed by Lett (1915: 140). H(33) listed by Blockeel & Long (1998: 124).
H33 1999: on ledges of N-facing sandstone scarp, 250 m alt., Meenameen Scarp, Lough Navar Forest, H05, RD Porley 2041 (Rothero 2000: 56).
H(34) listed by Lett (1915: 140).
†H34 listed by Blockeel & Long (1998: 124).
H35 2001: dry sheltered NE-facing rock crevice on hillside, 250 m alt., Altnandewon, Common Mt., Glengesh, G78, NG Hodgetts 3845 (Rothero 2003: 58).
H(36) listed by Lett (1915: 140) without locality.
†H36 listed by Blockeel & Long (1998: 124).
H(37) listed by Lett (1915: 140).
†H37 listed by Blockeel & Long (1998: 124).
H(38) listed by Lett (1915: 140).
H(38) 1928: Slieve Donard (BBS exc.) (Duncan 1928: 114, 117), as var. *crispa*.
†H38 listed by Blockeel & Long (1998: 124).
H(39) listed by Lett (1915: 140).
†H39 listed by Blockeel & Long (1998: 124).
H(40) listed by Lett (1915: 140).
†H40 listed by Blockeel & Long (1998: 124).

110/3 ***Bartramia ithyphylla*** Brid.

[H(1) listed by Lett (1915: 140). H1 deleted because no valid record or voucher specimen traced (Blockeel 1999: 7)].
H(6) listed by Lett (1915: 140). H(6) listed by Blockeel & Long (1998: 124).
H(7) listed by Lett (1915: 140).
†H7 listed by Blockeel & Long (1998: 124).
H(8) 1944: valley N of Corrig-na-binnian, AW Stelfox, comm. ALK King (Warburg 1964: 730).
†H8 listed by Blockeel & Long (1998: 124).
H16 1951: Kylemore, H Milne-Redhead (Warburg 1952: 103).
H(20) listed by Lett (1915: 140). H(20) listed by Blockeel & Long (1998: 124).
[H(21) listed by Lett (1915: 140) without details. H21 deleted because no valid record or voucher specimen traced (Blockeel 1999: 7)].
H22 1978: roadside wall, SE side of Hill 689, 4 miles NE of Moynalty, DM Synnott (Hill 1979: 31).
H(27) listed by Lett (1915: 140). H(27) listed by Blockeel & Long (1998: 124).
H(31) listed by Lett (1915: 140). H(31) listed by Blockeel & Long (1998: 124).
H(34) listed by Lett (1915: 140).
†H34 listed by Blockeel & Long (1998: 124).
H(35) listed by Lett (1915: 140). H(35) listed by Blockeel & Long (1998: 124).
H(36) listed by Lett (1915: 140).
†H36 listed by Blockeel & Long (1998: 124).
H(38) listed by Lett (1915: 140). H(38) listed by Blockeel & Long (1998: 124).
H(39) listed by Lett (1915: 140).
†H39 listed by Blockeel & Long (1998: 124).
†H40 listed by Blockeel & Long (1998: 124).

112/1 ***Philonotis rigida*** Brid.

H(1) listed by Lett (1915: 140).
†H1 listed by Blockeel & Long (1998: 125).
H(2) listed by Lett (1915: 140). H(2) listed by Blockeel & Long (1998: 125).
H(3) listed by Lett (1915: 140). H(3) listed by Blockeel & Long (1998: 125).
H16 1970: rock crevice on N side of Benbeg, AR Perry & HJ Perry (Crundwell 1974: 173).
H(20) listed by Lett (1915: 140). H(20) listed by Blockeel & Long (1998: 125).
H27 1970: rock in ravine, S slope of Ben Gorm, N of Killary Harbour, JA Paton (Crundwell 1971b: 381).
H33 1961: cracks of limestone, *ca* 200 ft [alt.], Stonefort, nr Boa I., RD Fitzgerald (Warburg 1962: 372).
H35 1963: wet shaded cliffs in bay N of Rossarrell Point, nr Malin Beg, AR Perry & RD Fitzgerald (Warburg 1964: 730).

112/3 ***Philonotis arnellii*** Husn.
(syn. *Philonotis capillaris* Lindb.)

H16 1969: moist shaded vertical bank at side of track nr Farravaun, Glann, NW of Oughterard, AR Perry & HJ Perry (BBSUK), conf. MO Hill (Crundwell 1970: 206, MO Hill MS).
H30 2001: on damp shale by stream, 460 m alt., W slope of Cuilcagh, H12, DT Holyoak 01-776 (BBSUK) (Rothero 2002: 52).
[H35 1969: E shore of L. Meela, nr Dunglow, JA Paton (Crundwell 1970: 206). Redet. by MO Hill (MS) as depauperate *P. fontana*, so omitted from *CC* by Corley & Hill (1981: 105)].
H(36) 1931: wet sand among rocks, R. Mourne, McGaw [*sic* = Megaw ?] (BBSUK), conf. MO Hill (MO Hill MS).
[H(39) 1928: wood nr Cave Hill, Belfast (BBS exc.) (Duncan 1928: 113, 116). H(39) not accepted for *CC* by Corley & Hill (1981: 105)].

Irish and British specimens were revised for the *CC* (Corley & Hill 1981: 105) by MO Hill (MS).

112/4 ***Philonotis caespitosa*** Jur.

H1 1951: nr Lough Coomacullen, Glenbeigh, EC Wallace, conf. MO Hill (Hill 1981: 32, MO Hill MS).
H4 1966: marsh by stream, Rylane Cross, Boggeragh Mts, MFV Corley & JS Parker, conf. MO Hill (Perry 1967: 418, MO Hill MS).
H8 1991: on boulders, 100 m alt., in Bilboa River, R85, N Lockhart & A O'Suillivan (Blockeel 1992: 27).
H16 1968: marshy area, edge of L. Corrib, Dooros Peninsula, AR Perry, conf. MO Hill (Hill 1978: 22, MO Hill MS).
H(20) 1867: Lugnaquilla, D McArdle (BM), conf. MO Hill (MO Hill MS). [Lett (1915:140) also lists 1871: Lugnaquilla, leg. Moore and Glenmalure, leg. Moore].
H29 2000: on mud in ditch by lough, Carrickaport Lough, SE edge, H00, DT Holyoak 00-749 (BBSUK) (Rothero 2001: 44).
H30 2001: on damp soil on track, 315 m alt., W of Bellavally Gap, H12, DT Holyoak 01-641C (Rothero 2002: 52).
H(31) no date: in trickling water on hillside, Feede, JS Thomson (anon. 1946c: 283).
1944: in trickling water on mountain side, Feede, JF Thomson (GALW), comm. NF Stewart (Blockeel 1994: 40).
H(33) 1865: Corel Glen, Chrashkill [*sic* = Correl Glen, Church Hill], D McArdle (BM), conf. MO Hill (MO Hill MS).
[H35 1955: side of small stream, Tory I., R Brown, comm. WWM Baron (Warburg 1956: 155). Not accepted for *CC* by Corley & Hill (1981: 105), following revision of specimen(s) by MO Hill)].
H37 2002: on firm mud in inundation zone by reservoir, 155 m alt., NE edge of Seagahan Reservoir, H93, DT Holyoak 02-1068 (Rothero 2003: 58).
H38 2002: on mud at edge of tarmac on disused moorland road, 335 m alt., nr S end of Spelga Dam, J22, DT Holyoak 02-977 (Rothero 2003: 58).
H40 2002: on open sandy soil by track in old quarry, 285 m alt., above Whitewater Bridge, NE of Lough Fea, H78, DT Holyoak 02-1151 (Rothero 2003: 58).

Irish and British specimens were revised for the *CC* (Corley & Hill 1981: 105) by MO Hill (MS).

112/5 ***Philonotis fontana*** (Hedw.) Brid.
(syn. *Philonotis adpressa* Fergusson, *P. fontana* var. *adpressa* (Fergusson) Limpr., *P. fontana* var. *compacta* Schimp., *P. fontana* var. *falcata* (Hook.) Brid.)

H(1) listed by Lett (1915: 140) without details.
†H1 listed by Blockeel & Long (1998: 125).
H(2) listed by Lett (1915: 140) without details.
H(2) 1945: Connor Hill, nr Dingle, Miss Fagan, per JS Thomson (anon. 1946c: 283).
†H2 listed by Blockeel & Long (1998: 125).
†H3 listed by Blockeel & Long (1998: 125).
H(4) listed by Lett (1915: 140) without details.
†H4 listed by Blockeel & Long (1998: 125).
H(5) listed by Lett (1915: 140) without details.
†H5 listed by Blockeel & Long (1998: 125).
H(6) listed by Lett (1915: 140) without

details.
†H6 listed by Blockeel & Long (1998: 125).
H(7) listed by Lett (1915: 140) without details.
†H7 listed by Blockeel & Long (1998: 125).
H(8) listed by Lett (1915: 140) without details.
†H8 listed by Blockeel & Long (1998: 125).
H(9) listed by Lett (1915: 140) without details.
†H9 listed by Blockeel & Long (1998: 125).
H(10) listed by Lett (1915: 140) without details.
†H10 listed by Blockeel & Long (1998: 125).
H11 1966: muddy ground by pond, Dysart Castle, J Appleyard *et al.* (BBS exc.) (Perry 1967: 418).
H(12) listed by Lett (1915: 140) without details.
†H12 listed by Blockeel & Long (1998: 125).
H(13) listed by Lett (1915: 140) without details.
†H13 listed by Blockeel & Long (1998: 125).
[H(14) listed by Lett (1915: 140) without details. H14 deleted because no valid record or voucher specimen traced (Blockeel 1999: 7)].
[H(15) listed by Lett (1915: 140) without details. H15 deleted because no valid record or voucher specimen traced (Blockeel 1999: 7)].
H(16) listed by Lett (1915: 140) without details.
†H16 listed by Blockeel & Long (1998: 125).
H17 1968: flush at edge of raised bog, Addergoule N[orth], R. Suck, nr Ballinasloe, HJB Birks (Crundwell 1969: 887).
[H(18) listed by Lett (1915: 140) without details. H18 deleted because no valid record or voucher specimen traced (Blockeel 1999: 7)].
H19 1957: gravel flat by R. Liffey below Ballymore Eustace, ALK King (Warburg 1958b: 482).
H(20) listed by Lett (1915: 140).
H20 1950: above waterfall, South Prison, Lugnacullia [*sic* = Lugnaquillia], MWR Graham, comm. JS Thomson (Warburg 1952: 103), as var. *adpressa.*
H(21) listed by Lett (1915: 140) without details.
†H21 listed by Blockeel & Long (1998: 125).
H23 1967: Scraw Bog, Portnashangan, ALK King (Crundwell 1968: 642).
H(24) 1941: Lough Leeben, JG Finlay (Duncan 1944: 212).
†H24 listed by Blockeel & Long (1998: 125).
H(25) listed by Lett (1915: 140) without details.
†H25 listed by Blockeel & Long (1998: 125).
H26 1965: bog, *ca* 750 ft alt., cliffs S of Glendaduff, [The] Ox Mts, RD Fitzgerald (Warburg 1966: 199).
H(27) listed by Lett (1915: 140) without details.
†H27 listed by Blockeel & Long (1998: 125).
H(28) listed by Lett (1915: 140) without details.
†H28 listed by Blockeel & Long (1998: 125).
H(29) listed by Lett (1915: 140) without details.
†H29 listed by Blockeel & Long (1998: 125).
H(30) listed by Lett (1915: 140) without details.
†H30 listed by Blockeel & Long (1998: 125).
H(31) listed by Lett (1915: 140). H(31) listed by Blockeel & Long (1998: 125).
H31 1999: on wet rock ledge by waterfall, 300 m alt., Two Mile River, Carlingford, J11, TL Blockeel 28/176 (Rothero 2000: 56).
H(32) listed by Lett (1915: 140) without details.
†H32 listed by Blockeel & Long (1998: 125).
H(33) listed by Lett (1915: 140) without details.
†H33 listed by Blockeel & Long (1998: 125).
H(34) listed by Lett (1915: 140) without locality.
†H34 listed by Blockeel & Long (1998: 125).
H(35) listed by Lett (1915: 140).
†H35 listed by Blockeel & Long (1998: 125).
H(36) listed by Lett (1915: 140) without details.
†H36 listed by Blockeel & Long (1998: 125).
H(37) listed by Lett (1915: 140) without details.
†H37 listed by Blockeel & Long (1998: 125).
H(38) listed by Lett (1915: 140, 141).
†H38 listed by Blockeel & Long (1998: 125).
H(39) listed by Lett (1915: 140, 141).
†H39 listed by Blockeel & Long (1998: 125).
H(40) listed by Lett (1915: 140) without details.
†H40 listed by Blockeel & Long (1998: 125).

112/6 ***Philonotis tomentella*** Molendo (syn. *Philonotis fontana* var. *tomentella* (Molendo) Dixon)

[H16 1970: base of dripping rock outcrop, corrie on N side of Benbeg, AR Perry & HJ Perry (Crundwell 1974: 173); H16 deleted because specimen (BBSUK) redet. as *P. fontana* by MO Hill (Hill 1978: 22, MO Hill MS)].
H34 2002: in bryophyte mat on rocks beneath overhang on N-facing crags, 488 m alt., Bulbin Mt. just NW of summit, C34, DT Holyoak 02-518 (BBSUK) (Rothero 2003: 58).
H35 2001: on crags just E of gully nr top of N-facing coire, 550 m alt., Lavagh More, G99, NG Hodgetts 3863 (BBSUK) (Rothero 2003: 58).

Listed for Co. Louth (H31) and W Co. Donegal (H35) by Smith (1978: 462), but not accepted for any Irish vice-county by MO Hill following revision of specimens for *CC* (Corley & Hill 1981: 106).

[112/7 ***Philonotis seriata*** Mitt.]

[Listed for H2, H31, H32 and H37 by Lett (1915: 140) but these records have been deleted as errors].

112/8 ***Philonotis calcarea*** (Hedw.) Brid.

H(1) listed by Lett (1915: 140). H(1) listed by Blockeel & Long (1998: 125).
H(2) listed by Lett (1915: 140). H(2) listed by Blockeel & Long (1998: 125).
H6 1968: wet limestone rocks, roadside on W bank of R. Nore, S of Cappoquin, JA Paton (Crundwell 1969: 887).
H(7) listed by Lett (1915: 140).
†H7 listed by Blockeel & Long (1998: 125).
[H8 deleted because no valid record or voucher specimen traced (Blockeel 1999: 7)].
H9 1960: calcareous spring on SE side of Cappanawalla, nr Ballyvaughan, MCF Proctor (Warburg 1961: 169).
H11 1966: bog, Derryfadda, nr Johnstown, RD Fitzgerald (BBS exc.) (Crundwell 1968: 642).
[H(14) listed by Lett (1915: 141). H14 deleted because specimen (DBN) is *P. fontana* (Crundwell 1968: 642)].
H15 1962: fen nr Cregg Point, Lough Derg, AJE Smith (Warburg 1963b: 500).
H16 1968: roadside ditch, fen 1 mile S of Carrowmoreknock, 4 miles N of Moycullen, AR Perry (Crundwell 1969: 887).
H17 1968: amongst fen vegetation at roadside ½ mile SE of Menlough, N of Galway City, AR Perry (Crundwell 1969: 887).
H18 1984: fen beside Fin Lough, nr Clonmacnoise, V Power (Hill 1986: 22).
H19 1951: calcareous tufa, Rye Water Valley, Leixlip, JP Brunker (Warburg 1952: 103), as ? var. *mollis* Vent.
H(20) listed by Lett (1915: 141).
†H20 listed by Blockeel & Long (1998: 125).
[H(21) listed by Lett (1915: 141) without details. H21 deleted because no valid record or voucher specimen traced (Blockeel 1999: 7)].
H22 1965: flush, Commons, Duleek, DM Synnott (Perry 1967: 418).
H23 1957: gravel flat by L. Ennell, nr Lilliput House, ALK King (Warburg 1958b: 482).
H(24) 1941: Lough Leeben, JG Finlay (Duncan 1944: 212).
†H24 listed by Blockeel & Long (1998: 125).
H25 1973: flush on peat, Kilmore Bay, shore of L. Ree, WV Rubers (U) (Crundwell 1975: 19).
H26 1981: calcareous fen, North L. Frank, nr L. Carra, N Lockhart (Hill 1983: 55).
H(27) listed by Lett (1915: 141).
†H27 listed by Blockeel & Long (1998: 125).
H(28) listed by Lett (1915: 141).
†H28 listed by Blockeel & Long (1998: 125).
H29 1961: old log above waterfall, Glencar, RD Fitzgerald & MPH Kertland (Warburg 1962: 372).
H(31) listed by Lett (1915: 141). H(31) listed by Blockeel & Long (1998: 125).
H(32) listed by Lett (1915: 141). H(32) listed by Blockeel & Long (1998: 125).
H(33) listed by Lett (1915: 141).
†H33 listed by Blockeel & Long (1998: 125).
H34 1962: flush, E side of Bulbin [Mt.], AC Crundwell (BBS exc.) (Warburg 1963b: 500).
H(35) listed by Lett (1915: 141).
†H35 listed by Blockeel & Long (1998: 125).
H36 1956: Glen Curry Bridge, nr Omagh, RD Fitzgerald & MPH Kertland (Warburg 1957: 333).

H(37) listed by Lett (1915: 141). H(37) listed by Blockeel & Long (1998: 125).
H(38) listed by Lett (1915: 141). H(38) listed by Blockeel & Long (1998: 125).
H(39) listed by Lett (1915: 141). H(39) listed by Blockeel & Long (1998: 125).
H(40) listed by Lett (1915: 141).
†H40 listed by Blockeel & Long (1998: 125).

112/9 ***Philonotis cernua*** (Wilson) D.G.Griffin & W.R.Buck
(syn. *Bartramidula wilsonii* Bruch, Schimp. & W.Gümbel, *Philonotis wilsonii* (Bruch, Schimp. & W.Gümbel) Mitt.)

H(1) listed by Lett (1915: 140).
†H1 listed by Blockeel & Long (1998: 126).
[H3 deleted because no valid record or voucher specimen traced (Blockeel 1999: 7)].
H(16) 1868: nr Maam, no collector's name (E) (Blockeel 1995c: 44).
H27 1987: on soil on gravelly scree slope, NE corrie of Mweelrea, DG Long (E) (Blockeel 1988: 38).

113/1 ***Breutelia chrysocoma*** (Hedw.) Lindb.

H(1) listed by Lett (1915: 141) without details.
†H1 listed by Blockeel & Long (1998: 126).
H(2) listed by Lett (1915: 141) without details.
†H2 listed by Blockeel & Long (1998: 126).
H3 1951: hillside, Pass of Keimaneigh, ALK King (Warburg 1952: 103).
H4 1966: boggy ground at 1200 ft alt., Seefin, Boggeragh Mts, MFV Corley & JS Parker (Perry 1967: 418).
H(5) listed by Lett (1915: 141) without details.
†H5 listed by Blockeel & Long (1998: 126).
H(6) listed by Lett (1915: 141) without details.
†H6 listed by Blockeel & Long (1998: 126).
H(7) listed by Lett (1915: 141) without details.
†H7 listed by Blockeel & Long (1998: 126).
H(8) listed by Lett (1915: 141) without details.
†H8 listed by Blockeel & Long (1998: 126).
H(9) listed by Lett (1915: 141) without details.
†H9 listed by Blockeel & Long (1998: 126).
H(10) listed by Lett (1915: 141) without details.
H10 1979: nr waterfall, W side of Keeper Hill, S of Silvermine Mts, HMH van Melick (Hill 1981: 32).
[H(11) listed by Lett (1915: 141) without details. H11 deleted because no valid record or voucher specimen traced (Blockeel 1999: 7)].
H12 1969: marshy ground, Pallis Bridge, Wicklow Gap, RD Fitzgerald (Crundwell 1970: 206).
H(13) listed by Lett (1915: 141) without details.
†H13 listed by Blockeel & Long (1998: 126).
H(14) listed by Lett (1915: 141) without details.
†H14 listed by Blockeel & Long (1998: 126).
H15 1957: cut-over bog, nr Loughrea, RE Parker (Warburg 1958b: 482).
H(16) listed by Lett (1915: 141) without details.
†H16 listed by Blockeel & Long (1998: 126).
H17 1957: boulders, turlough, Killower, nr Tuam, EM Lobley (BBS exc.) (Warburg 1958b: 482).
[H(18) listed by Lett (1915: 141) without details. H18 deleted because no valid record or voucher specimen traced (Blockeel 1999: 7)].
H(20) listed by Lett (1915: 141) without details.
†H20 listed by Blockeel & Long (1998: 126).
[H(21) listed by Lett (1915: 141) without details. H21 deleted because no valid record or voucher specimen traced (Blockeel 1999: 7)].
H24 1957: Carn Clonhugh hill, ALK King (Warburg 1958b: 482).
H(25) listed by Lett (1915: 141) without details.
†H25 listed by Blockeel & Long (1998: 126).
H(26) listed by Lett (1915: 141) without details.
†H26 listed by Blockeel & Long (1998: 126).
H(27) listed by Lett (1915: 141) without details.
†H27 listed by Blockeel & Long (1998: 126).
H(28) listed by Lett (1915: 141) without details.
†H28 listed by Blockeel & Long (1998: 126).
H(29) listed by Lett (1915: 141) without details.
†H29 listed by Blockeel & Long (1998: 126).
H(30) listed by Lett (1915: 141) without

details.
†H30 listed by Blockeel & Long (1998: 126).
[H(31) listed by Lett (1915: 141) without details. H31 deleted because no valid record or voucher specimen traced (Blockeel 1999: 7)].
H31 1999: among moist rocks on bank of stream, 150 m alt., Two Mile River, Carlingford, J11, TL Blockeel 28/153 (Rothero 2000: 56).
[H(32) listed by Lett (1915: 141) without details. H32 deleted because no valid record or voucher specimen traced (Blockeel 1999: 7)].
H(33) listed by Lett (1915: 141) without details.
†H33 listed by Blockeel & Long (1998: 126).
H(34) listed by Lett (1915: 141) without details.
†H34 listed by Blockeel & Long (1998: 126).
H(35) listed by Lett (1915: 141) without details.
†H35 listed by Blockeel & Long (1998: 126).
H(36) listed by Lett (1915: 141) without details.
†H36 listed by Blockeel & Long (1998: 126).
H(37) listed by Lett (1915: 141) without details.
†H37 listed by Blockeel & Long (1998: 126).
H(38) listed by Lett (1915: 141) without details.
†H38 listed by Blockeel & Long (1998: 126).
H(39) listed by Lett (1915: 141) without details.
†H39 listed by Blockeel & Long (1998: 126).
H(40) listed by Lett (1915: 141) without details.
†H40 listed by Blockeel & Long (1998: 126).

114/1 ***Timmia austriaca*** Hedw.

H28 1970: on rock ledge, Ben Bulben, EC Wallace & E Hegewald (Wallace 1972, Crundwell 1974: 173).

114/2 ***Timmia norvegica*** J.E.Zetterst.

[H(20) listed as dubious record by Lett (1915: 141) from Powerscourt leg. Orr].
H(28) 1928: Gleniff, Ben Bulben (BBS exc.) (Duncan 1928: 114-115, 118).
1928: Gleniff, Ben Bulben, leg. CH Binstead, HH Knight & A Sutton, comm. A Sutton (anon. 1929: 103).
†H28 listed by Blockeel & Long (1998: 126).
H29 2000: on thin soil over limestone with other bryophytes on W-facing rocky slope, 340 m alt., SE of Aghadunvane, G85, DT Holyoak 00-546 (BBSUK) (Rothero 2001: 44).

115/2 ***Amphidium mougeotii*** (Bruch & Schimp.) Schimp.
(syn. *Anoectangium mougeotii* (Bruch & Schimp.) Lindb., *Zygodon mougeotii* Bruch & Schimp.)

H(1) listed by Lett (1915: 126).
†H1 listed by Blockeel & Long (1998: 126).
H(2) listed by Lett (1915: 126).
†H2 listed by Blockeel & Long (1998: 126).
H(3) listed by Lett (1915: 126).
†H3 listed by Blockeel & Long (1998: 126).
H(4) listed by Lett (1915: 126) without locality.
†H4 listed by Blockeel & Long (1998: 126).
[H(5) listed by Lett (1915: 126) as 1850: Templemichael Glen, leg. Carroll. H5 deleted because no valid record or voucher specimen traced (Blockeel 1999: 7)].
H(6) listed by Lett (1915: 126).
†H6 listed by Blockeel & Long (1998: 126).
H(7) listed by Lett (1915: 126).
†H7 listed by Blockeel & Long (1998: 126).
H(8) listed by Lett (1915: 126) without details.
†H8 listed by Blockeel & Long (1998: 126).
[H(9) listed by Lett (1915: 126) as: Foynes, leg. Stewart. H9 deleted because no valid record or voucher specimen traced (Blockeel 1999: 7)].
H10 1967: on wet rocks in wooded valley, Clare Glen, nr Newport, HH Birks, HJB Birks & DA Ratcliffe (Crundwell 1968: 642).
H11 1968: wet roadside rocks W of R. Nore, SE of Thomastown, JA Paton (Crundwell 1969: 887).
H13 1954: siliceous rock on L.[eft] bank of R. Barrow above Graiguenamanagh, ALK King (Warburg 1955: 585).
H14 1956: rocky bank, nr Roundwood Bridge, AA Cridland (Warburg 1958b: 480).
H(16) listed by Lett (1915: 126).
†H16 listed by Blockeel & Long (1998: 126).
H(20) listed by Lett (1915: 126).
†H20 listed by Blockeel & Long (1998: 126).
H21 1952: rocks facing N, Ballinascorney

Gap, *ca* 800 ft [alt.], ALK King (Warburg 1953: 311).
H26 1965: rocks *ca* 600 ft alt., W of L. Talt, [The] Ox Mts, RD Fitzgerald (Warburg 1966: 200).
H(27) listed by Lett (1915: 126).
†H27 listed by Blockeel & Long (1998: 126).
H(28) listed by Lett (1915: 126).
†H28 listed by Blockeel & Long (1998: 126).
H29 1963: limestone, *ca* 900 ft [alt.], Peakadaw, Glenade, RD Fitzgerald & AR Perry (Warburg 1964: 730).
H(30) 1911: Waterfall, Swanlinbar River, WN Tetley (anon. 1912c: 7), labelled as *Cynodontium Bruntoni* but redet. as *Zygodon mougeotii* by GB Savery.
†H30 listed by Blockeel & Long (1998: 126).
[H(31) listed by Lett (1915: 126). H31 deleted because no valid record or voucher specimen traced (Blockeel 1999: 7)].
H31 1999: in rock crevice by stream, 300 m alt., Two Mile River, Carlingford, J11, TL Blockeel 28/160 (Rothero 2000: 56).
H(33) listed by Lett (1915: 126).
†H33 listed by Blockeel & Long (1998: 126).
H(34) listed by Lett (1915: 126).
†H34 listed by Blockeel & Long (1998: 126).
H(35) listed by Lett (1915: 126).
†H35 listed by Blockeel & Long (1998: 126).
H(36) listed by Lett (1915: 126) without details.
†H36 listed by Blockeel & Long (1998: 126).
H(37) listed by Lett (1915: 126).
†H37 listed by Blockeel & Long (1998: 126).
H(38) listed by Lett (1915: 126). H(38) listed by Blockeel & Long (1998: 126).
H38 1999: in crevice of large boulder on stream bank, 50 m alt., Tollymore Forest park, 4 km W of Newcastle, J33, TL Blockeel 28/351 (Rothero 2000: 56).
H(39) listed by Lett (1915: 126).
†H39 listed by Blockeel & Long (1998: 126).
H(40) listed by Lett (1915: 126).
†H40 listed by Blockeel & Long (1998: 126).

116/1a *Zygodon viridissimus* (Dicks.) Brid. **var. *viridissimus***
(syn. *Zygodon viridissimus* var. *occidentalis* (Correns) Malta)

H(1) listed by Lett (1915: 126) without details.
†H1 listed by Blockeel & Long (1998: 126).
H(2) listed by Lett (1915: 126) without details.
†H2 listed by Blockeel & Long (1998: 126).
H(3) listed by Lett (1915: 126) without details.
†H3 listed by Blockeel & Long (1998: 126).
H(4) listed by Lett (1915: 126) without details.
†H4 listed by Blockeel & Long (1998: 126).
H(5) listed by Lett (1915: 126) without details.
†H5 listed by Blockeel & Long (1998: 126).
H(6) listed by Lett (1915: 126) without details.
†H6 listed by Blockeel & Long (1998: 126).
H(7) listed by Lett (1915: 126) without details.
†H7 listed by Blockeel & Long (1998: 126).
H(8) listed by Lett (1915: 126) without details.
†H8 listed by Blockeel & Long (1998: 126).
H(9) listed by Lett (1915: 126) without details.
†H9 listed by Blockeel & Long (1998: 126).
H(10) listed by Lett (1915: 126) without details.
†H10 listed by Blockeel & Long (1998: 126).
H(11) listed by Lett (1915: 126) without details.
†H11 listed by Blockeel & Long (1998: 126).
H(12) listed by Lett (1915: 126) without details.
†H12 listed by Blockeel & Long (1998: 126).
H(13) listed by Lett (1915: 126) without details.
†H13 listed by Blockeel & Long (1998: 126).
H(14) listed by Lett (1915: 126) without details.
†H14 listed by Blockeel & Long (1998: 126).
H15 1957: scrub, nr Kilreekill, RE Parker (Warburg 1958b: 480).
H(16) listed by Lett (1915: 126) without details.
†H16 listed by Blockeel & Long (1998: 126).
H17 1957: trees in small wood, nr Kilgariff, nr Headford, EM Lobley (BBS exc.) (Warburg 1958b: 480).
[H(18) listed by Lett (1915: 126) without details. H18 deleted because no valid record or voucher specimen traced (Blockeel 1999: 7)].
H(19) listed by Lett (1915: 126) without details.
†H19 listed by Blockeel & Long (1998: 126).
H(20) listed by Lett (1915: 126) without details.
†H20 listed by Blockeel & Long (1998: 126).

H(21) listed by Lett (1915: 126) without details.
†H21 listed by Blockeel & Long (1998: 126).
H22 1950: stone, Slane Hill, JS Thomson (Warburg 1952: 102), as var. *occidentalis*.
1963: elm, wood above R. Boyne, Donore, Drogheda, DM Synnott (Warburg 1964: 731).
H(23) listed by Lett (1915: 126) without details.
†H23 listed by Blockeel & Long (1998: 126).
H24 1966: fallen ash, Cloondara, ALK King (Perry 1967: 418).
H(25) listed by Lett (1915: 126) without details.
†H25 listed by Blockeel & Long (1998: 126).
H26 1970: on elder E of Ballintober, MFV Corley (Crundwell 1971b: 381).
H(27) listed by Lett (1915: 126) without details.
†H27 listed by Blockeel & Long (1998: 126).
H(28) listed by Lett (1915: 126) without details.
†H28 listed by Blockeel & Long (1998: 126).
H29 1963: tree at E end of Lough Gill, nr Dromahair, RD Fitzgerald & AR Perry (Warburg 1964: 731).
H(30) listed by Lett (1915: 126) without details.
†H30 listed by Blockeel & Long (1998: 126).
[H(31) listed by Lett (1915: 126) without details. H31 deleted because no valid record or voucher specimen traced (Blockeel 1999: 7)].
H(32) listed by Lett (1915: 126) without details.
†H32 listed by Blockeel & Long (1998: 126).
H(33) listed by Lett (1915: 126) without details.
†H33 listed by Blockeel & Long (1998: 126).
H(34) listed by Lett (1915: 126) without details.
†H34 listed by Blockeel & Long (1998: 126).
H(35) 1946: rock, nr Clooney, JS Thomson (anon. 1947: 31).
†H35 listed by Blockeel & Long (1998: 126).
H(36) listed by Lett (1915: 126) without details.
†H36 listed by Blockeel & Long (1998: 126).
H(37) listed by Lett (1915: 126) without details.
†H37 listed by Blockeel & Long (1998: 126).
H(38) listed by Lett (1915: 126) without details. H(38) listed by Blockeel & Long (1998: 126).
H(39) listed by Lett (1915: 126) without details.
†H39 listed by Blockeel & Long (1998: 126).
H(40) listed by Lett (1915: 126) without details.
†H40 listed by Blockeel & Long (1998: 126).

116/1b *Zygodon viridissimus* var. *stirtonii*
(Schimp. ex Stirt.) I.Hagen
(syn. *Zygodon stirtonii* Schimp. ex Stirt.)

H(2) listed by Lett (1915: 126). H(2) listed by Blockeel & Long (1998: 126).
H(3) listed by Lett (1915: 126). H(3) listed by Blockeel & Long (1998: 126).
H4 1966: stone wall by estuary, mouth of R. Stick, S of Belgooly, MFV Corley & JS Parker (Perry 1967: 418).
H5 1956: willows, lane, nr Youghal, EC Wallace (Warburg 1958b: 480).
H(6) listed by Lett (1915: 126).
†H6 listed by Blockeel & Long (1998: 126).
†H8 listed by Blockeel & Long (1998: 126).
H(9) 1944: wall, Roughan, JS Thomson (GALW), comm. NF Stewart (Blockeel 1994: 40).
H9 1961: calcareous rocks nr Black Head, EM Lobley (Warburg 1962: 371; it was later noted by Hill 1983: 55 that this record was omitted from *CC* in error, comm. AR Perry).
†H10 listed by Blockeel & Long (1998: 126).
H(11) listed by Lett (1915: 126). H(11) listed by Blockeel & Long (1998: 126).
H13 1969: on old walls, St Mullins Abbey, nr Graiguenamanagh, RD Fitzgerald (Crundwell 1970: 207).
H16 1970: tree W of Kylemore Castle, JA Paton (Crundwell 1971b: 381; it was later noted by Hill 1983: 55 that this record was omitted from *Census Catalogue* in error, comm. AR Perry, because H16 was wrongly transcribed as H26).
H(20) listed by Lett (1915: 126).
H20 1975: basic boulder in woodland by Vartry River, the Devil's Glen, NW of Ashford, AR Perry (Hill 1981: 32). H20 is erroneously placed in brackets in Blockeel & Long (1998: 126).
H(21) listed by Lett (1915: 126).
†H21 listed by Blockeel & Long (1998: 126).
H(22) listed by Lett (1915: 126).
†H22 listed by Blockeel & Long (1998: 126).

H25 2002: on limestone wall by track, 45 m alt., Suck River Callows, Carrowntarriff, M84, NG Hodgetts 4080 (Rothero 2003: 58).
[H26 deleted because it was entered into *CC* as error in transcribing H16, comm. AR Perry, in Hill 1983: 55].
H27 1970: tree nr Erriff Bridge, N of Maumtrasna, JA Paton (Crundwell 1971b: 381).
H(28) 1928: rocks above Glencar Lough, N side (BBS exc.) (Duncan 1928: 119).
†H28 listed by Blockeel & Long (1998: 126).
H29 1963: limestone, *ca* 850 ft [alt.], Boggaun, nr Manorhamilton, RD Fitzgerald & AR Perry (Warburg 1964: 731).
H30 2001: on vertical limestone on low crag, 230 m alt., Giant's Leap, S of Blacklion, H03, DT Holyoak 01-750 (Rothero 2002: 52).
H(31) listed by Lett (1915: 126).
†H31 listed by Blockeel & Long (1998: 126).
H(33) listed by Lett (1915: 126).
†H33 listed by Blockeel & Long (1998: 126).
†H34 listed by Blockeel & Long (1998: 126).
H35 1962: rock on cliffs, Black Burrow, nr Dunfanaghy, EF Warburg (BBS exc.) (Warburg 1963b: 500).
H(38) listed by Lett (1915: 126). H(38) listed by Blockeel & Long (1998: 126).
H38 2002: on mortar of old wall, 7 m alt., SE of Castle I., Strangford Lough, J54, DT Holyoak 02-996 (Rothero 2003: 58).
H(39) listed by Lett (1915: 126).
†H39 listed by Blockeel & Long (1998: 126).
H(40) listed by Lett (1915: 126) without details.
†H40 listed by Blockeel & Long (1998: 126).

116/2 ***Zygodon rupestris*** Schimp. ex Lor. (syn. *Zygodon baumgartneri* Malta, *Z. viridissimus* var. *rupestris* C.Hartm., *Z. viridissimus* var. *vulgaris* Malta)

†H1 listed by Blockeel & Long (1998: 127).
†H2 listed by Blockeel & Long (1998: 127).
H3 1967: on old oaks, Glengarriff, RD Fitzgerald (Crundwell 1968: 642).
H6 1999: on bole of oak in grassy clearing, 60 m alt., Lismore, by junction of Glenakeefe R. and Owennashad R., S00, TL Blockeel 28/198 (Rothero 2000: 56).
[H(9) 1945: on a wall, Kilnaboy, JS Thomson (anon. 1946c: 282). Not accepted for H (9) in *CC* by Warburg (1963a: 64)].
H14 1957: trunk of old lime tree at edge of the conifer plantation, Emo Estate, AA Cridland (Warburg 1958b: 480).
H16 1994: on oak at lough margin, 15 m alt., Derryclare NNR, L84, GP Rothero 94/046 (Blockeel 1995c: 44).
†H20 listed by Blockeel & Long (1998: 127).
H28 1987: on trunk of *Quercus robur* in parkland, Temple House, nr Ballymote, A Orange (Blockeel 1988: 38).
[H(38) listed by Lett (1915: 127) as 1884: Newcastle, leg. HW Lett. Record not accepted for H38 in recent *CC*].
H38 2002: on trunk of large *Quercus*, 50 m alt., by Shimna River in Tollymore Forest Park, J33, DT Holyoak 02-919 (Rothero 2003: 58).

116/3 ***Zygodon conoideus*** (Dicks.) Hook. & Taylor

H(1) listed by Lett (1915: 127).
†H1 listed by Blockeel & Long (1998: 127).
H(2) listed by Lett (1915: 127).
†H2 listed by Blockeel & Long (1998: 127).
H(3) listed by Lett (1915: 127).
†H3 listed by Blockeel & Long (1998: 127).
H(4) listed by Lett (1915: 127) without details.
†H4 listed by Blockeel & Long (1998: 127).
H(5) listed by Lett (1915: 127). H(5) listed by Blockeel & Long (1998: 127).
H5 2002: on trunk of poplar, 110 m alt., River Bride, Ardarou Wood, Glenville, W78, TL Blockeel 31/366 (Rothero 2003: 58).
H6 1999: with *Harpalejeunea* on branch of oak in N-facing woodland, 70 m alt., Lismore, by junction of Glenakeefe R and Owennashad R, S00, TL Blockeel 28/197 (Rothero 2000: 56).
H8 1979: on willow, S side of Clare Glens, nr Newport, AC Crundwell (Hill 1980b: 44).
H10 1967: on trees in wood, Devils Bit Mt., RD Fitzgerald (Crundwell 1968: 642).
H12 1953: apple, Inch, WR Megaw (Warburg 1954: 482).
H13 1999: on sycamore in scrubby woodland, 30 m alt., Pollymounty River, N bank, Ballyknockcrumpin, TL Blockeel 28/303 (Rothero 2000: 56).
H(14) listed by Lett (1915: 127).
†H14 listed by Blockeel & Long (1998: 127).

H15 1957: trunk of ash, Garryland Wood, nr Gort, AC Crundwell (BBS exc.) (Warburg 1958b: 480).
H(16) listed by Lett (1915: 127).
†H16 listed by Blockeel & Long (1998: 127).
[H17 deleted because no valid record or voucher specimen traced (Blockeel 1999: 7)].
H(18) listed by Lett (1915: 127). H(18) listed by Blockeel & Long (1998: 127).
H(20) listed by Lett (1915: 127). H(20) listed by Blockeel & Long (1998: 127).
H20 2000: on *Fraxinus* by river in steep-sided, wooded valley, 130 m alt., The Devil's Glen above Ashford, nr waterfall, T29, DG Long 29462 (Rothero 2001: 45).
H22 1965: hedgerow stump nr Summerhill, ALK King (Warburg 1966: 200).
H24 1968: on *Corylus* in wood nr Elfeet Bay, L. Ree, WV Rubers *et al.* (U) (Crundwell 1974: 173).
H(25) listed by Lett (1915: 127).
†H25 listed by Blockeel & Long (1998: 127).
H(26) listed by Lett (1915: 127).
†H26 listed by Blockeel & Long (1998: 127).
†H27 listed by Blockeel & Long (1998: 127).
H28 1965: elder, nr Percy Mount, nr L. Gill, EF Warburg (Warburg 1966: 200).
H(29) listed by Lett (1915: 127).
†H29 listed by Blockeel & Long (1998: 127).
H30 2001: on hazel in scrub nr river, 95 m alt., Owenmore River, NW of Glengevlin, H02, DT Holyoak 01-649 (Rothero 2002: 53).
H(33) listed by Lett (1915: 127).
†H33 listed by Blockeel & Long (1998: 127).
H34 2001: on large ash by road, 90 m alt., Carricknahorna, N of crossroads, G96, NG Hodgetts 3906 (Rothero 2003: 58-59).
2001: on ash tree by disused railway, 100 m alt., Barnesmore Gap, SE of Ardinawark, H08, NG Hodgetts 3885 (Rothero 2003: 58-59).
H(35) listed by Lett (1915: 127).
†H35 listed by Blockeel & Long (1998: 127).
H36 2002: on bark of *Robinia* in ornamental grounds, 100 m alt., Drum Manor Forest Park, H77, DT Holyoak 02-1092 (Rothero 2003: 59).
H(38) listed by Lett (1915: 127). H(38) listed by Blockeel & Long (1998: 127).
H38 1999: on bole of sycamore with *Metzgeria furcata*, 55 m alt., Tollymore Forest park, 4 km W of Newcastle, J33, TL Blockeel 28/333 (Rothero 2000: 56).
H(39) listed by Lett (1915: 127).
†H39 listed by Blockeel & Long (1998: 127).
H(40) listed by Lett (1915: 127).
†H40 listed by Blockeel & Long (1998: 127).

[116/4 ***Zygodon gracilis*** Wilson]

[Listed for H16 by Lett (1915: 127) as: Connemara, leg. Wilson, but subsequently dismissed as an error].

117/1 ***Orthotrichum lyellii*** Hook. & Taylor

[H(1) listed by Lett (1915: 128) without details. H1 deleted because no valid record or voucher specimen traced (Blockeel 1999: 7)].
H(2) listed by Lett (1915: 128). H(2) listed by Blockeel & Long (1998: 127).
H4 1967: on tree, Dripsey Castle, nr Cork, RD Fitzgerald (Crundwell 1968: 642).
H(6) 1933: Cappagh, E Armitage (anon. 1934b: 121).
†H6 listed by Blockeel & Long (1998: 127).
H(7) listed by Lett (1915: 128) without locality.
†H7 listed by Blockeel & Long (1998: 127).
H8 1966: sycamore in hedge, Glenbrohane, nr Ballylanders, MFV Corley & JS Parker (Perry 1967: 419).
H10 1968: in wood, edge of R. Brosna, nr Birr, G Drennan (Crundwell 1969: 887).
H(11) listed by Lett (1915: 128).
†H11 listed by Blockeel & Long (1998: 127).
H(12) listed by Lett (1915: 128).
†H12 listed by Blockeel & Long (1998: 127).
H(13) listed by Lett (1915: 128).
†H13 listed by Blockeel & Long (1998: 127).
H14 1955: tree, Abbeyleix demesne, JS Thomson (Warburg 1956: 155).
H(18) listed by Lett (1915: 128). H(18) listed by Blockeel & Long (1998: 127).
H(19) listed by Lett (1915: 128).
†H19 listed by Blockeel & Long (1998: 127).
H(20) listed by Lett (1915: 128).
†H20 listed by Blockeel & Long (1998: 127).
H(21) listed by Lett (1915: 128).
†H21 listed by Blockeel & Long (1998: 127).
H(22) listed by Lett (1915: 128).
†H22 listed by Blockeel & Long (1998: 127).
H(23) listed by Lett (1915: 128).
†H23 listed by Blockeel & Long (1998: 127).
H24 1980: on sallow, shore of Lough Kinale,

DM Synnott (Hill 1981: 32).
H(30) listed by Lett (1915: 128). H(30) listed by Blockeel & Long (1998: 127).
H30 2001: on bark of sallow in carr, 75 m alt., N shore of Lough Sheelin, NW of Mount Nugent, N48, DT Holyoak 01-670 (Rothero 2002: 53).
H(31) listed by Lett (1915: 128). H(31) listed by Blockeel & Long (1998: 127).
H(32) listed by Lett (1915: 128). H(32) listed by Blockeel & Long (1998: 127).
H(33) listed by Lett (1915: 128).
†H33 listed by Blockeel & Long (1998: 127).
H(36) listed by Lett (1915: 128).
†H36 listed by Blockeel & Long (1998: 127).
H37 1964: ash tree, Derrylee, E of Verner's Bridge, RD Fitzgerald (Warburg 1965: 869).
H(38) listed by Lett (1915: 128).
†H38 listed by Blockeel & Long (1998: 127).
H(39) listed by Lett (1915: 128). H(39) listed by Blockeel & Long (1998: 127).
H39 1999: on *Acer pseudoplatanus* beside track in deciduous woodland, Glenarm Forest at N end, D31, DT Holyoak 99-836 (BBSUK) (Rothero 2000: 56).
H(40) listed by Blockeel & Long (1998: 127).
H40 1999: on ash tree at edge of deciduous plantation, Altalacky River, NW of Moneyeany [*sic* = Moneyneany], H79, DT Holyoak 99-718 (BBSUK) (Rothero 2000: 56).

117/2 ***Orthotrichum striatum*** Hedw.
(syn. *Orthotrichum leiocarpum* Bruch, Schimp. & W.Gümbel, *O. shawii* Wilson ex Schimp.)

H(1) listed by Lett (1915: 127) without details.
†H1 listed by Blockeel & Long (1998: 127).
H(2) listed by Lett (1915: 127). H(2) listed by Blockeel & Long (1998: 127).
H(3) listed by Lett (1915: 127).
†H3 listed by Blockeel & Long (1998: 127).
H(4) listed by Lett (1915: 127).
†H4 listed by Blockeel & Long (1998: 127).
H5 1956: sallows, Ballyvergan East, Youghal, EC Wallace (Warburg 1957: 332).
H(6) 1933: Cappagh Lake, E Armitage (anon. 1934b: 121).
†H6 listed by Blockeel & Long (1998: 127).
H9 1957: hawthorn scrub, Slievecarran, EM Lobley (BBS exc.) (Warburg 1958b: 481).
H10 1979: on *Salix* in wood below conifer plantation, S slope of Keeper Hill, JA Paton (Hill 1982: 28).
H12 1954: oak, Curragh Wood, Inch, JS Thomson (Warburg 1955: 585).
H(13) listed by Lett (1915: 127). H(13) listed by Blockeel & Long (1998: 127).
H(14) listed by Lett (1915: 127).
†H14 listed by Blockeel & Long (1998: 127).
H15 1994: branches of poplar tree in garden, Coole, M40, NG Hodgetts 2958 (Blockeel 1995c: 45).
H17 1990: on branch of Ash tree, 15 m alt., shore of L. Corrib, SW of Headford, M24, TL Blockeel 19/560 (Blockeel 1991c: 44).
H(20) listed by Lett (1915: 127).
†H20 listed by Blockeel & Long (1998: 127).
H(21) listed by Lett (1915: 127). H(21) listed by Blockeel & Long (1998: 127).
H23 1953: Forestry Dept., Clonhugh, NE end of L. Owel, JS Thomson (Warburg 1954: 483).
H25 1965: tree, *ca* 400 ft alt., 1 mile N of Ballyfarnan, RD Fitzgerald & EM Lobley (Warburg 1966: 200).
H28 1965: dead shrub nr Percy Mount, nr L. Gill, EF Warburg (Warburg 1966: 200).
H29 2000: on branch of *Corylus* in scrub on lough edge, Lough Gill, E shore, G73, DT Holyoak 00-558 (BBSUK) (Rothero 2001: 45).
H30 2001: on sallow in scrub on lough shore, 95 m alt., Lough Ramor at Deerpark, W of Virginia, N58, DT Holyoak 01-660 (Rothero 2002: 53).
H(31) 1943: Ravensdale, JS Thomson (Duncan 1944: 212).
[H32 deleted because no valid record or voucher specimen traced (Blockeel 1999: 7)].
H(33) listed by Lett (1915: 127).
†H33 listed by Blockeel & Long (1998: 127).
H(36) listed by Lett (1915: 127).
†H36 listed by Blockeel & Long (1998: 127).
[H(37) listed by Lett (1915: 127) without locality. H37 deleted because no valid record or voucher specimen traced (Blockeel 1999: 7)].
H(38) listed by Lett (1915: 127). H(38) listed by Blockeel & Long (1998: 127).
H(39) listed by Lett (1915: 127). H(39) listed by Blockeel & Long (1998: 127).
H39 1999: on *Acer pseudoplatanus* beside

track in deciduous woodland, Glenarm Forest at N end, D31, DT Holyoak 99-837 (BBSUK) (Rothero 2000: 56).
H(40) listed by Lett (1915: 127). H(40) listed by Blockeel & Long (1998: 127).
H40 1999: on hazel nr edge of clearing, Banagher Glen, C60, DT Holyoak 99-641 (BBSUK) (Rothero 2000: 56).

117/4 ***Orthotrichum affine*** Brid.
(syn. *Orthotrichum affine* var. *fastigiatum* (Brid.) Huebener, *O. affine* var. *rivale* Wilson ex Braithw.)

H(1) listed by Lett (1915: 127) without details.
†H1 listed by Blockeel & Long (1998: 127).
H(2) listed by Lett (1915: 127) without details.
†H2 listed by Blockeel & Long (1998: 127).
H(3) listed by Lett (1915: 127) without details.
†H3 listed by Blockeel & Long (1998: 127).
H(4) listed by Lett (1915: 127) without details.
†H4 listed by Blockeel & Long (1998: 127).
H(5) listed by Lett (1915: 127) without details.
†H5 listed by Blockeel & Long (1998: 127).
H(6) listed by Lett (1915: 127) without details.
†H6 listed by Blockeel & Long (1998: 127).
H(8) listed by Lett (1915: 127) without details.
†H8 listed by Blockeel & Long (1998: 127).
H(9) listed by Lett (1915: 127) without details.
†H9 listed by Blockeel & Long (1998: 127).
H(10) listed by Lett (1915: 127) without details.
†H10 listed by Blockeel & Long (1998: 127).
H(11) listed by Lett (1915: 127) without details.
†H11 listed by Blockeel & Long (1998: 127).
H(12) listed by Lett (1915: 127) without details.
†H12 listed by Blockeel & Long (1998: 127).
H(13) listed by Lett (1915: 127) without details.
†H13 listed by Blockeel & Long (1998: 127).
H(14) listed by Lett (1915: 127) without details.
†H14 listed by Blockeel & Long (1998: 127).
H15 1957: Garrylands Wood, J Appleyard (BBS exc.) (Warburg 1958b: 481).
[H(16) listed by Lett (1915: 127) without details. H16 deleted because no valid record or voucher specimen traced (Blockeel 1999: 7)].
[H(17) listed by Lett (1915: 127) without details. H17 deleted because no valid record or voucher specimen traced (Blockeel 1999: 7)].
[H(18) listed by Lett (1915: 127) without details. H18 deleted because no valid record or voucher specimen traced (Blockeel 1999: 7)].
H(19) listed by Lett (1915: 127) without details.
†H19 listed by Blockeel & Long (1998: 127).
H(20) listed by Lett (1915: 127) without details.
†H20 listed by Blockeel & Long (1998: 127).
H(21) listed by Lett (1915: 127).
†H21 listed by Blockeel & Long (1998: 127).
H22 1950: elder, Slane, JS Thomson (Warburg 1952: 103).
†H23 listed by Blockeel & Long (1998: 127).
H24 1965: trees in wood nr Cloonart Bridge, S of Roosky, EM Lobley & RD Fitzgerald (Warburg 1966: 200).
H(25) listed by Lett (1915: 127).
H25 1970: willow nr L. Ree, Barry Beg, N of Athlone, JA Paton (Crundwell 1971b: 381).
H(26) listed by Lett (1915: 127) without details.
†H26 listed by Blockeel & Long (1998: 127).
[H(27) listed by Lett (1915: 127) without details. H27 deleted because no valid record or voucher specimen traced (Blockeel 1999: 7)].
H(28) listed by Lett (1915: 127) without details.
†H28 listed by Blockeel & Long (1998: 127).
H(29) listed by Lett (1915: 127) without details.
†H29 listed by Blockeel & Long (1998: 127).
H(30) listed by Lett (1915: 127) without details.
†H30 listed by Blockeel & Long (1998: 127).
[H(31) listed by Lett (1915: 127) without details. H31 deleted because no valid record or voucher specimen traced (Blockeel 1999: 7)].
[H(32) listed by Lett (1915: 127) without details. H32 deleted because no valid record or voucher specimen traced (Blockeel 1999: 7)].
H(33) listed by Lett (1915: 127) without

details.
†H33 listed by Blockeel & Long (1998: 127).
H(34) listed by Lett (1915: 127) without details.
†H34 listed by Blockeel & Long (1998: 127).
H(35) listed by Lett (1915: 127) without details.
†H35 listed by Blockeel & Long (1998: 127).
H(36) listed by Lett (1915: 127) without details.
†H36 listed by Blockeel & Long (1998: 127).
H(37) listed by Lett (1915: 127) without details.
†H37 listed by Blockeel & Long (1998: 127).
H(38) listed by Lett (1915: 127) without details. H(38) listed by Blockeel & Long (1998: 127).
H38 1999: on bole of beech tree, 55 m alt., Tollymore Forest park, 4 km W of Newcastle, J33, TL Blockeel 28/343 (Rothero 2000: 56).
H(39) listed by Lett (1915: 127). H(39) listed by Blockeel & Long (1998: 127).
H39 1999: on bark of *Salix cinerea* in *Salix* scrub at edge of lough, Lough Guile, D02, DT Holyoak 99-136 (BBSUK) (Rothero 2000: 56).
H(40) listed by Lett (1915: 127) without details.
†H40 listed by Blockeel & Long (1998: 127).

117/5 ***Orthotrichum rupestre*** Schleich. ex Schwägr.
(syn. *Orthotrichum rupestre* var. *rupincola* (Funck) Huebener, *O. rupestre* var. *sturmii* (Hoppe & Hornsch.) Jur.)

H(1) listed by Lett (1915: 127). H(1) listed by Blockeel & Long (1998: 128).
H(2) listed by Lett (1915: 127).
†H2 listed by Blockeel & Long (1998: 128).
H(16) listed by Lett (1915: 127).
†H16 listed by Blockeel & Long (1998: 128).
H(20) listed by Lett (1915: 127). H(20) listed by Blockeel & Long (1998: 128).
H(21) listed by Lett (1915: 127).
†H21 listed by Blockeel & Long (1998: 128).
H25 1968: on limestone wall, Ballagh, 4 miles NW of Lanesborough, WV Rubers *et al.* (U) (Crundwell 1974: 173).
H(26) listed by Lett (1915: 127). H(26) listed by Blockeel & Long (1998: 128).
H(27) listed by Lett (1915: 127).
†H27 listed by Blockeel & Long (1998: 128).
H28 1965: rocks by L. Gill nr Ennisfree, EM Lobley & RD Fitzgerald (Warburg 1966: 200).
H29 1972: on siliceous outcrop, E end of L. Gill, N of Dromahair, WV Rubers (U) (Crundwell 1974: 173).
H(34) listed by Lett (1915: 127). H(34) listed by Blockeel & Long (1998: 128).
H34 2002: on open sloping shale rocks on slope below dunes, 10 m alt., Doagh Isle NE of Ballyliffin, C45, DT Holyoak 02-482 (Rothero 2003: 59).
H(35) listed by Lett (1915: 127) without details.
†H35 listed by Blockeel & Long (1998: 128).
H(37) listed by Lett (1915: 127). H(37) listed by Blockeel & Long (1998: 128).
H(38) listed by Lett (1915: 127). H(38) listed by Blockeel & Long (1998: 128).
H(39) listed by Lett (1915: 127).
†H39 listed by Blockeel & Long (1998: 128).
H(40) listed by Blockeel & Long (1998: 128).
H40 1999: on top of basalt boulder on slope below crags, 260 m alt., Binevenagh, W slopes, DT Holyoak 99-567A (BBSUK) (Rothero 2000: 56).

117/8 ***Orthotrichum anomalum*** Hedw.
(syn. *Orthotrichum anomalum* var. *cylindricum* Schimp., *O. anomalum* var. *saxatile* auct.)

H1 1951: wall nr station, Glenbeigh, J Appleyard (BBS exc.) (Warburg 1952: 103), as var. *saxatile*.
H(2) listed by Lett (1915: 128).
H2 1951: wall, Tralee, AC Crundwell (Warburg 1952: 103), as var. *saxatile*.
†H3 listed by Blockeel & Long (1998: 128).
H(4) listed by Lett (1915: 128, 129).
†H4 listed by Blockeel & Long (1998: 128).
H5 1966: bridge over R. Douglas, nr Kilworth, J Appleyard *et al.* (BBS exc.) (Perry 1967: 419).
H(6) 1933: Knock Mann, E Armitage (anon. 1934b: 121), as var. *saxatile*.
†H6 listed by Blockeel & Long (1998: 128).
H7 1966: wall by road, Bansha, J Appleyard *et al.* (BBS exc.) (Perry 1967: 419).
H(8) listed by Lett (1915: 129).
†H8 listed by Blockeel & Long (1998: 128).
H(9) listed by Lett (1915: 128, 129).
†H9 listed by Blockeel & Long (1998: 128).
H(10) listed by Lett (1915: 128, 129).
†H10 listed by Blockeel & Long (1998: 128).

H(11) listed by Lett (1915: 129).
†H11 listed by Blockeel & Long (1998: 128).
H12 1954: stone gatepost, Dumbrody Abbey, ALK King (Warburg 1955: 585), as var. *saxatile*.
H(13) listed by Lett (1915: 128).
†H13 listed by Blockeel & Long (1998: 128).
H(14) listed by Lett (1915: 128).
†H14 listed by Blockeel & Long (1998: 128).
H(15) listed by Lett (1915: 129).
†H15 listed by Blockeel & Long (1998: 128).
H(16) listed by Lett (1915: 129).
†H16 listed by Blockeel & Long (1998: 128).
H17 1955: limestone, Ballindooly, ALK King (Warburg 1956: 154), as var. *saxatile*.
H(18) listed by Lett (1915: 129).
†H18 listed by Blockeel & Long (1998: 128).
H(19) listed by Lett (1915: 129) without details.
†H19 listed by Blockeel & Long (1998: 128).
H(20) listed by Lett (1915: 129) without locality.
†H20 listed by Blockeel & Long (1998: 128).
H(21) listed by Lett (1915: 129).
†H21 listed by Blockeel & Long (1998: 128).
H22 1950: wall-top, Slane, JS Thomson (Warburg 1952: 103), as var. *saxatile*.
H(23) listed by Lett (1915: 129).
†H23 listed by Blockeel & Long (1998: 128).
H24 1965: wall, Cloonart Bridge, RD Fitzgerald & EM Lobley (Warburg 1966: 200).
H(25) listed by Lett (1915: 129).
†H25 listed by Blockeel & Long (1998: 128).
H(26) listed by Lett (1915: 129).
†H26 listed by Blockeel & Long (1998: 128).
H(27) listed by Lett (1915: 129).
†H27 listed by Blockeel & Long (1998: 128).
H(28) listed by Lett (1915: 129).
H(28) 1928: rocks above Glencar Lough, N side (BBS exc.) (Duncan 1928: 119), as var. *saxatile*.
†H28 listed by Blockeel & Long (1998: 128).
H(29) listed by Lett (1915: 129).
†H29 listed by Blockeel & Long (1998: 128).
H(30) listed by Lett (1915: 129).
†H30 listed by Blockeel & Long (1998: 128).
H(31) listed by Lett (1915: 129).
†H31 listed by Blockeel & Long (1998: 128).
H(32) listed by Lett (1915: 129).
H32 1952: limestone, Lisgall, nr Carrickmacross, RD Fitzgerald (Warburg 1953: 312), as var. *saxatile*.
H(33) listed by Lett (1915: 129).
†H33 listed by Blockeel & Long (1998: 128).
H(34) listed by Lett (1915: 129).
H(34) 1945: Fahan, W Inishowen, AM Irvin (anon. 1946c: 282).
†H34 listed by Blockeel & Long (1998: 128).
H(35) listed by Lett (1915: 129).
†H35 listed by Blockeel & Long (1998: 128).
H(36) listed by Lett (1915: 129).
†H36 listed by Blockeel & Long (1998: 128).
H(37) listed by Lett (1915: 129) without locality.
†H37 listed by Blockeel & Long (1998: 128).
H(38) listed by Lett (1915: 129). H(38) listed by Blockeel & Long (1998: 128).
H38 2002: on mortar of old wall, 7 m alt., SE of Castle I., Strangford Lough, J54, DT Holyoak 02-995 (Rothero 2003: 59).
H(39) listed by Lett (1915: 129).
†H39 listed by Blockeel & Long (1998: 128).
H(40) listed by Lett (1915: 129).
†H40 listed by Blockeel & Long (1998: 128).

117/9a *Orthotrichum cupulatum* Brid. **var. *cupulatum***

H1 1951: among boulders by L. Gab, Dingle Peninsula, AC Crundwell (Warburg 1952: 103).
H2 1951: stone steps, old Kenmare House, Killarney, JS Thomson (Warburg 1953: 312).
H(4) listed by Lett (1915: 128).
†H4 listed by Blockeel & Long (1998: 128).
H5 1951: Fermoy Station Platform, AC Crundwell & EF Warburg (Warburg 1952: 103).
H6 1972: roadside, Glenshelane River nr Broemountain, N of Cappoquin, WV Rubers (U) (Crundwell 1974: 173).
H7 1962: wall by left bank of R. Suir, Clonmel, ALK King (Warburg 1963b: 500).
H(8) listed by Lett (1915: 128).
†H8 listed by Blockeel & Long (1998: 128).
H9 1979: limestone boulder beside Fin Lough, NE of Newmarket on Fergus, JA Paton (Hill 1980b: 44).
H10 1952: rocks, Terryglass Bay, L. Derg, MPH Kertland & ALK King (Warburg 1953: 312).
H15 1952: limestone at Ross Quay, L. Derg, MPH Kertland & ALK King (Warburg 1953: 312).
H(16) listed by Lett (1915: 128).
†H16 listed by Blockeel & Long (1998: 128).
H17 1966: limestone wall, Derreen, N of

Monivea, MFV Corley & JS Parker (Perry 1967: 419).
H19 1968: on limestone rock by towpath of Grand Canal nr Naas, ALK King (Crundwell 1969: 887).
H(21) listed by Lett (1915: 128).
†H21 listed by Blockeel & Long (1998: 128).
H23 1952: rocks by R. Shannon, Carrickobreen, Athlone, JP Brunker & ALK King (Warburg 1953: 312).
H25 1959: by L. Funshinagh, ALK King (Warburg 1960: 777).
H(26) listed by Lett (1915: 128).
†H26 listed by Blockeel & Long (1998: 128).
H(28) listed by Lett (1915: 128). H(28) listed by Blockeel & Long (1998: 128).
H28 2001: on limestone steps, 35 m alt., Creevykeel megalithic tomb, G75, NG Hodgetts 3724 (Rothero 2002: 53).
H29 1959: rock by L. Gill at Parke's Castle, ALK King (Warburg 1960: 777).
H30 1956: wall, Virginia, JS Thomson (Warburg 1957: 332).
H32 1950: limestone, L. Aphuca, RD Fitzgerald (Warburg 1951: 500).
H33 2000: on large limestone boulder in grassland, Marble Arch, by visitor centre, H13, DT Holyoak 00-143 (BBSUK) (Rothero 2001: 45).
H34 1969: rock on shore below Soldier's Hill, NW of Malin, JA Paton (Crundwell 1970: 207).
H(35) listed by Lett (1915: 128).
†H35 listed by Blockeel & Long (1998: 128).
H(38) listed by Lett (1915: 128). H(38) listed by Blockeel & Long (1998: 128).
H(39) listed by Lett (1915: 128). H(39) listed by Blockeel & Long (1998: 128).
H39 1999: on chalk rock in disused quarry, E of Cranny Falls, D21, DT Holyoak 99-828 (BBSUK) (Rothero 2000: 56).
[H(40) listed by Lett (1915: 128) without locality. H40 deleted because no valid record or voucher specimen traced (Blockeel 1999: 7)].

117/9b *Orthotrichum cupulatum* var. *riparium* Huebener
(syn. *Orthotrichum cupulatum* var. *nudum* (Dicks.) Braithw.)

H6 1968: wall on W bank of R. Blackwater, S of Cappoquin, JA Paton (Crundwell 1969: 887).
[H(8) listed by Lett (1915: 128) as: Anacotty, leg. Miss Armitage. H8 deleted because no valid record or voucher specimen traced (Blockeel 1999: 7)].
[H(9) listed by Lett (1915: 128) without details. H9 deleted because no valid record or voucher specimen traced (Blockeel 1999: 7)].
H13 1999: at base of sycamore on bank of river, 5 m alt., R Barrow, nr canal lock, 1 km NW of Saint Mullins, S73, TL Blockeel 28/320 (Rothero 2000: 56).
†H21 listed by Blockeel & Long (1998: 128).
H22 1979: rocks by Lough Sheelin, Ross, DM Synnott (Hill 1980b: 44).
H24 1980: W shore of Lough Kinale, DM Synnott (Hill 1981: 32).
[H(26) 1910: Lough Carra, WN Tetley (anon. 1911c: 10). H(26) listed by Lett (1915: 128) as 1910: L. Carra, leg. Tetley. H26 deleted because no valid record or voucher specimen traced (Blockeel 1999: 7)].
H30 2001: on vertical concrete wall by lough, 75 m alt., N shore of Lough Sheelin, NW of Mount Nugent, N48, DT Holyoak 01-688 (Rothero 2002: 53).
[H(33) listed by Lett (1915: 128) as 1907: Devenish I., leg. Tetley. H33 deleted because no valid record or voucher specimen traced (Blockeel 1999: 7)].
H33 2000: on limestone boulders in grassland at lough edge, Upper Lough Erne, S of Carragh, H32, DT Holyoak 00-323 (BBSUK) (Rothero 2001: 45).
H(34) 1937: Bundoran, no collector named (BBS exc.) (Armitage 1938: 12), as var. *nudum*.
H36 1957: concrete gate-post, Benburb, RD Fitzgerald (Warburg 1960: 777).
H37 2002: on boulder at edge of lough, 14 m alt., Lough Neagh at Oxford I., J06, DT Holyoak 02-1009 (Rothero 2003: 59).
[H38 deleted because no valid record or voucher specimen traced (Blockeel 1999: 7)].
H(39) listed by Lett (1915: 128). H(39) listed by Blockeel & Long (1998: 128).
H(40) listed by Lett (1915: 128).
†H40 listed by Blockeel & Long (1998: 128).

117/10 *Orthotrichum rivulare* Turner

H(1) listed by Lett (1915: 129).
†H1 listed by Blockeel & Long (1998: 128).
H(2) listed by Lett (1915: 129). H(2) listed by

Blockeel & Long (1998: 128).
H(4) listed by Lett (1915: 129).
†H4 listed by Blockeel & Long (1998: 128).
H5 1999: on lower part of trunk of alder, 8 m alt., R Bride, Little Grace, *ca* 2 km W of Tallowbridge, W99, TL Blockeel & DH Wrench 28/262 (Rothero 2000: 56).
H(6) listed by Lett (1915: 129).
†H6 listed by Blockeel & Long (1998: 128).
H8 1994: on willow subject to inundation, 6 km E of Abbeyfeale, by bridge over Allaghaun River, R12, E Wiltshire & S Reynolds (Blockeel 1995c: 45).
H9 1972: on willow branch by stream, Parteen, N of Limerick, WV Rubers (U) (Crundwell 1974: 173).
H13 1969: on ash-tree by R. Slaney, Aghade Bridge, nr Tullow, RD Fitzgerald (Crundwell 1970: 207).
H(20) listed by Lett (1915: 129). H(20) listed by Blockeel & Long (1998: 128).
H(21) listed by Lett (1915: 129). H(21) listed by Blockeel & Long (1998: 128).
H29 1963: alder bole by stream, Bawn, 1 mile S of Dromahair, AR Perry & RD Fitzgerald (Warburg 1964: 731).
H30 2001: on sallow and alder by river, 95 m alt., Owenmore River, NW of Glengevlin, H02, DT Holyoak 01-648 (Rothero 2002: 53).
H(31) listed by Lett (1915: 129).
†H31 listed by Blockeel & Long (1998: 128).
†H36 listed by Blockeel & Long (1998: 128).
H(38) listed by Lett (1915: 129). H(38) listed by Blockeel & Long (1998: 128).
H38 2002: on branch of *Salix cinerea* in carr at edge of lake, 5 m alt., E side of Quoile Pondage Basin NNR, Downpatrick, J44, DT Holyoak 02-993 (Rothero 2003: 59).
H(39) listed by Lett (1915: 129). H(39) listed by Blockeel & Long (1998: 128).
H(40) 1937: Castledawson, WR Megaw (anon. 1938d: 40).

117/11 ***Orthotrichum sprucei*** Mont.

H(2) listed by Lett (1915: 129). H(2) listed by Blockeel & Long (1998: 128).
H5 1999: at the base of trunk of alder on bank of river, 8 m alt., R Bride, Little Grace, 2 km W of Tallowbridge, Tallow, W99, TL Blockeel 28/260 (Rothero 2000: 57).
H(6) listed by Lett (1915: 129). H(6) listed by Blockeel & Long (1998: 128).
H6 1999: on alder on bank of river, 8 m alt., Tallowbridge, Tallow, W99, TL Blockeel 28/259 (Rothero 2000: 57).
H12 1975: alder trunks nr R. Bann, Camolin, JA Paton (BBS exc.) (Crundwell 1976: 30).
H29 2000: on *Alnus* on river bank, Bonet River, below Gortgarrigan Bridge, G83, DT Holyoak 00-577 (BBSUK) (Rothero 2001: 45).
H(38) listed by Lett (1915: 129). H(38) listed by Blockeel & Long (1998: 128).
H38 2002: on silt-encrusted tree in flood zone, River Lagan, Drumbridge, R Weyl, conf. DT Holyoak (Rothero 2003: 59).
H(39) listed by Lett (1915: 129). H(39) listed by Blockeel & Long (1998: 128).

117/12 ***Orthotrichum stramineum*** Hornsch. ex Brid.

[H(1) listed by Lett (1915: 129) as: Ross Bay, leg. Carrington. H1 deleted because the only record traced (Ross Bay, B Carrington, in Lett 1915) is from H2, comm. NF Stewart (Blockeel 1995c: 45)].
H(2) listed by Lett (1915: 129). H(2) listed by Blockeel & Long (1998: 129).
H(10) listed by Lett (1915: 129). H(10) listed by Blockeel & Long (1998: 129).
H(11) listed by Lett (1915: 129). H(11) listed by Blockeel & Long (1998: 129).
H(12) listed by Lett (1915: 129).
†H12 listed by Blockeel & Long (1998: 129).
H(20) listed by Lett (1915: 129).
†H20 listed by Blockeel & Long (1998: 129).
H(38) listed by Lett (1915: 129). H(38) listed by Blockeel & Long (1998: 129).
H(39) listed by Lett (1915: 129). H(39) listed by Blockeel & Long (1998: 129).

117/13 ***Orthotrichum tenellum*** Bruch ex Brid.

H1 1951: old willow, nr L. Currane, J Appleyard (BBS exc.) (Warburg 1952: 103).
H(2) listed by Lett (1915: 130).
†H2 listed by Blockeel & Long (1998: 129).
H(3) listed by Lett (1915: 130). H(3) listed by Blockeel & Long (1998: 129).
H(5) listed by Lett (1915: 130). H(5) listed by Blockeel & Long (1998: 129).
H(6) listed by Lett (1915: 130).

H6 1966: tree nr L. Ballin, Kill, J Appleyard (BBS exc.) (Perry 1967: 419).
H7 1956: by R. Suir nr Knocklofty, EC Wallace (Warburg 1957: 332).
†H8 listed by Blockeel & Long (1998: 129).
H9 1979: on *Sambucus* nr Clonlea Lough. E of Kilkishen, JA Paton (Hill 1980b: 44).
H(11) listed by Lett (1915: 130). H(11) listed by Blockeel & Long (1998: 129).
H12 1953: apple trees, Inch, WR Megaw (Warburg 1954: 483).
H15 1960: bark of *Ulex europaeus*, by roadside between Gort and Derrybrien, MCF Proctor (Warburg 1961: 167).
H(20) listed by Lett (1915: 130). H(20) listed by Blockeel & Long (1998: 129).
H(21) listed by Lett (1915: 130). H(21) listed by Blockeel & Long (1998: 129).
H29 1963: alder at side of stream, Bawn, 1 mile S of Dromahair, RD Fitzgerald & AR Perry (Warburg 1964: 731).
H31 1967: woodland, Beaulieu, Drogheda, DM Synnott (Crundwell 1968: 642).
[H32 deleted because no valid record or voucher specimen traced (Blockeel 1999: 7)].
†H33 listed by Blockeel & Long (1998: 129).
H(34) 1937: on hawthorn by River Erne, Ballyshannon, no collector named (BBS exc.) (Armitage 1938: 12).
†H36 listed by Blockeel & Long (1998: 129).
H(38) listed by Lett (1915: 130). H(38) listed by Blockeel & Long (1998: 129).
H38 1999: on willow by river, River Lagan, Drum, J36, DT Holyoak 99-871 (BBSUK) (Rothero 2000: 57).
H(39) 1937: apple tree, Aghalee, nr Lurgan, JS Thomson, comm. RD Fitzgerald (Warburg 1966: 200).
†H40 listed by Blockeel & Long (1998: 129).

117/14 ***Orthotrichum pallens*** Bruch ex Brid.

H(4) no date: nr Cork, Carroll (Lett 1915: 130). H(4) listed by Blockeel & Long (1998: 129).
[H(16) listed by Lett (1915: 130) as: nr Galway, leg. Moore. H16 deleted because no valid record or voucher specimen traced (Blockeel 1999: 7)].
[H17 deleted because no valid record or voucher specimen traced (Blockeel 1999: 7)].
H(20) no date: Westaston, Moore (Lett 1915: 130). H(20) listed by Blockeel & Long (1998: 129).
H(21) 1871: Baldoyle, Moore (Lett 1915: 130). H(21) listed by Blockeel & Long (1998: 129).
H26 1970: on sycamore E of Ballintober, MFV Corley (Crundwell 1971b: 381).

[117/15 ***Orthotrichum pumilum*** Sw.]
(syn. *Orthotrichum schimperi* Hammar)

[Records from H3, H19, H21 and H37 listed by Lett (1915: 129) are all dismissed as errors and hence the species is absent from recent *CC*].

117/16 ***Orthotrichum diaphanum*** Brid.
(syn. *Orthotrichum diaphanum* var. *aquaticum* Davies ex Vent.)

[H(1) listed by Lett (1915: 128) without details. H1 deleted because no valid record or voucher specimen traced (Blockeel 1999: 7)].
H(2) listed by Lett (1915: 128).
†H2 listed by Blockeel & Long (1998: 129).
H3 1966: wall of bridge, Sandy Cove, S of Kinsale, MFV Corley & JS Parker (Perry 1967: 419).
H(4) listed by Lett (1915: 128).
†H4 listed by Blockeel & Long (1998: 129).
H(5) listed by Lett (1915: 128).
†H5 listed by Blockeel & Long (1998: 129).
H6 1956: wall, nr Dungarvan, EC Wallace (Warburg 1957: 333).
H7 1966: fallen branch, edge of bog S of Longfordpass Bridge, nr Urlingford, J Appleyard *et al.* (BBS exc.) (Perry 1967: 419).
H(8) listed by Lett (1915: 128).
†H8 listed by Blockeel & Long (1998: 129).
H(9) listed by Lett (1915: 128). H(9) listed by Blockeel & Long (1998: 129).
H10 1967: concrete gate post, Knockfine, Keeper Hill, RD Fitzgerald (Crundwell 1968: 643).
H(11) listed by Lett (1915: 128).
†H11 listed by Blockeel & Long (1998: 129).
H(12) listed by Lett (1915: 128).
†H12 listed by Blockeel & Long (1998: 129).
H13 1969: old elder, Burreen River, Sheean, nr Myshall, RD Fitzgerald (Crundwell 1970: 207).
H(14) listed by Lett (1915: 128).
†H14 listed by Blockeel & Long (1998: 129).
H(15) listed by Lett (1915: 128). H(15) listed

by Blockeel & Long (1998: 129).
H16 1950: nr Moycullen, ALK King (Warburg 1954: 483).
H(17) listed by Lett (1915: 128). H(17) listed by Blockeel & Long (1998: 129).
H(18) listed by Lett (1915: 128). H(18) listed by Blockeel & Long (1998: 129).
H(19) listed by Lett (1915: 128).
†H19 listed by Blockeel & Long (1998: 129).
H(20) listed by Lett (1915: 128) without locality.
†H20 listed by Blockeel & Long (1998: 129).
H(21) listed by Lett (1915: 128).
†H21 listed by Blockeel & Long (1998: 129).
H22 1964: stones in ditch, Hill of Tara, nr Navan, JW Fitzgerald & MPH Kertland (Warburg 1965: 869).
H(23) listed by Lett (1915: 128).
†H23 listed by Blockeel & Long (1998: 129).
H24 1965: elder, wood, Cloonart Bridge, RD Fitzgerald & EM Lobley (Warburg 1966: 200).
H25 1952: tree trunk in lane to Carrigynachten Bog, nr Athlone, ALK King (Warburg 1953: 312).
H(26) listed by Lett (1915: 128). H(26) listed by Blockeel & Long (1998: 129).
H(27) listed by Lett (1915: 128). H(27) listed by Blockeel & Long (1998: 129).
H(28) listed by Lett (1915: 128).
†H28 listed by Blockeel & Long (1998: 129).
H29 1963: alder beside stream, Bawn, 1 mile S of Dromahair, RD Fitzgerald & AR Perry (Warburg 1964: 731).
H(30) listed by Lett (1915: 128).
†H30 listed by Blockeel & Long (1998: 129).
H(31) listed by Lett (1915: 128). H(31) listed by Blockeel & Long (1998: 129).
H(32) 1947: alder, Hope Castle demesne, Castleblaney, JS Thomson (Warburg 1952: 103).
H(33) listed by Lett (1915: 128).
†H33 listed by Blockeel & Long (1998: 129).
H(34) listed by Lett (1915: 128). H(34) listed by Blockeel & Long (1998: 129).
H34 2002: on concrete fencepost in shallow ravine, 35 m alt., S of Soldiers Hill, NW of Malin, C45, DT Holyoak 02-568 (Rothero 2003: 59).
H35 1990: on wall top, 5 m alt., Dunfanaghy, C03, TL Blockeel 19/454 (Blockeel 1991c: 45).
H(36) listed by Lett (1915: 128).
†H36 listed by Blockeel & Long (1998: 129).
H(37) listed by Lett (1915: 128).
†H37 listed by Blockeel & Long (1998: 129).
H(38) listed by Lett (1915: 128). H(38) listed by Blockeel & Long (1998: 129).
H38 2002: on *Salix cinerea* in carr at edge of lake, 5 m alt., E side of Quoile Pondage Basin NNR, Downpatrick, J44, DT Holyoak 02-991 (Rothero 2003: 59).
H(39) listed by Lett (1915: 128).
†H39 listed by Blockeel & Long (1998: 129).
H(40) 1936: Kilrea, JD Houston (anon. 1937a: 367).
†H40 listed by Blockeel & Long (1998: 129).

117/17 *Orthotrichum pulchellum* Brunt.

H(2) listed by Lett (1915: 130). H(2) listed by Blockeel & Long (1998: 129).
H3 1964: *Fuchsia* bark, Bearhaven copper mines, nr Allihies, ERB Little (Perry 1967: 419).
H(4) listed by Lett (1915: 130).
†H4 listed by Blockeel & Long (1998: 129).
H(5) listed by Lett (1915: 130). H(5) listed by Blockeel & Long (1998: 129).
H5 2002: on *Salix* in wet ground, 40 m alt., Glenbower Wood, nr Killeagh, W97, TL Blockeel 31/312 (Rothero 2003: 59).
H6 1966: willow by R. Nier, nr Shanballyanne, Ballymacarbry, JA Paton (BBS exc.) (Perry 1967: 419).
H(8) listed by Lett (1915: 130).
†H8 listed by Blockeel & Long (1998: 129).
H(9) listed by Lett (1915: 130) without details.
†H9 listed by Blockeel & Long (1998: 129).
H10 1951: elder, wooded gully above Silvermines, AD Banwell, PJ Wanstall & EV Watson (Warburg 1953: 312).
H12 1975: *Salix* in old quarry, Carriganeagh River, S of Gorey, JA Paton (BBS exc.) (Crundwell 1976: 30).
H13 1999: on hazel on bank of stream, 30 m alt., Pollymounty River, N bank, Ballyknockcrumpin, S73, TL Blockeel 28/304 (Rothero 2000: 57).
H(14) listed by Lett (1915: 130).
†H14 listed by Blockeel & Long (1998: 129).
H15 1994: branch of elder, Pollboy, Boleyneendorish River, Slieve Aughty, M50, RC Stern (Blockeel 1995c: 45).
†H16 listed by Blockeel & Long (1998: 129).
H(19) listed by Lett (1915: 130). H(19) listed by Blockeel & Long (1998: 129).
H20 1974: elders by abandoned farm 1 miles [*sic*] W of Glendarragh, nr Newtown Mt

Kennedy, PH Pitkin (Crundwell 1975: 19).
H(21) listed by Lett (1915: 130). H(21) listed by Blockeel & Long (1998: 129).
H22 1967: on fallen larch, bank of R. Boyne, Glenmore, Oldbridge, DM Synnott (Crundwell 1968: 643).
H23 1953: apple, Woodlands garden, Ballinafid, JS Thomson (Warburg 1954: 483).
H24 1965: trees, wood, Cloonart Bridge, RD Fitzgerald & EM Lobley (Warburg 1966: 200).
H(25) listed by Lett (1915: 130).
†H25 listed by Blockeel & Long (1998: 129).
H26 1970: on sycamore E of Ballintober, MFV Corley (Crundwell 1971b: 381).
H27 1968: ash tree, Drummin Wood, W of Foxford, JA Paton (Crundwell 1969: 887).
H(28) 1939: Doonally river, JS Thomson (anon. 1940a: 174).
†H28 listed by Blockeel & Long (1998: 129).
H29 1963: hazel in wooded W-facing slope of limestone scarp, Boggaun, nr Manorhamilton, AR Perry & RD Fitzgerald (Warburg 1964: 731).
H30 1956: apple, Virginia, JS Thomson (Warburg 1957: 333).
H(32) 1947: on alder, Hope Castle demesne, Castleblaney, JS Thomson (anon. 1948b: 121).
H(33) listed by Lett (1915: 130).
†H33 listed by Blockeel & Long (1998: 129).
H(34) listed by Blockeel & Long (1998: 129).
H34 2002: on *Corylus* in scrub on steep slope above beach, 25 m alt., Kinnoge Bay, C64, DT Holyoak 02-540 (Rothero 2003: 59).
H(35) listed by Lett (1915: 130).
†H35 listed by Blockeel & Long (1998: 129).
H(36) listed by Lett (1915: 130).
†H36 listed by Blockeel & Long (1998: 129).
H(37) listed by Lett (1915: 130). H(37) listed by Blockeel & Long (1998: 129).
H(38) listed by Lett (1915: 130). H(38) listed by Blockeel & Long (1998: 129).
H38 2002: on *Fagus sylvatica* by pond, 45 m alt., Mill Pond, Tollymore Forest Park, J33, DT Holyoak 02-942 (Rothero 2003: 59).
H(39) listed by Lett (1915: 130). H(39) listed by Blockeel & Long (1998: 129).
H39 1999: on bark of *Salix cinerea* in *Salix* scrub at edge of lough, Lough Guile, D02, DT Holyoak 99-315 (BBSUK) (Rothero 2000: 57).
H(40) listed by Lett (1915: 130).
†H40 listed by Blockeel & Long (1998: 129).

118/1 ***Ulota coarctata*** (P.Beauv.) Hammar (syn. *Weissia coarctata* (P.Beauv.) Lindb.)

H(1) 1861: Glena Killarney, Carrington (Lett 1915: 130). H(1) listed by Blockeel & Long (1998: 129).
H(2) 1861: Torc Wood, Carrington (Lett 1915: 130).
†H2 listed by Blockeel & Long (1998: 129).

118/2 ***Ulota drummondii*** (Hook. & Grev.) Brid.
(syn. *Weissia drummondii* (Hook. & Grev.) Lindb.)

H(1) listed by Lett (1915: 130) without locality.
†H1 listed by Blockeel & Long (1998: 129).
H(2) listed by Lett (1915: 130). H(2) listed by Blockeel & Long (1998: 129).
H(6) listed by Lett (1915: 130). H(6) listed by Blockeel & Long (1998: 129).
H(7) listed by Lett (1915: 130).
†H7 listed by Blockeel & Long (1998: 129).
H10 1979: on *Salix*, E slope of Keeper Hill, S of Silvermine Mts, HMH van Melick (Hill 1981: 33).
H16 1994: tree branch, Derryclare Wood, L84, JA Paton 2702 (Blockeel 1995c: 45).
H(20) listed by Lett (1915: 130). H(20) listed by Blockeel & Long (1998: 129).
H21 1969: willow nr stream, N slope of Killakee Mt., JA Paton (Crundwell 1970: 207).
H(33) listed by Lett (1915: 130).
†H33 listed by Blockeel & Long (1998: 129).
H35 1962: trees in wood nr Mid Town, Mulroy Bay, EF Warburg (BBS exc.) (Warburg 1964: 731).
H36 1957: trees, Curraginhalt, RD Fitzgerald (Warburg 1960: 776).
H(39) listed by Lett (1915: 130).
H39 1957: trees in oak and birch woods, Breen, Glenshesk, RE Parker ('in *CC* but regarded as doubtful by Megaw 1938') (Warburg 1958b: 480).

118/3 ***Ulota crispa*** (Hedw.) Brid.
(syn. *Ulota crispa* var. *crispa*, *U. crispula* Brid., *U. nicholsonii* Culm., *Weissia ulophylla* Ehrh. ex Lindb., *W. ulophylla* var. *crispula* (Bruch) Braithw., *W. ulophylla* var. *intermedia* (Schimp.) Braithw.)

H(1) listed by Lett (1915: 131) without details.
†H1 listed by Blockeel & Long (1998: 130).
H(2) listed by Lett (1915: 131).
†H2 listed by Blockeel & Long (1998: 130).
H(3) listed by Lett (1915: 131).
†H3 listed by Blockeel & Long (1998: 130).
H(4) listed by Lett (1915: 131) without details.
†H4 listed by Blockeel & Long (1998: 130).
H(5) listed by Lett (1915: 131).
†H5 listed by Blockeel & Long (1998: 130).
H(6) listed by Lett (1915: 131) without details.
†H6 listed by Blockeel & Long (1998: 130).
H(7) 1945: boulder by Loch Diheen, Galtees, RD Meikle (anon. 1947: 31).
†H7 listed by Blockeel & Long (1998: 130).
H(8) listed by Lett (1915: 131) without details.
†H8 listed by Blockeel & Long (1998: 130).
H(9) listed by Lett (1915: 131) without details.
†H9 listed by Blockeel & Long (1998: 130).
H10 1951: elder, shaded gully above Silvermines, AD Banwell, PJ Wanstall & EV Watson (Warburg 1953: 311).
H(11) listed by Lett (1915: 131) without details.
†H11 listed by Blockeel & Long (1998: 130).
H(12) listed by Lett (1915: 131) without details.
†H12 listed by Blockeel & Long (1998: 130).
H(13) listed by Lett (1915: 131).
†H13 listed by Blockeel & Long (1998: 130).
H(14) listed by Lett (1915: 131).
†H14 listed by Blockeel & Long (1998: 130).
H(15) listed by Lett (1915: 131) without details.
H15 1952: tree trunk, Ross Quay, L. Derg, MPH Kertland & ALK King (Warburg 1953: 311).
H(16) listed by Lett (1915: 131).
†H16 listed by Blockeel & Long (1998: 130).
[H(17) listed by Lett (1915: 131) without details. H17 deleted because no valid record or voucher specimen traced (Blockeel 1999: 8)].
H(18) listed by Lett (1915: 131). H(18) listed by Blockeel & Long (1998: 130).
[H(19) listed by Lett (1915: 131) without details. H19 deleted because no valid record or voucher specimen traced (Blockeel 1999: 8)].
H(20) listed by Lett (1915: 131) without details.
†H20 listed by Blockeel & Long (1998: 130).
H(21) listed by Lett (1915: 131) without details.
†H21 listed by Blockeel & Long (1998: 130).
H22 1950: tree, Slane, JS Thomson (Warburg 1952: 102).
H(23) listed by Lett (1915: 131).
†H23 listed by Blockeel & Long (1998: 130).
H24 1965: trees, wood, Cloonart Bridge, RD Fitzgerald & EM Lobley (Warburg 1966: 200).
H(25) listed by Lett (1915: 131) without details.
†H25 listed by Blockeel & Long (1998: 130).
H(26) listed by Lett (1915: 131) without details.
†H26 listed by Blockeel & Long (1998: 130).
H(27) 1911: on rocks under Slievemore, Achill I., JB Duncan (anon.1927: 285).
H(27) listed by Lett (1915: 131).
1925: on rocks, Croaghaum [*sic* = Croaghaun], Achill I., JB Duncan, HH Knight & WE Nicholson [described new to science as *U. Nicholsonii* by Culmann 1926, *Revue Bryologique* p. 21] (anon.1927: 285).
1925: Croaghaun, Achill I., WE Nicholson, JB Duncan & HH Knight (isotype of *U. nicholsonii* (CGE), of which Warburg 1963c: 143 commented that [he] 'cannot see that it differs taxonomically from *U. crispa*') (cf. Warburg 1963a: 66, 1963c: 143, 1964: 731).
†H27 listed by Blockeel & Long (1998: 130).
H(28) listed by Lett (1915: 131).
†H28 listed by Blockeel & Long (1998: 130).
H(29) listed by Lett (1915: 131).
H29 1963: hazel in wooded W-facing slope of limestone scarp, Boggaun, nr Manorhamilton, AR Perry & RD Fitzgerald (Warburg 1964: 731).
H(30) listed by Lett (1915: 131) without details.
†H30 listed by Blockeel & Long (1998: 130).
[H(31) listed by Lett (1915: 131) without

details. H31 deleted because no valid record or voucher specimen traced (Blockeel 1999: 8)].
H(32) listed by Lett (1915: 131).
†H32 listed by Blockeel & Long (1998: 130).
H(33) listed by Lett (1915: 131).
†H33 listed by Blockeel & Long (1998: 130).
H(34) listed by Lett (1915: 131) without details.
†H34 listed by Blockeel & Long (1998: 130).
H(35) listed by Lett (1915: 131).
†H35 listed by Blockeel & Long (1998: 130).
H(36) listed by Lett (1915: 131).
†H36 listed by Blockeel & Long (1998: 130).
H(37) listed by Lett (1915: 131) without details.
†H37 listed by Blockeel & Long (1998: 130).
H(38) listed by Lett (1915: 131).
†H38 listed by Blockeel & Long (1998: 130).
H(39) listed by Lett (1915: 131).
†H39 listed by Blockeel & Long (1998: 130).
H(40) listed by Lett (1915: 131).
†H40 listed by Blockeel & Long (1998: 130).

118/4 ***Ulota bruchii*** Hornsch. ex Brid.
(syn. *Ulota crispa* var. *norvegica* (Grönvall) A.J.E.Sm. & M.O.Hill, *Weissia bruchii* (Hornsch.) Lindb.)

H(1) listed by Lett (1915: 130) without details.
†H1 listed by Blockeel & Long (1998: 130).
H(2) listed by Lett (1915: 130).
†H2 listed by Blockeel & Long (1998: 130).
H3 1966: ash trunks, woods W of Kilmurry, MFV Corley & JS Parker (Perry 1967: 419).
H(4) listed by Lett (1915: 130).
†H4 listed by Blockeel & Long (1998: 130).
H(5) listed by Lett (1915: 130).
†H5 listed by Blockeel & Long (1998: 130).
H(6) 1933: Knockmealdowns [*sic* = Knockmealdown], E Armitage (anon. 1934b: 121).
†H6 listed by Blockeel & Long (1998: 130).
H(7) listed by Lett (1915: 130).
†H7 listed by Blockeel & Long (1998: 130).
H(8) listed by Lett (1915: 130).
†H8 listed by Blockeel & Long (1998: 130).
H9 1957: Maghera Wood, Tulla, ALK King (Warburg 1958b: 480).
H10 1951: willow, wooded gully above Silvermines, AD Banwell, PJ Wanstall & EV Watson (Warburg 1953: 311).
H11 1966: oak tree, Foulkscourt House, nr Johnstown, JG Duckett (BBS exc.) (Perry 1967: 419).
H12 1953: apple, Inch, WR Megaw (Warburg 1954: 483).
H13 1969: on birch at edge of bog, St Mullins, nr Graiguenamanagh, RD Fitzgerald (Crundwell 1970: 207).
H(14) listed by Lett (1915: 130).
†H14 listed by Blockeel & Long (1998: 130).
H15 1957: trees, Garryland Wood, RE Parker (Warburg 1958b: 480).
H(16) listed by Lett (1915: 130).
†H16 listed by Blockeel & Long (1998: 130).
H17 1966: alders in wood by stream, Derreen, N of Monivea, MFV Corley & JS Parker (Perry 1966: 419).
H18 1965: by R. Camcor above Kinnity, ALK King (Warburg 1966: 200).
H(20) listed by Lett (1915: 130).
†H20 listed by Blockeel & Long (1998: 130).
H21 1969: willows nr stream, N slope of Killakee Mt., JA Paton (Crundwell 1970: 207).
H22 1978: on sallow by Lough Bane, Oldcastle, DM Synnott (Hill 1980b: 44).
H24 1965: trees in wood nr Cloonart Bridge, S of Roosky, EM Lobley & RD Fitzgerald (Warburg 1966: 200).
H25 2002: on hazel with *Frullania tamarisci* etc., 40 m alt., St John's Wood, Lough Ree, M95, NG Hodgetts 4059 (Rothero 2003: 59).
H(27) listed by Lett (1915: 130).
†H27 listed by Blockeel & Long (1998: 130).
H(28) listed by Lett (1915: 130).
†H28 listed by Blockeel & Long (1998: 130).
H29 1963: birch in roadside marsh, SE of Sriff Cottage, E of Lough Gill, AR Perry & RD Fitzgerald (Warburg 1964: 731).
H30 1967: on trees on hillside, Snuhanagh, NE of Dowra, ALK King (Crundwell 1969: 887).
H(31) 1943: Ravensdale, JS Thomson (Duncan 1944: 211).
H33 1999: on twigs of rowan at base of sandstone escarpment, 300 m alt., Letter [Scarp], Lough Navar Forest, H05, RD Porley 2040 (Rothero 2000: 57).
H(34) listed by Lett (1915: 130).
†H34 listed by Blockeel & Long (1998: 130).
H(35) listed by Lett (1915: 131).
†H35 listed by Blockeel & Long (1998: 130).
H(36) listed by Lett (1915: 131).
†H36 listed by Blockeel & Long (1998: 130).
H(38) listed by Lett (1915: 131). H(38) listed

by Blockeel & Long (1998: 130).
H38 1999: on bole of beech tree, 50 m alt., Tollymore Forest park, 4 km W of Newcastle, J33, TL Blockeel 28/342 (Rothero 2000: 57).
H(39) listed by Lett (1915: 131).
†H39 listed by Blockeel & Long (1998: 130).
H(40) listed by Lett (1915: 131).
†H40 listed by Blockeel & Long (1998: 130).

118/5 ***Ulota calvescens*** Wilson
(syn. *Ulota vittata* Mitt., *Weissia vittata* (Mitt.) Lindb.)

H(1) listed by Lett (1915: 131).
†H1 listed by Blockeel & Long (1998: 130).
H(2) listed by Lett (1915: 131).
†H2 listed by Blockeel & Long (1998: 130).
H3 2002: on twigs of *Salix* in gully, 340 m alt., Gougane Barra, below Lough Fadda, W06, TL Blockeel 31/327 (Rothero 2003: 59).
H9 1957: hazels on SE side of Slievecarran, AC Crundwell (BBS exc.) (Warburg 1958b: 480).
[H(14) listed by Lett (1915: 131) without details. H14 deleted because record not traced (Proctor 1964, Warburg 1966: 200)].
H15 1994: on willow with *U. crispa* var. *norvegica*, nr Pollboy, Slieve Aughty, M50, NG Hodgetts 2961 (Blockeel 1995c: 45).
H16 1957: hazels in ravine, Ballynahinch, AC Crundwell (BBS exc.) (Warburg 1958b: 480).
H(18) listed by Lett (1915: 131). H(18) listed by Blockeel & Long (1998: 130).
H(26) listed by Lett (1915: 131). H(26) listed by Blockeel & Long (1998: 130).
H27 1965: branches of hazels, W side of L. Conn, nr Errew, AMcG Stirling (Warburg 1966: 200).
H(28) listed by Lett (1915: 131).
†H28 listed by Blockeel & Long (1998: 130).
H(29) listed by Lett (1915: 131) without locality.
†H29 listed by Blockeel & Long (1998: 130).
H30 1957: willow, lane between Tiltinbane and Black Lion [*sic* = Blacklion], AC Crundwell (Warburg 1958b: 480).
H(33) listed by Lett (1915: 131).
†H33 listed by Blockeel & Long (1998: 130).
H(35) listed by Lett (1915: 131).
†H35 listed by Blockeel & Long (1998: 130).
H(39) listed by Lett (1915: 131). H(39) listed by Blockeel & Long (1998: 130).
H40 1952: young hazel, Attikeeragh, UK Duncan & RD Fitzgerald (Warburg 1957: 332).

118/6 ***Ulota hutchinsiae*** (Sm.) Hammar
(syn. *Weissia americana* (P.Beauv.) Lindb.)

H(1) listed by Lett (1915: 130).
†H1 listed by Blockeel & Long (1998: 130).
H(2) listed by Lett (1915: 130).
†H2 listed by Blockeel & Long (1998: 130).
H(3) listed by Lett (1915: 130).
†H3 listed by Blockeel & Long (1998: 130).
H(4) listed by Lett (1915: 130). H(4) listed by Blockeel & Long (1998: 130).
[H(5) listed by Lett (1915: 130) without details. H5 deleted because no valid record or voucher specimen traced (Blockeel 1999: 8)].
H(6) listed by Lett (1915: 130).
†H6 listed by Blockeel & Long (1998: 130).
H(7) listed by Lett (1915: 130). H(7) listed by Blockeel & Long (1998: 130).
H15 1957: rocks, moorland, E of Gort nr R. Owendalulleegh, DG Catcheside (BBS exc.) (Warburg 1958b: 481).
H(16) listed by Lett (1915: 130).
†H16 listed by Blockeel & Long (1998: 130).
H(20) listed by Lett (1915: 130). H(20) listed by Blockeel & Long (1998: 130).
H(21) listed by Lett (1915: 130). H(21) listed by Blockeel & Long (1998: 130).
H(27) listed by Lett (1915: 130).
†H27 listed by Blockeel & Long (1998: 130).
H28 1962: stone of dolmen, Carrowmore, nr Sligo, EF Warburg (Warburg 1963b: 500).
H30 1965: boulders in bog, Carricknacrannoge, nr Dowra, RD Fitzgerald & EM Lobley (Warburg 1966: 201).
H(32) listed by Lett (1915: 130). H(32) listed by Blockeel & Long (1998: 130).
H(34) listed by Lett (1915: 130). H(34) listed by Blockeel & Long (1998: 130).
H(35) listed by Lett (1915: 130).
†H35 listed by Blockeel & Long (1998: 130).
H(37) listed by Lett (1915: 130) without locality. H(37) listed by Blockeel & Long (1998: 130).
H(38) listed by Lett (1915: 130). H(38) listed by Blockeel & Long (1998: 130).

H(40) listed by Lett (1915: 130). H(40) listed by Blockeel & Long (1998: 130).

118/7 ***Ulota phyllantha*** Brid.

H(1) listed by Lett (1915: 131) without details.
†H1 listed by Blockeel & Long (1998: 130).
H(2) listed by Lett (1915: 131) without details.
†H2 listed by Blockeel & Long (1998: 130).
H(3) listed by Lett (1915: 131) without details.
†H3 listed by Blockeel & Long (1998: 130).
H4 1955: beech, nr Knocknagree, MJP Scannell, comm. ALK King (Warburg 1956: 154).
†H5 listed by Blockeel & Long (1998: 130).
H(6) listed by Lett (1915: 131) without details.
†H6 listed by Blockeel & Long (1998: 130).
H(7) listed by Lett (1915: 131) without details.
†H7 listed by Blockeel & Long (1998: 130).
H(8) listed by Lett (1915: 131) without details.
†H8 listed by Blockeel & Long (1998: 130).
H(9) listed by Lett (1915: 131) without details.
†H9 listed by Blockeel & Long (1998: 130).
H(10) listed by Lett (1915: 131) without details.
†H10 listed by Blockeel & Long (1998: 130).
H(11) listed by Lett (1915: 131) without details.
†H11 listed by Blockeel & Long (1998: 130).
H(12) listed by Lett (1915: 131) without details.
†H12 listed by Blockeel & Long (1998: 130).
H(13) listed by Lett (1915: 131) without details.
†H13 listed by Blockeel & Long (1998: 130).
H(14) listed by Lett (1915: 131) without details.
†H14 listed by Blockeel & Long (1998: 130).
H15 1956: wood at Hearnesbrook, nr Killimor, ALK King (Warburg 1957: 332).
H(16) listed by Lett (1915: 131) without details.
†H16 listed by Blockeel & Long (1998: 130).
H(17) listed by Lett (1915: 131) without details.
†H17 listed by Blockeel & Long (1998: 130).
[H(18) listed by Lett (1915: 131) without details. H18 deleted because no valid record or voucher specimen traced (Blockeel 1999: 8)].
[H(19) listed by Lett (1915: 131) without details. H19 deleted because no valid record or voucher specimen traced (Blockeel 1999: 8)].
H(20) listed by Lett (1915: 131) without details.
†H20 listed by Blockeel & Long (1998: 130).
H(21) listed by Lett (1915: 131) without details.
†H21 listed by Blockeel & Long (1998: 130).
H(22) listed by Lett (1915: 131) without details.
†H22 listed by Blockeel & Long (1998: 130).
H(23) listed by Lett (1915: 131) without details.
†H23 listed by Blockeel & Long (1998: 130).
H(24) listed by Lett (1915: 131) without details.
†H24 listed by Blockeel & Long (1998: 130).
H(25) listed by Lett (1915: 131) without details.
†H25 listed by Blockeel & Long (1998: 130).
H(26) listed by Lett (1915: 131) without details.
†H26 listed by Blockeel & Long (1998: 130).
H(27) listed by Lett (1915: 131) without details.
†H27 listed by Blockeel & Long (1998: 130).
H(28) listed by Lett (1915: 131) without details.
†H28 listed by Blockeel & Long (1998: 130).
H(29) listed by Lett (1915: 131) without details.
†H29 listed by Blockeel & Long (1998: 130).
H(30) listed by Lett (1915: 131) without details.
†H30 listed by Blockeel & Long (1998: 130).
[H(31) listed by Lett (1915: 131) without details. H31 deleted because no valid record or voucher specimen traced (Blockeel 1999: 8)].
H(32) listed by Lett (1915: 131) without details.
†H32 listed by Blockeel & Long (1998: 130).
H(33) listed by Lett (1915: 131) without details.
†H33 listed by Blockeel & Long (1998: 130).
H(34) listed by Lett (1915: 131) without details.
†H34 listed by Blockeel & Long (1998: 130).
H(35) listed by Lett (1915: 131) without details.

†H35 listed by Blockeel & Long (1998: 130).
H(36) listed by Lett (1915: 131) without details.
†H36 listed by Blockeel & Long (1998: 130).
H(37) listed by Lett (1915: 131) without details.
†H37 listed by Blockeel & Long (1998: 130).
H(38) listed by Lett (1915: 131) without details. H(38) listed by Blockeel & Long (1998: 130).
H38 2002: on *Salix cinerea* in carr at edge of lake, 5 m alt., E side of Quoile Pondage Basin NNR, Downpatrick, J44, DT Holyoak 02-990 (Rothero 2003: 59).
H(39) listed by Lett (1915: 131) without details.
†H39 listed by Blockeel & Long (1998: 130).
H(40) listed by Lett (1915: 131) without details.
†H40 listed by Blockeel & Long (1998: 130).

119/1a *Hedwigia ciliata* (Hedw.) P.Beauv. **var. *ciliata***
(syn. *Hedwigia albicans* auct. pro parte)

H6 1966: boulders by lake edge, *ca* 1250 ft [alt.], Sgilloge Loughs, Comeragh Mts, RD Fitzgerald (NMW) (Crundwell 1995: 808, Blockeel 1996: 47).

This species and the next were confused until the study by Hedenäs (1994). The Irish and British records were revised by Crundwell (1995). Older records (e.g. from Lett 1915: 165) are not listed because they can only be assigned to either of these two species when specimens have been reidentified.

119/2 *Hedwigia stellata* Hedenäs
(syn. *Hedwigia albicans* auct. pro parte)

H1 1952: on sandstone boulder by the river, Cloghane, ALK King (AC Crundwell MS). H1 listed (Crundwell 1995: 807, Blockeel 1996: 47).
H2 1967: on rocks, *ca* 900 ft [alt.], The Paps, RD Fitzgerald (AC Crundwell MS). H2 listed (Crundwell 1995: 807, Blockeel 1996: 47).
H3 1987: on slaty rock outcrop above the marsh 2 miles N of Enniskean, M Scannell (DBN) (AC Crundwell MS). H3 listed (Crundwell 1995: 807, Blockeel 1996: 47).
H4 1967: on rocks, Shournegh River, nr Blarney, RD Fitzgerald (NMW) (AC Crundwell MS). H4 listed (Crundwell 1995: 807, Blockeel 1996: 47).
H6 1961: on conglomerate rocks, 1800 ft [alt.], above Crotty's Lake, JK Ferguson (DBN) (AC Crundwell MS). H6 listed (Crundwell 1995: 807, Blockeel 1996: 47).
H(8) 1946: on stones, Knockseefin, nr Nicker, RD Fitzgerald (NMW) (AC Crundwell MS). H(8) listed (Crundwell 1995: 807, Blockeel 1996: 47).
H8 1992: on rock outcrop in grassland, Foynes I., Shannon estuary, R25, E Wiltshire (Rothero 2000: 57).
H12 1969: on rocks in scree, *ca* 1400 ft [alt.], Caher Roe's Den, RD Fitzgerald (NMW) (AC Crundwell MS). H12 listed (Crundwell 1995: 807, Blockeel 1996: 47).
[H13 record (1969: below Caher Roe's Den, Blackstairs Mts, RD Fitzgerald, NMW) not listed because the locality appears to be in H12 (AC Crundwell MS)].
H15 1957: sandstone boulders on hills E of Gort, RE Parker (BBSUK) (Warburg 1958b: 477, as *H. ciliata*; AC Crundwell MS). H15 listed (Crundwell 1995: 807, Blockeel 1996: 47).
H16 1999: on boulder on open hillside, 30 m alt., Errisbeg, W of bog road, L64, DG Long 28447 (Rothero 2000: 57).
H19 1953: on granite boulder on Cupidstown Hill, ALK King (BBSUK) (Warburg 1954: 481, as *H. ciliata*; AC Crundwell MS). H19 listed (Crundwell 1995: 807, Blockeel 1996: 47).
H20 1975: granite boulder by car park, E end of Upper Lake, Vale of Glendalough, AR Perry (NMW) (AC Crundwell MS). H20 listed (Crundwell 1995: 807, Blockeel 1996: 47).
H21 1988: partly shaded rock outcrops, S side of plantation, by duck pond, Lambay [I.], DM Synnott (DBN) (AC Crundwell MS). H21 listed (Crundwell 1995: 807, Blockeel 1996: 47).
H22 1960: on Ordovician shale at Grangegeath nr Slane, ALK King (DBN) (Warburg 1961: 163, as *H. ciliata*; AC Crundwell MS). H22 listed (Crundwell 1995: 807, Blockeel 1996: 47).
H24 1957: on Carn Clonhugh, ALK King

(DBN) (Warburg 1958b: 477 as *H. ciliata*; AC Crundwell MS). H24 listed (Crundwell 1995: 807, Blockeel 1996: 47).

H(25) 1910: Sheegorey nr Boyle, WN Tetley (BBSUK) (AC Crundwell MS). H(25) listed (Crundwell 1995: 807, Blockeel 1996: 47).

H26 1987: woodland on N side of the Srah-Partry road, DM Synnott (DBN) (AC Crundwell MS). H26 listed (Crundwell 1995: 807, Blockeel 1996: 47).

H27 1987: summit above Kildownet Castle, Achill I., DM Synnott (DBN) (AC Crundwell MS). H27 listed (Crundwell 1995: 807, Blockeel 1996: 47).

H28 1963: on schistose rocks, *ca* 900 ft [alt.], S of Knockachree, [The] Ox Mts, AR Perry & RD Fitzgerald (NMW) (AC Crundwell MS). H28 listed (Crundwell 1995: 807, Blockeel 1996: 47).

H29 1963: on stone in bog, Sriff Cottage, nr Dromahair, AR Perry & RD Fitzgerald (NMW) (AC Crundwell MS). H29 listed (Crundwell 1995: 807, Blockeel 1996: 47).

H30 1968: Cornasaus Mt., G Drennan (NMW) (AC Crundwell MS). H30 listed (Crundwell 1995: 807, Blockeel 1996: 47).

H31 1965: summit of Trumpet Hill, NE of Dundalk, DM Synnott (DBN) (AC Crundwell MS). H31 listed (Crundwell 1995: 807, Blockeel 1996: 47).

H32 1986: hill SE of Cleeve L., DM Synnott (DBN) det. AC Crundwell (Crundwell 1995: 807, AC Crundwell MS, Blockeel 1996: 47).

H33 1959: on rocks, *ca* 900 ft [alt.], Aghahoolin, RD Fitzgerald (NMW) (AC Crundwell MS). H33 listed (Crundwell 1995: 807, Blockeel 1996: 47).

H35 1950: on rock, Baines Gap, RD Fitzgerald (NMW) (AC Crundwell MS). H35 listed (Crundwell 1995: 807, Blockeel 1996: 47).

H36 1950: Moymore Td [Townsland], Pomeroy, RD Fitzgerald (NMW) (AC Crundwell MS). H36 listed (Crundwell 1995: 807, Blockeel 1996: 47).

H37 1964: on rock, *ca* 800 ft [alt.], Annacloghmullin, S of Belfast, MPH Kertland (NMW) (AC Crundwell MS). H37 listed (Crundwell 1995: 807, Blockeel 1996: 47).

H(38) 1883: Tievedockeragh, Mournes, HW Lett (DBN) (AC Crundwell MS). H(38) listed (Crundwell 1995: 807, Blockeel 1996: 47).

H38 2002: on low outcrop on hillside, 205 m alt., W slope of Slievenabrock, J33, DT Holyoak 02-1019 (Rothero 2003: 59).

H(39) 1949: heath nr level crossing, Larne-Ballynure Rd [Road], RD Fitzgerald (NMW) (AC Crundwell MS). H(39) listed (Crundwell 1995: 807, Blockeel 1996: 47).

H39 1999: on dolerite boulders on exposed slope above cliff, Murlough Bay, D14, DT Holyoak 99-768 (BBSUK) (Rothero 2000: 57).

H40 1952: basalt outcrops, 600 ft [alt.], Altikeeragh, RD Fitzgerald (NMW) (AC Crundwell MS). H40 listed (Crundwell 1995: 807, Blockeel 1996: 47).

H. stellata was recognised as a species distinct from *H. ciliata* in the study by Hedenäs (1994). The Irish and British records were revised by Crundwell (1995), but for *H. stellata* only a list of vice-counties was published. Details of the specimens forming the basis of records from each vice-county are given above from an unpublished list that AC Crundwell lodged with the BBS Recorder of Mosses.

119/3 *Hedwigia integrifolia* P.Beauv.
(syn. *Hedwigia imberbis* (Sm.) Spruce)

†H1 listed by Blockeel & Long (1998: 131).

H(1) listed by Lett (1915: 164).

†H2 listed by Blockeel & Long (1998: 131).

[H(3) listed by Lett (1915: 164)].

H6 1966: damp rocks at *ca* 1500 ft alt., Coumshingaun, Comeragh Mts, ERB Little *et al.* (BBS exc.) (Perry 1967: 419).

H(20) listed by Lett (1915: 164).

†H20 listed by Blockeel & Long (1998: 131).

H(39) listed by Lett (1915: 164).

†H39 listed by Blockeel & Long (1998: 131).

120/1a *Fontinalis antipyretica* Hedw. **var. *antipyretica***

H(1) listed by Lett (1915: 163) without details.

†H1 listed by Blockeel & Long (1998: 131).

H(2) listed by Lett (1915: 163) without details.
†H2 listed by Blockeel & Long (1998: 131).
H3 1951: wet flush, SE coast of Sherkin I., IA Rorison (Warburg 1952: 105).
H(4) listed by Lett (1915: 163) without details.
†H4 listed by Blockeel & Long (1998: 131).
H5 1966: stones in R. Douglas nr Kilworth, RD Fitzgerald (BBS exc.) (Crundwell 1968: 643).
H(6) listed by Lett (1915: 163) without details.
†H6 listed by Blockeel & Long (1998: 131).
H(7) listed by Lett (1915: 163) without details.
†H7 listed by Blockeel & Long (1998: 131).
H(8) listed by Lett (1915: 163) without details.
†H8 listed by Blockeel & Long (1998: 131).
H(9) listed by Lett (1915: 163) without details.
†H9 listed by Blockeel & Long (1998: 131).
H10 1967: in stream, Knockfine, Keeper Hill, RD Fitzgerald (Crundwell 1968: 643).
H(11) listed by Lett (1915: 163) without details.
†H11 listed by Blockeel & Long (1998: 131).
H12 1954: stream, Inch, JS Thomson (Warburg 1955: 586).
H(13) listed by Lett (1915: 163) without details.
†H13 listed by Blockeel & Long (1998: 131).
H(14) listed by Lett (1915: 163) without details.
†H14 listed by Blockeel & Long (1998: 131).
†H15 listed by Blockeel & Long (1998: 131).
H(16) listed by Lett (1915: 163) without details.
†H16 listed by Blockeel & Long (1998: 131).
H(17) listed by Lett (1915: 163) without details.
†H17 listed by Blockeel & Long (1998: 131).
H(18) listed by Lett (1915: 163) without details.
†H18 listed by Blockeel & Long (1998: 131).
H(19) listed by Lett (1915: 163) without details.
†H19 listed by Blockeel & Long (1998: 131).
H(20) listed by Lett (1915: 163) without details.
†H20 listed by Blockeel & Long (1998: 131).
H(21) listed by Lett (1915: 163) without details.
†H21 listed by Blockeel & Long (1998: 131).
H22 1963: Mattock River, Dowth, DM Synnott (Warburg 1964: 731).
H23 1952: boulder in R. Shannon, Wren's I., nr Athlone, JP Brunker & ALK King (Warburg 1953: 314).
†H24 listed by Blockeel & Long (1998: 131).
H(25) listed by Lett (1915: 163) without details.
†H25 listed by Blockeel & Long (1998: 131).
H(26) listed by Lett (1915: 163) without details.
†H26 listed by Blockeel & Long (1998: 131).
H(27) listed by Lett (1915: 163) without details.
†H27 listed by Blockeel & Long (1998: 131).
H(28) listed by Lett (1915: 163) without details.
†H28 listed by Blockeel & Long (1998: 131).
H(29) listed by Lett (1915: 163) without details.
†H29 listed by Blockeel & Long (1998: 131).
H(30) listed by Lett (1915: 163) without details.
†H30 listed by Blockeel & Long (1998: 131).
[H(31) listed by Lett (1915: 163) without details. H31 deleted because no valid record or voucher specimen traced (Blockeel 1999: 8)].
H(32) listed by Lett (1915: 163) without details.
†H32 listed by Blockeel & Long (1998: 131).
H(33) listed by Lett (1915: 163) without details.
†H33 listed by Blockeel & Long (1998: 131).
H(34) listed by Lett (1915: 163) without details.
†H34 listed by Blockeel & Long (1998: 131).
H(35) listed by Lett (1915: 163) without details.
†H35 listed by Blockeel & Long (1998: 131).
H(36) listed by Lett (1915: 163) without details.
†H36 listed by Blockeel & Long (1998: 131).
H(37) listed by Lett (1915: 163) without details.
†H37 listed by Blockeel & Long (1998: 131).
H(38) listed by Lett (1915: 163) without details.
†H38 listed by Blockeel & Long (1998: 131).
H(39) listed by Lett (1915: 163) without details.
†H39 listed by Blockeel & Long (1998: 131).
H(40) listed by Lett (1915: 163) without details.
†H40 listed by Blockeel & Long (1998: 131).

120/1b *Fontinalis antipyretica* var. *gracilis* (Hedw.) Schimp.
(syn. *Fontinalis gracilis* Lindb.)

[H(1) listed by Lett (1915: 163). H1 deleted because no valid record or voucher specimen traced (Blockeel 1999: 8)].
H7 1966: stones in stream E of Knockastackeen, Galtee Mts, JA Paton (BBS exc.) (Perry 1967: 419).
[H(12) 1911: Aughnabrisky Stream, WN Tetley (anon. 1912c: 10). H(12) listed by Lett (1915: 163). H12 deleted because no valid record or voucher specimen traced (Blockeel 1999: 8)].
H16 1970: rocks in the Bunowen River nr Tullyconor Bridge, S of Killary Harbour, JA Paton (Crundwell 1971b: 381).
[H(21) listed by Lett (1915: 163) without details. H21 deleted because no valid record or voucher specimen traced (Blockeel 1999: 8)].
[H(38) listed by Lett (1915: 163). H38 deleted because no valid record or voucher specimen traced (Blockeel 1999: 8)].
[H(39) listed by Lett (1915: 163). H39 deleted because no valid record or voucher specimen traced (Blockeel 1999: 8)].
H39 1999: on basalt in small stream, Garron Plateau, D21, DT Holyoak 99-823 (BBSUK) (Rothero 2001: 45).
H40 1999: on rock in quick-flowing river, Banagher Glen, C60, DT Holyoak 99-644 (BBSUK) (Rothero 2000: 57).

120/1c *Fontinalis antipyretica* var. *gigantea* (Sull.) Sull.

H1 1983: NE shore, Coomnacronia Lake, SW of Glenbeigh, JA Paton (Hill 1984b: 29).
H9 1961: fringe of Ballycullinan Lough nr Corrofin, EM Lobley (Warburg 1962: 374).
H12 1975: stream nr Croghan, Croghan Mt., JA Paton (BBS exc.) (Crundwell 1976: 30).
H15 1968: boulders by turlough, Tirneevin, 3 miles W of Gort, AR Perry (Crundwell 1969: 887).
H16 1994: boulder on margin of Ballynahinch Lake, E of Clifden, L74, JA Paton 2704 (Blockeel 1995c: 45).
H20 2001: on margin of ornamental lake, 120 m alt., Powerscourt House, O21, DG Long 29930 (Rothero 2002: 53).
H(22) listed by Lett (1915: 163).
†H22 listed by Blockeel & Long (1998: 131).
[H25 deleted because no valid record or voucher specimen traced (Blockeel 1999: 8)].
H25 2002: in very wet fen on lough shore, 35 m alt., Portrunny Bay, Lough Ree, M96, NG Hodgetts 4069 (Rothero 2003: 59).
H(26) listed by Lett (1915: 163).
†H26 listed by Blockeel & Long (1998: 131).
H28 1965: stones at water's edge, S shore of L. Gill, E of Ennisfree, AR Perry & EF Warburg (Warburg 1966: 201).
H29 1965: small submerged boulders on N shore of Glencar Lough, S of Glencar Waterfall, EF Warburg & AR Perry (Warburg 1966: 201).
H(36) 1907: between Raughan Park and Stewartstown, HW Lett (anon. 1910: 346).
1907: on roadside in a wall, Stewartstown, J Glover (anon. 1912c: 10).
H(36) listed by Lett (1915: 163).
†H36 listed by Blockeel & Long (1998: 131).
H(38) listed by Lett (1915: 163). H(38) listed by Blockeel & Long (1998: 131).
[H(39) listed by Lett (1915: 163). H39 deleted because no valid record or voucher specimen traced (Blockeel 1999: 8)].
H(40) listed by Lett (1915: 163). H(40) listed by Blockeel & Long (1998: 131).

120/1d *Fontinalis antipyretica* var. *cymbifolia* W.E.Nicholson

H9 1968: stones submerged in R. Fergus nr Elmvale House, W of Killinaboy, AR Perry (Crundwell 1969: 887).

120/2a *Fontinalis squamosa* Hedw. **var. *squamosa***

H(1) listed by Lett (1915: 164).
†H1 listed by Blockeel & Long (1998: 131).
H(2) listed by Lett (1915: 164).
†H2 listed by Blockeel & Long (1998: 131).
H3 1953: upper waters of R. Lee, Gougane Barra, ALK King (Warburg 1958b: 485).
H(4) listed by Lett (1915: 164) without locality
†H4 listed by Blockeel & Long (1998: 131).
H(5) listed by Lett (1915: 164). H(5) listed by

Blockeel & Long (1998: 131).
H5 2002: submerged on stones, 105 m alt., River Bride, Ardarou Wood, Glenville, W78, TL Blockeel 31/360 (Rothero 2003: 59).
H(6) listed by Lett (1915: 164).
†H6 listed by Blockeel & Long (1998: 131).
H7 1966: rocks in stream above Cooper's Wood, S side of Galtymore, RD Fitzgerald (BBS exc.) (Crundwell 1968: 643).
H(8) listed by Lett (1915: 164) without locality.
†H8 listed by Blockeel & Long (1998: 131).
H12 1951: rocks in R. Urrin, Mocurry Cross, nr Kilteely, ALK King (Warburg 1952: 105).
H13 1969: stones in stream, Burreen River, Sheean, nr Myshall, RD Fitzgerald (Crundwell 1970: 207).
H15 1994: on stones in upland stream, nr Pollboy, Slieve Aughty, M50, NG Hodgetts 2967 (Blockeel 1995c: 45).
H(16) listed by Lett (1915: 164).
†H16 listed by Blockeel & Long (1998: 131).
H(20) listed by Lett (1915: 164).
†H20 listed by Blockeel & Long (1998: 131).
H(21) listed by Lett (1915: 164).
†H21 listed by Blockeel & Long (1998: 131).
H(27) listed by Lett (1915: 164).
†H27 listed by Blockeel & Long (1998: 131).
H30 2001: on rock in shallow river, 95 m alt., Owenmore River, NW of Glengevlin, H02, DT Holyoak 01-651 (Rothero 2002: 53).
H33 1959: stones in stream, Quilcagh [*sic* = Cuilcagh], RD Fitzgerald (Warburg 1960: 779).
H34 1967: on rocks, Crana River, nr Buncrana, RD Fitzgerald (Crundwell 1968: 643).
H35 1962: pool on cliff-top at Bunglass, nr Slieve League, ALK King (Warburg 1963b: 501).
†H36 listed by Blockeel & Long (1998: 131).
H37 1966: rock in stream, Ballinasack Bridge, nr Cashel Lakes, RD Fitzgerald (Perry 1967: 419).
H(38) listed by Lett (1915: 164). H(38) listed by Blockeel & Long (1998: 131).
H38 1999: on rocks in stream, 50 m alt., Tollymore Forest park, 4 km W of Newcastle, J33, TL Blockeel 28/337 (Rothero 2000: 57).
H(40) listed by Lett (1915: 164).
†H40 listed by Blockeel & Long (1998: 131).

Most records are undoubtedly of non-fertile plants and therefore only presumed to be this form rather than var. *curnowii* Cardot.

120/2c *Fontinalis squamosa* var. *dixonii* (Cardot) A.J.E.Sm.

H33 1950: rocky bed of stream, Owenbrean River, J Taylor (Warburg 1951: 502, Taylor 1951).
[H35 report by RD Fitzgerald (1951) was apparently judged to be erroneous since the record did not appear in any *CC*].

121/1 *Climacium dendroides* (Hedw.) F. Weber & D.Mohr

H(1) listed by Lett (1915: 163).
†H1 listed by Blockeel & Long (1998: 131).
H(2) listed by Lett (1915: 163).
†H2 listed by Blockeel & Long (1998: 131).
H(3) listed by Lett (1915: 163) without details.
†H3 listed by Blockeel & Long (1998: 131).
H(4) listed by Lett (1915: 163).
†H4 listed by Blockeel & Long (1998: 131).
H5 1956: margin of lough, Ballydekin, E of Midleton, EC Wallace (Warburg 1957: 335).
H(6) listed by Lett (1915: 163).
†H6 listed by Blockeel & Long (1998: 131).
H7 1966: cut-away bog, Longfordpass South, nr Urlingford, RD Fitzgerald (BBS exc.) (Crundwell 1968: 643).
H(8) listed by Lett (1915: 163).
†H8 listed by Blockeel & Long (1998: 131).
H(9) no date: nr Kilnaboy, JS Thomson (anon. 1946c: 284).
†H9 listed by Blockeel & Long (1998: 131).
H10 1967: in marsh, Knockfine, Keeper Hill, RD Fitzgerald (Crundwell 1968: 643).
H11 1966: bog, Derryfadda, nr Johnstown, J Appleyard *et al.* (BBS exc.) (Perry 1967: 419).
†H12 listed by Blockeel & Long (1998: 131).
H(13) listed by Lett (1915: 163).
†H13 listed by Blockeel & Long (1998: 131).
H(14) listed by Lett (1915: 163).
†H14 listed by Blockeel & Long (1998: 131).
H(15) listed by Lett (1915: 163) without locality.
†H15 listed by Blockeel & Long (1998: 131).

H16 1953: by Cregduff Lough, nr Roundstone, R Mackechnie, comm. EC Wallace (Warburg 1954: 485).
H(17) listed by Lett (1915: 163).
†H17 listed by Blockeel & Long (1998: 131).
H18 1967: Ballyduff Bog, nr Clonmacnoise, MP Horan (Crundwell 1968: 643).
H(19) 1949: bank of stream, grounds of Calverstown House, JS Thomson (Warburg 1950: 386).
†H19 listed by Blockeel & Long (1998: 131).
†H20 listed by Blockeel & Long (1998: 131).
H(21) listed by Lett (1915: 163). H(21) listed by Blockeel & Long (1998: 131).
†H22 listed by Blockeel & Long (1998: 131).
H(23) 1946: Scraw Bog, Portnashangan, Mullingar, KC Harris (anon. 1947: 33).
†H23 listed by Blockeel & Long (1998: 131).
H(24) listed by Lett (1915: 163).
†H24 listed by Blockeel & Long (1998: 131).
H(25) listed by Lett (1915: 163).
†H25 listed by Blockeel & Long (1998: 131).
H(26) listed by Lett (1915: 163).
†H26 listed by Blockeel & Long (1998: 131).
H(27) listed by Lett (1915: 163).
†H27 listed by Blockeel & Long (1998: 131).
H(28) listed by Lett (1915: 163).
†H28 listed by Blockeel & Long (1998: 131).
H(29) listed by Lett (1915: 163).
†H29 listed by Blockeel & Long (1998: 131).
H(30) listed by Lett (1915: 163).
†H30 listed by Blockeel & Long (1998: 131).
[H31 deleted because no valid record or voucher specimen traced (Blockeel 1999: 8)].
H(32) listed by Lett (1915: 163).
†H32 listed by Blockeel & Long (1998: 131).
H(33) listed by Lett (1915: 163).
†H33 listed by Blockeel & Long (1998: 131).
H(34) listed by Lett (1915: 163).
†H34 listed by Blockeel & Long (1998: 131).
H(35) listed by Lett (1915: 163).
†H35 listed by Blockeel & Long (1998: 131).
H(36) listed by Lett (1915: 163).
†H36 listed by Blockeel & Long (1998: 131).
H(37) listed by Lett (1915: 163).
†H37 listed by Blockeel & Long (1998: 131).
H(38) listed by Lett (1915: 163).
†H38 listed by Blockeel & Long (1998: 131).
H(39) listed by Lett (1915: 163).
†H39 listed by Blockeel & Long (1998: 131).
H(40) listed by Lett (1915: 163).
†H40 listed by Blockeel & Long (1998: 131).

122/1 ***Cryphaea heteromalla*** (Hedw.) D.Mohr (syn. *Cryphaea arborea* (P.Beauv.) Lindb.)

H(2) listed by Lett (1915: 164).
†H2 listed by Blockeel & Long (1998: 132).
H3 1966: ash trunk by river, W bank of R. Bandon, nr Ballinadee, MFV Corley & JS Parker (Perry 1967: 419).
H(4) listed by Lett (1915: 164).
†H4 listed by Blockeel & Long (1998: 132).
H5 1956: willows in lane, Ballyvergan East, Youghal, EC Wallace (Warburg 1957: 334).
H(6) 1933: Cappagh Lake, E Armitage (anon. 1934b: 127).
†H6 listed by Blockeel & Long (1998: 132).
H7 1956: thorns, hillside nr Knocklofty, EC Wallace (Warburg 1957: 334).
H(8) listed by Lett (1915: 164).
†H8 listed by Blockeel & Long (1998: 132).
H(9) listed by Lett (1915: 164).
†H9 listed by Blockeel & Long (1998: 132).
H(10) listed by Lett (1915: 164).
†H10 listed by Blockeel & Long (1998: 132).
H(11) listed by Lett (1915: 164).
†H11 listed by Blockeel & Long (1998: 132).
H(12) listed by Lett (1915: 164).
†H12 listed by Blockeel & Long (1998: 132).
H(13) listed by Lett (1915: 164).
†H13 listed by Blockeel & Long (1998: 132).
H(14) listed by Lett (1915: 164).
†H14 listed by Blockeel & Long (1998: 132).
H15 1957: shrubs in fen carr, nr L. Cultra [*sic* = Cutra?], RE Parker (BBS exc.) (Warburg 1958b: 485).
H(16) listed by Lett (1915: 164). H(16) listed by Blockeel & Long (1998: 132).
[H17 deleted because no valid record or voucher specimen traced (Blockeel 1999: 8)].
H(18) listed by Lett (1915: 164). H(18) listed by Blockeel & Long (1998: 132).
H(19) listed by Lett (1915: 164).
†H19 listed by Blockeel & Long (1998: 132).
H(20) listed by Lett (1915: 164) without locality.
†H20 listed by Blockeel & Long (1998: 132).
H(21) listed by Lett (1915: 164).
†H21 listed by Blockeel & Long (1998: 132).
H22 1950: elder, Slane, JS Thomson (Warburg 1952: 105).
H(23) listed by Lett (1915: 164).
†H23 listed by Blockeel & Long (1998: 132).
†H24 listed by Blockeel & Long (1998: 132).

†H25 listed by Blockeel & Long (1998: 132).
H26 1953: bushes by L. Carra, nr Keel Bridge, EC Wallace (Warburg 1954: 484).
H27 1968: ash tree, Drummin Wood, W of Foxford, JA Paton (Crundwell 1969: 887).
H(28) listed by Lett (1915: 164).
†H28 listed by Blockeel & Long (1998: 132).
H29 1965: trees at roadside, Drumkeeran, N of L. Allen, RD Fitzgerald & EM Lobley (Warburg 1966: 201).
H(30) listed by Lett (1915: 164).
†H30 listed by Blockeel & Long (1998: 132).
H(31) 1943: Ravensdale, JS Thomson (Duncan 1944: 213).
H(32) listed by Lett (1915: 164).
†H32 listed by Blockeel & Long (1998: 132).
H(33) listed by Lett (1915: 164).
†H33 listed by Blockeel & Long (1998: 132).
[H35 deleted because no valid record or voucher specimen traced (Blockeel 1999: 8)].
H35 2002: on *Salix cinerea* in carr on lough shore, 21 m alt., NE shore of Lough Fern, C12, DT Holyoak 02-745 (Rothero 2003: 59).
†H36 listed by Blockeel & Long (1998: 132).
H(37) listed by Lett (1915: 164).
†H37 listed by Blockeel & Long (1998: 132).
H(38) listed by Lett (1915: 164). H(38) listed by Blockeel & Long (1998: 132).
H38 2002: on *Sambucus nigra* at edge of plantation, 65 m alt., S of Shimna River in Tollymore Forest Park, J33, DT Holyoak 02-981 (Rothero 2003: 59).
H(39) listed by Lett (1915: 164). H(39) listed by Blockeel & Long (1998: 132).
H39 1999: on *Acer pseudoplatanus* beside track in deciduous woodland, Glenarm Forest at N end, D31, DT Holyoak 99-835 (BBSUK) (Rothero 2000: 57-58).
H(40) listed by Lett (1915: 164).
†H40 listed by Blockeel & Long (1998: 132).

123/1a *Leucodon sciuroides* (Hedw.) Schwägr. **var. *sciuroides***

H(3) listed by Lett (1915: 164). H(3) listed by Blockeel & Long (1998: 132).
H6 1956: beech by Knocklofty Bridge, EC Wallace (Warburg 1957: 334).
H7 1956: elm nr Knocklofty Bridge, EC Wallace (Warburg 1957: 334).
H(9) listed by Lett (1915: 164). H(9) listed by Blockeel & Long (1998: 132).
H(11) listed by Lett (1915: 164). H(11) listed by Blockeel & Long (1998: 132).
H(14) listed by Lett (1915: 164).
†H14 listed by Blockeel & Long (1998: 132).
H(16) listed by Lett (1915: 164). H(16) listed by Blockeel & Long (1998: 132).
H(18) listed by Lett (1915: 164). H(18) listed by Blockeel & Long (1998: 132).
H(19) 1938: Monasterevan, JG Finlay (Duncan 1944: 214).
H(20) listed by Lett (1915: 164).
†H20 listed by Blockeel & Long (1998: 132).
H(21) listed by Lett (1915: 164). H(21) listed by Blockeel & Long (1998: 132).
H(22) listed by Lett (1915: 164).
†H22 listed by Blockeel & Long (1998: 132).
[H23 record dismissed because details not traced (Rose 1975, Crundwell 1976: 30)].
H23 1987: on *Sorbus* tree beside main road, Moate town centre, MV Fletcher & DA Newman (Blockeel 1998: 38).
H31 1965: trunk of fallen chestnut, bank of R. Boyne nr Townley Hall, Tullyallen, DM Synnott (Warburg 1966: 201).
H33 2002: on old *Fraxinus* in parkland, 80 m alt., Florence Court House, H13, DG Long 30787 (Rothero 2003: 60).
H(39) listed by Lett (1915: 164). H(39) listed by Blockeel & Long (1998: 132).

124/1 *Antitrichia curtipendula* (Hedw.) Brid.

H(1) listed by Lett (1915: 164).
†H1 listed by Blockeel & Long (1998: 132).
H3 1979: steep shaded rocks, NE slope of Lackawee, HMH van Melick (Hill 1981: 33).
H(6) listed by Lett (1915: 164).
†H6 listed by Blockeel & Long (1998: 132).
H(12) listed by Lett (1915: 164). H(12) listed by Blockeel & Long (1998: 132).
H(20) listed by Lett (1915: 164). H(20) listed by Blockeel & Long (1998: 132).
[H(21) listed by Lett (1915: 164) without locality. H21 record dismissed because it was not localised (Smith 1974, Crundwell 1975: 19)].
H(28) listed by Lett (1915: 164). H(28) listed by Blockeel & Long (1998: 132).
H(32) listed by Lett (1915: 164). H(32) listed by Blockeel & Long (1998: 132).
H33 1950: hazel copse, Marble Arch, J Taylor (Warburg 1951: 502).

H(34) listed by Lett (1915: 164). H(34) listed by Blockeel & Long (1998: 132).
H36 1956: rocky promontory nr Wolf's Hill, 6 miles NW of Cookstown, RE Parker (Warburg 1957: 335).
H(39) listed by Lett (1915: 164). H(39) listed by Blockeel & Long (1998: 132).
H(40) 1897: Dungiven, JB Parker (anon. 1899: 17).
H(40) listed by Lett (1915: 164).
†H40 listed by Blockeel & Long (1998: 132).

125/1 ***Pterogonium gracile*** (Hedw.) Sm.
(syn. *Pterogonium ornithopodioides* (F. Weber & D.Mohr) Lindb. nom. illeg.)

H(1) listed by Lett (1915: 155).
†H1 listed by Blockeel & Long (1998: 132).
H(2) listed by Lett (1915: 155).
†H2 listed by Blockeel & Long (1998: 132).
H(3) listed by Lett (1915: 155).
†H3 listed by Blockeel & Long (1998: 132).
H(4) listed by Lett (1915: 155). H(4) listed by Blockeel & Long (1998: 132).
[H(5) listed by Lett (1915: 155). H5 deleted because no valid record or voucher specimen traced (Blockeel 1999: 8)].
†H6 listed by Blockeel & Long (1998: 132).
H7 1966: rocks by L. Muskry, Galtee Mts, JG Duckett *et al.* (BBS exc.) (Perry 1967: 419).
H8 1966: basalt rocks, Knockroe, nr Caherconlish, MFV Corley & JS Parker (Perry 1967: 419).
H13 1969: rocks by R. Slaney, Aghade Bridge, nr Tullow, RD Fitzgerald (Crundwell 1970: 208).
†H16 listed by Blockeel & Long (1998: 132).
H(20) listed by Lett (1915: 155).
†H20 listed by Blockeel & Long (1998: 132).
H(21) listed by Lett (1915: 155).
†H21 listed by Blockeel & Long (1998: 132).
H27 1987: rocks at outlet of L. Bunnafreva East, Achill I., DM Synnott (Blockeel 1998: 38).
H28 1965: rocks at lake edge, L. Gill, E of Ennisfree, RD Fitzgerald & EM Lobley (Warburg 1966: 201).
H(31) listed by Lett (1915: 155). H(31) listed by Blockeel & Long (1998: 132).
H(33) listed by Blockeel & Long (1998: 132).
H35 1951: boulder, Innishkeel, WR Megaw (Warburg 1953: 314).
H(38) listed by Blockeel & Long (1998: 132).
H(39) listed by Lett (1915: 155). H(39) listed by Blockeel & Long (1998: 132).

126/1 ***Myurium hochstetteri*** (Schimp.) Kindb.
(syn. *Myurium hebridarum* Schimp.)

H16 1969: along rivulet, Roundstone, G Harmsen (Crundwell 1973: 513).

127/1 ***Leptodon smithii*** (Hedw.) F.Weber & D.Mohr

H3 1957: on *Rhododendron ponticum* in shade in mixed woods in ground of Bantry House, Bantry, SW Greene (Warburg 1959: 637).
H6 1956: beech by Knocklofty Bridge, EC Wallace (Warburg 1957: 335).

[128/1 ***Neckera pennata*** Hedw.]

[The origin of specimens labelled as collected in H39 (1849: Colin Glen, leg. D Orr, BM, DBN) is dismissed as doubtful by Lett (1915: 163)].

128/2 ***Neckera crispa*** Hedw.
(syn. *Neckera crispa* var. *falcata* Boulay)

H(1) listed by Lett (1915: 162).
†H1 listed by Blockeel & Long (1998: 133).
H(2) listed by Lett (1915: 162).
†H2 listed by Blockeel & Long (1998: 133).
H3 1955: cliffs above Glen Lough, H Milne-Redhead (Warburg 1957: 334).
H(4) listed by Lett (1915: 162). H(4) listed by Blockeel & Long (1998: 133).
H(5) listed by Lett (1915: 162). H(5) listed by Blockeel & Long (1998: 133).
H(6) listed by Lett (1915: 162).
†H6 listed by Blockeel & Long (1998: 133).
H(7) listed by Lett (1915: 162).
†H7 listed by Blockeel & Long (1998: 133).
H(8) listed by Lett (1915: 162) without locality.
†H8 listed by Blockeel & Long (1998: 133).
H(9) listed by Lett (1915: 162).
H(9) 1945: rocks nr Lough Bunny, JS Thomson (anon. 1946c: 284), as var. *falcata*.
†H9 listed by Blockeel & Long (1998: 133).
H10 1967: on shaded basic rocks, Clare Glen, nr Newport, HH Birks, HJB Birks & DA Ratcliffe (Crundwell 1968: 643).
[H(15) listed by Lett (1915: 162) without

details. H15 deleted because no valid record or voucher specimen traced (Blockeel 1999: 8)].

H(16) listed by Lett (1915: 162).
†H16 listed by Blockeel & Long (1998: 133).
H(17) listed by Lett (1915: 162).
†H17 listed by Blockeel & Long (1998: 133).
H18 base of hazel on limestone pavement, Clorhane, nr Clonmacnoise, DL Kelly & D Doogue (Hill 1986: 23).
H(20) 1938: Devil's Glen, DB Bradshaw (anon. 1940a: 174).
†H20 listed by Blockeel & Long (1998: 133).
H23 1968: limestone quarry, Rock of Curry, 5 miles NNW of Castlepollard, G Drennan (Crundwell 1969: 887).
H24 1968: in wood, Rathcline House, 2 miles SW of Lanesborough, WV Rubers *et al.* (U) (Crundwell 1974: 173).
†H25 listed by Blockeel & Long (1998: 133).
H(26) listed by Lett (1915: 162).
†H26 listed by Blockeel & Long (1998: 133).
H27 1965: basic rocks, 900 ft alt., E end of Sheeffry Hills, nr Gortmore, AMcG Stirling (Warburg 1966: 201).
H(28) listed by Lett (1915: 162).
H(28) 1928: rocks above Glencar Lough, N side (BBS exc.) (Duncan 1928: 119), as var. *falcata*.
†H28 listed by Blockeel & Long (1998: 133).
H(29) listed by Lett (1915: 162).
†H29 listed by Blockeel & Long (1998: 133).
H(30) listed by Lett (1915: 162). H(30) listed by Blockeel & Long (1998: 133).
H30 2001: on limestone rock in hazel scrub, 265 m alt., Legnaveagh, S of Blacklion, H03, DT Holyoak 01-743 (Rothero 2002: 54).
H(31) listed by Lett (1915: 162). H(31) listed by Blockeel & Long (1998: 133).
H31 1999: on moist rock face on bank of stream, 150 m alt., Two Mile River, Carlingford, J11, TL Blockeel 28/152 (Rothero 2000: 58).
H(33) listed by Lett (1915: 162).
†H33 listed by Blockeel & Long (1998: 133).
H(34) listed by Lett (1915: 162) without details.
†H34 listed by Blockeel & Long (1998: 133).
H(35) listed by Lett (1915: 162).
†H35 listed by Blockeel & Long (1998: 133).
H36 1956: limestone, Carrickaness, RD Fitzgerald (Warburg 1957: 334).
H37 1966: limestone, old canal, Carrickaness, nr Benburb, RD Fitzgerald (Perry 1967: 419).
H(38) listed by Lett (1915: 162). H(38) listed by Blockeel & Long (1998: 133).
H(39) listed by Lett (1915: 162).
†H39 listed by Blockeel & Long (1998: 133).
H(40) listed by Lett (1915: 162).
†H40 listed by Blockeel & Long (1998: 133).

128/3 ***Neckera pumila*** Hedw.
(syn. *Neckera fontinaloides* Lindb. nom. illeg., *N. fontinaloides* var. *philippei* (Dufour) Lindb., *N. pumila* var. *philippeana* (Bruch, Schimp. & W. Gümbel) Milde)

H(1) listed by Lett (1915: 163). H(1) listed by Blockeel & Long (1998: 133).
H2 1951: fallen elm, grounds of Kenmare House, Killarney, ALK King (Warburg 1952: 105).
H3 1966: ash trunks, woods W of Kilmurry, MFV Corley & JS Parker (Perry 1967: 420).
H(4) listed by Lett (1915: 163).
†H4 listed by Blockeel & Long (1998: 133).
H(5) listed by Lett (1915: 163).
†H5 listed by Blockeel & Long (1998: 133).
H(6) listed by Lett (1915: 163) without locality.
†H6 listed by Blockeel & Long (1998: 133).
H(7) 1945: Glen of Aberlow, RD Meikle (anon. 1947: 33).
†H7 listed by Blockeel & Long (1998: 133).
H8 1966: hawthorn in hedge, Glenbrohane, nr Ballylanders, MFV Corley & JS Parker (Perry 1967: 420).
H(9) listed by Lett (1915: 163).
†H9 listed by Blockeel & Long (1998: 133).
H10 1951: trunk of willow in wooded gorge, Silvermines, AD Banwell, PJ Wanstall & EV Watson (Warburg 1953: 314).
H11 1952: Farmley Wood, nr Cuffe's Grange, MPH Kertland & ALK King (Warburg 1953: 314).
H12 1953: apple tree, Inch, WR Megaw (Warburg 1954: 484).
H13 1999: on sycamore in scrubby woodland, 30 m alt., Pollymounty River, N bank, Ballyknockcrumpin, S73, TL Blockeel 28/302 (Rothero 2000: 58).
H(14) listed by Lett (1915: 163).
†H14 listed by Blockeel & Long (1998: 133).
H15 1957: small trees in scrub, nr Kilreekill, RE Parker (Warburg 1958b: 485).
H16 1955: Ross Forest, Moycullen, ALK

King (Warburg 1956: 156).
H17 1966: ash trunk, Ryehill, N of Monivea, MFV Corley & JS Parker (Perry 1967: 420).
H(18) listed by Lett (1915: 163). H(18) listed by Blockeel & Long (1998: 133).
H(19) 1938: Moore Abbey, JG Finlay (Duncan 1944: 214).
H(20) listed by Lett (1915: 163).
†H20 listed by Blockeel & Long (1998: 133).
H21 1956: old beech stump in Kilakee Wood, ALK King (Warburg 1957: 334).
H(22) listed by Lett (1915: 163).
†H22 listed by Blockeel & Long (1998: 133).
†H23 listed by Blockeel & Long (1998: 133).
H24 1965: birch and rhododendron in wood, Cloonart Bridge, RD Fitzgerald & EM Lobley (Warburg 1966: 201).
H25 1959: fallen beech by L. Funshinagh, ALK King (Warburg 1960: 779).
H26 1970: tree trunk in wood W of Pollagh River, NE of Balla, JA Paton (Crundwell 1971b: 381).
H27 1987: *Rhododendron* branch, woodland nr Glendarary House, W of Achill Sound, Achill I., JA Paton (Blockeel 1998: 38).
H28 1963: tree, Lissadell Wood, Lissadell, nr Sligo, RD Fitzgerald & AR Perry (Warburg 1964: 731).
H29 1965: conifers, Creevelea Abbey, Dromahair, RD Fitzgerald & EM Lobley (Warburg 1966: 201).
H(30) no date: Farnham Wood, J Glover (anon. 1912c: 10), as var. *Philippeana*. H(30) listed by Lett (1915: 163).
1941: Farnham Demesne, JG Finlay (Duncan 1944: 214).
†H30 listed by Blockeel & Long (1998: 133).
H(31) 1943: Ravensdale, JS Thomson (Duncan 1944: 214), as var. *philippeana*.
[H32 deleted because no valid record or voucher specimen traced (Blockeel 1999: 8)].
H(33) listed by Lett (1915: 163).
H33 1957: hazel in wood, nr Hanging Rock, L. Macnean Lower, AC Crundwell (Warburg 1958b: 485).
H36 1951: beech, Aghnahoe, nr Ballygawley, RD Fitzgerald (Warburg 1952: 105).
H37 1966: elder, Tullydonnel, nr Forkhill, RD Fitzgerald (Perry 1967: 420).
H(38) listed by Blockeel & Long (1998: 133).
H(39) 1928: Glenariff (BBS exc.) (Duncan 1928: 114, 117). H(39) listed by Blockeel & Long (1998: 133).
H40 1999: on hazel nr edge of clearing, Banagher Glen, C60, DT Holyoak 99-640 (BBSUK) (Rothero 2000: 58).

128/4 ***Neckera complanata*** (Hedw.) Huebener

H(1) listed by Lett (1915: 162) without details.
†H1 listed by Blockeel & Long (1998: 133).
H(2) listed by Lett (1915: 162) without details.
†H2 listed by Blockeel & Long (1998: 133).
†H3 listed by Blockeel & Long (1998: 133).
H(4) listed by Lett (1915: 162) without details.
†H4 listed by Blockeel & Long (1998: 133).
H(5) listed by Lett (1915: 162) without details.
†H5 listed by Blockeel & Long (1998: 133).
H(6) listed by Lett (1915: 162) without details.
†H6 listed by Blockeel & Long (1998: 133).
†H7 listed by Blockeel & Long (1998: 133).
H(8) listed by Lett (1915: 162) without details.
†H8 listed by Blockeel & Long (1998: 133).
H(9) listed by Lett (1915: 162) without details.
†H9 listed by Blockeel & Long (1998: 133).
H(10) listed by Lett (1915: 162) without details.
†H10 listed by Blockeel & Long (1998: 133).
H(11) listed by Lett (1915: 162) without details.
†H11 listed by Blockeel & Long (1998: 133).
H(12) listed by Lett (1915: 162) without details.
†H12 listed by Blockeel & Long (1998: 133).
H(13) listed by Lett (1915: 162) without details.
†H13 listed by Blockeel & Long (1998: 133).
H(14) listed by Lett (1915: 162) without details.
†H14 listed by Blockeel & Long (1998: 133).
H(15) listed by Lett (1915: 162) without details.
†H15 listed by Blockeel & Long (1998: 133).
H(16) listed by Lett (1915: 162) without details.
†H16 listed by Blockeel & Long (1998: 133).
H(17) listed by Lett (1915: 162) without details.
†H17 listed by Blockeel & Long (1998: 133).
[H(18) listed by Lett (1915: 162) without

details. H18 deleted because no valid record or voucher specimen traced (Blockeel 1999: 8)].
H(19) listed by Lett (1915: 162) without details.
†H19 listed by Blockeel & Long (1998: 133).
H(20) listed by Lett (1915: 162) without details.
†H20 listed by Blockeel & Long (1998: 133).
H(21) listed by Lett (1915: 162) without details.
†H21 listed by Blockeel & Long (1998: 133).
H(22) listed by Lett (1915: 162) without details.
†H22 listed by Blockeel & Long (1998: 133).
H(23) listed by Lett (1915: 162) without details.
†H23 listed by Blockeel & Long (1998: 133).
H(24) listed by Lett (1915: 162) without details.
†H24 listed by Blockeel & Long (1998: 133).
H(25) listed by Lett (1915: 162) without details.
†H25 listed by Blockeel & Long (1998: 133).
H(26) listed by Lett (1915: 162) without details.
†H26 listed by Blockeel & Long (1998: 133).
H(27) listed by Lett (1915: 162) without details.
†H27 listed by Blockeel & Long (1998: 133).
H(28) listed by Lett (1915: 162) without details.
†H28 listed by Blockeel & Long (1998: 133).
†H29 listed by Blockeel & Long (1998: 133).
H(30) listed by Lett (1915: 162) without details.
†H30 listed by Blockeel & Long (1998: 133).
[H(31) listed by Lett (1915: 162) without details. H31 deleted because no valid record or voucher specimen traced (Blockeel 1999: 8)].
H(32) listed by Lett (1915: 162) without details.
†H32 listed by Blockeel & Long (1998: 133).
H(33) listed by Lett (1915: 162) without details.
†H33 listed by Blockeel & Long (1998: 133).
H(34) listed by Lett (1915: 162) without details.
†H34 listed by Blockeel & Long (1998: 133).
H(35) 1946: wall nr Clooney, JS Thomson (anon. 1947: 33).
†H35 listed by Blockeel & Long (1998: 133).
H(36) listed by Lett (1915: 162) without details.
†H36 listed by Blockeel & Long (1998: 133).
H(37) listed by Lett (1915: 162) without details.
†H37 listed by Blockeel & Long (1998: 133).
H(38) listed by Lett (1915: 162) without details. H(38) listed by Blockeel & Long (1998: 133).
H38 1999: on mortared wall of the Hermitage, 55 m alt., Tollymore Forest park, 4 km W of Newcastle, J33, TL Blockeel 28/340 (Rothero 2000: 58).
H(39) listed by Lett (1915: 162) without details.
†H39 listed by Blockeel & Long (1998: 133).
H(40) listed by Lett (1915: 162) without details.
†H40 listed by Blockeel & Long (1998: 133).

129/1 ***Homalia trichomanoides*** (Hedw.) Bruch, Schimp. & W.Gümbel
(syn. *Omalia trichomanoides* auct.)

H1 1966: boulder on W shore of L. Leane, Killarney, JA Paton & GCG Argent (Perry 1967: 420).
H2 1972: sandstone boulder in wood edge, Derreencullig, SE of Killarney, WV Rubers (U) (Crundwell 1974: 173).
[H(3) listed by Lett (1915: 162). H3 deleted because no valid record or voucher specimen traced (Blockeel 1999: 8)].
H3 2002: on boulder at edge of stream, 30 m alt., Kerry River, Glengarriff, V85, TL Blockeel 31/354 (Rothero 2003: 60).
H(4) listed by Lett (1915: 162). H(4) listed by Blockeel & Long (1998: 133).
H(5) listed by Lett (1915: 162) without details.
†H5 listed by Blockeel & Long (1998: 133).
H(6) listed by Lett (1915: 162).
†H6 listed by Blockeel & Long (1998: 133).
H(8) listed by Lett (1915: 162). H(8) listed by Blockeel & Long (1998: 133).
H(9) listed by Lett (1915: 162).
†H9 listed by Blockeel & Long (1998: 133).
H10 1951: banks, Silvermines, AD Banwell, PJ Wanstall & EV Watson (Warburg 1953: 314).
H11 1968: bank of the Dinin River nr Dysart Bridge, S of Castlecomber, JA Paton (Crundwell 1969: 887).
H12 1969: on stone in bank, Sculloge Gap, nr Kiltealy, RD Fitzgerald (Crundwell 1970: 208).
H(13) listed by Lett (1915: 162). H(13) listed

by Blockeel & Long (1998: 133).
H(14) listed by Lett (1915: 162).
†H14 listed by Blockeel & Long (1998: 133).
H15 1957: stumps, Garryland Wood, nr Gort, RE Parker (BBS exc.) (Warburg 1958b: 485).
H(16) listed by Lett (1915: 162).
†H16 listed by Blockeel & Long (1998: 133).
H(18) listed by Lett (1915: 162). H(18) listed by Blockeel & Long (1998: 133).
H(19) 1937: Straffan, JS Thomson (anon. 1938d: 40).
H(20) listed by Lett (1915: 162).
†H20 listed by Blockeel & Long (1998: 133).
H(21) listed by Lett (1915: 162). H(21) listed by Blockeel & Long (1998: 133).
H22 1966: exposed sycamore root, woodland above R. Boyne, Stalleen, Donore, DM Synnott (Perry 1967: 420).
H23 1970: tree base, wood on E shore of L. Ennell, Mullingar, JA Paton (Crundwell 1971b: 381).
H24 1980: base of *Acer pseudoplatanus* by marsh S of Currygrane Lough, Ballinalera, DM Synnott (Hill 1981: 33).
H25 1965: stone by stream, *ca* 400 ft alt., 1 mile N of Ballyfarnan, RD Fitzgerald & EM Lobley (Warburg 1966: 201).
H(26) listed by Lett (1915: 162).
†H26 listed by Blockeel & Long (1998: 133).
H27 1987: on roots of Horse Chestnut by roadside, Rose Cottage woods nr Westport, DA Newman (Blockeel 1998: 38).
H(28) listed by Lett (1915: 162).
†H28 listed by Blockeel & Long (1998: 133).
H(29) listed by Lett (1915: 162).
†H29 listed by Blockeel & Long (1998: 133).
H30 1965: bankside, Cavanagarvan, nr Monaghan, EM Lobley & RD Fitzgerald (Warburg 1966: 201).
H31 1952: rock by stream, Little Ash, nr Dundalk, RD Fitzgerald (Warburg 1953: 314).
†H33 listed by Blockeel & Long (1998: 133).
H(34) listed by Lett (1915: 162) without locality. H(34) listed by Blockeel & Long (1998: 133).
[H(35) listed by Lett (1915: 162) as: Bundoran, leg. Waddell [Bundoran is in H34!]. H35 deleted because no valid record or voucher specimen traced (Blockeel 1999: 8)].
H(36) listed by Lett (1915: 162).
†H36 listed by Blockeel & Long (1998: 133).
H(37) listed by Lett (1915: 162).
†H37 listed by Blockeel & Long (1998: 133).
H(38) listed by Lett (1915: 162).
†H38 listed by Blockeel & Long (1998: 133).
H(39) listed by Lett (1915: 162).
†H39 listed by Blockeel & Long (1998: 133).
H(40) listed by Lett (1915: 162).
†H40 listed by Blockeel & Long (1998: 133).

130/1 ***Thamnobryum alopecurum*** (Hedw.) Gangulee
(syn. *Porotrichum alopecurum* (Hedw.) Dixon, *P. alopecurum* var. *acutum* Braithw.)

H(1) listed by Lett (1915: 162).
†H1 listed by Blockeel & Long (1998: 133).
H(2) listed by Lett (1915: 162) without details.
†H2 listed by Blockeel & Long (1998: 133).
H(3) listed by Lett (1915: 162) without details.
†H3 listed by Blockeel & Long (1998: 133).
H(4) listed by Lett (1915: 162) without details.
†H4 listed by Blockeel & Long (1998: 133).
H(5) listed by Lett (1915: 162) without details.
†H5 listed by Blockeel & Long (1998: 133).
H(6) listed by Lett (1915: 162) without details.
†H6 listed by Blockeel & Long (1998: 133).
H(7) listed by Lett (1915: 162) without details.
†H7 listed by Blockeel & Long (1998: 133).
H(8) listed by Lett (1915: 162) without details.
†H8 listed by Blockeel & Long (1998: 133).
H(9) listed by Lett (1915: 162) without details.
†H9 listed by Blockeel & Long (1998: 133).
H(10) listed by Lett (1915: 162) without details.
†H10 listed by Blockeel & Long (1998: 133).
H(11) listed by Lett (1915: 162) without details.
†H11 listed by Blockeel & Long (1998: 133).
H(12) listed by Lett (1915: 162) without details.
†H12 listed by Blockeel & Long (1998: 133).
H(13) listed by Lett (1915: 162) without details.
†H13 listed by Blockeel & Long (1998: 133).
H(14) listed by Lett (1915: 162) without details.

†H14 listed by Blockeel & Long (1998: 133).
H(15) listed by Lett (1915: 162) without details.
†H15 listed by Blockeel & Long (1998: 133).
H(16) 1945: Ashford Demesne, Cong, KC Harris (anon. 1946c: 284).
†H16 listed by Blockeel & Long (1998: 133).
H(17) listed by Lett (1915: 162) without details.
†H17 listed by Blockeel & Long (1998: 133).
H(18) listed by Lett (1915: 162) without details.
†H18 listed by Blockeel & Long (1998: 133).
H(19) listed by Lett (1915: 162) without details.
†H19 listed by Blockeel & Long (1998: 133).
H(20) listed by Lett (1915: 162) without details.
†H20 listed by Blockeel & Long (1998: 133).
H(21) listed by Lett (1915: 162) without details.
†H21 listed by Blockeel & Long (1998: 133).
H(22) listed by Lett (1915: 162) without details.
†H22 listed by Blockeel & Long (1998: 133).
H(23) listed by Lett (1915: 162) without details.
†H23 listed by Blockeel & Long (1998: 133).
H24 1957: R.[ight] bank of R. Inny, Ballymacarrow Bridge, MPH Kertland & ALK King (Warburg 1958b: 485).
H(25) listed by Lett (1915: 162) without details.
†H25 listed by Blockeel & Long (1998: 133).
H(26) listed by Lett (1915: 162) without details.
†H26 listed by Blockeel & Long (1998: 133).
H(27) listed by Lett (1915: 162) without details.
†H27 listed by Blockeel & Long (1998: 133).
H(28) listed by Lett (1915: 162) without details.
†H28 listed by Blockeel & Long (1998: 133).
H(29) listed by Lett (1915: 162) without details.
†H29 listed by Blockeel & Long (1998: 133).
H(30) listed by Lett (1915: 162) without details.
†H30 listed by Blockeel & Long (1998: 133).
H(31) listed by Lett (1915: 162) without details.
†H31 listed by Blockeel & Long (1998: 133).
[H(32) listed by Lett (1915: 162) without details. H32 deleted because no valid record or voucher specimen traced (Blockeel 1999: 8)].
H(33) listed by Lett (1915: 162) without details.
†H33 listed by Blockeel & Long (1998: 133).
H(34) listed by Lett (1915: 162) without details.
†H34 listed by Blockeel & Long (1998: 133).
H(35) listed by Lett (1915: 162) without details.
†H35 listed by Blockeel & Long (1998: 133).
H(36) listed by Lett (1915: 162) without details.
†H36 listed by Blockeel & Long (1998: 133).
H(37) listed by Lett (1915: 162) without details.
†H37 listed by Blockeel & Long (1998: 133).
H(38) listed by Lett (1915: 162) without details. H(38) listed by Blockeel & Long (1998: 133).
H38 1999: on rocks on bank of stream, 50 m alt., Tollymore Forest park, 4 km W of Newcastle, J33, TL Blockeel 28/349 (Rothero 2000: 58).
H(39) listed by Lett (1915: 162) without details.
†H39 listed by Blockeel & Long (1998: 133).
H(40) listed by Lett (1915: 162) without details.
†H40 listed by Blockeel & Long (1998: 133).

[**130/2** ***Thamnobryum angustifolium*** (Holt) Nieuwl.
(syn. *Porotrichum angustifolium* (Holt) Dixon)]

[H(1) 1906: Derrycunihy, HW Lett in Lett (1915: 162). Specimen (DBN) reidentified as a form of *T. alopecurum* by Dixon 1923: 45. Locality originally given as H2 is in H1 (see Kelly 1984b)].
[H(40)?1898: Glen ... [illegible, but looks like Glenlive], c.[oll.] J Shipley (Dixon 1923, who suggests the correctly identified specimen might be from H39 as the same collector obtained a *Dicranum* at Glenariff in 1898). This is the basis of the 'doubtful record from Antrim' mentioned by Smith (1978: 510), but not accepted by him or by Blockeel & Long (1998: 134).]

131/1a *Pterigynandrum filiforme* Hedw. **var. *filiforme***

[H(1) listed by Lett (1915: 155)].
H(20) listed by Lett (1915: 155). H(20) listed by Blockeel & Long (1998: 134).
H(21) listed by Lett (1915: 155). H(21) listed by Blockeel & Long (1998: 134).
H(38) listed by Lett (1915: 155). H(38) listed by Blockeel & Long (1998: 134).
H(40) listed by Lett (1915: 155). H(40) listed by Blockeel & Long (1998: 134).

131/1b *Pterigynandrum filiforme* **var. *majus*** (De Not.) De Not.

H(38) listed by Blockeel & Long (1998: 134).

133/1 *Hookeria lucens* (Hedw.) Sm. (syn. *Pterygophyllum lucens* (Hedw.) Brid.)

H(1) listed by Lett (1915: 161).
†H1 listed by Blockeel & Long (1998: 134).
H(2) listed by Lett (1915: 161).
†H2 listed by Blockeel & Long (1998: 134).
†H3 listed by Blockeel & Long (1998: 134).
H(4) listed by Lett (1915: 161).
†H4 listed by Blockeel & Long (1998: 134).
H5 1966: clay bank, Jeffry's Wood, nr Kilworth, JG Duckett (BBS exc.) (Perry 1967: 420).
H(6) listed by Lett (1915: 161).
†H6 listed by Blockeel & Long (1998: 134).
H(7) listed by Lett (1915: 161).
†H7 listed by Blockeel & Long (1998: 134).
H(8) listed by Lett (1915: 161).
†H8 listed by Blockeel & Long (1998: 134).
H(9) listed by Lett (1915: 161).
†H9 listed by Blockeel & Long (1998: 134).
H10 1951: wooded gorge, Silvermines, AD Banwell, PJ Wanstall & EV Watson (Warburg 1953: 314).
H(11) listed by Lett (1915: 161).
†H11 listed by Blockeel & Long (1998: 134).
H12 1958: bank of drain, Camolin State Forest, ALK King (Warburg 1959: 637).
H(13) listed by Lett (1915: 161) without details.
†H13 listed by Blockeel & Long (1998: 134).
H(14) listed by Lett (1915: 161).
†H14 listed by Blockeel & Long (1998: 134).
H(15) listed by Lett (1915: 161).
†H15 listed by Blockeel & Long (1998: 134).
H(16) listed by Lett (1915: 161).
†H16 listed by Blockeel & Long (1998: 134).
H(20) listed by Lett (1915: 161).
†H20 listed by Blockeel & Long (1998: 134).
H(21) listed by Lett (1915: 161).
†H21 listed by Blockeel & Long (1998: 134).
H22 1963: wood above R. Boyne, Donore, Drogheda, DM Synnott (Warburg 1964: 732).
H24 1968: wood on E shore of L. Forbes, W of Castle Forbes, WV Rubers (U) (Crundwell 1974: 173).
H25 1960: Rockingham Woods, Boyle, ALK King (Warburg 1962: 171).
H26 1965: clefts of rocks, *ca* 600 ft alt., W of L. Talt, [The] Ox Mts, RD Fitzgerald (Warburg 1966: 201).
H(27) listed by Lett (1915: 161).
†H27 listed by Blockeel & Long (1998: 134).
H(28) listed by Lett (1915: 161).
†H28 listed by Blockeel & Long (1998: 134).
H(29) listed by Lett (1915: 161).
†H29 listed by Blockeel & Long (1998: 134).
H30 1965: shaded bank, Corrakeeldrum Lough, nr Dowra, RD Fitzgerald & EM Lobley (Warburg 1966: 201).
H(31) listed by Lett (1915: 161). H(31) listed by Blockeel & Long (1998: 134).
H(32) listed by Lett (1915: 161). H(32) listed by Blockeel & Long (1998: 134).
H(33) listed by Lett (1915: 161).
†H33 listed by Blockeel & Long (1998: 134).
H(34) listed by Lett (1915: 161) without locality.
†H34 listed by Blockeel & Long (1998: 134).
H(35) listed by Lett (1915: 161).
†H35 listed by Blockeel & Long (1998: 134).
H(36) listed by Lett (1915: 161).
†H36 listed by Blockeel & Long (1998: 134).
H37 1964: in flush at *ca* 1100 ft [alt.], Slieve Gullion, RD Fitzgerald (Warburg 1965: 870).
H(38) listed by Lett (1915: 161).
†H38 listed by Blockeel & Long (1998: 134).
H(39) listed by Lett (1915: 161).
†H39 listed by Blockeel & Long (1998: 134).
H(40) listed by Lett (1915: 161).
†H40 listed by Blockeel & Long (1998: 134).

[*Hypopterygium immigrans* Lett]

[Lett (1915: 161) lists this species as introduced in H21 (1887: Easton Lodge, Monkstown, leg. G Pim, 'On surface of earth in pots and on rock-work of walls, in a cold fern house where it has flourished and fruited freely for some years. An immigrant.'). It was named as *H. immigrans* by Lett in *Journal of Botany* **42**: 249-252, 1904. The geographical origin of the moss is unclear].

134/1 ***Cyclodictyon laetevirens*** (Hook. & Taylor) Mitt.

H(1) listed by Lett (1915: 162).
†H1 listed by Blockeel & Long (1998: 134).
H(2) listed by Lett (1915: 162).
†H2 listed by Blockeel & Long (1998: 134).
H3 1963: deep shaded and dripping rock cleft at 400 ft [alt.], Hungry Hill, nr Adrigole, DA Ratcliffe (Warburg 1964: 732).
H(4) listed by Lett (1915: 162). H(4) listed by Blockeel & Long (1998: 134).
H(6) listed by Lett (1915: 162). H(6) placed in brackets, comm. HJB Birks (Hill 1981: 33). H(6) listed by Blockeel & Long (1998: 134).
H27 1962: dark deep wet overhang in stream, N side of Menawn [*sic* = Menaun], Achill I., EF Warburg (Warburg 1963b: 501).
H29 1967: on wet shaded rocks between Glencar and Glenfarne, DA Ratcliffe, HH Birks & HJB Birks (Crundwell 1968: 644).

135/1 ***Daltonia splachnoides*** (Sm.) Hook. & Taylor

H(1) listed by Lett (1915: 162).
†H1 listed by Blockeel & Long (1998: 134).
H(2) listed by Lett (1915: 162).
†H2 listed by Blockeel & Long (1998: 134).
H3 1955: wet rocks by rivulet, NE slope of Lackawee, H Milne-Redhead (Warburg 1956: 156).
H8 1994: stream valley at edge of forestry, slopes of Knockanimpaha, R23, E Wiltshire & MV O'Brien (Blockeel 1995c: 46).
H(21) listed by Lett (1915: 162). H(21) a pre-1950 record, comm. AJE Smith (Hill 1980b: 45). H(21) listed by Blockeel & Long (1998: 134).
H27 1987: on sloping rock slab by stream, ravine below N ridge of Devil's Mother, DG Long (Blockeel 1998: 38).
H29 1963: rotting log in stream above Glencar Waterfall, AR Perry & RD Fitzgerald (Warburg 1964: 732).
H30 1965: twigs of willow, *ca* 1150 ft alt., dripping rock face, Englishman's House, 3 miles S of Glenfarne, RD Fitzgerald (Warburg 1966: 201).
H33 2000: on *Salix cinerea* amongst tall *Vaccinium myrtillus* and *Luzula sylvatica* in block scree below N-facing sandstone crag, Culcarrick Scarp, H05, DT Holyoak 00-242 (BBSUK) (Rothero 2001: 46).

138/1 ***Leskea polycarpa*** Hedw.

H(1) listed by Lett (1915: 143) without details.
†H1 listed by Blockeel & Long (1998: 135).
H(2) listed by Lett (1915: 143).
†H2 listed by Blockeel & Long (1998: 135).
H3 2002: on base of tree by lake, 4 m alt., Kilkeran Lake, Castlefreke, W33, TL Blockeel 31/378 (Rothero 2003: 60).
H4 1966: alders by R. Lee, Innishcarra Bridge, MFV Corley & JS Parker (Perry 1967: 420).
H5 1999: on alder by river, Tallow, W99, DH Wrench (Rothero 2000: 58).
H6 1966: chestnut by river, Tikincor, nr Clonmel, J Appleyard & JG Duckett (Perry 1967: 420).
H7 1956: tree root by R. Suir, Knocklofty, EC Wallace (Warburg 1957: 335).
[H(8) listed by Lett (1915: 143) without locality. H8 deleted because no valid record or voucher specimen traced (Blockeel 1999: 8)].
H12 1975: alders beside stream S of Clonough Bridge, E of Inch, JA Paton (BBS exc.) (Crundwell 1976: 30).
H13 1969: ash tree by R. Slaney, Aghade Bridge, nr Tullow, RD Fitzgerald (Crundwell 1970: 208).
H15 1957: trees and rocks around turlough, Garryland Wood, nr Gort, RE Parker (BBS exc.) (Warburg 1958b: 485).
[H(19) 1938: Co. Kildare, JS Thomson (anon. 1939b: 110); record lacks a precise

locality. H19 deleted because no valid record or voucher specimen traced (Blockeel 1999: 8)].
H(20) listed by Lett (1915: 143). H(20) listed by Blockeel & Long (1998: 135).
[H21 deleted because no valid record or voucher specimen traced (Blockeel 1999: 8)].
H22 1965: base of ash above water level, canal bank, Oldbridge, DM Synnott (Warburg 1966: 201).
H24 1957: tree root by right bank of R. Inny, Ballymacarrow Bridge, MPH Kertland & ALK King (Warburg 1958b: 485).
H(25) listed by Lett (1915: 143).
†H25 listed by Blockeel & Long (1998: 135).
H26 1987: on silty boulder on wooded river bank, E bank of Cloon River nr Partry, DG Long (Blockeel 1998: 39).
†H28 listed by Blockeel & Long (1998: 135).
H(29) listed by Lett (1915: 143).
†H29 listed by Blockeel & Long (1998: 135).
H(30) 1941: Lough Oughter, JS Thomson (Duncan 1944: 214).
H30 2001: on *Salix viminalis* by river, 95 m alt., Owenmore River, NW of Glengevlin, H02, DT Holyoak 01-650 (Rothero 2002: 54).
H31 1965: willow, bank of R. Boyne, nr Townley Hall, Tullyallen, DM Synnott (Warburg 1966: 201).
H(32) 1947: stump in swamp, Black I., Lough Muckno, Hope Castle demesne, Castleblaney, JS Thomson (anon. 1948b: 123).
H33 1957: tree roots in woodland stream, nr Hanging Rock, L. Macnean Lower, AC Crundwell (Warburg 1958b: 485).
H(34) listed by Lett (1915: 143). H(34) listed by Blockeel & Long (1998: 135).
H(35) listed by Lett (1915: 143). H(35) listed by Blockeel & Long (1998: 135).
H35 2002: on *Salix cinerea* in carr on lough shore, 21 m alt., NE shore of Lough Fern, C12, DT Holyoak 02-746 (Rothero 2003: 60).
†H36 listed by Blockeel & Long (1998: 135).
H(37) listed by Lett (1915: 143).
†H37 listed by Blockeel & Long (1998: 135).
H(38) listed by Lett (1915: 143). H(38) listed by Blockeel & Long (1998: 135).
H38 1999: on willow and alder on river bank, Drum, beside River Lagan, J36, DT Holyoak 99-868 (BBSUK) (Rothero 2000: 58).
H(39) listed by Lett (1915: 143). H(39) listed by Blockeel & Long (1998: 135).
H(40) listed by Lett (1915: 143). H(40) listed by Blockeel & Long (1998: 135).

143/3 ***Anomodon viticulosus*** (Hedw.) Hook. & Taylor

H(1) listed by Lett (1915: 143) without details.
†H1 listed by Blockeel & Long (1998: 136).
H(2) listed by Lett (1915: 143) without details.
†H2 listed by Blockeel & Long (1998: 136).
[H(3) listed by Lett (1915: 143) without details. H3 deleted because no valid record or voucher specimen traced (Blockeel 1999: 8)].
H(4) listed by Lett (1915: 143) without details.
†H4 listed by Blockeel & Long (1998: 136).
H(5) listed by Lett (1915: 143) without details.
H(5) 1920: Fermoy, DB Bradshaw (anon. 1924: 76).
H5 2002: on limestone rocks in arboretum, 10 m alt., Fota House, Foaty I., W77, TL Blockeel 31/346 (Rothero 2003: 60).
H(6) 1933: Kilgreany, E Armitage (anon. 1934b: 128).
†H6 listed by Blockeel & Long (1998: 136).
H(7) listed by Lett (1915: 143) without details.
†H7 listed by Blockeel & Long (1998: 136).
H(8) listed by Lett (1915: 143) without details.
†H8 listed by Blockeel & Long (1998: 136).
H(9) listed by Lett (1915: 143) without details.
†H9 listed by Blockeel & Long (1998: 136).
[H(10) listed by Lett (1915: 143) without details. H10 deleted because no valid record or voucher specimen traced (Blockeel 1999: 8)].
H10 2002: on limestone wall by road, alt. 40 m, Sedboro, nr Dromineer, E side of Loch Derg, R88, DG Long 31464 (Rothero 2003: 60).
H(11) listed by Lett (1915: 143) without details.
†H11 listed by Blockeel & Long (1998: 136).
[H(13) listed by Lett (1915: 143) without details. H13 deleted because no valid record or voucher specimen traced (Blockeel 1999: 8)].

H13 1999: on embankment wall by river, 4 m alt., Saint Mullins, banks of R Barrow, S73, TL Blockeel 28/318 (Rothero 2000: 58).
H(14) listed by Lett (1915: 143) without details.
†H14 listed by Blockeel & Long (1998: 136).
[H(15) listed by Lett (1915: 143) without details. H15 deleted because no valid record or voucher specimen traced (Blockeel 1999: 8)].
H(16) listed by Lett (1915: 143) without details.
†H16 listed by Blockeel & Long (1998: 136).
H(17) listed by Lett (1915: 143) without details.
†H17 listed by Blockeel & Long (1998: 136).
H(18) listed by Lett (1915: 143) without details.
†H18 listed by Blockeel & Long (1998: 136).
[H(19) listed by Lett (1915: 143) without details. H19 deleted because no valid record or voucher specimen traced (Blockeel 1999: 8)].
[H(20) listed by Lett (1915: 143) without details. H20 deleted because no valid record or voucher specimen traced (Blockeel 1999: 8)].
H(21) listed by Lett (1915: 143) without details. H(21) listed by Blockeel & Long (1998: 136).
H(22) listed by Lett (1915: 143) without details.
†H22 listed by Blockeel & Long (1998: 136).
H(23) listed by Lett (1915: 143) without details.
†H23 listed by Blockeel & Long (1998: 136).
H24 1957: bank, Ballymacarrow Bridge, MPH Kertland & ALK King (Warburg 1958b: 485).
†H25 listed by Blockeel & Long (1998: 136).
H(26) listed by Lett (1915: 143) without details.
†H26 listed by Blockeel & Long (1998: 136).
H27 1987: on rock face in woodland, by R. Bunanakee, S bank, W slopes of Mweelrea, DA Newman (Blockeel 1998: 39).
H(28) listed by Lett (1915: 143) without details.
†H28 listed by Blockeel & Long (1998: 136).
H(29) listed by Lett (1915: 143) without details.
†H29 listed by Blockeel & Long (1998: 136).
H(30) listed by Lett (1915: 143) without details.
†H30 listed by Blockeel & Long (1998: 136).
[H(31) 1912: Co. Louth [no locality given], J Glover (anon. 1916c: 8). H(31) listed by Lett (1915: 143) without details. H31 deleted because no valid record or voucher specimen traced (Blockeel 1999: 8)].
H32 1950: limestone, L. Aphuca, RD Fitzgerald (Warburg 1951: 502).
H(33) listed by Lett (1915: 143) without details. H(33) listed by Blockeel & Long (1998: 136).
H33 2000: on rock at base of limestone crag in woodland, Hanging Rock, H13, DT Holyoak 00-126 (BBSUK) (Rothero 2001: 46).
[H(34) listed by Lett (1915: 143) without details. H34 deleted because no valid record or voucher specimen traced (Blockeel 1999: 8)].
H(35) listed by Lett (1915: 143) without details. H(35) listed by Blockeel & Long (1998: 136).
H(36) listed by Lett (1915: 143) without details.
†H36 listed by Blockeel & Long (1998: 136).
H37 1964: limestone rocks by towpath, Carrickaness, nr Benburb, RD Fitzgerald (Warburg 1965: 870).
[H(38) listed by Lett (1915: 143) without details. H38 deleted because no valid record or voucher specimen traced (Blockeel 1999: 8)].
H(39) listed by Lett (1915: 143) without details.
†H39 listed by Blockeel & Long (1998: 136).
H(40) listed by Lett (1915: 143) without details.
†H40 listed by Blockeel & Long (1998: 136).

144/1a ***Heterocladium heteropterum*** Bruch, Schimp. & W.Gümbel **var.** ***heteropterum***
(syn. *Heterocladium macounii* auct. non Best)

H(1) listed by Lett (1915: 155).
†H1 listed by Blockeel & Long (1998: 136).
H(2) listed by Lett (1915: 155).
[H2 record (1951: rotting tree stump, Derrycunihy Wood, Killarney, RE Parker (BBS exc.): Warburg 1953: 315, as *H. macounii*) should be deleted because the locality is in H1 (see Kelly

1984b)].
H(3) listed by Lett (1915: 155).
†H3 listed by Blockeel & Long (1998: 136).
H(4) listed by Lett (1915: 155).
†H4 listed by Blockeel & Long (1998: 136).
H5 1956: stones in wood, Tourig river valley, NW of Youghal, EC Wallace (Warburg 1957: 335).
H(6) listed by Lett (1915: 155).
†H6 listed by Blockeel & Long (1998: 136).
H(7) listed by Lett (1915: 155).
†H7 listed by Blockeel & Long (1998: 136).
H8 1966: stone in wood by sea, by Ballydonohoe House, E of Tarbert, MFV Corley & JS Parker (Perry 1967: 420).
H9 1957: ground in Cratloe Wood, ALK King (Warburg 1958b: 485).
H10 1967: on wet rocks in wooded valley, Clare Glen, nr Newport, HH Birks, HJB Birks & DA Ratcliffe (Crundwell 1968: 644).
H11 1966: rocks in wood, Inistioge, JA Appleyard *et al.*(BBS exc.) (Perry 1967: 420).
H12 1969: on boulder in wood, Wicklow Gap, RD Fitzgerald (Crundwell 1970: 208).
H(13) listed by Lett (1915: 155). H(13) listed by Blockeel & Long (1998: 136).
H14 1952: ground in plantation, Ossory Forest, *ca* 1000 ft [alt.], ALK King (Warburg 1953: 315).
H(15) listed by Lett (1915: 155). H(15) listed by Blockeel & Long (1998: 136).
H(16) listed by Lett (1915: 155).
†H16 listed by Blockeel & Long (1998: 136).
H(20) listed by Lett (1915: 155).
†H20 listed by Blockeel & Long (1998: 136).
H(21) listed by Lett (1915: 155). H(21) listed by Blockeel & Long (1998: 136).
[H22 should be removed from *CC* because specimen (1965: on tree roots in wood by R. Boyne, Oldbridge, ALK King, Crundwell 1968: 644) (DBN) redet. as *H. wulfsbergii* by AC Crundwell, *fide* AJE Smith MS list].
H25 1981: ravine below waterfall, ESE of Kilronan Mt., Arigna, DM Synnott (Hill 1982: 29).
H26 1965: shaded sides of boulders, *ca* 600 ft alt., W of L. Talt, [The] Ox Mts, RD Fitzgerald (Warburg 1966: 201).
H(27) listed by Lett (1915: 155).
†H27 listed by Blockeel & Long (1998: 136).
H28 1963: schistose rocks, *ca* 1000 ft [alt.], S of Knockachree, Slieve Gamph, RD Fitzgerald & AR Perry (Warburg 1964: 732).
†H29 listed by Blockeel & Long (1998: 136).
H30 1965: rock cleft *ca* 2000 ft alt., top of Cuilcagh, RD Fitzgerald & EM Lobley (Warburg 1966: 201).
H(31) listed by Lett (1915: 155). H(31) listed by Blockeel & Long (1998: 136).
H33 1961: rock face in wood, *ca* 200 ft [alt.], Stonefort, nr Boa I., RD Fitzgerald (Warburg 1962: 374).
H(34) listed by Lett (1915: 155).
†H34 listed by Blockeel & Long (1998: 136).
H(35) listed by Lett (1915: 155).
†H35 listed by Blockeel & Long (1998: 136).
H36 1950: wet boulders by stream, nr Glashagh Bridge, J Taylor (Warburg 1951: 502).
H37 1951: wet stones, Rough I., RD Fitzgerald (Warburg 1952: 105).
H(38) listed by Lett (1915: 155).
†H38 listed by Blockeel & Long (1998: 136).
H(39) listed by Lett (1915: 155).
†H39 listed by Blockeel & Long (1998: 136).
†H40 listed by Blockeel & Long (1998: 136).

H. wulfsbergii was not usually recognised in Ireland or Britain until the revision by Crundwell & Smith (2000); some of the older specimens placed as *H. heteropterum* have not been revised and these may include some material of the rarer *H. wulfsbergii*.

144/1b *Heterocladium heteropterum* var. *flaccidum* Bruch, Schimp. & W.Gümbel (syn. *Heterocladium heteropterum* var. *fallax* Milde)

H(1) 1936: Derrycunihy Woods, Killarney, PWM Richards (anon. 1938d: 41), as var. *fallax*.
†H1 listed by Blockeel & Long (1998: 136).
H(2) 1913: Killarney, EA Richards (anon. 1915a: 134).
†H2 listed by Blockeel & Long (1998: 136).
†H3 listed by Blockeel & Long (1998: 136).
H5 1966: shaded rocks, Jeffry's Wood, Kilworth, JG Duckett *et al.* (BBS exc.) (Perry 1967: 420).
H6 1956: stones in wood, Deelish, nr Dungarvan, EC Wallace (Warburg 1957: 335).
H8 1993: bank by estuary shore,

Ringmoylan, R45, E Wiltshire (Blockeel 1994: 41).

H10 1979: shaded rock in wood above Clare River, Clare Glens, S of Newport, JA Paton (Hill 1980b: 45).

H11 1968: shaded block of sandstone, wood on W bank of R. Nore, SE of Thomastown, JA Paton (Crundwell 1969: 888).

H13 1999: on stone on woodland floor on bank of stream, 30 m alt., Pollymounty River, N bank, Ballyknockcrumpin, S73, TL Blockeel 28/312 (Rothero 2000: 58).

H16 1957: wooded ravine, Ballynahinch, RE Parker (BBS exc.) (Warburg 1958b: 485).

H20 1975: shaded rocks beside Vartry River, Devil's Glen, Ashford, JA Paton (BBS exc.) (Crundwell 1976: 30).

H25 2002: on shaded wet limestone rock, 45 m alt., Tawnytaskin Wood, Lough Key, M80, NG Hodgetts 4100 (Rothero 2003: 60).

H26 1987: boulder in mixed woodland, woodland E of Cloon River nr Partry, DG Long (Blockeel 1998: 39).

H27 1987: on large boulder under trees, N of Bunanakee River, W of Mweelrea, DG Long (Blockeel 1998: 39).

H(28) 1937: River Duff, no collector named (BBS exc.) (Armitage 1938: 12), as var. *fallax*.

†H28 listed by Blockeel & Long (1998: 136).

H29 1972: half-buried block, Kilmore, E shore of L. Gill, WV Rubers (U) (Crundwell 1974: 19).

H(33) 1912: Correll Glen, WN Tetley (anon. 1913b: 11). H(33) listed by Lett (1915: 155).

†H33 listed by Blockeel & Long (1998: 136).

[H34 deleted because no valid record or voucher specimen traced (Blockeel 1999: 8)].

H34 2001: on limestone in plantation woodland, 60 m alt., Ederamone, G96, NG Hodgetts 3913 (Rothero 2003: 60).

H(35) listed by Lett (1915: 155).

†H35 listed by Blockeel & Long (1998: 136).

H36 2002: on overhanging sandstone nr river in wooded gorge, 160 m alt., Sloughan Glen, H27, DT Holyoak 02-1125 (Rothero 2003: 60).

H(38) listed by Lett (1915: 155). H(38) listed by Blockeel & Long (1998: 136).

[H(39) listed by Lett (1915: 155). H39 deleted because no valid record or voucher specimen traced (Blockeel 1999: 8)].

H(40) 1936: Kilrea, JD Houston (anon. 1937a: 368), as var. *fallax*.

†H40 listed by Blockeel & Long (1998: 136).

144/2 *Heterocladium wulfsbergii* I.Hagen (syn. *Heterocladium heteropterum* auct. pro parte, non Bruch, Schimp. & W. Gümbel)

H(1) 1925: Loch Doon, Connor Pass, Dingle Peninsula [= 01/50], CB Marquand (E), det. AC Crundwell (AJE Smith MS).

H1 1951: on rock in stream, lower end of L. Caragh, Glenbeigh [= 11/79], RD Fitzgerald (NMW), det. AC Crundwell (AJE Smith MS). H1 listed by Crundwell & Smith (2000: 47).

H2 1954: stone in deep shade by stream pool, Foley's Glade, AP Fanning (DBN), det. AC Crundwell (AJE Smith MS). H2 listed by Crundwell & Smith (2000: 47).

H(6) no date: Lough Coumshingaun, Comeragh Mts [= 21/31], HW Lett (DBN), det. AC Crundwell (AJE Smith MS). H(6) listed by Crundwell & Smith (2000: 47).

H6 1962: among rocks in moraine below L. Coumshingaun [= 21/31], ALK King (?) (DBN), det. AC Crundwell (AJE Smith MS). †H6 listed by Blockeel & Long (1998: 136).

H7 1962: on stony bank by stream in glen, between Roche's Hill and Sugarloaf Mt., Knockmealdown Mts, no collector named (DBN), det. AC Crundwell (AJE Smith MS). H7 listed by Crundwell & Smith (2000: 47).

[H(12) or [H(13) 1867: on rocks in the clody, Mount Leinster [= 21/85], no collector named (DBN), det. AC Crundwell (AJE Smith MS). H(12) or H(13) listed by Crundwell & Smith (2000: 47), but not by Blockeel & Long (1998: 136) because record not securely assigned to a single vice-county].

H(20) 1863: Powerscourt [= 32/11], D Moore (DBN), det. AC Crundwell (AJE Smith MS). H(20) listed by Crundwell & Smith (2000: 47).

H21 1962: growing through *Solenostoma sphaerocarpum*, Upper Dodder Valley [= 32/02], ALK King (?) (DBN), det.

AC Crundwell (AJE Smith MS). H21 listed by Crundwell & Smith (2000: 47).

H22 1965: on tree roots in wood by R. Boyne, Oldbridge [= 32/07], ALK King (DBN), det. AC Crundwell (AJE Smith MS). This record was originally published (Crundwell 1968: 644) as *H. heteropterum* var. *heteropterum*. H22 listed by Crundwell & Smith (2000: 47).

H(27) 1909: Achill, Curran [= 02/79], HW Lett (DBN), det. AC Crundwell (AJE Smith MS). H(27) listed by Crundwell & Smith (2000: 47).

H35 2001: on rocks by waterfall, 10 m alt., Carrick Lower Bridge, Carrick, G57, NG Hodgetts 3758 (Rothero 2002: 54).

H40 1999: on rocks under trees on banks of river, S of Dogleap House, C62, DT Holyoak 99-625 (BBSUK) (Rothero 2000: 58).

Irish and British records of this species were not usually separated from those of *H. heteropterum* var. *heteropterum* until the study by Crundwell & Smith (2000). The details of specimens listed above are taken from an unpublished list prepared by AJE Smith based on determinations by AC Crundwell.

145/1a ***Thuidium abietinum*** (Hedw.) Bruch, Schimp. & W.Gümbel **subsp. *abietinum***

H(16) listed by Lett (1915: 143). H(16) listed by Blockeel & Long (1998: 136).

H(21) listed by Lett (1915: 143). H(21) listed by Blockeel & Long (1998: 136).

H(27) listed by Lett (1915: 143). H(27) listed by Blockeel & Long (1998: 136).

H(28) listed by Lett (1915: 143).

†H28 listed by Blockeel & Long (1998: 136).

H(34) listed by Lett (1915: 143). H(34) listed by Blockeel & Long (1998: 136).

†H35 listed by Blockeel & Long (1998: 136).

H(40) listed by Lett (1915: 143).

†H40 listed by Blockeel & Long (1998: 136).

Specimens should be checked to confirm the subspecific identity of these records since it seems surprising that most old records of *T. abietinum* are apparently referred to subsp. *abietinum* whereas numerous recent records represent subsp. *hystricosum*.

145/1b ***Thuidium abietinum* subsp. *hystricosum*** (Mitt.) Kindb.
(syn. *Thuidium hystricosum* Mitt.)

H27 1999: in very short vegetation close to road edge on damp, sandy machair, Garter Hill, F84, DT Holyoak 99-330, conf. TL Blockeel (BBSUK) (Rothero 2000: 58).

H(28) 1939: sandhills, Strandhill, JS Thomson (Duncan 1944: 214).

†H28 listed by Blockeel & Long (1998: 137).

H(34) listed by Blockeel & Long (1998: 137).

H34 2001: in dune grassland, 10 m alt., Finner Camp, Ballyshannon, G86, NG Hodgetts 3725 (Rothero 2002: 54).

H(35) 1946: sand dunes, Dunfanaghy, AM Irwin (anon. 1948b: 123).

†H35 listed by Blockeel & Long (1998: 137).

H(40) 1935: Magilligan Sandhills, WR Megaw (anon. 1936: 281).
1937: Magilligan, leg. WR Megaw, det. HN Dixon (anon. 1939a: 97).

†H40 listed by Blockeel & Long (1998: 137).

145/2 ***Thuidium tamariscinum*** (Hedw.) Bruch, Schimp. & W.Gümbel
(syn. *Thuidium tamariscifolium* Lindb. nom. illeg.)

H(1) listed by Lett (1915: 142) without details.

†H1 listed by Blockeel & Long (1998: 137).

H(2) listed by Lett (1915: 142) without details.

†H2 listed by Blockeel & Long (1998: 137).

H(3) listed by Lett (1915: 142) without details.

†H3 listed by Blockeel & Long (1998: 137).

H(4) listed by Lett (1915: 142) without details.

†H4 listed by Blockeel & Long (1998: 137).

H(5) listed by Lett (1915: 142) without details.

†H5 listed by Blockeel & Long (1998: 137).

H(6) listed by Lett (1915: 142) without details.

†H6 listed by Blockeel & Long (1998: 137).

H(7) listed by Lett (1915: 142) without details.

†H7 listed by Blockeel & Long (1998: 137).

H(8) listed by Lett (1915: 142) without details.

†H8 listed by Blockeel & Long (1998: 137).

H(9) listed by Lett (1915: 142) without

details.
†H9 listed by Blockeel & Long (1998: 137).
H(10) listed by Lett (1915: 142) without details.
†H10 listed by Blockeel & Long (1998: 137).
H(11) listed by Lett (1915: 142) without details.
†H11 listed by Blockeel & Long (1998: 137).
H(12) listed by Lett (1915: 142) without details.
†H12 listed by Blockeel & Long (1998: 137).
H(13) listed by Lett (1915: 142) without details.
†H13 listed by Blockeel & Long (1998: 137).
H(14) listed by Lett (1915: 142) without details.
†H14 listed by Blockeel & Long (1998: 137).
H(15) listed by Lett (1915: 142) without details.
†H15 listed by Blockeel & Long (1998: 137).
H(16) listed by Lett (1915: 142) without details.
†H16 listed by Blockeel & Long (1998: 137).
H(17) listed by Lett (1915: 142) without details.
†H17 listed by Blockeel & Long (1998: 137).
H(18) listed by Lett (1915: 142) without details.
†H18 listed by Blockeel & Long (1998: 137).
H(19) listed by Lett (1915: 142) without details.
†H19 listed by Blockeel & Long (1998: 137).
H(20) listed by Lett (1915: 142) without details.
†H20 listed by Blockeel & Long (1998: 137).
H(21) listed by Lett (1915: 142) without details.
†H21 listed by Blockeel & Long (1998: 137).
H(22) listed by Lett (1915: 142) without details.
†H22 listed by Blockeel & Long (1998: 137).
H(23) listed by Lett (1915: 142) without details.
†H23 listed by Blockeel & Long (1998: 137).
H(24) listed by Lett (1915: 142) without details.
†H24 listed by Blockeel & Long (1998: 137).
H(25) listed by Lett (1915: 142) without details.
†H25 listed by Blockeel & Long (1998: 137).
H(26) listed by Lett (1915: 142) without details.
†H26 listed by Blockeel & Long (1998: 137).
H(27) listed by Lett (1915: 142) without details.
†H27 listed by Blockeel & Long (1998: 137).
H(28) listed by Lett (1915: 142) without details.
†H28 listed by Blockeel & Long (1998: 137).
H(29) listed by Lett (1915: 142) without details.
†H29 listed by Blockeel & Long (1998: 137).
H(30) listed by Lett (1915: 142) without details.
†H30 listed by Blockeel & Long (1998: 137).
H(31) listed by Lett (1915: 142) without details.
†H31 listed by Blockeel & Long (1998: 137).
H(32) listed by Lett (1915: 142) without details.
†H32 listed by Blockeel & Long (1998: 137).
H(33) listed by Lett (1915: 142) without details.
†H33 listed by Blockeel & Long (1998: 137).
H(34) listed by Lett (1915: 142) without details.
†H34 listed by Blockeel & Long (1998: 137).
H(35) listed by Lett (1915: 142) without details.
†H35 listed by Blockeel & Long (1998: 137).
H(36) listed by Lett (1915: 142) without details.
†H36 listed by Blockeel & Long (1998: 137).
H(37) listed by Lett (1915: 142) without details.
†H37 listed by Blockeel & Long (1998: 137).
H(38) listed by Lett (1915: 142) without details.
†H38 listed by Blockeel & Long (1998: 137).
H(39) listed by Lett (1915: 142) without details.
†H39 listed by Blockeel & Long (1998: 137).
H(40) listed by Lett (1915: 142) without details.
†H40 listed by Blockeel & Long (1998: 137).

145/3 ***Thuidium delicatulum*** (Hedw.) Mitt. (syn. *Thuidium erectum* Duby)

H(1) listed by Lett (1915: 142).
†H1 listed by Blockeel & Long (1998: 137).
H(2) listed by Lett (1915: 142) without details.
H(2) 1935: Torc Mt., no collector named (BBS exc.) (Watson 1936: 265).
†H2 listed by Blockeel & Long (1998: 137).
H3 1953: roadside runnel on Coomataggart Mt., ALK King (Warburg 1954: 485).
H6 1966: boulders by R. Nire, nr Shanballyanne, JA Paton (BBS exc.)

(Perry 1967: 420).

H7 1966: marshy valley below Bay Lough, Knockmealdown Mts, JA Paton *et al.* (BBS exc.) (Perry 1967: 420).

H8 1966: in quarry, Pallas Green, RD Fitzgerald (BBS exc.) (Crundwell 1968: 644).

H9 1957: limestone woodlands, Slievecarran, nr Kinvarra, RE Parker (BBS exc.) (Warburg 1958b: 485).

H10 1979: mine waste, Silvermines, N Lockhart & RC Stern (Hill 1980b: 45).

H12 1975: roadside gravel, Pallis Bridge, Wicklow Gap, W of Coolgreany, AR Perry (Hill 1977a: 23).

H15 1957: tree bases, Garryland Wood, nr Gort, RE Parker (BBS exc.) (Warburg 1958b: 485).

H(16) listed by Lett (1915: 142) without details.

†H16 listed by Blockeel & Long (1998: 137).

H18 1986: sedge-dominated meadow, Clonmacnoise Callows, N Lockhart (Blockeel 1989: 31).

H19 1979: Newbridge Fen, AC Crundwell *et al.* (Hill 1980b: 45).

H(20) listed by Lett (1915: 142) without details.

†H20 listed by Blockeel & Long (1998: 137).

[H(21) listed by Lett (1915: 142) without details. H21 deleted because no valid record or voucher specimen traced (Blockeel 1999: 8)].

[H23 deleted because record not traced (Synnott 1982, Hill 1983: 55)].

H25 1968: on tree stump, St John's Wood, 3 miles SE of Knockcroghery, WV Rubers *et al.* (U) (Crundwell 1974: 174).

H26 1965: limestone grassland, Carrowagower Bridge, between Clonbur and Ballinrobe, AMcG Stirling (Warburg 1966: 202).

†H27 listed by Blockeel & Long (1998: 137).

H(28) 1937: Ben Bulben, no collector named (BBS exc.) (Armitage 1938: 12).

†H28 listed by Blockeel & Long (1998: 137).

†H29 listed by Blockeel & Long (1998: 137).

H(30) 1949: shady ground in wood, Farnham, JP Brunker (Warburg 1950: 386).

†H30 listed by Blockeel & Long (1998: 137).

H31 1965: side of drain, Spruce Forest, Omeath Road, N of Dundalk, DM Synnott (Warburg 1966: 202).

H(33) listed by Lett (1915: 142) without details.

†H33 listed by Blockeel & Long (1998: 137).

H(34) 1939: Tullach Bay, Inishowen, JD Houston (anon. 1940a: 174).

†H34 listed by Blockeel & Long (1998: 137).

H(35) listed by Lett (1915: 142) without details.

†H35 listed by Blockeel & Long (1998: 137).

H36 1952: marshy ground, L. Bradan, RD Fitzgerald (Warburg 1953: 315).

H(38) 1900: Ballykinler, CH Waddell (anon.1903: 141, Lett 1915: 142).

H(39) listed by Blockeel & Long (1998: 137).

H(40) listed by Lett (1915: 142) without details. H(40) listed by Blockeel & Long (1998: 137).

H40 1999: in short grassland on fixed dunes, Benone, C73, DT Holyoak 99-530 (BBSUK) (Rothero 2000: 58).

145/4 ***Thuidium assimile*** (Mitt.) Jaeg.
(syn. *Thuidium philibertii* Limpr.)

H1 1951: dunes, Castlegregory, AC Crundwell (Warburg 1952: 105).

H7 1966: bank amongst limestone rocks, Rock of Cashel, JA Paton (BBS exc.) (Perry 1967: 420).

H9 1953: turf on limestone crags, Poulsallagh, R Mackechnie & EC Wallace (Warburg 1954: 485).

H10 1979: foot of spoil-heap, Silvermines Mt., EC Wallace (Hill 1980b: 45).

H11 1968: turfy bank in old limestone quarry N of Thomastown, JA Paton (Crundwell 1969: 888).

H14 1956: calcareous grassland, esker SW of Portlaoise, AA Cridland (Warburg 1958b: 485).

H16 1957: fixed dunes, Dog's Bay, Roundstone, JH Tallis (BBS exc.) (Warburg 1958b: 485).

H17 1970: calcareous turf nr edge of L. Corrib, SW of Keekill, AR Perry & HJ Perry (Crundwell 1974: 174).

H(19) 1949: bank in sand quarry, nr Calverstown, JS Thomson (Warburg 1950: 386).

H22 1965: grassland, Commons, Duleek, DM Synnott (Warburg 1966: 202).

H23 1979: top of lock wall, Royal Canal between Ballinla and Footy's Hill, Killucan, DM Synnott (Hill 1980b: 45). [Also 1980: limestone quarry N of Bunbrosna, DM Synnott (Hill 1981: 34), but this apparently the 2nd record

published in error].
H25 1981: old limestone quarry, Maddysrulla, W of Portrunny Bay, L. Ree, DM Synnott (Hill 1982: 29).
H(28) 1928: nr Rosses Point, Sligo (BBS exc.) (Duncan 1928: 119).
†H28 listed by Blockeel & Long (1998: 137).
H32 1952: floor of limestone quarry, Lisgall, nr Carrickmacross, RD Fitzgerald (Warburg 1953: 315).
H(34) 1937: Bundoran, no collector named (BBS exc.) (Armitage 1938: 12).
H35 1962: calcareous turf, Tramore Strand, Murroe, nr Dunfanaghy, EM Lobley (BBS exc.) (Warburg 1963b: 501).
H37 1964: floor of old limestone quarry, Loughgall, RD Fitzgerald (Warburg 1966: 202).
H38 2000: in short turf on calcareous sand dunes, Cloughy, J65, R Weyl (BBSUK) (Rothero 2001: 46).
H(39) 1928: sandhills, Portrush (BBS exc.) (Duncan 1928: 113, 116).
H(40) listed by Blockeel & Long (1998: 137).
H40 1990: in dune grassland, Balmaclary, C63, DM Synnott (Rothero 2001: 46).
H40 1999: on N-facing bank in dunes, W of Portstewart, C83, DT Holyoak 99-603 (BBSUK) (Rothero 2000: 58).

The name *T. assimile* is adopted in place of *T. philibertii* following the taxonomic review of tropical Asian and Pacific *Thuidium* by Touw (2001: 17-18), which concludes that these taxa are inseparable.

145/5 *Thuidium recognitum* (Hedw.) Lindb.

[H(1) listed by Lett (1915: 142)].
[H(3) listed by Lett (1915: 142)].
[H(8) listed by Lett (1915: 142)].
H9 1959: limestone rocks in patch of scrub N of Lake Trabaun, MCF Proctor (Warburg 1961: 172).
H16 1999: on dry sand in short grass on machair, Truska, L54, DT Holyoak 99-407 (BBSUK) (Rothero 2000: 58).
[H(19) 1938: nr Naas, JG Finlay (Duncan 1944: 214). H19 listed as doubtful (in square brackets) in *CC* by Warburg (1963a: 71)].
[H(25) listed by Lett (1915: 142)].
H26 1953: limestone pavement under bushy scrub, E shore of L. Carra, EC Wallace (Warburg 1954: 485).
[H(29) listed by Lett (1915: 143)].
[H(29) 1928: wooded glen, NE end of Glencar Lough (BBS exc.) (Duncan 1928: 118). Record from H29 treated as doubtful in *CC* by Warburg (1963a: 71)].
H29 1963: amongst grass on limestone ledges, scarp at Boggaun, nr Manorhamilton, AR Perry & RD Fitzgerald (Warburg 1964: 732).
[H(31) listed by Lett (1915: 143)].
[H(34) listed by Lett (1915: 143)].
H34 2002: in short grassland in dune slack, 10 m alt., Doagh Isle NE of Ballyliffin, C45, DT Holyoak 02-481 (Rothero 2003: 60).
H35 2002: in moss mat in dune slack with *Salix repens*, 5 m alt., N of Lough Nagreany, C14, DT Holyoak 02-882 (Rothero 2003: 60).
[H(38) listed by Lett (1915: 143)].
H(40) 1913: The Umbra, Downhill, CH Waddell (anon. 1914a: 105).
†H40 listed by Blockeel & Long (1998: 137).

147/1a *Palustriella commutata* (Hedw.) Ochyra **var. *commutata***
(syn. *Amblystegium glaucum* Lindb. nom. illeg., *Cratoneuron commutatum* (Hedw.) Roth var. *commutatum*, *Hypnum commutatum* Hedw.)

H1 1951: flush, Coomeeneragh, Glenbeigh, RE Parker (BBS exc.) (Warburg 1952: 107).
H(2) listed by Lett (1915: 145).
†H2 listed by Blockeel & Long (1998: 137).
H3 1953: roadside runnel by old road to Ballingcary, Gougane Barra, ALK King (Warburg 1954: 487).
H(4) listed by Lett (1915: 145).
†H4 listed by Blockeel & Long (1998: 137).
H(5) listed by Lett (1915: 145). H(5) listed by Blockeel & Long (1998: 137).
H(6) listed by Lett (1915: 145). H(6) listed by Blockeel & Long (1998: 137).
H6 1999: in base-rich flush on steep slope, 400 m alt., Coumshingaun, SW corner of corrie, Comeragh Mts, S31, TL Blockeel 28/286 (Rothero 2000: 58).
H(7) listed by Lett (1915: 145).
†H7 listed by Blockeel & Long (1998: 137).
H(8) listed by Lett (1915: 145).
†H8 listed by Blockeel & Long (1998: 137).
H(9) listed by Lett (1915: 145).
†H9 listed by Blockeel & Long (1998: 137).

H10 1979: Old Red Sandstone face, N side of Clare Glens, nr Newport, AC Crundwell (Hill 1980b: 45).
H11 2000: amongst spring vegetation at edge of stream, 24 m alt., Dysart Wood, S side of R. Nore, 3 km downstream of Thomastown, S53, M Wyse Jackson, conf. N Lockhart (Rothero 2001: 46).
H(13) listed by Lett (1915: 145).
†H13 listed by Blockeel & Long (1998: 137).
H(14) listed by Lett (1915: 145).
†H14 listed by Blockeel & Long (1998: 137).
[H(15) listed by Lett (1915: 145). H15 deleted because no valid record or voucher specimen traced (Blockeel 1999: 8)].
H(16) listed by Lett (1915: 145).
†H16 listed by Blockeel & Long (1998: 137).
H17 1968: fen by roadside ½ mile SE of Menlough, N of Galway City, AR Perry (Crundwell 1969: 888).
H(18) listed by Lett (1915: 145).
†H18 listed by Blockeel & Long (1998: 137).
H(19) 1949: waterfall by Rye Water, Leixlip, JP Brunker (Warburg 1950: 388).
†H19 listed by Blockeel & Long (1998: 137).
H(20) listed by Lett (1915: 145).
†H20 listed by Blockeel & Long (1998: 137).
H(21) listed by Lett (1915: 145). H(21) listed by Blockeel & Long (1998: 137).
H22 1966: in calcareous flush, Commons, Duleek, DM Synnott (DBN) (Blockeel 1989: 31).
H23 1953: ditch nr shore, NE end of L. Owel, JS Thomson (Warburg 1954: 487).
H24 1966: wall of lock, Aghnaskea Bridge, Royal Canal, ALK King (Perry 1967: 420).
H25 1973: marsh, Kilmore Bay, shore of L. Ree, WV Rubers (U) (Crundwell 1975: 19).
H(26) 1945: bogs, Partry, KC Harris (anon. 1946c: 286).
†H26 listed by Blockeel & Long (1998: 137).
†H27 listed by Blockeel & Long (1998: 137).
H(28) listed by Lett (1915: 145).
†H28 listed by Blockeel & Long (1998: 137).
H(29) listed by Lett (1915: 145).
†H29 listed by Blockeel & Long (1998: 137).
H30 2001: on unshaded tufa in flush, 225 m alt., N of Manragh, H03, DT Holyoak 01-766 (Rothero 2002: 54).
H(31) listed by Lett (1915: 145). H(31) listed by Blockeel & Long (1998: 137).
H31 1999: in base-rich seepage area among rocks, 160 m alt., Two Mile River, Carlingford, J11, TL Blockeel 28/155 (Rothero 2000: 58).
H(32) listed by Lett (1915: 145). H(32) listed by Blockeel & Long (1998: 137).
H(33) listed by Lett (1915: 145).
†H33 listed by Blockeel & Long (1998: 137).
H(34) listed by Lett (1915: 145).
†H34 listed by Blockeel & Long (1998: 137).
H(35) listed by Lett (1915: 145).
†H35 listed by Blockeel & Long (1998: 137).
H(36) listed by Lett (1915: 145).
†H36 listed by Blockeel & Long (1998: 137).
[H(37) listed by Lett (1915: 145) as 1898: Camlough Mt., leg. HW Lett. H37 deleted: specimen from Camlough Mt., 1898, leg. HW Lett (DBN), is *Ctenidium molluscum*, comm. DM Synnott (Blockeel 1989: 30)].
H37 1964: in flush, 300 m, Slieve Gullion, RD Fitzgerald (NMW), comm. AR Perry (Blockeel 1990: 32-33).
H(38) listed by Lett (1915: 145). H(38) listed by Blockeel & Long (1998: 137).
H38 2002: on damp schistose rock above river, 70 m alt., Spinkwee River, Tollymore Forest Park, J33, DT Holyoak, 02-986 (Rothero 2003: 60).
H(39) listed by Lett (1915: 145).
†H39 listed by Blockeel & Long (1998: 137).
H(40) listed by Lett (1915: 145).
†H40 listed by Blockeel & Long (1998: 137).

147/1b *Palustriella commutata* var. *falcata* (Brid.) Ochyra
(syn. *Amblystegium falcatum* (Brid.) De Not., *Cratoneuron commutatum* (Hedw.) Roth var. *falcatum* (Brid.) Mönk., *Hypnum falcatum* Brid., *H. falcatum* var. *gracilescens* Schimp.)

H(1) listed by Blockeel & Long (1998: 137).
H(2) listed by Lett (1915: 145) without details.
†H2 listed by Blockeel & Long (1998: 137).
H(3) listed by Lett (1915: 145).
†H3 listed by Blockeel & Long (1998: 137).
H8 1975: marshy field, Clogh, Rathkeale, PH Pitkin (Crundwell 1976: 30).
H(9) listed by Lett (1915: 145).
†H9 listed by Blockeel & Long (1998: 137).
H11 1966: bog, Derryfadda, nr Johnstown, J Appleyard (BBS exc.) (Perry 1967: 420).
H(12) listed by Lett (1915: 145). H(12) listed by Blockeel & Long (1998: 137).

H13 1969: in flush, the Nine Stones, N of Mt Leinster, RD Fitzgerald (Crundwell 1970: 208).
H14 1965: alkaline marsh, Derry Hills, nr Clonaslee, ALK King (Warburg 1966: 202).
[H(15) listed by Lett (1915: 145). H15 deleted because no valid record or voucher specimen traced (Blockeel 1999: 8)].
H(16) listed by Lett (1915: 145).
†H16 listed by Blockeel & Long (1998: 137).
H(17) listed by Lett (1915: 145).
†H17 listed by Blockeel & Long (1998: 137).
H(18) 1949: bog beyond Kennedy's Cross, Birr, AP Fanning (Warburg 1951: 503).
†H18 listed by Blockeel & Long (1998: 137).
H(19) 1949: Mullamoy Bog, nr Calverstown, JS Thomson (Warburg 1950: 388).
H(21) listed by Lett (1915: 145). H(21) listed by Blockeel & Long (1998: 137).
H22 1963: cement wall under dripping water nr sea, Gormanstown, DM Synnott (Warburg 1964: 732).
H23 1953: Scraw Bog, nr Portnashangan, JF Thompson, comm. JS Thomson (Warburg 1954: 487).
H24 1966: marsh on E shore of L. Ree, ALK King (Perry 1967: 420).
H25 1968: Annaghmore Lough, 3 miles NW of Strokestown, WV Rubers *et al.* (U) (Crundwell 1975: 19).
H(26) 1945: bogs, Partry, KC Harris (anon. 1946c: 286).
†H26 listed by Blockeel & Long (1998: 137).
H27 1962: wet flush by Keel Lough, Achill I. (Warburg 1963b: 501).
H(28) 1928: nr Rosses Point, Sligo (BBS exc.) (Duncan 1928: 119).
1937: Annacoona, no collector named (BBS exc.) (Armitage 1938: 13), as *Hypnum falcatum* var. *gracilescens*.
†H28 listed by Blockeel & Long (1998: 137).
H(29) listed by Lett (1915: 145).
†H29 listed by Blockeel & Long (1998: 137).
H(30) listed by Lett (1915: 145). H(30) listed by Blockeel & Long (1998: 137).
H30 2001: on open wet soil on flushed bank, 220 m alt., N of Legeelan, H03, DT Holyoak 01-742 (Rothero 2002: 54).
H(31) listed by Lett (1915: 145). H(31) listed by Blockeel & Long (1998: 137).
H31 1999: in stony, base-rich flush on moorland slope by stream, 300 m alt., Two Mile River, Carlingford, J11, TL Blockeel 28/180 (Rothero 2000: 58).
[H32 deleted because no valid record or voucher specimen traced (Blockeel 1999: 8)].
†H33 listed by Blockeel & Long (1998: 137).
H(34) listed by Lett (1915: 145).
†H34 listed by Blockeel & Long (1998: 137).
H(35) listed by Lett (1915: 145).
†H35 listed by Blockeel & Long (1998: 137).
H36 1952: bog, 600 ft [alt.], L. Avadan, RD Fitzgerald (Warburg 1959: 638).
H(37) listed by Lett (1915: 145). H(37) listed by Blockeel & Long (1998: 137).
H(38) listed by Lett (1915: 145). H(38) listed by Blockeel & Long (1998: 137).
H(39) listed by Lett (1915: 146). H(39) listed by Blockeel & Long (1998: 137).
H(40) listed by Lett (1915: 146).
†H40 listed by Blockeel & Long (1998: 137).

147/1c *Palustriella commutata* var. *virescens* (Schimp.) Ochyra
(syn. *Cratoneuron commutatum* (Hedw.) Roth var. *virescens* (Schimp.) P.W. Richards & E.C.Wallace)

H29 1972: submerged just below Glencar Waterfall, WV Rubers (U) (Crundwell 1975: 19).

148/1 *Cratoneuron filicinum* (Hedw.) Spruce
(syn. *Amblystegium fallax* (Brid.) Milde, *A.* filicinum (Hedw.) De Not., *A. filicinum* var. *trichodes* (Brid.) Molendo, *Cratoneuron filicinum* var. *fallax* (Brid.) Roth)

H(1) listed by Lett (1915: 143) without details.
†H1 listed by Blockeel & Long (1998: 138).
H(2) listed by Lett (1915: 143) without details.
H2 1972: boulder, lake shore at Tomies Wood, WV Rubers (U) (Crundwell 1975: 19), as var. *fallax*.
H3 1951: stream bed in intertidal zone, Sherkin I., IA Rorison (Warburg 1952: 107).
H(4) listed by Lett (1915: 143) without details.
†H4 listed by Blockeel & Long (1998: 138).
H(5) listed by Lett (1915: 143) without details.
†H5 listed by Blockeel & Long (1998: 138).
H(6) listed by Lett (1915: 143) without details.

†H6 listed by Blockeel & Long (1998: 138).
H(7) listed by Lett (1915: 143) without details.
†H7 listed by Blockeel & Long (1998: 138).
H(8) listed by Lett (1915: 143).
†H8 listed by Blockeel & Long (1998: 138).
H(9) listed by Lett (1915: 143) without details.
†H9 listed by Blockeel & Long (1998: 138).
H(10) listed by Lett (1915: 143) without details.
†H10 listed by Blockeel & Long (1998: 138).
H(11) listed by Lett (1915: 143) without details.
†H11 listed by Blockeel & Long (1998: 138).
H12 1953: stone jetty in pond, Ballynestragh, JP Brunker (Warburg 1954: 486).
H(13) listed by Lett (1915: 143) without details.
†H13 listed by Blockeel & Long (1998: 138).
H(14) listed by Lett (1915: 143) without details.
†H14 listed by Blockeel & Long (1998: 138).
H15 1957: marshy ground, Loughrea, RE Parker (Warburg 1958b: 487).
H(16) listed by Lett (1915: 143) without details.
†H16 listed by Blockeel & Long (1998: 138).
H(17) listed by Lett (1915: 143) without details.
†H17 listed by Blockeel & Long (1998: 138).
H(18) listed by Lett (1915: 143).
†H18 listed by Blockeel & Long (1998: 138).
†H19 listed by Blockeel & Long (1998: 138).
H(20) listed by Lett (1915: 143) without details.
†H20 listed by Blockeel & Long (1998: 138).
H(21) listed by Lett (1915: 143).
†H21 listed by Blockeel & Long (1998: 138).
H22 1950: marsh, Slane, JS Thomson (Warburg 1952: 107).
H23 1953: stone, NE shore of L. Owel, JS Thomson (Warburg 1954: 486).
H24 1955: roadside drain, Derryad Bog, nr Kilashee, TA Barry, comm. ALK King (Warburg 1956: 158).
H(25) 1940: nr Boyle, JS Thomson (Duncan 1944: 216).
†H25 listed by Blockeel & Long (1998: 138).
H(26) listed by Lett (1915: 143) without details.
†H26 listed by Blockeel & Long (1998: 138).
H(27) listed by Lett (1915: 143) without details.
H27 1965: flush just above sea level, S of Currane village, Currane Achill, DF Chamberlain (Warburg 1966: 202), as var. *fallax*.
H(28) listed by Lett (1915: 143) without details.
H28 1965: stones in stream at 400 ft alt., SE of Tormore, N of Glencar Lough, EF Warburg & AR Perry (Warburg 1966: 202), as var. *fallax*.
H(29) listed by Lett (1915: 143) without details.
†H29 listed by Blockeel & Long (1998: 138).
H(30) listed by Lett (1915: 143) without details.
†H30 listed by Blockeel & Long (1998: 138).
H(31) listed by Lett (1915: 143) without details.
†H31 listed by Blockeel & Long (1998: 138).
H(32) listed by Lett (1915: 143) without details.
†H32 listed by Blockeel & Long (1998: 138).
H(33) listed by Lett (1915: 143).
†H33 listed by Blockeel & Long (1998: 138).
H(34) listed by Lett (1915: 143).
†H34 listed by Blockeel & Long (1998: 138).
H(35) listed by Lett (1915: 143) without details.
†H35 listed by Blockeel & Long (1998: 138).
H(36) listed by Lett (1915: 143) without details.
†H36 listed by Blockeel & Long (1998: 138).
H(37) listed by Lett (1915: 143) without details.
H37 1950: well, Edenappe, J Taylor (Warburg 1954: 486), as var. *fallax*.
H(38) listed by Lett (1915: 143).
†H38 listed by Blockeel & Long (1998: 138).
H(39) listed by Lett (1915: 143).
†H39 listed by Blockeel & Long (1998: 138).
H(40) listed by Lett (1915: 143) without details.
†H40 listed by Blockeel & Long (1998: 138).

150/1a *Campylium stellatum* (Hedw.) J.Lange & C.E.O.Jensen **var. *stellatum***
(syn. *Amblystegium stellatum* (Hedw.) Lindb., *Hypnum stellatum* Hedw.)

H(1) listed by Lett (1915: 145) without details.
†H1 listed by Blockeel & Long (1998: 138).
H(2) listed by Lett (1915: 145) without details.
†H2 listed by Blockeel & Long (1998: 138).
†H3 listed by Blockeel & Long (1998: 138).

H(4) listed by Lett (1915: 145) without details.
†H4 listed by Blockeel & Long (1998: 138).
H5 1967: in bog, *ca* 800 ft [alt.], Lyrenamon, NW of Carrignavar, RD Fitzgerald (Crundwell 1968: 644).
H6 1966: boggy place nr pine wood below Coumshingaun, J Appleyard *et al.* (BBS exc.) (Perry 1967: 420).
H7 1966: L. Curra, J Appleyard & JG Duckett (BBS exc.) (Perry 1967: 420).
H(8) listed by Lett (1915: 145) without details.
†H8 listed by Blockeel & Long (1998: 138).
H(9) listed by Lett (1915: 145) without details.
†H9 listed by Blockeel & Long (1998: 138).
H(10) 1949: among heather, moor nr Longnaminch, The Pike, Balinganny, AP Fanning (Warburg 1951: 503).
†H10 listed by Blockeel & Long (1998: 138).
H(11) listed by Lett (1915: 145) without details.
†H11 listed by Blockeel & Long (1998: 138).
H12 1954: bank, Inch, JS Thomson (Warburg 1955: 586).
H(13) listed by Lett (1915: 145) without details.
†H13 listed by Blockeel & Long (1998: 138).
H(14) listed by Lett (1915: 145) without details.
†H14 listed by Blockeel & Long (1998: 138).
H(15) listed by Lett (1915: 145) without details.
†H15 listed by Blockeel & Long (1998: 138).
H(16) listed by Lett (1915: 145) without details.
†H16 listed by Blockeel & Long (1998: 138).
H17 1957: fens, Cloonboo, RE Parker (Warburg 1958b: 487).
H(18) listed by Lett (1915: 145) without details.
†H18 listed by Blockeel & Long (1998: 138).
H(19) 1949: Ballymount Bog, nr Calverstown, JS Thomson (Warburg 1950: 387).
†H19 listed by Blockeel & Long (1998: 138).
H(20) listed by Lett (1915: 145) without details.
†H20 listed by Blockeel & Long (1998: 138).
[H(21) listed by Lett (1915: 145) without details. H21 deleted because no valid record or voucher specimen traced (Blockeel 1999: 8)].
H22 1965: wet channel, Commons, Duleek, DM Synnott (Warburg 1966: 202).
H23 1953: Scraw Bog, nr Portnashangan, JS Thomson (Warburg 1954: 486).
†H24 listed by Blockeel & Long (1998: 138).
H(25) listed by Lett (1915: 145) without details.
†H25 listed by Blockeel & Long (1998: 138).
H(26) listed by Lett (1915: 145) without details.
†H26 listed by Blockeel & Long (1998: 138).
H(27) listed by Lett (1915: 145) without details.
†H27 listed by Blockeel & Long (1998: 138).
H(28) listed by Lett (1915: 145) without details.
†H28 listed by Blockeel & Long (1998: 138).
H(29) listed by Lett (1915: 145) without details.
†H29 listed by Blockeel & Long (1998: 138).
H30 1955: Farren Connell Bog, nr Mt Nugent, ALK King (Warburg 1956: 158).
[H(31) listed by Lett (1915: 145) without details. H31 deleted because no valid record or voucher specimen traced (Blockeel 1999: 8)].
H31 1999: in base-rich flush on steep slope above stream, 350 m alt., Two Mile River, Carlingford, J11, TL Blockeel 28/181 (Rothero 2000: 59).
[H(32) listed by Lett (1915: 145) without details. H32 deleted because no valid record or voucher specimen traced (Blockeel 1999: 8)].
H32 2002: in blanket bog flush with *Drepanocladus cossonii*, 250 m alt., 1 km downstream of outflow from Lough Bradan, H54, N Lockhart 2002/04a (Rothero 2003: 60).
H(33) listed by Lett (1915: 145) without details.
†H33 listed by Blockeel & Long (1998: 138).
H(34) listed by Lett (1915: 145) without details.
†H34 listed by Blockeel & Long (1998: 138).
H(35) listed by Lett (1915: 145) without details.
†H35 listed by Blockeel & Long (1998: 138).
H(36) listed by Lett (1915: 145) without details.
†H36 listed by Blockeel & Long (1998: 138).
H(37) listed by Lett (1915: 145) without details.
†H37 listed by Blockeel & Long (1998: 138).
[H(38) listed by Lett (1915: 145) without details. H38 deleted because no valid

record or voucher specimen traced (Blockeel 1999: 8)].

H38 2002: on peat in flush on hillside, 200 m alt., W slope of Slievenabrock, J33, DT Holyoak 02-1017 (Rothero 2003: 60).

H(39) listed by Lett (1915: 145) without details.

†H39 listed by Blockeel & Long (1998: 138).

H(40) listed by Lett (1915: 145) without details.

†H40 listed by Blockeel & Long (1998: 138).

150/1b *Campylium stellatum* var. *protensum* (Brid.) Bryhn
(syn. *Amblystegium protensum* (Brid.) Lindb., *Campylium protensum* (Brid.) Kindb., *Hypnum stellatum* var. *protensum* (Brid.) Röhl.)

H(1) 1946: coast, N of Drom, AW Stelfox (per JS Thomson) (anon. 1949c: 221).

†H2 listed by Blockeel & Long (1998: 138).

H4 1966: damp rocks at edge of ditch, Ringnanean Wood, by mouth of R. Stick, MFV Corley & JS Parker (Perry 1967: 420).

H(7) listed by Lett (1915: 145). H(7) listed by Blockeel & Long (1998: 138).

H(8) listed by Lett (1915: 145) without locality.

†H8 listed by Blockeel & Long (1998: 138).

[H(9) listed by Lett (1915: 145) without locality. H9 deleted because no valid record or voucher specimen traced (Blockeel 1999: 8)].

H11 1966: damp place by roadside, Foulkscourt House, nr Johnstown, J Appleyard (BBS exc.) (Perry 1967: 420).

†H16 listed by Blockeel & Long (1998: 138).

H18 1957: roadside bank, nr Ballinagar, JS Thomson (Warburg 1958b: 488).

H19 1962: grassy bank by Gravel Canal at Boyninge's Bridge, ALK King (Warburg 1963b: 501).

H22 1960: roadside bank, Ballinrig nr Summer hill, ALK King (Warburg 1962: 174).

H23 1980: steep roadside bank, Coolamber Lissmacaffrey, DM Synnott (Hill 1981: 34).

H25 1968: lime-rich clay with *Juncus,* Hind River at Cloonsellan, 5 miles SE of Roscommon, WV Rubers *et al.* (U) (Crundwell 1975: 20).

H26 1987: side of boulder on limestone pavement, W side of Keel Bridge, DM Synnott (Blockeel 1998: 39).

H27 1962: dunes, Keel Bay, Achill I., EF Warburg (Warburg 1963b: 501).

H(28) listed by Lett (1915: 145).

†H28 listed by Blockeel & Long (1998: 138).

H29 1965: Carboniferous limestone outcrop at 700 ft alt., gully nr county boundary, S of Glencar Lough, AR Perry & EF Warburg (Warburg 1966: 202).

H(30) 1941: Lough Oughter, JS Thomson (Duncan 1944: 216).

H30 2001: on N-facing mortared wall of bridge, 45 m alt., River Erne at Carratraw Bridge, H31, DT Holyoak 01-839 (Rothero 2002: 54).

[H(31) listed by Lett (1915: 145) without locality. H31 deleted because no valid record or voucher specimen traced (Blockeel 1999: 8)].

[H(32) listed by Lett (1915: 145) without locality. H32 deleted because no valid record or voucher specimen traced (Blockeel 1999: 8)].

H(33) listed by Lett (1915: 145).

†H33 listed by Blockeel & Long (1998: 138).

H(34) listed by Lett (1915: 145). H(34) listed by Blockeel & Long (1998: 138).

H34 2002: in moss carpet on steep damp sand on N-facing slope above beach, 15 m alt., Kinnoge Bay, C64, DT Holyoak 02-535 (Rothero 2003: 60).

†H35 listed by Blockeel & Long (1998: 138).

H36 1953: old wall nr Annahavil Hill, nr Dungannon, MPH Kertland & EM Lobley (Warburg 1955: 586).

H(37) listed by Lett (1915: 145). H(37) listed by Blockeel & Long (1998: 138).

H(39) listed by Blockeel & Long (1998: 138).

H(40) 1913: at foot of cliff, Dounhill [*sic* = Downhill], JD Houston (anon. 1915b: 14).

H(40) listed by Blockeel & Long (1998: 138).

H40 1999: on damp clay bank on hillside, 300 m alt., Benbradagh, SW slope, C71, DT Holyoak 99-673 (BBSUK) (Rothero 2000: 59).

151/1 ***Campyliadelphus chrysophyllus*** (Brid.) Kanda
(syn. *Amblystegium chrysophyllum* (Brid.) De Not., *A. chrysophyllum var. erectum* (Bagn.) Braithw., *Campylium chrysophyllum* (Brid.) J.Lange, *Hypnum chrysophyllum* Brid., *H. chrysophyllum* var. *erectum* Bagn.)

H1 1951: rocks nr coast, West Cove, J Appleyard (BBS exc.) (Warburg 1952: 107).
H(2) listed by Lett (1915: 144).
†H2 listed by Blockeel & Long (1998: 138).
[H(4) listed by Lett (1915: 144) without locality. H4 deleted because no valid record or voucher specimen traced (Blockeel 1999: 8)].
H(5) listed by Lett (1915: 144). H(5) listed by Blockeel & Long (1998: 138).
H8 1966: soil on calcareous bank, Slievereagh, nr Ballylanders, MFV Corley & JS Parker (Perry 1967: 420).
H(9) listed by Lett (1915: 145).
H9 1960: The Burren, AW Stelfox, comm. RD Fitzgerald (Warburg 1962: 376).
H(10) listed by Lett (1915: 145).
H10 1965: stones by shore of L. Derg, Kilbarron Quay, ALK King (Warburg 1966: 202).
H(11) listed by Lett (1915: 144).
†H11 listed by Blockeel & Long (1998: 138).
H(12) listed by Lett (1915: 144). H(12) listed by Blockeel & Long (1998: 138).
H14 1955: wall nr Abbeyleix, JS Thomson (Warburg 1956: 158).
H15 1957: wall top, Garryland Wood, J Appleyard (BBS exc.) (Warburg 1958b: 488).
H16 1957: among rocks by sea, Bunowen Bay, AC Crundwell (BBS exc.) (Warburg 1958b: 488).
H(17) listed by Lett (1915: 144).
†H17 listed by Blockeel & Long (1998: 138).
H(18) listed by Lett (1915: 144).
†H18 listed by Blockeel & Long (1998: 138).
H(19) 1949: top of muddy wall, nr Calverstown, JS Thomson (Warburg 1950: 387).
H(20) listed by Lett (1915: 144). H(20) listed by Blockeel & Long (1998: 138).
H(21) listed by Lett (1915: 144). H(21) listed by Blockeel & Long (1998: 138).
H22 1978: damp flat in sand dunes, Mornington, DM Synnott (Hill 1980b: 45).
H23 1952: wall below Woodlands, NE end of L. Owel, JS Thomson (Warburg 1954: 486).
H24 1980: limestone wall, Draper Bridge, Royal Canal, DM Synnott (Hill 1981: 34).
H25 1952: limestone boulder in bog, Kilnamanagh, nr Athlone, JP Brunker & ALK King (Warburg 1953: 317).
H(26) listed by Lett (1915: 144).
†H26 listed by Blockeel & Long (1998: 138).
H(27) listed by Lett (1915: 144).
†H27 listed by Blockeel & Long (1998: 138).
[H(28) listed by Lett (1915: 144) without details].
H(28) 1928: Strand Hill, nr Sligo (BBS exc.) (Duncan 1928: 119), as *Hypnum chrysophyllum* var. *erectum.* H(28) listed by Blockeel & Long (1998: 138).
H(29) listed by Lett (1915: 144).
†H29 listed by Blockeel & Long (1998: 138).
H(30) listed by Lett (1915: 144). H(30) listed by Blockeel & Long (1998: 138).
H(31) listed by Lett (1915: 144). H(31) listed by Blockeel & Long (1998: 138).
[H(32) listed by Lett (1915: 144). H32 deleted because no valid record or voucher specimen traced (Blockeel 1999: 8)].
†H33 listed by Blockeel & Long (1998: 138).
H(34) listed by Lett (1915: 144, 145). H(34) listed by Blockeel & Long (1998: 138).
H34 2002: on thin sandy soil on top of low crag in dunes, 15 m alt., Doagh Isle NE of Ballyliffin, C45, DT Holyoak 02-493 (Rothero 2003: 60).
H(35) listed by Lett (1915: 144, 145). H(35) listed by Blockeel & Long (1998: 138).
H35 2002: on open damp sand in hollow on hillside nr dunes, 10 m alt., Cruit I., B72, DT Holyoak 02-383 (Rothero 2003: 60).
H(36) listed by Lett (1915: 144).
†H36 listed by Blockeel & Long (1998: 138).
H(37) listed by Lett (1915: 144). H(37) listed by Blockeel & Long (1998: 138).
H(38) listed by Lett (1915: 144). H(38) listed by Blockeel & Long (1998: 138).
H(39) 1928: sandhills, Portrush (BBS exc.) (Duncan 1928: 113, 116), as *Hypnum chrysophyllum* var. *erectum.*
H(39) listed by Lett (1915: 144).
†H39 listed by Blockeel & Long (1998: 138).
H(40) listed by Lett (1915: 144, 145).
†H40 listed by Blockeel & Long (1998: 138).

151/2 ***Campyliadelphus elodes*** (Lindb.) Kanda (syn. *Amblystegium elodes* Lindb., *Campylium elodes* (Lindb.) Kindb., *Hypnum elodes* Spruce hom. illeg.)

H(2) listed by Lett (1915: 144).
†H2 listed by Blockeel & Long (1998: 139).
H7 1966: in drain of cutaway bog, Longfordpass South, nr Urlingford, RD Fitzgerald (BBS exc.) (Crundwell 1968: 644).
H8 1975: marshy fields, Clogh, nr Rathkeale, PH Pitkin (Crundwell 1976: 30).
H(9) 1945: bog nr L. Bunny, JS Thomson (anon. 1946c: 285).
†H9 listed by Blockeel & Long (1998: 139).
H10 1965: marsh by L. Nahinch, nr Borrisokane, ALK King (Warburg 1966: 202).
H12 1969: in dune slack, Cahore Point, RD Fitzgerald (Crundwell 1970:208).
H15 1957: marshy place, nr Loughrea, RE Parker (Warburg 1958b: 487).
H(16) listed by Lett (1915: 144). H(16) listed by Blockeel & Long (1998: 139).
H17 1957: fen, Ballindooly, nr Galway City, RE Parker (BBS exc.) (Warburg 1958b: 487).
H18 1951: bog at railway bridge, Shararoque, Birr, AP Fanning (Warburg 1953: 317).
H(19) 1949: Ballymount Bog, nr Calverstown, JS Thomson (Warburg 1950: 387).
†H19 listed by Blockeel & Long (1998: 139).
H(20) listed by Lett (1915: 144). H(20) listed by Blockeel & Long (1998: 139).
H(21) listed by Lett (1915: 144). H(21) listed by Blockeel & Long (1998: 139).
H22 1978: damp limestone rocks by L. Bane, Oldcastle, DM Synnott (Hill 1980b: 45).
H23 1970: fen on W shore of Killinure Lough, S of Glassan, JA Paton (Crundwell 1971b: 382).
H25 1968: with *Schoenus* on W shore of R. Shannon 1 mile E of Athlone, WV Rubers *et al.* (U) (Crundwell: 1975: 20).
H26 1953: limestone pavement, E shore of L. Carra, nr Clogher House, EC Wallace (Warburg 1954: 486).
H28 1965: shore of L. Gill, nr Ennisfree, EM Lobley & RD Fitzgerald (Warburg 1966: 202).
H(30) 1941: Lough Oughter, JS Thomson (Duncan 1944: 216).
1941: L. Gowna, JS Thomson (Duncan 1944: 216).
1942: bog at Aghalee, JS Thomson, comm. ALK King (Warburg 1964: 732).
H(33) 1909: upper wall, Portora narrows, Lakeshae, Enniskillen, WN Tetley, comm. AJ Pettifer (Perry 1967: 420). Lett (1915: 144) gives 1910: Portora, leg Tetley.
H34 2001: around stems of reeds in rich fen, 90 m alt., Carricknahorna Lough, G96, NG Hodgetts 3908 (Rothero 2003: 60).
H(35) 1946: shore of Loch Clooney, Naran, JS Thomson (anon. 1947: 34).
H35 2002: in dune slack, 5 m alt., NW of New Lake, Dunfanaghy, B93, DT Holyoak 02-704 (Rothero 2003: 60).
H36 1956: marsh, L. More, Slieve Beagh, nr Favor Royal, RD Fitzgerald & MPH Kertland (Warburg 1957: 337).
H(37) 1917: Lurgan, JD Houston (anon. 1937a: 368).
H(39) listed by Blockeel & Long (1998: 139).
H(40) 1913: sandhills, Magilligan, JD Houston (anon. 1915b: 14).
H(40) listed by Lett (1915: 144). H(40) listed by Blockeel & Long (1998: 139).

152/1 ***Campylophyllum calcareum*** (Crundw. & Nyholm) Hedenäs (syn. *Campylium calcareum* Crundw. & Nyholm, *C. hispidulum* (Brid.) Mitt. var. *sommerfeltii* auct. non (Myrin) Lindb.)

H(16) listed by Lett (1915: 156). H(16) listed by Blockeel & Long (1998: 139).
[H(21) listed by Lett (1915: 156). H21 discounted because provenance of specimen dubious (Hill 1981: 34)].
[H(23) listed by Lett (1915: 156) without locality. H23 discounted because source of record not traced (Hill 1981: 34)].
H(26) listed by Lett (1915: 156) without details.
H(26) listed by Blockeel & Long (1998: 139).
H27 1987: sandy bank in lee of storm beach, Bull's Mouth, Achill I., DM Synnott (Blockeel 1998: 39).
H(39) listed by Lett (1915: 156). H(39) listed by Blockeel & Long (1998: 139).
H(40) listed by Lett (1915: 156). H(40) listed by Blockeel & Long (1998: 139).

153/1a *Amblystegium serpens* (Hedw.) Bruch, Schimp. & W.Gümbel **var. *serpens*** (syn. *Amblystegium juratzkae* Schimp. ex Kindb. err. orthogr., *A. juratzkanum* Schimp., *A. serpens* var. *depauperatum* (Boul.) Husn.)

H(1) listed by Lett (1915: 143) without details.
†H1 listed by Blockeel & Long (1998: 139).
H(2) listed by Lett (1915: 143) without details.
†H2 listed by Blockeel & Long (1998: 139).
H(3) listed by Lett (1915: 143) without details.
†H3 listed by Blockeel & Long (1998: 139).
H(4) listed by Lett (1915: 143) without details.
†H4 listed by Blockeel & Long (1998: 139).
H5 1956: sallows, fen W of Youghal, EC Wallace (Warburg 1957: 337).
H(6) 1933: Kilgreany, E Armitage (anon. 1934b: 131).
†H6 listed by Blockeel & Long (1998: 139).
†H7 listed by Blockeel & Long (1998: 139).
H(8) listed by Lett (1915: 143) without details.
†H8 listed by Blockeel & Long (1998: 139).
H(9) listed by Lett (1915: 143) without details.
H9 1959: turf on floor of turlough, Turlough, MCF Proctor & RB Ivimey-Cook (Warburg 1962: 174), as *A. juratzkanum*.
H(10) listed by Lett (1915: 143) without details.
†H10 listed by Blockeel & Long (1998: 139).
H(11) listed by Lett (1915: 143) without details.
†H11 listed by Blockeel & Long (1998: 139).
H(12) listed by Lett (1915: 143) without details.
†H12 listed by Blockeel & Long (1998: 139).
H(13) listed by Lett (1915: 143) without details.
†H13 listed by Blockeel & Long (1998: 139).
H(14) listed by Lett (1915: 143) without details.
†H14 listed by Blockeel & Long (1998: 139).
H15 1952: tree roots, Ross Quay, L. Derg, MPH Kertland & ALK King (Warburg 1953: 317).
H(16) listed by Lett (1915: 143) without details.
†H16 listed by Blockeel & Long (1998: 139).
H17 1957: limestone rocks, Ballindooly Castle, RE Parker (Warburg 1958b: 487).
H(18) listed by Lett (1915: 143) without details.
†H18 listed by Blockeel & Long (1998: 139).
[H(19) listed by Lett (1915: 143) without details. H19 deleted because no valid record or voucher specimen traced (Blockeel 1999: 8)].
H(20) listed by Lett (1915: 143) without details.
†H20 listed by Blockeel & Long (1998: 139).
H(21) listed by Lett (1915: 143, 144).
H21 1951: clay, Brook's End, Rush, JP Brunker (Warburg 1952: 107), as *A. juratzkanum*.
H(22) listed by Lett (1915: 143) without details.
†H22 listed by Blockeel & Long (1998: 139).
H(23) listed by Lett (1915: 143) without details.
†H23 listed by Blockeel & Long (1998: 139).
H(24) listed by Lett (1915: 143) without details.
†H24 listed by Blockeel & Long (1998: 139).
H(25) listed by Lett (1915: 143) without details.
H25 1968: Trinity I., L. Key, WV Rubers *et al.* (U) (Crundwell 1975: 20), as *A. juratzkanum*.
H26 1970: tree nr pool W of Pollagh River, NE of Balla, JA Paton (Crundwell 1971b: 382).
†H27 listed by Blockeel & Long (1998: 139).
H(28) listed by Lett (1915: 143) without details.
H28 1969: base of willow on edge of Bunduff L., N of Cliffony, JA Paton (Crundwell 1970: 208), as *A. juratzkanum*.
H(29) listed by Lett (1915: 143) without details.
H29 1963: recess in limestone face at 800 ft [alt.], Peakadaw, Glenade, AR Perry & RD Fitzgerald (Warburg 1964: 732), as *A. juratzkanum*.
H(30) listed by Lett (1915: 143) without details.
†H30 listed by Blockeel & Long (1998: 139).
[H(31) listed by Lett (1915: 143) without details. H31 deleted because no valid record or voucher specimen traced (Blockeel 1999: 8)].
[H(32) listed by Lett (1915: 143) without details. H32 deleted because no valid

record or voucher specimen traced (Blockeel 1999: 8)].
H(33) listed by Lett (1915: 143) without details.
†H33 listed by Blockeel & Long (1998: 139).
H(34) listed by Lett (1915: 143, 144).
†H34 listed by Blockeel & Long (1998: 139).
H(35) listed by Lett (1915: 143) without details.
H35 1969: salt marsh below cliffs S of Ards House, Ballymore, JA Paton (Crundwell 1970: 208), as *A. juratzkanum*.
H(36) listed by Lett (1915: 143) without details.
†H36 listed by Blockeel & Long (1998: 139).
H(37) listed by Lett (1915: 143) without details.
†H37 listed by Blockeel & Long (1998: 139).
H(38) listed by Lett (1915: 143, 144). H(38) listed by Blockeel & Long (1998: 139).
H38 2002: on *Salix cinerea* in carr at edge of lake, 5 m alt., E side of Quoile Pondage Basin NNR, Downpatrick, J44, DT Holyoak 02-989 (Rothero 2003: 60).
H(39) listed by Lett (1915: 143, 144).
†H39 listed by Blockeel & Long (1998: 139).
H(40) listed by Lett (1915: 143, 144).
†H40 listed by Blockeel & Long (1998: 139).

153/1b ***Amblystegium serpens* var. *salinum*** Carrington

H1 1966: dunes nr Castlegregory, Dingle Peninsula, JA Paton & GCG Argent (Perry 1967: 421).
H2 1952: dunes, Banna Strand, ALK King (Warburg 1953: 317).
H6 1962: sand dunes, Bunmahon, AJE Smith (Warburg 1963b: 502).
†H9 listed by Blockeel & Long (1998: 139).
H12 1956: fixed dune nr Ballymoney, ALK King (Warburg 1957: 337).
[H16 1957: among mosses on sandblown boulders, nr Dog's Bay, Roundstone, DG Catcheside & EM Lobley (Warburg 1958b: 487). H16 deleted because specimen in BBSUK is var. *serpens*, redet. AJE Smith (Crundwell 1976: 30)].
[H19 1953: sandstone boulder by lane below Cupidstown Hill, ALK King (Warburg 1954: 486). H19 deleted because specimen in BBSUK is var. *serpens*, redet. AJE Smith (Crundwell 1976: 30)].
†H21 listed by Blockeel & Long (1998: 139).
H27 1962: dunes, Caraun Point, Achill I., EF Warburg (Warburg 1963b: 502).
H28 1965: among basic coastal rocks, nr Dromore West, EM Lobley & RD Fitzgerald (Warburg 1966: 202).
†H34 listed by Blockeel & Long (1998: 139).
H35 1951: sandy ground, Inishkeel, 'W.A. M.' (Warburg 1953: 317).
H(38) listed by Blockeel & Long (1998: 139).
[H39 deleted because specimen in BBSUK is var. *serpens*, redet. AJE Smith (Crundwell 1976: 30)].
H(40) listed by Blockeel & Long (1998: 139).
H40 1999: on damp sand in low, sparse vegetation at edge of dune slack, Ballymaclary NNR, C63, DT Holyoak 99-287 (BBSUK) (Rothero 2000: 59).

153/2 ***Amblystegium fluviatile*** (Hedw.) Bruch, Schimp. & W.Gümbel
(syn. *Hygroamblystegium fluviatile* (Hedw.) Loeske)

[H(4) listed by Lett (1915: 143)].
H4 1966: rock in stream, Owenagearagh River, below Cloghroe, MFV Corley & JS Parker (Perry 1967: 421).
H(5) listed by Lett (1915: 143). H(5) listed by Blockeel & Long (1998: 139).
H5 2002: at water level on stonework of bridge, 105 m alt., River Bride, Ardarou Wood, Glenville, W78, TL Blockeel 31/362 (Rothero 2003: 61).
H6 1966: rocks in R. Nire, nr Shanballyanne, ERB Little (BBS exc.) (Perry 1967: 421).
H8 1994: stream valley at edge of forestry, slopes of Knockanimpaha, R23, E Wiltshire & MV O'Brien (Blockeel 1995c: 46).
H10 1979: rocks in river, N side of Clare Glens, nr Newport, AC Crundwell (Hill 1980b: 46).
H12 1975: stone in stream nr bridge S of Clonough Bridge, Coolgreany, AR Perry (Hill 1977a: 23).
H13 1969: stones in stream, Burreen River, Sheean, nr Myshall, RD Fitzgerald (Crundwell 1970: 208).
[H(15) listed by Lett (1915: 143) without details. H15 deleted because no valid record or voucher specimen traced (Blockeel 1999: 8)].
H(19) 1939: stone by Golden Falls, nr Ballymore-Eustace, JF Thomson, comm. ALK King [record previously attributed

in error to H20 by anon. 1940a: 175] (Warburg 1965: 870).

[H(20) 1939: Golden Falls, Hollywood, JS Thomson (anon. 1940a: 175). H20 deleted because record (1939: stone by Golden Falls, nr Ballymore-Eustace, JF Thomson, comm. ALK King, anon. 1940a: 175) is from a locality in H19 (Warburg 1965: 870)].

H20 1969: rocks in Aughrim River, between Aughrim and Woodenbridge, RD Fitzgerald (Crundwell 1970: 208).

H25 2002: on vertical limestone wall of harbour, 35 m alt., Lecarrow Harbour, M95, NG Hodgetts 4066 (Rothero 2003: 61).

H(35) listed by Lett (1915: 143). H(35) listed by Blockeel & Long (1998: 139).

H(38) listed by Lett (1915: 143). H(38) listed by Blockeel & Long (1998: 139).

H(39) listed by Lett (1915: 143). H(39) listed by Blockeel & Long (1998: 139).

153/3 ***Amblystegium tenax*** (Hedw.) C.E.O. Jensen
(syn. *Amblystegium irriguum* (Wilson) Bruch, Schimp. & W.Gümbel, *Hygroamblystegium tenax* (Hedw.) Jenn.)

H(1) listed by Lett (1915: 143). H(1) listed by Blockeel & Long (1998: 139).

H(2) 1935: Muckross, no collector named (BBS exc.) (Watson 1936: 265).

H(5) listed by Lett (1915: 143).

†H5 listed by Blockeel & Long (1998: 139).

H6 1956: stone in stream, Deelish, nr Dungarvan, EC Wallace (Warburg 1957: 337).

H7 1956: stream, Marlfield, Clonmel, EC Wallace (Warburg 1957: 337).

H(8) listed by Lett (1915: 143) without locality.

†H8 listed by Blockeel & Long (1998: 139).

[H(9) listed by Lett (1915: 143). H9 deleted because no valid record or voucher specimen traced (Blockeel 1999: 8)].

H11 1966: rocks in R. Nore, Castle Dysart, nr Thomastown, RD Fitzgerald (BBS exc.) (Crundwell 1968: 644).

H15 1957: rock in calcareous stream, nr Punchbowl, 1 mile S of Gort, RE Parker (BBS exc.) (Warburg 1958b: 487).

H19 1963: bridge wall at Porterstown, ALK King (Warburg 1966: 202).

H(20) 1940: Devil's Glen, JS Thomson (Duncan 1944: 216).

H(21) listed by Lett (1915: 143). H(21) listed by Blockeel & Long (1998: 139).

H(25) listed by Lett (1915: 143). H(25) listed by Blockeel & Long (1998: 139).

H27 1970: stone in river nr Erriff Bridge, N of Maumtrasna, JA Paton (Crundwell 1971b: 382).

[H(28) listed by Lett (1915: 143). H28 deleted: specimen from Collooney, 1904, leg. D McArdle (DBN), is a mixture of *Hygrohypnum luridum* and *Cratoneuron filicinum*, comm. DM Synnott (Blockeel 1989: 31)].

H(33) 1911: The Cladagh, Florence Court, WN Tetley (anon. 1912c: 12), labelled as '*Amblystegium filicinum* (form of)' but redet. by GB Savery as 'a rather robust form of *A. irriguum* B. & S.'

H(33) listed by Lett (1915: 143).

†H33 listed by Blockeel & Long (1998: 139).

[H(37) listed by Lett (1915: 143) as 1885: Ardmore Glebe, leg. HW Lett. H37 deleted: specimen from Ardmore Glebe, 1885, leg. HW Lett (DBN), is *Cratoneuron filicinum*, comm. DM Synnott (Blockeel 1989: 31)].

H(38) listed by Lett (1915: 143). H(38) listed by Blockeel & Long (1998: 139).

H38 2002: on exposed tree roots at edge of lake, 115 m alt., SE edge of Castlewellan Lake, J33, DT Holyoak 02-1037 (Rothero 2003: 61).

H(39) listed by Lett (1915: 143). H(39) listed by Blockeel & Long (1998: 139).

H(40) 1913: Garvagh, JD Houston (anon. 1937a: 368).

H40 1999: on basalt boulder in stream in woodland, Downhill Forest, C73, DT Holyoak 99-279 (BBSUK) (Rothero 2000: 59).

153/4 ***Amblystegium varium*** (Hedw.) Lindb.

H6 1972: blocks in stream, Mill Wood, 1 mile W of Carrick on Suir, WV Rubers (U) (Crundwell 1975: 20).

H(8) listed by Lett (1915: 143). H(8) listed by Blockeel & Long (1998: 140).

H9 1973: boulders at edge of turlough, Castletown, Carran, PH Pitkin (Crundwell 1974: 174).

H15 1957: floor of dried-up turlough, Garryland Wood, nr Gort, RE Parker

(BBS exc.) (Warburg 1958b: 487).
H16 1968: bole of *Salix* overhanging Aughnanure Castle, Ardnasillagh, SE of Oughterard, AR Perry (Crundwell 1969: 888).
H17 1957: fallen rotting tree, small wood, nr Kilgariff, Headford, EM Lobley (BBS exc.) (Warburg 1958b: 487).
H22 1966: rock in fast-flowing stream, Commons, Duleek, DM Synnott (Perry 1967: 421).
[H(24) listed by Lett (1915: 143) without locality. H24 deleted because no valid record or voucher specimen traced (Blockeel 1999: 8)].
[H(25) listed by Lett (1915: 143)].
H25 1952: roadside bank, Kilnamanagh, nr Athlone, ALK King (Warburg 1953: 317).
H26 1970: tree nr pool W of Pollagh river, NE of Balla, JA Paton (Crundwell 1971b: 382).
H27 1987: on tree roots on wooded lake shore, by lake, Westport House, DG Long (Blockeel 1998: 39).
H28 1972: boulder on N shore of L. Gill, WV Rubers (U) (Crundwell 1975: 20).
H(30) 1941: Lough Oughter, JS Thomson (Duncan 1944: 216).
†H30 listed by Blockeel & Long (1998: 140).
H(33) listed by Lett (1915: 143).
†H33 listed by Blockeel & Long (1998: 140).
H(34) 1937: in grass in meadow, Bundoran, CH Binstead (BBS exc.), comm. EM Lobley, based on redet. of specimen formerly placed as *A. kochii* (Warburg 1963b: 502).
H(35) listed by Lett (1915: 143). H(35) listed by Blockeel & Long (1998: 140).
†H36 listed by Blockeel & Long (1998: 140).
H(37) listed by Lett (1915: 143).
†H37 listed by Blockeel & Long (1998: 140).
H(38) listed by Blockeel & Long (1998: 140).
H(39) listed by Lett (1915: 143). H(39) listed by Blockeel & Long (1998: 140).
H(40) listed by Lett (1915: 143). H(40) listed by Blockeel & Long (1998: 140).

153/5 ***Amblystegium humile*** (P.Beauv.) Crundw.
(syn. *Amblystegium kochii* Bruch, Schimp. & W.Gümbel)

H25 1968: shore of L. Ree 1 mile W of Lanesborough, WV Rubers *et al.* (U) (Crundwell 1975: 20).
[H(34) 1937: Bundoran, no collector named (BBS exc.) (Armitage 1938: 12-13). H34 deleted because specimen on which record was probably based (1937: Bundoran, BBS exc.) is *A. varium* (Warburg 1963b: 502)].
H39 1951: ground in fen, shore of L. Neagh, RD Fitzgerald (Warburg 1952: 107).
H(40) listed by Lett (1915: 144). H(40) listed by Blockeel & Long (1998: 140).

153/7 ***Amblystegium confervoides*** (Brid.) Bruch, Schimp. & W.Gümbel
(syn. *Amblystegiella confervoides* (Brid.) Loeske, *Platydictya confervoides* (Brid.) H.A.Crum)

H8 1979: limestone wall, Barrigone, nr Askeaton, RC Stern (Hill 1980b: 46).
H9 1957: limestone rocks in hazel scrub on SE side of Slievecarran, J Appleyard, AC Crundwell & E Nyholm (BBS exc.) (Warburg 1958b: 487).
H15 1994: limestone rock, Garryland Wood, Coole, 3 km NW of Gort, M40, HLK Whitehouse (Blockeel 1995c: 46).
H(16) listed by Lett (1915: 144). H(16) listed by Blockeel & Long (1998: 140).
H(20) listed by Lett (1915: 144). H(20) listed by Blockeel & Long (1998: 140).
H(21) listed by Lett (1915: 144). H(21) listed by Blockeel & Long (1998: 140).
H(28) listed by Lett (1915: 144). H(28) listed by Blockeel & Long (1998: 140).

154/1 ***Leptodictyum riparium*** (Hedw.) Warnst.
(syn. *Amblystegium riparium* (Hedw.) Bruch, Schimp. & W.Gümbel, *A. riparium* var. *longifolium* (Schultz) Schimp., *Hypnum riparium* Hedw., *H. riparium* var. *longifolium* (Schultz) Röhl.)

H(1) listed by Lett (1915: 144). H(1) listed by Blockeel & Long (1998: 140).
H2 1952: dunes, Banna Strand, ALK King (Warburg 1953: 317).
H3 2002: on log at edge of lake, 4 m alt., Kilkeran Lake, Castlefreke, W33, TL Blockeel 31/377 (Rothero 2003: 61).
[H4 deleted because no valid record or voucher specimen traced (Blockeel 1999: 8)].
H(5) listed by Lett (1915: 144). H(5) listed by

Blockeel & Long (1998: 140).
H(6) listed by Lett (1915: 144). H(6) listed by Blockeel & Long (1998: 140).
H(8) listed by Lett (1915: 144) without locality.
†H8 listed by Blockeel & Long (1998: 140).
H9 1979: in carr, N end of Fin Lough, NW of Sixmilebridge, AC Crundwell (Hill 1980b: 45).
H(11) listed by Lett (1915: 144).
†H11 listed by Blockeel & Long (1998: 140).
H(12) listed by Lett (1915: 144).
†H12 listed by Blockeel & Long (1998: 140).
H13 1999: on log in overgrown ditch, 8 m alt., R Barrow, nr canal, 1 km NW of Saint Mullins, S73, TL Blockeel 28/321 (Rothero 2000: 59).
H14 1956: side of ditch by Barranagh's Bridge, nr Mountmellick, AA Cridland (Warburg 1958b: 487).
H15 1951: rotting stump in drain, Clonfert, AP Fanning (Warburg 1953: 317).
H16 1957: willow carr, nr sea, Spiddle, RE Parker (Warburg 1958b: 487).
H18 1983: meadow between the National Monument at Clonmacnoise and the Shannon, M Tubridy (Hill 1986: 23).
H(19) 1949: waterfall, Rye Water, Leixlip, JP Brunker (Warburg 1950: 387).
†H19 listed by Blockeel & Long (1998: 140).
H(20) listed by Lett (1915: 144) without locality.
†H20 listed by Blockeel & Long (1998: 140).
H(21) 1947: well by roadside, Finglas, ALK King (per JS Thomson) (anon. 1949c: 221), as *Hypnum riparium* var. *longifolium*.
H(21) listed by Lett (1915: 144).
†H21 listed by Blockeel & Long (1998: 140).
H22 1966: rock in fast-flowing stream, Commons, Duleek, DM Synnott (Perry 1967: 421).
H23 1953: side of well, Woodlands, NE end of L. Owel, JS Thomson (Warburg 1954: 486).
H(24) 1941: Ardnacliff, JG Finlay (Duncan 1944: 216), as *Hypnum riparium* var. *longifolium*.
†H24 listed by Blockeel & Long (1998: 140).
H(25) 1940: nr Boyle, JS Thomson (Duncan 1944: 216), as *Hypnum riparium*.
1940: nr Boyle, JS Thomson (Duncan 1944: 216), as *Hypnum riparium* var. *longifolium*.
†H25 listed by Blockeel & Long (1998: 140).
H26 1970: willow trunk, pool W of Pollagh River, NE of Balla, JA Paton (Crundwell 1971b: 382).
H(27) listed by Lett (1915: 144).
†H27 listed by Blockeel & Long (1998: 140).
H28 1969: base of willow on edge of Bunduff L., N of Cliffony, JA Paton (Crundwell 1970: 208).
H(29) 1948: roadside ditch, Carrick-on-Shannon, ALK King (Warburg 1954: 486).
H29 2000: on top of small sandstone rock at lough edge, Carrickaport Lough, SE edge, H00, DT Holyoak 00-744 (BBSUK) (Rothero 2001: 46).
H(30) listed by Lett (1915: 144). H(30) listed by Blockeel & Long (1998: 140).
H30 2001: on sandstone by stream, 75 m alt., N shore of Lough Sheelin, NW of Mount Nugent, N48, DT Holyoak 01-669 (Rothero 2002: 54).
H(31) listed by Lett (1915: 144). H(31) listed by Blockeel & Long (1998: 140).
H(32) 1947: shore of Lough Muckno, Castleblaney, JS Thomson (anon. 1948b: 123), as *H. riparium* var. *longifolium*.
H32 1950: wall at stream, Carrickmacross, RD Fitzgerald (Warburg 1951: 503).
H33 1950: boulders at edge of water nr Youth Hostel, L. Macnean, J Taylor (Warburg 1954: 486).
H(35) listed by Lett (1915: 144).
†H35 listed by Blockeel & Long (1998: 140).
H(36) listed by Lett (1915: 144).
†H36 listed by Blockeel & Long (1998: 140).
H(37) listed by Lett (1915: 144).
†H37 listed by Blockeel & Long (1998: 140).
H(38) listed by Lett (1915: 144). H(38) listed by Blockeel & Long (1998: 140).
H38 2002: on soil beneath *Salix cinerea* by path at edge of lake, 5 m alt., E side of Quoile Pondage Basin NNR, Downpatrick, J44, DT Holyoak, 02-988 (Rothero 2003: 61).
H(39) listed by Lett (1915: 144). H(39) listed by Blockeel & Long (1998: 140).
H(40) 1939: Benone, JS Thomson (anon. 1940a: 175), as *Hypnum riparium* var. *longifolium*.
†H40 listed by Blockeel & Long (1998: 140).

155/1 ***Conardia compacta*** (Müll.Hal.) H.Rob. (syn. *Amblystegium compactum* (Müll. Hal.) Austin)

H(28) 1928: Gleniff, Ben Bulben (BBS exc.) (Duncan 1928: 114-115, 118). H(28) listed by Blockeel & Long (1998: 140).

156/1 ***Warnstorfia fluitans*** (Hedw.) Loeske (syn. *Amblystegium fluitans* (Hedw.) De Not., *A. fluitans* var. *submersum* (Schimp.) Braithw., *Drepanocladus falcatus* auct., *D. fluitans* (Hedw.) Warnst. var. *fluitans*, *D. fluitans* var. *falcatus* (Sanio ex C.E.O.Jensen) Roth, *Hypnum fluitans* Hedw., *H. fluitans* var. *atlanticum* Renauld)

[H(1) listed by Lett (1915: 147)].
H(1) 1935: Brandon, no collector named (BBS exc.) (Watson 1936: 265), as *Drepanocladus falcatus* [this name is a *nomen nudum* and does not appear to have been validly published; it can only be presumed that it refers to this species rather than to *Palustriella commutata* var. *falcata*].
H1 1966: marshy ground in wood N of O'Sullivan's Cascade, L. Leane, EM Lobley *et al.* (Perry 1967: 421), as var. *falcatus*.
[H(2) listed by Lett (1915: 147)].
H3 1951: L. Ordree, Sherkin I., IA Rorison (Warburg 1952: 107).
[H(4) listed by Lett (1915: 147)].
[H(5) listed by Lett (1915: 147)].
H6 1999: in wet ground by drainage channel at edge of relict bog, 165 m alt., Monaneea Lake, 7 km N of Ardmore, X28, TL Blockeel 28/224 (Rothero 2000: 59).
[H(7) listed by Lett (1915: 147)]
H7 1966: damp track on moorland N of L. Muskry, J Appleyard (BBS exc.) (Perry 1967: 421), as var. *falcatus*.
[H(8) listed by Lett (1915: 147) without locality].
[H(12) listed by Lett (1915: 147)].
H12 1975: heathy bank W of Cloroge, Mt Leinster, JA Paton (BBS exc.) (Crundwell 1976: 31), as var. *falcatus*.
H13 1969: on wet path, *ca* 600 ft [alt.], below Caher Roe's Den, Blackstairs Mts, RD Fitzgerald (Crundwell 1970: 209).
H15 1952: marsh by L. Derg, nr Ross Quay, MPH Kertland & ALK King (Warburg 1953: 317).
H16 1957: brackish pool, nr sea, Bunowen Bay, RE Parker (Warburg 1958b: 488).
[H(18) listed by Lett (1915: 147)].
H19 1971: in bog-chain at Allenwood, ALK King (Crundwell 1972: 142), as var. *falcatus*.
[H(20) listed by Lett (1915: 147) without locality. H20 deleted because no valid record or voucher specimen traced (Blockeel 1999: 8)].
[H(21) listed by Lett (1915: 147)].
H(21) 1924: Dublin Mts, WR Megaw (anon. 1925: 162), as *Hypnum fluitans* var. *atlanticum*.
H23 1952: The Derries Bog, nr Athlone, JP Brunker & ALK King (Warburg 1953: 317).
[H(25) listed by Lett (1915: 147)].
H25 2002: by stream and waterfall on crags, 150 m alt., Kilronan Mt., Arigna, G91, NG Hodgetts 4148 (Rothero 2003: 61).
[H(27) listed by Lett (1915: 147)].
†H27 listed by Blockeel & Long (1998: 141).
[H(28) listed by Lett (1915: 147)].
[H(29) listed by Lett (1915: 147)].
H30 1956: bog pool, Virginia, JS Thomson (Warburg 1957: 337).
[H(31) listed by Lett (1915: 147)].
H32 1962: bog, Darraghlan, nr Monaghan, RD Fitzgerald (Warburg 1962: 376), as var. *falcatus*.
[H(33) listed by Lett (1915: 147)].
†H33 listed by Blockeel & Long (1998: 141).
[H(34) listed by Lett (1915: 147) without locality].
H34 1962: peaty pool nr top of Croaghconnellagh, EF Warburg (BBS exc.) (Warburg 1963b: 502).
[H(35) listed by Lett (1915: 147)].
H35 1970: shallow peaty pool nr sea nr Portnoo, N of Ardara, MFV Corley (Crundwell 1971b: 382), as var. *falcatus*.
[H36 1950: bog drain, nr Trillick, J Taylor (Warburg 1951: 503). H36 omitted from *CC* by Corley & Hill (1981: 118), presumably because record rejected].
[H(37) listed by Lett (1915: 147)].
[H(38) listed by Lett (1915: 147)].
[H(39) listed by Lett (1915: 147)]. H(39) listed by Blockeel & Long (1998: 141).
[H(40) listed by Lett (1915: 147)].
H40 1968: wet bog nr Hellhole, Binevanagh [*sic* = Binevenagh], H Bulls & RD

Fitzgerald (Crundwell 1971b: 382), as var. *falcatus*.

Old records (e.g. from Lett 1915: 147) were often based on misidentification of other species, so that they cannot be accepted unless voucher specimens have been checked.

156/2 ***Warnstorfia exannulata*** (Bruch, Schimp. & W.Gümbel) Loeske
(syn. *Amblystegium exannulatum* (Bruch, Schimp. & W.Gümbel) De Not., *A. exannulatum* var. *rotae* (De Not.) Braithw., *Drepanocladus exannulatus* (Bruch, Schimp. & W.Gümbel) Warnst. var. *exannulatus*, *D. exannulatus* var. *rotae* (De Not.) Loeske, *Hypnum exannulatum* Bruch, Schimp. & W. Gümbel, *Hypnum exannulatum* var. *brachydictyon* (Renauld) Paris nom. illeg.)

H(1) listed by Lett (1915: 147).
H2 1967: in flush, *ca* 900 ft [alt.], The Paps, RD Fitzgerald (Crundwell 1968: 645).
H3 1951: fen, Cape Clear, IA Rorison (Warburg 1952: 107).
1979: peaty soil on rocks above the shore, S of League Point, Sheep's Head Peninsula, JA Paton (Hill 1980b: 46); as var. *rotae*.
H4 1967: on moor, *ca* 1200 ft [alt.], Mushera, Boggeragh Mts, RD Fitzgerald (Crundwell 1968: 645).
H5 1967: in bog, *ca* 800 ft [alt.], Lyrenamon, NW of Garrignavar, RD Fitzgerald (Crundwell 1968: 645), as var. *rotae*.
1967: in bog, Lyrenamon, RD Fitzgerald (Crundwell 1968: 645).
H(6) listed by Lett (1915: 147).
H(6) 1933: Poolvona, E Armitage (anon. 1934b: 132), as *Hypnum exannulatum* var. *brachydictyon*.
H6 1966: marshy slope nr Sgilloge Loughs, Comeragh Mts, JA Paton (BBS exc.) (Perry 1967: 421).
1999: in bottom of drainage channel by relict bog, 165 m alt., Monaneea Lake, 7 km N of Ardmore, X28, TL Blockeel 28/225 (Rothero 2000: 59).
H7 1966: boggy ground nr Bay Lough, Knockmealdown Mts, ERB Little & JA Paton (BBS exc.) (Perry 1967: 421).
H(8) listed by Lett (1915: 147).
H8 1966: marshy moorland, Monabrack, J Appleyard (BBS exc.) (Perry 1967: 421).
H12 1961: drain on Forth Mt., ALK King (Warburg 1962: 376).
1975: flush by moorland stream, Croghan, S side of Mt., AR Perry (Hill 1977a: 24), as var. *rotae*.
H16 1966: small flush in field by shore, W side of Doorus Pennisula, L. Corrib, G Halliday & GCG Argent (Perry 1967: 421).
1970: on margin of lough W of Errisberg, Roundstone, MFV Corley (Crundwell 1971b: 382), as var. *rotae*.
H18 2002: in flush in blanket bog, 300 m alt., Glenletter, Slieve Bloom Mts, N20, N Lockhart 2002/15a (Rothero 2003: 61).
H19 1993: shallow ephemeral pool, The Curragh, S of Thornton Lodge, N80, NF Stewart & RJ Stewart (Blockeel 1994: 41), as var. *rotae*.
H20 1958: pool on lower slope of Great Sugarloaf Mt., *ca* 800 ft [alt.], ALK King (Warburg 1959: 638).
1975: bog 1½ miles NE of Avoca, JA Paton (BBS exc.) (Crundwell 1976: 31).
H(21) listed by Lett (1915: 147).
H(21) 1949: Corrig Brook, 1100-1500 ft [alt.], Glenasmole, AW Stelfox (per JS Thomson) (Warburg 1950: 387), as *Hypnum exannulatum* var. brachydictyon.
H22 1970: in swamp below moraine at Galtrim, ALK King (Crundwell 1972: 142).
H24 1957: among *Sphagnum* on raised bog, Newtonforbes [*sic* = Newtown Forbes], MPH Kertland & ALK King (Warburg 1958b: 488).
H25 1966: drainage ditch, peat bog SW of Termonbarry, G Halliday & GCG Argent (Perry 1967: 421).
H26 1987: boggy ground, E of Srah village, E of bridge over Cloon River, GP Rothero (Blockeel 1998: 39), as var. *rotae*.
H(27) listed by Lett (1915: 147).
H27 1962: flush, W side of Corraun Hill, EF Warburg (Warburg 1963b: 502).
1987: in stony flush on roadside, coast nr Dugort Quay, Achill I., DG Long (Blockeel 1998: 39), as var. *rotae*.
H(28) listed by Lett (1915: 147).
H28 1963: roadside bog at 1000 ft [alt.], S of

Knockachree, Slieve Gamph, AR Perry & RD Fitzgerald (Warburg 1964: 733).

H29 1965: bare peat by cutting in roadside bog, 4½ miles E of Manorhamilton, AR Perry & EF Warburg (Warburg 1966: 202).

H30 1970: in a flush below the crags, below Englishman's House, Glenfarne, nr Belcoo, JA Paton (BBS exc.) (Crundwell 1971b: 382, Appleyard 1971: 389-390).

H(31) listed by Lett (1915: 147). H (31) listed by Blockeel & Long (1998: 141).

H(32) listed by Lett (1915: 147) without locality.

H32 1980: submerged in bog pool, Lisnashannagh Lough, N Lockhart (Hill 1983: 56), as var. *rotae*.

H(33) listed by Lett (1915: 147).

†H33 listed by Blockeel & Long (1998: 141).

H(34) listed by Lett (1915: 147).

H34 1967: wet ground by lough, Gap of Mamore, nr Buncrana, RD Fitzgerald (Crundwell 1968: 645).

H(35) listed by Lett (1915: 147).

H35 1963: stream, nr Laragh Lake, Crovehy, ALK King (Warburg 1964: 733).

H36 1952: bog, L. Bradan, RD Fitzgerald (Warburg 1953: 317). Omitted from *CC* by Corley & Hill (1981: 119), apparently in error.
2002: in carpet on wet ground at edge of lake, 235 m alt., E edge of Loughahull, H07, DT Holyoak 02-1137 (Rothero 2003: 61).

H37 1964: flush *ca* 1000 ft [alt.], Slieve Gullion, RD Fitzgerald (Warburg 1965: 871).
1964: bog, Derryadd townland, E of Lough Gullion, RD Fitzgerald (Warburg 1965: 871), as var *rotae*.

H(38) listed by Lett (1915: 147). H(38) listed by Blockeel & Long (1998: 141).

H38 2002: on peat in inundation zone of reservoir, 330 m alt., nr S edge of Spelga Dam, J22, DT Holyoak 02-975 (Rothero 2003: 61).

H(39) listed by Lett (1915: 147).

†H39 listed by Blockeel & Long (1998: 141).

[H(40) listed by Lett (1915: 147)].

157/1 ***Drepanocladus polygamus*** (Bruch, Schimp. & W.Gümbel) Hedenäs
(syn. *Amblystegium polygamum* Bruch, Schimp. & W.Gümbel, *A. polygamum* var. *stagnatum* (Wilson) Braithw., *Campylium polygamum* (Bruch, Schimp. & W.Gümbel) J.Lange & C.E.O.Jensen)

†H3 listed by Blockeel & Long (1998: 141).

H9 1959: turf by shore of brackish turlough, Ballyvaughan, MCF Proctor (Warburg 1962: 174).

H(12) listed by Lett (1915: 145). H(12) listed by Blockeel & Long (1998: 141).

H13 1973: Rahill Bog, Rathvilly, MJP Scannell (Crundwell 1974: 174).

[H(16) listed by Lett (1915: 145) as 1872: Connemara, leg. Moore. H16 deleted: specimen from Connemara, 1872, leg. D Moore (DBN), is *Campylium chrysophyllum*, comm. DM Synnott (Blockeel 1989: 31)].

H19 1951: calcareous swamp by Louisa Bridge, nr Leixlip, ALK King (Warburg 1953: 317).

H(20) listed by Lett (1915: 145). H(20) listed by Blockeel & Long (1998: 141).

H(21) listed by Lett (1915: 145). H(21) listed by Blockeel & Long (1998: 141).

H22 1969: dune slack at Laytown, ALK King (Crundwell 1970: 208).

H23 1971: Scraw Bog, NW of Mullingar, ALK King (Crundwell 1972: 142).

H24 1968: among *Phragmites*, Begnagh Bridge, 1.5 miles S of Cloondara, WV Rubers *et al.* (U) (Crundwell 1975: 20).

H25 1960: limy shore of L. Ree, Hodson's Bay, AW Stelfox (Crundwell 1970: 208).

H(27) listed by Lett (1915: 145).

†H27 listed by Blockeel & Long (1998: 141).

H(28) listed by Blockeel & Long (1998: 141).

[H31 deleted because no valid record or voucher specimen traced (Blockeel 1999: 8)].

[H(32) listed by Lett (1915: 145) without locality. H32 deleted because no valid record or voucher specimen traced (Blockeel 1999: 8)].

H(33) listed by Lett (1915: 145). H(33) listed by Blockeel & Long (1998: 141).

H(34) listed by Lett (1915: 145). H(34) listed by Blockeel & Long (1998: 141).

H34 2002: on damp soil in grass just above saltmarsh, 5 m alt., Binnion, NW of

Clonmany, C34, DT Holyoak 02-498 (Rothero 2003: 61).
[H35 deleted because no valid record or voucher specimen traced (Blockeel 1999: 8)].
H35 1999: on damp bare soil close to stream, Sheskinmore Lough, G79, DT Holyoak 99-756 (BBSUK) (Rothero 2000: 59).
H(37) listed by Lett (1915: 145).
†H37 listed by Blockeel & Long (1998: 141).
H(38) listed by Lett (1915: 145). H(38) listed by Blockeel & Long (1998: 141).
H(39) listed by Lett (1915: 145). H(39) listed by Blockeel & Long (1998: 141).
H(40) listed by Blockeel & Long (1998: 141).

157/2 ***Drepanocladus aduncus*** (Hedw.) Warnst.
(syn. *Amblystegium aduncum* (Hedw.) De Not., *A. kneiffii* Bruch, Schimp. & W.Gümbel, *A. kneiffii* var. *polycarpon* Bland., *Drepanocladus polycarpos* (Bland. ex Voit.) Warnst., *Hypnum aduncum* Hedw., *Hypnum aduncum* var. *gracilescens* auct., *Hypnum aduncum* var. *polycarpon* (Bland. ex Voit) Schimp., *Hypnum aduncum* var. *polycarpum* (Voit) Bruch, Schimp. & W. Gümbel)

H(1) listed by Lett (1915: 146).
H1 1951: damp sandy roadside, Glenbeigh, EW Jones (BBS exc.) (Warburg 1952: 107).
H(2) listed by Lett (1915: 146, 147).
†H2 listed by Blockeel & Long (1998: 141).
H3 1951: watery mat of fen, Sherkin I., IA Rorison (OXF) (Warburg 1962: 174), as var. *kneiffii*.
[H(4) listed by Lett (1915: 147). H4 deleted because no valid record or voucher specimen traced (Blockeel 1999: 8)].
H5 1956: fen W of Youghal, EC Wallace (Warburg 1957: 337).
H(6) listed by Lett (1915: 147).
H6 1999: in wet ground at edge of lake with *Hypericum elodes*, 165 m alt., Monaneea Lake, 7 km N of Ardmore, X28, TL Blockeel 28/223 (Rothero 2000: 59).
H(7) listed by Lett (1915: 147).
H7 1991: poor fen, 100 m alt., Ballydonagh Townland, nr Grange, R94, N Lockhart & A O'Suillivan (Blockeel 1992: 28).
H(8) listed by Lett (1915: 147).
†H8 listed by Blockeel & Long (1998: 141).
H(9) listed by Lett (1915: 147).
H(9) 1945: bog by L. Bunny, JS Thomson (anon. 1946c: 285).
†H9 listed by Blockeel & Long (1998: 141).
H(12) listed by Lett (1915: 147). H(12) listed by Blockeel & Long (1998: 141).
H(14) listed by Lett (1915: 147).
H14 1955: in water, Abbeyleix demesne, JS Thomson (Warburg 1956: 158).
[H15 deleted because no valid record or voucher specimen traced (Blockeel 1999: 8)].
H(16) listed by Lett (1915: 147).
H16 1957: marshy place among dunes, nr Roundstone, J Appleyard (BBS exc.) (Warburg 1958b: 488). This vice-county record for *D. aduncus* was subsequently deleted by Blockeel (1989: 31) in error [because specimen from Leenane, 1901, leg. HW Lett (DBN), is *Cratoneuron commutatum*, comm. DM Synnott]; Blockeel (1999: 10) reinstates the record, pointing out that the deletion was not based on the voucher for the original record.
H19 1998: submerged in small eutrophic pond, Sillagh House, Ballymore Eustace, M Wyse Jackson, det. N Lockhart (Rothero 2000: 59).
H(20) listed by Lett (1915: 147). H(20) listed by Lett (1915: 147).
†H20 listed by Blockeel & Long (1998: 141).
H(21) listed by Lett (1915: 147).
H(21) 1916: Portmarnock, DA Jones, PGM Rhodes & E Cleminshaw (E) (Żarnowiec 2001: 143, Hill 2002: 61). H (21) listed by Blockeel & Long (1998: 141).
H(23) 1946: Scraw Bog, Portnashangan, Mullingar, KC Harris (anon. 1947: 34), as ? var. *gracilescens* Schp.
H24 1968: stony river bed, Schrule Bridge, 2 miles SW of Ballymahon, P Hessel, J Klein & WV Rubers (U) (Crundwell 1975: 20; Żarnowiec 2001: 194-195 as *D. aduncus s.s.*; record apparently overlooked by Hill 2002: 61).
H25 1959: pool in quarry by roadside, 2 miles E of Boyle, ALK King (Warburg 1960: 780).
H27 1962: wet sandy edge of Keel Lough, Achill I., EF Warburg (Warburg 1963b: 502).
†H28 listed by Blockeel & Long (1998: 141).
H(29) listed by Lett (1915: 147). H(29) listed

by Blockeel & Long (1998: 141).
H(31) listed by Lett (1915: 147).
H31 1964: under *Iris*, Bragabstown Bog, Dunleer, DM Synnott (Warburg 1966: 202).
H(33) listed by Lett (1915: 147).
H(33) 1919: Kinarla Lough, nr Enniskillen, WN Tetley, comm. RD Fitzgerald (Perry 1967: 421).
H(34) listed by Lett (1915: 147, 148).
†H34 listed by Blockeel & Long (1998: 141).
H(35) listed by Lett (1915: 147, 148).
H35 1999: on damp bare soil close to stream, Sheskinmore Lough, G79, DT Holyoak 99-756 (BBSUK) (Rothero 2000: 59).
H(36) listed by Lett (1915: 148).
H36 1957: bog, Tullygiven Lake, nr Benburb, RD Fitzgerald (Warburg 1959: 638).
(H37) 1886: Lough Neagh, Bird's I., CH Waddell (E) (Żarnowiec 2001: 195 as *D. aduncus s.s.*; Hill 2002: 61).
H(37) listed by Lett (1915: 147, 148).
†H37 listed by Blockeel & Long (1998: 141).
H(38) 1906: in a pool at Glostry, Kircubbin, J Glover (E) (Żarnowiec 2001: 143 as *D. polycarpos*; Hill 2002: 61).
H(38) listed by Lett (1915: 147, 148).
1916: floating in Lurgan canal, and in ditch, Kilmore, JD Houston (anon. 1916a: 165), as *Hypnum aduncum* var. *polycarpon*.
H(39) listed by Lett (1915: 147, 148).
†H39 listed by Blockeel & Long (1998: 141).
H(40) listed by Lett (1915: 147).
†H40 listed by Blockeel & Long (1998: 141).

A revision by Żarnowiec (2001) divided *D. aduncus* into three species, of which two (*D. aduncus s.s.* and *D. polycarpos* (Bland. ex Voit) Warnst.) were recorded in Ireland (cf. Hill 2002). However, studies of British specimens by Hill (2003) show that these more narrowly defined taxa cannot be maintained as distinct species.

157/3 ***Drepanocladus sendtneri*** (Schimp. ex H.Müll.) Warnst.
(syn. *Amblystegium sendtneri* (Schimp.) De Not., *A. sendtneri* var. *hamatum* (Bruch, Schimp. & W.Gümbel) Braithw., *A. sendtneri* var. *wilsoni* (Schimp.) Braithw., *Drepanocladus sendtneri* var. *wilsonii* (Schimp. ex Lorb.) Warnst., *Hypnum wilsonii* Schimp. ex Lorb.)

H(9) 1945: bog nr L. Bunny, JS Thomson (anon. 1946c: 285), as *Hypnum wilsoni*.
†H9 listed by Blockeel & Long (1998: 141).
H15 1966: turlough, Tirneevin, nr Gort, N Chuter, comm. ALK King (Perry 1967: 421, King 1968), as var. *wilsonii*.
H23 1970: fen on W shore of Killinure Lough, S of Glassan, JA Paton (Crundwell 1971b: 382).
H24 1968: among *Phragmites*, Begnagh Bridge, 1½ miles S of Cloondara, WV Rubers *et al.* (U) (Crundwell 1975: 20).
H25 1962: fen by shore of Lough Ree at Hodson's Bay, EF Warburg (Warburg 1963b: 502), as var. *wilsonii*.
1970: calcareous shore of L. Ree, Portrunny Bay, JA Paton (Crundwell 1971b: 382).
H26 1953: shore of L. Carra, opposite Otter Point, EC Wallace (Warburg 1955: 587).
[H(28) listed by Lett (1915: 146) as 1913: Benbulben, leg. Porter. H28 deleted because specimen from nr Ben Bulben, 1913, leg. W Porter (DBN), is *D.* cf. *revolvens*, comm. DM Synnott (Blockeel 1989: 31)].
[H31 deleted because no valid record or voucher specimen traced (Blockeel 1999: 8)].
H(34) 1939: Ballyliffin, 'DDH' [*sic* = JD Houston ?] (anon. 1940a: 176).
H(35) listed by Lett (1915: 146). H(35) listed by Blockeel & Long (1998: 141).
H(36) listed by Lett (1915: 146). H(36) listed by Blockeel & Long (1998: 141).
H(37) listed by Lett (1915: 146). H(37) listed by Blockeel & Long (1998: 141).
H(39) listed by Lett (1915: 146). H(39) listed by Blockeel & Long (1998: 141).
[H(40) listed by Lett (1915: 146) as 1904: Magilligan, leg. HW Lett. H40 deleted because specimen from Magilligan, 1904, leg. HW Lett & CH Waddell (DBN), is *D.* cf. *revolvens*, comm. DM

Synnott (Blockeel 1989: 31)].

H40 1990: in slack with *Carex elata*, Balmaclary [*sic* = Ballymaclary] NNR, C63, R Weyl (Rothero 2001: 46).

157/4 ***Drepanocladus lycopodioides*** (Brid.) Warnst.
(syn. *Amblystegium lycopodioides* (Brid.) De Not., *Hypnum lycopodioides* Brid.)

H(9) 1945: bog by L. Bunny, JS Thomson (anon. 1946c: 285).
†H9 listed by Blockeel & Long (1998: 142).
H15 1962: fen nr Clegg Point, L. Derg, AJE Smith (Warburg 1963b: 502).
H17 1957: fen, Ballindooly, nr Galway City, RE Parker (BBS exc.) (Warburg 1958b: 488).
H(20) listed by Lett (1915: 146). H(20) listed by Blockeel & Long (1998: 141).
H(21) listed by Lett (1915: 146) without locality. H(21) listed by Blockeel & Long (1998: 141).
H23 1968: submerged in lake, Bethlehem House, L. Ree, WV Rubers *et al.* (U) (Crundwell1975: 20).
H25 2002: abundant in inundated sedge and reed beds by small lough, 50 m alt., Fin Lough, nr Lough Key, G80, NG Hodgetts, 4116 (Rothero 2003: 61).
H26 1966: shallow pools on limestone pavement, SW corner of Inishcoog, L. Mask, G Halliday (Perry 1967: 421).
H35 1962: dried-up margin of pool, nr the lake, Congreagen, J Appleyard (BBS exc.) (Warburg 1963b: 502).
H(37) 1888: shore of Lough Neagh, Raughlan I., HW Lett (DBN), comm. DM Synnott (Blockeel 1989: 31).
H(38) listed by Lett (1915: 146). H(38) listed by Blockeel & Long (1998: 141).
H(39) listed by Lett (1915: 146). H(39) listed by Blockeel & Long (1998: 141).
H(40) 1936: Magilligan, WR Megaw (anon. 1937a: 368).
H40 1999: in damp hollow in dune slack, Ballymaclary NNR, C73, DT Holyoak 99-285 (BBSUK) (Rothero 2000: 59).

157/5 ***Drepanocladus revolvens*** (Sw.) Warnst. *s.s.*

H1 1953: drain nr river from L. Adoon, Brandon, AP Fanning 2005 (DBN) (Blockeel 2000: 37).
H(2) 1949: from boggy bank above first waterfall, 500 ft [alt.], Derrymore, AP Fanning 347 (DBN) (Blockeel 2000: 37).
†H2 listed by Blockeel & Long (1998: 142).
H3 1967: in flush, Aghacunna, 92/14, RD Fitzgerald (NMW) (Blockeel 2000: 37).
H4 1966: marshy ground at edge of stream, nr Kilcullen House, Rylane Cross, Boggeragh Mts, 9325, MFV Corley & JS Parker (BBSUK) (Perry 1967: 421, Blockeel 2000: 37).
H5 1967: in bog, *ca* 800 ft [alt.], Lyrenamon, 92/5050, RD Fitzgerald (NMW) (Blockeel 2000: 37).
H6 1966: in flush, *ca* 1150 ft [alt.], Laghtnafrankee, Comeragh Mts, 02/17, RD Fitzgerald (BBSUK, NMW) (Crundwell 1968: 645, Blockeel 2000: 37).
H7 1966: wet rocks above L. Curra, Galtee Mts, DM Synnott (DBN) (Blockeel 2000: 37).
[H8 1975: edge of marsh, Diggity Bog, Ballyvogue, nr Askeaton, PH Pitkin (Crundwell 1976: 31); record not accepted by Blockeel 2000].
H10 1965: in bog by L. Nahinch, ALK King (DBN) (Blockeel 2000: 37).
H12 1975: channels at foot of boggy slope, Croghan, PH Pitkin (BBSUK) (Hill 1979: 32, Blockeel 2000: 37).
H(14) 1912: on wet sandstone rock in bog at low alt., nr R. Gorragh, WR Tetley (BBSUK) (Blockeel 2000: 37).
H15 1951: bottom of drain in bog by Grand Canal, Clonfert, AP Fanning (BBSUK, DBN) (Warburg 1953: 317, Blockeel 2000: 37).
H16 1999: in *Schoenus* fen, 40 m alt., Errisbeg, NW side of Lough Nalawney, L64, DG Long 28455 (BBSUK) (Blockeel 2000: 37, Rothero 2000: 59).
H17 1968: in marginal lagg of raised bog complex, Addergoule North, River Suck, nr Ballinasloe, HJB Birks (BBSUK) (Blockeel 2000: 37).
H20 1975: flush on SW side of Lough Ouler, Tonelagee, 42/0802, AR Perry (NMW) (Blockeel 2000: 37).
H(21) 1852: Three Rock Mt., D Orr (DBN) (Blockeel 2000: 37).
H23 1967: Scraw Bog, Portnashangan, [no name = ALK King], (DBN) (Blockeel

2000: 37).

H27 1994: in wet boggy ground in hollow, below N side of Knockaveen, Clare I., TL Blockeel 23/219 (Hb. Blockeel) (Blockeel 2000: 37).

H28 1963: 1000 ft [alt.], bog below siliceous crags S of Knockachree, Slieve Gamph, AR Perry (NMW) (Blockeel 2000: 37).

H29 2000: in calcareous flush on NE-facing hillside, 520 m alt., E slope of Truskmore, G74, DT Holyoak 00-710 (BBSUK) (Rothero 2001: 46).

H31 1999: in peaty flush on moorland, Two Mile River, Carlingford Mt., J11, TL Blockeel (BBSUK) (Blockeel 2000: 37).

H33 1959: in bog, *ca* 1200 ft [alt.], Quilcagh [*sic* = Cuilcagh], RD Fitzgerald (NMW) (Blockeel 2000: 37).

H34 2002: in flush on slope above sea-cliff, 30 m alt., Dunree Head, C23, DT Holyoak 02-787 (Rothero 2003: 61).

H35 1963: with *Schoenus*, above Muckish Gap, DM Synnott (DBN) (Blockeel 2000: 37).

H36 2002: in flush on N-facing hillside, 290 m alt., NE slope of Bolaght Mt., H27, DT Holyoak 02-1128 (Rothero 2003: 61).

H37 1964: in flush, *ca* 700 ft [alt.], below Tower, Slieve Gullion, 14/18, RD Fitzgerald (NMW) (Blockeel 2000: 37).

H(38) listed by Blockeel & Long (1998: 142).

H38 1952: Conlig Bog, 400 ft [alt.], RD Fitzgerald (NMW) (Blockeel 2000: 37).

H(39) listed by Blockeel & Long (1998: 142).

H39 1951: in bog, 1100 ft [alt.], Agnew's Hill, nr Larne, RD Fitzgerald (NMW) (Blockeel 2000: 37).

H40 1999: on wet peat in disturbed area of open blanket bog, Windy Hill, C73, DT Holyoak 99-547 (BBSUK) (Blockeel 2000: 37, Rothero 2000: 59).

Separation of *D. revolvens* and *D. cossonii* (formerly known as *D. revolvens* var. *intermedius*) was inconsistent in Ireland and Britain until the taxonomic review by Hedenäs (1989) clarified their characters and Blockeel (2000) revised identification of many of the voucher specimens. Only records accepted by Blockeel (2000) and subsequently are assigned to *D. revolvens* and *D. cossonii* here, older records that have not been revised being listed merely as '*D. revolvens* aggregate'.

157/5 *Drepanocladus revolvens* (Sw.) Warnst. aggregate

H(1) listed by Lett (1915: 146).

H1 1953: peaty mud by shore of L. Slat, AP Fanning, comm. EC Wallace (Warburg 1960: 781).

H(2) listed by Lett (1915: 146).

H(3) listed by Lett (1915: 146).

H(5) listed by Lett (1915: 146).

H(6) listed by Lett (1915: 146).

H(7) listed by Lett (1915: 146).

H(9) 1945: bog nr L. Bunny, JS Thomson (anon. 1946c: 286), as *Hypnum revolvens*.

H9 1956: calcareous marsh, nr L. Bunny, ALK King (Warburg 1957: 337), as *D. revolvens* var. *intermedius*.

H(10) listed by Lett (1915: 146).

H(13) 1867: Sandbrook, S of Tullow, RC Browne (DBN) (Crundwell 1968: 645), as *D. revolvens* var. *intermedius*.

H(13) listed by Lett (1915: 146).

H(14) listed by Lett (1915: 146).

H(16) listed by Lett (1915: 146).

H17 1957: fens, Cloonboo, RE Parker (Warburg 1958b: 488), as *D. revolvens* var. *intermedius*.

H(19) 1949: Mullamoy Bog, nr Calverstown, JS Thomson (Warburg 1950: 388), as *Hypnum intermedium.*

H(20) listed by Lett (1915: 146).

H(21) listed by Lett (1915: 146).

H22 1960: alkaline marsh nr Lough Shesk, ALK King (Warburg 1962: 175), as *D. revolvens* var. *intermedius*.
1965: marsh by small lake, S of L. Shesk, ALK King (Warburg 1966: 203).

H23 1952: Scraw Bog, Portnashangan, JS Thomson (Warburg 1954: 487), as *D. revolvens* var *intermedius*.

H(26) listed by Lett (1915: 146).

H26 1957: shore of L. Carra nr Clogher House, EC Wallace (Warburg 1960: 781), as *D. revolvens* var. *intermedius*.

H(27) listed by Lett (1915: 146).

H(28) listed by Lett (1915: 146).

H(29) listed by Lett (1915: 146).

H29 1963: calcareous flush in field below limestone scarp, Boggaun, nr Manorhamilton, AR Perry & RD Fitzgerald (Warburg 1964: 733), as *D.*

revolvens var. *intermedius*.
H(30) listed by Lett (1915: 146).
H(31) listed by Lett (1915: 146).
H(32) listed by Lett (1915: 146).
H(33) listed by Lett (1915: 146).
H33 1961: boggy field, Garvary Wood, nr Boa I., RD Fitzgerald (Warburg 1962: 376), as *D. revolvens* var. *intermedius*.
H(34) listed by Lett (1915: 146).
H(35) listed by Lett (1915: 146).
H(36) listed by Lett (1915: 146).
H(37) listed by Lett (1915: 146).
H(38) listed by Lett (1915: 146).
H(39) listed by Lett (1915: 146).
H(40) listed by Lett (1915: 146).

This list for the 'aggregate' comprises records published by Lett (1915: 146) as *Amblystegium intermedium* or *A. revolvens*, along with records published as new for vice-counties from before the revision by Blockeel (2000), for which the voucher specimens have apparently not been revised.

157/6 ***Drepanocladus cossonii*** (Schimp.) Loeske
(syn. *Amblystegium intermedium* (Lindb.) Lindb., *Drepanocladus revolvens* var. *intermedius* (Lindb.) P.W. Richards & E.C.Wallace, *Hypnum intermedium* Lindb.)

H1 1951: with *Salix repens* and *Preissia quadrata* on sand-dunes, Castlegregory, AC Crundwell (BBS exc.) (BBSUK, E) (Blockeel 2000: 39).
H2 1954: swampy field N of village, Ardfert, AP Fanning (DBN), comm. EC Wallace (Warburg 1960: 781, Blockeel 2000: 39).
H7 1966: edge of bog nr Urlingford, DM Synnott (DBN) (Blockeel 2000: 39).
H8 1975: edge of marsh, nr road, Diggity Bog, Ballyvogue, nr Askeaton, PH Pitkin (BBSUK) (Blockeel 2000: 39).
H9 1994: wet ground at edge of Watt's Lough, S of Mullaghmore, Burren, R39, HLK Whitehouse (Hb. Whitehouse), conf. L. Hedenäs (Blockeel 2000: 39).
H10 1965: marsh by L. Nahinch, nr Borrisokane, ALK King (BBSUK) (Blockeel 2000: 39).
H11 1966: in pool on bog, Derryfadda, W of Johnstown, ERB Little (BBS exc.) (BBSUK) (Perry 1967: 421, Blockeel 2000: 39).
H14 1965: marsh at Derry Hills, nr Clonaslee, ALK King (BBSUK) (Warburg 1966: 203, Blockeel 2000: 39).
H15 1957: fen, Loughrea, RE Parker (BBSUK) (Warburg 1958b: 488, Blockeel 2000: 39).
H16 1960: Maam Bridge, AW Stelfox (NMW) (Blockeel 2000: 39).
H17 1968: fen at roadside ½ mile SE of Galway City, AR Perry (BBSUK) (Blockeel 2000: 39).
H18 1984: *Schoenus*-dominated fen, Fin Lough, nr Clonmacnoise, V Power (BBSUK) (Blockeel 2000: 39).
H19 1998: margin of calcareous spring-fed fen with *Calliergon cuspidatum, Rhizomnium pseudopunctatum* and *Homalothecium nitens*, Pollardstown Fen, N Lockhart (DBN) (Blockeel 2000: 39).
H20 1964: Ballybetagh Bog, ALK King (DBN) (Blockeel 2000: 39).
H(21) 1856: Kilsaughlin, D Orr (DBN) (Blockeel 2000: 39).
H22 1966: with *Philonotis calcarea* in calcareous flush, Commons, Duleek, DM Synnott (DBN) (Blockeel 2000: 39).
H23 1999: in calcareous fen with *Schoenus nigricans, Calliergonella cuspidata, Ctenidium molluscum, Palustriella commutata, Cratoneuron filicinum, ca* 85 m alt., SE shore of Lough Ennell (opposite Cherry I.), N44, M Wyse Jackson (DBN) (Blockeel 2000: 39).
H24 1966: in marsh on E shore of L. Ree below Cashel Lodge, ALK King (BBSUK, DBN) (Blockeel 2000: 39).
H25 1970: with *D. sendtneri*, fen nr Lough Ree, Barry Beg, N of Athlone, JA Paton (BBSUK) (Blockeel 2000: 39).
H26 1960: marsh by lane at Down Hill, Ballina, ALK King (BBSUK, DBN) (Warburg 1962: 175, Blockeel 2000: 39).
H27 1958: blanket bog outside iron flush area, T.A.E. bog, between Dooleeg and Bellacorrick, ALK King (BBSUK) (Blockeel 2000: 39).
H28 1963: fen below limestone crags, 800 ft [alt.], NE end of Bricklieve Mts, AR Perry & RD Fitzgerald (NMW)

(Blockeel 2000: 39).

H29 1963: basic flush below limestone outcrop, Ballinlig, Glenade, AR Perry & RD Fitzgerald (BBSUK) (Blockeel 2000: 39).

H(31) 1882: rocks by stream, Carlingford Mount, CH Waddell (DBN) (Blockeel 2000: 39).

H(32) 1907: Drumreaske, WFdeV Kane (DBN) (Blockeel 2000: 39).

H33 1970: flushed hillside, Carrickbrawn, EC Nelson (DBN, ex UCW Aberystwyth) (Blockeel 2000: 39).

H34 1967: in marsh below Barnan More, Inishowen, 06/50, RD Fitzgerald (NMW) (Blockeel 2000: 39).

H35 1990: in calcareous marsh by lough, L. Sheshkinmore, NW of Ardara, G69, TL Blockeel 19/537 (Hb. Blockeel) (Blockeel 2000: 39-40).

H(37) 1900: Camlough Mt., HW Lett & CH Waddell (Hb. Lett, DBN) (Blockeel 2000: 40).

H39 1990: on stony wet ground in *Spiranthes romanzoffiana* site, Garron, above Carnlough, DM Synnott (DBN) (Blockeel 2000: 40).

H40 1999: in low vegetation of damp hollow in dune slack, Ballymaclary NNR, C63, DT Holyoak 99-288, conf. TL Blockeel (BBSUK) (Blockeel 2000: 40, Rothero 2000: 59).

See note under *D. revolvens* (above). Only records accepted in the revision by Blockeel (2000) or subsequently are accepted as *D. cossonii* here. Old records (e.g. of *Amblystegium intermedium* in Lett 1915: 146) should not be accepted without reidentification of the voucher specimens.

158/1 ***Hamatocaulis vernicosus*** (Mitt.) Hedenäs
(syn. *Amblystegium vernicosum* (Lindb.) Lindb., *Drepanocladus vernicosus* (Mitt.) Warnst.)

[H1 1951: dunes, Castlegregory, AC Crundwell (Warburg 1952: 107); redet. as *D. cossonii* by TL Blockeel (Blockeel 2000: 39)].

H6 1963: basic flush bogs at 1000 ft [alt.], beside R. Nire, Comeragh Mts, DA Ratcliffe (BBSUK, E), conf. TL Blockeel (Warburg 1964: 733, Blockeel 1997b: 13).

[H9 1970: among *Schoenus nigricans*, S edge of L. Bunny, AR Perry & HJ Perry (BBSUK) (Crundwell 1974: 174), redet. as *D. cossonii* by TL Blockeel (Blockeel 1997b: 19, where erroneously listed as from H17)].

H12 1969: marshy ground, Pallis Bridge, Wicklow Gap, RD Fitzgerald (BBSUK), conf. TL Blockeel (Crundwell 1970: 209, Blockeel 1997b: 13).

H16 1983: wet area with *Juncus* and *Calliergon* by road, W side of Lough Mask, SL Jury, FJ Rumsey & DA Webb (BBSUK), conf. TL Blockeel (Blockeel 1987: 26, 1997b: 13).

[H17 1968: amongst fen vegetation at roadside ½ mile SE of Menlough, N of Galway City, AR Perry (Crundwell 1970: 209), redet. as *D. cossonii* by TL Blockeel (Blockeel 1997b: 19, where erroneously listed as from H9)].

[H19 1970: bank of runnel on calcareous slope at Louisa Bridge, Leixlip, ALK King (BBSUK) (Crundwell 1972: 143), redet. as *D. cossonii* by TL Blockeel (Blockeel 1997b: 19)].

H20 1975: small bog on S side of road about ¼ mile E of Yellowford Cross Roads, N of Rathvilly, AR Perry (NMW), conf. TL Blockeel (Blockeel 1997b: 13). H20 was apparently omitted in error by Blockeel & Long (1998: 142).

H22 1978: cut-over bog between L. Bane and Drumone, Oldcastle, DM Synnott (BBSUK, DBN), conf. TL Blockeel (Hill 1980b: 46, Blockeel 1997b: 13).

H(23) 1946: Scraw Bog, Portnashangan, Mullingar, KC Harris (BBSUK, DBN, E), conf. TL Blockeel (anon. 1947: 34, Blockeel 1997b: 13).

H23 1966: Scraw Bog, Portnashangan, JS Thomson (DBN), conf. TL Blockeel (Blockeel 1997b: 13).

[H25 1970: With *D. sendtneri*, fen nr L. Ree, Barry Beg, N of Athlone, 04/0509, JA Paton (BBSUK) (Crundwell 1971b: 382), redet. as *D. cossonii* by TL Blockeel (Blockeel 1997b: 19)].

H27 1958: blanket bog outside iron flush area, T.A.E. bog, between Dooleeg and Bellacorick, ALK King (DBN; BBSUK specimen is *D. cossonii*), conf. TL Blockeel (Warburg 1959: 638, Blockeel

1997b: 14).

[H29 1963: basic flush below limestone outcrops, Ballinlig, Glenade, AR Perry & RD Fitzgerald (BBSUK) (Warburg 1964: 733), redet. as *D. cossonii* by TL Blockeel (Blockeel 1997b: 19)].

[H35 1962: marshy ground at edge of Mullaghderg Lough, The Rosses, AC Crundwell (BBS exc.) (BBSUK, E) (Warburg 1963b: 502), redet. as *D. cossonii* by TL Blockeel (Blockeel 1997b: 19)].

H35 1999: in mesotrophic flush with *Sphagnum contortum, S. teres, S. warnstorfii, Carex nigra* and *Juncus acutiflorus*, 150 m alt., Meentygrannagh Bog, 2 km S of Altinierin, C00, N Lockhart, conf. TL Blockeel (Rothero 2000: 60).

H(38) 1901: bog by river Lagan, above Lisburn, JH Davies (BM; Hb. Lett, DBN), conf. TL Blockeel (Blockeel 1997b: 14).
1901: wet bog nr Lisburn, JH Davies (DBN), conf. TL Blockeel (Blockeel 1997b: 14).

The commoner *Drepanocladus cossonii* has often been confused with this species in Ireland and Britain. The records listed in the *CC* by Blockeel & Long (1998: 142, 172) result from revision of specimens by TL Blockeel (1997b). Old records (e.g. from Lett 1915: 146) were often erroneous, so they are listed above only when specimens have been reidentified recently.

159/1 ***Tomentypnum nitens*** (Hedw.) Loeske (syn. *Camptothecium nitens* (Hedw.) Schimp., *Homalothecium nitens* (Hedw.) H.Rob.)

H8 1996: in *Phragmites/Molinia* flush in blanket bog, 330 m alt., Slieve Felim, R75, R Goodwillie (Blockeel 1997a: 45, Goodwillie 1999).

H16 1988: iron-rich flush, Bunscannive, Connemara, N Lockhart (Lockhart 1988, 1991, Blockeel 1989: 31).

H19 1957: along margin of large fen, nr Newbridge, RE Parker (Warburg 1958b: 485, King 1958a).

H23 1971: fen-bog transition, Scraw Bog, Ballynagall, N of L. Owel, DM Synnott (Crundwell 1974: 175).

H27 1957: iron flush in blanket bog, Dooleeg, TA Barry, comm. ALK King (Warburg 1958b: 485-486, King 1958a, King & Scannell 1960).

H33 1957: large flush-bog complex, W of L. Meenameen, L. Navar Forest, RE Parker (Warburg 1958b: 485-486). Now extinct in this area due to afforestation with conifers (DT Holyoak unpublished, 2000).

H35 1998: in calcareous flush with *Sphagnum warnstorfii, S. teres* and *Calliergon stramineum*, 150 m alt., Meentygrannagh Bog, 2 km S of Altinierin, C00, N Lockhart (Rothero 1999b: 46).

160/1 ***Sanionia uncinata*** (Hedw.) Loeske (syn. *Drepanocladus uncinatus* (Hedw.) Warnst., *Hypnum uncinatum* Hedw.)

†H1 listed by Blockeel & Long (1998: 142).

[H2 deleted: specimen from Torc Waterfall, 1899, leg. HW Lett (DBN), is *Ctenidium molluscum*, comm. DM Synnott (Blockeel 1989: 31)].

H(4) listed by Blockeel & Long (1998: 142).

†H6 listed by Blockeel & Long (1998: 142).

H(7) listed by Blockeel & Long (1998: 142).

H(8) listed by Blockeel & Long (1998: 142).

†H9 listed by Blockeel & Long (1998: 142).

†H10 listed by Blockeel & Long (1998: 142).

H12 1975: floor of old quarry, Cummer Vale 4 miles NE of Carnew, AR Perry (Hill 1977a: 24).

†H14 listed by Blockeel & Long (1998: 142).

H15 1957: wall top, Coole Lough, Garryland Wood, nr Gort, AC Crundwell (BBS exc.) (Warburg 1958b: 488).

†H16 listed by Blockeel & Long (1998: 142).

†H17 listed by Blockeel & Long (1998: 142).

†H20 listed by Blockeel & Long (1998: 142).

H(21) listed by Blockeel & Long (1998: 142).

H22 1978: under *Salix cinerea* by Ballyhoe Lough, DM Synnott (Hill 1979: 32).

H24 1968: wood on E shore of L. Forbes, W of Castle Forbes, WV Rubers *et al.* (U) (Crundwell 1974: 174).

H26 1970: willow trunk, pool W of Pollagh River, NE of Balla, JA Paton (Crundwell 1971b: 382).

†H28 listed by Blockeel & Long (1998: 142).

H29 1965: *Sphagnum* bog, *ca* 900 ft alt., Dergvone, nr Drumkeeran, EM Lobley

& RD Fitzgerald (Perry 1967: 421).
H30 2001: on sallow in carr at edge of lough, 60 m alt., Lough Gowna, NW of Dermaferst Bridge, N28, DT Holyoak 01-699 (Rothero 2002: 54).
H(31) listed by Blockeel & Long (1998: 142).
H(32) 1947: amongst roots of trees in wet ground, Black I., Lough Muckno, Castleblaney, JS Thomson (anon. 1948b: 124).
†H32 listed by Blockeel & Long (1998: 142).
†H33 listed by Blockeel & Long (1998: 142).
†H34 listed by Blockeel & Long (1998: 142).
†H35 listed by Blockeel & Long (1998: 142).
H36 1951: Black Bog, nr Creggan, RD Fitzgerald (Warburg 1952: 107).
H(37) listed by Blockeel & Long (1998: 142).
H(38) listed by Blockeel & Long (1998: 142).
†H39 listed by Blockeel & Long (1998: 142).
†H40 listed by Blockeel & Long (1998: 142).

161/1 ***Hygrohypnum ochraceum*** (Turner ex Wilson) Loeske
(syn. *Amblystegium ochraceum* (Turner ex Wilson) Lindb.)

H(1) listed by Lett (1915: 148).
†H1 listed by Blockeel & Long (1998: 143).
H(2) listed by Lett (1915: 148).
†H2 listed by Blockeel & Long (1998: 143).
H(3) listed by Lett (1915: 148). H(3) listed by Blockeel & Long (1998: 143).
H5 1966: stones in river, Araglin, J Appleyard *et al.* (BBS exc.) (Perry 1967: 422).
H(6) listed by Lett (1915: 148).
†H6 listed by Blockeel & Long (1998: 143).
H7 1966: rocks in stream *ca* 1300 ft alt., S side of Galtymore, RD Fitzgerald (BBS exc.) (Perry 1967: 422).
H8 1966: rocks in stream *ca* 1300 ft alt., S side of Galtymore, RD Fitzgerald (BBS exc.) (Perry 1967: 422).
H(9) listed by Lett (1915: 148) without details.
†H9 listed by Blockeel & Long (1998: 143).
H10 1979: Clare Glen, EW Jones (Hill 1980b: 46); [another record given as 1979: rotten stem beside stream, W side of Keeper Hill, S of Silvermine Mts, HMH van Melick (Hill 1981: 34) apparently 2nd record published in error].
†H12 listed by Blockeel & Long (1998: 143).
H15 1994: on rocks in stream, nr Pollboy, Slieve Aughty, M50, NG Hodgetts 2962 (Blockeel 1995c: 46).
H(16) listed by Lett (1915: 148).
†H16 listed by Blockeel & Long (1998: 143).
H19 1957: gravel by R. Liffey below Ballymore-Eustace, ALK King (Warburg 1958b: 489).
H(20) listed by Lett (1915: 148).
†H20 listed by Blockeel & Long (1998: 143).
H(21) listed by Lett (1915: 148).
†H21 listed by Blockeel & Long (1998: 143).
H(31) listed by Lett (1915: 148). H(31) listed by Blockeel & Long (1998: 143).
H33 1950: boulders in the Sruh Croppagh stream, Cats Hole, J Taylor (Warburg 1954: 487).
H(34) listed by Lett (1915: 148).
†H34 listed by Blockeel & Long (1998: 143).
†H35 listed by Blockeel & Long (1998: 143).
H36 1951: stones in bottom of Bywash Omagh Reservoir, Glenhordial, RD Fitzgerald (Warburg 1952: 107).
H(38) listed by Lett (1915: 148).
†H38 listed by Blockeel & Long (1998: 143).
H(39) listed by Lett (1915: 148). H(39) listed by Blockeel & Long (1998: 143).
H(40) listed by Lett (1915: 148).
†H40 listed by Blockeel & Long (1998: 143).

161/3a ***Hygrohypnum luridum*** (Hedw.) Jenn. **var. *luridum***
(syn. *Amblystegium palustre* (Brid.) Lindb., *Hypnum luridum* Hedw., *Hypnum palustre* Huds.)

H(1) listed by Lett (1915: 148).
†H1 listed by Blockeel & Long (1998: 143).
H(2) listed by Lett (1915: 148).
†H2 listed by Blockeel & Long (1998: 143).
H(3) listed by Lett (1915: 148). H(3) listed by Blockeel & Long (1998: 143).
H(4) listed by Lett (1915: 148).
†H4 listed by Blockeel & Long (1998: 143).
H6 1966: dead wood, quarry N of Lismore, J Appleyard & JG Duckett (BBS exc.) (Perry 1967: 422).
H(7) 1945: Bocheen, Galtees, RD Meikle (anon. 1947: 34).
H(8) listed by Lett (1915: 148). H(8) listed by Blockeel & Long (1998: 143).
H9 1956: rock by R. Caher, Fanore Bridge, nr Black Head, ALK King (Warburg 1957: 338).
H10 1952: Terryglass Bay, shore of L. Derg, MPH Kertland & ALK King (Warburg

1953: 318).
H11 1968: bank of Dinin River nr Dysart Bridge, S of Castlecomber, JA Paton (Crundwell 1969: 889).
H(13) listed by Lett (1915: 148). H(13) listed by Blockeel & Long (1998: 143).
H(14) listed by Lett (1915: 148).
†H14 listed by Blockeel & Long (1998: 143).
H15 1962: fen nr Cregg Pt, by Lough Derg, AJE Smith (Warburg 1964: 733).
H(16) listed by Lett (1915: 148).
†H16 listed by Blockeel & Long (1998: 143).
H18 1951: rock in shallow river, Sandymount, Birr, AP Fanning (Warburg 1954: 487).
H19 1957: gravel by R. Liffey below Ballymore-Eustace, ALK King (Warburg 1958b: 489).
H(20) listed by Lett (1915: 148).
†H20 listed by Blockeel & Long (1998: 143).
H(21) listed by Lett (1915: 148). H(21) listed by Blockeel & Long (1998: 143).
†H22 listed by Blockeel & Long (1998: 143).
H(23) listed by Lett (1915: 148).
†H23 listed by Blockeel & Long (1998: 143).
H24 1968: wet rock in limestone quarry 1 mile S of Lanesborough, WV Rubers *et al.* (U) (Crundwell 1975: 20).
H(25) 1940: nr Boyle, JS Thomson (Duncan 1944: 217).
†H25 listed by Blockeel & Long (1998: 143).
H(26) listed by Lett (1915: 148). H(26) listed by Blockeel & Long (1998: 143).
H(27) listed by Lett (1915: 148).
†H27 listed by Blockeel & Long (1998: 143).
H(28) listed by Lett (1915: 148).
†H28 listed by Blockeel & Long (1998: 143).
H(29) listed by Lett (1915: 148).
†H29 listed by Blockeel & Long (1998: 143).
H(30) listed by Lett (1915: 148). H(30) listed by Blockeel & Long (1998: 143).
H30 2001: on boulder in stream, 315 m alt., W of Bellavally Gap, H12, DT Holyoak 01-643 (Rothero 2002: 54).
H(31) listed by Lett (1915: 148). H(31) listed by Blockeel & Long (1998: 143).
H(32) listed by Lett (1915: 148). H(32) listed by Blockeel & Long (1998: 143).
H(33) listed by Lett (1915: 148).
†H33 listed by Blockeel & Long (1998: 143).
H(34) 1937: Ballyshannon, no collector named (BBS exc.) (Armitage 1938: 13).
H(35) listed by Lett (1915: 148). H(35) listed by Blockeel & Long (1998: 143).
H35 2002: in flush on steep E-facing slope in coire, 330 m alt., Slieve Tooey above Lough Croaghballaghdown, G69, NG Hodgetts 3794 (Rothero 2003: 61).
H(36) listed by Lett (1915: 148).
†H36 listed by Blockeel & Long (1998: 143).
H37 2002: on open vertical concrete at edge of lough, 14 m alt., Lough Neagh at Oxford I., J06, DT Holyoak 02-1008 (Rothero 2003: 61).
H(38) listed by Lett (1915: 149). H(38) listed by Blockeel & Long (1998: 143).
H(39) listed by Lett (1915: 149).
†H39 listed by Blockeel & Long (1998: 143).
H(40) listed by Lett (1915: 149).
†H40 listed by Blockeel & Long (1998: 143).

[**161/3b *Hygrohypnum luridum*** (Hedw.) Jenn. **var. *subsphaericarpon*** (Schleich. Ex Brid.) C.E.O.Jensen
(syn. *Amblystegium palustre* var. *subsphaericarpon* (Brid.) Lindb.)]

[Listed for H2 and H39 by Lett (1915: 149) and H2 by Smith (1978: 573), but not accepted for any Irish vice-county by Blockeel & Long (1998: 143).]

161/5 *Hygrohypnum eugyrium* (Schimp.) Broth.
(syn. *Amblystegium eugyrium* (Bruch, Schimp. & W.Gümbel) Lindb., *A. eugyrium* var. *mackayi* (Schimp.) Braithw., *Hypnum eugyrium* (Bruch, Schimp. & W.Gümbel) Sull. & Lesq., *H. eugyrium* var. *mackayi* Schimp.)

H(1) listed by Lett (1915: 149).
†H1 listed by Blockeel & Long (1998: 143).
H(2) listed by Lett (1915: 149).
†H2 listed by Blockeel & Long (1998: 143).
H(3) listed by Lett (1915: 149).
H3 1955: rocks in waterfall, below Glenkeel Lough, H Milne-Redhead (Warburg 1957: 338).
H(6) listed by Lett (1915: 149).
†H6 listed by Blockeel & Long (1998: 143).
H7 1963: rocks in stream by cascade, N side of Galtymore, DA Ratcliffe (Warburg 1964: 733).
H8 1966: rocks in stream S of Paradise Hill, Galtee Mts, MFV Corley & JS Parker (Perry 1967: 422).
H16 1967: on rocks in stream flowing through woods, Kylemore, nr Letterfrack, HH Birks, HJB Birks & DA

Ratcliffe (Crundwell 1968: 645).

H(20) 1939: Devil's Glen, JS Thomson (anon. 1940a: 176).

H27 1987: wet rocks by waterfall in ravine on S side of Ben Gorm, above Killary Harbour, GP Rothero (Blockeel 1998: 39).

H(31) listed by Lett (1915: 149). H(31) listed by Blockeel & Long (1998: 143).

H(33) listed by Lett (1915: 149). H(33) listed by Blockeel & Long (1998: 143).

H(34) listed by Lett (1915: 149). H(34) listed by Blockeel & Long (1998: 143).

H(35) listed by Lett (1915: 149). H(35) listed by Blockeel & Long (1998: 143).

H35 2001: on rock in stream in scrub in woodland, 20 m alt., The Commons, Killybegs, G77, NG Hodgetts 3754 (Rothero 2002: 54).

H36 1957: rocks in stream, Corrick Bridge, nr Plumbridge, RD Fitzgerald (Warburg 1958b: 489).

H(38) listed by Lett (1915: 149). H(38) listed by Blockeel & Long (1998: 143).

H(39) listed by Lett (1915: 149).

H(39) 1928: Glenariff (BBS exc.) (Duncan 1928: 117), as *Hypnum eugyrium* var. *mackayi*.

H39 1999: on basalt boulder above water level in stream, E of Cranny Falls, D21, DT Holyoak 99-829 (BBSUK) (Rothero 2000: 60).

161/8 ***Hygrohypnum duriusculum*** (De Not.) Jamieson
(syn. *Amblystegium dilatatum* (Wilson ex Schimp.) Lindb., *Hygrohypnum dilatatum* (Wilson ex Schimp.) Loeske)

H(1) 1897: Connor Hill Pass, HW Lett (Lett 1915: 148).

H(2) 1865: Torc Waterfall, Hutton (Lett 1915: 148).

163/1 ***Scorpidium scorpioides*** (Hedw.) Limpr.
(syn. *Amblystegium scorpioides* (Hedw.) Lindb., *Hypnum scorpioides* Hedw.)

H(1) listed by Lett (1915: 148).

†H1 listed by Blockeel & Long (1998: 144).

H2 1967: in flush, *ca* 900 ft [alt.], The Paps, RD Fitzgerald (Crundwell 1968: 645).

H(3) listed by Lett (1915: 148).

†H3 listed by Blockeel & Long (1998: 144).

H(4) listed by Lett (1915: 148). H(4) listed by Blockeel & Long (1998: 144).

[H(8) listed by Lett (1915: 148) without details. H8 deleted because no valid record or voucher specimen traced (Blockeel 1999: 9)].

H(9) 1945: bog nr L. Bunny, JS Thomson (anon. 1946c: 286).

†H9 listed by Blockeel & Long (1998: 144).

H10 1952: shore of Terryglass Bay, L. Derg, MPH Kertland & ALK King (Warburg 1953: 318).

H11 1966: on bog, Derryfadda, W of Johnstown, J Appleyard *et al.* (BBS exc.) (Crundwell 1968: 645).

H13 1975: fen ¼ mile S of Yellow Ford Cross Roads, N Kirby (BBS exc.) (Crundwell 1976: 31).

H14 1956: marshy calcareous ground by Grand Canal, Mountmellick, AA Cridland (Warburg 1958b: 489).

H(15) listed by Lett (1915: 148) without locality.

†H15 listed by Blockeel & Long (1998: 144).

H(16) listed by Lett (1915: 148).

†H16 listed by Blockeel & Long (1998: 144).

H17 1957: fens, Cloonboo, RE Parker (Warburg 1958b: 489).

H18 1951: wet peat, Skaravogue, Birr, AP Fenning (Warburg 1954: 487).

H(19) 1938: nr Naas, JG Finlay (Duncan 1944: 217).

[H(20) listed by Lett (1915: 148) without locality. H20 deleted because no valid record or voucher specimen traced (Blockeel 1999: 9)].

H(21) listed by Lett (1915: 148). H(21) listed by Blockeel & Long (1998: 144).

H22 1965: wet channel, Commons, Duleek, DM Synnott (Warburg 1966: 203).

H(23) listed by Lett (1915: 148).

†H23 listed by Blockeel & Long (1998: 144).

H24 1980: Drapers Bridge, Royal Canal, DM Synnott (Hill 1981: 35).

H25 1959: on shore of Lake Funshinagh, ALK King (Warburg 1962: 175).

H26 1953: pools by E shore of L. Carra, by Otter Point, EC Wallace (Warburg 1954: 487).

H(27) listed by Lett (1915: 148).

†H27 listed by Blockeel & Long (1998: 144).

H28 1963: boggy ground, *ca* 900 ft [alt.], S of Knockachree, Slieve Gamph, RD Fitzgerald & AR Perry (Warburg 1964: 733).

H(30) listed by Lett (1915: 148). H(30) listed

by Blockeel & Long (1998: 144).
H(31) listed by Lett (1915: 148). H(31) listed by Blockeel & Long (1998: 144).
[H(32) listed by Lett (1915: 148) without details. H32 deleted because no valid record or voucher specimen traced (Blockeel 1999: 9)].
H(33) listed by Lett (1915: 148). H(33) listed by Blockeel & Long (1998: 144).
H33 2000: in calcareous flush with *Carex* spp., N edge of Glencreawan Lough, H05, DT Holyoak 00-302 (BBSUK) (Rothero 2001: 47).
H(34) listed by Lett (1915: 148).
†H34 listed by Blockeel & Long (1998: 144).
H(35) listed by Lett (1915: 148).
†H35 listed by Blockeel & Long (1998: 144).
H36 1951: wet peaty bog, L. Bradan, RD Fitzgerald (Warburg 1952: 108).
H(37) listed by Lett (1915: 148). H(37) listed by Blockeel & Long (1998: 144).
H(38) listed by Lett (1915: 148).
†H38 listed by Blockeel & Long (1998: 144).
H(39) listed by Lett (1915: 148).
†H39 listed by Blockeel & Long (1998: 144).
H(40) listed by Lett (1915: 148).
†H40 listed by Blockeel & Long (1998: 144).

164/1 ***Calliergon stramineum*** (Brid.) Kindb. (syn. *Acrocladium stramineum* (Brid.) P. W.Richards & E.C.Wallace, *Amblystegium stramineum* (Brid.) De Not., *Hypnum stramineum* Brid.)

H(1) listed by Lett (1915: 149).
†H1 listed by Blockeel & Long (1998: 144).
H(5) listed by Lett (1915: 149). H(5) listed by Blockeel & Long (1998: 144).
H6 1966: among *Sphagnum*, Laghtnafrankee, Comeragh Mts, EM Lobley (BBS exc.) (Perry 1967: 422).
H7 1966: among *Sphagnum*, bog betwen Seefin and Knockeenatoung, Galtee Mts, EM Lobley & RJ Murphy (BBS exc.) (Perry 1967: 422).
H9 1973: Lough Goller Bog, Lisdoonvarna, PH Pitkin (Crundwell 1974: 174).
H10 1979: wet ground on W side of Keeper Hill, S of Silvermine Mts, HMH van Melick (Hill 1981: 35).
H12 1969: among *Sphagnum* in marshy ground, Sculloge Gap, nr Kiltealy, RD Fitzgerald (Crundwell 1970: 209).
H13 1966: bog, Crannagh, SW of Mt Leinster, E Booth, comm. DM Synnott (Perry 1967: 422).
H(14) listed by Lett (1915: 149). H(14) listed by Blockeel & Long (1998: 144).
H16 1959: wet flush, Gortmore townland, nr W shore of L. Mask, MCF Proctor (Warburg 1963b: 502).
H17 1985: flush on raised bog, Monivea, H Grogan & C Douglas (Blockeel 1987: 26).
H18 1986: minerotrophic soak, Clara Bog, C O'Connell (Blockeel 1987: 26, O'Connell & Foss 1987).
H(20) listed by Lett (1915: 149).
†H20 listed by Blockeel & Long (1998: 144).
H(21) listed by Lett (1915: 149). H(21) listed by Blockeel & Long (1998: 144).
H22 1971: fen-bog transition, site of L. Frehaun, ½ mile S of L. Shesk, Clonmellon, DM Synnott (Crundwell 1974: 174).
H23 1971: poor fen, Fore, DM Synnott (Crundwell 1974: 174).
H24 1965: *Sphagnum* bog, Corn Hill, *ca* 700 ft alt., nr Drumlish, EM Lobley & RD Fitzgerald (Warburg 1966: 203).
[H26 deleted because no valid record or voucher specimen traced (Blockeel 1999: 9)].
H27 1958: iron flush in bog between Dooleeg and Bellacorick, ALK King (Warburg 1959: 639).
H(28) 1937: Ben Bulben, no collector named (BBS exc.) (Armitage 1938: 13).
†H28 listed by Blockeel & Long (1998: 144).
H29 1965: *Sphagnum* bog, Dergvone, NE of Drumkeeran, EM Lobley & RD Fitzgerald (Warburg 1966: 203).
H30 1955: marsh at edge of Carrigabruse Bog, nr Loch Ramor, ALK King (Warburg 1956: 158).
H(31) listed by Lett (1915: 149). H(31) listed by Blockeel & Long (1998: 144).
H32 2002: in blanket bog flush, 350 m alt., E of Three Counties Hollow, Eshbrack, H54, N Lockhart 2002/05a (Rothero 2003: 61).
H(33) listed by Lett (1915: 149). H(33) listed by Blockeel & Long (1998: 144).
H33 2000: in small flush on N-facing slope, 600 m alt., SE of Lough Atona, H12, DT Holyoak 00-182 (BBSUK) (Rothero 2001: 47).
H(34) listed by Lett (1915: 149).
†H34 listed by Blockeel & Long (1998: 144).
H35 1998: calcareous flush with *Sphagnum*

warnstorfii and *Tomentypnum nitens*, 150 m alt., Meentygrannagh Bog, 2 km S of Altinierin, C00, N Lockhart (Rothero 1999b: 46).
H(36) listed by Lett (1915: 149).
†H36 listed by Blockeel & Long (1998: 144).
H(37) listed by Lett (1915: 149).
†H37 listed by Blockeel & Long (1998: 144).
H(38) listed by Lett (1915: 149). H(38) listed by Blockeel & Long (1998: 144).
H38 2002: on peat in inundation zone of reservoir, 330 m alt., nr S edge of Spelga Dam, J22, DT Holyoak 02-974 (Rothero 2003: 61).
H(39) listed by Lett (1915: 149).
†H39 listed by Blockeel & Long (1998: 144).
H(40) listed by Lett (1915: 149).
†H40 listed by Blockeel & Long (1998: 144).

164/2 ***Calliergon trifarium*** (F.Weber & D. Mohr) Kindb.
(syn. *Acrocladium trifarium* (F.Weber & D.Mohr) P.W.Richards & E.C.Wallace)

H9 1953: dried floor of turlough, S of Mullagh More, MCF Proctor (Warburg 1954: 487, Proctor 1959).
H16 1980: among *Scorpidium scorpioides*, S side of Errisbeg, Roundstone, A Moen (Hill 1982: 29).

164/3 ***Calliergon cordifolium*** (Hedw.) Kindb.
(syn. *Acrocladium cordifolium* (Hedw.) P.W.Richards & E.C.Wallace, *Amblystegium cordifolium* (Hedw.) De Not., *Hypnum cordifolium* Hedw.)

[H(1) listed by Lett (1915: 149) without locality. H1 deleted because no valid record or voucher specimen traced (Blockeel 1999: 9)].
H(2) listed by Lett (1915: 149) without details.
†H2 listed by Blockeel & Long (1998: 144).
†H3 listed by Blockeel & Long (1998: 144).
H(4) listed by Lett (1915: 149).
†H4 listed by Blockeel & Long (1998: 144).
[H5 deleted because no valid record or voucher specimen traced (Blockeel 1999: 9)].
H6 1966: wet meadow, Ballin Lough, nr Bunmahon, JG Duckett *et al.* (BBS exc.) (Perry 1967: 422).
H7 1991: swamp, 100 m alt., Doonoor Townland, 1 km S of Grange, R94, N Lockhart & A O'Suillivan (Blockeel 1992: 28).
H(8) listed by Lett (1915: 149) without locality. H(8) listed by Blockeel & Long (1998: 144).
H10 1991: in wet, sedge-dominated cutaway bog, 50 m alt., 3 km W of Newport, R66, N Lockhart & A O'Suillivan (Blockeel 1992: 28).
†H12 listed by Blockeel & Long (1998: 144).
H13 1975: bog nr Yellowford Cross Roads, Rathvilly, AR Perry (Hill 1977a: 24).
H15 1957: boggy thicket by roadside, nr L. Cutra, J Appleyard (BBS exc.) (Warburg 1958b: 489).
H(16) listed by Lett (1915: 149).
†H16 listed by Blockeel & Long (1998: 144).
H18 1986: in seasonally flooded meadows, Clonmacnoise Callows, N Lockhart (Blockeel 1989: 31).
H(20) listed by Lett (1915: 149).
†H20 listed by Blockeel & Long (1998: 144).
H(21) listed by Lett (1915: 149). H(21) listed by Blockeel & Long (1998: 144).
H22 1966: by small lake nr Carraigobann, N of Duleek, DM Synnott (Perry 1967: 422).
H23 1953: wet ditch, Barronstown, nr Lough Iron, JS Thomson (Warburg 1954: 487).
H(24) 1941: Ardnacliff, JG Finlay (Duncan 1944: 217).
H(25) 1940: nr Boyle, JS Thomson (Duncan 1944: 217).
†H25 listed by Blockeel & Long (1998: 144).
H(27) listed by Lett (1915: 149).
†H27 listed by Blockeel & Long (1998: 144).
H(28) 1928: nr Rosses Point, Sligo (BBS exc.) (Duncan 1928: 119).
†H28 listed by Blockeel & Long (1998: 144).
H(29) listed by Lett (1915: 149).
†H29 listed by Blockeel & Long (1998: 144).
H(30) 1941: Killykeen, JG Finlay (Duncan 1944: 217).
H30 2001: on soil in sallow carr, 60 m alt., Lough Gowna, NW of Dermaferst Bridge, N28, DT Holyoak 01-698 (Rothero 2002: 55).
H(31) listed by Lett (1915: 149). H(31) listed by Blockeel & Long (1998: 144).
H(32) 1947: swampy ground among reeds, side of Lough Muckno, Castleblaney, JS Thomson (anon. 1948b: 124).
†H32 listed by Blockeel & Long (1998: 144).
H33 1959: shores of Lough at Derrynawilt Cross Roads, RD Fitzgerald (Warburg

1960: 782).
H(34) listed by Lett (1915: 149).
†H34 listed by Blockeel & Long (1998: 144).
H(36) listed by Lett (1915: 149).
†H36 listed by Blockeel & Long (1998: 144).
H(37) listed by Lett (1915: 149).
†H37 listed by Blockeel & Long (1998: 144).
H(38) listed by Lett (1915: 149). H(38) listed by Blockeel & Long (1998: 144).
H(39) listed by Lett (1915: 149).
†H39 listed by Blockeel & Long (1998: 144).
H(40) 1945: Umbra Swamp, Downhill, AM Irvin (anon. 1946a: 268).
†H40 listed by Blockeel & Long (1998: 144).

164/4 ***Calliergon giganteum*** (Schimp.) Kindb. (syn. *Acrocladium giganteum* (Schimp.) P.W.Richards & E.C.Wallace, *Amblystegium giganteum* (Schimp.) De Not., *Hypnum giganteum* Schimp.)

H1 1968: marsh on the edge of L. Gill, Castlegregory, Dingle Peninsula, JA Paton (Crundwell 1969: 889).
H6 1999: in wet ground among tall herbs in mire, 60 m alt., Fennor, *ca* 5 km W of Tramore, S50, TL Blockeel 28/296 (Rothero 2000: 60).
H7 1966: edge of raised bog, Longfordpass South, nr Urlingford, JG Duckett *et al.* (BBS exc.) (Perry 1967: 422).
H8 1975: marsh, Clogh, nr Rathkeale, PH Pitkin (Crundwell 1976: 31).
H(9) 1945: bog by L. Bunny, JS Thomson (anon. 1946c: 286).
†H9 listed by Blockeel & Long (1998: 144).
H10 1952: shore of Terryglass Bay, L. Derg, MPH Kertland & ALK King (Warburg 1953: 318).
H11 1966: ditch in young plantation nr Foulkscourt House, nr Johnstown, ERB Little (BBS exc.) (Perry 1967: 422).
H13 1969: edge of bog, St Mullins, nr Graiguenamanagh, RD Fitzgerald (Crundwell 1970: 209).
†H15 listed by Blockeel & Long (1998: 144).
H16 1965: marsh nr shore of L. Mask, nr mouth of Owenbrin R., AMcG Stirling (Warburg 1966: 203).
H17 1957: fens, Cloonboo, RE Parker (Warburg 1958b: 489).
H18 1984: old drain nr Fin Lough, nr Clonmacnoise, V Power (Hill 1986: 23).
H19 1953: basic marsh, Morristown Lattin, nr Newbridge, ALK King (Warburg 1954: 487).
H(20) 1949: Buckroney Marsh, Brittas, JP Brunker (Warburg 1950: 388).
H(21) listed by Lett (1915: 149). H(21) listed by Blockeel & Long (1998: 144).
H22 1960: alkaline marsh nr Lough Shesk, ALK King (Warburg 1962: 175).
H(23) 1946: Scraw Bog, Portnashangan, Mullingar, KC Harris (anon. 1947: 34).
†H23 listed by Blockeel & Long (1998: 144).
H24 1966: wall of canal lock, Cloondara, ALK King (Perry 1967: 422).
†H25 listed by Blockeel & Long (1998: 144).
H26 1953: pool by shore of L. Carra, opposite Otter Point, EC Wallace (Warburg 1954: 487).
H(27) listed by Lett (1915: 149).
†H27 listed by Blockeel & Long (1998: 144).
H28 1959: roadside drain nr Knocknarea, ALK King (Warburg 1960: 782).
H29 1965: fen and ditch *ca* 1 mile NE of Dromahair, EF Warburg (Warburg 1966: 203).
H(31) 1943: Feede, JS Thomson (Duncan 1944: 217).
H(32) listed by Lett (1915: 149). H(32) listed by Blockeel & Long (1998: 144).
†H33 listed by Blockeel & Long (1998: 144).
[H(34) listed by Lett (1915: 149)].
H(35) listed by Lett (1915: 149) without details.
†H35 listed by Blockeel & Long (1998: 144).
H(36) listed by Lett (1915: 149).
†H36 listed by Blockeel & Long (1998: 144).
H(37) 1915: Lurgan, JD Houston (anon. 1916c: 11).
†H37 listed by Blockeel & Long (1998: 144).
H(38) listed by Lett (1915: 149).
†H38 listed by Blockeel & Long (1998: 144).
H(39) listed by Lett (1915: 149).
†H39 listed by Blockeel & Long (1998: 144).
H(40) 1900: pool among sandhills, Magilligan, CH Waddell (anon. 1915a: 138).
H(40) listed by Lett (1915: 149) as: Magilligan, leg. HW Lett.
†H40 listed by Blockeel & Long (1998: 144).

164/5 ***Calliergon sarmentosum*** (Wahlenb.) Kindb.
(syn. *Acrocladium sarmentosum* (Wahlenb.) P.W.Richards & E.C. Wallace, *Amblystegium sarmentosum* (Wahlenb.) De Not.)

H(1) listed by Lett (1915: 149).
†H1 listed by Blockeel & Long (1998: 144).
H(2) listed by Lett (1915: 149).
†H2 listed by Blockeel & Long (1998: 144).
H3 1953: stream on slope of Coomataggart Mt., nr Gougane Barra, ALK King (Warburg 1954: 487).
H(16) listed by Lett (1915: 149).
†H16 listed by Blockeel & Long (1998: 144).
H(20) listed by Lett (1915: 149). H(20) listed by Blockeel & Long (1998: 144).
H(27) 1909: Clare I., RL Praeger (DBN) (Crundwell 1970: 209).
[H27 1957: flush, edge of summit plateau, Maumtrasna, RE Parker (BBS exc.) (Warburg 1958b: 489). H27 deleted because based on locality (E of Skeltia, Maumtrasna) in H16 (Crundwell 1970: 209)].
H(34) listed by Lett (1915: 149).
†H34 listed by Blockeel & Long (1998: 144).
H35 1962: flush at 800 ft [alt.], N side of Muckish Mt., AC Crundwell (BBS exc.) (Warburg 1963b: 502).
H(38) listed by Lett (1915: 149). H(38) listed by Blockeel & Long (1998: 144).
H(39) listed by Lett (1915: 149).
†H39 listed by Blockeel & Long (1998: 144).

165/1 ***Calliergonella cuspidata*** (Hedw.) Loeske
(syn. *Acrocladium cuspidatum* (Hedw.) Lindb., *Calliergon cuspidatum* (Hedw.) Kindb., *Hypnum cuspidatum* Hedw., *H. cuspidatum* var. *pungens* Weis nom. inval.)

H(1) listed by Lett (1915: 161) without details.
†H1 listed by Blockeel & Long (1998: 144).
H(2) listed by Lett (1915: 161) without details.
†H2 listed by Blockeel & Long (1998: 144).
H(3) listed by Lett (1915: 161) without details.
†H3 listed by Blockeel & Long (1998: 144).
H(4) listed by Lett (1915: 161) without details.
†H4 listed by Blockeel & Long (1998: 144).
H(5) listed by Lett (1915: 161) without details.
†H5 listed by Blockeel & Long (1998: 144).
H(6) listed by Lett (1915: 161) without details.
†H6 listed by Blockeel & Long (1998: 144).
H(7) listed by Lett (1915: 161) without details.
†H7 listed by Blockeel & Long (1998: 144).
H(8) listed by Lett (1915: 161) without details.
†H8 listed by Blockeel & Long (1998: 144).
H(9) listed by Lett (1915: 161) without details.
†H9 listed by Blockeel & Long (1998: 144).
H(10) listed by Lett (1915: 161) without details.
†H10 listed by Blockeel & Long (1998: 144).
H(11) listed by Lett (1915: 161) without details.
†H11 listed by Blockeel & Long (1998: 144).
H(12) listed by Lett (1915: 161) without details.
†H12 listed by Blockeel & Long (1998: 144).
H(13) listed by Lett (1915: 161) without details.
†H13 listed by Blockeel & Long (1998: 144).
H(14) listed by Lett (1915: 161) without details.
†H14 listed by Blockeel & Long (1998: 144).
H(15) listed by Lett (1915: 161) without details.
†H15 listed by Blockeel & Long (1998: 144).
H(16) listed by Lett (1915: 161) without details.
†H16 listed by Blockeel & Long (1998: 144).
H(17) listed by Lett (1915: 161) without details.
†H17 listed by Blockeel & Long (1998: 144).
H(18) listed by Lett (1915: 161) without details.
†H18 listed by Blockeel & Long (1998: 144).
H(19) listed by Lett (1915: 161) without details.
†H19 listed by Blockeel & Long (1998: 144).
H(20) listed by Lett (1915: 161) without details.
†H20 listed by Blockeel & Long (1998: 144).
H(21) listed by Lett (1915: 161) without details.
†H21 listed by Blockeel & Long (1998: 144).
H(22) listed by Lett (1915: 161) without details.
†H22 listed by Blockeel & Long (1998: 144).

H(23) listed by Lett (1915: 161) without details.
†H23 listed by Blockeel & Long (1998: 144).
H(24) listed by Lett (1915: 161) without details.
†H24 listed by Blockeel & Long (1998: 144).
H(25) listed by Lett (1915: 161) without details.
†H25 listed by Blockeel & Long (1998: 144).
H(26) listed by Lett (1915: 161) without details.
H(26) 1945: Cong, W Mayo [*sic*], ML Anderson, per JS Thomson (anon. 1946c: 286).
†H26 listed by Blockeel & Long (1998: 144).
H(27) listed by Lett (1915: 161) without details.
†H27 listed by Blockeel & Long (1998: 144).
H(28) listed by Lett (1915: 161) without details.
†H28 listed by Blockeel & Long (1998: 144).
H(29) listed by Lett (1915: 161) without details.
†H29 listed by Blockeel & Long (1998: 144).
H(30) listed by Lett (1915: 161) without details.
†H30 listed by Blockeel & Long (1998: 144).
H(31) listed by Lett (1915: 161) without details.
†H31 listed by Blockeel & Long (1998: 144).
H(32) listed by Lett (1915: 161) without details.
†H32 listed by Blockeel & Long (1998: 144).
H(33) listed by Lett (1915: 161) without details.
†H33 listed by Blockeel & Long (1998: 144).
H(34) listed by Lett (1915: 161) without details.
†H34 listed by Blockeel & Long (1998: 144).
H(35) listed by Lett (1915: 161) without details.
†H35 listed by Blockeel & Long (1998: 144).
H(36) listed by Lett (1915: 161) without details.
†H36 listed by Blockeel & Long (1998: 144).
H(37) listed by Lett (1915: 161) without details.
†H37 listed by Blockeel & Long (1998: 144).
H(38) listed by Lett (1915: 161) without details.
†H38 listed by Blockeel & Long (1998: 144).
H(39) listed by Lett (1915: 161) without details.
†H39 listed by Blockeel & Long (1998: 144).
H(40) listed by Lett (1915: 161) without details.
H(40) 1940: damp sandy soil, Portstewart, WR Megaw (anon. 1948b: 124), as '*Hypnum cuspidatum* var. *pungens* Schp.'
†H40 listed by Blockeel & Long (1998: 144).

166/1a *Isothecium myosuroides* Brid. **var. *myosuroides***
(syn. *Eurhynchium myosuroides* (Brid.) Schimp., *Isothecium myosuroides* var. *tenuinerve* (Kindb.) Braithw.)

H(1) listed by Lett (1915: 154) without details.
†H1 listed by Blockeel & Long (1998: 145).
H(2) listed by Lett (1915: 154) without details.
†H2 listed by Blockeel & Long (1998: 145).
H(3) listed by Lett (1915: 154) without details.
†H3 listed by Blockeel & Long (1998: 145).
H(4) listed by Lett (1915: 154) without details.
†H4 listed by Blockeel & Long (1998: 145).
H(5) listed by Lett (1915: 154) without details.
†H5 listed by Blockeel & Long (1998: 145).
H(6) listed by Lett (1915: 154) without details.
†H6 listed by Blockeel & Long (1998: 145).
H(7) listed by Lett (1915: 154) without details.
†H7 listed by Blockeel & Long (1998: 145).
H(8) 1945: S Tipperary and Limerick boundary, AW Stelfox, per JS Thomson (anon. 1946c: 285).
†H8 listed by Blockeel & Long (1998: 145).
H(9) listed by Lett (1915: 154) without details.
†H9 listed by Blockeel & Long (1998: 145).
H(10) listed by Lett (1915: 154) without details.
†H10 listed by Blockeel & Long (1998: 145).
H(11) listed by Lett (1915: 154) without details.
†H11 listed by Blockeel & Long (1998: 145).
H(12) listed by Lett (1915: 154) without details.
†H12 listed by Blockeel & Long (1998: 145).
H(13) listed by Lett (1915: 154) without details.
†H13 listed by Blockeel & Long (1998: 145).
H(14) listed by Lett (1915: 154) without details.
†H14 listed by Blockeel & Long (1998: 145).

H15 1956: wood at Hearnesbrook, nr Killimor, ALK King (Warburg 1957: 336).
H(16) listed by Lett (1915: 154) without details.
†H16 listed by Blockeel & Long (1998: 145).
H(17) listed by Lett (1915: 154) without details.
†H17 listed by Blockeel & Long (1998: 145).
H(18) listed by Lett (1915: 154) without details.
†H18 listed by Blockeel & Long (1998: 145).
H(19) 1949: root of tree, Calverstown House, JS Thomson (Warburg 1950: 387).
H(20) listed by Lett (1915: 154) without details.
†H20 listed by Blockeel & Long (1998: 145).
H(21) listed by Lett (1915: 154) without details.
†H21 listed by Blockeel & Long (1998: 145).
H(22) listed by Lett (1915: 154) without details.
†H22 listed by Blockeel & Long (1998: 145).
H23 1952: tree, Clonhugh Demesne, NE end of L. Owel, JS Thomson (Warburg 1953: 316).
H24 1965: tree, *ca* 600 ft alt., Corn Hill, nr Drumlish, RD Fitzgerald & EM Lobley (Warburg 1966: 203).
H(25) listed by Lett (1915: 154).
†H25 listed by Blockeel & Long (1998: 145).
H(26) listed by Lett (1915: 154) without details.
†H26 listed by Blockeel & Long (1998: 145).
H(27) listed by Lett (1915: 154) without details.
†H27 listed by Blockeel & Long (1998: 145).
H(28) listed by Lett (1915: 154) without details.
†H28 listed by Blockeel & Long (1998: 145).
H(29) listed by Lett (1915: 154) without details.
†H29 listed by Blockeel & Long (1998: 145).
H(30) listed by Lett (1915: 154) without details.
†H30 listed by Blockeel & Long (1998: 145).
[H(31) listed by Lett (1915: 154) without details. H31 deleted because no valid record or voucher specimen traced (Blockeel 1999: 9)].
H31 1999: on shaded boulder in plantation, 120 m alt., Two Mile River, Carlingford, J11, TL Blockeel 28/148 (Rothero 2000: 60).
H(32) listed by Lett (1915: 154) without details.
†H32 listed by Blockeel & Long (1998: 145).
H(33) listed by Lett (1915: 154) without details.
†H33 listed by Blockeel & Long (1998: 145).
H(34) listed by Lett (1915: 154) without details.
†H34 listed by Blockeel & Long (1998: 145).
H(35) listed by Lett (1915: 154).
†H35 listed by Blockeel & Long (1998: 145).
H(36) listed by Lett (1915: 154) without details.
†H36 listed by Blockeel & Long (1998: 145).
H(37) listed by Lett (1915: 154) without details.
†H37 listed by Blockeel & Long (1998: 145).
H(38) listed by Lett (1915: 154) without details.
†H38 listed by Blockeel & Long (1998: 145).
H(39) listed by Lett (1915: 154) without details.
†H39 listed by Blockeel & Long (1998: 145).
H(40) listed by Lett (1915: 154) without details.
†H40 listed by Blockeel & Long (1998: 145).

166/1b *Isothecium myosuroides* var. *brachythecioides* (Dixon) Braithw.
(syn. *Eurhynchium myosuroides* var. *brachythecioides* Dixon)

H(1) listed by Lett (1915: 154). H(1) listed by Blockeel & Long (1998: 145).
H(2) 1935: Mangerton, no collector named (BBS exc.) (Watson 1936: 265).
H7 1963: sandstone rocks at 1500 ft on N side of Galtymore Mt., DA Ratcliffe (Warburg 1964: 733).
H8 1966: basic rock at 2000 ft alt., Temple Hill, Galtee Mts, MFV Corley & JS Parker (Perry 1967: 422).
†H16 listed by Blockeel & Long (1998: 145).
†H27 listed by Blockeel & Long (1998: 145).
H28 1963: limestone outcrops at 1350 ft [alt.], Lugnagall, Glencar, AR Perry & RD Fitzgerald (Warburg 1964: 733).
H29 1963: limestone outcrops at 900 ft [alt.], Boggaun, nr Manorhamilton, AR Perry & RD Fitzgerald (Warburg 1964: 733).
H(30) listed by Blockeel & Long (1998: 145).
H(33) 1914: Cuilcagh, WN Tetley (anon. 1915b: 13), labelled as *Eurhynchium crassinervium*, but redet. by HN Dixon as *E. myosuroides* var. *brachythecioides*.
H(33) listed by Blockeel & Long (1998: 145).

H33 2000: on sandstone at base of N-facing crag, Culcarrick Scarp, E part, H05, DT Holyoak 00-250 (BBSUK) (Rothero 2001: 47).
H(34) listed by Lett (1915: 154).
†H34 listed by Blockeel & Long (1998: 145).
H35 1955: Horn Head, AW Stelfox, comm. JS Thomson (Warburg 1956: 157).
H36 1958: rocks, 1800 ft [alt.], Dart Mt., RD Fitzgerald (Warburg 1959: 638), as record from H40. 'Dart Mt. (H.40)' from Warburg (1959: 638) revised to 'Dart Mt. (H.36)' (Warburg 1961: 173).
H39 1999: on stable scree of basalt boulders on slope above coast, Giant's Causeway, C94, DT Holyoak 99-247 (BBSUK) (Rothero 2000: 60).
['H40' 1958: rocks 1800 ft [alt.], Dart Mt., RD Fitzgerald (Warburg 1959: 638). Revised to 'Dart Mt. (H.36)' (Warburg 1961: 173)].
H40 1999: on basalt boulder below crags, 260 m alt., Binevenagh, W slopes, C63, DT Holyoak 99-564 (BBSUK) (Rothero 2000: 60).

166/2 ***Isothecium alopecuroides*** (Dubois) Isov.
(syn. *Eurhynchium myurum* (Brid.) Dixon, *Isothecium myurum* Brid., *I. viviparum* Lindb.)

H(1) listed by Lett (1915: 155) without details.
†H1 listed by Blockeel & Long (1998: 145).
H(2) listed by Lett (1915: 155) without details.
†H2 listed by Blockeel & Long (1998: 145).
H3 1953: roots of tree on island in Lake Gougane Barra, ALK King (Warburg 1954: 486).
H(4) listed by Lett (1915: 155) without details.
†H4 listed by Blockeel & Long (1998: 145).
H(5) listed by Lett (1915: 155) without details.
†H5 listed by Blockeel & Long (1998: 145).
H(6) listed by Lett (1915: 155) without details.
†H6 listed by Blockeel & Long (1998: 145).
H7 1956: roots of beech, Marlfield, Clonmel, EC Wallace (Warburg 1957: 336).
H(8) listed by Lett (1915: 155) without details.
†H8 listed by Blockeel & Long (1998: 145).
H(9) listed by Lett (1915: 155) without details.
†H9 listed by Blockeel & Long (1998: 145).
H(10) listed by Lett (1915: 155) without details.
†H10 listed by Blockeel & Long (1998: 145).
H(11) listed by Lett (1915: 155) without details.
†H11 listed by Blockeel & Long (1998: 145).
H(12) listed by Lett (1915: 155) without details.
†H12 listed by Blockeel & Long (1998: 145).
H(13) listed by Lett (1915: 155) without details.
†H13 listed by Blockeel & Long (1998: 145).
H(14) listed by Lett (1915: 155) without details.
†H14 listed by Blockeel & Long (1998: 145).
H15 1956: wood at Hearnesbrook, nr Killimor, ALK King (Warburg 1957: 336).
H(16) listed by Lett (1915: 155) without details.
†H16 listed by Blockeel & Long (1998: 145).
H(17) listed by Lett (1915: 155) without details.
†H17 listed by Blockeel & Long (1998: 145).
H(18) 1949: tree-stump, copse at edge of Ballywilliam Bog, Birr, AP Fanning (Warburg 1954: 486).
†H18 listed by Blockeel & Long (1998: 145).
H(19) 1938: Monasterevan, JG Finlay (Duncan 1944: 215).
H(20) listed by Lett (1915: 155) without details.
†H20 listed by Blockeel & Long (1998: 145).
H(21) listed by Lett (1915: 155) without details.
†H21 listed by Blockeel & Long (1998: 145).
H22 1950: tree-trunk, Slane, JS Thomson (Warburg 1952: 106).
H23 1952: tree, Clonhugh Demesne, NE end of L. Owel, JS Thomson (Warburg 1953: 316).
H(24) listed by Lett (1915: 155) without details.
†H24 listed by Blockeel & Long (1998: 145).
H(25) listed by Lett (1915: 155) without details.
†H25 listed by Blockeel & Long (1998: 145).
H(26) listed by Lett (1915: 155) without details.
†H26 listed by Blockeel & Long (1998: 145).
H(27) listed by Lett (1915: 155) without

details.

†H27 listed by Blockeel & Long (1998: 145).

H(28) 1928: nr Sligo (BBS exc.) (Duncan 1928: 119).

†H28 listed by Blockeel & Long (1998: 145).

H(29) listed by Lett (1915: 155) without details.

†H29 listed by Blockeel & Long (1998: 145).

[H(30) listed by Lett (1915: 155) without details. H30 deleted because no valid record or voucher specimen traced (Blockeel 1999: 9)].

H30 2001: on sandstone blocks of ruined wall, 305 m alt., W of Bellavally Gap, H12, DT Holyoak 01-629 (Rothero 2002: 55).

[H(31) listed by Lett (1915: 155) without details. H31 deleted because no valid record or voucher specimen traced (Blockeel 1999: 9)].

H(32) listed by Lett (1915: 155) without details.

†H32 listed by Blockeel & Long (1998: 145).

H(33) listed by Lett (1915: 155) without details.

†H33 listed by Blockeel & Long (1998: 145).

H(34) listed by Lett (1915: 155) without details.

†H34 listed by Blockeel & Long (1998: 145).

H(35) listed by Lett (1915: 155) without details.

†H35 listed by Blockeel & Long (1998: 145).

†H36 listed by Blockeel & Long (1998: 145).

†H37 listed by Blockeel & Long (1998: 145).

H(38) listed by Lett (1915: 155) without details. H(38) listed by Blockeel & Long (1998: 145).

H38 2002: on bark of *Quercus*, 50 m alt., by Shimna River in Tollymore Forest Park, J33, DT Holyoak 02-921 (Rothero 2003: 62).

H(39) listed by Lett (1915: 155) without details.

†H39 listed by Blockeel & Long (1998: 145).

H(40) listed by Lett (1915: 155) without details.

†H40 listed by Blockeel & Long (1998: 145).

166/3 ***Isothecium holtii*** Kindb.
(syn. *Isothecium myosuroides* var. *rivulare* Holt ex Limpr.)

H(1) listed by Lett (1915: 154).

†H1 listed by Blockeel & Long (1998: 145).

H(2) listed by Lett (1915: 154) without details.

†H2 listed by Blockeel & Long (1998: 145).

[H(3) listed by Lett (1915: 154) without details. H3 deleted because no valid record or voucher specimen traced (Blockeel 1999: 9)].

H6 1966: rocks by Owennashad River, J Appleyard *et al.* (BBS exc.) (Perry 1967: 422).

H20 1960: granite by L. Dan, nr Roundwood, ALK King (Warburg 1961: 173).

H35 1962: rocks in stream, Lough Beagh, S of Glenveagh Castle, EC Wallace (BBS exc.) (Warburg 1963b: 502).

H38 1950: rock in R. Bann, Spelja [*sic* = Spelga], RD Fitzgerald (Warburg 1951: 502). Preston & Stone (1999) also report this species from the Shimna River.

H40 1958: wet rocks, 1800 ft [alt.], Dart Mt., RD Fitzgerald (Warburg 1959: 638).

167/1 ***Scorpiurium circinatum*** (Brid.) M. Fleisch. & Loeske
(syn. *Hypnum circinatum* Brid.)

H(1) listed by Lett (1915: 150) without details. H(1) reported as a pre-1950 record, comm. AJE Smith (Hill 1980b: 46). H(1) listed by Blockeel & Long (1998: 145).

H(2) listed by Lett (1915: 150).

†H2 listed by Blockeel & Long (1998: 145).

H(5) listed by Lett (1915: 150).

†H5 listed by Blockeel & Long (1998: 145).

H6 1956: wall of park, Kilmanahan Castle, nr Clonmel, EC Wallace (Warburg 1957: 336).

H(8) listed by Lett (1915: 150).

†H8 listed by Blockeel & Long (1998: 145).

H(9) listed by Lett (1915: 150).

†H9 listed by Blockeel & Long (1998: 145).

H15 1952: limestone boulder by stream, Medick, AP Fanning (Warburg 1953: 316).

H23 1974: limestone boulders at water's edge, Hare I., L. Ree, PH Pitkin (Crundwell 1975: 20).

H24 1981: limestone boulders, shore of Lough Ree, Inchenagh, DM Synnott (DBN) (Blockeel 1989: 31).

H25 1981: limestone boulder on shore of L. Ree, John's Wood, DM Synnott (Hill 1982: 29).

168/1 ***Homalothecium sericeum*** (Hedw.) Bruch, Schimp. & W.Gümbel (syn. *Camptothecium sericeum* (Hedw.) Kindb., *Hypnum sericeum* (Hedw.) L. ex With.)

H(1) listed by Lett (1915: 154) without details.
†H1 listed by Blockeel & Long (1998: 145).
H(2) listed by Lett (1915: 154) without details.
†H2 listed by Blockeel & Long (1998: 145).
H(3) listed by Lett (1915: 154) without details.
†H3 listed by Blockeel & Long (1998: 145).
H(4) listed by Lett (1915: 154) without details.
†H4 listed by Blockeel & Long (1998: 145).
†H5 listed by Blockeel & Long (1998: 145).
H(6) listed by Lett (1915: 154) without details.
†H6 listed by Blockeel & Long (1998: 145).
H(7) listed by Lett (1915: 154) without details.
†H7 listed by Blockeel & Long (1998: 145).
H(8) listed by Lett (1915: 154) without details.
†H8 listed by Blockeel & Long (1998: 145).
H(9) listed by Lett (1915: 154) without details.
†H9 listed by Blockeel & Long (1998: 145).
H(10) listed by Lett (1915: 154) without details.
†H10 listed by Blockeel & Long (1998: 145).
H(11) listed by Lett (1915: 154) without details.
†H11 listed by Blockeel & Long (1998: 145).
H(12) listed by Lett (1915: 154) without details.
†H12 listed by Blockeel & Long (1998: 145).
H(13) listed by Lett (1915: 154) without details.
†H13 listed by Blockeel & Long (1998: 145).
H(14) listed by Lett (1915: 154) without details.
†H14 listed by Blockeel & Long (1998: 145).
H(15) listed by Lett (1915: 154) without details.
†H15 listed by Blockeel & Long (1998: 145).
H(16) listed by Lett (1915: 154) without details.
†H16 listed by Blockeel & Long (1998: 145).
H(17) listed by Lett (1915: 154) without details.
†H17 listed by Blockeel & Long (1998: 145).
[H(18) listed by Lett (1915: 154) without details. H18 deleted because no valid record or voucher specimen traced (Blockeel 1999: 9)].
H(19) listed by Lett (1915: 154) without details.
†H19 listed by Blockeel & Long (1998: 145).
H(20) listed by Lett (1915: 154) without details.
†H20 listed by Blockeel & Long (1998: 145).
H(21) listed by Lett (1915: 154) without details.
†H21 listed by Blockeel & Long (1998: 145).
H(22) listed by Lett (1915: 154) without details.
†H22 listed by Blockeel & Long (1998: 145).
H(23) listed by Lett (1915: 154) without details.
†H23 listed by Blockeel & Long (1998: 145).
H(24) listed by Lett (1915: 154) without details.
†H24 listed by Blockeel & Long (1998: 145).
H(25) listed by Lett (1915: 154) without details.
†H25 listed by Blockeel & Long (1998: 145).
H(26) listed by Lett (1915: 154) without details.
†H26 listed by Blockeel & Long (1998: 145).
H(27) listed by Lett (1915: 154) without details.
†H27 listed by Blockeel & Long (1998: 145).
H(28) listed by Lett (1915: 154) without details.
†H28 listed by Blockeel & Long (1998: 145).
H(29) listed by Lett (1915: 154) without details.
†H29 listed by Blockeel & Long (1998: 145).
H(30) listed by Lett (1915: 154) without details.
†H30 listed by Blockeel & Long (1998: 145).
[H31 deleted because no valid record or voucher specimen traced (Blockeel 1999: 9)].
H(32) listed by Lett (1915: 154) without details.
†H32 listed by Blockeel & Long (1998: 145).
H(33) listed by Lett (1915: 154) without details.
†H33 listed by Blockeel & Long (1998: 145).
H(34) listed by Lett (1915: 154) without details.
†H34 listed by Blockeel & Long (1998: 145).
H(35) listed by Lett (1915: 154) without details.
†H35 listed by Blockeel & Long (1998: 145).

H(36) listed by Lett (1915: 154) without details.
†H36 listed by Blockeel & Long (1998: 145).
H(37) listed by Lett (1915: 154) without details.
†H37 listed by Blockeel & Long (1998: 145).
H(38) listed by Lett (1915: 154) without details.
†H38 listed by Blockeel & Long (1998: 145).
H(39) listed by Lett (1915: 154) without details.
†H39 listed by Blockeel & Long (1998: 145).
H(40) listed by Lett (1915: 154) without details.
†H40 listed by Blockeel & Long (1998: 145).

168/2 ***Homalothecium lutescens*** (Hedw.) H. Rob.
(syn. *Camptothecium lutescens* (Hedw.) Bruch, Schimp. & W.Gümbel, *Hypnum lutescens* Hedw.)

H(1) listed by Lett (1915: 154) without details.
†H1 listed by Blockeel & Long (1998: 145).
H(2) listed by Lett (1915: 154) without details.
†H2 listed by Blockeel & Long (1998: 145).
H3 1975: wall between sea and marsh, Hare I., P Whelan (Hill 1978: 24, Whelan 1978).
H(4) listed by Lett (1915: 154) without details. H(4) listed by Blockeel & Long (1998: 145).
H(5) listed by Lett (1915: 154) without details.
†H5 listed by Blockeel & Long (1998: 145).
H(6) listed by Lett (1915: 154) without details.
†H6 listed by Blockeel & Long (1998: 145).
H7 1956: top of limestone wall, lane nr Knocklofty, EC Wallace (Warburg 1957: 335).
H(8) listed by Lett (1915: 154) without details.
†H8 listed by Blockeel & Long (1998: 145).
H(9) listed by Lett (1915: 154) without details.
†H9 listed by Blockeel & Long (1998: 145).
H(10) listed by Lett (1915: 154) without details.
†H10 listed by Blockeel & Long (1998: 145).
H(11) listed by Lett (1915: 154) without details.
†H11 listed by Blockeel & Long (1998: 145).
H(12) listed by Lett (1915: 154) without details.
†H12 listed by Blockeel & Long (1998: 145).
H(13) listed by Lett (1915: 154) without details.
†H13 listed by Blockeel & Long (1998: 145).
H(14) listed by Lett (1915: 154) without details.
†H14 listed by Blockeel & Long (1998: 145).
[H(15) listed by Lett (1915: 154) without details. H15 deleted because no valid record or voucher specimen traced (Blockeel 1999: 9)].
H(16) listed by Lett (1915: 154) without details.
†H16 listed by Blockeel & Long (1998: 145).
H17 1957: bank of calcareous soil, Balindooly Castle, RE Parker (Warburg 1958b: 485).
H(18) listed by Lett (1915: 154) without details.
†H18 listed by Blockeel & Long (1998: 145).
H(19) listed by Lett (1915: 154) without details.
†H19 listed by Blockeel & Long (1998: 145).
H(20) listed by Lett (1915: 154) without details.
†H20 listed by Blockeel & Long (1998: 145).
H(21) listed by Lett (1915: 154) without details. H(21) listed by Blockeel & Long (1998: 145).
H(22) 1941: Ross House Estate, JG Finlay (Duncan 1944: 215).
†H22 listed by Blockeel & Long (1998: 145).
H(23) listed by Lett (1915: 154) without details.
†H23 listed by Blockeel & Long (1998: 145).
H(24) listed by Lett (1915: 154) without details.
†H24 listed by Blockeel & Long (1998: 145).
H(25) listed by Lett (1915: 154) without details.
†H25 listed by Blockeel & Long (1998: 145).
H26 1953: wall-top, Ballinrobe, EC Wallace (Warburg 1954: 485).
H(27) listed by Lett (1915: 154) without details.
†H27 listed by Blockeel & Long (1998: 145).
H(28) listed by Lett (1915: 154) without details.
†H28 listed by Blockeel & Long (1998: 145).
H(29) listed by Lett (1915: 154) without details.
†H29 listed by Blockeel & Long (1998: 145).
[H(30) listed by Lett (1915: 154) without

details. H30 deleted because no valid record or voucher specimen traced (Blockeel 1999: 9)].
H30 2001: amongst limestone boulders on bank, 50 m alt., River Erne, W bank, W of Belturbet, H31, DT Holyoak 01-703 (Rothero 2002: 55).
[H(31) listed by Lett (1915: 154) without details. H31 deleted because no valid record or voucher specimen traced (Blockeel 1999: 9)].
[H(32) listed by Lett (1915: 154) without details. H32 deleted because no valid record or voucher specimen traced (Blockeel 1999: 9)].
H(33) listed by Lett (1915: 154) without details. H(33) listed by Blockeel & Long (1998: 145).
H33 2000: on edge of limestone scree on SE-facing hillside, NW of Marble Arch, H13, DT Holyoak 00-166 (BBSUK) (Rothero 2001: 47).
H(34) listed by Lett (1915: 154) without details.
†H34 listed by Blockeel & Long (1998: 145).
H(35) listed by Lett (1915: 154) without details.
†H35 listed by Blockeel & Long (1998: 145).
H(37) listed by Lett (1915: 154) without details.
†H37 listed by Blockeel & Long (1998: 145).
H(38) listed by Lett (1915: 154) without details. H(38) listed by Blockeel & Long (1998: 145).
H(39) listed by Lett (1915: 154) without details.
†H39 listed by Blockeel & Long (1998: 145).
H(40) listed by Lett (1915: 154) without details.
†H40 listed by Blockeel & Long (1998: 145).

169/1 ***Brachythecium albicans*** (Hedw.) Bruch, Schimp. & W.Gümbel
(syn. *Hypnum albicans* Neck. ex Hedw.)

H(1) listed by Lett (1915: 154).
†H1 listed by Blockeel & Long (1998: 145).
†H3 listed by Blockeel & Long (1998: 145).
H(4) listed by Lett (1915: 154).
†H4 listed by Blockeel & Long (1998: 145).
H(5) listed by Lett (1915: 154). H(5) listed by Blockeel & Long (1998: 145).
H6 1956: wall-top, Kilminnin, Dungarvan, EC Wallace (Warburg 1957: 335).
H9 1963: sandhills at Fanore, DM Synnott (Warburg 1964: 733).
H12 1950: sand dunes, Curracloe, ALK King (Warburg 1951: 502).
H16 1969: amongst grass on sand by sea-wall *ca* 2 miles W of Spiddle, AR Perry & HJ Perry (Crundwell 1970: 209).
H19 1951: railway ballast pits, Newbridge, JP Brunker (Warburg 1952: 106).
H(20) 1940: Sutton Golf Course, JG Finlay (Duncan 1944: 215).
H20 1975: dunes nr Pennycomequick Bridge, NE of Arklow, JA Paton (BBS exc.) (Crundwell 1976: 31).
H(21) listed by Lett (1915: 154).
†H21 listed by Blockeel & Long (1998: 145).
H22 1954: fixed dunes, Gormanstown, ALK King (Warburg 1955: 586).
H(27) listed by Lett (1915: 154).
†H27 listed by Blockeel & Long (1998: 145).
H28 1963: sand-dunes, Rosses Point, RD Fitzgerald & AR Perry (Warburg 1964: 733).
[H(31) listed by Lett (1915: 154) without locality. H31 deleted because no valid record or voucher specimen traced (Blockeel 1999: 9)].
H(34) listed by Lett (1915: 154).
†H34 listed by Blockeel & Long (1998: 145).
H(35) listed by Lett (1915: 154).
†H35 listed by Blockeel & Long (1998: 145).
H(37) listed by Lett (1915: 154). H(37) listed by Blockeel & Long (1998: 145).
H(38) listed by Lett (1915: 154). H(38) listed by Blockeel & Long (1998: 145).
H38 2002: on open sandy shingle in dune heathland, 5 m alt., Murlough NNR, J33, DT Holyoak 02-951 (Rothero 2003: 62).
H(39) listed by Lett (1915: 154). H(39) listed by Blockeel & Long (1998: 145).
H39 1999: on bare sand and amongst short vegetation on bank in dunes, E of Portballintrae, C94, DT Holyoak 99-243 (BBSUK) (Rothero 2000: 60).
H(40) listed by Lett (1915: 154).
†H40 listed by Blockeel & Long (1998: 145).

169/3 ***Brachythecium glareosum*** (Spruce) Bruch, Schimp. & W.Gümbel
(syn. *Hypnum glareosum* Bruch ex Spruce)

H(1) listed by Lett (1915: 154) without details.
†H1 listed by Blockeel & Long (1998: 146).

H2 1950: grassy bank by roadside at cross, Skeharagh, Tralee, AP Fanning (Warburg 1953: 315).
H(3) listed by Lett (1915: 154). H(3) listed by Blockeel & Long (1998: 146).
H6 1956: bank in wood by R. Suir, Knocklofty Bridge, EC Wallace (Warburg 1957: 335).
H8 1966: turf on wall top, Paradise Hill, Galtee Mts, MFV Corley & JS Parker (Perry 1967: 422).
H9 1957: old wall, Slievecarran, DG Catcheside & EM Lobley (BBS exc.) (Warburg 1958b: 486).
H(16) listed by Lett (1915: 154).
†H16 listed by Blockeel & Long (1998: 146).
H18 1957: Charleville Castle grounds, Tullamore, JS Thomson (Warburg 1958b: 486).
H(19) 1938: Rathmore, JG Finlay (Duncan 1944: 215).
H(20) listed by Lett (1915: 154).
†H20 listed by Blockeel & Long (1998: 146).
H(21) listed by Lett (1915: 154). H(21) listed by Blockeel & Long (1998: 146).
H22 1978: clay bank in lane with high hedges, 400 m N of Ratoath, DM Synnott (Hill 1980b: 46).
H25 1968: shore of Annaghmore L., 3 miles NW of Strokestown, WV Rubers *et al.* (U) (Crundwell 1975: 20).
H26 1970: side of track, Keel Bridge, 3 miles N of Ballinrobe, J Appleyard (BBS exc.) (Crundwell 1971b: 382, Appleyard 1971: 388).
H(28) listed by Lett (1915: 154). H(28) listed by Blockeel & Long (1998: 146).
H(29) listed by Lett (1915: 154). H(29) listed by Blockeel & Long (1998: 146).
H29 2000: on soil on ledge of limestone crag on N-facing hillside, 400 m alt., S of Glencar Lough, G74, DT Holyoak 00-634 (BBSUK) (Rothero 2001: 47).
H(31) listed by Lett (1915: 154). H(31) listed by Blockeel & Long (1998: 146).
H(33) listed by Lett (1915: 154). H(33) listed by Blockeel & Long (1998: 146).
H33 2000: in moss mat growing over limestone in *Corylus* scrub, E of Pollreagh, H13, DT Holyoak 00-153 (BBSUK) (Rothero 2001: 47).
H34 2002: on damp sand in grassland, 25 m alt., SW of Lagacurry, Doagh Isle, C45, DT Holyoak 02-553 (Rothero 2003: 62).
H35 1962: dunes, Dunfanaghy, AC Crunwell & EC Wallace (Warburg 1963b: 503).
1962: sandy ground, Dooros Point, J Appleyard (BBS exc.) (Warburg 1963b: 503).
H(38) listed by Lett (1915: 154). H(38) listed by Blockeel & Long (1998: 146).
H(39) listed by Lett (1915: 154).
†H39 listed by Blockeel & Long (1998: 146).
H(40) listed by Lett (1915: 154).
†H40 listed by Blockeel & Long (1998: 146).

[**169/4** ***Brachythecium salebrosum*** (F.Weber & D.Mohr) Bruch, Schimp. & W.Gümbel]

[H2 1951: wall-top, Tralee, AC Crundwell (Warburg 1952: 106). H2 not listed in *CC* by Corley & Hill 1981: 122].
[H24 1972: limestone boulder, Rathcline House, WV Rubers (U) (Crundwell 1975: 20). H24 not listed in *CC* by Corley & Hill 1981: 122].

[*B. salebrosum* was listed for 19 Irish vice-counties by Smith (1978: 592), but revision of specimens by MO Hill for *CC* (Corley & Hill 1981: 122) led to rejection of all Irish records].

169/5 ***Brachythecium mildeanum*** (Schimp.) Schimp. ex Milde
(syn. *Brachythecium salebrosum* var. *palustre* Schimp.)

H1 1951: sandy bank, West Cove, nr Waterville, JS Thomson, etc. (BBS exc.) (BBSUK), conf. MO Hill (Warburg 1952: 106, MO Hill MS).
H2 1951: top of wall, Tralee, AC Crundwell (BBSUK), conf. MO Hill (MO Hill MS).
1966: fixed dunes, Ballybunnion, MFV Corley & JS Parker (Perry 1967: 422).
H(5) 1852: quarry, Cobh I., Cork Harbour, I Carroll (BM, CRK), conf. MO Hill (Hill 1979: 32, MO Hill MS).
[H6 1966: sand dunes, Bunmahon, J Appleyard (BBS exc.) (Perry 1967: 422). This record is apparently among those rejected by MO Hill (H6 was excluded from Corley & Hill 1981: 122)].
[H12 1966: sand dunes, Cahore Point, J Appleyard & JG Duckett (Perry 1967: 422). This record is apparently among those rejected by MO Hill (H12

excluded from Corley & Hill 1981: 122)].

H13 1975: hummock in fen, SW of Yellowford Cross Roads, S of Baltinglass, JA Paton (BBS exc.) (BBSUK), conf. MO Hill (Crundwell 1976: 31, MO Hill MS).

H16 1957: sand dunes, Errisbeg, J Appleyard (BBS exc.) (BBSUK), conf. MO Hill (Warburg 1958b: 486, MO Hill MS).

H17 1957: bog S of R. Clare, J Appleyard (BBS exc.) (BBSUK), conf. MO Hill (Warburg 1958b: 486, MO Hill MS).

H20 1975: base-rich bank and roadside above Glencullin River, NW of Enniskerry, JA Paton (BBS exc.), conf. MO Hill (Crundwell 1976: 31, MO Hill MS).

H(21) 1836: grassy banks nr Glasnevin, D Orr (BM), conf. MO Hill (MO Hill MS).

H22 1961: damp sandy roadside nr Kells, EM Lobley, conf. MO Hill (Warburg 1962: 374, MO Hill MS).

H23 1970: roadside nr Bryanstown House, SW of Mullingar, JA Paton (BBSUK), conf. MO Hill (Crundwell 1971b: 382, MO Hill MS).

H27 1987: damp sandy ground on open grassy dunes, nr Lough Nambrack, E of Dugort, Achill I., DG Long & TL Blockeel (Blockeel 1998: 39).

H(28) 1928: Rosses Point, Binstead (BM), conf. MO Hill (MO Hill MS).

H28 1963: sand dunes, Rosses Point, RD Fitzgerald & AR Perry, conf. MO Hill (MO Hill MS).

[H(34) 1937: Bundoran, no collector named (BBS exc.) (Armitage 1938: 12). This record is apparently among those rejected by MO Hill (not listed for H34 in Corley & Hill 1981: 122)].

H34 2002: in moss carpet in dune slack, 5 m alt., N of Fahan, C32, DT Holyoak 02-767 (Rothero 2003: 62).

H(35) 1918: Inishkeel, Portroo, WN Tetley (BBSUK), conf. MO Hill (MO Hill MS).

H(37) 1885: creeping up old hollies in bog, Ardmore Glebe, HW Lett (DBN), comm. DM Synnott (Blockeel 1989: 31).

H(39) 1900: bog, Derryaghy [2 miles N of Lisburn], JH Davies (Hb. Dixon, BM), conf. MO Hill (MO Hill MS).

[H(40) 1940: roadside, Cappagh, nr Portstewart, WR Megaw (anon. 1949c: 221), as *B. salebrosum* var. *palustre*. This record is apparently among those rejected by MO Hill. (H(40) is not listed by Corley & Hill 1981: 122)].

Irish and British records were revised by MO Hill for the *CC* (Corley & Hill 1981). Details of some Irish specimens given above are from an unpublished list by MO Hill.

169/6 *Brachythecium rutabulum* (Hedw.) Bruch, Schimp. & W.Gümbel
(syn. *Hypnum rutabulum* L. ex Hedw., *H. rutabulum* var. *robustum* (Bruch, Schimp. & W.Gümbel) Lesq. & James)

H(1) listed by Lett (1915: 153) without details.

†H1 listed by Blockeel & Long (1998: 146).

H(2) listed by Lett (1915: 153) without details.

†H2 listed by Blockeel & Long (1998: 146).

H(3) listed by Lett (1915: 153) without details.

†H3 listed by Blockeel & Long (1998: 146).

H(4) listed by Lett (1915: 153) without details.

†H4 listed by Blockeel & Long (1998: 146).

H(5) listed by Lett (1915: 153) without details.

†H5 listed by Blockeel & Long (1998: 146).

H(6) listed by Lett (1915: 153) without details.

†H6 listed by Blockeel & Long (1998: 146).

H(7) listed by Lett (1915: 153) without details.

†H7 listed by Blockeel & Long (1998: 146).

H(8) listed by Lett (1915: 153) without details.

†H8 listed by Blockeel & Long (1998: 146).

H(9) listed by Lett (1915: 153) without details.

†H9 listed by Blockeel & Long (1998: 146).

H(10) listed by Lett (1915: 153) without details.

†H10 listed by Blockeel & Long (1998: 146).

H(11) listed by Lett (1915: 153) without details.

†H11 listed by Blockeel & Long (1998: 146).

H(12) listed by Lett (1915: 153) without details.

†H12 listed by Blockeel & Long (1998: 146).

H(13) listed by Lett (1915: 153) without details.

†H13 listed by Blockeel & Long (1998: 146).

H(14) listed by Lett (1915: 153) without

details.
†H14 listed by Blockeel & Long (1998: 146).
H(15) listed by Lett (1915: 153) without details.
†H15 listed by Blockeel & Long (1998: 146).
H(16) listed by Lett (1915: 153) without details.
†H16 listed by Blockeel & Long (1998: 146).
H(17) listed by Lett (1915: 153) without details.
†H17 listed by Blockeel & Long (1998: 146).
H(18) listed by Lett (1915: 153) without details.
†H18 listed by Blockeel & Long (1998: 146).
H(19) listed by Lett (1915: 153) without details.
†H19 listed by Blockeel & Long (1998: 146).
H(20) listed by Lett (1915: 153) without details.
†H20 listed by Blockeel & Long (1998: 146).
H(21) listed by Lett (1915: 153) without details.
†H21 listed by Blockeel & Long (1998: 146).
H(22) listed by Lett (1915: 153).
†H22 listed by Blockeel & Long (1998: 146).
H(23) listed by Lett (1915: 153) without details.
†H23 listed by Blockeel & Long (1998: 146).
H(24) listed by Lett (1915: 153) without details.
†H24 listed by Blockeel & Long (1998: 146).
H(25) listed by Lett (1915: 153) without details.
†H25 listed by Blockeel & Long (1998: 146).
H(26) listed by Lett (1915: 153) without details.
†H26 listed by Blockeel & Long (1998: 146).
H(27) listed by Lett (1915: 153) without details.
†H27 listed by Blockeel & Long (1998: 146).
H(28) listed by Lett (1915: 153) without details.
†H28 listed by Blockeel & Long (1998: 146).
H(29) listed by Lett (1915: 153) without details.
†H29 listed by Blockeel & Long (1998: 146).
H(30) listed by Lett (1915: 153) without details.
†H30 listed by Blockeel & Long (1998: 146).
H(31) listed by Lett (1915: 153) without details.
†H31 listed by Blockeel & Long (1998: 146).
H(32) listed by Lett (1915: 153) without details.
†H32 listed by Blockeel & Long (1998: 146).
H(33) listed by Lett (1915: 153) without details.
†H33 listed by Blockeel & Long (1998: 146).
H(34) listed by Lett (1915: 153) without details.
†H34 listed by Blockeel & Long (1998: 146).
H(35) listed by Lett (1915: 153) without details.
†H35 listed by Blockeel & Long (1998: 146).
H(36) listed by Lett (1915: 153) without details.
†H36 listed by Blockeel & Long (1998: 146).
H(37) listed by Lett (1915: 153) without details.
†H37 listed by Blockeel & Long (1998: 146).
H(38) listed by Lett (1915: 153) without details.
†H38 listed by Blockeel & Long (1998: 146).
H(39) listed by Lett (1915: 153) without details.
†H39 listed by Blockeel & Long (1998: 146).
H(40) listed by Lett (1915: 153) without details.
†H40 listed by Blockeel & Long (1998: 146).

169/7 ***Brachythecium rivulare*** Bruch, Schimp. & W.Gümbel
(syn. *Brachythecium rivulare* var. *latifolium* (Kindb.) Husn., *Hypnum rivulare* (Bruch, Schimp. & W.Gümbel) Bruch, *H. rivulare* var. *tenue* (Dixon) Braithw.)

H(1) listed by Lett (1915: 153) without details.
†H1 listed by Blockeel & Long (1998: 146).
H(2) listed by Lett (1915: 153) without details.
†H2 listed by Blockeel & Long (1998: 146).
H3 1951: bog, Cape Clear, IA Rorison (Warburg 1952: 106).
H(5) listed by Lett (1915: 153) without details.
†H5 listed by Blockeel & Long (1998: 146).
H(6) listed by Lett (1915: 153) without details.
†H6 listed by Blockeel & Long (1998: 146).
H(7) listed by Lett (1915: 153) without details.
†H7 listed by Blockeel & Long (1998: 146).
H(8) listed by Lett (1915: 153) without details.
†H8 listed by Blockeel & Long (1998: 146).
H(9) listed by Lett (1915: 153) without details.

†H9 listed by Blockeel & Long (1998: 146).
H(10) listed by Lett (1915: 153) without details.
†H10 listed by Blockeel & Long (1998: 146).
H(11) listed by Lett (1915: 153) without details.
†H11 listed by Blockeel & Long (1998: 146).
H(12) listed by Lett (1915: 153) without details.
†H12 listed by Blockeel & Long (1998: 146).
H(13) listed by Lett (1915: 153) without details.
†H13 listed by Blockeel & Long (1998: 146).
H(15) listed by Lett (1915: 153) without details.
†H15 listed by Blockeel & Long (1998: 146).
H(16) listed by Lett (1915: 153) without details.
†H16 listed by Blockeel & Long (1998: 146).
H17 1966: rock by river, Derreen, N of Monivea, MFV Corley & JS Parker (Perry 1967: 423).
H(18) listed by Lett (1915: 153) without details.
†H18 listed by Blockeel & Long (1998: 146).
H19 1953: basic marsh, Morristown Latten, nr Newbridge, ALK King (Warburg 1954: 485).
H(20) listed by Lett (1915: 153) without details.
†H20 listed by Blockeel & Long (1998: 146).
H(21) listed by Lett (1915: 153).
†H21 listed by Blockeel & Long (1998: 146).
H22 1965: marshy ground between canal and R. Boyne, W of bridge at Beauparc, DM Synnott (Warburg 1966: 203).
H23 1952: marshy ground NE end of L. Owel, JS Thomson (Warburg 1954: 485).
H24 1986: flushed area along channel on raised bog, Clontymullen, H Grogan & C Douglas (Blockeel 1987: 26).
H25 1968: limestone boulder, shore of L. Ree, St John's Wood, 3 miles SE of Knockcroghery, WV Rubers *et al.* (U) (Crundwell 1975: 20).
H(26) listed by Lett (1915: 153) without details.
†H26 listed by Blockeel & Long (1998: 146).
H(27) listed by Lett (1915: 153) without details.
†H27 listed by Blockeel & Long (1998: 146).
H(28) listed by Lett (1915: 153) without details.
†H28 listed by Blockeel & Long (1998: 146).
H(29) listed by Lett (1915: 153) without details.
†H29 listed by Blockeel & Long (1998: 146).
H(30) listed by Lett (1915: 153) without details.
†H30 listed by Blockeel & Long (1998: 146).
[H(31) listed by Lett (1915: 153) without details. H31 deleted because no valid record or voucher specimen traced (Blockeel 1999: 9)].
H(32) listed by Lett (1915: 153) without details.
†H32 listed by Blockeel & Long (1998: 146).
H(33) listed by Lett (1915: 153) without details.
†H33 listed by Blockeel & Long (1998: 146).
H(34) listed by Lett (1915: 153) without details.
†H34 listed by Blockeel & Long (1998: 146).
H(35) listed by Lett (1915: 153) without details.
†H35 listed by Blockeel & Long (1998: 146).
†H36 listed by Blockeel & Long (1998: 146).
H(37) listed by Lett (1915: 153) without details.
†H37 listed by Blockeel & Long (1998: 146).
H(38) listed by Lett (1915: 153) without details. H(38) listed by Blockeel & Long (1998: 146).
H38 2002: on rocks by river, 45 m alt., edge of Shimna River, Tollymore Forest Park, J33, DT Holyoak 02-940 (Rothero 2003: 62).
H(39) listed by Lett (1915: 153) without details.
H39 1951: slow-moving water, 1100 ft [alt.], Agnew's Hill, nr Larne, RD Fitzgerald (Warburg 1952: 106), as var. *latifolium.*
H(40) listed by Lett (1915: 153) without details.
†H40 listed by Blockeel & Long (1998: 146).

169/11 ***Brachythecium velutinum*** (Hedw.) Bruch, Schimp. & W.Gümbel (syn. *Hypnum velutinum* L. ex Hedw., *H. velutinum* var. *praelongum* (Bruch, Schimp. & W.Gümbel) Braithw.)

H(1) listed by Lett (1915: 153). H(1) listed by Blockeel & Long (1998: 146).
H(2) listed by Lett (1915: 153).
†H2 listed by Blockeel & Long (1998: 146).
H(5) listed by Lett (1915: 153). H(5) listed by Blockeel & Long (1998: 146).
H(6) listed by Lett (1915: 153). H(6) listed by

Blockeel & Long (1998: 146).
[H(7) listed by Lett (1915: 153) without details. H7 deleted because no valid record or voucher specimen traced (Blockeel 1999: 9)].
[H(8) listed by Lett (1915: 153) without details. H8 deleted because no valid record or voucher specimen traced (Blockeel 1999: 9)].
H(9) listed by Lett (1915: 153). H(9) listed by Blockeel & Long (1998: 146).
H(12) listed by Lett (1915: 153). H(12) listed by Blockeel & Long (1998: 146).
H(13) listed by Lett (1915: 153). H(13) listed by Blockeel & Long (1998: 146).
H(16) listed by Lett (1915: 153). H(16) listed by Blockeel & Long (1998: 146).
†H20 listed by Blockeel & Long (1998: 146).
H(21) listed by Lett (1915: 153).
†H21 listed by Blockeel & Long (1998: 146).
H(22) listed by Lett (1915: 153). H(22) listed by Blockeel & Long (1998: 146).
H(23) listed by Lett (1915: 153). H(23) listed by Blockeel & Long (1998: 146).
H(24) listed by Lett (1915: 153). H(24) listed by Blockeel & Long (1998: 146).
H(26) listed by Lett (1915: 153). H(26) listed by Blockeel & Long (1998: 146).
H(27) listed by Lett (1915: 153).
†H27 listed by Blockeel & Long (1998: 146).
H(28) listed by Lett (1915: 153).
†H28 listed by Blockeel & Long (1998: 146).
H(30) listed by Lett (1915: 153). H(30) listed by Blockeel & Long (1998: 146).
H(32) listed by Lett (1915: 153). H(32) listed by Blockeel & Long (1998: 146).
H(33) listed by Lett (1915: 153).
†H33 listed by Blockeel & Long (1998: 146).
[H(34) listed by Lett (1915: 153) without locality. H34 deleted because no valid record or voucher specimen traced (Blockeel 1999: 9)].
H(35) listed by Lett (1915: 153).
†H35 listed by Blockeel & Long (1998: 146).
H(36) listed by Lett (1915: 153).
†H36 listed by Blockeel & Long (1998: 146).
H(37) listed by Lett (1915: 153). H(37) listed by Blockeel & Long (1998: 146).
H(38) listed by Lett (1915: 153).
†H38 listed by Blockeel & Long (1998: 146).
H(39) listed by Lett (1915: 153). H(39) listed by Blockeel & Long (1998: 146).
[H(40) listed by Lett (1915: 153) without details. H40 deleted because no valid record or voucher specimen traced (Blockeel 1999: 9)].

169/12 ***Brachythecium appleyardiae*** McAdam & A.J.E.Sm.

H30 2001: on limestone boulders below overhang nr cave in N-facing crag, 225 m alt., N of Manragh, H03, DT Holyoak 01-764 (Rothero 2002: 55).
H33 2000: on ledge beneath overhangs on steep limestone crag shaded by *Fraxinus*/*Corylus* woodland, Hanging Rock, H13, DT Holyoak 00-128, conf. TL Blockeel (BBSUK) (Rothero 2001: 47).

169/14 ***Brachythecium populeum*** (Hedw.) Bruch, Schimp. & W.Gümbel
(syn. *Hypnum viride* Lam. ex Boucher, *H. viride* var. *majus* (Bruch, Schimp. & W.Gümbel) Moell.)

H(1) listed by Lett (1915: 153) without details.
†H1 listed by Blockeel & Long (1998: 147).
H(2) listed by Lett (1915: 153) without details.
†H2 listed by Blockeel & Long (1998: 147).
H3 1979: stone beside woodland path nr Ardnagashel House, N side of Bantry Bay, JA Paton & AC Crundwell (Hill 1980b: 46).
H(4) listed by Lett (1915: 153) without details.
†H4 listed by Blockeel & Long (1998: 147).
[H(5) listed by Lett (1915: 153) without details. H5 deleted because no valid record or voucher specimen traced (Blockeel 1999: 9)].
H(6) listed by Lett (1915: 153) without details.
†H6 listed by Blockeel & Long (1998: 147).
[H(7) listed by Lett (1915: 153) without details. H7 deleted because no valid record or voucher specimen traced (Blockeel 1999: 9)].
H(8) listed by Lett (1915: 153) without details.
†H8 listed by Blockeel & Long (1998: 147).
H9 1957: path in Cratloe Wood, ALK King (Warburg 1958b: 486).
H(10) listed by Lett (1915: 153) without details.
†H10 listed by Blockeel & Long (1998: 147).
[H(11) listed by Lett (1915: 153) without

details. H11 deleted because no valid record or voucher specimen traced (Blockeel 1999: 9)].
H(12) listed by Lett (1915: 153) without details.
†H12 listed by Blockeel & Long (1998: 147).
H(13) listed by Lett (1915: 153) without details.
†H13 listed by Blockeel & Long (1998: 147).
H14 1956: flagstone in field by Taverton Cross Roads, AA Cridland (Warburg 1958b: 486).
[H(15) listed by Lett (1915: 153) without details. H15 deleted because no valid record or voucher specimen traced (Blockeel 1999: 9)].
H16 1968: siliceous boulder in lane 4 miles NW of Oughterard, AR Perry (Crundwell 1969: 890).
H(19) 1949: branch of apple, nr Kildare, JS Thomson (Warburg 1950: 387).
H(20) listed by Lett (1915: 153) without details.
†H20 listed by Blockeel & Long (1998: 147).
H(21) listed by Lett (1915: 153) without details.
†H21 listed by Blockeel & Long (1998: 147).
H(22) listed by Lett (1915: 153) without details.
†H22 listed by Blockeel & Long (1998: 147).
H23 1980: shaded limestone wall, S side of Hill of Ushnagh, W of Mullingar, DM Synnott (Hill 1981: 35).
H24 1980: roadside wall, crossroads N of Lisryan, DM Synnott (Hill 1981: 35).
H(25) listed by Lett (1915: 153) without details.
†H25 listed by Blockeel & Long (1998: 147).
H26 1987: stone on NE shore, Cooley Lough, S of Ballyhean, JA Paton (Blockeel 1998: 39).
H(27) listed by Lett (1915: 153).
†H27 listed by Blockeel & Long (1998: 147).
[H(28) listed by Lett (1915: 153) without details. H28 deleted because no valid record or voucher specimen traced (Blockeel 1999: 9)].
†H29 listed by Blockeel & Long (1998: 147).
H(30) listed by Lett (1915: 153). H(30) listed by Blockeel & Long (1998: 147).
H31 1967: rock outcrop by marsh E of Tenure, DM Synnott (Crundwell 1968: 646).
H(32) listed by Lett (1915: 153) without details.
†H32 listed by Blockeel & Long (1998: 147).
H(33) listed by Lett (1915: 153) without details.
†H33 listed by Blockeel & Long (1998: 147).
H(34) listed by Lett (1915: 153) without details.
†H34 listed by Blockeel & Long (1998: 147).
H(35) listed by Lett (1915: 153) without details.
†H35 listed by Blockeel & Long (1998: 147).
H(36) listed by Lett (1915: 153) without details.
†H36 listed by Blockeel & Long (1998: 147).
[H(37) listed by Lett (1915: 153) without details. H37 deleted because no valid record or voucher specimen traced (Blockeel 1999: 9)].
H(38) listed by Lett (1915: 153) without details. H(38) listed by Blockeel & Long (1998: 147).
H38 2002: on sandstone block on floor of old quarry, 100 m alt., Scrabo Quarry, J47, DT Holyoak 02-1029 (Rothero 2003: 62).
H(39) listed by Lett (1915: 153) without details.
†H39 listed by Blockeel & Long (1998: 147).
H(40) listed by Lett (1915: 153) without details.
†H40 listed by Blockeel & Long (1998: 147).

169/15 *Brachythecium plumosum* (Hedw.) Bruch, Schimp. & W.Gümbel
(syn. *Hypnum plumosum* Hedw., *H. pseudoplumosum* Brid., *H. pseudoplumosum* var. *homomallum* (Bruch, Schimp. & W.Gümbel) Braithw.)

H(1) listed by Lett (1915: 153, 154).
†H1 listed by Blockeel & Long (1998: 147).
H(2) listed by Lett (1915: 153).
†H2 listed by Blockeel & Long (1998: 147).
H(3) listed by Lett (1915: 153).
†H3 listed by Blockeel & Long (1998: 147).
H(4) listed by Lett (1915: 153, 154).
†H4 listed by Blockeel & Long (1998: 147).
H(5) listed by Lett (1915: 154).
H5 1956: stone in damp quarry, Youghal, EC Wallace (Warburg 1957: 335).
H(6) listed by Lett (1915: 153, 154).
†H6 listed by Blockeel & Long (1998: 147).
H(7) listed by Lett (1915: 153).
†H7 listed by Blockeel & Long (1998: 147).
H(8) listed by Lett (1915: 153).

†H8 listed by Blockeel & Long (1998: 147).
H(9) listed by Lett (1915: 153) without details.
†H9 listed by Blockeel & Long (1998: 147).
H(10) listed by Lett (1915: 153).
†H10 listed by Blockeel & Long (1998: 147).
H(12) listed by Lett (1915: 153, 154).
†H12 listed by Blockeel & Long (1998: 147).
H(13) listed by Lett (1915: 153).
†H13 listed by Blockeel & Long (1998: 147).
H(14) listed by Lett (1915: 153).
†H14 listed by Blockeel & Long (1998: 147).
H15 1957: stones, in R. Owendalulleegh, RE Parker, (Warburg 1958b: 486).
H(16) listed by Lett (1915: 154) without locality.
H16 1957: rocks in stream, Ballynahinch, AC Crundwell (BBS exc.) (Warburg 1958b: 486).
H(18) listed by Lett (1915: 153).
†H18 listed by Blockeel & Long (1998: 147).
H(20) listed by Lett (1915: 153, 154).
†H20 listed by Blockeel & Long (1998: 147).
H(21) listed by Lett (1915: 153, 154). H(21) listed by Blockeel & Long (1998: 147).
H24 1965: boulder in small stream, Corn Hill, nr Drumlish, EM Lobley & RD Fitzgerald (Warburg 1966: 203).
H25 1965: boulders in stream, Kilronan, nr Ballyfarnan, EM Lobley & RD Fitzgerald (Warburg 1966: 203).
H(27) listed by Lett (1915: 153, 154).
†H27 listed by Blockeel & Long (1998: 147).
H(28) listed by Lett (1915: 153).
†H28 listed by Blockeel & Long (1998: 147).
H(29) listed by Lett (1915: 153).
†H29 listed by Blockeel & Long (1998: 147).
H(30) listed by Lett (1915: 154).
†H30 listed by Blockeel & Long (1998: 147).
H(31) listed by Lett (1915: 153). H(31) listed by Blockeel & Long (1998: 147).
[H(32) listed by Lett (1915: 153, 154) without locality. H32 deleted because no valid record or voucher specimen traced (Blockeel 1999: 9)].
H(33) listed by Lett (1915: 153, 154).
†H33 listed by Blockeel & Long (1998: 147).
H(34) listed by Lett (1915: 153).
†H34 listed by Blockeel & Long (1998: 147).
H(35) listed by Lett (1915: 153, 154).
†H35 listed by Blockeel & Long (1998: 147).
H(36) listed by Lett (1915: 153).
†H36 listed by Blockeel & Long (1998: 147).
H(37) listed by Lett (1915: 154).
H37 1964: stones in stream, *ca* 1000 ft [alt.], Slieve Gullion, RD Fitzgerald (Warburg 1965: 871).
H(38) listed by Lett (1915: 153, 154).
†H38 listed by Blockeel & Long (1998: 147).
H(39) listed by Lett (1915: 153, 154).
†H39 listed by Blockeel & Long (1998: 147).
H(40) listed by Lett (1915: 153, 154).
†H40 listed by Blockeel & Long (1998: 147).

170/1 ***Scleropodium purum*** (Hedw.) Limpr. (syn. *Hypnum purum* L. ex Hedw., *Pseudoscleropodium purum* (Hedw.) M. Fleisch. ex Broth.)

H(1) listed by Lett (1915: 150) without details.
†H1 listed by Blockeel & Long (1998: 147).
H(2) listed by Lett (1915: 150) without details.
†H2 listed by Blockeel & Long (1998: 147).
H(3) listed by Lett (1915: 150) without details.
†H3 listed by Blockeel & Long (1998: 147).
H(4) listed by Lett (1915: 150) without details.
†H4 listed by Blockeel & Long (1998: 147).
†H5 listed by Blockeel & Long (1998: 147).
H(6) listed by Lett (1915: 150) without details.
†H6 listed by Blockeel & Long (1998: 147).
H(7) listed by Lett (1915: 150) without details.
†H7 listed by Blockeel & Long (1998: 147).
H(8) listed by Lett (1915: 150) without details.
†H8 listed by Blockeel & Long (1998: 147).
H(9) listed by Lett (1915: 150) without details.
†H9 listed by Blockeel & Long (1998: 147).
H10 1951: grassy hillside above Silvermines, AD Banwell, PJ Wanstall & EV Watson (Warburg 1953: 315).
H(11) listed by Lett (1915: 150) without details.
†H11 listed by Blockeel & Long (1998: 147).
H(12) listed by Lett (1915: 150) without details.
†H12 listed by Blockeel & Long (1998: 147).
H(13) listed by Lett (1915: 150) without details.
†H13 listed by Blockeel & Long (1998: 147).
†H14 listed by Blockeel & Long (1998: 147).
H(15) listed by Lett (1915: 150) without details.
†H15 listed by Blockeel & Long (1998: 147).

H(16) listed by Lett (1915: 150) without details.
†H16 listed by Blockeel & Long (1998: 147).
H(17) listed by Lett (1915: 150) without details.
†H17 listed by Blockeel & Long (1998: 147).
H(18) listed by Lett (1915: 150) without details.
†H18 listed by Blockeel & Long (1998: 147).
†H19 listed by Blockeel & Long (1998: 147).
H(20) listed by Lett (1915: 150) without details.
†H20 listed by Blockeel & Long (1998: 147).
H(21) listed by Lett (1915: 150) without details.
†H21 listed by Blockeel & Long (1998: 147).
H(22) listed by Lett (1915: 150) without details.
†H22 listed by Blockeel & Long (1998: 147).
H(23) listed by Lett (1915: 150) without details.
†H23 listed by Blockeel & Long (1998: 147).
H(24) listed by Lett (1915: 150) without details.
†H24 listed by Blockeel & Long (1998: 147).
H(25) listed by Lett (1915: 150) without details.
†H25 listed by Blockeel & Long (1998: 147).
H(26) listed by Lett (1915: 150) without details.
†H26 listed by Blockeel & Long (1998: 147).
H(27) listed by Lett (1915: 150) without details.
†H27 listed by Blockeel & Long (1998: 147).
H(28) listed by Lett (1915: 150) without details.
†H28 listed by Blockeel & Long (1998: 147).
H(29) listed by Lett (1915: 150) without details.
†H29 listed by Blockeel & Long (1998: 147).
H(30) listed by Lett (1915: 150) without details.
†H30 listed by Blockeel & Long (1998: 147).
H(31) listed by Lett (1915: 150) without details.
†H31 listed by Blockeel & Long (1998: 147).
H(32) listed by Lett (1915: 150) without details.
†H32 listed by Blockeel & Long (1998: 147).
H(33) listed by Lett (1915: 150) without details.
†H33 listed by Blockeel & Long (1998: 147).
H(34) listed by Lett (1915: 150) without details.
†H34 listed by Blockeel & Long (1998: 147).
H(35) listed by Lett (1915: 150) without details.
†H35 listed by Blockeel & Long (1998: 147).
H(36) listed by Lett (1915: 150) without details.
†H36 listed by Blockeel & Long (1998: 147).
H(37) listed by Lett (1915: 150) without details.
†H37 listed by Blockeel & Long (1998: 147).
H(38) listed by Lett (1915: 150) without details.
†H38 listed by Blockeel & Long (1998: 147).
H(39) listed by Lett (1915: 150) without details.
†H39 listed by Blockeel & Long (1998: 147).
H(40) listed by Lett (1915: 150) without details.
†H40 listed by Blockeel & Long (1998: 147).

170/2 ***Scleropodium cespitans*** (Müll.Hal.) L.F. Koch
(syn. *Brachythecium caespitosum* (Wilson) Dixon, *Scleropodium caespitosum* (Wilson) Bruch, Schimp. & W.Gümbel)

[H3 deleted because no valid record or voucher specimen traced (Blockeel 1999: 9)].
H5 1956: foot of wall, Castlemartyr, EC Wallace (Warburg 1957: 335).
H6 1956: foot of wall, Kilmanahan, nr Knocklofty Bridge, EC Wallace (Warburg 1957: 335).
H7 1956: foot of wall, Clonmel, EC Wallace (Warburg 1957: 335).
H9 1994: on large limestone boulder by lough, 25 m alt., L. Inchiquin, NW of Corofin, R28, TL Blockeel, GM Dirkse & JA Paton, TL Blockeel 23/147 (Blockeel 1995c: 46).
H13 1969: on rocks by R. Slaney, Aghade Bridge, nr Tullow, RD Fitzgerald (Crundwell 1970: 209).
H28 1972: on boulder on N shore of L. Gill, WV Rubers (U) (Crundwell 1974: 175).
H(30) 1948: Virginia State Forest, ALK King (Warburg 1950: 387, King 1950).
H33 1950: boulder, shore of L. Erne, J Taylor (Warburg 1954: 485).
H35 2002: on boulder nr lough shore, 21 m alt., E shore of Lough Fern, C12, DT Holyoak 02-748 (Rothero 2003: 62).
H(39) 1948: tree roots by river nr Antrim Town, WR Megaw (anon. 1949c: 221).

170/3 ***Scleropodium tourettii*** (Brid.) L.F.Koch (syn. *Hypnum illecebrum* Hedw., *Scleropodium illecebrum* auct., *S. tourretii* auct.)

[H(1) listed by Lett (1915: 150) without details. H1 deleted because no record was traced (Sowter 1972, Crundwell 1973: 514)].
H(2) listed by Lett (1915: 150). H(2) listed by Blockeel & Long (1998: 147).
H(3) listed by Blockeel & Long (1998: 147).
H(4) listed by Lett (1915: 150). H(4) listed by Blockeel & Long (1998: 147).
H(5) listed by Lett (1915: 150)
†H5 listed by Blockeel & Long (1998: 147).
H6 1956: hedgebank nr old Pike Bridge, Dungarvan, EC Wallace (Warburg 1957: 335).
H(7) listed by Lett (1915: 150). H(7) listed by Blockeel & Long (1998: 147).
H(12) listed by Lett (1915: 150). H(12) listed by Blockeel & Long (1998: 147).
H(21) listed by Lett (1915: 150). H(21) listed by Blockeel & Long (1998: 147).
H(37) listed by Lett (1915: 150). H(37) listed by Blockeel & Long (1998: 147).
H(39) listed by Lett (1915: 150). H(39) listed by Blockeel & Long (1998: 147).

171/1 ***Cirriphyllum piliferum*** (Hedw.) Grout (syn. *Eurhynchium piliferum* (Hedw.) Bruch, Schimp. & W.Gümbel, *Hypnum piliferum* Schreb. ex Hedw.)

H(1) listed by Lett (1915: 152) without details.
†H1 listed by Blockeel & Long (1998: 147).
H2 1953: bank in wood, Ballyseedy Wood, AP Fanning (Warburg 1954: 485).
†H3 listed by Blockeel & Long (1998: 147).
H(4) listed by Lett (1915: 152).
†H4 listed by Blockeel & Long (1998: 147).
H(5) listed by Lett (1915: 152).
†H5 listed by Blockeel & Long (1998: 147).
H(6) listed by Lett (1915: 152).
H6 1956: wooded slope by R. Suir, Knocklofty Bridge, EC Wallace (Warburg 1957: 336).
H(7) listed by Lett (1915: 152) without details.
†H7 listed by Blockeel & Long (1998: 147).
†H8 listed by Blockeel & Long (1998: 147).
H(9) listed by Lett (1915: 152).
†H9 listed by Blockeel & Long (1998: 147).
H(11) listed by Lett (1915: 152).
†H11 listed by Blockeel & Long (1998: 147).
H(12) listed by Lett (1915: 152).
†H12 listed by Blockeel & Long (1998: 147).
[H(13) 1937: Kilkea Park, JS Thomson (anon. 1939b: 110). H13 deleted because Kilkea Park locality is in H19, comm. JS Thomson (Warburg 1953: 316)].
H(13) 1867: Browne's Hill, Carlow, RC Browne (DBN) (Crundwell 1968: 646).
H(14) listed by Lett (1915: 152).
†H14 listed by Blockeel & Long (1998: 147).
[H(15) listed by Lett (1915: 152) without locality. H15 deleted because no valid record or voucher specimen traced (Blockeel 1999: 9)].
H16 1955: grass track, Ashford Woods, nr Cong, ALK King (Warburg 1956: 157).
H(18) 1949: under hedge on grassy bank, Comber Kinitty, AP Fanning (Warburg 1953: 316).
†H18 listed by Blockeel & Long (1998: 147).
†H19 listed by Blockeel & Long (1998: 147).
H(20) listed by Lett (1915: 152) without locality.
†H20 listed by Blockeel & Long (1998: 147).
H(21) listed by Lett (1915: 152).
†H21 listed by Blockeel & Long (1998: 147).
H22 1950: grassy bank, Slane, JS Thomson (Warburg 1952: 106).
H23 1952: bank, Clonhugh Demesne, NE of L. Owel, JS Thomson (Warburg 1954: 485).
H(24) 1941: Ardnacliff, JG Finlay (Duncan 1944: 215).
†H24 listed by Blockeel & Long (1998: 147).
H25 1968: disturbed soil 1 mile W of Lanesborough, WV Rubers *et al.* (U) (Crundwell 1974: 175).
H26 1970: woodland W of Pollagh River, NE of Balla, JA Paton (Crundwell 1971b: 383).
H27 1987: on bank in damp woodland, nr lake, Westport House, DG Long (Blockeel 1998: 39).
H(28) listed by Lett (1915: 152).
†H28 listed by Blockeel & Long (1998: 147).
H(29) listed by Lett (1915: 152).
†H29 listed by Blockeel & Long (1998: 147).
H30 1956: grassy bank, Virginia, JS Thomson (Warburg 1957: 336).
H31 1967: woodland, Mosstown, Rathescar, Ardee, DM Synnott (Crundwell 1968: 646).
H(33) listed by Lett (1915: 152).

†H33 listed by Blockeel & Long (1998: 147).
[H(34) listed by Lett (1915: 152) without locality. H34 deleted because no valid record or voucher specimen traced (Blockeel 1999: 9)].
H34 2001: in grass on roadside verge, 40 m alt., roadside nr Lough Lareen, G96, NG Hodgetts 3911 (Rothero 2003: 62).
H(35) listed by Lett (1915: 152).
†H35 listed by Blockeel & Long (1998: 147).
H36 1959: edge of wood on river bank, Drumlea Wood, nr Gortin, RD Fitzgerald (Warburg 1960: 780).
H(37) listed by Lett (1915: 152). H(37) listed by Blockeel & Long (1998: 147).
H(38) listed by Lett (1915: 152). H(38) listed by Blockeel & Long (1998: 147).
H38 2002: on soil by track at edge of lake, 45 m alt., E edge of The Lake, Tollymore Forest Park, J33, DT Holyoak 02-945 (Rothero 2003: 62).
H(39) listed by Lett (1915: 152).
†H39 listed by Blockeel & Long (1998: 147).
†H40 listed by Blockeel & Long (1998: 147).

172/1 ***Rhynchostegium riparioides*** (Hedw.) Cardot
(syn. *Eurhynchium riparioides* (Hedw.) P.W.Richards, *Hypnum rusciforme* Weiss ex Brid. nom. illeg., *H. rusciforme* var. *atlanticum* (Brid.) Brid.)

H(1) listed by Lett (1915: 152).
†H1 listed by Blockeel & Long (1998: 148).
H(2) listed by Lett (1915: 152) without details.
†H2 listed by Blockeel & Long (1998: 148).
H(3) listed by Lett (1915: 152) without details.
†H3 listed by Blockeel & Long (1998: 148).
H(4) listed by Lett (1915: 152) without details.
†H4 listed by Blockeel & Long (1998: 148).
H(5) listed by Lett (1915: 152) without details.
†H5 listed by Blockeel & Long (1998: 148).
H(6) listed by Lett (1915: 152) without details.
†H6 listed by Blockeel & Long (1998: 148).
H(7) listed by Lett (1915: 152).
†H7 listed by Blockeel & Long (1998: 148).
H(8) listed by Lett (1915: 152).
H8 1993: in shaded overgrown garden plot, Foynes I., R25, E Wiltshire (Rothero 1999a: 100).
H(9) listed by Lett (1915: 152) without details.
†H9 listed by Blockeel & Long (1998: 148).
H(10) listed by Lett (1915: 152) without details.
†H10 listed by Blockeel & Long (1998: 148).
H(11) listed by Lett (1915: 152) without details.
†H11 listed by Blockeel & Long (1998: 148).
H(12) listed by Lett (1915: 152) without details.
†H12 listed by Blockeel & Long (1998: 148).
H(13) listed by Lett (1915: 152) without details.
†H13 listed by Blockeel & Long (1998: 148).
H(14) listed by Lett (1915: 152) without details.
†H14 listed by Blockeel & Long (1998: 148).
H15 1957: boulders in calcareous stream, nr Punchbowl, 1 mile S of Gort, RE Parker (BBS exc.) (Warburg 1958b: 486).
H(16) listed by Lett (1915: 152) without details.
†H16 listed by Blockeel & Long (1998: 148).
[H(17) listed by Lett (1915: 152) without details. H17 deleted because no valid record or voucher specimen traced (Blockeel 1999: 9)].
H(18) listed by Lett (1915: 152) without details.
†H18 listed by Blockeel & Long (1998: 148).
H(19) listed by Lett (1915: 152) without details.
†H19 listed by Blockeel & Long (1998: 148).
H(20) listed by Lett (1915: 152) without details.
†H20 listed by Blockeel & Long (1998: 148).
H(21) listed by Lett (1915: 152).
†H21 listed by Blockeel & Long (1998: 148).
H22 1950: damp wall, Glebe House, Slane, JS Thomson (Warburg 1952: 106).
H23 1953: ditch nr shore, NE end of L. Owel, JS Thomson (Warburg 1954: 486).
H(24) listed by Lett (1915: 152) without details.
†H24 listed by Blockeel & Long (1998: 148).
H(25) listed by Lett (1915: 152) without details.
†H25 listed by Blockeel & Long (1998: 148).
H(26) listed by Lett (1915: 152) without details.
†H26 listed by Blockeel & Long (1998: 148).
H(27) listed by Lett (1915: 152) without details.
†H27 listed by Blockeel & Long (1998: 148).

H(28) listed by Lett (1915: 152) without details.
†H28 listed by Blockeel & Long (1998: 148).
H(29) listed by Lett (1915: 152) without details.
†H29 listed by Blockeel & Long (1998: 148).
H(30) listed by Lett (1915: 152) without details.
†H30 listed by Blockeel & Long (1998: 148).
H(31) listed by Lett (1915: 152) without details.
†H31 listed by Blockeel & Long (1998: 148).
[H(32) listed by Lett (1915: 152) without details. H32 deleted because no valid record or voucher specimen traced (Blockeel 1999: 9)].
H(33) listed by Lett (1915: 152).
†H33 listed by Blockeel & Long (1998: 148).
H(34) listed by Lett (1915: 152) without details.
†H34 listed by Blockeel & Long (1998: 148).
H(35) listed by Lett (1915: 152).
†H35 listed by Blockeel & Long (1998: 148).
H(36) listed by Lett (1915: 152) without details.
†H36 listed by Blockeel & Long (1998: 148).
H(37) listed by Lett (1915: 152) without details.
†H37 listed by Blockeel & Long (1998: 148).
H(38) listed by Lett (1915: 152) without details.
†H38 listed by Blockeel & Long (1998: 148).
H(39) listed by Lett (1915: 152) without details.
†H39 listed by Blockeel & Long (1998: 148).
H(40) listed by Lett (1915: 152) without details.
†H40 listed by Blockeel & Long (1998: 148).

172/2 ***Rhynchostegium alopecuroides*** (Brid.) A.J.E.Sm.
(syn. *Eurhynchium alopecuroides* (Brid.) P.W.Richards & E.C.Wallace, *Eurhynchium alopecurum* auct., *Eurhynchium riparioides* var. *alopecuroides* auct., *Hypnum rusciforme* var. *alopecuroides* Brid., *Rhynchostegium lusitanicum* (Schimp.) A.J.E.Sm.)

H1 1968: stream below Coomrooanig Lough, E of Waterville, JA Paton (Crundwell 1969: 890).
H(2) 1905: stream, Mangerton Mt., JB Duncan (Warburg 1951: 502).
†H2 listed by Blockeel & Long (1998: 148).
H6 1963: partly submerged rocks by cascade at 1200 ft [alt.], head of R. Nire, Comeragh Mts, DA Ratcliffe (Warburg 1964: 734).
H16 1994: on rock in swift-flowing river, 100 m alt., Kylemore River, Glencorbet, L75, TL Blockeel 23/217, first found by GP Rothero (Blockeel 1995c: 46).
H(19) listed by Lett (1915: 152) without details. H(19) listed by Blockeel & Long (1998: 148).
H(20) 1949: 2000-2700 ft [alt.], Lugnaquillia, AW Stelfox, per JS Thomson (Warburg 1950: 387).
†H20 listed by Blockeel & Long (1998: 148).
[H21 deleted because no valid record or voucher specimen traced (Blockeel 1999: 9)].
H27 1987: submerged on rock in waterfall in small stream, Keem Bay, Achill I., TL Blockeel (Blockeel 1998: 39).
H(35) listed by Lett (1915: 152) without details.
†H35 listed by Blockeel & Long (1998: 148).

172/3 ***Rhynchostegium murale*** (Hedw.) Bruch, Schimp. & W.Gümbel
(syn. *Eurhynchium murale* (Hedw.) Milde, syn. *E. murale* var. *julaceum* (Bruch, Schimp. & W.Gümbel) Milde, *Hypnum murale* Neck. Ex Hedw.)

H1 1979: rock by R. Roughty at Roughty Bridge, ½ km W of Greenlane, G Bloom (Hill 1980b: 47).
H2 1951: wall top, Clogher House, Tralee, AP Fanning (Warburg 1953: 316).
H(4) listed by Lett (1915: 152). H(4) listed by Blockeel & Long (1998: 148).
H(5) listed by Lett (1915: 152). H(5) listed by Blockeel & Long (1998: 148).
H(7) listed by Lett (1915: 152). H(7) listed by Blockeel & Long (1998: 148).
H(8) listed by Lett (1915: 152). H(8) listed by Blockeel & Long (1998: 148).
H(9) 1945: by Lough Inchiquin, JS Thomson (anon. 1946c: 285).
†H9 listed by Blockeel & Long (1998: 148).
H(12) listed by Lett (1915: 152). H(12) listed by Blockeel & Long (1998: 148).
H14 1955: Abbeyleix demesne, JS Thomson (Warburg 1956: 158).
H15 1968: boulders by roadside nr turlough, Tirneevin, *ca* 3 miles W of Gort, AR

Perry (Crundwell 1969: 890).
H17 1966: rock in wood, Derreen, N of Monivea, MFV Corley & JS Parker (Perry 1967: 423).
H(18) listed by Lett (1915: 152). H(18) listed by Blockeel & Long (1998: 148).
H(19) 1938: Rathmore, JG Finlay (Duncan 1944: 215).
H(20) listed by Lett (1915: 152). H(20) listed by Blockeel & Long (1998: 148).
H(21) listed by Lett (1915: 152).
†H21 listed by Blockeel & Long (1998: 148).
†H22 listed by Blockeel & Long (1998: 148).
H(23) listed by Lett (1915: 152).
†H23 listed by Blockeel & Long (1998: 148).
H24 1972: limestone boulder, Rathcline House, WV Rubers (U) (Crundwell 1975: 21).
H25 1968: sheltered limestone wall, Ballagh, 4 miles NW of Lanesborough, WV Rubers *et al.* (U) (Crundwell 1975: 21).
[H(26) listed by Lett (1915: 152)].
H27 1962: concrete shed on top of Croaghpatrick, EF Warburg (Warburg 1963b: 503).
H(28) listed by Lett (1915: 152).
H(28) 1928: Gleniff, Ben Bulben (BBS exc.) (Duncan 1928: 114-115, 118), as var. *julaceum*.
†H28 listed by Blockeel & Long (1998: 148).
H29 1963: limestone boulders in woodland at 800 ft above Glencar Waterfall, AR Perry & RD Fitzgerald (Warburg 1964: 734).
H33 1957: stone in roadside bank, Enniskillen, AC Crundwell (Warburg 1958b: 486).
H(34) listed by Lett (1915: 152). H(34) listed by Blockeel & Long (1998: 148).
H(36) listed by Lett (1915: 152).
†H36 listed by Blockeel & Long (1998: 148).
H(37) listed by Lett (1915: 152).
†H37 listed by Blockeel & Long (1998: 148).
H(38) listed by Lett (1915: 152). H(38) listed by Blockeel & Long (1998: 148).
H(39) listed by Lett (1915: 152). H(39) listed by Blockeel & Long (1998: 148).
H39 1999: on chalk boulder at base of cliffs, White Park Bay, D04, DT Holyoak 99-616 (BBSUK) (Rothero 2000: 60).
[H(40) listed by Lett (1915: 152) without locality. H40 deleted because no valid record or voucher specimen traced (Blockeel 1999: 9)].

172/4 *Rhynchostegium confertum* (Dicks.) Bruch, Schimp. & W.Gümbel
(syn. *Eurhynchium confertum* (Dicks.) Milde, *Hypnum confertum* Dicks.)

H(1) listed by Lett (1915: 152).
†H1 listed by Blockeel & Long (1998: 148).
H(2) listed by Lett (1915: 152).
†H2 listed by Blockeel & Long (1998: 148).
H(3) listed by Lett (1915: 152).
†H3 listed by Blockeel & Long (1998: 148).
H(4) listed by Lett (1915: 152).
†H4 listed by Blockeel & Long (1998: 148).
H(5) listed by Lett (1915: 152).
†H5 listed by Blockeel & Long (1998: 148).
H6 1956: roadside, Dungarvan Harbour, EC Wallace (Warburg 1957: 336).
H7 1966: tree by dried-up lake, Thomastown, E of Tipperary, J Appleyard *et al.* (BBS exc.) (Perry 1967: 423).
H(8) listed by Lett (1915: 152).
†H8 listed by Blockeel & Long (1998: 148).
H(9) listed by Lett (1915: 152).
†H9 listed by Blockeel & Long (1998: 148).
H(10) listed by Lett (1915: 152).
†H10 listed by Blockeel & Long (1998: 148).
H(11) listed by Lett (1915: 152).
†H11 listed by Blockeel & Long (1998: 148).
H(12) listed by Lett (1915: 152).
†H12 listed by Blockeel & Long (1998: 148).
[H(13) listed by Lett (1915: 152). H13 deleted because no valid record or voucher specimen traced (Blockeel 1999: 9)].
H13 2002: on concrete at base of old fence post, 335 m alt., S slope of Croaghaun, nr car park, S85, DT Holyoak 02-357 (Rothero 2003: 62).
H(14) listed by Lett (1915: 152).
†H14 listed by Blockeel & Long (1998: 148).
H16 1957: old wall, Clifden, EM Lobley (BBS exc.) (Warburg 1958b: 486).
H(17) listed by Lett (1915: 152).
†H17 listed by Blockeel & Long (1998: 148).
[H(18) listed by Lett (1915: 152). H18 deleted because no valid record or voucher specimen traced (Blockeel 1999: 9)].
[H(19) listed by Lett (1915: 152). H19 deleted because no valid record or voucher specimen traced (Blockeel 1999: 9)].
H(20) listed by Lett (1915: 152).
†H20 listed by Blockeel & Long (1998: 148).
H(21) listed by Lett (1915: 152).
†H21 listed by Blockeel & Long (1998: 148).
H22 1951: earth bank, Julianstown, RD

Fitzgerald (Warburg 1952: 106).
H23 1952: garden path, Woodlands, NE end of L. Owel, JS Thomson (Warburg 1954: 486).
H24 1957: root of hawthorn by right bank of R. Inny, Ballymacarrow Bridge, ALK King (Warburg 1958b: 486).
H25 1973: shaded limestone wall, St John's Wood, shore of L. Ree, WV Rubers (U) (Crundwell 1975: 21).
H26 1973: dead wood, mixed ashwood on limestone, Hogs I., L. Carra, nr Ballinrobe, DL Kelly (Crundwell 1975: 21).
H(27) listed by Lett (1915: 152).
†H27 listed by Blockeel & Long (1998: 148).
H(28) listed by Lett (1915: 152).
†H28 listed by Blockeel & Long (1998: 148).
H(29) listed by Lett (1915: 152).
†H29 listed by Blockeel & Long (1998: 148).
H(30) listed by Lett (1915: 152).
†H30 listed by Blockeel & Long (1998: 148).
H(31) listed by Lett (1915: 152).
†H31 listed by Blockeel & Long (1998: 148).
[H(32) listed by Lett (1915: 152). H32 deleted because no valid record or voucher specimen traced (Blockeel 1999: 9)].
[H(33) listed by Lett (1915: 152). H33 deleted because no valid record or voucher specimen traced (Blockeel 1999: 9)].
H33 2000: on concrete block, Hanging Rock, H13, DT Holyoak 00-124 (BBSUK) (Rothero 2001: 47).
H(34) listed by Lett (1915: 152).
†H34 listed by Blockeel & Long (1998: 148).
†H35 listed by Blockeel & Long (1998: 148).
H(36) listed by Lett (1915: 152).
†H36 listed by Blockeel & Long (1998: 148).
H(37) listed by Lett (1915: 152).
†H37 listed by Blockeel & Long (1998: 148).
H(38) listed by Lett (1915: 152). H(38) listed by Blockeel & Long (1998: 148).
H38 2002: on top of wall of bridge, 50 m alt., by Shimna River in Tollymore Forest Park, J33, DT Holyoak 02-924 (Rothero 2003: 62).
H(39) listed by Lett (1915: 152).
†H39 listed by Blockeel & Long (1998: 148).
[H(40) listed by Lett (1915: 152). H40 deleted because no valid record or voucher specimen traced (Blockeel 1999: 9)].
H40 1999: on bark of *Fraxinus* in scrub at edge of dunes and saltmarsh, W of Portstewart, C83, DT Holyoak 99-172 (BBSUK) (Rothero 2000: 60).

172/5 ***Rhynchostegium megapolitanum*** (F. Weber & D.Mohr) Bruch, Schimp. & W. Gümbel
(syn. *Eurhynchium megapolitanum* (F. Weber & D.Mohr) Milde, *Hypnum megapolitanum* Bland. ex F.Weber & D. Mohr)

H(1) listed by Lett (1915: 152). H(1) listed by Blockeel & Long (1998: 148).
H6 1962: sand-dunes at end of beach, Tramore, IK Ferguson, comm. DM Synnott (Warburg 1965: 872).
H20 1972: dunes N of Arcklow [*sic* = Arklow], WV Rubers (U) (Crundwell 1974: 175).
H(21) listed by Lett (1915: 152). H(21) listed by Blockeel & Long (1998: 148).
H33 1957: gravel at roadside on S side of L. Macnean Lower, AC Crundwell (Warburg 1958b: 487).

173/1 ***Eurhynchium striatum*** (Hedw.) Schimp.
(syn. *Hypnum striatum* Schreb. ex Hedw.)

H(1) listed by Lett (1915: 150) without details.
†H1 listed by Blockeel & Long (1998: 148).
H(2) listed by Lett (1915: 150) without details.
†H2 listed by Blockeel & Long (1998: 148).
H(3) listed by Lett (1915: 150) without details.3
†H3 listed by Blockeel & Long (1998: 148).
H(4) listed by Lett (1915: 150) without details.
†H4 listed by Blockeel & Long (1998: 148).
H(5) listed by Lett (1915: 150) without details.
†H5 listed by Blockeel & Long (1998: 148).
H(6) listed by Lett (1915: 150) without details.
†H6 listed by Blockeel & Long (1998: 148).
H(7) listed by Lett (1915: 150) without details.
†H7 listed by Blockeel & Long (1998: 148).
H(8) listed by Lett (1915: 150) without details.
†H8 listed by Blockeel & Long (1998: 148).
H(9) listed by Lett (1915: 150) without details.
†H9 listed by Blockeel & Long (1998: 148).
H(10) listed by Lett (1915: 150) without

details.
†H10 listed by Blockeel & Long (1998: 148).
H(11) listed by Lett (1915: 150) without details.
†H11 listed by Blockeel & Long (1998: 148).
H(12) listed by Lett (1915: 150) without details.
†H12 listed by Blockeel & Long (1998: 148).
H(13) listed by Lett (1915: 150) without details.
†H13 listed by Blockeel & Long (1998: 148).
H(14) listed by Lett (1915: 150) without details.
†H14 listed by Blockeel & Long (1998: 148).
H(15) listed by Lett (1915: 150) without details.
†H15 listed by Blockeel & Long (1998: 148).
H(16) listed by Lett (1915: 150) without details.
†H16 listed by Blockeel & Long (1998: 148).
H(17) listed by Lett (1915: 150) without details.
†H17 listed by Blockeel & Long (1998: 148).
H(18) listed by Lett (1915: 150) without details.
†H18 listed by Blockeel & Long (1998: 148).
H(19) listed by Lett (1915: 150) without details.
†H19 listed by Blockeel & Long (1998: 148).
H(20) listed by Lett (1915: 150) without details.
†H20 listed by Blockeel & Long (1998: 148).
H(21) listed by Lett (1915: 150) without details.
†H21 listed by Blockeel & Long (1998: 148).
H(22) listed by Lett (1915: 150) without details.
†H22 listed by Blockeel & Long (1998: 148).
H(23) listed by Lett (1915: 150) without details.
†H23 listed by Blockeel & Long (1998: 148).
H(24) listed by Lett (1915: 150) without details.
†H24 listed by Blockeel & Long (1998: 148).
H(25) listed by Lett (1915: 150) without details.
†H25 listed by Blockeel & Long (1998: 148).
H(26) listed by Lett (1915: 150) without details.
†H26 listed by Blockeel & Long (1998: 148).
H(27) listed by Lett (1915: 150) without details.
†H27 listed by Blockeel & Long (1998: 148).
H(28) listed by Lett (1915: 150) without details.
†H28 listed by Blockeel & Long (1998: 148).
H(29) listed by Lett (1915: 150) without details.
†H29 listed by Blockeel & Long (1998: 148).
H(30) listed by Lett (1915: 150) without details.
†H30 listed by Blockeel & Long (1998: 148).
[H(31) listed by Lett (1915: 150) without details. H31 deleted because no valid record or voucher specimen traced (Blockeel 1999: 9)].
H(32) listed by Lett (1915: 150) without details.
†H32 listed by Blockeel & Long (1998: 148).
H(33) listed by Lett (1915: 150) without details.
†H33 listed by Blockeel & Long (1998: 148).
H(34) listed by Lett (1915: 150) without details.
†H34 listed by Blockeel & Long (1998: 148).
H(35) listed by Lett (1915: 150) without details.
†H35 listed by Blockeel & Long (1998: 148).
H(36) listed by Lett (1915: 150) without details.
†H36 listed by Blockeel & Long (1998: 148).
H(37) listed by Lett (1915: 150) without details.
†H37 listed by Blockeel & Long (1998: 148).
H(38) listed by Lett (1915: 150) without details.
†H38 listed by Blockeel & Long (1998: 148).
H(39) listed by Lett (1915: 150) without details.
†H39 listed by Blockeel & Long (1998: 148).
H(40) listed by Lett (1915: 150) without details.
†H40 listed by Blockeel & Long (1998: 148).

173/3 ***Eurhynchium striatulum*** (Spruce) Bruch, Schimp. & W.Gümbel
(syn. *Hypnum striatulum* Spruce, *Isothecium striatulum* (Spruce) Kindb.)

H(1) listed by Lett (1915: 150). H(1) listed by Blockeel & Long (1998: 148).
H(2) listed by Lett (1915: 150).
†H2 listed by Blockeel & Long (1998: 148).
H5 1956: limestone, Carrigshane Hill, Midleton, EC Wallace (Warburg 1957: 336).
H(8) listed by Lett (1915: 150).
†H8 listed by Blockeel & Long (1998: 148).
H(9) 1945: Blackhead [*sic* = Black Head], JS Thomson (anon. 1946c: 285).

†H9 listed by Blockeel & Long (1998: 148).
H16 1957: shaded sloping rock-face on shore of Derryclare Lough, AC Crundwell (BBS exc.) (Warburg 1958b: 486).
H17 1957: shaded limestone rocks, Ballindooly Castle, RE Parker (Warburg 1958b: 486).
H(20) listed by Lett (1915: 150). H(20) listed by Blockeel & Long (1998: 148).
H25 1981: limestone wall above turlough at Mullygollan, NE of Castleplunket, DM Synnott (Hill 1982: 29).
H26 1970: with *Cirriphyllum crassinervium* on limestone wall, W shore of Lough Carra, DM Synnott (DBN) (Blockeel 1989: 31).
H28 1963: limestone wall at roadside nr Grange, S of Knocknarea, nr Sligo, AR Perry & RD Fitzgerald (Warburg 1964: 733).
H29 1963: limestone wall at E end of Lough Gill, W of Sriff Cottage, AR Perry & RD Fitzgerald (Warburg 1964: 733).

173/4 *Eurhynchium pulchellum* (Hedw.) Jenn. **var. *diversifolium*** (Bruch, Schimp. & W.Gümbel) C.E.O.Jensen

H40 1964: decomposed basalt, *ca* 1400 ft [alt.], Benbradagh, RD Fitzgerald (NMW), conf. MO Hill (Warburg 1965: 871, Fitzgerald & Fitzgerald 1966a, Hill 1993, Blockeel 1994: 41; record was inadvertently omitted from Corley & Hill 1981: 124).

173/5 *Eurhynchium pumilum* (Wilson) Schimp.
(syn. *Hypnum pallidirostre* Braun, *Rhynchostegiella pallidirostra* (Brid.) Loeske, *Rhynchostegiella pumila* (Wilson) E.F.Warb.)

[H1 deleted because no valid record or voucher specimen traced (Blockeel 1999: 9)].
H(2) listed by Lett (1915: 150) without locality.
†H2 listed by Blockeel & Long (1998: 149).
[H3 deleted because no valid record or voucher specimen traced (Blockeel 1999: 9)].
H(4) listed by Lett (1915: 150).
†H4 listed by Blockeel & Long (1998: 149).
H(5) listed by Lett (1915: 150). H(5) listed by Blockeel & Long (1998: 149).
H5 2002: on earthy underhang on river bank, 110 m alt., River Bride, Ardarou Wood, Glenville, W78, TL Blockeel 31/367 (Rothero 2003: 62).
H6 1956: bank of R. Suir, Knocklofty Bridge, EC Wallace (Warburg 1957: 336).
H(8) 1945: wood nr Galtymore, Galtees, RD Meikle (anon. 1947: 33).
†H8 listed by Blockeel & Long (1998: 149).
H9 1960: base of boulder in birch-hazel wood, Poulavallan, SW of Slievecarran, MCF Proctor (Warburg 1961: 173).
[H(11) listed by Lett (1915: 150) as 1911: S of Royal Oak, leg. Tetley. H(11) deleted because the locality (E [*sic* = S] of Royal Oak, 1911, WN Tetley, in Lett 1915) is in H13, *teste* ALK King (Warburg 1955: 586)].
H11 1958: ground in deep shade in ravine, nr Coolhill Castle, ALK King (Warburg 1959: 638).
H12 1975: shaded bank by track, Tara Hill, Coolgreany, AR Perry (Hill 1977a: 24).
H(13) 1911: S of Royal Oak, WN Tetley (in Lett 1915), originally listed as in H11 but corrected to H13 *teste* ALK King (Warburg 1955: 586).
H13 2002: on steep soil on bank in woodland, 70 m alt., just W of Bunclody, S95, DT Holyoak 02-371 (Rothero 2003: 62).
H14 1955: ground under trees, Abbeyleix demesne, JS Thomson (Warburg 1956: 157).
H15 1957: rocks by stream, nr the Punchbowl, nr L. Cutra, J Appleyard (BBS exc.) (Warburg 1958b: 486).
H(16) listed by Lett (1915: 150). H(16) listed by Blockeel & Long (1998: 149).
[H19 deleted because no valid record or voucher specimen traced (Blockeel 1999: 9)].
H(20) listed by Lett (1915: 150).
†H20 listed by Blockeel & Long (1998: 149).
H(21) listed by Lett (1915: 150). H(21) listed by Blockeel & Long (1998: 149).
H22 1973: shaded earth nr archaeological site, Newgrange, MO Hill (Crundwell 1974: 175).
H23 1980: clay bank in wet woodland, Bunbrosna, DM Synnott (Hill 1982: 29).
H25 1982: top of roadside wall, in shade, Mt Druid Ho., Ballanagare, DM Synnott (DBN) (Blockeel 1989: 31).

H27 1965: damp loamy bank under hazels, shore of L. Conn, nr Errew, AMcG Stirling (Warburg 1966: 203).
†H28 listed by Blockeel & Long (1998: 149).
H(29) listed by Lett (1915: 150).
†H29 listed by Blockeel & Long (1998: 149).
H30 2001: on damp limestone of ledge in cave entrance, 220 m alt., Giant's Leap, S of Blacklion, H03, DT Holyoak 01-755 (Rothero 2002: 55).
H(32) listed by Lett (1915: 150) without locality.
†H32 listed by Blockeel & Long (1998: 149).
H(33) listed by Lett (1915: 150).
†H33 listed by Blockeel & Long (1998: 149).
H(34) 1937: Erne Valley, no collector named (BBS exc.) (Armitage 1938: 12).
1937: Erme [*sic* = Erne] Valley, E Armitage (anon. 1938b: 30).
H34 2002: on tufa under overhanging sea cliff, 5 m alt, coast of Ballyliffin, C34, DT Holyoak (Rothero 2003: 62).
H35 1962: coastal rocks, Ards, nr Dunfanaghy, EM Lobley & MPH Kertland (BBS exc.) (Warburg 1963b: 503).
H36 2002: on thin soil over limestone on outcrop, 95 m alt., nr Carrickaness Bridge W of Drumquin, H27, DT Holyoak 02-1123 (Rothero 2003: 62).
H(37) listed by Lett (1915: 150) without details. H(37) listed by Blockeel & Long (1998: 149).
H37 2002: on steep soil on bank above stream, 65 m alt., Gosford Forest Park, H94, DT Holyoak 02-1082 (Rothero 2003: 62).
H(38) listed by Lett (1915: 150). H(38) listed by Blockeel & Long (1998: 149).
H(39) listed by Lett (1915: 150).
†H39 listed by Blockeel & Long (1998: 149).
†H40 listed by Blockeel & Long (1998: 149).

173/6 ***Eurhynchium praelongum*** (Hedw.) Bruch, Schimp. & W.Gümbel
(syn. *Eurhynchium praelongum* var. *stokesii* (Turner) Dixon, *Hypnum praelongum* L. ex Hedw., *H. praelongum* var. *stokesii* (Turner) Brid.)

H(1) listed by Lett (1915: 150) without details.
H1 1951: boulders in oakwoods, nr Blackstones Bridge, Caragh Lake, PW Richards (BBS exc.) (Warburg 1952: 106), as var. *stokesii*.
†H1 listed by Blockeel & Long (1998: 149).
H(2) listed by Lett (1915: 150).
†H2 listed by Blockeel & Long (1998: 149).
H(3) listed by Lett (1915: 150) without details.
H3 1951 [given as 1921, but apparently in error]: stone walls, Cape Clear, IA Rorison (Warburg 1952: 106), as var. *stokesii*.
H(4) listed by Lett (1915: 150) without details.
†H4 listed by Blockeel & Long (1998: 149).
H(5) listed by Lett (1915: 150) without details.
†H5 listed by Blockeel & Long (1998: 149).
H(6) listed by Lett (1915: 150) without details.
†H6 listed by Blockeel & Long (1998: 149).
H(7) listed by Lett (1915: 150).
†H7 listed by Blockeel & Long (1998: 149).
H(8) listed by Lett (1915: 150) without details.
†H8 listed by Blockeel & Long (1998: 149).
H(9) listed by Lett (1915: 150) without details.
†H9 listed by Blockeel & Long (1998: 149).
H10 1951: on elder above Silvermines, AD Banwell, PJ Wanstall & EV Watson (Warburg 1953: 316).
1967: on shaded blocks in wooded valley, Clare Glen, nr Newport, HH Birks, HJB Birks & DA Ratcliffe (Crundwell 1968: 646), as var. *stokesii*.
H(11) listed by Lett (1915: 150) without details.
†H11 listed by Blockeel & Long (1998: 149).
H(12) listed by Lett (1915: 150) without details.
H12 1975: woodland bank W of Courtown, JA Paton (BBS exc.) (Crundwell 1976: 31), as var. *stokesii*.
H(13) listed by Lett (1915: 150).
†H13 listed by Blockeel & Long (1998: 149).
H14 1956: decaying stump, pine plantation nr Durrow, AA Cridland (Warburg 1958b: 486), as var. *stokesii*.
H(15) listed by Lett (1915: 150) without details.
H15 1972: on ground in acid oakwood, Woodford, DL Kelly (Crundwell 1974: 175), as var. *stokesii*.
H(16) listed by Lett (1915: 150) without details.
H16 1970: on edge of track through wood,

Kylemore Castle, MFV Corley (Crundwell 1971b: 383), as var. *stokesii*.
H(17) listed by Lett (1915: 150).
†H17 listed by Blockeel & Long (1998: 149).
H(18) listed by Lett (1915: 150).
†H18 listed by Blockeel & Long (1998: 149).
H(19) listed by Lett (1915: 150) without details.
†H19 listed by Blockeel & Long (1998: 149).
H(20) listed by Lett (1915: 150).
†H20 listed by Blockeel & Long (1998: 149).
H(21) listed by Lett (1915: 150).
†H21 listed by Blockeel & Long (1998: 149).
H(22) listed by Lett (1915: 150) without details.
H22 1965: woods, Oldbridge, ALK King (Warburg 1966: 203), as var. *stokesii*.
H(23) listed by Lett (1915: 150) without details.
H23 1953: Packenham Hall woods, ALK King (Warburg 1966: 203), as var. *stokesii*.
H(24) listed by Lett (1915: 150) without details.
†H24 listed by Blockeel & Long (1998: 149).
H(25) listed by Lett (1915: 150).
†H25 listed by Blockeel & Long (1998: 149).
H(26) listed by Lett (1915: 150).
†H26 listed by Blockeel & Long (1998: 149).
H(27) listed by Lett (1915: 150) without details.
†H27 listed by Blockeel & Long (1998: 149).
H(28) listed by Lett (1915: 150).
†H28 listed by Blockeel & Long (1998: 149).
H(29) listed by Lett (1915: 150).
†H29 listed by Blockeel & Long (1998: 149).
H(30) listed by Lett (1915: 150) without details.
H30 1955: wood by L. Sheelin, ALK King (Warburg 1958b: 486), as var. *stokesii*.
H(31) listed by Lett (1915: 150).
†H31 listed by Blockeel & Long (1998: 149).
H(32) listed by Lett (1915: 150).
†H32 listed by Blockeel & Long (1998: 149).
H(33) listed by Lett (1915: 150).
†H33 listed by Blockeel & Long (1998: 149).
H(34) listed by Lett (1915: 150) without locality.
†H34 listed by Blockeel & Long (1998: 149).
H35 1990: stream side in oak woodland, Glenlack, Glenbeagh, DM Synnott (Blockeel 1991c: 45), as var. *stokesii*.
H(36) listed by Lett (1915: 150).
†H36 listed by Blockeel & Long (1998: 149).
H(37) listed by Lett (1915: 150).
†H37 listed by Blockeel & Long (1998: 149).
H(38) listed by Lett (1915: 150).
†H38 listed by Blockeel & Long (1998: 149).
H(39) listed by Lett (1915: 150).
†H39 listed by Blockeel & Long (1998: 149).
H(40) listed by Lett (1915: 150).
†H40 listed by Blockeel & Long (1998: 149).

173/7 ***Eurhynchium hians*** (Hedw.) Sande Lac.
(syn. *Eurhynchium swartzii* (Turner) Curn. var. *swartzii*, *E. swartzii* var. *rigidum* (Boulay) Thér., *Hypnum hians* Hedw., *H. swartzii* Turner)

H(1) listed by Lett (1915: 150).
†H1 listed by Blockeel & Long (1998: 149).
H(2) listed by Lett (1915: 150).
†H2 listed by Blockeel & Long (1998: 149).
H3 1951: island in Gougane Barra Lake, ALK King (Warburg 1952: 106).
H(4) listed by Lett (1915: 150).
†H4 listed by Blockeel & Long (1998: 149).
[H(5) listed by Lett (1915: 150) without details. H5 deleted because no valid record or voucher specimen traced (Blockeel 1999: 9)].
H(6) 1933: Cappagh Lake, E Armitage (anon. 1934b: 130).
1933: Kilgreany, E Armitage (anon. 1934b: 130).
†H6 listed by Blockeel & Long (1998: 149).
H(7) 1945: above Loch Curra, Galtees, RD Meikle (anon. 1947: 33).
†H7 listed by Blockeel & Long (1998: 149).
H(8) listed by Lett (1915: 150).
†H8 listed by Blockeel & Long (1998: 149).
H(9) 1945: nr Roughan Ho.[use], Kilnaboy, JS Thomson (anon. 1946c: 284), as *E. swartzii*.
1945: Kilnaboy, JS Thomson (anon. 1946c: 284), as var. *rigidum*.
†H9 listed by Blockeel & Long (1998: 149).
H10 1965: scrub on shore of L. Derg nr Kilbarron Quay, ALK King (Warburg 1966: 203).
H(11) listed by Lett (1915: 151).
†H11 listed by Blockeel & Long (1998: 149).
H(12) listed by Lett (1915: 151).
†H12 listed by Blockeel & Long (1998: 149).
H(13) listed by Lett (1915: 151). H(13) listed by Blockeel & Long (1998: 149).
H13 2002: on soil on slope at woodland edge nr road, 70 m alt., just W of Bunclody, S95, DT Holyoak 02-369 (Rothero

2003: 62).
H(14) listed by Lett (1915: 151).
†H14 listed by Blockeel & Long (1998: 149).
H(15) listed by Lett (1915: 151).
†H15 listed by Blockeel & Long (1998: 149).
H16 1957: old wall, Clifden, EM Lobley (BBS exc.) (Warburg 1958b: 486).
H(17) listed by Lett (1915: 151).
†H17 listed by Blockeel & Long (1998: 149).
H18 1954: Gloster Woods, Brosna, ALK King (Warburg 1955: 586).
H(19) 1938: Rathmore, JG Finlay (Duncan 1944: 215).
H19 2002: in stubble field (winter wheat), 70 m alt., Furry Field, Courttown East townland, Athy, S69, HF Fox & CD Preston (Rothero 2003: 62).
H(20) listed by Lett (1915: 151).
†H20 listed by Blockeel & Long (1998: 149).
H(21) listed by Lett (1915: 151).
†H21 listed by Blockeel & Long (1998: 149).
H22 1950: log, grounds of Slane Castle, JS Thomson (Warburg 1952: 106).
H(23) listed by Lett (1915: 151).
†H23 listed by Blockeel & Long (1998: 149).
H24 1965: ground in wood, Cloonart Bridge, RD Fitzgerald & EM Lobley (Warburg 1966: 203).
H(25) 1940: nr Boyle, JS Thomson (Duncan 1944: 215).
†H25 listed by Blockeel & Long (1998: 149).
H(26) listed by Lett (1915: 151).
H26 1970: limestone boulder, Keel Bridge, S end of L. Carra, J Appleyard (BBS exc.) (Crundwell 1972: 143), as var. *rigidum*.
H(27) listed by Lett (1915: 151).
†H27 listed by Blockeel & Long (1998: 149).
H(28) listed by Lett (1915: 151).
†H28 listed by Blockeel & Long (1998: 149).
H(29) listed by Lett (1915: 151).
H29 1963: limestone scarp, Boggaun, nr Manorhamilton, AR Perry & RD Fitzgerald (Warburg 1964: 734), as var. *rigidum*.
[H30 deleted because no valid record or voucher specimen traced (Blockeel 1999: 9)].
H30 2001: on open damp soil on track in plantation, 315 m alt., W of Ballyvally Gap, H12, DT Holyoak 01-641D (Rothero 2002: 55).
H31 1967: woodland bank, Beaulieu, E of Drogheda, DM Synnott (Crundwell 1968: 646).
H(32) listed by Lett (1915: 151).
†H32 listed by Blockeel & Long (1998: 149).
H(33) listed by Lett (1915: 151).
H(33) 1923: Portora, Enniskillen, WN Tetley (anon. 1924: 78).
†H33 listed by Blockeel & Long (1998: 149).
H(34) listed by Lett (1915: 151) without locality.
H(34) 1937: River Erne, no collector named (BBS exc.) (Armitage 1938: 12), as var. *rigidum*.
†H34 listed by Blockeel & Long (1998: 149).
H(35) 1946: road nr Loch Birrog, Portnoo, JS Thomson (anon. 1947: 33).
†H35 listed by Blockeel & Long (1998: 149).
[H(36) listed by Lett (1915: 151) as 1909: Dungannon, leg. Porter. H36 deleted because specimen from Tyrone, 1912, leg. W Porter (DBN), is *Isothecium myosuroides*, comm. DM Synnott (Blockeel 1989: 31)].
H(37) listed by Lett (1915: 151) without details.
†H37 listed by Blockeel & Long (1998: 149).
H(38) listed by Lett (1915: 151) [misprint as 33]. H(38) listed by Blockeel & Long (1998: 149).
H38 2002: on thin soil over rocks by river, 45 m alt., by Shimna River in Tollymore Forest Park, J33, DT Holyoak 02-932 (Rothero 2003: 62).
H(39) listed by Lett (1915: 151).
†H39 listed by Blockeel & Long (1998: 149).
H(40) listed by Lett (1915: 151). H(40) listed by Blockeel & Long (1998: 149).
H40 1999: on thin soil over rocks at edge of small pool beside path in garden, SW of Castlerock, C73, DT Holyoak 99-153 (BBSUK) (Rothero 2000: 60).

173/8 *Eurhynchium schleicheri* (R.Hedw.) Jur.

H10 1979: loamy soil in woodland, Keeper Hill, S of Silvermine Mts, HMH van Melick (Hill 1981: 35).

173/9 ***Eurhynchium speciosum*** (Brid.) Jur. (syn. *Hypnum speciosum* Brid.)

H(2) listed by Lett (1915: 151).
†H2 listed by Blockeel & Long (1998: 149).
H(4) listed by Lett (1915: 151). H(4) listed by Blockeel & Long (1998: 149).
H(5) listed by Blockeel & Long (1998: 149).
H(6) listed by Blockeel & Long (1998: 149).
H9 1959: fringe of brackish turlough, Ballyvaughan, MCF Proctor (Warburg 1961: 173).
H19 1969: beside stream, Belan Lodge, nr Moone, RD Fitzgerald (Crundwell 1970: 210). H19 was apparently omitted in error from Corley & Hill (1981: 125) and Blockeel & Long (1998: 149).
H(20) listed by Lett (1915: 151). H(20) listed by Blockeel & Long (1998: 149).
H(21) listed by Lett (1915: 151).
†H21 listed by Blockeel & Long (1998: 149).
H22 1965: damp path under trees by R. Boyne, Oldbridge, ALK King (Warburg 1966: 203).
H25 1973: on moist limestone boulder in ashwood, St Johns Wood, shore of L. Ree, WV Rubers (U) (Crundwell 1974: 175).
H28 1967: in deeply shaded entrance to mine working, Glenyf [*sic* = Gleniff], Annacoona, PD Coker & JJ Barkman (Crundwell 1968: 646).
H32 1980: damp soil subject to flooding, under alder and hawthorn, N shore of Emy Lough, N Lockhart (Hill 1983: 56-57).
H35 1962: damp hollow in cliffs, Black Burrow, nr Dunfanaghy, EF Warburg *et al.* (BBS exc.) (Warburg 1963b: 503).
H36 1957: on litter, Killycolpy, RD Fitzgerald (Warburg 1960: 780).
H37 1950: clay base of wall, Magheny, J Taylor (BEL), comm. MPH Kertland (Warburg 1962: 375).
H(38) listed by Lett (1915: 151). H(38) listed by Blockeel & Long (1998: 149).
H(39) listed by Lett (1915: 151).
†H39 listed by Blockeel & Long (1998: 149).
H(40) 1947: lawn nr edge of path, Macosquin, nr Coleraine, J Taylor (BEL), comm. MPH Kertland (Warburg 1962: 375).

173/10 ***Eurhynchium crassinervium*** (Wilson) Schimp. (syn. *Cirriphyllum crassinervium* (Wilson) Loeske & M.Fleisch., *Hypnum crassinerve* auct., *H. crassinervium* Wilson)

H(1) listed by Lett (1915: 151).
†H1 listed by Blockeel & Long (1998: 149).
H(2) listed by Lett (1915: 151).
†H2 listed by Blockeel & Long (1998: 149).
H(4) listed by Lett (1915: 151).
†H4 listed by Blockeel & Long (1998: 149).
H(5) listed by Lett (1915: 151). H(5) listed by Blockeel & Long (1998: 149).
H6 1956: wooded hillside, Knocklofty Bridge, EC Wallace (Warburg 1957: 336).
H7 1956: roots of beech, Marlfield, Clonmel, EC Wallace (Warburg 1957: 336).
H(8) listed by Lett (1915: 151).
†H8 listed by Blockeel & Long (1998: 149).
H(9) listed by Lett (1915: 151).
†H9 listed by Blockeel & Long (1998: 149).
H(10) listed by Lett (1915: 151).
†H10 listed by Blockeel & Long (1998: 149).
H11 1958: shady ground, Rosbercon, nr New Ross, ALK King (Warburg 1959: 637).
H(12) listed by Lett (1915: 151). H(12) listed by Blockeel & Long (1998: 149).
H13 1999: on mortared wall of bridge, 4 m alt., Saint Mullins, banks of R Barrow, S73, TL Blockeel 28/319 (Rothero 2000: 60).
H(15) listed by Lett (1915: 151).
†H15 listed by Blockeel & Long (1998: 149).
H(16) listed by Lett (1915: 151) without details.
†H16 listed by Blockeel & Long (1998: 149).
H17 1955: sandy ground by Headford road at Ballindooly, ALK King (Warburg 1956: 157).
H(18) 1949: stone in grove, Roscrea-Mount Heaton, AP Fanning (Warburg 1954: 485).
[H19 deleted because no valid record or voucher specimen traced (Blockeel 1999: 9)].
H(20) listed by Lett (1915: 151).
†H20 listed by Blockeel & Long (1998: 149).
H(21) no date: Carrick Mines, F Winder, per JS Thomson (anon. 1946c: 284).
H(22) listed by Lett (1915: 151).
†H22 listed by Blockeel & Long (1998: 149).

H23 1957: limestone boulder at base of wall, nr Ballymahon, RE Parker (Warburg 1958b: 486). H23 omitted from *CC* by Warburg (1963b: 79), apparently in error.
1970: rocks by shore of Killinure Lough, S of Glassan, JA Paton (Crundwell 1971b: 383).
H24 1957: bank of ditch under trees, nr Carrickboy, ALK King (Warburg 1958b: 486).
H(25) 1940: nr Lough Key, JS Thomson (Duncan 1944: 215).
†H25 listed by Blockeel & Long (1998: 149).
H(26) listed by Lett (1915: 151).
†H26 listed by Blockeel & Long (1998: 149).
H(27) listed by Lett (1915: 151).
†H27 listed by Blockeel & Long (1998: 149).
H(28) 1928: rocks above Glencar Lough, N side (BBS exc.) (Duncan 1928: 119).
†H28 listed by Blockeel & Long (1998: 149).
H(29) 1928: wooded glen, NE end of Glencar Lough (BBS exc.) (Duncan 1928: 118).
†H29 listed by Blockeel & Long (1998: 149).
[H30 deleted because no valid record or voucher specimen traced (Blockeel 1999: 9)].
H30 2001: on sloping limestone boulder, 70 m alt., SE shore of Lough Sheelin, NE of Ross, N48, DT Holyoak 01-654 (Rothero 2002: 55).
H32 1950: limestone, L. Aphuca, RD Fitzgerald (Warburg 1951: 502).
H(33) listed by Blockeel & Long (1998: 149).
H33 2000: on top of mortared stone wall of bridge, Cladagh River below Marble Arch, H13, DT Holyoak 00-91 (BBSUK) (Rothero 2001: 47).
H35 2001: on rocks by waterfall, 10 m alt., Carrick Lower Bridge, Carrick, G57, NG Hodgetts 3759 (Rothero 2002: 55).
H(36) listed by Lett (1915: 151).
†H36 listed by Blockeel & Long (1998: 149).
H(38) listed by Blockeel & Long (1998: 149).
H(39) listed by Lett (1915: 151).
†H39 listed by Blockeel & Long (1998: 149).
†H40 listed by Blockeel & Long (1998: 149).

174/1 ***Rhynchostegiella tenella*** (Dicks.) Limpr.
(syn. *Eurhynchium tenellum* (Dicks.) Milde, *Hypnum algirianum* (P.Beauv.) Brid., *Rhynchostegiella tenella* var. *tenella* (Dicks.) Limpr.)

H(1) listed by Lett (1915: 151) without details.
†H1 listed by Blockeel & Long (1998: 150).
H(2) listed by Lett (1915: 151).
†H2 listed by Blockeel & Long (1998: 150).
H3 1966: wall of bridge, Sandy Cove, S of Kinsale, MFV Corley & JS Parker (Perry 1967: 423).
H(4) listed by Lett (1915: 151).
†H4 listed by Blockeel & Long (1998: 150).
H(5) listed by Lett (1915: 151).
†H5 listed by Blockeel & Long (1998: 150).
H(6) 1933: Knock Maun, E Armitage (anon. 1934b: 130).
1933: Kilgreany, E Armitage (anon. 1934b: 130).
†H6 listed by Blockeel & Long (1998: 150).
H7 1956: stone, nr Knocklofty, EC Wallace (Warburg 1957: 336).
H(8) listed by Lett (1915: 151).
†H8 listed by Blockeel & Long (1998: 150).
H(9) 1944: on a wall, JS Thomson (anon. 1946c: 285). This record should probably be rejected because it lacks an exact locality.
†H9 listed by Blockeel & Long (1998: 150).
H10 1967: wall of bridge, Rossaguile Bridge, Keeper Hill, RD Fitzgerald (Crundwell 1968: 646).
H(11) listed by Lett (1915: 151).
†H11 listed by Blockeel & Long (1998: 150).
H(12) listed by Lett (1915: 151).
†H12 listed by Blockeel & Long (1998: 150).
H(13) listed by Lett (1915: 151).
†H13 listed by Blockeel & Long (1998: 150).
H14 1955: wall, Abbeyleix, JS Thomson (Warburg 1956: 157).
H15 1957: old wall, Garryland Woods, nr Gort, EM Lobley (BBS exc.) (Warburg 1958b: 486).
H(16) listed by Lett (1915: 151).
†H16 listed by Blockeel & Long (1998: 150).
H(17) listed by Lett (1915: 152).
†H17 listed by Blockeel & Long (1998: 150).
H(18) listed by Lett (1915: 152). H(18) listed by Blockeel & Long (1998: 150).
H(19) 1949: between stones in wall, Calverstown, JS Thomson (Warburg

1950: 387).
†H19 listed by Blockeel & Long (1998: 150).
H(20) listed by Lett (1915: 152) without locality.
†H20 listed by Blockeel & Long (1998: 150).
H(21) listed by Lett (1915: 152).
†H21 listed by Blockeel & Long (1998: 150).
H(22) listed by Lett (1915: 152).
†H22 listed by Blockeel & Long (1998: 150).
H(23) listed by Lett (1915: 152).
†H23 listed by Blockeel & Long (1998: 150).
H(25) 1940: nr Boyle, JS Thomson (Duncan 1944: 215).
†H25 listed by Blockeel & Long (1998: 150).
H26 1970: on limestone wall E of Ballinober, MFV Corley (Crundwell 1971b: 383).
H(27) listed by Lett (1915: 152) without details.
†H27 listed by Blockeel & Long (1998: 150).
†H28 listed by Blockeel & Long (1998: 150).
†H29 listed by Blockeel & Long (1998: 150).
H(30) listed by Lett (1915: 152). H(30) listed by Blockeel & Long (1998: 150).
H30 2001: on ruined mortared wall, 305 m alt., W of Bellavally Gap, H12, DT Holyoak 01-631 (Rothero 2002: 55).
H(31) listed by Lett (1915: 152).
†H31 listed by Blockeel & Long (1998: 150).
[H32 deleted because no valid record or voucher specimen traced (Blockeel 1999: 9)].
H(33) listed by Lett (1915: 152).
†H33 listed by Blockeel & Long (1998: 150).
H(34) 1937: Erne Valley, no collector named (BBS exc.) (Armitage 1938: 12).
1937: Bundoran, no collector named (BBS exc.) (Armitage 1938: 12).
†H34 listed by Blockeel & Long (1998: 150).
H(35) 1946: road nr Loch Clooney, Naran, JS Thomson (anon. 1947: 33).
†H35 listed by Blockeel & Long (1998: 150).
H36 1959: wall, Loughrey, nr Cookstown, RD Fitzgerald (Warburg 1960: 780).
H37 1962: old wall, Gosford Castle nr Markethill, EM Lobley & MPH Kertland (Warburg 1963b: 503).
H(38) listed by Lett (1915: 152).
†H38 listed by Blockeel & Long (1998: 150).
H(39) listed by Lett (1915: 152).
†H39 listed by Blockeel & Long (1998: 150).
†H40 listed by Blockeel & Long (1998: 150).

174/3 ***Rhynchostegiella curviseta*** (Brid.) Limpr.
(syn. *Eurhynchium curvisetum* (Brid.) Husnot, *Hypnum curvisetum* Brid.)

H(1) 1935: Dingle, no collector named (BBS exc.) (Watson 1936: 265).
[H27 1962: overhung rock in stream, N side of Menawn [*sic* = Menaun], Achill I., EF Warburg (Warburg 1963b: 503). H27 record (from Warburg 1963b: 503) deleted (Warburg 1964: 734)].
H(29) 1928: wooded glen, NE end of Glencar Lough (BBS exc.) (Duncan 1928: 118).
H(29) listed by Blockeel & Long (1998: 150).
H33 1965: wet boulders by Cladagh R., Marble Arch, S of L. Macnean Lower, AR Perry (Warburg 1966: 204).
H(39) listed by Lett (1915: 151). H(39) listed by Blockeel & Long (1998: 150).

174/4 ***Rhynchostegiella teneriffae*** (Mont.) Dirkse & Bouman
(syn. *Eurhynchium teesdalei* (Bruch, Schimp. & W.Gümbel) Milde, *Hypnum teesdalii* Sm. hom. illeg., *Rhynchostegiella teesdalei* (Bruch, Schimp. & W.Gümbel) Limpr.)

H(3) listed by Lett (1915: 151). H(3) listed by Blockeel & Long (1998: 150).
H4 2002: on wet rocks in small stream in oak woodland, 10 m alt., E bank of River Bandon, SE of Innishannon, W55, TL Blockeel 31/376 (Rothero 2003: 62).
H6 1972: sandstone boulder by stream, Mill Wood, W of Carrick on Suir, WV Rubers (U) (Crundwell 1975: 21).
H8 1992: deep cleft in shale cliff, shore line between Foynes and Cooleen Point, R25, E Wiltshire (Blockeel 1993: 54).
H9 1977: limestone in stream-bed, tributary of Aille River, Spa Wells, Lisdoonvarna, PH Pitkin (Hill 1979: 32).
H10 1967: stones in stream, Devils Bit Mt., RD Fitzgerald (Crundwell 1968: 646).
H11 1966: on stones in stream, Dysart Castle, Inistioge, J Appleyard & RD Fitzgerald (BBS exc.) (Crundwell 1968: 646).
H15 1957: rocks by stream, nr the Punchbowl, nr L. Cutra, J Appleyard (BBS exc.) (Warburg 1958b: 486).
H(16) listed by Lett (1915: 151).
†H16 listed by Blockeel & Long (1998: 150).
H(20) listed by Lett (1915: 151) without

details.
†H20 listed by Blockeel & Long (1998: 150).
H(21) listed by Lett (1915: 151). H(21) listed by Blockeel & Long (1998: 150).
†H28 listed by Blockeel & Long (1998: 150).
H(29) 1928: wooded glen, NE end of Glencar Lough (BBS exc.) (Duncan 1928: 118).
†H29 listed by Blockeel & Long (1998: 150).
H(33) listed by Lett (1915: 151).
H(33) 1937: nr River Erne, Belleek, no collector named (BBS exc.) (Armitage 1938: 12).
†H33 listed by Blockeel & Long (1998: 150).
H(34) listed by Blockeel & Long (1998: 150).
H35 1990: on wet rock at edge of stream in Oak/Birch wood, 50 m alt., L. Eske, G98, TL Blockeel 19/550 (Blockeel 1991c: 46).
H(38) listed by Lett (1915: 151). H(38) listed by Blockeel & Long (1998: 150).
H(39) listed by Lett (1915: 151).
†H39 listed by Blockeel & Long (1998: 150).
H(40) listed by Lett (1915: 151).
†H40 listed by Blockeel & Long (1998: 150).

175/1 ***Entodon concinnus*** (De Not.) Paris (syn. *Cylindrothecium concinnum* (De Not.) Schimp., *Entodon orthocarpus* (Brid.) Lindb.)

H(1) listed by Lett (1915: 161).
†H1 listed by Blockeel & Long (1998: 150).
H(6) listed by Lett (1915: 161). H(6) listed by Blockeel & Long (1998: 150).
H8 1953: grassy roadside on limestone, nr Askeaton, EC Wallace (Warburg 1954: 485).
†H9 listed by Blockeel & Long (1998: 150).
H15 1970: old limestone quarry 4 miles W of Ballinasloe, JA Paton (Crundwell 1971b: 383).
H16 1951: Dog's Bay, H Milne-Redhead (Warburg 1952: 105).
H(19) 1949: bank of sand quarry, nr Calverstown, JS Thomson (Warburg 1950: 386).
H(20) listed by Lett (1915: 161). H(20) listed by Blockeel & Long (1998: 150).
H(21) listed by Lett (1915: 161).
†H21 listed by Blockeel & Long (1998: 150).
H22 1977: dunes nr Maiden Tower, Mornington, DM Synnott (Hill 1978: 24).
H25 1970: sandy railway bank, Barry Beg, N of Athlone, JA Paton (Crundwell 1971b: 383).
H26 1953: limestone rocks, N end of L. Carra nr Clogher House, EC Wallace (Warburg 1954: 485).
H27 1958: sandhills on the Mullet, nr Belmullet, ALK King (Warburg 1959: 637).
H(28) 1928: nr Rosses Point, Sligo (BBS exc.) (Duncan 1928: 119).
†H28 listed by Blockeel & Long (1998: 150).
H29 1963: base of limestone scarp, Boggaun, nr Manorhamilton, AR Perry & RD Fitzgerald (Warburg 1964: 734).
H30 1957: turf at foot of limestone rocks, Legeelan, nr Black Lion [*sic* = Blacklion], AC Crundwell (Warburg 1958b: 485).
[H33 deleted because no valid record or voucher specimen traced (Blockeel 1999: 9)].
H33 2000: on edge of limestone scree on SE-facing hillside, NW of Marble Arch, H13, DT Holyoak 00-167 (BBSUK) (Rothero 2001: 47).
H(34) listed by Lett (1915: 161).
†H34 listed by Blockeel & Long (1998: 150).
H(35) listed by Lett (1915: 161).
†H35 listed by Blockeel & Long (1998: 150).
H(38) listed by Blockeel & Long (1998: 150).
H38 2000: on calcareous sand dunes, Cloughy, J65, R Weyl (Rothero 2001: 47).
H(39) listed by Blockeel & Long (1998: 150).
H(40) listed by Lett (1915: 161).
†H40 listed by Blockeel & Long (1998: 150).

176/1 ***Pleurozium schreberi*** (Brid.) Mitt. (syn. *Hylocomium parietinum* Lindb. nom. illeg.)

H(1) listed by Lett (1915: 156) without details.
†H1 listed by Blockeel & Long (1998: 150).
H(2) listed by Lett (1915: 156) without details.
†H2 listed by Blockeel & Long (1998: 150).
†H3 listed by Blockeel & Long (1998: 150).
H(4) listed by Lett (1915: 156) without details.
†H4 listed by Blockeel & Long (1998: 150).
H5 1956: wooded hillside, Tourig valley, above Park House, NW of Youghal, EC Wallace (Warburg 1957: 338).
H(6) listed by Lett (1915: 156) without details.

†H6 listed by Blockeel & Long (1998: 150).
H(7) listed by Lett (1915: 156) without details.
†H7 listed by Blockeel & Long (1998: 150).
H(8) listed by Lett (1915: 156) without details.
†H8 listed by Blockeel & Long (1998: 150).
H(9) listed by Lett (1915: 156) without details.
†H9 listed by Blockeel & Long (1998: 150).
H10 1951: moorland above 1000 ft [alt.], nr Silvermines, AD Banwell, PJ Wanstall & EV Watson (Warburg 1953: 318).
H(11) listed by Lett (1915: 156) without details.
†H11 listed by Blockeel & Long (1998: 150).
H(12) listed by Lett (1915: 156) without details.
†H12 listed by Blockeel & Long (1998: 150).
H(13) listed by Lett (1915: 156) without details.
†H13 listed by Blockeel & Long (1998: 150).
H(14) listed by Lett (1915: 156) without details.
†H14 listed by Blockeel & Long (1998: 150).
H15 1952: marsh by shore of L. Derg, nr Ross Quay, MPH Kertland & ALK King (Warburg 1953: 318).
H(16) listed by Lett (1915: 156) without details.
†H16 listed by Blockeel & Long (1998: 150).
H(17) listed by Lett (1915: 156) without details.
†H17 listed by Blockeel & Long (1998: 150).
H(18) listed by Lett (1915: 156) without details.
†H18 listed by Blockeel & Long (1998: 150).
H(19) 1938: Moire Abbey, JG Finlay (Duncan 1944: 217).
†H19 listed by Blockeel & Long (1998: 150).
H(20) listed by Lett (1915: 156) without details.
†H20 listed by Blockeel & Long (1998: 150).
H(21) listed by Lett (1915: 156) without details.
†H21 listed by Blockeel & Long (1998: 150).
H22 1950: rocky hill, Slane, JS Thomson (Warburg 1952: 107).
H(23) listed by Lett (1915: 156) without details.
†H23 listed by Blockeel & Long (1998: 150).
H24 1957: raised bog, Newtonforbes [*sic* = Newtown Forbes], MPH Kertland & ALK King (Warburg 1958b: 489).
H(25) listed by Lett (1915: 156) without details.
†H25 listed by Blockeel & Long (1998: 150).
H(26) listed by Lett (1915: 156) without details.
†H26 listed by Blockeel & Long (1998: 150).
H(27) listed by Lett (1915: 156) without details.
†H27 listed by Blockeel & Long (1998: 150).
H(28) listed by Lett (1915: 156) without details.
†H28 listed by Blockeel & Long (1998: 150).
H(29) listed by Lett (1915: 156) without details.
†H29 listed by Blockeel & Long (1998: 150).
H(30) listed by Lett (1915: 156) without details.
†H30 listed by Blockeel & Long (1998: 150).
H(31) listed by Lett (1915: 156) without details.
†H31 listed by Blockeel & Long (1998: 150).
H(32) listed by Lett (1915: 156) without details.
†H32 listed by Blockeel & Long (1998: 150).
H(33) listed by Lett (1915: 156) without details.
†H33 listed by Blockeel & Long (1998: 150).
H(34) listed by Lett (1915: 156) without details.
†H34 listed by Blockeel & Long (1998: 150).
H(35) listed by Lett (1915: 156) without details.
†H35 listed by Blockeel & Long (1998: 150).
H(36) listed by Lett (1915: 156) without details.
†H36 listed by Blockeel & Long (1998: 150).
H(37) listed by Lett (1915: 156) without details.
†H37 listed by Blockeel & Long (1998: 150).
H(38) listed by Lett (1915: 156) without details.
†H38 listed by Blockeel & Long (1998: 150).
H(39) listed by Lett (1915: 156) without details.
†H39 listed by Blockeel & Long (1998: 150).
H(40) listed by Lett (1915: 156) without details.
†H40 listed by Blockeel & Long (1998: 150).

177/1a ***Myurella julacea*** (Schwägr.) Bruch, Schimp. & W.Gümbel, **var.** ***julacea***

H(6) listed by Lett (1915: 155). H(6) listed by Blockeel & Long (1998: 150).
H(16) listed by Lett (1915: 155). H(16) listed by Blockeel & Long (1998: 150).

H34 2002: on thin soil in crevices beneath overhang on schist crags, 485 m alt., Bulbin Mt. just NW of summit, C34, DT Holyoak 02-503B (Rothero 2003: 63).
H40 1964: decomposed basalt *ca* 1400 ft [alt.], Benbradagh, RD Fitzgerald & MPH Kertland (Warburg 1965: 870).

177/1b *Myurella julacea* var. *scabrifolia* Lindb. ex Limpr.

H29 1963: shaded cleft of limestone, *ca* 900 ft [alt.], Peakadaw, Glenade, RD Fitzgerald & AR Perry (Warburg 1964: 732, Fitzgerald & Fitzgerald 1966a).

178/1 *Platydictya jungermannioides* (Brid.) H. A.Crum
(syn. *Amblystegiella sprucei* (Bruch) Loeske, *Amblystegium sprucei* (Bruch) Bruch, Schimp. & W.Gümbel)

H11 1973: limestone rock in cave mouth, Dunmore Cave, DL Kelly (Crundwell 1974: 174).
[H(21) listed by Lett (1915: 144) as 1856: Portmarnock, leg. Orr. H21 deleted because record believed to be an error (Stirling 1968, Crundwell 1969: 889)].
[H23 deleted because record not traced (Stirling 1968, Crundwell 1969: 889)].
†H28 listed by Blockeel & Long (1998: 151).
H(29) 1937: Glenade, no collector named (BBS exc.) (Armitage 1938: 12).
†H29 listed by Blockeel & Long (1998: 151).
H(33) 1905: Correll Glen, nr Church Hill, D McArdle (DBN), comm. RD Fitzgerald (Lett 1915: 144, Perry 1967: 421).
H33 2000: on ledge under overhang on N-facing sandstone crag, Culcarrick Scarp, E part, H05, DT Holyoak 00-248 (BBSUK) (Rothero 2001: 47).
H35 2002: on soil on marble outcrop, 15 m alt., W of Melmore Lough, C14, DT Holyoak 02-608 (Rothero 2003: 63).

179/1 *Orthothecium rufescens* (Brid.) Bruch, Schimp. & W.Gümbel
(syn. *Stereodon rufescens* (Brid.) Mitt.)

H9 1959: damp limestone rock-face on low cliff, shallow valley behind Black Head, MCF Proctor (Warburg 1960: 780).
H(28) listed by Lett (1915: 159).
†H28 listed by Blockeel & Long (1998: 151).
H(29) listed by Lett (1915: 159).
†H29 listed by Blockeel & Long (1998: 151).
H33 2000: on damp limestone at base of N-facing crags, N of Glencreawan Lough, H05, DT Holyoak 00-278 (BBSUK) (Rothero 2001: 47).
H35 1967: on N-facing calcareous schistose rocks, Slieve League, nr Carrick, 1300 ft [alt.], HH Birks, HJB Birks & DA Ratcliffe (BBSUK) (published by Crundwell 1968: 646 and HJB Birks, HH Birks & Ratcliffe 1969, but subsequently 'lost' from the records; reinstated by Blockeel 1999: 10).

179/2 *Orthothecium intricatum* (Hartm.) Bruch, Schimp. & W.Gümbel
(syn. *Stereodon subrufus* Lindb.)

H(1) listed by Lett (1915: 159).
†H1 listed by Blockeel & Long (1998: 151).
H(2) listed by Lett (1915: 159).
†H2 listed by Blockeel & Long (1998: 151).
H(7) 1943: Lough Muskry, AW Stelfox, per JS Thomson (Duncan 1944: 215).
†H7 listed by Blockeel & Long (1998: 151).
H9 1994: in damp hollow on shaded limestone crag, 180 m alt., Glen of Clab, M20, TL Blockeel & NG Hodgetts, TL Blockeel 23/170 (Blockeel 1995c: 46).
H(16) 1933: Muckanaght, Twelve Bens, PWM Richards (anon. 1938d: 41).
†H16 listed by Blockeel & Long (1998: 151).
H27 1965: basic rocks, 1500 ft alt., E end of Sheefry Hills, nr Gortmore, AMcG Stirling (Warburg 1966: 204).
H(28) listed by Lett (1915: 159).
†H28 listed by Blockeel & Long (1998: 151).
H(29) listed by Lett (1915: 159).
†H29 listed by Blockeel & Long (1998: 151).
H30 2001: on vertical limestone in cave at base of crag, 200 m alt., Legnaveagh, S of Blacklion, H03, DT Holyoak 01-746 (Rothero 2002: 55).
†H33 listed by Blockeel & Long (1998: 151).
H(34) listed by Lett (1915: 159).
†H34 listed by Blockeel & Long (1998: 151).
H(35) listed by Lett (1915: 159).
†H35 listed by Blockeel & Long (1998: 151).
†H39 listed by Blockeel & Long (1998: 151).
H40 1990: on shaded rock in Big Cleft, Binevenagh, DM Synnott (Blockeel 1991: 46).

180/1 ***Plagiothecium latebricola*** Bruch, Schimp. & W.Gümbel

H29 1974: on rotting wood in mixed woodland, Garadice Lough, nr Ballinamore, DL Kelly, det. DM Synnott, conf. AC Crundwell (Crundwell 1975: 21, DL Kelly in Hackney 1980).

180/3a ***Plagiothecium denticulatum*** (Hedw.) Bruch, Schimp. & W.Gümbel **var.** ***denticulatum***

H3 1968: shaded rocky bank above the shore, Ballycrovana Harbour, N of Eyeries, JA Paton (Crundwell 1969: 890).
H4 1983: stream bank, woodland N of Belgooly, nr Kinsale, RC Stern (Hill 1984b: 30).
H6 1999: on bank by track in woodland, 70 m alt., Lismore, by junction of Glenakeefe R. and Owennashad R., S00, TL Blockeel 28/190 (Rothero 2000: 61).
H8 1966: tree roots in sunken lane, Paradise Hill, Galtee Mts, MFV Corley & JS Parker (Perry 1967: 423).
H10 1979: woodland bank above Clare River, Clare Glens, S of Newport, JA Paton (Hill 1980b: 47).
H(12) listed by Blockeel & Long (1998: 151).
[H12 1953: elm, Inch, WR Megaw (Warburg 1954: 486). Record no longer accepted for *CC*].
H(13) 1867: rocks in the Clody, Mt Leinster, RC Browne (DBN) (Crundwell 1968: 647).
†H13 listed by Blockeel & Long (1998: 151).
H20 1952: wall below graveyard, Glendalough, JS Thomson, comm. ALK King (Warburg 1965: 872).
H22 1970: ditch bank, moorland W of An Uaimh, JA Paton (Crundwell 1971b: 383).
H24 1965: raised bog S of Roosky, RD Fitzgerald & EM Lobley (Warburg 1966: 204).
H25 1965: tree stump, hedgeside, Kilronan, nr Ballyfarnan, EM Lobley & RD Fitzgerald (Crundwell 1968: 647).
H26 1965: cliffs, *ca* 750 ft alt., S of Glendaduff, [The] Ox Mts, RD Fitzgerald (Warburg 1966: 204).
†H33 listed by Blockeel & Long (1998: 151).
†H36 listed by Blockeel & Long (1998: 151).
H37 1951: roots of trees, Rough I., RD Fitzgerald (Warburg 1952: 107).
H(38) listed by Blockeel & Long (1998: 151).
†H39 listed by Blockeel & Long (1998: 151).
H40 1999: on steep bank above river in woodland, S of Dogleap House, C62, DT Holyoak 99-630 (BBSUK) (Rothero 2000: 61).

Prior to the revision by Greene (1957) records of this species were often confused with those of *P. succulentum* or *P. nemorale* through reliance on unreliable characters (e.g. from Dixon 1924: 478). Hence old records of *P. denticulatum* (e.g. from Lett 1915: 160) are not listed here.

180/3b ***Plagiothecium denticulatum*** **var.** ***obtusifolium*** (Turner) Moore

H1 1966: mossy ledge on cliffs, Brandon Mt., JA Paton (Crundwell 1968: 647).
H3 1967: cleft of rocks, *ca* 1400 ft [alt.], Gougane Barra, RD Fitzgerald (Crundwell 1968: 647).
†H7 listed by Blockeel & Long (1998: 152).
H16 1994: wet rocks in gully on N-facing cliffs, 420 m alt., Twelve Bens, NE corrie of Bengower, L75, DG Long 25845 (Blockeel 1995c: 46).
H35 1969: rocky stream bank, S slope Muckish Mt., JA Paton (Crundwell 1970: 210).
†H40 listed by Blockeel & Long (1998: 152).

180/5 ***Plagiothecium curvifolium*** Schlieph. ex Limpr.

H20 1981: extensive glossy patches on bare soil, Bellvue Wood, Glen of the Downs Nature Reserve, N Lockhart (Hill 1983: 57).
[H29 1965: ground nr waterfall, Dergvone, N of L. Allen, RD Fitzgerald & EM Lobley (Warburg 1966: 204). H29 deleted because specimen (BBSUK) is incorrectly named (Hill 1981: 36)].
H29 2000: on damp, rotting wood on ground in woodland, Garadice Lough, N edge, H11, DT Holyoak 00-764 (BBSUK) (Rothero 2001: 47).
[H33 deleted because specimen (Hb. RD Fitzgerald) is *P. laetum* (Hill 1981: 36)].

180/6 ***Plagiothecium laetum*** Bruch, Schimp. & W.Gümbel

H21 1969: shaded stream-bank, N slope of Killakee Mt., JA Paton (Crundwell 1970: 210).
H33 1961: on raw humus in wood nr Carrick Lough, Derrygonnelly, RD Fitzgerald (Hill 1981: 36).

180/8 ***Plagiothecium platyphyllum*** Mönk.

H20 1975: flush, cliffs on S side of L. Ouler, DM Synnott (BBS exc.) (Crundwell 1976: 32).
[H21 deleted because no valid record or voucher specimen traced (Blockeel 1999: 9)].

180/9 ***Plagiothecium cavifolium*** (Brid.) Z. Iwats.
(syn. *Plagiothecium roeseanum* Bruch, Schimp. & W.Gümbel)

H(1) 1946: Brandon Mt., AW Stelfox, comm. ALK King (Warburg 1965: 872).
H27 1987: on mossy cliff ledge, E corrie of Slievemore, Achill I., DG Long (Blockeel 1998: 39-40).
H(34) 1907: among rocks, summit of Bulbein [*sic* = Bulbin] Mt., J Hunter (CGE) (Crundwell 1968: 647).
H34 2002: with other bryophytes on thin soil under overhang of N-facing crags, 490 m alt., NW of summit of Bulbin Mt., C34, DT Holyoak 02-523 (Rothero 2003: 63).

180/10 ***Plagiothecium succulentum*** (Wilson) Lindb.

†H1 listed by Blockeel & Long (1998: 152).
†H2 listed by Blockeel & Long (1998: 152).
†H3 listed by Blockeel & Long (1998: 152).
H4 1966: bank by road nr Rylane Cross, Boggeragh Mts, MFV Corley & JS Parker (Perry 1967: 423).
H5 1966: river bank, R. Douglas, nr Kilworth, RD Fitzgerald (BBS exc.) (Crundwell 1968: 647).
H6 1964: in heavy shade under scrub in upper valley of R. Licky, ALK King (Warburg 1965: 872).
H7 1966: crevices in sandstone, cliffs above L. Muskry, Galtee Mts, ERB Little (BBS exc.) (Perry 1967: 423-424).
H8 1966: bank of sunken lane, Paradise Hill, Galtee Mts, MFV Corley & JS Parker (Perry 1967: 423-424).
H9 1979: stream bank in wood on SE side of Woodcock Hill, Sixmilebridge, JA Paton (Hill 1980b: 47).
H10 1979: wood below conifer plantation, S slope of Keeper Hill, JA Paton (Hill 1980b: 47).
H12 1958: ground in Camolin Forest, ALK King (Warburg 1964: 735).
H14 2001: on soil under Sitka [Spruce] in plantation, Garafin, S29, L French, S O'Donoghue & A McKee, comm. DL Kelly (Rothero 2003: 63).
[H15 deleted because no valid record or voucher specimen traced (Blockeel 1999: 9)].
†H16 listed by Blockeel & Long (1998: 152).
H17 1966: ground in wood, Ryehill, N of Monivea, MFV Corley & JS Parker (Perry 1967: 423-424).
H18 1973: base of tree, moist alder wood, Camcor River, Kinnitty, DL Kelly (Crundwell 1974: 176).
H20 1950: roadside bank nr Clone, Aughrim, ALK King (Warburg 1964: 735).
H22 1970: ditch bank, moorland W of An Uaimh, JA Paton (Crundwell 1971b: 383).
H24 1965: damp bank, *ca* 750 ft alt., Corn Hill, nr Drumlish, RD Fitzgerald & EM Lobley (Warburg 1966: 204).
H25 1981: on bank by stream in ditch, E side of Slieve Baurn, DM Synnott (Hill 1982: 29).
H26 1965: cliffs, *ca* 750 ft alt., S of Glendaduff, [The] Ox Mts, RD Fitzgerald (Warburg 1966: 204).
H27 1962: rock by stream, N side of Menawn [*sic* = Menaun], Achill I., EF Warburg (Warburg 1963b: 503).
†H28 listed by Blockeel & Long (1998: 152).
H29 1963: overhanging bank below limestone crags at 800 ft [alt.], Peakadaw, Glenade, AR Perry & RD Fitzgerald (Warburg 1964: 735).
H30 1955: damp ground by L. Ramor, Virginia, ALK King (Perry 1967: 423-424).
H32 1965: tree, Cavanagarvan, nr Monaghan, RD Fitzgerald (Warburg 1966: 204).
†H33 listed by Blockeel & Long (1998: 152).
H34 1962: rock crevice, E side of Bulbin

[Mt.], Inishowen, EF Warburg (BBS exc.) (Warburg 1963b: 503).
H35 1963: clay in rock cleft, Silver Strand, Malin Beg, RD Fitzgerald & AR Perry (Warburg 1964: 735).
[H38 deleted because no valid record or voucher specimen traced (Blockeel 1999: 9)].
H38 1999: on rocky bank of stream, 50 m alt., Tollymore Forest park, 4 km W of Newcastle, J33, TL Blockeel 28/335 (Rothero 2000: 61).
†H39 listed by Blockeel & Long (1998: 152).
†H40 listed by Blockeel & Long (1998: 152).

Irish and British material of *P. succulentum, P. nemorale* and allied species was much confused prior to the revision by Greene (1957). Most old records (e.g. from Lett 1915: 160-161) are not listed here because they should only be referred to the species currently recognised after reidentification of voucher specimens.

180/11 *Plagiothecium nemorale* (Mitt.) A. Jaeger
(syn. *Plagiothecium silvaticum* auct., *P. sylvaticum* auct. non *Hypnum sylvaticum* Brid.)

†H1 listed by Blockeel & Long (1998: 152).
†H2 listed by Blockeel & Long (1998: 152).
H3 1951: shaded sandstone lip of Lisamore Well, Cape Clear, IA Rorison (Warburg 1952: 107).
1979: shaded bank nr Ardnagashel House, N side of Bantry Bay, JA Paton & AC Crundwell (Hill 1980b: 47).
H4 1983: stream-bank, woodland N of Belgooly, nr Kinsale, RC Stern (Hill 1984b: 30).
H5 1966: earthy bank by stream, R. Douglas valley, N of Kilworth, ERB Little (BBS exc.) (Perry 1967: 424).
H6 1972: on shaded dripping rock, Coumshingaun Lough, Commeragh [*sic* = Comeragh] Mts, WV Rubers (U) (Crundwell 1974: 176).
H7 1966: stream bank below Bay L., Knockmealdown Mts, JA Paton (BBS exc.) (Crundwell 1968: 647).
[H(8) 1945: Tipperary and Limerick boundary, AW Stelfox, per JS Thomson (anon. 1946c: 285). Not accepted for H(8) in *CC* by Warburg (1963a: 83)].
H8 1992: in mature woodland, NE shore of Foynes I., Shannon Estuary, R25, E Wiltshire (Blockeel 1993: 54).
H9 1979: hedgebank nr Killuran River, NW slope of Slieve Bernagh, N of Broadford, JA Paton (Hill 1980b: 47).
H10 1973: mixed woodland, Clare Glens, N side, DL Kelly (Crundwell 1974: 176).
H11 1954: shady roadside bank nr Graiguenamanagh, ALK King (Warburg 1964: 735).
H16 1968: woodland floor, Hill of Doon, L. Corrib, AR Perry (Crundwell 1969: 891).
H20 1962: deep shade on wooded slope, Glen of the Downs, ALK King (Warburg 1964: 735).
†H21 listed by Blockeel & Long (1998: 152).
[H(24) 1941: Ardnacliff, JG Finlay (Duncan 1944: 216). H24 not accepted for *CC* by Warburg (1963a: 83)].
†H25 listed by Blockeel & Long (1998: 152).
†H27 listed by Blockeel & Long (1998: 152).
H28 1963: rock cleft, *ca* 900 ft [alt.], NE side of Carrowkeel, Bricklieve Mts, RD Fitzgerald & AR Perry (Warburg 1964: 735).
H29 1963: cleft in limestone, *ca* 900 ft [alt.], Peakadaw, Glenade, RD Fitzgerald & AR Perry (Warburg 1964: 735).
H30 1965: amongst calcareous rocks, Moneygashel Fort, nr Blacklion, AR Perry & EF Warburg (Warburg 1966: 205).
H33 2000: at base of *Crataegus* in *Corylus* scrub on rocky limestone slope, Crossmurrin Nature Reserve, SE part, H13, DT Holyoak 00-201 (BBSUK) (Rothero 2001: 47).
H34 1962: rock crevice, E side of Bulbin [Mt.], AC Crundwell (BBS exc.) (Warburg 1963b: 504).
H35 1962: rocks in wood, Glenbeagh Castle, EF Warburg & AC Crundwell (BBS exc.) (Warburg 1963b: 504).
†H36 listed by Blockeel & Long (1998: 152).
H37 1967: shore, Mullaghmore Lake, nr Markethill, MPH Kertland (Crundwell 1968: 647).
H(38) listed by Blockeel & Long (1998: 152).
H39 1964: ground, Craigagh Wood, nr Cushendun, RD Fitzgerald (Warburg 1965: 873).
[H(40) 1936: Ness Glen, WR Megaw (anon.

1937a: 368). Not accepted for H(40) in *CC* by Warburg (1963a: 83)].
H40 1964: under tree at edge of bog nr Ringsend, RD Fitzgerald (Warburg 1965: 873).

See note under preceding species.

180/12 ***Plagiothecium undulatum*** (Hedw.) Bruch, Schimp. & W.Gümbel

H(1) listed by Lett (1915: 160) without details.
†H1 listed by Blockeel & Long (1998: 152).
H(2) listed by Lett (1915: 160) without details.
†H2 listed by Blockeel & Long (1998: 152).
H(3) listed by Lett (1915: 160) without details.
†H3 listed by Blockeel & Long (1998: 152).
H(4) listed by Lett (1915: 160) without details.
†H4 listed by Blockeel & Long (1998: 152).
H(5) listed by Lett (1915: 160) without details.
†H5 listed by Blockeel & Long (1998: 152).
H(6) listed by Lett (1915: 160) without details.
†H6 listed by Blockeel & Long (1998: 152).
H(7) listed by Lett (1915: 160) without details.
†H7 listed by Blockeel & Long (1998: 152).
H(8) listed by Lett (1915: 160) without details.
†H8 listed by Blockeel & Long (1998: 152).
H(9) listed by Lett (1915: 160) without details.
†H9 listed by Blockeel & Long (1998: 152).
H10 1951: moorland above 1000 ft [alt.], nr Silvermines, AD Banwell, PJ Wanstall & EV Watson (Warburg 1953: 316).
[H(11) listed by Lett (1915: 160) without details. H11 deleted because no valid record or voucher specimen traced (Blockeel 1999: 9)].
H(12) listed by Lett (1915: 160) without details.
†H12 listed by Blockeel & Long (1998: 152).
H(13) listed by Lett (1915: 160) without details.
†H13 listed by Blockeel & Long (1998: 152).
H(14) listed by Lett (1915: 160) without details.
†H14 listed by Blockeel & Long (1998: 152).
H(16) listed by Lett (1915: 160) without details.
†H16 listed by Blockeel & Long (1998: 152).
H17 1968: under heather on raised bog, Addergoule N[orth], R. Suck, nr Ballinasloe, HJB Birks (Crundwell 1969: 891).
H(20) listed by Lett (1915: 160) without details.
†H20 listed by Blockeel & Long (1998: 152).
H(21) listed by Lett (1915: 160) without details.
†H21 listed by Blockeel & Long (1998: 152).
H23 1979: wooded peninsula, SE end of L. Derravaragh (Hill 1980b: 47).
[H(24) listed by Lett (1915: 160) without details. H24 deleted because no valid record or voucher specimen traced (Blockeel 1999: 9)].
H(25) listed by Lett (1915: 160) without details.
†H25 listed by Blockeel & Long (1998: 152).
H(26) listed by Lett (1915: 160) without details.
†H26 listed by Blockeel & Long (1998: 152).
H(27) listed by Lett (1915: 160) without details.
†H27 listed by Blockeel & Long (1998: 152).
H(28) listed by Lett (1915: 160) without details.
†H28 listed by Blockeel & Long (1998: 152).
H(29) listed by Lett (1915: 160) without details.
†H29 listed by Blockeel & Long (1998: 152).
H(30) listed by Lett (1915: 160) without details.
†H30 listed by Blockeel & Long (1998: 152).
[H(31) listed by Lett (1915: 160) without details. H31 deleted because no valid record or voucher specimen traced (Blockeel 1999: 9)].
[H(32) listed by Lett (1915: 160) without details. H32 deleted because no valid record or voucher specimen traced (Blockeel 1999: 9)].
H(33) listed by Lett (1915: 160) without details.
†H33 listed by Blockeel & Long (1998: 152).
H(34) listed by Lett (1915: 160) without details.
†H34 listed by Blockeel & Long (1998: 152).
H(35) listed by Lett (1915: 160) without details.
†H35 listed by Blockeel & Long (1998: 152).
H(36) listed by Lett (1915: 160) without details.

†H36 listed by Blockeel & Long (1998: 152).
H37 1950: Slieve Gullion, *ca* 1400 ft [alt.], J Taylor (Warburg 1951: 503).
H(38) listed by Lett (1915: 160) without details.
†H38 listed by Blockeel & Long (1998: 152).
H(39) listed by Lett (1915: 160) without details.
†H39 listed by Blockeel & Long (1998: 152).
H(40) listed by Lett (1915: 160) without details.
†H40 listed by Blockeel & Long (1998: 152).

181/1 ***Isopterygiopsis muelleriana*** (Schimp.) Z.Iwats.
(syn. *Isopterygium muellerianum* (Schimp.) A.Jaeger)

H1 1951: rock crevice, Coomeeneragh, nr Glenbeigh, EF Warburg (BBS exc.) (Warburg 1952: 106).

181/2 ***Isopterygiopsis pulchella*** (Hedw.) Z. Iwats.
(syn. *Isopterygium pulchellum* (Hedw.) A.Jaeger, *Plagiothecium pulchellum* (Hedw.) Bruch, Schimp. & W.Gümbel)

H(1) listed by Lett (1915: 160).
†H1 listed by Blockeel & Long (1998: 153).
H(2) listed by Lett (1915: 160).
†H2 listed by Blockeel & Long (1998: 153).
H3 1979: rock crevice above Glenbeg Lough, Ardgroom, RC Stern (Hill 1980b: 47).
H6 1966: ledge on cliffs above Sgillage (*sic* = Sgilloge) Loughs, Comeragh Mts, JA Paton (BBS exc.) (Crundwell 1968: 646).
H(7) listed by Lett (1915: 160). H(7) listed by Blockeel & Long (1998: 153).
H(8) 1945: Galtees, RD Meikle (anon. 1947: 33).
†H8 listed by Blockeel & Long (1998: 153).
H10 1979: among *Amphidium mougeotii*, wet rocks by stream, Keeper Hill, RC Stern (Hill 1980b: 47).
H16 1957: moist rock ledges, NW face of Ben Lettery, EV Watson (BBS exc.) (Warburg 1958b: 487).
H(20) listed by Lett (1915: 160). H(20) listed by Blockeel & Long (1998: 153).
[H(21) listed by Lett (1915: 160) without details. H21 deleted because no valid record or voucher specimen traced (Blockeel 1999: 9)].
H(27) listed by Lett (1915: 160).
†H27 listed by Blockeel & Long (1998: 153).
†H28 listed by Blockeel & Long (1998: 153).
H29 1969: limestone crags SE of Kinlough, nr Bundoran, JA Paton (Crundwell 1970: 210).
H(33) listed by Blockeel & Long (1998: 153).
H(34) listed by Lett (1915: 160).
†H34 listed by Blockeel & Long (1998: 153).
H(35) listed by Lett (1915: 160).
†H35 listed by Blockeel & Long (1998: 153).
H(38) listed by Lett (1915: 160). H(38) listed by Blockeel & Long (1998: 153).
H(39) listed by Lett (1915: 160).
†H39 listed by Blockeel & Long (1998: 153).
H(40) listed by Lett (1915: 160). H(40) listed by Blockeel & Long (1998: 153).

182/1 ***Pseudotaxiphyllum elegans*** (Brid.) Z. Iwats.
(syn. *Isopterygium elegans* (Brid.) Lindb., *Plagiothecium elegans* (Brid.) Schimp.)

H(1) listed by Lett (1915: 159).
†H1 listed by Blockeel & Long (1998: 153).
H(2) listed by Lett (1915: 159).
†H2 listed by Blockeel & Long (1998: 153).
H(3) listed by Lett (1915: 159).
†H3 listed by Blockeel & Long (1998: 153).
H4 1966: bank in wood, above R. Lee, Innishcarra Bridge, MFV Corley & JS Parker (Perry 1967: 423).
H5 1956: wooded hillside by Tourig river, above Park House, NW of Youghal, EC Wallace (Warburg 1957: 336).
H(6) listed by Lett (1915: 159).
†H6 listed by Blockeel & Long (1998: 153).
H(7) listed by Lett (1915: 159).
†H7 listed by Blockeel & Long (1998: 153).
H(8) listed by Lett (1915: 159) without details.
†H8 listed by Blockeel & Long (1998: 153).
H(9) listed by Lett (1915: 159) without details.
†H9 listed by Blockeel & Long (1998: 153).
H10 1967: clay bank in shade, Knockfine, Keeper Hill, RD Fitzgerald (Crundwell 1968: 646).
H(11) listed by Lett (1915: 159).
†H11 listed by Blockeel & Long (1998: 153).
H(12) listed by Lett (1915: 160).
†H12 listed by Blockeel & Long (1998: 153).
H(13) listed by Lett (1915: 160).

†H13 listed by Blockeel & Long (1998: 153).
H14 1956: conifer plantation, *ca* 1200 ft [alt.], Slieve Bloom, AA Cridland (Warburg 1958b: 487). H16 1957: rock crevice, NE side of Benchoona, nr Killary Harbour, AC Crundwell (BBS exc.) (Warburg 1958b: 487).
H19 1953: Cromwellstown Hill, ALK King (Warburg 1954: 486).
H(20) listed by Lett (1915: 160).
†H20 listed by Blockeel & Long (1998: 153).
†H21 listed by Blockeel & Long (1998: 153).
H22 1966: shale by R. Boyne, Stalleen, Donore, DM Synnott (Perry 1967: 423).
H23 1957: by road to bog, Ballinafid, ALK King (Warburg 1960: 780).
H(25) listed by Lett (1915: 160).
†H25 listed by Blockeel & Long (1998: 153).
H(26) listed by Lett (1915: 160).
†H26 listed by Blockeel & Long (1998: 153).
H(27) listed by Lett (1915: 160).
†H27 listed by Blockeel & Long (1998: 153).
H(28) listed by Lett (1915: 160).
†H28 listed by Blockeel & Long (1998: 153).
H(29) listed by Lett (1915: 160).
†H29 listed by Blockeel & Long (1998: 153).
H(30) listed by Lett (1915: 160).
†H30 listed by Blockeel & Long (1998: 153).
H(31) listed by Lett (1915: 160). H(31) listed by Blockeel & Long (1998: 153).
H(32) 1947: muddy bank of ditch, road outside Hope Castle, Castleblaney, JS Thomson (anon. 1948b: 123).
H(33) listed by Lett (1915: 160).
†H33 listed by Blockeel & Long (1998: 153).
H(34) listed by Lett (1915: 160).
†H34 listed by Blockeel & Long (1998: 153).
H(35) listed by Lett (1915: 160).
†H35 listed by Blockeel & Long (1998: 153).
H(36) listed by Lett (1915: 160).
†H36 listed by Blockeel & Long (1998: 153).
H(37) listed by Lett (1915: 160).
†H37 listed by Blockeel & Long (1998: 153).
H(38) listed by Lett (1915: 160).
†H38 listed by Blockeel & Long (1998: 153).
H(39) listed by Lett (1915: 160).
†H39 listed by Blockeel & Long (1998: 153).
H(40) 1936: Ness Glen, WR Megaw (anon. 1937a: 368).
†H40 listed by Blockeel & Long (1998: 153).

184/1 ***Taxiphyllum wissgrillii*** (Garov.) Wijk & Margad.
(syn. *Isopterygium depressum* (Brid.) Mitt., *Plagiothecium depressum* (Brid.) Spruce)

H(2) listed by Lett (1915: 159).
†H2 listed by Blockeel & Long (1998: 153).
H9 1957: limestone rocks in hazel scrub on SE side of Slievecarran, J Appleyard, AC Crundwell & E Nyholm (Warburg 1958b: 487).
H11 1973: on rock in mouth of cave, Dunmore Cave, DL Kelly (Crundwell 1974: 175).
H(13) listed by Lett (1915: 159).
H(16) listed by Lett (1915: 159).
†H16 listed by Blockeel & Long (1998: 153).
H(21) listed by Lett (1915: 159). H(21) listed by Blockeel & Long (1998: 153).
H23 1980: on stone of limestone in wood, W of Killavally Torque, NE of Kilbeggan, DM Synnott (Hill 1981: 35).
H(28) 1937: Annacoona, no collector named (BBS exc.) (Armitage 1938: 12).
†H28 listed by Blockeel & Long (1998: 153).
†H29 listed by Blockeel & Long (1998: 153).
H30 2001: on damp limestone in cave, 220 m alt., Giant's Leap, S of Blacklion, H03, DT Holyoak 01-756 (Rothero 2002: 55).
H33 1960: on limestone stones in wood, Hanging Rock, RD Fitzgerald (Warburg 1961: 173).
H(34) 1937: River Erne, no collector named (BBS exc.) (Armitage 1938: 12).
H34 2001: on rock in stream at edge of conifer plantation, 50 m alt., Ederamone, G96, NG Hodgetts 3919 (Rothero 2003: 63).
H(38) listed by Lett (1915: 159). H(38) listed by Blockeel & Long (1998: 153).
H39 1950: Crow Glen, RD Fitzgerald (Warburg 1951: 502).
H40 1952: moist earth in rock crevice, wood by stream, Downhill, EW Jones (Warburg 1953: 316).

185/1 ***Rhytidium rugosum*** (Hedw.) Kindb.
(syn. *Hypnum rugosum* Hedw.)

H(40) 1900: sandhills, Magilligan, HW Lett & CH Waddell (see *Journ. Bot.* 1900) (anon. 1901: 92, Lett 1915: 156).
†H40 listed by Blockeel & Long (1998: 153).

186/1 ***Sematophyllum micans*** (Mitt.) Braithw. (syn. *Sematophyllum novae-caesareae* (Austin) E.Britton)

H(1) listed by Lett (1915: 157).
†H1 listed by Blockeel & Long (1998: 153).
H(2) listed by Lett (1915: 157).
†H2 listed by Blockeel & Long (1998: 153).
H(3) listed by Lett (1915: 157). H(3) listed by Blockeel & Long (1998: 153).
H16 1968: shaded rocks at side of waterfall one mile NE of Maumwee Lough, L. Corrib, AR Perry (Crundwell 1969: 891).

186/2 ***Sematophyllum demissum*** (Wilson) Mitt.

H(1) listed by Lett (1915: 157).
H1 1951: Cavagh Lough, PW Richards (BBS exc.) (NMW) (PD Coker MS).
H(2) 1829: Cromaglown, W Wilson (DBN, NMW) (Lett 1915: 157, PD Coker MS). 1831: Turk Mt., Bowman (E, Type) (PD Coker MS).
†H2 listed by Blockeel & Long (1998: 153).
H(3) listed by Lett (1915: 157).
H(3) 1867: Glengarriff, GE Hunt & JD Hooker (BM) (PD Coker MS).
H3 1967: Pass of Keimaneigh, HH Birks, HJB Birks & DA Ratcliffe, comm. HJB Birks (PD Coker MS).
H16 1982: inclined slab of rock in light shade under trees, nr Leenane, Killary Harbour, DA Ratcliffe (Hill 1983: 57).

187/1 ***Pylaisia polyantha*** (Hedw.) Schimp.

†H1 listed by Blockeel & Long (1998: 154).
†H2 listed by Blockeel & Long (1998: 154).
H(5) listed by Blockeel & Long (1998: 154).

[**189/1** ***Homomallium incurvatum*** (Brid.) Loeske]

[H33 deleted because the specimen (1993: trunk of ash tree, Marble Arch, H13, T Hallingbäck, comm. NG Hodgetts (BBSUK): Blockeel 1994: 41, Hodgetts & Hallingbäck 1994) lacks sporophytes and is probably a form of *Hypnum resupinatum* (Blockeel 1999: 2).]

190/3 ***Hypnum cupressiforme*** Hedw. s.s. (syn. *Hypnum cupressiforme* var. *cupressiforme*, *Stereodon cupressiformis* (Hedw.) Brid. ex Mitt., *S. cupressiformis* var. *longirostris* (Bruch, Schimp. & W. Gümbel) Braithw.)

H(1) listed by Lett (1915: 157).
†H1 listed by Blockeel & Long (1998: 154).
H(2) listed by Lett (1915: 157).
†H2 listed by Blockeel & Long (1998: 154).
H(3) listed by Lett (1915: 157).
†H3 listed by Blockeel & Long (1998: 154).
H(4) listed by Lett (1915: 157).
†H4 listed by Blockeel & Long (1998: 154).
H(5) listed by Lett (1915: 157).
†H5 listed by Blockeel & Long (1998: 154).
H(6) listed by Lett (1915: 157).
†H6 listed by Blockeel & Long (1998: 154).
H(7) listed by Lett (1915: 157).
†H7 listed by Blockeel & Long (1998: 154).
H(8) listed by Lett (1915: 157).
†H8 listed by Blockeel & Long (1998: 154).
H(9) listed by Lett (1915: 158).
†H9 listed by Blockeel & Long (1998: 154).
H(10) listed by Lett (1915: 157).
†H10 listed by Blockeel & Long (1998: 154).
H(11) listed by Lett (1915: 157).
†H11 listed by Blockeel & Long (1998: 154).
H(12) listed by Lett (1915: 157).
†H12 listed by Blockeel & Long (1998: 154).
H(13) listed by Lett (1915: 157).
†H13 listed by Blockeel & Long (1998: 154).
H(14) listed by Lett (1915: 157).
†H14 listed by Blockeel & Long (1998: 154).
H(15) listed by Lett (1915: 157).
†H15 listed by Blockeel & Long (1998: 154).
H(16) listed by Lett (1915: 157).
†H16 listed by Blockeel & Long (1998: 154).
†H17 listed by Blockeel & Long (1998: 154).
H(18) listed by Lett (1915: 157).
†H18 listed by Blockeel & Long (1998: 154).
H(19) listed by Lett (1915: 157).
†H19 listed by Blockeel & Long (1998: 154).
H(20) listed by Lett (1915: 157).
†H20 listed by Blockeel & Long (1998: 154).
H(21) listed by Lett (1915: 157).
†H21 listed by Blockeel & Long (1998: 154).
H(22) listed by Lett (1915: 157).
†H22 listed by Blockeel & Long (1998: 154).
†H23 listed by Blockeel & Long (1998: 154).
H(24) listed by Lett (1915: 157).
†H24 listed by Blockeel & Long (1998: 154).
H(25) listed by Lett (1915: 157).
†H25 listed by Blockeel & Long (1998: 154).

H(26) listed by Lett (1915: 157).
†H26 listed by Blockeel & Long (1998: 154).
H(27) listed by Lett (1915: 157).
†H27 listed by Blockeel & Long (1998: 154).
H(28) listed by Lett (1915: 157).
†H28 listed by Blockeel & Long (1998: 154).
H(29) listed by Lett (1915: 157).
†H29 listed by Blockeel & Long (1998: 154).
H(30) listed by Lett (1915: 157).
†H30 listed by Blockeel & Long (1998: 154).
H(31) listed by Lett (1915: 157).
†H31 listed by Blockeel & Long (1998: 154).
H(32) listed by Lett (1915: 157).
†H32 listed by Blockeel & Long (1998: 154).
H(33) listed by Lett (1915: 157).
†H33 listed by Blockeel & Long (1998: 154).
H(34) listed by Lett (1915: 157).
†H34 listed by Blockeel & Long (1998: 154).
H(35) listed by Lett (1915: 157).
†H35 listed by Blockeel & Long (1998: 154).
H(36) listed by Lett (1915: 157).
†H36 listed by Blockeel & Long (1998: 154).
H(37) listed by Lett (1915: 157).
†H37 listed by Blockeel & Long (1998: 154).
H(38) listed by Lett (1915: 157).
[H(38) 1936: Rostrevor Mt., WR Megaw (anon. 1937a: 368), as *Hypnum cupressiforme* var. *minus* Wilson. Identification of this gathering should be established by checking the specimen].
†H38 listed by Blockeel & Long (1998: 154).
H(39) listed by Lett (1915: 157).
†H39 listed by Blockeel & Long (1998: 154).
H(40) listed by Lett (1915: 157).
[H(40) 1937: Ness Glen, 'JHD' [*sic* = JD Houston ?] (anon. 1938d: 41), as *H. cupressiforme* var. *minus*. Identification of this gathering should be established by checking the specimen].
†H40 listed by Blockeel & Long (1998: 154).

190/4a *Hypnum lacunosum* (Brid.) Hoffm. ex Brid. **var. *lacunosum***
(syn. *Hypnum cupressiforme* var. *elatum* Brid., *H. cupressiforme* var. *lacunosum* Brid., *Stereodon cupressiformis* var. *elatus* (Bruch, Schimp. & W.Gümbel) Braithw.)

H(1) listed by Lett (1915: 158).
†H1 listed by Blockeel & Long (1998: 154).
H(2) listed by Lett (1915: 158).
†H2 listed by Blockeel & Long (1998: 154).
H3 1975: clay banks, NW side of Hare I., P Whelan (Hill 1978: 24, Whelan 1978).
†H5 listed by Blockeel & Long (1998: 154).
H6 1964: dunes at mouth of R. Mahon, Bunmahon, ALK King (Warburg 1965: 873).
†H7 listed by Blockeel & Long (1998: 154).
H(8) listed by Lett (1915: 158).
†H8 listed by Blockeel & Long (1998: 154).
H(9) no date: Burren (ex Hb. W West) (anon. 1915a: 138).
†H9 listed by Blockeel & Long (1998: 154).
†H11 listed by Blockeel & Long (1998: 154).
H(12) listed by Lett (1915: 158).
†H12 listed by Blockeel & Long (1998: 154).
†H13 listed by Blockeel & Long (1998: 154).
†H14 listed by Blockeel & Long (1998: 154).
†H15 listed by Blockeel & Long (1998: 154).
H16 1957: dunes, nr Dog's Bay, Roundstone, EM Lobley, (Warburg 1958b: 488-489).
H17 1955: limy ground nr Ballinooly Lough, ALK King (Warburg 1956: 158).
†H19 listed by Blockeel & Long (1998: 154).
H20 1954: dunes, Arklow, JS Thomson (Warburg 1955: 587).
H(21) listed by Lett (1915: 158).
†H21 listed by Blockeel & Long (1998: 154).
H22 1969: fixed dunes, Laytown, ALK King (Crundwell 1970: 211).
H(23) listed by Lett (1915: 158).
†H23 listed by Blockeel & Long (1998: 154).
H24 1966: limestone by E shore of L. Ree below Cashel Lodge, ALK King (Perry 1967: 424).
H(25) listed by Lett (1915: 158).
†H25 listed by Blockeel & Long (1998: 154).
H(26) listed by Lett (1915: 158).
†H26 listed by Blockeel & Long (1998: 154).
H(27) listed by Lett (1915: 158).
†H27 listed by Blockeel & Long (1998: 154).
H(28) listed by Lett (1915: 158).
†H28 listed by Blockeel & Long (1998: 154).
H(29) listed by Lett (1915: 158).
†H29 listed by Blockeel & Long (1998: 154).
H(30) listed by Lett (1915: 158).
†H30 listed by Blockeel & Long (1998: 154).
H(31) listed by Lett (1915: 158) without details.
†H31 listed by Blockeel & Long (1998: 154).
H(33) listed by Lett (1915: 158) without locality.
†H33 listed by Blockeel & Long (1998: 154).
H(34) listed by Lett (1915: 158).
†H34 listed by Blockeel & Long (1998: 154).
H(35) 1911: Killybegs, CA Cheetham (anon. 1915a: 138).
H(35) listed by Lett (1915: 158).

†H35 listed by Blockeel & Long (1998: 154).
†H36 listed by Blockeel & Long (1998: 154).
H(37) listed by Lett (1915: 158).
†H37 listed by Blockeel & Long (1998: 154).
H(38) listed by Lett (1915: 158).
†H38 listed by Blockeel & Long (1998: 154).
H(39) listed by Lett (1915: 158).
†H39 listed by Blockeel & Long (1998: 154).
H(40) listed by Lett (1915: 158).
†H40 listed by Blockeel & Long (1998: 154).

This var. and the next were not consistently identified until the revision by Smith (1997). A few of the older records of var. *lacunosum* (e.g. from Lett 1915: 158) may therefore be based on specimens of var. *tectorum*.

190/4b *Hypnum lacunosum* var. *tectorum* (Brid.) J.-P.Frahm
(syn. *Hypnum cupressiforme* var. *tectorum* Brid.)

H5 1951: wall top, Mallow [= W59], EF Warburg & EC Wallace (BBSUK) (Warburg 1952: 107, Rothero 1999a: 101). H5 listed by Smith (1997: 763).
[H7 1966: on limestone, Rock of Cashel, RD Fitzgerald (BBS exc.) (Crundwell 1968: 647-648). H7 record not accepted by Smith (1997: 763)].
H(9) 1863: limestone rocks, Blackhead [*sic* = Black Head] [= M11], J Nowell (DBN) (Rothero 1999a: 101). H(9) listed by Smith (1997: 763).
[1966: limestone rocks nr Poulsallagh, MFV Corley & JS Parker (Perry 1967: 424). H9 record not accepted by Smith (1997: 763)].
[H11 1966: bridge, Dysart Castle, J Appleyard *et al.* (BBS exc.) (Perry 1967: 424). H11 record not accepted by Smith (1997: 763)].
H12 1966: wall, Kiltealy, Blackstairs Mts, [= S84], J Appleyard & JG Duckett (BBSUK) (Perry 1967: 424, Rothero 1999a: 101). H12 listed by Smith (1997: 763).
H13 1975: bank in field, Yellowford Cross Roads, Rathvilly, AR Perry (Hill 1977a: 24).
[H14 1956: flagstone wall, W of Garrintaggart, AA Cridland (Warburg 1958b: 488). H14 record not accepted by Smith (1997: 763)].
[H15 1957: limestone rocks, Garryland Woods, nr Gort, EM Lobley (BBS exc.) (Warburg 1958b: 488). H15 record not accepted by Smith (1997: 763)].
[H16 1968: siliceous boulder by roadside, Costelloe Bridge, AR Perry (Crundwell 1969: 891). H16 record not accepted by Smith (1997: 763)].
H16 1994: turf in machair, Mannin Strand, Ballyconnolly [*sic* = Ballyconneely], L64, AJE Smith (Rothero 1999a: 101). H16 listed by Smith (1997: 763).
[H17 1957: boulders, turlough, Killower, nr Tuam, EM Lobley (BBS exc.) (Warburg 1958b: 488). H17 record not accepted by Smith (1997: 763)].
[H19 1954: roadside boulder, Glending, between Blessington and Naas, ALK King (Warburg 1955: 587). H19 record not accepted by Smith (1997: 763)].
[H22 1960: Bray Hill, nr Laracor, ALK King (Warburg 1962: 377). H22 record not accepted by Smith (1997: 763)].
[H24 1957: wall, Ardagh Hill, MPH Kertland & ALK King (Warburg 1958b: 488-489). H24 record not accepted by Smith (1997: 763)].
[H25 1965: limestone, Caslan's Wood, nr Strokestown, RD Fitzgerald & EM Lobley (Warburg 1966: 205). H25 record not accepted by Smith (1997: 763)].
[H26 1970: on boulder on roadside, Glendaduff, NE of Foxford, MFV Corley (Crundwell 1971b: 383). H26 record not accepted by Smith (1997: 763)].
H(28) 1904: Arand Hill, D McArdle (DBN) (Rothero 1999a: 101). H(28) listed by Smith (1997: 763) on basis of preceding record.
[1928: nr Rosses Point, Sligo (BBS exc.) (Duncan 1928: 119)].
H(29) 1948: growing through *Camptothecium lutescens*, Carrick-on-Shannon [= M99], ALK King (DBN) (Warburg 1962: 175, Rothero 1999a: 101). H(29) listed by Smith (1997: 763).
[H30 1955: rock, Carrickasimon Hill, nr Lough Ramor, ALK King (Warburg 1956: 158). H30 record not accepted by Smith (1997: 763)].
H31 1966: rock by waterfall, Two Mile River, N of Carlingford Mt., J11, DM Synnott (DBN) (Rothero 1999a: 101).

H31 listed by Smith (1997: 763).
[H33 1960: on top of rocks, Altnamollyboy, RD Fitzgerald (Warburg 1962: 175). H33 record not accepted by Smith (1997: 763)].
[H(34) 1937: Bundoran, no collector named (BBS exc.) (Armitage 1938: 13). H(34), 1937: Bundoran, EM Lobley (anon. 1938b: 32). H34 record not accepted by Smith (1997: 763)].
[H35 1963: siliceous rock nr Clooney, ALK King (Warburg 1964: 735). H35 record not accepted by Smith (1997: 763)].
[H36 1957: old wall, Loughrey nr Cookstown, RD Fitzgerald (Warburg 1959: 638). H36 record not accepted by Smith (1997: 763)].
[H37 1962: old wall base, Gosford Castle nr Markethill, EM Lobley & MPH Kertland (Warburg 1963b: 504). H37 record not accepted by Smith (1997: 763)].
H(38) 1890: Newtownards Glen, J47, SA Stewart (DBN) (Rothero 1999a: 101). 1906: roofs, Lemaderg, JH Davies (DBN) (Rothero 1999a: 101). H(38) listed by Smith (1997: 763) on basis of two preceding records.
[H40 1968: chalk rocks, Benbradagh, HH Birks & RD Fitzgerald (Crundwell 1969: 891). H40 record not accepted by Smith (1997: 763)].

Smith (1997) showed that var. *tectorum* had often been confused with var. *lacunosum*. Hence only those records confirmed by Smith (1997: 763 and MS list) or subsequently are accepted here.

190/5 ***Hypnum resupinatum*** Taylor (syn. *Hypnum cupressiforme* var. *resupinatum* (Taylor) Schimp., *Stereodon resupinatus* (Taylor) Braithw.)

H(1) listed by Lett (1915: 159).
†H1 listed by Blockeel & Long (1998: 155).
H(2) listed by Lett (1915: 159).
†H2 listed by Blockeel & Long (1998: 155).
†H3 listed by Blockeel & Long (1998: 155).
H(4) listed by Lett (1915: 159).
†H4 listed by Blockeel & Long (1998: 155).
†H5 listed by Blockeel & Long (1998: 155).
H6 1956: trunks of oaks, Knocklofty Bridge, EC Wallace (Warburg 1957: 337).
H(7) 1945: on alder, Glen of Aberlow [*sic* = Aherlow], RD Meikle (anon. 1947: 34).
†H7 listed by Blockeel & Long (1998: 155).
H(8) listed by Lett (1915: 159) without locality.
†H8 listed by Blockeel & Long (1998: 155).
H(9) listed by Lett (1915: 159) without details.
†H9 listed by Blockeel & Long (1998: 155).
H10 1967: on trees, Knockfine, Keeper Hill, RD Fitzgerald (Crundwell 1968: 647).
H11 1966: trees nr Foulkscourt House, W of Johnstown, ERB Little (BBS exc.) (Perry 1967: 424).
H(12) listed by Lett (1915: 159).
†H12 listed by Blockeel & Long (1998: 155).
H(13) listed by Lett (1915: 159).
†H13 listed by Blockeel & Long (1998: 155).
H(14) listed by Lett (1915: 159).
†H14 listed by Blockeel & Long (1998: 155).
H15 1956: wood at Hearnesbrook, nr Killimor, ALK King (Warburg 1957: 337).
H(16) listed by Lett (1915: 159).
†H16 listed by Blockeel & Long (1998: 155).
H17 1957: trees in small wood, nr Kilgariff, nr Headford, EM Lobley (BBS exc.) (Warburg 1958b: 488).
H(18) listed by Lett (1915: 159). H(18) listed by Blockeel & Long (1998: 155).
†H19 listed by Blockeel & Long (1998: 155).
H20 1964: elm by roadside S of The Scalp, ALK King (Warburg 1965: 873).
H(21) listed by Lett (1915: 159).
†H21 listed by Blockeel & Long (1998: 155).
H(22) listed by Lett (1915: 159) without locality.
†H22 listed by Blockeel & Long (1998: 155).
†H23 listed by Blockeel & Long (1998: 155).
H(24) listed by Lett (1915: 159).
†H24 listed by Blockeel & Long (1998: 155).
†H25 listed by Blockeel & Long (1998: 155).
†H26 listed by Blockeel & Long (1998: 155).
H(27) listed by Lett (1915: 159).
†H27 listed by Blockeel & Long (1998: 155).
H(28) 1928: nr Sligo (BBS exc.) (Duncan 1928: 119).
†H28 listed by Blockeel & Long (1998: 155).
H(29) listed by Lett (1915: 159).
†H29 listed by Blockeel & Long (1998: 155).
H(30) listed by Lett (1915: 159).
†H30 listed by Blockeel & Long (1998: 155).
H31 1953: Ravensdale State Forest, ALK King (Warburg 1954: 487).
H(32) listed by Lett (1915: 159).

†H32 listed by Blockeel & Long (1998: 155).
H(33) listed by Lett (1915: 159).
†H33 listed by Blockeel & Long (1998: 155).
H(34) listed by Lett (1915: 159) without locality.
†H34 listed by Blockeel & Long (1998: 155).
H(35) listed by Lett (1915: 159).
†H35 listed by Blockeel & Long (1998: 155).
H(36) listed by Lett (1915: 159).
†H36 listed by Blockeel & Long (1998: 155).
H(37) listed by Lett (1915: 159).
†H37 listed by Blockeel & Long (1998: 155).
H(38) listed by Lett (1915: 159).
†H38 listed by Blockeel & Long (1998: 155).
H(39) listed by Lett (1915: 159).
†H39 listed by Blockeel & Long (1998: 155).
H(40) listed by Lett (1915: 159).
†H40 listed by Blockeel & Long (1998: 155).

190/6 ***Hypnum andoi*** A.J.E.Sm.
(syn. *Hypnum cupressiforme* var. *filiforme* Brid., *H. cupressiforme* var. *mammillatum* Brid., *H. mammillatum* (Brid.) Loeske, *Stereodon cupressiformis var. filiformis* (Brid.) Braithw., *S. cupressiformis* var. *mammillatus* (Brid.) Brid. ex Braithw.)

H(1) listed by Lett (1915: 158). H(1) listed by Blockeel & Long (1998: 155).
H(2) listed by Lett (1915: 158).
†H2 listed by Blockeel & Long (1998: 155).
H3 1962: tree in wood by Lough Glenbeg, AJE Smith (Warburg 1963b: 504).
H4 1966: hawthorns on bank by road, Rylane Cross, Boggeragh Mts, MFV Corley & JS Parker (Perry 1967: 424), as *H. cupressiforme* var. *filiforme*.
1967: on alders, *ca* 1300 ft [alt.], Musherabeg, RD Fitzgerald (Crundwell 1968: 647).
H5 2002: on *Salix*, River Bride, Ardarou Wood, Glenville, W78, TL Blockeel 31/368 (Rothero 2003: 63).
H6 1966: logs in ravine S of the Punchbowl, Comeragh Mts, ERB Little (BBS exc.) (Perry 1967: 424).
1966: on trees in wood by R. Nier nr Clonmel, RD Fitzgerald (BBS exc.) (Crundwell 1968: 647).
[H(7) or [H(8) 1945: Galtees, RD Meikle (anon. 1947: 34), as *H. cupressiforme* var. *filiforme*. Record not used in *CC* because not assigned to a unique vice-county].
H7 1966: on larch, *ca* 1300 ft [alt.], Cooper's Wood, S side of Galtymore, RD Fitzgerald (BBS exc.) (Crundwell 1968: 647), as *H. cupressiforme* var. *filiforme*.
1966: on *Salix* in wood, *ca* 1000 ft [alt.], Knockastakeen, Galtee Mts, RD Fitzgerald (BBS exc.) (Crundwell 1968: 647), as *H. cupressiforme* var. *mammillatum*.
H8 1966: tree in gully, Monabrack, J Appleyard (BBS exc.) (Perry 1967: 424).
H12 1954: on tree, Curragh Wood, Inch, JS Thomson (BBSUK) (Warburg 1955: 587, Hill 1980b: 48).
H13 1999: on bole of birch in scrubby woodland, 30 m alt., Pollymounty River, N bank, Ballyknockcrumpin, S73, TL Blockeel 28/311 (Rothero 2000: 61).
H16 1957: trunk of tree, Kylemore Woods, DG Catcheside (BBS exc.), comm. AC Crundwell (Warburg 1958b: 488).
[H18 1957: beech, nr Ballingall, JS Thomson (Warburg 1958b: 488), as *H. cupressiforme* var. *filiforme*. Not accepted as *H. andoi* in *CC*].
[H(20) 1939: Devil's Glen, JS Thomson (Duncan 1944: 217), as *H. cupressiforme* var. *filiforme*. Not accepted as *H. andoi* in *CC*].
H20 1975: on log in pine wood by R. Ow nr Aghavannagh, WD Foster (BBS exc.) (Crundwell 1976: 32).
[H(21) 1939: Slade of Saggart, JS Thomson (Duncan 1944: 217), as *H. cupressiforme* var. *filiforme*. Not accepted as *H. andoi* in *CC*].
[H23 1953: tree trunk, Clonhugh Demesne, NE end of L. Owel, JS Thomson (Warburg 1954: 487), as *H. cupressiforme* var. *filiforme*. Not accepted as *H. andoi* in *CC*].
H23 1970: tree trunk, wood on E shore of L. Ennell, Mullingar, JA Paton (Crundwell 1971b: 383).
H25 1960: in Rockingham Woods nr Boyle, ALK King (BBSUK) (Warburg 1962: 175, Hill 1980b: 48).
[H26 1957: pines, nr L. Carra, RE Parker (Warburg 1958b: 488), as *H. cupressiforme* var. *filiforme*. Not accepted as *H. andoi* in *CC*].
H26 1970: tree trunk in wood W of Pollagh River, NE of Balla, JA Paton (Crundwell 1971b: 383).

H27 1970: rotting log in wood nr Erriff Bridge, N of Maumtrasna, JA Paton (Crundwell 1971b: 383).
H28 1970: woodland nr Drumcliff, N of Sligo, J Appleyard (Hill 1981: 36).
H(29) 1928: wooded glen, NE end of Glencar Lough (BBS exc.) (Duncan 1928: 118), as *H. cupressiforme* var. *mamillatum*.
†H29 listed by Blockeel & Long (1998: 155).
H(30) 1909: rock top of Quilcagh [*sic* = Cuilcagh], WN Tetley (BBSUK) (Hill 1980b: 48).
H30 2001: on dead branch, 95 m alt., Deerpark, W of Virginia, H58, DT Holyoak 01-652 (Rothero 2002: 56).
H33 1957: dead gorse stems in wood on SE side of Belmore Mt., AC Crundwell (Warburg 1958b: 488).
H34 2001: on fallen tree in scrubby woodland, 70 m alt., S of Glenmore Bridge, Welchtown, H09, NG Hodgetts 3856 (Rothero 2003: 63).
2001: on tree trunk in woodland, 70 m alt., Cloghan More, NG Hodgetts 3857 (Rothero 2003: 63).
H35 1990: on bole of Oak tree in deciduous woodland, 60 m alt., Ballyarr Wood, *ca* 5 km E of Kilmacrenan, C12, TL Blockeel 19/508 (Blockeel 1991c: 46).
H36 2002: on *Salix cinerea* at edge of woodland, 100 m alt., Drum Manor Forest Park, H77, DT Holyoak 02-1088 (Rothero 2003: 63).
[H37 1964: trees, Derrylee, E of Verner's Bridge, RD Fitzgerald (Warburg 1965: 873), as *H. cupressiforme* var. *filiforme*. H37 was not listed by Corley & Hill 1981: 128, but it is unclear whether the preceding record was overlooked or deliberately discounted].
H(38) listed by Blockeel & Long (1998: 155).
H38 1999: on fallen branch in mixed woodland, 50 m alt., Tollymore Forest park, 4 km W of Newcastle, J33, TL Blockeel 28/345 (Rothero 2000: 61).
[H(39) 1928: Glenariff (BBS exc.) (Duncan 1928: 117), as *H. cupressiforme* var. *filiforme*. *H. mamillatum* not accepted for H39 in *CC* by Warburg (1963a: 83)].
H39 1999: on hazel in scrub on N-facing slope, Sallagh Braes, D30, DT Holyoak 99-880 (BBSUK) (Rothero 2000: 61).
H40 1999: on trunk of *Betula* at edge of track in *Picea* plantation, Garvagh Forest, C81, DT Holyoak 99-291 (BBSUK) (Rothero 2000: 61).

Old records of var. *filiforme* (e.g. in Lett 1915: 158-159 as *Stereodon cupressiformis* var. *filiformis*) are not listed above. They will mainly be referable to *H. andoi*, but many were based on non-fertile gatherings and careful study of specimens is needed to establish whether they can safely be referred to any of the taxa currently recognised.

190/7 *Hypnum uncinulatum* Jur.
(syn. *Stereodon canariensis* Mitt., *S. circinalis* sensu Lett 1915: 159)

[H(1) listed by Lett (1915: 159), but determination regarded by HN Dixon as 'indecisive in the absence of fruit'].
[H(1) listed by Lett (1915: 159) as *Stereodon circinalis*, but Dixon (1924: 537) referred the material to *S. canariensis*, i. e. *Hypnum uncinulatum*. They have not been accepted as the latter species in recent *CC*].
H(2) 1829: Torc [Turk] Mt., Killarney, W Wilson (Ando & Townsend 1980, Hill 1981: 36, Smith 1997: 767).
[H(2) listed by Lett (1915: 159), but determination regarded by HN Dixon as 'indecisive in the absence of fruit'. However, capsules are present on the gathering made in 1829 by Wilson].
[Other H(2) records were listed by Lett (1915: 159) as *Stereodon circinalis*, but Dixon (1924: 537) referred the material to *S. canariensis*, i.e. *Hypnum uncinulatum*. They have not been accepted as the latter species in recent *CC*].

190/8 *Hypnum jutlandicum* Holmen & E. Warncke
(syn. *Hypnum cupressiforme* var. *ericetorum* Bruch, Schimp. & W. Gümbel, *Stereodon cupressiformis* var. *ericetorum* (Bruch, Schimp. & W. Gümbel) C.E.O.Jensen)

H(1) listed by Lett (1915: 157) without details.
†H1 listed by Blockeel & Long (1998: 155).
H2 1966: woods by Torc Cascade, nr Killarney, MFV Corley & JS Parker

(Perry 1967: 424).
†H3 listed by Blockeel & Long (1998: 155).
H(4) listed by Lett (1915: 157) without details.
†H4 listed by Blockeel & Long (1998: 155).
H5 1951: moorland, SE of Mallow, EC Wallace & EF Warburg (Warburg 1952: 107).
†H6 listed by Blockeel & Long (1998: 155).
H(7) 1943: Lough Curra, AW Stelfox, per JS Thomson (Duncan 1944: 217).
†H7 listed by Blockeel & Long (1998: 155).
H8 1959: bog nr Castleconnell, ALK King (Warburg 1962: 175).
H(9) listed by Lett (1915: 158).
†H9 listed by Blockeel & Long (1998: 155).
H(10) listed by Lett (1915: 158).
†H10 listed by Blockeel & Long (1998: 155).
H(11) listed by Lett (1915: 158).
†H11 listed by Blockeel & Long (1998: 155).
H(12) listed by Lett (1915: 158).
†H12 listed by Blockeel & Long (1998: 155).
H(13) listed by Lett (1915: 158).
†H13 listed by Blockeel & Long (1998: 155).
H(14) listed by Lett (1915: 158).
†H14 listed by Blockeel & Long (1998: 155).
H15 1957: moorland, hills E of Gort, RE Parker (Warburg 1958b: 488).
H(16) listed by Lett (1915: 158).
†H16 listed by Blockeel & Long (1998: 155).
H(17) listed by Lett (1915: 158).
†H17 listed by Blockeel & Long (1998: 155).
H(18) listed by Lett (1915: 158).
†H18 listed by Blockeel & Long (1998: 155).
†H19 listed by Blockeel & Long (1998: 155).
H(20) 1948: hillside wood, nr Drumgoff, Glenmalure, ALK King (Warburg 1950: 388).
†H20 listed by Blockeel & Long (1998: 155).
†H21 listed by Blockeel & Long (1998: 155).
H22 1958: Ballivor Bog, ALK King (Warburg 1959: 638).
†H23 listed by Blockeel & Long (1998: 155).
H(24) listed by Lett (1915: 158).
†H24 listed by Blockeel & Long (1998: 155).
H(25) listed by Lett (1915: 158).
†H25 listed by Blockeel & Long (1998: 155).
H(26) listed by Lett (1915: 158).
†H26 listed by Blockeel & Long (1998: 155).
H(27) listed by Lett (1915: 158).
†H27 listed by Blockeel & Long (1998: 155).
H(28) listed by Lett (1915: 158).
†H28 listed by Blockeel & Long (1998: 155).
H(29) listed by Lett (1915: 158) without details.
†H29 listed by Blockeel & Long (1998: 155).
H(30) listed by Lett (1915: 158).
†H30 listed by Blockeel & Long (1998: 155).
H(31) listed by Lett (1915: 158). H(31) listed by Blockeel & Long (1998: 155).
H31 1999: on heathy bank by track in conifer plantation, 50 m alt., Two Mile River, Carlingford, J11, TL Blockeel 28/145 (Rothero 2000: 61).
H(32) listed by Lett (1915: 158) without locality.
†H32 listed by Blockeel & Long (1998: 155).
H(33) listed by Lett (1915: 158).
†H33 listed by Blockeel & Long (1998: 155).
H(34) listed by Lett (1915: 158) without locality.
†H34 listed by Blockeel & Long (1998: 155).
H(35) listed by Lett (1915: 158).
†H35 listed by Blockeel & Long (1998: 155).
H(36) listed by Lett (1915: 158).
†H36 listed by Blockeel & Long (1998: 155).
H(37) listed by Lett (1915: 158).
†H37 listed by Blockeel & Long (1998: 155).
H(38) listed by Lett (1915: 158).
†H38 listed by Blockeel & Long (1998: 155).
H(39) listed by Lett (1915: 158) without details.
†H39 listed by Blockeel & Long (1998: 155).
H(40) 1936: Sixtowns, WR Megaw (anon. 1937a: 368).
†H40 listed by Blockeel & Long (1998: 155).

[190/9 ***Hypnum imponens*** Hedw.]

[Records from H(1) and H(38) in Lett (1915: 157) are dismissed as errors following Megaw (1950)].

190/11 ***Hypnum lindbergii*** Mitt.
(syn. *Hypnum patientiae* Lindb. ex Milde, *Stereodon lindbergii* (Mitt.) Braithw.)

H(1) listed by Lett (1915: 157).
†H1 listed by Blockeel & Long (1998: 155).
H(2) listed by Lett (1915: 157).
†H2 listed by Blockeel & Long (1998: 155).
H(3) listed by Lett (1915: 157).
†H3 listed by Blockeel & Long (1998: 155).
H(4) listed by Lett (1915: 157) without details.
†H4 listed by Blockeel & Long (1998: 155).
H5 1951: track, SE of Mallow, EC Wallace & EF Warburg (Warburg 1952: 107).
H6 1956: grassy path, Tourig valley, NW of

Youghal, EC Wallace (Warburg 1957: 337).
H7 1979: damp bankside, Seefin, Galtee Mts, EM Lobley & RD Fitzgerald (BBS exc.) (Perry 1967: 424).
H(8) listed by Lett (1915: 157).
†H8 listed by Blockeel & Long (1998: 155).
H9 1979: verge beside lane, W side of Slievebernagh, AC Crundwell (Hill 1980b: 48).
H10 1967: floor of old quarry, Knockfine, Keeper Hill, RD Fitzgerald (Crundwell 1968: 648).
H11 1968: woodland track on W bank of R. Nore, SE of Thomastown, JA Paton (Crundwell 1969: 891).
H(12) listed by Lett (1915: 157).
†H12 listed by Blockeel & Long (1998: 155).
H13 1969: on track in old quarry, Lackan, nr Oldleighlin, RD Fitzgerald (Crundwell 1970: 211).
H14 1956: marshy field by waterfall above Clonaslee, AA Cridland (Warburg 1958b: 489).
H15 1957: side of moorland road, hills E of Gort, RE Parker (Warburg 1958b: 489).
H16 1957: sandy soil on rocks, Owenglin R., Clifden, DH Dalby, EM Lobley & JH Tallis (BBS exc.) (Warburg 1958b: 489).
H(19) listed by Lett (1915: 157). H(19) listed by Blockeel & Long (1998: 155).
H(20) listed by Lett (1915: 157).
†H20 listed by Blockeel & Long (1998: 155).
H22 1978: floor of quarry, Teevurcher, N of Moynalty, DM Synnott (Hill 1979: 33).
H23 1957: roadside, Ballinafid, nr Multyfarnham, JS Thomson (Warburg 1958b: 489).
H25 2002: in wet pasture at edge of turlough, 250 m alt., Newtown Turlough, M77, NG Hodgetts 4093 (Rothero 2003: 63).
H26 1970: track-side, Glendaduff, NE of Foxford, MFV Corley (Crundwell 1971b: 383).
†H27 listed by Blockeel & Long (1998: 155).
H28 1963: turf, *ca* 700 ft [alt.], Lugnagall, Glencar, RD Fitzgerald & AR Perry (Warburg 1964: 736).
H(29) 1928: wooded glen, NE end of Glencar Lough (BBS exc.) (Duncan 1928: 118).
†H29 listed by Blockeel & Long (1998: 155).
H(31) 1945: Ravensdale, ML Anderson, per JS Thomson (anon. 1946c: 286).
H32 1961: track in old sandpit, Castleshane, nr Monaghan, RD Fitzgerald (Warburg 1962: 377).
H(33) listed by Lett (1915: 157).
†H33 listed by Blockeel & Long (1998: 155).
H(34) listed by Lett (1915: 157).
†H34 listed by Blockeel & Long (1998: 155).
H35 1962: edge of track, Corcreagan, W of Dunfanaghy, AC Crundwell (BBS exc.) (Warburg 1963b: 504).
H(36) listed by Lett (1915: 157).
†H36 listed by Blockeel & Long (1998: 155).
†H37 listed by Blockeel & Long (1998: 155).
H(38) listed by Lett (1915: 157). H(38) listed by Blockeel & Long (1998: 155).
H38 2002: at edge of gravel track in plantation, 135 m alt., SE of Glen River in Donards Wood nr Newcastle, J32, DT Holyoak 02-1039 (Rothero 2003: 63).
H(39) listed by Lett (1915: 157). H(39) listed by Blockeel & Long (1998: 155).
H39 2000: on side of path, Glenariff Waterfalls NNR, D22, DM Synnott (Rothero 2001: 47).
H(40) 1914: Kibua, JD Houston (anon. 1915b: 15). H(40) listed by Blockeel & Long (1998: 155).
H40 1999: on thin, compressed soil on stony track in *Picea* plantation, Garvagh Forest, C81, DT Holyoak 99-299 (BBSUK) (Rothero 2000: 61).

190/12 ***Hypnum callichroum*** Brid.
(syn. *Stereodon callichrous* (Brid.) Braithw.)

H(1) listed by Lett (1915: 159).
†H1 listed by Blockeel & Long (1998: 155).
H(2) listed by Lett (1915: 159).
†H2 listed by Blockeel & Long (1998: 155).
[H(16) record dismissed as doubtful by Lett (1915: 159)].
H16 1957: rock ledges, Benchoona, nr L. Fee, RE Parker (BBS exc.) (Warburg 1958b: 489).
†H27 listed by Blockeel & Long (1998: 155).
H28 1963: limestone outcrops at 1300 ft [alt.], Lugnagall, Glencar, AR Perry & RD Fitzgerald (Warburg 1964: 736).
†H29 listed by Blockeel & Long (1998: 155).
H34 1968: on rocks, Kindrohid, nr Clonmany, RD Fitzgerald & HH Birks (Crundwell 1969: 891).
H35 1961: shady rocks in woods at 500 ft [alt.], Glenkeagh, nr Dunlewy, DA Ratcliffe (Warburg 1962: 377).

191/1 *Ptilium crista-castrensis* (Hedw.) De Not.

H27 1987: on steep grass covered scree at *ca* 2000 ft on the W side of the N-facing corrie, Mweelrea, DM Synnott (Blockeel 1998: 40).
[H(39) records (1847: Colin Glen, leg. Orr) dismissed as error of locality by Lett (1915: 157)].

192/1a *Ctenidium molluscum* (Hedw.) Mitt. **var. *molluscum***
(syn. *Hypnum molluscum* Hedw.)

H(1) listed by Lett (1915: 156) without details.
†H1 listed by Blockeel & Long (1998: 156).
H(2) listed by Lett (1915: 156) without details.
†H2 listed by Blockeel & Long (1998: 156).
H(3) listed by Lett (1915: 156) without details.
†H3 listed by Blockeel & Long (1998: 156).
H(4) listed by Lett (1915: 156) without details.
†H4 listed by Blockeel & Long (1998: 156).
†H5 listed by Blockeel & Long (1998: 156).
H(6) listed by Lett (1915: 156) without details.
†H6 listed by Blockeel & Long (1998: 156).
H(7) listed by Lett (1915: 156) without details.
H(7) 1945: cliffs at 2700 ft [alt.], Loch Curra, RD Meikle (anon. 1947: 34).
†H7 listed by Blockeel & Long (1998: 156).
H(8) listed by Lett (1915: 156) without details.
†H8 listed by Blockeel & Long (1998: 156).
H(9) listed by Lett (1915: 156) without details.
†H9 listed by Blockeel & Long (1998: 156).
H(10) listed by Lett (1915: 156) without details.
†H10 listed by Blockeel & Long (1998: 156).
H(11) listed by Lett (1915: 156) without details.
†H11 listed by Blockeel & Long (1998: 156).
H(12) listed by Lett (1915: 156) without details.
†H12 listed by Blockeel & Long (1998: 156).
H(13) listed by Lett (1915: 156) without details.
†H13 listed by Blockeel & Long (1998: 156).
H(14) listed by Lett (1915: 156) without details.
†H14 listed by Blockeel & Long (1998: 156).
H(15) listed by Lett (1915: 156) without details.
†H15 listed by Blockeel & Long (1998: 156).
H(16) listed by Lett (1915: 156) without details.
†H16 listed by Blockeel & Long (1998: 156).
H(17) listed by Lett (1915: 156) without details.
†H17 listed by Blockeel & Long (1998: 156).
H(18) listed by Lett (1915: 156) without details.
†H18 listed by Blockeel & Long (1998: 156).
†H19 listed by Blockeel & Long (1998: 156).
H(20) listed by Lett (1915: 156) without details.
†H20 listed by Blockeel & Long (1998: 156).
H(21) listed by Lett (1915: 156) without details.
†H21 listed by Blockeel & Long (1998: 156).
H(22) listed by Lett (1915: 156) without details.
†H22 listed by Blockeel & Long (1998: 156).
H(23) listed by Lett (1915: 156) without details.
†H23 listed by Blockeel & Long (1998: 156).
H24 1955: drained edge by roadside, Derryad Bog, nr Killashee, TA Barry, comm. ALK King (Warburg 1956: 158).
H(25) listed by Lett (1915: 156) without details.
†H25 listed by Blockeel & Long (1998: 156).
H(26) listed by Lett (1915: 156) without details.
†H26 listed by Blockeel & Long (1998: 156).
H(27) listed by Lett (1915: 156) without details.
†H27 listed by Blockeel & Long (1998: 156).
H(28) listed by Lett (1915: 156) without details.
†H28 listed by Blockeel & Long (1998: 156).
H(29) listed by Lett (1915: 156) without details.
†H29 listed by Blockeel & Long (1998: 156).
H(30) listed by Lett (1915: 156) without details.
†H30 listed by Blockeel & Long (1998: 156).
H(31) listed by Lett (1915: 156) without details.
†H31 listed by Blockeel & Long (1998: 156).
H(32) listed by Lett (1915: 156) without details.
†H32 listed by Blockeel & Long (1998: 156).
H(33) listed by Lett (1915: 156) without

details.
†H33 listed by Blockeel & Long (1998: 156).
H(34) listed by Lett (1915: 156) without details.
†H34 listed by Blockeel & Long (1998: 156).
H(35) listed by Lett (1915: 156) without details.
†H35 listed by Blockeel & Long (1998: 156).
H(36) listed by Lett (1915: 156) without details.
†H36 listed by Blockeel & Long (1998: 156).
H(37) listed by Lett (1915: 156) without details.
†H37 listed by Blockeel & Long (1998: 156).
H(38) listed by Lett (1915: 156) without details.
†H38 listed by Blockeel & Long (1998: 156).
H(39) listed by Lett (1915: 156) without details.
†H39 listed by Blockeel & Long (1998: 156).
H(40) listed by Lett (1915: 156) without details.
†H40 listed by Blockeel & Long (1998: 156).

192/1b *Ctenidium molluscum* var. *fastigiatum* (Bosw. ex Hobk.) Braithw.
(syn. *Hypnum molluscum* var. *fastigiatum* Bosw. ex Hobk.)

H1 1951: dry rocks on crags above L. Coomeathcun, nr Waterville, EC Wallace (BBS exc.) (Warburg 1952: 108).
H(2) 1935: Torc Mt., no collector named (BBS exc.) (Watson 1936: 265).
1935: Muckross, no collector named (BBS exc.) (Watson 1936: 265).
[H2 deleted because no valid record or voucher specimen traced (Blockeel 1999: 10), but preceding records suggest it should be reinstated].
[H9 deleted because no valid record or voucher specimen traced (Blockeel 1999: 10)].
H(28) 1928: Gleniff, Ben Bulben (BBS exc.) (Duncan 1928: 118).
[H28 deleted because no valid record or voucher specimen traced (Blockeel 1999: 10), but preceding record suggests it should be reinstated].
H29 1965: limestone, *ca* 1000 ft alt., Aghadunvane, L. Melvin, RD Fitzgerald & EM Lobley (Warburg 1966: 205).
H33 1959: limestone rocks, Lough Scolban, RD Fitzgerald (Warburg 1960: 782).

192/1c *Ctenidium molluscum* var. *condensatum* (Schimp.) E.Britton
(syn. *Hypnum molluscum* var. *condensatum* Schimp.)

[H(1) listed by Lett (1915: 156). H1 deleted because no valid record or voucher specimen traced (Blockeel 1999: 10)].
[H(2) listed by Lett (1915: 156). H2 deleted because no valid record or voucher specimen traced (Blockeel 1999: 10)].
H(3) listed by Lett (1915: 156).
†H3 listed by Blockeel & Long (1998: 156).
[H(6) listed by Lett (1915: 156). H6 deleted because no valid record or voucher specimen traced (Blockeel 1999: 10)].
H(7) listed by Blockeel & Long (1998: 156).
H16 1968: rocks in basic flush, W-facing slope at ca 1100 ft [alt.], Lissoughter, Recess, AR Perry (Crundwell 1969: 891).
H20 1965: dripping schistose cliffs, Raven's Glen, Glencree, ALK King (Warburg 1966: 205).
[H27 1957: damp soil at foot of rocks, SE valley of Maumtrasna, AC Crundwell (BBS exc.) (Warburg 1958b: 489). H27 deleted because the locality (E of Skeltia, Maumtrasna) is in H16 (Crundwell 1970: 211)].
H27 1987: on wet rock in N corrie, Slievemore, Achill I., TL Blockeel (Blockeel 1998: 40).
H29 2001: on flushed vertical NW-facing sandstone at base of crag, 375 m alt., Slieve Anierin, W slope, H01, DT Holyoak 01-846 (Rothero 2002: 56).
H31 1970: in quarry, Barnavave Hill, Carlingford, M Carson (Crundwell 1972: 144).
[H(33) listed by Lett (1915: 156). H33 deleted because no valid record or voucher specimen traced (Blockeel 1999: 10)].
H34 2002: on flushed slope below crags, 425 m alt., NW slope of Bulbin Mt., C34, DT Holyoak 02-800 (Rothero 2003: 63).
H35 1962: foot of dripping rocks, 900 ft alt., NE side of Crocknalaragagh, by Muckish Mt., AC Crundwell & J Appleyard (BBS exc.) (Warburg 1963b: 504).
H36 1952: boggy ground, 600 ft [alt.], L. Braden, RD Fitzgerald (Warburg 1958b: 489).
[H(38) listed by Lett (1915: 156) without

details].

[H(39) listed by Lett (1915: 156). H39 deleted because no valid record or voucher specimen traced (Blockeel 1999: 10)].

H40 1999: on steep flushed rock beside track in woodland, Banagher Glen, C60, DT Holyoak 99-647 (BBSUK) (Rothero 2000: 61).

192/1d *Ctenidium molluscum* var. *robustum* Boulay
(syn. *Ctenidium molluscum* var. *croceum* Braithw).

[H(1) listed by Lett (1915: 156). H1 deleted because no valid record or voucher specimen traced (Blockeel 1999: 10)].

[H2 deleted because no valid record or voucher specimen traced (Blockeel 1999: 10)].

[H(6) listed by Lett (1915: 156). H6 deleted because no valid record or voucher specimen traced (Blockeel 1999: 10)].

H(38) listed by Lett (1915: 156). H(38) listed by Blockeel & Long (1998: 156).

[H39 deleted because no valid record or voucher specimen traced (Blockeel 1999: 10)].

193/1 *Hyocomium armoricum* (Brid.) Wijk & Margad.
(syn. *Hyocomium flagellare* Bruch, Schimp. & W.Gümbel)

H(1) listed by Lett (1915: 156).

†H1 listed by Blockeel & Long (1998: 156).

H(2) listed by Lett (1915: 156).

†H2 listed by Blockeel & Long (1998: 156).

H(3) listed by Lett (1915: 157).

†H3 listed by Blockeel & Long (1998: 156).

H(4) listed by Lett (1915: 157).

†H4 listed by Blockeel & Long (1998: 156).

H5 1966: by R. Douglas, nr Kilworth. J Appleyard *et al.* (BBS exc.) (Perry 1967: 424).

H(6) listed by Lett (1915: 157).

†H6 listed by Blockeel & Long (1998: 156).

H(7) listed by Lett (1915: 157).

†H7 listed by Blockeel & Long (1998: 156).

H8 1966: rocks in stream, S of Paradise Hill, Galtee Mts, MFV Corley & JS Parker (Perry 1967: 424).

H9 1963: rocks, small stream on W side of Slieve Elva, *ca* 850 ft [alt.], Lisdoonvarna, G Halliday (Warburg 1964: 735).

H10 1967: on wet rocks nr river level in wooded valley, Clare Glen, nr Newport, HH Birks, HJB Birks & DA Ratcliffe (Crundwell 1968: 648).

H(11) listed by Lett (1915: 157). H(11) listed by Blockeel & Long (1998: 156).

H(12) listed by Lett (1915: 157).

†H12 listed by Blockeel & Long (1998: 156).

H(13) listed by Lett (1915: 157).

†H13 listed by Blockeel & Long (1998: 156).

†H14 listed by Blockeel & Long (1998: 156).

†H16 listed by Blockeel & Long (1998: 156).

H(16) listed by Lett (1915: 157).

H18 1952: rocks in stream, forestry plantation nr Letter Cross, Slieve Bloom, Kinitty, AP Fanning (Warburg 1954: 485).

H(20) listed by Lett (1915: 157).

†H20 listed by Blockeel & Long (1998: 156).

H(21) listed by Lett (1915: 157).

†H21 listed by Blockeel & Long (1998: 156).

H25 1981: rocks by waterfall, E of Kilronan Mt., Arigna, DM Synnott (Hill 1982: 30).

H(26) listed by Lett (1915: 157). H(26) listed by Blockeel & Long (1998: 156).

H(27) listed by Lett (1915: 157).

†H27 listed by Blockeel & Long (1998: 156).

H(28) listed by Lett (1915: 157).

†H28 listed by Blockeel & Long (1998: 156).

H(29) 1937: Glenade, no collector named (BBS exc.) (Armitage 1938: 12).

†H29 listed by Blockeel & Long (1998: 156).

H(30) listed by Lett (1915: 157).

†H30 listed by Blockeel & Long (1998: 156).

H(31) listed by Lett (1915: 157). H(31) listed by Blockeel & Long (1998: 156).

H(33) listed by Lett (1915: 157).

†H33 listed by Blockeel & Long (1998: 156).

H(34) listed by Lett (1915: 157).

†H34 listed by Blockeel & Long (1998: 156).

H(35) listed by Lett (1915: 157).

†H35 listed by Blockeel & Long (1998: 156).

H(36) listed by Lett (1915: 157).

†H36 listed by Blockeel & Long (1998: 156).

H(37) listed by Lett (1915: 157). H(37) listed by Blockeel & Long (1998: 156).

H(38) listed by Lett (1915: 157).

†H38 listed by Blockeel & Long (1998: 156).

H(39) listed by Lett (1915: 157). H(39) listed by Blockeel & Long (1998: 156).

H(40) listed by Lett (1915: 157).

†H40 listed by Blockeel & Long (1998: 156).

194/1 ***Rhytidiadelphus triquetrus*** (Hedw.) Warnst.
(syn. *Hylocomium triquetrum* (Hedw.) Bruch, Schimp. & W.Gümbel)

H(1) listed by Lett (1915: 156) without details.
†H1 listed by Blockeel & Long (1998: 156).
H(2) listed by Lett (1915: 156) without details.
†H2 listed by Blockeel & Long (1998: 156).
H(3) listed by Lett (1915: 156) without details.
†H3 listed by Blockeel & Long (1998: 156).
H(4) listed by Lett (1915: 156) without details.
†H4 listed by Blockeel & Long (1998: 156).
H(5) listed by Lett (1915: 156) without details.
†H5 listed by Blockeel & Long (1998: 156).
H(6) listed by Lett (1915: 156) without details.
†H6 listed by Blockeel & Long (1998: 156).
H(7) listed by Lett (1915: 156) without details.
†H7 listed by Blockeel & Long (1998: 156).
H(8) listed by Lett (1915: 156) without details.
†H8 listed by Blockeel & Long (1998: 156).
H(9) listed by Lett (1915: 156) without details.
†H9 listed by Blockeel & Long (1998: 156).
H(10) listed by Lett (1915: 156) without details.
†H10 listed by Blockeel & Long (1998: 156).
H(11) listed by Lett (1915: 156) without details.
†H11 listed by Blockeel & Long (1998: 156).
H(12) listed by Lett (1915: 156) without details.
†H12 listed by Blockeel & Long (1998: 156).
H(13) listed by Lett (1915: 156) without details.
†H13 listed by Blockeel & Long (1998: 156).
H(14) listed by Lett (1915: 156) without details.
†H14 listed by Blockeel & Long (1998: 156).
H(15) listed by Lett (1915: 156) without details.
†H15 listed by Blockeel & Long (1998: 156).
H(16) listed by Lett (1915: 156) without details.
†H16 listed by Blockeel & Long (1998: 156).
H(17) listed by Lett (1915: 156) without details.
†H17 listed by Blockeel & Long (1998: 156).
H(18) listed by Lett (1915: 156) without details.
†H18 listed by Blockeel & Long (1998: 156).
H(19) listed by Lett (1915: 156) without details.
†H19 listed by Blockeel & Long (1998: 156).
H(20) listed by Lett (1915: 156) without details.
†H20 listed by Blockeel & Long (1998: 156).
H(21) listed by Lett (1915: 156) without details.
†H21 listed by Blockeel & Long (1998: 156).
H(22) listed by Lett (1915: 156) without details.
†H22 listed by Blockeel & Long (1998: 156).
H(23) listed by Lett (1915: 156) without details.
†H23 listed by Blockeel & Long (1998: 156).
H(24) listed by Lett (1915: 156) without details.
†H24 listed by Blockeel & Long (1998: 156).
H(25) listed by Lett (1915: 156) without details.
†H25 listed by Blockeel & Long (1998: 156).
H(26) listed by Lett (1915: 156) without details.
†H26 listed by Blockeel & Long (1998: 156).
H(27) listed by Lett (1915: 156) without details.
†H27 listed by Blockeel & Long (1998: 156).
H(28) listed by Lett (1915: 156) without details.
†H28 listed by Blockeel & Long (1998: 156).
H(29) listed by Lett (1915: 156) without details.
†H29 listed by Blockeel & Long (1998: 156).
H(30) listed by Lett (1915: 156) without details.
†H30 listed by Blockeel & Long (1998: 156).
[H(31) listed by Lett (1915: 156) without details. H31 deleted because no valid record or voucher specimen traced (Blockeel 1999: 10)].
H31 1999: on grassy bank by track in conifer plantation, 50 m alt., Two Mile River, Carlingford, J11, TL Blockeel 28/144 (Rothero 2000: 61).
H(32) listed by Lett (1915: 156) without details.
†H32 listed by Blockeel & Long (1998: 156).
H(33) listed by Lett (1915: 156) without details.
†H33 listed by Blockeel & Long (1998: 156).
H(34) listed by Lett (1915: 156) without

details.
†H34 listed by Blockeel & Long (1998: 156).
H(35) listed by Lett (1915: 156) without details.
†H35 listed by Blockeel & Long (1998: 156).
H(36) listed by Lett (1915: 156) without details.
†H36 listed by Blockeel & Long (1998: 156).
H(37) listed by Lett (1915: 156) without details.
†H37 listed by Blockeel & Long (1998: 156).
H(38) listed by Lett (1915: 156) without details.
†H38 listed by Blockeel & Long (1998: 156).
H(39) listed by Lett (1915: 156) without details.
†H39 listed by Blockeel & Long (1998: 156).
H(40) listed by Lett (1915: 156) without details.
†H40 listed by Blockeel & Long (1998: 156).

194/2 *Rhytidiadelphus squarrosus* (Hedw.) Warnst.
(syn. *Hylocomium squarrosum* (Hedw.) Bruch, Schimp. & W.Gümbel)

H(1) listed by Lett (1915: 156) without details.
†H1 listed by Blockeel & Long (1998: 156).
H(2) listed by Lett (1915: 156) without details.
†H2 listed by Blockeel & Long (1998: 156).
H(3) listed by Lett (1915: 156) without details.
†H3 listed by Blockeel & Long (1998: 156).
H(4) listed by Lett (1915: 156) without details.
†H4 listed by Blockeel & Long (1998: 156).
†H5 listed by Blockeel & Long (1998: 156).
H(6) listed by Lett (1915: 156) without details.
†H6 listed by Blockeel & Long (1998: 156).
H(7) listed by Lett (1915: 156) without details.
†H7 listed by Blockeel & Long (1998: 156).
H(8) listed by Lett (1915: 156) without details.
†H8 listed by Blockeel & Long (1998: 156).
H(9) listed by Lett (1915: 156) without details.
†H9 listed by Blockeel & Long (1998: 156).
H(10) listed by Lett (1915: 156) without details.
†H10 listed by Blockeel & Long (1998: 156).
H(11) listed by Lett (1915: 156) without details.
†H11 listed by Blockeel & Long (1998: 156).
H(12) listed by Lett (1915: 156) without details.
†H12 listed by Blockeel & Long (1998: 156).
H(13) listed by Lett (1915: 156) without details.
†H13 listed by Blockeel & Long (1998: 156).
H(14) listed by Lett (1915: 156) without details.
†H14 listed by Blockeel & Long (1998: 156).
H(15) listed by Lett (1915: 156) without details.
†H15 listed by Blockeel & Long (1998: 156).
†H16 listed by Blockeel & Long (1998: 156).
H(17) listed by Lett (1915: 156) without details. H(17) listed by Blockeel & Long (1998: 156).
H17 2002: in lawn in cemetery, 80 m alt., Kildaree graveyard, nr Williamstown, M56, NG Hodgetts 4134 (Rothero 2003: 63).
H(18) listed by Lett (1915: 156) without details.
†H18 listed by Blockeel & Long (1998: 156).
†H19 listed by Blockeel & Long (1998: 156).
H(20) listed by Lett (1915: 156) without details.
†H20 listed by Blockeel & Long (1998: 156).
H(21) listed by Lett (1915: 156) without details.
†H21 listed by Blockeel & Long (1998: 156).
H(22) listed by Lett (1915: 156) without details.
†H22 listed by Blockeel & Long (1998: 156).
H(23) listed by Lett (1915: 156) without details.
†H23 listed by Blockeel & Long (1998: 156).
H(24) listed by Lett (1915: 156) without details.
†H24 listed by Blockeel & Long (1998: 156).
H(25) listed by Lett (1915: 156) without details.
†H25 listed by Blockeel & Long (1998: 156).
H(26) listed by Lett (1915: 156) without details.
†H26 listed by Blockeel & Long (1998: 156).
H(27) listed by Lett (1915: 156) without details.
†H27 listed by Blockeel & Long (1998: 156).
H(28) listed by Lett (1915: 156) without details.
†H28 listed by Blockeel & Long (1998: 156).
H(29) listed by Lett (1915: 156) without details.

†H29 listed by Blockeel & Long (1998: 156).
H(30) listed by Lett (1915: 156) without details.
†H30 listed by Blockeel & Long (1998: 156).
H(31) listed by Lett (1915: 156) without details.
†H31 listed by Blockeel & Long (1998: 156).
H(32) listed by Lett (1915: 156) without details.
†H32 listed by Blockeel & Long (1998: 156).
H(33) listed by Lett (1915: 156) without details.
†H33 listed by Blockeel & Long (1998: 156).
H(34) listed by Lett (1915: 156) without details.
†H34 listed by Blockeel & Long (1998: 156).
H(35) listed by Lett (1915: 156) without details.
†H35 listed by Blockeel & Long (1998: 156).
H(36) listed by Lett (1915: 156) without details.
†H36 listed by Blockeel & Long (1998: 156).
H(37) listed by Lett (1915: 156) without details.
†H37 listed by Blockeel & Long (1998: 156).
H(38) listed by Lett (1915: 156) without details.
†H38 listed by Blockeel & Long (1998: 156).
H(39) listed by Lett (1915: 156) without details.
†H39 listed by Blockeel & Long (1998: 156).
H(40) listed by Lett (1915: 156) without details.
†H40 listed by Blockeel & Long (1998: 156).

194/3 ***Rhytidiadelphus subpinnatus*** (Lindb.) T.J.Kop.
(syn. *Rhytidiadelphus squarrosus* var. *calvescens* (Lindb.) Warnst.)

H6 1966: wooded valley, Glendine Bridge, N of Youghal, J Appleyard (Hill 1981: 36).

194/4 ***Rhytidiadelphus loreus*** (Hedw.) Warnst.
(syn. *Hylocomium loreum* (Hedw.) Bruch, Schimp. & W.Gümbel)

H(1) listed by Lett (1915: 156) without details.
†H1 listed by Blockeel & Long (1998: 156).
H(2) listed by Lett (1915: 156) without details.
†H2 listed by Blockeel & Long (1998: 156).
H(3) listed by Lett (1915: 156) without details.
†H3 listed by Blockeel & Long (1998: 156).
H4 1966: boggy ground at 1200 ft alt., Seefin, Boggeragh Mts, MFV Corley & JS Parker (Perry 1967: 424).
H(5) listed by Lett (1915: 156) without details.
†H5 listed by Blockeel & Long (1998: 156).
H(6) listed by Lett (1915: 156) without details.
†H6 listed by Blockeel & Long (1998: 156).
H(7) listed by Lett (1915: 156) without details.
†H7 listed by Blockeel & Long (1998: 156).
H(8) listed by Lett (1915: 156) without details.
†H8 listed by Blockeel & Long (1998: 156).
H(9) listed by Lett (1915: 156) without details.
†H9 listed by Blockeel & Long (1998: 156).
H10 1967: moorland, Knockfine, Keeper Hill, RD Fitzgerald (Crundwell 1968: 648).
H(11) listed by Lett (1915: 156) without details.
†H11 listed by Blockeel & Long (1998: 156).
H(12) listed by Lett (1915: 156) without details.
†H12 listed by Blockeel & Long (1998: 156).
H(13) listed by Lett (1915: 156) without details.
†H13 listed by Blockeel & Long (1998: 156).
H(14) listed by Lett (1915: 156) without details.
†H14 listed by Blockeel & Long (1998: 156).
H15 1957: moorland on hills E of Gort, RE Parker (Warburg 1958b: 489).
H(16) listed by Lett (1915: 156) without details.
†H16 listed by Blockeel & Long (1998: 156).
[H(17) listed by Lett (1915: 156) without details. H17 deleted because no valid record or voucher specimen traced (Blockeel 1999: 10)].
H(18) listed by Lett (1915: 156) without details.
†H18 listed by Blockeel & Long (1998: 156).
H19 1958: shaded bank under beeches, Elverstown, ALK King (Warburg 1959: 639).
H(20) listed by Lett (1915: 156) without details.
†H20 listed by Blockeel & Long (1998: 156).
H(21) listed by Lett (1915: 156) without details.

†H21 listed by Blockeel & Long (1998: 156).
H22 1967: Carnbane East, Slieve na Callaigh, Oldcastle, DM Synnott (Crundwell 1968: 648).
H24 1965: moorland *ca* 800 ft alt., Corn Hill, nr Drumlish, RD Fitzgerald & EM Lobley (Warburg 1966: 205).
H(25) listed by Lett (1915: 156) without details.
†H25 listed by Blockeel & Long (1998: 156).
H(26) listed by Lett (1915: 156) without details.
†H26 listed by Blockeel & Long (1998: 156).
H(27) listed by Lett (1915: 156) without details.
†H27 listed by Blockeel & Long (1998: 156).
H(28) listed by Lett (1915: 156) without details.
†H28 listed by Blockeel & Long (1998: 156).
H(29) listed by Lett (1915: 156) without details.
†H29 listed by Blockeel & Long (1998: 156).
H(30) listed by Lett (1915: 156) without details.
†H30 listed by Blockeel & Long (1998: 156).
[H(31) listed by Lett (1915: 156) without details. H31 deleted because no valid record or voucher specimen traced (Blockeel 1999: 10)].
H(32) listed by Lett (1915: 156) without details.
†H32 listed by Blockeel & Long (1998: 156).
H(33) listed by Lett (1915: 156) without details.
†H33 listed by Blockeel & Long (1998: 156).
H(34) listed by Lett (1915: 156) without details.
†H34 listed by Blockeel & Long (1998: 156).
H(35) listed by Lett (1915: 156) without details.
†H35 listed by Blockeel & Long (1998: 156).
H(36) listed by Lett (1915: 156) without details.
†H36 listed by Blockeel & Long (1998: 156).
H(37) listed by Lett (1915: 156) without details.
†H37 listed by Blockeel & Long (1998: 156).
H(38) listed by Lett (1915: 156) without details.
†H38 listed by Blockeel & Long (1998: 156).
H(39) listed by Lett (1915: 156) without details.
†H39 listed by Blockeel & Long (1998: 156).
H(40) listed by Lett (1915: 156) without details.
†H40 listed by Blockeel & Long (1998: 156).

195/1 ***Hylocomium brevirostre*** (Brid.) Bruch, Schimp. & W.Gümbel
(syn. *Hypnum brevirostre* (Brid.) Ehrh.)

H(1) listed by Lett (1915: 156).
†H1 listed by Blockeel & Long (1998: 157).
H(2) listed by Lett (1915: 156).
†H2 listed by Blockeel & Long (1998: 157).
H(3) listed by Lett (1915: 156).
†H3 listed by Blockeel & Long (1998: 157).
H(4) listed by Lett (1915: 156).
†H4 listed by Blockeel & Long (1998: 157).
H(5) listed by Lett (1915: 156). H(5) listed by Blockeel & Long (1998: 157).
H(6) 1933: Unishad Valley, E Armitage (anon. 1934b: 134).
†H6 listed by Blockeel & Long (1998: 157).
H(7) 1945: Ballynacourt, Glen of Aberlow [*sic* = Aherlow], RD Meikle (anon. 1947: 34).
†H7 listed by Blockeel & Long (1998: 157).
H(8) listed by Lett (1915: 156).
†H8 listed by Blockeel & Long (1998: 157).
H(9) 1945: rocks, Roughan Ho.[use], Kilnaboy, JS Thomson (anon. 1946c: 286).
†H9 listed by Blockeel & Long (1998: 157).
H(10) listed by Lett (1915: 156).
†H10 listed by Blockeel & Long (1998: 157).
H(12) listed by Lett (1915: 156).
†H12 listed by Blockeel & Long (1998: 157).
H(13) listed by Lett (1915: 156).
†H13 listed by Blockeel & Long (1998: 157).
H(14) listed by Lett (1915: 156).
†H14 listed by Blockeel & Long (1998: 157).
H(15) listed by Lett (1915: 156).
†H15 listed by Blockeel & Long (1998: 157).
H(16) listed by Lett (1915: 156).
†H16 listed by Blockeel & Long (1998: 157).
H17 1957: boulders, turlough, Killower, nr Tuam, EM Lobley (BBS exc.) (Warburg 1958b: 489).
H(18) listed by Lett (1915: 156). H(18) listed by Blockeel & Long (1998: 157).
H(20) listed by Lett (1915: 156) without locality.
†H20 listed by Blockeel & Long (1998: 157).
H(21) listed by Lett (1915: 156). H(21) listed by Blockeel & Long (1998: 157).
H22 1967: oak woodland, N of Balrath, Duleek, DM Synnott (Crundwell 1968: 648).
H23 1952: grounds of Woodlands, NE end of

L. Owel, JS Thomson (Warburg 1954: 487).
H24 1965: tree stump in wood, Cloonart Bridge, RD Fitzgerald & EM Lobley (Warburg 1966: 205).
H(25) listed by Lett (1915: 156).
†H25 listed by Blockeel & Long (1998: 157).
H(26) listed by Lett (1915: 156).
†H26 listed by Blockeel & Long (1998: 157).
H(27) listed by Lett (1915: 156).
†H27 listed by Blockeel & Long (1998: 157).
H(28) listed by Lett (1915: 156).
†H28 listed by Blockeel & Long (1998: 157).
†H29 listed by Blockeel & Long (1998: 157).
H(30) listed by Lett (1915: 156). H(30) listed by Blockeel & Long (1998: 157).
H30 2001: on old limestone wall in hazel scrub, 235 m alt., Legnaveagh, S of Blacklion, H03, DT Holyoak 01-745 (Rothero 2002: 56).
H31 1966: beechwood, Trumpet Hill, Carlingford Peninsula, DM Synnott (Perry 1967: 424).
H(32) listed by Lett (1915: 156). H(32) listed by Blockeel & Long (1998: 157).
H(33) listed by Lett (1915: 156).
†H33 listed by Blockeel & Long (1998: 157).
H(34) listed by Lett (1915: 156) without locality. H(34) listed by Blockeel & Long (1998: 157).
H34 2001: on limestone in railway cutting, 30 m alt., nr Lough Naharash, Ballyshannon Turloughs, G86, NG Hodgetts 3730 (Rothero 2002: 56).
H(35) listed by Lett (1915: 156).
†H35 listed by Blockeel & Long (1998: 157).
H36 1950: wood, Stewartstown Castle, RD Fitzgerald (Warburg 1951: 503).
H(38) listed by Lett (1915: 156). H(38) listed by Blockeel & Long (1998: 157).
H(39) listed by Lett (1915: 156).
†H39 listed by Blockeel & Long (1998: 157).
H(40) listed by Lett (1915: 156).
†H40 listed by Blockeel & Long (1998: 157).

195/3 ***Hylocomium umbratum*** (Hedw.) Bruch, Schimp. & W.Gümbel

[H(1) listed by Lett (1915: 155)].
H1 1951: above Coomeeneragh Lake, nr Glenbeigh, EW Jones (BBS exc.) (Warburg 1952: 107).
†H2 listed by Blockeel & Long (1998: 157).
H16 1957: steep N-facing grassy slopes, Benchoona, nr L. Fee, RE Parker (BBS exc.) (Warburg 1958b: 489).
H(27) listed by Lett (1915: 155).
†H27 listed by Blockeel & Long (1998: 157).
H28 1967: shaded rocks and humus, Slish Wood, F Rose (Crundwell 1968: 648).
H29 1965: among limestone boulders, Peakadaw, Glenade, EM Lobley & RD Fitzgerald (Warburg 1966: 205).
H35 1961: damp shady rocks in oakwoods at 500 ft [alt.], Glenbeagh, nr Dunlewy, DA Ratcliffe (Warburg 1962: 377).
H39 1957: moist N-facing bank in oakwood, 600 ft [alt.], Breen, Glenshesk, RE Parker (Warburg 1958b: 489).

195/4 ***Hylocomium splendens*** (Hedw.) Bruch, Schimp. & W.Gümbel
(syn. *Hylocomium proliferum* (Brid.) Lindb. nom. illeg., *H. proliferum* var. *lambayensis* McArdle in Lett 1915: 156, *H. splendens* var. *gracilius* (Boulay) Husn.)

H(1) listed by Lett (1915: 156) without details.
†H1 listed by Blockeel & Long (1998: 157).
H(2) listed by Lett (1915: 156) without details.
†H2 listed by Blockeel & Long (1998: 157).
†H3 listed by Blockeel & Long (1998: 157).
H(4) listed by Lett (1915: 156) without details.
†H4 listed by Blockeel & Long (1998: 157).
H(5) listed by Lett (1915: 156) without details.
†H5 listed by Blockeel & Long (1998: 157).
H(6) listed by Lett (1915: 156) without details.
†H6 listed by Blockeel & Long (1998: 157).
H(7) listed by Lett (1915: 156) without details.
†H7 listed by Blockeel & Long (1998: 157).
H(8) listed by Lett (1915: 156) without details.
†H8 listed by Blockeel & Long (1998: 157).
H(9) listed by Lett (1915: 156) without details.
†H9 listed by Blockeel & Long (1998: 157).
H(10) listed by Lett (1915: 156) without details.
†H10 listed by Blockeel & Long (1998: 157).
H(11) listed by Lett (1915: 156) without details.
†H11 listed by Blockeel & Long (1998: 157).
H(12) listed by Lett (1915: 156) without

details.
†H12 listed by Blockeel & Long (1998: 157).
H(13) listed by Lett (1915: 156) without details.
†H13 listed by Blockeel & Long (1998: 157).
H(14) listed by Lett (1915: 156) without details.
†H14 listed by Blockeel & Long (1998: 157).
H(15) listed by Lett (1915: 156) without details.
†H15 listed by Blockeel & Long (1998: 157).
H(16) listed by Lett (1915: 156) without details.
†H16 listed by Blockeel & Long (1998: 157).
H(17) listed by Lett (1915: 156) without details.
†H17 listed by Blockeel & Long (1998: 157).
H(18) listed by Lett (1915: 156) without details.
†H18 listed by Blockeel & Long (1998: 157).
H(19) 1946: Cupidstown Hill, AW Stelfox (per JS Thomson) (anon. 1947: 34).
†H19 listed by Blockeel & Long (1998: 157).
H(20) listed by Lett (1915: 156) without details.
†H20 listed by Blockeel & Long (1998: 157).
H(21) listed by Lett (1915: 156).
†H21 listed by Blockeel & Long (1998: 157).
H(22) listed by Lett (1915: 156) without details.
†H22 listed by Blockeel & Long (1998: 157).
H(23) listed by Lett (1915: 156) without details.
†H23 listed by Blockeel & Long (1998: 157).
H(24) listed by Lett (1915: 156) without details.
†H24 listed by Blockeel & Long (1998: 157).
H(25) listed by Lett (1915: 156) without details.
†H25 listed by Blockeel & Long (1998: 157).
H(26) listed by Lett (1915: 156) without details.
†H26 listed by Blockeel & Long (1998: 157).
H(27) listed by Lett (1915: 156) without details.
†H27 listed by Blockeel & Long (1998: 157).
H(28) listed by Lett (1915: 156) without details.
†H28 listed by Blockeel & Long (1998: 157).
H(29) listed by Lett (1915: 156) without details.
†H29 listed by Blockeel & Long (1998: 157).
H(30) listed by Lett (1915: 156) without details.
†H30 listed by Blockeel & Long (1998: 157).
H(31) listed by Lett (1915: 156) without details.
†H31 listed by Blockeel & Long (1998: 157).
H(32) listed by Lett (1915: 156) without details.
†H32 listed by Blockeel & Long (1998: 157).
H(33) listed by Lett (1915: 156) without details.
†H33 listed by Blockeel & Long (1998: 157).
H(34) listed by Lett (1915: 156) without details.
†H34 listed by Blockeel & Long (1998: 157).
H(35) listed by Lett (1915: 156) without details.
†H35 listed by Blockeel & Long (1998: 157).
H(36) listed by Lett (1915: 156) without details.
†H36 listed by Blockeel & Long (1998: 157).
H(37) listed by Lett (1915: 156) without details.
†H37 listed by Blockeel & Long (1998: 157).
H(38) listed by Lett (1915: 156) without details.
†H38 listed by Blockeel & Long (1998: 157).
H(39) listed by Lett (1915: 156) without details.
H(39) 1928: sandhills, Portrush (BBS exc.) (Duncan 1928: 113, 116), as var. *gracilius*.
†H39 listed by Blockeel & Long (1998: 157).
H(40) listed by Lett (1915: 156) without details.
†H40 listed by Blockeel & Long (1998: 157).

APPENDIX
SYMBOLS AND ABBREVIATIONS

APPENDIX. Symbols and abbreviations.

†	Entry in latest *CC* (Blockeel & Long 1998) apparently lacking brackets only because an (unverified) post-1949 record exists in data held at the Biological Records Centre (Monks Wood, Great Britain)
[ ]	Square brackets used to denote rejected or problematical records
( )	Round brackets around vice-county number used to denote pre-1950 record (round brackets used in very early *CC* to denote doubtful records are never copied in citations in the present work)
agg.	aggregate (group of closely related species)
alt.	altitude above mean sea-level
anon.	anonymous
ASSI	Area of Special Scientific Interest
BBS	British Bryological Society
BBS exc.	Field Meeting [excursion] of British Bryological Society
(BBSUK)	BBS Hb. at National Museum and Gallery, Cardiff, Wales
(BEL)	Hb. Ulster Museum, Belfast
(BFT)	Hb. Department of Botany, The Queen's University, Belfast
(BIRM)	Hb. Department of Botany, The University, Birmingham, Great Britain
(BM)	Hb. Department of Botany, The Natural History Museum, London, Great Britain.
(BRIST)	Hb. Department of Botany, The University, Bristol, Great Britain
CC	*Census Catalogue* of MEC or BBS (see Bibliographical Notes in Introduction for list and References below for bibliographical details)
(CGE)	Hb. Botany School, University of Cambridge
comm.	communicated by
conf.	confirmed by
(CRK)	Hb. University College, Cork (see Cullinane & Whelan 1977)
(DBN)	Hb. National Botanic Gardens, Glasnevin, Dublin (see Synnott 1980)
det.	determined (identified) by
DNFC	Dublin Naturalists' Field Club
(DUKE)	Duke University Herbarium, Dept. of Botany, Durham, North Carolina, U.S.A.
(E)	Hb. Royal Botanic Garden, Edinburgh, Scotland
E	East
ENE	East-north-east
ESE	East-south-east
exc.	Excursion [note that this abbreviation which was formerly in frequent use invites confusion with 'Exchange']
f.	*forma*, form
ft	feet
(GALW)	Hb. University College, Galway
(GL)	Hb. Department of Botany, University of Glasgow, Scotland
(H)	Hb. Botanical Museum, University of Helsinki, Helsinki, Finland
H1-H40	Numbers representing each of the Vice-Counties in Ireland (see end of this book for a list)
Hb.	herbarium
hom. illeg.	illegitimate homonym
incl.	includes
INJ	*Irish Naturalists' Journal*
I.	Island
(JE)	Hb. Haussknecht, Sektion Biologie der Friedrich-Schiller-Universität, Jena, Germany
(K)	Hb. Royal Botanic Gardens, Kew, Great Britain
L.	Lough
(LDS)	Hb. Plant Sciences Department, The University, Leeds, Great Britain
leg.	collected by [*legit* = he gathered]
(LIV)	Hb. Merseyside County Museum, Liverpool, Great Britain
m	metres
(MANCH)	Hb. The Manchester Museum, The University, Manchester, Great Britain
MEC	Moss Exchange Club
MS	manuscript
MSS	manuscripts
Mt	Mount
Mt., Mts	Mountain, mountains
N	North
NE	North-east
(NMW)	Hb. BIOSYB, The National Museum and Gallery of Wales, Cardiff, Wales
NNE	North-north-east
NNR	National Nature Reserve
NNW	North-north-west

nom. illeg.	illegitimate name
nom. nud.	*nomen nudum* (name published without description)
nr	near
NW	North-west
(NY)	Hb. The New York Botanical Garden, New York, U.S.A.
orth.	orthographic (spelling) variant
(OXF)	Fielding-Druce Hb., Department of Botany, Oxford University, Great Britain
pro parte	in part
R.	River
redet.	redetermined by
(RNG)	Hb. Plant Science Laboratories, The University, Reading, Great Britain
S	South
SE	South-east
s.n.	without number (of specimen)
s.s.	*sensu stricto* (in the strict sense)
SSE	South-south-east
SSW	South-south-west
subf.	*subforma*, sub-form
subsp.	subspecies
SW	South-west
syn.	synonym(s)
(TCD)	Hb. School of Botany, Trinity College, Dublin (cf. Parnell 1982)
(TRH)	Hb. Botanical Department, Museum of the Royal Norwegian Society for Science and Letters, Trondheim, Norway
(U)	Hb. Institute for Systematic Botany, Utrecht, Netherlands
var.	variety
W	West
WNW	West-north-west
WSW	West-south-west.

REFERENCES

anon. 1899. Extracts from M. E. C. notebook for 1898. *The Third Annual Report of the Moss Exchange Club* (*M.E.C. Reports*) **1**: 16-19.
anon. 1901. [Untitled = Mosses; Hepaticae]. *Moss Exchange Club. Reports and extracts from the Club note book for the year 1901* (*M.E.C. Reports*) **1**: 72-97.
anon. 1902. List of mosses and hepatics. *Moss Exchange Club. Report for the year 1902* (*M.E.C. Reports*) **1**: 112-125.
anon. 1903. List of mosses and hepatics. *Moss Exchange Club. Report for the year 1903* (*M.E.C. Reports*) **1**: 133-148.
anon. 1906. List of mosses and hepatics. *Moss Exchange Club. Report for the year 1906* (*M.E.C. Reports*) **1**: 210-230.
anon. 1909a. Mosses. *Moss Exchange Club. The fourteenth Annual Report, April 1909* (*M.E.C. Reports*) **1**: 301-318.
anon. 1909b. Hepatics. *Moss Exchange Club. The fourteenth Annual Report, April 1909* (*M.E.C. Reports*) **1**: 318-325.
anon. 1910. Mosses. *Moss Exchange Club. The fifteenth Annual Report, March 1910* (*M.E.C. Reports*) **1**: 334-353.
anon. 1911a. Mosses. *Moss Exchange Club. The sixteenth Annual Report, March 1911* (*M.E.C. Reports*) **2**: 7-26.
anon. 1911b. Hepatics. *Moss Exchange Club. The sixteenth Annual Report, March 1911* (*M.E.C. Reports*) **2**: 27-35.
anon. 1911c. Mosses. *Moss Exchange Club. Section II. Report for the year 1910*: 6-13.
anon. 1911d. Hepatics. *Moss Exchange Club. Section II. Report for the year 1910*: 14-16.
anon. 1912a. Mosses. *Moss Exchange Club. The seventeenth Annual Report, April 1912* (*M.E.C. Reports*) **2**: 43-54.
anon. 1912b. Hepatics. *Moss Exchange Club. The seventeenth Annual Report, April 1912* (*M.E.C. Reports*) **2**: 55-60.
anon. 1912c. Mosses. *Moss Exchange Club. Section II. Report for the year 1911*: 6-13.
anon. 1913a. Mosses. *Moss Exchange Club. The eighteenth Annual Report, March 1913* (*M.E.C. Reports*) **2**: 67-80.
anon. 1913b. Mosses. *Moss Exchange Club. Section II. Report for the year 1912*: 6-13.
anon. 1914a. Mosses. *Moss Exchange Club. The nineteenth Annual Report, March* 1914 (*M.E.C. Reports*) **2**: 94-109.
anon. 1914b. Hepatics. *Moss Exchange Club. The nineteenth Annual Report, March 1914* (*M.E.C. Reports*) **2**: 110-115.
anon. 1915a. Mosses. *Moss Exchange Club. The twentieth Annual Report, April 1915* (*M.E.C. Reports*) **2**: 123-138.
anon. 1915b. Mosses. *Moss Exchange Club. Section II. Report for the year 1914*: 7-16.
anon. 1916a. Mosses. *Moss Exchange Club. The twenty-first Annual Report, April 1916* (*M.E.C. Reports*) **2**: 151-168.
anon. 1916b. Hepatics. *Moss Exchange Club. The twenty-first Annual Report, April 1916* (*M.E.C. Reports*) **2**: 169-175.
anon. 1916c. Mosses. *Moss Exchange Club. Section II. Report for the year 1915*: 5-11.
anon. 1917a. Sphagna. *Moss Exchange Club. The twenty-second Annual Report, April 1917* (*M.E.C. Reports*) **2**: 183-186.
anon. 1917b. Hepatics. *Moss Exchange Club. The twenty-second Annual Report, April 1917* (*M.E.C. Reports*) **2**: 194-199.
anon. 1917c. Mosses. *Moss Exchange Club. Section II. Report for the year 1916*: 8-12.
anon. 1918a. Sphagna. *Moss Exchange Club. The twenty-third Annual Report, June 1918* (*M.E.C. Reports*) **2**: 205-210.
anon. 1918b. Hepatics. *Moss Exchange Club. Section II. Report for the year 1917*: 14-18.
anon. 1919a. Sphagna. *Moss Exchange Club. The twenty-fourth Annual Report, July 1919* (*M.E.C. Reports*) **2**: 229-234.
anon. 1919b. Hepatics. *Moss Exchange Club. The twenty-fourth Annual Report, July 1919* (*M.E.C. Reports*) **2**: 244-247.
anon. 1921. Sphagna. *Moss Exchange Club. The twenty-sixth Annual Report, August 1921* (*M.E.C.

Reports) **2**: 271-273.
anon. 1923. [Reports on plants sent in by members.] Hepatics. *The British Bryological Society Report for 1923* **1**: 33-38.
anon. 1924. Reports on plants sent in by members. True mosses. *The British Bryological Society Report for 1924* **1**: 64-82.
anon. 1925. Reports on plants sent in by members. True mosses. European (British and Continental). *The British Bryological Society Report for 1925* **1**: 131-165.
anon. 1926. Reports on plants sent in by members. True mosses. European (British and Continental). *The British Bryological Society Report for 1926* **1**: 209-233.
anon. 1927. Reports on plants sent in by members. True mosses. European (British and Continental). *The British Bryological Society Report for 1926-7* **1**: 276-300.
anon. 1929. Reports on plants sent in by members. True mosses. European (British and Continental). *The British Bryological Society Report for 1928* **2**: 91-114.
anon. 1931a. Reports on plants sent in by members for distribution. True mosses. European (British and Continental). *The British Bryological Society Report for 1930* **2**: 243-272.
anon. 1931b. Reports on plants sent in by members for distribution. Hepatics. European (British and Continental). *The British Bryological Society Report for 1930* **2**: 281-288.
anon. 1932. Reports on plants sent in by members for distribution. True mosses. European (British and Continental). *The British Bryological Society Report for 1931* **2**: 332-351.
anon. 1934a. Reports on plants sent in by members. Sphagna. *The British Bryological Society Report for 1933* **3**: 103-106.
anon. 1934b. Reports on plants sent in by members.True mosses. European (British and Continental). *The British Bryological Society Report for 1933* **3**: 107-134.
anon. 1934c. Reports on plants sent in by members. Hepatics. European (British and Continental). *The British Bryological Society Report for 1933* **3**: 140-148.
anon. 1936. Reports on plants sent in by members. True mosses. European (British and Continental). *The British Bryological Society Report for 1935* **3**: 270-285.
anon. 1937a. Census Catalogues. List of additional V.C. records since the issue of Supplements in 1935, but not distributed or otherwise published. Mosses. *The British Bryological Society Report for 1936* **3**: 366-368.
anon. 1937b. [Census Catalogues.] List of Hepatic records, additional v.c.'s, etc., since the issue of the Supplement and not distributed or otherwise published. *The British Bryological Society Report for 1936* **3**: 369-370.
anon. 1938a. Reports on plants sent in by members. Sphagna. *The British Bryological Society Report for 1937* **4**: 19-22.
anon. 1938b. Reports on plants sent in by members. True mosses. European (British and Continental). *The British Bryological Society Report for 1937* **4**: 22-32.
anon. 1938c. Reports on plants sent in by members. Hepatics European, (British and Continental). *The British Bryological Society Report for 1937* **4**: 33-38.
anon. 1938d. Census Catalogues. List of additional V.C. records since the issue of the Report for 1936. Mosses. *The British Bryological Society Report for 1937* **4**: 38-42.
anon. 1938e. [Census Catalogues.] Hepatics. List of additional V.C. records since the issue of the Report for 1936. *The British Bryological Society Report for 1937* **4**: 42-45.
anon. 1939a. Reports on plants sent in by members. True mosses. European (British and Continental). *The British Bryological Society Report for 1938* **4**: 87-100.
anon. 1939b. Census Catalogues. List of additional V.C. records since the issue of the Report for 1937. Mosses. *The British Bryological Society Report for 1938* **4**: 108-110.
anon. 1939c. [Census Catalogues.] Hepatics. List of additional V.C. records since the issue of the Report for 1937. *The British Bryological Society Report for 1938* **4**: 111.
anon. 1940a. Census Catalogues. List of additional V.C. records since the issue of the Report for 1938. Mosses. *The* British *Bryological Society Report for 1939* **4**: 172-176.
anon. 1940b. [Census Catalogues.] Hepatics. List of additional V.C. records since the issue of the Report for 1938. *The British Bryological Society Report for 1939* **4**: 177-179.
anon. 1946a. Report on plants sent in by members for distribution. True mosses. European (British and Continental). *The British Bryological Society Report for 1944-45* **4**: 252-268.

anon. 1946b. Census Catalogues. Lists of new vice-county records. Sphagna. *The British Bryological Society Report for 1944-45* **4**: 277-278.

anon. 1946c. [Census Catalogues.] List of additional V.C. records for the years 1944-45. Mosses. *The British Bryological Society Report for 1944-45* **4**: 279-286.

anon. 1947. New vice-county records. Musci. *Transactions of the British Bryological Society* **1**: 28-35.

anon. 1948a. New vice-county records. Sphagna. *Transactions of the British Bryological Society* **1**: 117-118.

anon. 1948b. New vice-county records. Musci. *Transactions of the British Bryological Society* **1**: 118-124.

anon. 1949a. New vice-county records. Hepaticae. *Transactions of the British Bryological Society* **1**: 212-214.

anon. 1949b. New vice-county records. Sphagna. *Transactions of the British Bryological Society* **1**: 214-216.

anon. 1949c. New vice-county records. Musci. *Transactions of the British Bryological Society* **1**: 216-222.

anon. 1989. *Gazetteer of Ireland. Names of centres of population and physical features.* Dublin: Prepared by the Placenames Branch of the Ordnance Survey.

Ando, H. & Townsend, C.C. 1980. *Hypnum uncinulatum* Jur. reinstated as an Irish species. *Journal of Bryology* **11**: 185-189.

Appleyard, J. 1971. The Summer Meeting 1970. *Transactions of the British Bryological Society* **6**: 387-390.

Appleyard, J., Hill, M.O. & Whitehouse, H.L.K. 1985. *Leptobarbula berica* (De Not.) Schimp. in Britain. *Journal of Bryology* **13**: 461-470.

Armitage, E.[A]. 1938. Report of the Annual Meeting, 1937. *The British Bryological Society Report for 1937*, **4**: 9-14.

Armitage, E.A. 1944. *A short account of the Moss Exchange Club and the British Bryological Society.* Privately published.

Armitage, E.A. 1956. *A short account of the Moss Exchange Club and the British Bryological Society.* 2nd ed. Privately published. 24 pp.

Babington, C.C. 1859. Hints towards a Cybele Hibernica. *Proceedings of Dublin University Zoological and Botanical Association* **1**: 246-250, and *Natural History Review* **6** (Proceedings): 533-537.

Bakalin, V.A. 2001. Notes on *Lophozia* III. Some taxonomic problems in *Lophozia* sect. *Lophozia*. *Arctoa* **10**: 207-218.

Barker, [T.], Ingham, W., Jones, D.A., Meldrum, R.H., Waddell, C.H., Lett, M.A. & Marquand, E.D. 1907. *A* Census *Catalogue of British Mosses with Lists of the Botanical Vice Counties and their boundaries, and Lists of Sources of Records, compiled under the Direction of the Moss Exchange Club.* York: Coultas & Volans, for M.E.C.

Barry, T.A. & Synnott, D.M. 1970. Recent Quaternary bryophyte records. *Irish Naturalists' Journal* **16**: 351-352.

Barry, T.A. & Synnott, D.M. 1973. Subfossil *Meesia longiseta* in Ireland. *Irish Naturalists' Journal* **17**: 318.

Belfast Naturalists' Field Club. 1952. Crow Glen, Co. Antrim. *Irish Naturalists' Journal* **10**: 266-273.

Birks, H.H., Birks, H.J.B. & Ratcliffe, D.A. 1969. *Geocalyx graveolens* (Schrad.) Nees in Kerry, a hepatic new to Ireland. *Irish Naturalists' Journal* **16**: 204-205.

Birks, H.J.B. 1974. Distribution maps of bryophytes – *Tortula vahliana. Journal of Bryology* **8**: 125.

Birks, H.J.B. 1975. Distribution maps of bryophytes – *Dicranum scottianum. Journal of Bryology* **8**: 498.

Birks, H.J.B. 1976. Distribution maps of bryophytes in Britain and Ireland – *Glyphomitrium daviesii. Journal of Bryology* **9**: 122.

Birks, H.J.B., Birks, H.H. & Ratcliffe, D.A. 1969. Mountain plants on Slieve League, Co. Donegal. *Irish Naturalists' Journal* **16**: 203.

Birks, H.J.B. & Ratcliffe, D.A. 1976a. Distribution maps of bryophytes in Britain and Ireland – *Frullania germana. Journal of Bryology* **9**: 113.

Birks, H.J.B. & Ratcliffe, D.A. 1976b. Distribution maps of bryophytes in Britain and Ireland –

Sphagnum fuscum. *Journal of Bryology* **9**: 118.

Bischler-Causse, H. & Boisselier-Dubayle, M.C. 1991. Lectotypification of *Marchantia polymorpha* L. *Journal of Bryology* **16**: 361-365.

Blackstock, T.H. 1999. New vice-county records and amendments to the Census Catalogue. Hepaticae. *Bulletin of the British Bryological Society* **73**: 36-39.

Blackstock, T.H. 2000. New vice-county records and amendments to the *Census Catalogue*. Hepaticae. *Bulletin of the British Bryological Society* **75**: 40-45.

Blackstock, T.H. 2001. New vice-county records and amendments to the *Census Catalogue*. Hepaticae. *Bulletin of the British Bryological Society* **77**: 33-37.

Blackstock, T.H. 2002. New vice-county records and amendments to the *Census Catalogue*. Hepaticae. *Bulletin of the British Bryological Society* **79**: 38-42.

Blackstock, T.H. 2003. New vice-county records and amendments to the *Census Catalogue*. Hepaticae. *Bulletin of the British Bryological Society* **81**: 39-46.

Blackstock, T.H. & Long, D.G. 2002. *Heteroscyphus fissistipus* (Hook.f. & Taylor) Schiffn. established in south-west Ireland, new to the Northern Hemisphere. *Journal of Bryology* **24**: 147-150.

Blockeel, T.L. 1987. New vice-county records and amendments to the Census Catalogues. Musci. *Bulletin of the British Bryological Society* **50**: 20-26.

Blockeel, T.L. 1988. New vice-county records and amendments to the Census Catalogue. Musci. *Bulletin of the British Bryological Society* **52**: 33-40.

Blockeel, T.L. 1989. New vice-county records and amendments to the Census Catalogue. Hepaticae. *Bulletin of the British Bryological Society* **54**: 24-32.

Blockeel, T.L. 1990. New vice-county records and amendments to the Census Catalogue. Musci. *Bulletin of the British Bryological Society* **56**: 29-34.

Blockeel, T.L. 1991a. The Summer Meeting, 1990, Ireland. *Bulletin of the British Bryological Society* **57**: 5-11.

Blockeel, T.L. 1991b. The *Racomitrium heterostichum* group in the British Isles. *Bulletin of the British Bryological Society* **58**: 29-35.

Blockeel, T.L. 1991c. New vice-county records and amendments to the Census Catalogue. Musci. *Bulletin of the British Bryological Society* **58**: 40-46.

Blockeel, T.L. 1992. New vice-county records and amendments to the Census Catalogue. Musci. *Bulletin of the British Bryological Society* **60**: 25-29.

Blockeel, T.L. 1993. New vice-county records and amendments to the Census Catalogue. Musci. *Bulletin of the British Bryological Society* **62**: 47-55.

Blockeel, T.L. 1994. New vice-county records and amendments to the Census Catalogue. Musci. *Bulletin of the British Bryological Society* **64**: 35-42.

Blockeel, T.[L.] 1995a. Summer Field Meeting, 1994, Second week, Clifden. *Bulletin of the British Bryological Society* **65**: 12-18.

Blockeel, T.L. 1995b. A note on *Phascum cuspidatum* ssp. *papillosum* in the British Isles. *Bulletin of the British Bryological Society* **65**: 59-60.

Blockeel, T.L. 1995c. New vice-county records and amendments to the Census Catalogue. Musci. *Bulletin of the British Bryological Society* **66**: 40-47.

Blockeel, T.L. 1996. New vice-county records and amendments to the Census Catalogue. Musci. *Bulletin of the British Bryological Society* **68**: 44-48.

Blockeel, T.L. 1997a. New vice-county records and amendments to the Census Catalogue. Hepaticae. *Bulletin of the British Bryological Society* **70**: 41-46.

Blockeel, T.L. 1997b. A revision of British specimens of *Drepanocladus vernicosus*. Unpublished Report to Joint Nature Conservation Committee, 20 pp.

Blockeel, T.L. 1998. *Cinclidotus riparius* re-instated as a British and Irish moss. *Journal of Bryology* **20**: 109-119.

Blockeel, T.L. 1999. Musci, pp. 1-25 in Blockeel, T.L. & Long, D.G., The New Census Catalogue: supplementary lists of deleted, recent and replacement records. *Bulletin of the British Bryological Society* **73**, Supplement: 1-28.

Blockeel, T.L. 2000. The identification of *Drepanocladus revolvens* and *D.* cossonii, and their distribution in Britain and Ireland. *Bulletin of the British Bryological Society* **75**: 32-40.

Blockeel, T.L. in Blockeel, T.L. *et al.* 2002. New national and regional bryophyte records, 5. *Journal of Bryology* **24**: 88-91.

Blockeel, T.L. & Long, D.G. 1998. *A check-list and census catalogue of British and Irish bryophytes.* Cardiff: British Bryological Society.

Blockeel, T.L., Fuertes, E., Oliván, G., Holyoak, D.T. & Long, D.G. 2000a. New national and regional bryophyte records, 2. *Journal of Bryology* **22**: 68-70.

Blockeel, T.L., Ochyra, R. & Gos, L. 2000b. *Seligeria campylopoda* Kindb. in the British Isles. *Journal of Bryology* **22**: 29-33.

Blom, H.H. 1996. A revision of the *Schistidium apocarpum* complex in Norway and Sweden. *Bryophytorum Bibliotheca* **49**.

Buch, H. 1938. *Telaranea nematodes* aus Irland. *Annales Bryologici* **11**: 32-33.

Caffrey, J.M. 1987. *Ricciocarpus natans* (L.) Corda in Co Meath. *Irish Naturalists' Journal* **22**: 339-340.

Castell, C.P. 1950. New vice-county records. Hepaticae. *Transactions of the British Bryological Society* **1**: 374-380.

Castell, C.P. 1951. New vice-county records. Hepaticae. *Transactions of the British Bryological Society* **1**: 491-496.

Castell, C.P. 1952. New vice-county records. Hepaticae. *Transactions of the British Bryological Society* **2**: 89-97.

Castell, C.P. 1953. New vice-county records. Hepaticae. *Transactions of the British Bryological Society* **2**: 297-304.

Castell, C.P. 1954. New vice-county records. Hepaticae. *Transactions of the British Bryological Society* **2**: 471-477.

Castell, C.P. 1955. New vice-county records. Hepaticae. *Transactions of the British Bryological Society* **2**: 578-582.

Castell, C.P. 1956. New vice-county records. Hepaticae. *Transactions of the British Bryological Society* **3**: 146-150.

Castell, C.P. 1957. New vice-county records. Hepaticae. *Transactions of the British Bryological Society* **3**: 322-326.

Castell, C.P. 1958. New vice-county records. Hepaticae. *Transactions of the British Bryological Society* **3**: 461-470.

Castell, C.P. 1959. New vice-county records. Hepaticae. *Transactions of the British Bryological Society* **3**: 626-630.

Castell, C.P. 1960. New vice-county records. Hepaticae. *Transactions of the British Bryological Society* **3**: 763-769.

C.[hase], C.D. 1954. William Rutledge Megaw, 1885-1953. *Irish Naturalists' Journal* **11**: 181-183.

Colgan, N. & Scully, R.W. 1898. *Contributions towards a Cybele Hibernica, being outlines of the geographical distribution of plants in Ireland.* 2nd ed. Dublin: Edward Ponsonby & London: Gurney & Jackson.

Corley, M.F.V. 1976. The taxonomy of *Campylopus pyriformis* (Schultz) Brid. and related species. *Journal of Bryology* **9**: 193-212.

Corley, M.F.V. 1978. New vice-county records and amendments to the Census Catalogues. Hepaticae. Bulletin *of the British Bryological Society* **32**: 12-15.

Corley, M.F.V. 1979. New vice-county records and amendments to the Census Catalogues. Hepaticae. *Bulletin of the British Bryological Society* **34**: 22-25.

Corley, M.F.V. 1980a. New vice-county records and amendments to the Census Catalogues. Hepaticae. *Bulletin of the British Bryological Society* **36**: 25-32.

Corley, M.F.V. 1980b. The *Fissidens viridulus* complex in the British Isles and Europe. *Journal of Bryology* **11**: 191-208.

Corley, M.F.V. 1981. New vice-county records and amendments to the Census Catalogues. Hepaticae. *Bulletin of the British Bryological Society* **38**: 17-21.

Corley, M.F.V. 1982. New vice-county records and amendments to the Census Catalogues. Hepaticae. *Bulletin of the British Bryological Society* **40**: 19-23.

Corley, M.F.V. 1983. New vice-county records and amendments to the Census Catalogues. Hepaticae. *Bulletin of the British Bryological Society* **42**: 47-49.

Corley, M.F.V. 1984. New vice-county records and amendments to the Census Catalogues. Hepaticae. *Bulletin of the British Bryological Society* **44**: 23-25.
Corley, M.F.V. 1985. New vice-county records and amendments to the Census Catalogues. Hepaticae. *Bulletin of the British Bryological Society* **46**: 20-22.
Corley, M.F.V. 1986. New vice-county records and amendments to the Census Catalogues. Hepaticae. *Bulletin of the British Bryological Society* **48**: 17-18.
Corley, M.F.V. 1987. New vice-county records and amendments to the Census Catalogues. Hepaticae. *Bulletin of the British Bryological Society* **50**: 18-20.
Corley, M.F.V. & Hill, M.O. 1981. *Distribution of bryophytes in the British Isles. A census catalogue of their occurrence in vice-counties.* Cardiff: British Bryological Society.
Cridland, A.A. 1958. An outline of the bryophytes of County Laois (Queen's County). *Transactions of the British Bryological Society* **3**: 339-417.
Crundwell, A.C. 1952. Some bryophytes from the Dingle Peninsula. *Irish Naturalists' Journal* **10**: 309-311.
Crundwell, A.C. 1959. Some bryophytes from Counties Cavan and Fermanagh. *Irish Naturalists' Journal* **13**: 36-39.
Crundwell, A.C. 1968. New vice-county records and amendments to the Census Catalogues. Musci. *Transactions of the British Bryological Society* **5**: 629-649.
Crundwell, A.C. 1969. New vice-county records and amendments to the Census Catalogues. Musci. *Transactions of the British Bryological Society* **5**: 876-892.
Crundwell, A.C. 1970. New vice-county records and amendments to the Census Catalogues. Musci. *Transactions of the British Bryological Society* **6**: 195-211.
Crundwell, A.C. 1971a. *Weissia perssonii* Kindb., a neglected West European moss. *Transactions of the British Bryological Society* **6**: 221-224.
Crundwell, A.C. 1971b. New vice-county records and amendments to the Census Catalogues. Musci. *Transactions of the British Bryological Society* **6**: 374-384.
Crundwell, A.C. 1972. New vice-county records and amendments to the Census Catalogues. Musci. *Journal of Bryology* **7**: 135-144.
Crundwell, A.C. 1973. New vice-county records and amendments to the Census Catalogues. Musci. *Journal of Bryology* **7**: 506-515.
Crundwell, A.C. 1974. New vice-county records and amendments to the Census Catalogues. Musci. *Journal of Bryology* **8**: 165-176.
Crundwell, A.C. 1975. New vice-county records and amendments to the Census Catalogues. Musci. *Bulletin of the British Bryological Society* **26**: 12-22.
Crundwell, A.C. 1976. New vice-county records and amendments to the Census Catalogues. Musci. *Bulletin of the British Bryological Society* **28**: 21-33.
Crundwell, A.C. 1980. The Irish Meeting, August 1979. *Bulletin of the British Bryological Society* **36**: 9-11.
Crundwell, A.C. 1995. *Hedwigia stellata* and *H. ciliata* in the British Isles. *Journal of Bryology* **18**: 807-810.
Crundwell, A.C. & Nyholm, E. 1964. The European species of the *Bryum erythrocarpum* Complex. *Transactions of the British Bryological Society* **4**: 597-637.
Crundwell, A.C. & Nyholm, E. 1974. *Funaria muhlenbergii* and related European species. *Lindbergia* **2**: 222-229.
Crundwell, A.C. & Smith, A.J.E. 2000. *Heterocladium wulfsbergii* I.Hagen in the British Isles. *Journal of Bryology* **22**: 43-47.
Crundwell, A.C. & Warburg, E.F. 1963. *Seligeria oelandica* in Ireland, new to the British Isles. *Transactions of the British Bryological Society* **4**: 426-428.
Crundwell, A.C. & Whitehouse, H.L.K. 2001. A revision of *Bryum bornholmense* Wink. & R.Ruthe. *Journal of Bryology* **23**: 171-176.
Cullinane, J.P. & Whelan, P.M. 1977. The Bryophyte Herbarium, University College, Cork. *Irish Naturalists' Journal* **19**: 90-91.
Daniels, R.E. & Eddy, A. 1990. *Handbook of European Sphagna.* 2nd impression with minor corrections. London: HMSO.

Demaret, F. & Geissler, P. 1990. L'identité de *Bryum inclinatum* (Brid.) Turner homonyme illégitime et les espèces voisines. *Bull. Jardin Bot. National Belg.* **60**: 223-228.

Derda, G.S. & Wyatt, R. 1990. Genetic variation in the common hair-cap moss, *Polytrichum commune*. *Systematic Botany* **15**: 592-605.

Dickson, J.H. 1969. *Cryptothallus mirabilis* in Ireland. *Irish Naturalists' Journal* **16**: 135, Pl. 4.

Dixon, H.N. 1923. *Porotrichum angustifolium* in Ireland. *The Irish Naturalist* 1923, pp. 45-47.

Dixon, H.N. 1924. *The student's handbook of British mosses.* 3rd ed. Eastbourne: Sumfield & Day.

Douglas, C. 1987. The distribution and ecology of *Sphagnum pulchrum* (Braithw.) Warnst. in Ireland. *Glasra* **10**: 75-81.

Duncan, J.B. 1926. *A Census Catalogue of British Mosses with Lists of the Botanical Vice Counties and their boundaries, and Lists of Sources of Records (2nd Edition), compiled for The British Bryological Society (Formerly The Moss Exchange Club) ...* Berwick-on-Tweed, Martin's Printing Works, for BBS.

Duncan, J.B. 1928. British Bryological Society. Annual Meeting and Excursion. Belfast, 25th to 31st August, 1928. *Irish Naturalists' Journal* **2**: 112-119.

Duncan, J.B. 1929a. Report of the Annual Meeting, 1928. *The British Bryological Society Report for 1928*, **2**: 128.

D.[uncan], J.B. 1929b. *British Bryological Society. Census Catalogue of British Mosses (2nd Edition, 1926), Supplement.* Berwick-on-Tweed: Martin's Printing Works, for BBS.

D.[uncan], J.B. 1935. British Bryological Society. Census Catalogue of British Mosses (2nd Edition, 1926) [Supplement], 6 pp. in *The British Bryological Society. Supplements to Census Catalogue of British Mosses (2nd Edition), and Census Catalogue of British Hepatics (3rd Edition).* Berwick-on-Tweed: Martin's Printing Works, for BBS.

D.[uncan], J.B. 1944. [Census Catalogues]. List of additional V.C. Records since the issue of the Report for 1939. Mosses. *The British Bryological Society Report for 1940-43* **4**: 208-217.

Duncan, U.K. 1967. Distribution maps of bryophytes in Britain – *Sphagnum riparium. Transactions of the British Bryological Society* **5**: 361.

Farrington, A. 1954. Robert Lloyd Praeger, 1865-1953. *Irish Naturalists' Journal* **11**: 141-171.

Fitzgerald, J.W. 1950. Some Irish liverwort records. *Irish Naturalists' Journal* **10**: 107.

Fitzgerald, J.W. 1951. Some Irish liverwort records: II. *Irish Naturalists' Journal* **10**: 214.

Fitzgerald, J.W. 1952. *Scapania umbrosa* (Schrad.) Dum. on Ben Bulben, 1892. *Irish Naturalists' Journal* **10**: 298.

Fitzgerald, J.W. 1958. *Eucalyx paroicus* (Schiffn.) Macv. new to Ireland. *Irish Naturalists' Journal* **12**: 247.

Fitzgerald, J.W. 1960. *Calypogeia suecica* (Arn. & Pers.) K. Müll. and the epixylic bryophyte communities at Sheskinawaddy. *Irish Naturalists' Journal* **13**: 129-133.

Fitzgerald, J.W. 1962. *Calypogeia suecica* (Arn. & Pers.) K. Müll. growing on peat. *Irish Naturalists' Journal* **14**: 18.

Fitzgerald, J.W. 1969. Two hepatics new to Ireland. *Irish Naturalists' Journal* **16**: 241.

Fitzgerald, J.W. & Fitzgerald, R.D. 1960a. Bryophytes found in Counties Tyrone, Londonderry and Fermanagh, including some new to the Irish list. *Irish Naturalists' Journal* **13**: 174-177.

Fitzgerald, J.W. & Fitzgerald, R.D. 1960b. A bryophyte flora of Co. Tyrone. *Transactions of the British Bryological Society* **3**: 653-687.

Fitzgerald, J.W. & Fitzgerald, R.D. 1961. Gleanings among the Waddell MSS. *Irish Naturalists' Journal* **13**: 227-231.

Fitzgerald, J.W. & Fitzgerald, R.D. 1966a. Bryophytes new to the Irish list. *Irish Naturalists' Journal* **15**: 178-180.

Fitzgerald, J.W. & Fitzgerald, R.D. 1966b. Bryophyte additions to *A Flora of the North-east of Ireland'*. *Irish Naturalists' Journal* **15**: 180-182.

Fitzgerald, J.W. & Fitzgerald, R.D. 1967. Bryophytes of County Armagh. *Irish Naturalists' Journal* **15**: 324-326.

Fitzgerald, J.W. & Fitzgerald, R.D. 1968a. Bryophyte additions to *A Flora of the North-east of Ireland'*. *Irish Naturalists' Journal* **16**: 77.

Fitzgerald, J.W. & Fitzgerald, R.D. 1968b. *Calypogeia suecica* (Arn. & Pers.) K. Mull. in Kerry. *Irish Naturalists' Journal* **16**: 79-80.

Fitzgerald, J.W. & Fitzgerald, R.D. 1969. Bryophyte additions to *A Flora of the North-east of Ireland'*. *Irish Naturalists' Journal* **16**: 240-241.

Fitzgerald, J.W. & Perry, A.R. 1964. *Herberta* in Ireland, and its occur[r]ence at Fair Head, County Antrim. *Irish Naturalists' Journal* **14**: 229-232.

Fitzgerald, R.D. 1950. Some Irish moss records. *Irish Naturalists' Journal* **10**: 108.

Fitzgerald, R.D. 1951. The discovery of *Fontinalis dixoni* Card. et Dix. in Ireland. *Irish Naturalists' Journal* **10**: 164-166.

Fitzgerald, R.D. 1952a. Report of the Autumn Meeting in Ireland, 1951. *Transactions of the British Bryological Society* **2**: 125-128.

Fitzgerald, R.D. 1952b. *Brachythecium rivulare* (Bruch) B. & S. var. *latifolium* Husn. new to Ireland. *Irish Naturalists' Journal* **10**: 249.

Fitzgerald, R.D. 1952c. Some Irish moss records: II. *Irish Naturalists' Journal* **10**: 250.

Fitzgerald, R.D. 1952d. Some Irish moss records: III. *Irish Naturalists' Journal* **10**: 320.

Fitzgerald, R.D. & Fitzgerald, J.W. 1952. British Bryological Society excursion to Glenbeigh and Waterville, Co. Kerry, 1st to 14th Sept. 1951. *Revue Bryologique et Lichénologique* **21**: 179-182.

Flatberg, K.I. 1985. Studies in *Sphagnum subfulvum* Sjörs, and related morphotypes. *Lindbergia* **11**: 38-54.

Fox, H., Blockeel, T.[L.] & Perry, A.R. 2001. Summer field meeting, Dungarvan and New Ross, Ireland, 1999. *Bulletin of the British Bryological Society* **76**: 3-10.

Frahm, J.P. 1999. A survey of the *Campylopus* species from the Azores. *Cryptogamie* Bryologie **20**: 145-152.

Frisvoll, A.A. 1983. A taxonomic revision of the *Racomitrium canescens* group (Bryophyta, Grimmiales). *Gunneria* **41**: 1-181.

Frisvoll, A.A. 1988. A taxonomic revision of the *Racomitrium heterostichum* group (Bryophyta, Grimmiales) in N. and C. America, N. Africa, Europe and Asia. *Gunneria* **59**: 1-289.

Geissler, P. 1984. Notulae Bryofloristicae Helveticae. *Candollea* **39**: 641-646.

Goodwillie, R. 1999. *Homalothecium nitens* (Hedw.) Robins. – new to Co Limerick (H8). *Irish Naturalists' Journal* **26**: 288.

Greene, S.W. 1957. The British species of the *Plagiothecium denticulatum– P. silvaticum* group. *Transactions of the British Bryological Society* **3**: 181-190.

Greig-Smith, P. 1954. Notes on Lejeuneaceae. II. A quantitative assessment of criteria used in distinguishing some British species of *Lejeunea*. *Transactions of the British Bryological Society* **2**: 458-469.

Greven, H.C. 1995. Grimmia *Hedw. (Grimmiaceae, Musci) in Europe*. Leiden: Backhuys.

Greven, H.C. 1997. *Grimmia austro-funalis* C. Müll., a species with a misleading name and a disjunct distribution. *Journal of Bryology* **19**: 827-830.

Grolle, R. & Long, D.G. 2000. An annotated check-list of the Hepaticae and Anthocerotae of Europe and Macaronesia. *Journal of Bryology* **22**: 103-140.

Guerra, J., Jiménez, M.N., Ros, R.M. & Carrión, J.S. 1991. El genero *Phascum* (Pottiaceae) en la Península Ibérica. *Cryptogamie, Bryologie-Lichénologie* **12(4)**: 379-423.

Hackney, P. 1973. *Orthodontium lineare* Schwaegr. in County Antrim. *Irish Naturalists' Journal* **17**: 425.

Hackney, P. 1980. Plant Notes. Bryophytes and Lichens. *Irish Naturalists' Journal* **20**: 170.

Halliday, G., Argent, G.C. & Hawksworth, D.L. 1967. Some Irish plant records. *Irish Naturalists' Journal* **15**: 313-316.

Hedenäs, L. 1989. The genera *Scorpidium* and *Hamatocaulis*, gen. nov., in northern Europe. *Lindbergia* **15**: 8-36.

Hedenäs, L. 1994. The *Hedwigia ciliata* complex in Sweden, with notes on the occurrence of the taxa in Fennoscandia. *Journal of Bryology* **18**: 139-157.

Hegewald, E. 1973. *Campylopus polytrichoides* De Not. with sporophytes in Ireland. *Journal of Bryology* **7**: 443-445.

Heinrichs, J., Grolle, R. & Drehwald, U. 1998. The conspecificity of *Plagiochila killarniensis* Pearson and *P. bifaria* (Sw.) Lindenb. (Hepaticae). *Journal of Bryology* **20**: 495-497.

Hill, M.O. 1977a. New vice-county records and amendments to the Census Catalogues. Musci. *Bulletin of the British Bryological Society* **30**: 16-26.

Hill, M.O. 1977b. *Sphagnum flexuosum* and its varieties in Britain. *Bulletin of the British Bryological Society* **29**: 19.

Hill, M.O. 1978. New vice-county records and amendments to the Census Catalogues. Musci. *Bulletin of the British Bryological Society* **32**: 15-25.

Hill, M.O. 1979. New vice-county records and amendments to the Census Catalogues. Musci. *Bulletin of the British Bryological Society* **34**: 25-33.

Hill, M.O. 1980a. Vice-county distributions of segregates of *Pottia starkeana. Bulletin of the British Bryological Society* **35**: 9.

Hill, M.O. 1980b. New vice-county records and amendments to the Census Catalogues. Musci. *Bulletin of the British Bryological Society* **36**: 32-49.

Hill, M.O. 1981. New vice-county records and amendments to the Census Catalogues. Musci. *Bulletin of the British Bryological Society* **38**: 21-37.

Hill, M.O. 1982. New vice-county records and amendments to the Census Catalogues. Musci. *Bulletin of the British Bryological Society* **40**: 23-30.

Hill, M.O. 1983. New vice-county records and amendments to the Census Catalogues. Musci. *Bulletin of the British Bryological Society* **42**: 49-58.

Hill, M.O. 1984a. *Racomitrium elongatum* Frisvoll in Britain and Ireland. *Bulletin of the British Bryological Society* **43**: 21-25.

Hill, M.O. 1984b. New vice-county records and amendments to the Census Catalogues. Musci. *Bulletin of the British Bryological Society* **44**: 25-30.

Hill, M.O.1985. New vice-county records and amendments to the Census Catalogues. Musci. *Bulletin of the British Bryological Society* **46**: 22-28.

Hill, M.O. 1986. New vice-county records and amendments to the Census Catalogues. Musci. *Bulletin of the British Bryological Society* **48**: 18-24.

Hill, M.O. 1993. *Eurhynchium pulchellum* (Hedw.) Jenn. in Britain and Ireland. *Journal of Bryology* **17**: 683-684.

Hill, M.O. 2002. The *Drepanocladus aduncus* group in Britain and Ireland. *Bulletin of the British Bryological Society* **78**: 59-61.

Hill, M.O. 2003. Observations on *Drepanocladus aduncus* in Britain. *Bulletin of the British Bryological Society* **81**: 64-65.

Hill, M.O., Preston, C.D. & Smith, A.J.E. 1991. *Atlas of the bryophytes of Britain and Ireland. 1. Liverworts (Hepaticae and Anthocerotae).* Colchester: Harley Books.

Hill, M.O., Preston, C.D. & Smith, A.J.E. 1992. *Atlas of the bryophytes of Britain and Ireland. 2. Mosses (except Diplolepideae).* Colchester: Harley Books.

Hill, M.O., Preston, C.D. & Smith, A.J.E. 1994. *Atlas of the bryophytes of Britain and Ireland. 3. Mosses (Diplolepideae).* Colchester: Harley Books.

Hodgetts, N.G. 2001. A re-evaluation of *Bryum subelegans* Kindb. in Britain. *Journal of Bryology* **23**: 177-180.

Hodgetts, N.G. & Hallingbäck, T. 1994. Some bryophytes new to Ireland. *Irish Naturalists' Journal* **24**: 517-518.

Holmgren, P.K. & Keuken, W. 1974. *Index Herbariorum. Part I. The Herbaria of the World.* 6th ed. Utrecht: International Bureau for Plant Taxonomy and Nomenclature.

Holyoak, D.T. 2001a. Starry earth-moss *Ephemerum stellatum*. Report to Plantlife on work carried out during 2000. *Plantlife Report* no. **180**: 1-37.

Holyoak, D.T. 2001b. Tiny fern-moss *Fissidens exiguus*. Report to Plantlife on work carried out during 2000. *Plantlife Report* no. **181**: 1-23.

Holyoak, D.T. 2001c. *Ephemerum spinulosum* Bruch & Schimp. (Ephemeraceae) in Northern Ireland: a moss new to Europe. *Journal of Bryology* **23**: 139-141.

Holyoak, D.T. 2003. A taxonomic review of some British coastal species of the *Bryum bicolor* complex, with a description of *Bryum dyffrynense* sp. nov. *Journal of Bryology* **25**: 107-113.

Hooker, W.K. & Taylor, T. 1818. *Muscologia britannica*. London.

Ingham, W. 1913. *A Census Catalogue of British Hepatics, with List of the Botanical Vice-Counties and their boundaries and lists of Sources of Records. Compiled for the Moss Exchange*

Club ... 2nd ed. Darwen: W. H. Western, for M.E.C.
Ivimey-Cook, R.B. & Proctor, M.C.F. 1966. The plant communities of the Burren, Co. Clare. *Proceedings of the Royal Irish Academy* **64 B**: 211-301, pls. XIV-XXI.
Johnson, T. 1923. Canon Lett's Irish Sphagna. Determined by J. A. Wheldon. *Irish Naturalist* pp. 55-61.
Jones, D.A. 1917. Muscineae of Achill Island. *Journal of Botany* **55**: 240-246.
Jones, D.A. 1936a. *Cephalozia affinis* Lindb., in Ireland. *The British Bryological Society Report for 1935* **3**: 294.
Jones, D.A. 1936b. The hepatic, *Cephalozia affinis* Lind., in Ireland. *Irish Naturalists' Journal* **6**: 149.
J[ones], E.W. 1949. New vice-county records. Hepaticae. *Transactions of the British Bryological Society* **1**: 212-214.
Jones, E.W. 1954. Bryophytes seen in north-eastern Ireland, 1952. *Irish Naturalists' Journal* **11**: 115-120.
Jones, E.W. & Rose, F. 1975. *Plagiochila atlantica* F. Rose, sp. nov.–*P. ambagiosa* auct. *Journal of Bryology* **8**: 417-422.
Kelly, D.L. 1981. The native forest vegetation of Killarney, South-west Ireland: an ecological account. *Journal of Ecology* **69**: 437-472.
Kelly, D.L. 1984a. The summer meeting, 1983, Kerry. First week: Killorglin, 21-23 July. *Bulletin of the British Bryological Society* **43**: 5-6.
Kelly, D.L. 1984b. A note on the vice-county boundary between South and North Kerry: Is Derrycunihy in H1 or H2. *Irish Naturalists' Journal* **21**: 365.
Kelly, D.L. 1984c. Bryophytes – retraction of a record. *Irish Naturalists' Journal* **21**: 367.
Kelly, D.L. & Synnott, D.M. 1993. Bryophytes of the Phoenix Park, Dublin. *Glasra* **2**: 73-81.
Kertland, M.P.H. 1991. Obituary. Jean Wilgar Fitzgerald 1908-1988. Robert Desmond Fitzgerald 1914-1990. *Irish Naturalists' Journal* **23**: 345-346.
King, A.L.K. 1950. *Brachythecium caespitosum* Dixon in Co. Cavan. *Irish Naturalists' Journal* **10**: 21.
King, A.L.K. 1952. *Pohlia rothii* (Correns) Broth new to Ireland. *Irish Naturalists' Journal* **10**: 273.
King, A.L.K. 1953a. Bryophyte records from the Athlone district. *Irish Naturalists' Journal* **11**: 50-51.
King, A.L.K. 1953b. Bryophyte records made on one-day excursions from Dublin during 1952. *Irish Naturalists' Journal* **11**: 98-99.
King, A.L.K. 1954a. The hepatic *Ptilidium pulcherrimum* (Web.) Hampe new to Ireland. *Irish Naturalists' Journal* **11**: 205.
King, A.L.K. 1954b. New records of bryophytes found during a botanical tour in June, 1952. *Irish Naturalists' Journal* **11**: 230-231.
King, A.L.K. 1954c. Findings of the old bryologists. *Irish Naturalists' Journal* **11**: 235.
King, A.L.K. 1956a. Some interesting bryophytes. *Irish Naturalists' Journal* **12**: 70.
King, A.L.K. 1956b. *Camptothecium nitens* (Hedw.) Schp. as a fossil. *Irish Naturalists' Journal* **12**: 70-71.
King, A.L.K. 1957a. "Ireland and the Isle of Man": a correction. *Irish Naturalists' Journal* **12**: 201.
King, A.L.K. 1957b. Two interesting hepatics. *Irish Naturalists' Journal* **12**: 201.
King, A.L.K. 1958a. *Camptothecium nitens* (Hedw.) Schp. in Ireland. *Irish Naturalists' Journal* **12**: 247-248.
King, A.L.K. 1958b. *Meesia tristicha* Bruch & Schimp. in Ireland. *Irish Naturalists' Journal* **12**: 332.
King, A.L.K. 1960. Some interesting bryophytes. *Irish Naturalists' Journal* **13**: 171.
King, A.L.K. 1963a. *Campylopus brevipilus* B. & S., fruiting. *Irish Naturalists' Journal* **14**: 123.
King, A.L.K. 1963b. *Campylopus introflexus* (Hedw.) Brid., with capsules. *Irish Naturalists' Journal* **14**: 123.
King, A.L.K. 1966a. Some interesting bryophytes: 1. Hepatics. *Irish Naturalists' Journal* **15**: 207-208.
King, A.L.K. 1966b. Some interesting bryophytes: 2. Mosses. *Irish Naturalists' Journal* **15**: 234-236.
King, A.L.K. 1967a. Some interesting bryophytes: Mosses. *Irish Naturalists' Journal* **15**: 304-305.
King, A.L.K. 1967b. *Cinclidium stygium* Sw. in Co. Westmeath. *Irish Naturalists' Journal* **15**: 331.
King, A.L.K. 1968. *Nardia geoscyphus* (De Not.) Lindb., new to Ireland and *Drepanocladus sendtneri* var. β *wilsonii* (Schimp. ex Lor.) Warnst. new to South East Galway. *Irish Naturalists' Journal* **16**: 23.

King, A.L.K. 1970. Recent additions to the Irish bryophyte census lists. *Irish Naturalists' Journal* **16**: 350-351.

King, A.L.K. & Morrison, M.E.S. 1956. *Sphagnum imbricatum* Hornsch. ex Russ. *Irish Naturalists' Journal* **12**: 105-107.

King, A.L.K. & Scannell, M. 1960. Notes on the vegetation of a mineral flush in Co. Mayo. *Irish Naturalists' Journal* **13**: 137-140.

Kirby, N., Lockhart, N.D. & Synnott, D.M. 1980. Observations on the bryology at Gleniff, Co. Sligo (H28). *Bulletin of the Irish Biogeographical Society* **4**: 30-32.

Koponen, T. 1971. A monograph of *Plagiomnium* sect. *Rosulata* (Mniaceae). *Annales botanici* fennici **8**: 305-367.

Kučera, J. 2000. Illustrierter Bestimmungsschlüssel zu den mitteleuropäischen Arten der Gattung *Didymodon*. *Meylania* **19**: 1-49.

Lee, W.A. 1923a. Irish Sphagna. *Irish Naturalist* pp. 28-29.

Lee, W.A. 1923b. Irish Sphagna. *Irish Naturalist* pp. 121-123.

Lee, W.A. 1924. Irish Sphagna. *Irish Naturalist* p. 98.

Lett, H.W. 1902. *A list, with descriptive notes, of all the species of hepatics hitherto found in the British Islands.* Eastbourne.

Lett, H.W. 1912. Clare Island Survey. Parts 11-12. Musci and Hepaticae. *Proceedings of the Royal Irish Academy* **31**, Nos. 11-12: 1-18.

Lett, H.W. 1913. Mosses and hepatics of the Saltees. *Irish Naturalist* **22**: 192-194.

Lett, H.W. 1915. Census report on the mosses of Ireland. *Proceedings of the Royal Irish Academy* **32**, Section **B**, No. 7: 65-166.

Lewis, K. 1991. The Summer Meeting, 1990, Ireland. *Bulletin of the British Bryological Society* **57**: 5-8.

Lewis, K. & Smith, A.J.E. 1978. Studies on some bulbiliferous species of *Pohlia* section *Pohliella*. II. Taxonomy. *Journal of Bryology* **10**: 9-27.

Little, E.R.B. 1967. *Fissidens celticus* Paton, new to Ireland. *Irish Naturalists' Journal* **15**: 271.

Lobley, E.M. 1954. Notes on sphagna and other bryophytes from the north of Ireland. *Irish Naturalists' Journal* **11**: 197-198.

Lobley, E.M. 1955. Some Irish bryophyte records and localities. *Irish Naturalists' Journal* **11**: 253.

Lobley, E.M. 1958. The meeting of the British Bryological Society in Co. Galway, 1957. *Irish Naturalists' Journal* **12**: 285-290.

Lobley, E.M. 1962. Some records for bryophytes. *Irish Naturalists' Journal* **14**: 43-44.

Lobley, E.M. 1963. Bryophyte records for County Armagh. *Irish Naturalists' Journal* **14**: 98-99.

Lobley, E.M. & Fitzgerald, J.W. 1970. A revision of the genus *Sphagnum* L. in *A Flora of the North-east of Ireland. Irish Naturalists' Journal* **16**: 357-365.

Lockhart, N.[D.] 1984. The summer meeting, 1983, Kerry. First week: Killorglin, 24-26 July. *Bulletin of the British Bryological Society* **43**: 7-8.

Lockhart, N.D. 1987. The occurrence of *Homalothecium nitens* (Hedw.) Robins. in Ireland. *Journal of Bryology* **14**: 511-517.

Lockhart, N.D. 1988. Further records for *Homalothecium nitens* (Hedw.) Robins. in north County Mayo, Ireland. *Journal of Bryology* **15**: 234-235.

Lockhart, N.D. 1989a. Three new localities for *Saxifraga hirculus* L. in Ireland. *Irish Naturalists' Journal* **23**: 65-69.

Lockhart, N.D. 1989b. *Leiocolea rutheana* (Limpr.) K. Muell. new to Ireland. *Journal of Bryology* **15**: 525-529.

Lockhart, N.D. 1991. *Phytosociological and Ecological Studies of Lowland Blanket Bog Flushes in West Galway and North Mayo.* Unpublished Ph.D. Thesis, National University of Ireland, 301 pp.

Lockhart, N.[D.] 1999. *Paludella squarrosa* (Hedw.) Brid., a Boreal relict moss new to Ireland. *Journal of Bryology* **21**: 305-308.

Long, D.G. 1978. On the distinction between *Scapania aequiloba* and *S. aspera*. *Bulletin of the British Bryological Society* **31**: 26-29.

Long, D.G. 1984a. The moss *Fissidens rivularis* (Spruce) B.S.G. in Kerry, new to Ireland. *Irish Naturalists' Journal* **21**: 347-348.

Long, D.G. 1984b. Bryophytes and lichens from Skellig Michael, Co Kerry. *Irish Naturalists' Journal* **21**: 368.
Long, D.G. 1988. New vice-county records and amendments to the Census Catalogue. Hepaticae. *Bulletin of the British Bryological Society* **52**: 30-33.
Long, D.G. 1989. New vice-county records and amendments to the Census Catalogue. Hepaticae. *Bulletin of the British Bryological Society* **54**: 20-23.
Long, D.G. 1990a. New vice-county records and amendments to the Census Catalogue. Hepaticae. *Bulletin of the British Bryological Society* **56**: 23-29.
Long, D.G. 1990b. The bryophytes of Achill Island – Hepaticae. *Glasra* N.S., **1**: 47-64.
Long, D.G. 1991. New vice-county records and amendments to the Census Catalogue. Hepaticae. *Bulletin of the British Bryological Society* **58**: 37-40.
Long, D.G. 1992. New vice-county records and amendments to the Census Catalogue. Hepaticae. *Bulletin of the British Bryological Society* **60**: 24-25.
Long, D.G. 1993a. *Scapania uliginosa* (Sw. ex Lindenb.) Dum. erroneously recorded in Ireland. *Bulletin of the British Bryological Society* **61**: 43.
Long, D.G. 1993b. New vice-county records and amendments to the Census Catalogue. Hepaticae. *Bulletin of the British Bryological Society* **62**: 44-47.
Long, D.G. 1994. New vice-county records and amendments to the Census Catalogue. Hepaticae. *Bulletin of the British Bryological Society* **64**: 33-35.
Long, D.G. 1995a. *Marchantia polymorpha* in Britain and Ireland. *Bulletin of the British Bryological Society* **66**: 29-36.
Long, D.G. 1995b. New vice-county records and amendments to the Census Catalogue. Hepaticae. *Bulletin of the British Bryological Society* **66**: 37-40.
Long, D.G. 1996. New vice-county records and amendments to the Census Catalogue. Hepaticae. *Bulletin of the British Bryological Society* **68**: 42-44.
Long, D.G. 1997. New vice-county records and amendments to the Census Catalogue. Hepaticae. *Bulletin of the British Bryological Society* **70**: 38-41.
Long, D.G. 1999a. New vice-county records and amendments to the Census Catalogue. Hepaticae. *Bulletin of the British Bryological Society* **72**: 93-96.
Long, D.G. 1999b. Hepaticae, pp. 25-28 in Blockeel, T.L. & Long, D.G., The New Census Catalogue: supplementary lists of deleted, recent and replacement records. *Bulletin of the British Bryological Society* **73**, Supplement: 1-28.
McArdle, D. 1904. A list of Irish Hepaticae. *Proceedings of the Royal Irish Academy*, B **24**: 387-502.
McArdle, D. 1907. Musci and Hepaticae from Co. Mayo. *Irish Naturalist* **16**: 332-337.
McArdle, D. 1909. Mosses and liverworts from Co. Fermanagh, and Slieve League, Co. Donegal. *Irish Naturalist* **18**: 144-149.
Macvicar, S.M. 1905. *Moss Exchange Club. Census Catalogue of British Hepatics.* York: Coultas & Volans for M.E.C.
Macvicar, S.M. 1926. *The Student's Handbook of British Hepatics.* 2nd ed. Eastbourne: V.V. Sumfield.
Margadant, W.D. & During, H. 1982. *Beknopte flora van Nederlandse Blad- en Levermossen.* 517 pp., 68 figs.
Megaw, W.R. 1924. Mosses of Rathlin Island. *Irish Naturalist* p. 144.
M.[egaw], W.R. 1925. James Glover, 1844-1925. *The British Bryological Society Report for 1925* **1**: 183.
Megaw, W.R. 1926a. Irish moss records. *Irish Naturalists' Journal* **1**: 77.
Megaw, W.R. 1926b. Irish moss records. *Irish Naturalists' Journal* **1**: 158.
Megaw, W.R. 1929a. Report on recent additions to the Irish fauna and flora: Musci and Hepaticae. *Proceedings of the Royal Irish Academy* **39 B**: 78-91.
Megaw, W.R. 1929b. Further Irish moss records. *Irish Naturalists' Journal* **2**: 186-187.
Megaw, W.R. 1929c. Corrections and additions. *Irish Naturalists' Journal* **2**: 187.
Megaw, W.R. 1930. Irish bryological records. *Irish Naturalists' Journal* **3**: 130.
Megaw, W.R. 1932. Irish bryological records. *Irish Naturalists' Journal* **4**: 54-55.
Megaw, W.R. 1936. Two new Irish mosses. *Irish Naturalists' Journal* **6**: 149-150.
Megaw, W.R. 1937. Irish moss records. *Irish Naturalists' Journal* **6**: 196.

Megaw, W.R. 1938. Mosses and liverworts, in Stewart, S.A. & Corry, T.H. *A Flora of the North-east of Ireland*, 2nd ed. Belfast.

Megaw, W.R. 1950. The moss, *Hypnum imponens* Hedw. *Irish Naturalists' Journal* **10**: 57-58.

Milne-Redhead, H. 1969. Distribution maps of bryophytes in Britain – *Aphanolejeunea* microscopica. *Transactions of the British Bryological Society* **5**: 836.

Mitchell, M.E. (ed.) 1999. Early observations on the Flora of Southwest Ireland. Selected letters of Ellen Hutchins and Dawson Turner 1807-1814. *National Botanic Gardens, Glasnevin, Dublin, Occasional Papers* **12**: 1-124.

Moen, A. & Synnott, D.[M.] 1983. *Sphagnum subfulvum* Sjörs in Ireland compared with the occurrences in Norway. *Journal of Bryology* **12**: 331-336.

The Moss Group, Dublin Naturalists' Field Club. 1951. Bryological records. *Irish Naturalists' Journal* **10**: 186-188.

Muñoz, J. & Pando, F. 2000. *A world synopsis of the genus* Grimmia *(Musci, Grimmiaceae)*. St. Louis: Missouri Botanical Garden Press.

Murray, B.M. 1988. The genus *Andreaea* in Britain and Ireland. *Journal of Bryology* **15**: 17-82.

Nyholm, E. 1987. *Illustrated flora of nordic mosses. Fasc. 1. Fissidentaceae - Seligeriaceae.* Copenhagen & Lund: Nordic Bryological Society.

Nyholm, E. & Crundwell, A.C. 1958. *Bryum salinum* Hagen ex Limpr. in Britain and in America. *Transactions of the British Bryological Society* **3**: 375-377.

Ochi, H. 1972. A revision of African Bryoidea, Musci (First Part). *Journal of the Faculty of Education, Tottori University, Natural Sciences* **23**: 1-126.

Ochi, H. 1980. A revision of the neotropical Bryoideae, Musci (First part). *Journal of the Faculty of Education, Tottori University, Natural Sciences* **29**: 49-154.

O'Connell, C.A. & Foss, P.J. 1987. New records for *Calliergon stramineum* (Brid.) Kindb. and *Sphagnum squarrosum* Crome on Clara Bog Co Offaly (H18). *Irish Naturalists' Journal* **22**: 363.

Orange, A. 1995. Riparian taxa of *Schistidium* in the British Isles. *Bulletin of the British Bryological Society* **65**: 51-58.

Parker, R.E. 1958. The Summer Meeting in Ireland, 1957. *Transactions of the British Bryological Society* **3**: 493-498.

Parnell, J. 1982. Some remarks on the bryophyte herbarium of H. W. Lett in Trinity College Dublin. *Irish Naturalists' Journal* **20**: 489.

Paton, J.A. 1961. New vice-county records. Hepaticae. *Transactions of the British Bryological Society* **4**: 150-157.

Paton, J.A. 1962. New vice-county records. Hepaticae. *Transactions of the British Bryological Society* **4**: 482-491.

Paton, J.A. 1963. New vice-county records. Hepaticae. *Transactions of the British Bryological Society* **4**: 482-491.

Paton, J.A. 1964. New vice-county records and amendments to the Census Catalogue. Hepaticae. *Transactions of the British Bryological Society* **4**: 711-721.

Paton, J.A. 1965a. New vice-county records and amendments to the Census Catalogue. Hepaticae. *Transactions of the British Bryological Society* **4**: 851-858.

Paton, J.A. 1965b. *Census catalogue of British hepatics (4th edition).* Ipswich: British Bryological Society.

Paton, J.A. 1966. New vice-county records and amendments to the Census Catalogues. Hepaticae. *Transactions of the British Bryological Society* **5**: 180-189.

Paton, J.A. 1967a. *Riccia crystallina* L. and *R. cavernosa* Hoffm. in Britain. *Transactions of the British Bryological Society* **5**: 222-225.

Paton, J.A. 1967b. Distribution maps of bryophytes in Britain – *Cephalozia leucantha. Transactions of the British Bryological Society* **5**: 359.

Paton, J.A. 1967c. New vice-county records and amendments to the Census Catalogues. Hepaticae. *Transactions of the British Bryological Society* **5**: 392-405.

Paton, J.A. 1968. New vice-county records and amendments to the Census Catalogues. Hepaticae. *Transactions of the British Bryological Society* **5**: 618-629.

Paton, J.A. 1969a. New vice-county records and amendments to the Census Catalogues. Hepaticae.

Transactions of the British Bryological Society **5**: 865-876.
Paton, J.A. 1969b. Four hepatics new to Ireland. *Irish Naturalists' Journal* **16**: 171-173.
Paton, J.A. 1970. New vice-county records and amendments to the Census Catalogues. Hepaticae. *Transactions of the British Bryological Society* **6**: 185-194.
Paton, J.A. 1971a. New vice-county records and amendments to the Census Catalogues. Hepaticae. *Transactions of the British Bryological Society* **6**: 368-373.
Paton, J.A. 1971b. Three hepatics new to Ireland on Bulbin Mountain, Co. Donegal. *Irish Naturalists' Journal* **17**: 97-99.
Paton, J.A. 1972a. New vice-county records and amendments to the Census Catalogues. Hepaticae. *Journal of Bryology* **7**: 131-135.
Paton, J.A. 1972b. *Leiocolea heterocolpos* (Thed.) Buch new to Ireland. *Irish Naturalists' Journal* **17**: 180.
Paton, J.A. 1973a. Taxonomic studies in the genus *Fossombronia* Raddi. *Journal of Bryology* **7**: 243-252.
Paton, J.A. 1973b. New vice-county records and amendments to the Census Catalogues. Hepaticae. *Journal of Bryology* **7**: 503-515.
Paton, J.A. 1974a. *Fossombronia fimbriata* sp. nov. *Journal of Bryology* **8**: 1-4.
Paton, J.A. 1974b. New vice-county records and amendments to the Census Catalogues. Hepaticae. *Journal of Bryology* **8**: 161-165.
Paton, J.A. 1975. New vice-county records and amendments to the Census Catalogues. Hepaticae. *Bulletin of the British Bryological Society* **26**: 9-12.
Paton, J.A. 1976. New vice-county records and amendments to the Census Catalogues. Hepaticae. *Bulletin of the British Bryological Society* **28**: 16-21.
Paton, J.A. 1977a. New vice-county records and amendments to the Census Catalogue. Hepaticae. *Bulletin of the British Bryological Society* **30**: 11-16.
Paton, J.A. 1977b. *Metzgeria temperata* Kuwah. in the British Isles, and *M. fruticulosa* (Dicks.) Evans with sporophytes. *Journal of Bryology* **9**: 441-449.
Paton, J.A. 1977c. *Plagiochila killarniensis* Pears. in the British Isles. *Journal of Bryology* **9**: 451-459.
Paton, J.A. 1979. *Plagiochila britannica*, a new species in the British Isles. *Journal of Bryology* **10**: 245-256.
Paton, J.A. 1980. Observations on *Riccia bifurca* Hoffm. and other species of *Riccia* L. in the British Isles. *Journal of Bryology* **11**: 1-6.
Paton, J.A. 1984. *Cephaloziella nicholsonii* Douin & Schiffn. distinguished from *C. massalongi* (Spruce) K. Muell. *Journal of Bryology* **13**: 1-8.
Paton, J.A. 1990. *Riccia subbifurca* Warnst. ex Crozals in the British Isles. *Journal of Bryology* **16**: 5-8.
Paton, J.A. 1995. A new combination for a variety of *Leiocolea rutheana*. *Journal of Bryology* **18**: 823.
Paton, J.A. 1999. *The liverwort flora of the British Isles*. Colchester: Harley Books.
Paton, J.A., Blackstock, T.H. & Long, D.G. 1996. *Cephalozia macrostachya* Kaal. var. *spiniflora* (Schiffn.) Müll.Frib. in Britain and Ireland. *Journal of Bryology* **19**: 333-339.
Paton, J.A. & Perry, A.R. 1995. *Leiocolea fitzgeraldiaee sp. nov.* in Britain and Ireland. *Journal of Bryology* **18**: 469-47; Errata, *ibid.*, p. 863.
Pearson, W.H. 1919. The genus *Herberta* – as represented in the Manchester Museum. *Journal of Botany* **57**: 43.
Perring, F.H. & Walters, S.M. 1962. *Atlas of the British Flora*. London.
Perry, A.R. 1967. New vice-county records and amendments to the Census Catalogues. Musci. *Transactions of the British Bryological Society* **5**: 405-425.
Perry, A.R. 1983. Mosses and liverworts. Pp. 279-283, in Webb, D.A. & Scannell, M.J.P. *Flora of Connemara and the Burren*. Cambridge: Royal Dublin Society & Cambridge University Press.
Perry, A.R. 1990. Obituaries. Jean Wilgar Fitzgerald B.Sc. (1908-1988). *Journal of Bryology* **16**: 133-137.
Perry, A.R. 1991a. Obituary. Robert Desmond Fitzgerald (1914-1990). *Journal of Bryology* **16**: 495-496.

Perry, A.R. 1991b. Dates of publication of *Transactions of the British Bryological Society* and of *Journal of Bryology*. *Journal of Bryology* **16**: 644-647.

Porley, R.D. 2001. Mosses and liverworts of the sandstone scarps of the Lough Navar Forest region, Co Fermanagh. *Irish Naturalists' Journal* **26**: 393-404.

Porley, R.D. & Matcham, H.W. 2003. The status of *Orthodontium gracile* in Britain and Ireland. *Journal of Bryology* **25**: 64-66.

Praeger, R.Ll. 1901. Irish Topographical Botany. *Proceedings of the Royal Irish Academy* **23** (3rd series, **7**): 1-410.

Preston, S.J. & Stone, R.E. 1999. *Isothecium holtii* Kindb., a new record in Co Down (H38). *Irish Naturalists' Journal* **26**: 287-288.

Proctor, M.C.F. 1959. A note on *Acrocladium trifarium* in Ireland. *Transactions of the British Bryological Society* **3**: 571-574.

Proctor, M.C.F. 1964. Distribution maps of bryophytes in Britain – *Ulota vittata. Transactions of the British Bryological Society* **4**: 746.

Ratcliffe, D.A. 1962. The habitat of *Adelanthus unciformis* (Tayl.) Mitt., and *Jamesoniella carringtonii* (Balf.) Spr. in Ireland. *Irish Naturalists' Journal* **14**: 38-40.

Ratcliffe, D.A. 1965. Distribution maps of bryophytes in Britain – *Fossombronia angulosa. Transactions of the British Bryological Society* **4**: 876.

Richards, P.W. 1938a. *Telaranea nematodes* in Ireland. *The British Bryological Society Report for 1937* **4**: 61-62.

Richards, P.W. 1938b. The bryophyte communities of a Killarney oakwood. *Annales Bryologici* **11**: 108-130.

Richards, P.W. 1952. Meeting of the British Bryological Society in Southwestern Ireland, September 1951. *Revue Bryologique et Lichénologique* **21**: 177-179.

Richards, P.W. 1963. *Campylopus introflexus* (Hedw.) Brid. and *C. polytrichoides* De Not. in the British Isles; a preliminary account. *Transactions of the British Bryological Society* **4**: 404-417.

Risse, S. 1996. *Ephemerum minutissimum* Lindb. and *E. serratum* (Hedw.) Hampe. *The Bryological Times* **90**: 6.

Risse, S. 1997. Errata. *The Bryological Times* **92**: 7.

Rose, F. 1975. Distribution maps of bryophytes – *Leucodon sciuroides. Journal of Bryology* **8**: 502.

Rothero, G.P. 1984. The summer meeting, 1983, Kerry. Second Week: Kenmare, 27 July - 3 August. *Bulletin of the British Bryological Society* **43**: 8-11.

Rothero, G.P. 1988. The summer meeting, 1987, Co. Mayo. Second week at Westport: 12-18 August. *Bulletin of the British Bryological Society* **51**: 10-15.

Rothero, G.P. 1999a. New vice-county records and amendments to the Census Catalogue. Musci. *Bulletin of the British Bryological Society* **72**: 96-102.

Rothero, G.P. 1999b. New vice-county records and amendments to the Census Catalogue. Musci. *Bulletin of the British Bryological Society* **73**: 39-47.

Rothero, G.P. 2000. New vice-county records and amendments to the *Census Catalogue*. Musci. *Bulletin of the British Bryological Society* **75**: 45-62.

Rothero, G.P. 2001. New vice-county records and amendments to the *Census Catalogue*. Musci. *Bulletin of the British Bryological Society* **77**: 37-48.

Rothero, G.P. 2002. New vice-county records and amendments to the *Census Catalogue*. Musci. *Bulletin of the British Bryological Society* **79**: 42-56.

Rothero, G.P. 2003. New vice-county records and amendments to the *Census Catalogue*. Musci. *Bulletin of the British Bryological Society* **81**: 46-63.

Rothero, G.P. 2004. Current distribution of the *Schistidium apocarpum* complex in the British Isles. *Bulletin of the British Bryological Society* **82** (in press).

Rothero, G.P. & Synnott, D.[M.] 1988. The British Bryological Society in Ireland, August 1987. *Irish Naturalists' Journal* **22**: 495.

Rubers, W.V. 1975. Notes on some bryophytes from the Lough Ree area. *Irish Naturalists' Journal* **18**: 177-183.

Rycroft, D.S., Cole, W.J., Aslam, N., Lamont, Y.M. & Gabriel, R. 1999. Killarniensolide, methyl orsellinates and 9.10-dihydrophenanthrenes from the liverwort *Plagiochila killarniensis* from

Scotland and the Azores. *Phytochemistry* **50**: 1167-1173.
Sanderson, A.R. & Cheetham, C.A. 1912. Notes from the west coast. *Irish Naturalist* pp. 54-55.
Scannell, M.J.P. 1977. The bryophyte collection of Mrs A. L. K. King. *Irish Naturalists' Journal* **19**: 130.
Scannell, M.J.P. & Synnott, D.M. 1987. *Census Catalogue of the Flora of Ireland. Clár de Phlandaí na hÉireann. 2nd ed.* Dublin: Stationery Office.
Seaward, M.R.D. 1973. Distribution maps of bryophytes in Britain – *Bryum warneum. Journal of Bryology* **7**: 451.
Sherrin, W.R. 1937. *The British Bryological Society. Census Catalogue of British Sphagna. Compiled for the B.B.S. ...* [1st ed.] Berwick-on-Tweed: Martin's Printing Works, for BBS.
Sherrin, W.R. revised by Thompson, A. 1946. *The British Bryological Society. Census Catalogue of British Sphagna. Compiled for the B.B.S. ...* [2nd ed.] Berwick-on-Tweed: Martin's Printing Works, for BBS.
Smith, A.J.E. 1971. Distribution maps of bryophytes in Britain – *Grimmia ovalis. Transactions of the British Bryological Society* **6**: 341.
Smith, A.J.E. 1972. Distribution maps of bryophytes in Britain – *Fissidens crassipes. Journal of Bryology* **7**: 90.
Smith, A.J.E. 1973a. Distribution maps of bryophytes in Britain – *Rhacomitrium ellipticum. Journal of Bryology* **7**: 447.
Smith, A.J.E. 1973b. Distribution maps of bryophytes in Britain – *Bryum uliginosum. Journal of Bryology* **7**: 454.
Smith, A.J.E. 1973c. Distribution maps of bryophytes in Britain – *Bryum turbinatum. Journal of Bryology* **7**: 455.
Smith, A.J.E. 1974. Distribution maps of bryophytes – *Antitrichia curtipendula. Journal of Bryology* **8**: 128.
Smith, A.J.E. 1978. *The moss flora of Britain and Ireland.* Cambridge: Cambridge University Press.
Smith, A.J.E. 1990a. *The liverworts of Britain and Ireland.* Cambridge: Cambridge University Press.
Smith, A.J.E. 1990b. The bryophytes of Achill Island – Musci. *Glasra* N.S., **1**: 27-46.
Smith, A.J.E. 1992. The taxonomic status of the British varieties of *Grimmia trichophylla* Grev. *Journal of Bryology* **17**: 269-273.
Smith, A.J.E. 1993. *Ditrichum flexicaule* and *D. crispatissimum* in Great Britain and Ireland. *Bulletin of the British Bryological Society* **61**: 45-54.
Smith, A.J.E. 1997. The *Hypnum cupressiforme* complex in the British Isles. *Journal of Bryology* **19**: 751-774.
Smith, A.J.E. & Whitehouse, H.L.K. 1978. An account of the British species of the *Bryum bicolor* complex including *B. dunense* sp. nov. *Journal of Bryology* **10**: 29-47.
Sowter, F.A. 1972. Distribution maps of bryophytes in Britain – *Scleropodium tourretii. Journal of Bryology* **7**: 95.
Stelfox, A.W. 1965. The liverwort *Herberta* in Ireland. *Irish Naturalists' Journal* **15**: 56.
Stewart, S.A. 1890. Report on the botany of South Clare and the Shannon. *Proceedings of the Royal Irish Academy*, 3rd ser., **1**: 343-369.
Stewart, S.A. & Corry, T.H. 1888. *A flora of the North-east of Ireland.* Belfast: Belfast Naturalists' Field Club & Cambridge: Macmillan & Bowes.
Stirling, A.McG. 1968. Distribution maps of bryophytes in Britain – *Amblystegiella sprucei. Transactions of the British Bryological Society* **5**: 600.
Stotler, R.E., Ford, C.H. & Crandall-Stotler, B.J. 2002. Typifications in the Genus *Petalophyllum* (Marchantiophyta). *The Bryologist* **105**: 400-406.
Syed, H. 1973. A taxonomic study of *Bryum capillare* Hedw. and related species. *Journal of Bryology* **7**: 265-326.
Syed, H. & Crundwell, A.C. 1973. *Barbula maxima*, nom. nov., an endemic Irish species. *Journal of Bryology* **7**: 527-529.
Synnott, D.M. 1964. Contributions to the bryophyte census of Counties Meath and Louth. *Irish Naturalists' Journal* **14**: 210.
Synnott, D.[M.] 1967a. The summer meeting, 1966. *Transactions of the British Bryological Society* **5**: 428-431.

Synnott, D.M. 1967b. Contributions to the bryophyte census of Counties Meath and Louth: II. *Irish Naturalists' Journal* **15**: 293-296.

Synnott, D.M. 1967c.The summer meeting of the British Bryological Society in Ireland, 1966. *Irish Naturalists' Journal* **15**: 306-307.

Synnott, D.[M.] 1976a. The summer meeting, 1975. *Bulletin of the British Bryological Society* **27**: 5-9.

Synnott, D.[M.] 1976b. *Plagiochila atlantica* F. Rose (*P. ambagiosa* auct.) *Irish Naturalists' Journal* **18**: 347.

Synnott, D.[M.] 1976c. The British Bryological Society in Ireland, August1975. *Irish Naturalists' Journal* **18**: 366.

Synnott, D.M. [1977]. Progress in Irish Bryology: Hepaticae. Unpublished typescript, 66 pp.

Synnott, D.M. 1978. The bryophyte herbarium of Henry William Lett in the Herbarium, National Botanic Gardens, Glasnevin. *Glasra* **2**: 43-48.

Synnott, D.[M.] 1979. Bryophytes. Pp. 146-148, in Booth, E.M. *The Flora of County Carlow*. Dublin: Royal Dublin Society.

Synnott, D.M. 1980. A catalogue of collectors in the bryophyte herbarium, National Botanic Gardens, Glasnevin (DBN). *Glasra* **4**: 17-30.

Synnott, D.[M]. 1981. *Barbula maxima* in Canada and its significance for Irish vegetational history. *Irish Naturalists' Journal* **20**: 305-307.

Synnott, D.[M.] 1982. An outline of the bryophytes of Meath and Westmeath. *Glasra* **6**: 1-71.

Synnott, D.[M]. 1983a. *Anoectangium warburgii* - a new Irish moss. *Irish Naturalists' Journal* **21**: 91-92.

Synnott, D.[M]. 1983b. *Barbula icmadophila* Schimp. ex C Muell. – a delayed addition to the Irish moss flora. *Irish Naturalists' Journal* **21**: 177-178.

Synnott, D.[M]. 1984. The bryological collection of Arnold Patrick Fanning (1905-1980). *Irish Naturalists' Journal* **21**: 233-235.

Synnott, D.[M.] 1988. The summer meeting, 1987, Co. Mayo. First week in Achill Island: 5-12 August. *Bulletin of the British Bryological Society* **51**: 7-10.

Synnott, D.M. 1990a. The bryophytes of Achill Island – a preliminary note. *Glasra* N.S., **1**: 21-26.

Synnott, D.M. 1990b. The bryophytes of Lambay Island. *Glasra* N.S., **1**: 65-81.

Synnott, D.M. & Robinson, D.W. 1989. The moss *Trichostomopsis umbrosa* (C.Müll.) Robins. in Ireland. *Irish Naturalists' Journal* **23**: 113-114.

Synnott, D.M. & Robinson, D.W. 1990. The moss *Trichostomopsis umbrosa* (C.Mueller) H.Robinson in Ireland. *Glasra* **1**: 15-19.

Synnott, D.[M.] & Wyse Jackson, P. 1984. Mosses and liverworts. Pp. 47-50, in Wyse Jackson, P. & Skeffington, M.S. (eds.) *Flora of Inner Dublin.* Dublin: Royal Dublin Society.

Taylor, J. 1951. Some Irish bryophyta records. *Irish Naturalists' Journal* **10**: 131-133.

Taylor, J. 1954. Bryophyta–new vice-county records. *Irish Naturalists' Journal* **11**: 205-206.

T.[hompson], A. 1944. Census Catalogues. Lists of new vice-county records. Sphagna. *The British Bryological Society Report for 1940-43* **4**: 201-207.

Thompson, A. 1951. New vice-county records. Sphagna. *Transactions of the British Bryological Society* **1**: 496-497.

Thompson, A. & Lobley, E.M. 1950. New vice-county records. Sphagna. *Transactions of the British Bryological Society* **1**: 380-382.

Thomson, J.S. 1953. Possible *Scapania paludosa* in Co. Kerry. *Irish Naturalists' Journal* **11**: 21.

Touw, A. 2001. A taxonomic revision of the Thuidiaceae (Musci) of tropical Asia, the western Pacific and Hawaii. *Journal of the Hattori Botanical Laboratory* **91**: 1-136.

Turner, Dawson 1804. *Muscologiae Hibernicae Spicilegium.* Yermuthae: J. Black & Londini: J. White. (Facsimile reprint: 1998, Presses universitaires de Namur, Belgium).

Váňa, J. 1973. Studien über die *Jungermannioideae* (Hepaticae). 2, *Jungermannia* subg. *Jungermannia. Folia Geobotanica et Phytotaxonomica; Praha* **8**: 255-309.

Wallace, E.C. 1952. The British Bryological Society's Field Meeting in Co. Kerry, 1951. *Irish Naturalists' Journal* **10**: 259-263.

Wallace, E.C. 1963. The Summer Meeting in Ireland, 1962. *Transactions of the British Bryological Society* **4**: 531-534.

Wallace, E.C. 1972. A second *Timmia* in Ireland. *Irish Naturalists' Journal* **17**: 245.

Wallace, E.C. 1976. *Fissidens taxifolius* Hedw. ssp. *pallidicaulis* (Mitt.) Mönkm. in the British Isles. *Journal of Bryology* **9**: 161-162.

Warburg, E.F. 1950. New vice-county records. Musci. *Transactions of the British Bryological Society* **1**: 382-388.

Warburg, E.F. 1951. New vice-county records. Musci. *Transactions of the British Bryological Society* **1**: 497-503.

Warburg, E.F. 1952. New vice-county records. Musci. *Transactions of the British Bryological Society* **2**: 97-108.

Warburg, E.F. 1953. New vice-county records. Musci. *Transactions of the British Bryological Society* **2**: 304-318.

Warburg, E.F. 1954. New vice-county records. Musci. *Transactions of the British Bryological Society* **2**: 477-487.

Warburg, E.F. 1955. New vice-county records. Musci. *Transactions of the British Bryological Society* **2**: 582-587.

Warburg, E.F. 1956. New vice-county records. Musci. *Transactions of the British Bryological Society* **3**: 150-159.

Warburg, E.F. 1957. New vice-county records. Musci. *Transactions of the British Bryological Society* **3**: 326-338.

Warburg, E.F. 1958a. *Meesia tristicha* Bruch & Schimp. in the British Isles. *Transactions of the British Bryological Society* **3**: 378-381.

Warburg, E.F. 1958b. New vice-county records. Musci. *Transactions of the British Bryological Society* **3**: 471-490.

Warburg, E.F. 1959. New vice-county records. Musci. *Transactions of the British Bryological Society* **3**: 630-639.

Warburg, E.F. 1960. New vice-county records. Musci. *Transactions of the British Bryological Society* **3**: 769-782.

Warburg, E.F. 1961. New vice-county records. Musci. *Transactions of the British Bryological Society* **4**: 158-176.

Warburg, E.F. 1962. New vice-county records. Musci. *Transactions of the British Bryological Society* **4**: 364-377.

Warburg, E.F. 1963a. *Census catalogue of British mosses (3rd edition).* Ipswich: British Bryological Society.

Warburg, E.F. 1963b. New vice-county records. Musci. *Transactions of the British Bryological Society* **4**: 492-504.

Warburg, E.F. 1963c. Notes on the bryophytes of Achill Island. *Irish Naturalists' Journal* **14**: 139-145.

Warburg, E.F. 1964. New vice-county records and amendments to the Census Catalogue. Musci. *Transactions of the British Bryological Society* **4**: 722-736.

Warburg, E.F. 1965. New vice-county records and amendments to the Census Catalogue. Musci. *Transactions of the British Bryological Society* **4**: 859-873.

Warburg, E.F. 1966. New vice-county records and amendments to the Census Catalogues. Musci. *Transactions of the British Bryological Society* **5**: 189-206.

Watson, E.V. 1968. *Pohlia lutescens* (Limpr.) Lindb. f. in Britain and Ireland. *Transactions of the British Bryological Society* **5**: 443-447.

Watson, H.C. 1852. *Cybele Britannica.* Vol. 3. London.

Watson, H.C. 1883. *Topographical Botany.* 2nd ed. London: Bernard Quaritch.

Watson, W. 1936. Report of the Annual Meeting, 1935. *The British Bryological Society Report for 1935* **3**: 263-265.

Watson, W. 1937. British Bryological Society at Killarney, 1935. List of records. *Irish Naturalists' Journal* **6**: 161-165.

Wear, S. 1923. *A second supplement to, and summary of Stewart and Corry's Flora of the North*-east *of Ireland.* Belfast: Belfast Naturalists' Field Club.

Webb, D.A. 1980. The biological vice-counties of Ireland. *Proceedings of the Royal Irish Academy* **80B**: 179-196.

Werner, J. 2002. A comparison of *Dichodontium flavescens* (Dicks.) Lindb. and *D. pellucidum* (Hedw.) Lindb. (Bryopsida). *Journal of Bryology* **24**: 215-221.

Whelan, P. 1978. Some bryophytes of Hare Island, Co. Cork. *Irish Naturalists' Journal* **19**: 171.

Wheldon, J.A. 1919. Recent new *Sphagnum* records. *Moss Exchange Club. The twenty-fourth Annual Report, July 1919* (*M.E.C. Reports*) **2**: 247-252.

Wheldon, J.A. 1924. New forms of *Sphagnum*. *The British Bryological Society Report for 1924* **1**: 55-56.

White, J. 1985. The Gearagh Woodland, Co Cork. *Irish Naturalists' Journal* **21**: 391-396.

Whitehouse, H.L.K. 1963. *Bryum riparium* Hagen in the British Isles. *Transactions of the British Bryological Society* **4**: 389-403.

Whitehouse, H.L.K. 1969. *Dicranella staphylina*, a new European species. *Transactions of the British Bryological Society* **5**: 757-765.

Whitehouse, H.[L.K.] 1995. Summer Field Meeting, 1994, First week, The Burren. *Bulletin of the British Bryological Society* **65**: 8-12.

Whitehouse, H.L.K. & Crundwell, A.C. 1991. *Gymnostomum calcareum* Nees & Hornsch. and allied plants in Europe, North Africa and the Middle East. *Journal of Bryology* **16**: 561-579.

Whitehouse, H.L.K. & Crundwell, A.C. 1992. *Gymnostomum calcareum* Nees & Hornsch. and *G. viridulum* Brid. in Europe, North Africa and the Middle East. *Bulletin of the British Bryological Society* **59**: 35-50.

Whitehouse, H.L.K. & During, H.J. 1987. *Leptobarbula berica* (De Not.) Schimp. in Belgium and The Netherlands. *Lindbergia* **12**: 135-138.

Whitehouse, H.L.K. & Newton, M.E. 1988. *Tortula brevis* sp. nov. and *T. stanfordensis* Steere: morphology, cytology and geographical distribution. *Journal of Bryology* **15**: 83-99.

Wijk, R. van der, Margadant, W.D. & Florschütz, P.A. 1967. *Index Muscorum*. vol. 4. Utrecht, Netherlands: The International Bureau for Plant Taxonomy and Nomenclature.

Wilson, A. 1930. *A Census Catalogue of British Hepatics, with List of the Botanical Vice-Counties and their boundaries and lists of Sources of Records. Compiled for the British Bryological Society (Formerly The Moss Exchange Club) ...* 3rd ed. Berwick-on-Tweed: Martin's Printing Works, for BBS.

W.[ilson], A. 1935. British Bryological Society. Census Catalogue of British Hepatics (3rd Edition, 1930) [supplementary records], 3 pp. in *The British Bryological Society. Supplements to Census Catalogue of British Mosses (2nd Edition), and Census Catalogue of British Hepatics (3rd Edition).* Berwick-on-Tweed: Martin's Printing Works, for BBS.

W.[ilson], A. 1944. [Census Catalogues]. Hepatics. List of additional V.C. Records since the issue of the Report for 1939. Mosses. *The British Bryological Society Report for 1940-43* **4**: 218-222.

Wiltshire, E. 1995. The mosses and liverworts of Foynes Island and adjacent mainland, Co Limerick (H8). *Irish Naturalists' Journal* **25**: 123-128.

Wyatt, R. & Derda, G.S. 1997. Population biology of the Polytrichaceae. *Advances in Bryology* **6**: 265-296.

Żarnowiec, J. 2001. *A taxonomic monograph of the* Drepanocladus aduncus *group (Bryopsida: Amblystegiaceae).* Bielsko-Biała: Łódż Technical University.

VICE COUNTIES OF IRELAND

Map 1. Vice-counties of Ireland.

See the following page for list of names of vice-counties.

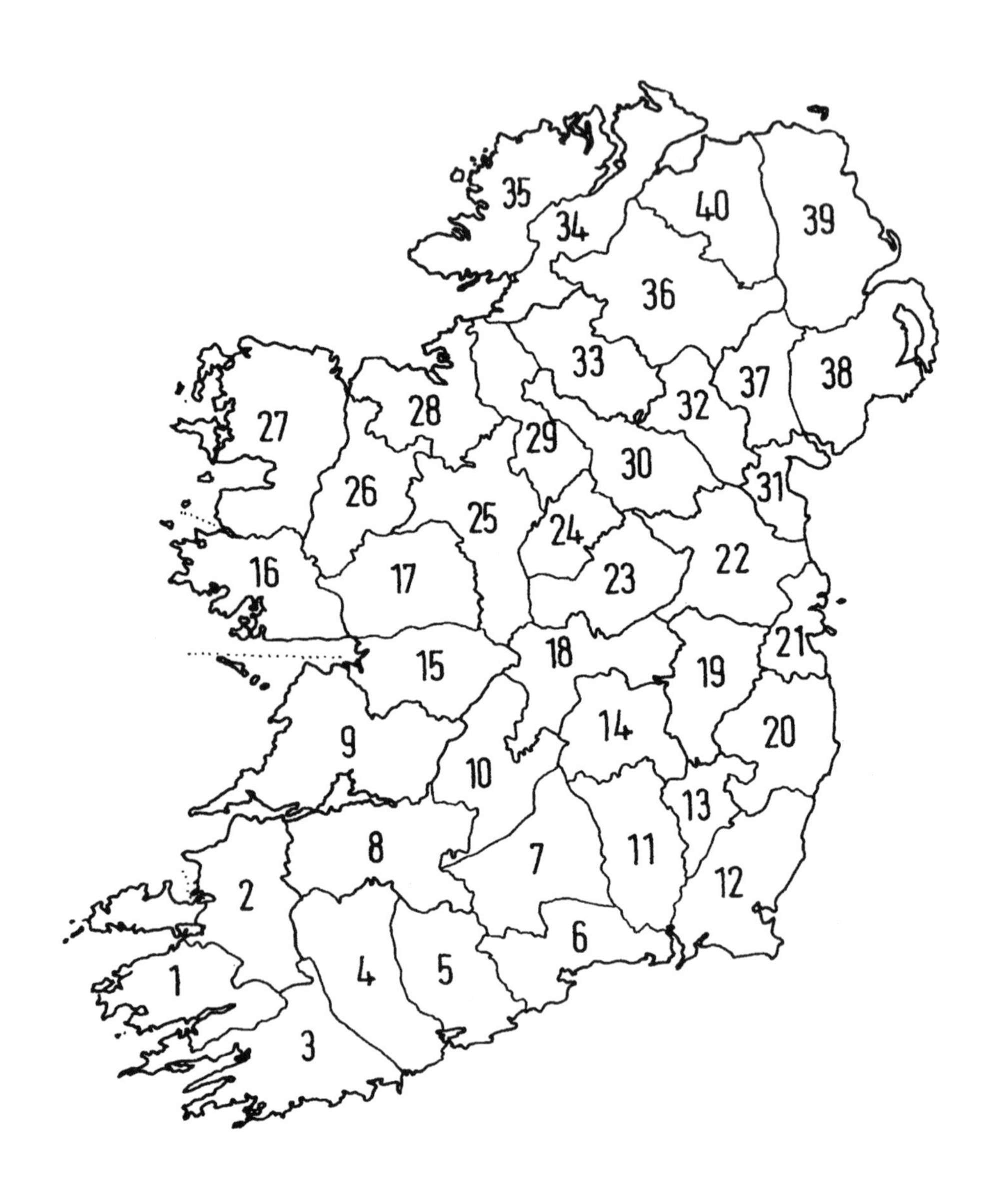

The Vice Counties of Ireland

The names and boundaries of Irish Vice Counties follow Praeger (1901). They differ in a number of details from the modern administrative boundaries for practical and historical reasons. One notable difference is that the Aran Islands, being geologically an extension of the Burren limestones, are placed in vice-county H9 (Clare). The points of difference and the formal definitions of the vice-county boundaries are given by Webb (1980). An important correction affecting H1 and H2 is noted by Kelly (1984b), who establishes that the famous oakwood at Derrycunihy is in H1. Webb (1980) asserts the principle that the vice-county boundaries were fixed for all time by Praeger (1901), so that they remain unaffected by recent (and future) changes in boundaries of the administrative counties. Scannell & Synnott (1987: end paper) provide a useful large coloured map of the Irish Vice Counties based on the definitive map from Praeger (1901), but Webb (1980) should be consulted for an authoritative account of the details of boundaries. (H = Hibernia precedes the vice-county numbers to differentiate between the British and Irish vice-counties. I = Ireland was used for the same purpose in some earlier lists.)

H1	South Kerry	H21	Dublin
H2	North Kerry	H22	Meath
H3	West Cork	H23	Westmeath
H4	Mid-Cork	H24	Longford
H5	East Cork	H25	Roscommon
H6	Waterford	H26	East Mayo
H7	South Tipperary	H27	West Mayo
H8	Limerick	H28	Sligo
H9	Clare (including Aran Islands)	H29	Leitrim
H10	North Tipperary	H30	Cavan
H11	Kilkenny	H31	Louth
H12	Wexford	H32	Monaghan
H13	Carlow	H33	Fermanagh
H14	Laois (= Leix, Queen's County)	H34	East Donegal
H15	South-east Galway	H35	West Donegal
H16	West Galway	H36	Tyrone
H17	North-east Galway	H37	Armagh
H18	Offaly (= King's County)	H38	Down
H19	Kildare	H39	Antrim
H20	Wicklow	H40	Londonderry

INDEX

INDEX

Synonyms and other excluded names are in *italics*.

Acaulon
minus 296
muticum 296
Acrobolbus
wilsonii 96
Acrocladium
cordifolium 456
cuspidatum 458
giganteum 457
sarmentosum 458
stramineum 455
trifarium 456
Adelanthus
decipiens 31
dugortiensis 31
lindenbergianus 31
unciformis 31
Alicularia
compressa 65
compressa var. *rigida* 65
scalaris 66
scalaris var. *distans* 66
scalaris var. *rivularis* 66
Aloina
aloides 285
aloides var. *aloides* 285
aloides var. *ambigua* 286
ambigua 286
rigida 284
Amblyodon
dealbatus 382
Amblystegiella
confervoides 440
sprucei 489
Amblystegium
aduncum 445
chrysophyllum 435
chrysophyllum var. *erectum* 435
compactum 442
confervoides 440
cordifolium 456
dilatatum 454
elodes 436
eugyrium 453
eugyrium var. *mackayi* 453
exannulatum 443
exannulatum var. *rotae* 443
falcatum 430
fallax 431
filicinum 431
filicinum var. *trichodes* 431
Amblystegium
fluitans 442
fluitans var. *submersum* 442
fluviatile 438
giganteum 457
glaucum 429
humile 440
intermedium 449
irriguum 439
juratzkae 437
juratzkanum 437
kneiffii 445
kneiffii var. *polycarpon* 445
kochii 440
lycopodioides 447
ochraceum 452
palustre 452
palustre var. *subsphaericarpon* 453
polygamum 444
polygamum var. *stagnatum* 444
protensum 434
riparium 440
riparium var. *longifolium* 440
sarmentosum 458
scorpioides 454
sendtneri 446
sendtneri var. *hamatum* 446
sendtneri var. *wilsoni* 446
serpens var. *depauperatum* 437
serpens var. salinum 438
serpens var. serpens 437
sprucei 489
stellatum 432
stramineum 455
tenax 439
varium 439
vernicosum 450
Amphidium
mougeotii 389
Anastrepta
orcadensis 46
Anastrophyllum
hellerianum 57
minutum 56
Andreaea
alpina 184
crassinervia 185, 186
crassinervia subsp. *huntii* 185, 186
crassinervia var. *huntii* 185
megistospora 187
obovata var. *papillosa* 185
petrophila 184
petrophila var. *acuminata* 184
petrophila var. *gracilis* 184
rothii subsp. falcata 186

Andreaea
rothii subsp. rothii 186
rothii subsp. uncertain 185
rupestris var. papillosa 185
rupestris var. rupestris 184
Aneura
ambrosioides 127
latifrons 130
major 128
multifida 127
palmata 129
pinguis 126
sinuata 128
sinuata var. *major* 128
Anisothecium
crispum 214
crispum var. *elatum* 214
grevillei 216
rubrum 216
rubrum var. *callistomum* 216
rubrum var. *tenellum* 216
rubrum var. *tenuifolium* 216
rufescens 217
squarrosum 214
Anoectangium
aestivum 268
compactum 268
mougeotii 389
warburgii 272
Anomobryum
concinnatum 346
filiforme var. *concinnatum* 346
filiforme var. *filiforme* 346
julaceum var. concinnatum 346
julaceum var. julaceum 346
Anomodon
viticulosus 422
Anthelia
julacea 44
julacea var. *gracilis* 44
juratzkana 44
Anthoceros
agrestis 150
husnotii 150
laevis 150
punctatus 150
punctatus 150
Antitrichia
curtipendula 413
Aphanolejeunea
microscopica 117
Aphanorhegma
patens 329
Aplozia
cordifolia 62
Aplozia
crenulata 63
crenulata var. *gracillima* 63
crenulata var. *inundata* 63
pumila 61
riparia 60
sphaerocarpa 62
Apometgeria
pubescens 136
Archidium
alternifolium 202
Arctoa
fulvella 222
Atrichum
angustatum 200
angustatum var. *rhystophyllum* 200
crispum 198
tenellum 198
undulatum var. undulatum 199
Aulacomnium
androgynum 381
palustre 380
Barbilophozia
atlantica 45
attenuata 46
barbata 46
floerkei 45
kunzeana 45
Barbula
acuta 275
brevifolia 280
brevifolia var. *acutifolia* 280
convoluta 272
convoluta var. *commutata* 272
convoluta var. *sardoa* 272
curvirostris 267
cylindrica 277
cylindrica var. *vinealis* 277
fallax 282
fallax var. *brevifolia* 282
ferruginascens 266
gracilis 275
hornschuchiana 263
hornschuchii 263
icmadophila 275
lurida 278
maxima 284
nicholsonii 276
recurvifolia 283
recurvifolia var. *robusta* 284
recurvirostra 265
reflexa 283
reflexa var. *maxima* 284
reflexa var. *robusta* 284
revoluta 264

Barbula
rigidula 275
rubella 265
rubella var. *dentata* 265
rubella var. *ruberrima* 266
sinuosa 279
spadicea 281
tomaculosus 283
tophacea 280
trifaria 278
unguiculata 274
unguiculata var. *apiculata* 274
unguiculata var. *cuspidata* 274
unguiculata var. *fastigiata* 274
vinealis 277
Bartramia
halleriana 383
ithyphylla 384
norvegica 383
oederi 383
pomiformis 383
pomiformis var. *crispa* 383
Bartramidula
wilsonii 388
Bazzania
pearsonii 25
triangularis 25
tricrenata 25
tricrenata var. *triangularis* 25
trilobata 24
trilobata var. *minor* 24
Blasia
pusilla 125
Blepharostoma
trichophyllum 19
Blindia
acuta 321
acuta var. *arenacea* 321
acuta var. *trichodes* 321
Brachydontium
trichodes 324
Brachyodus
trichodes 324
Brachythecium
albicans 465
appleyardiae 470
caespitosum 473
glareosum 465
mildeanum 466
plumosum 471
populeum 470
rivulare 468
rivulare var. *latifolium* 468
rutabulum 467
salebrosum 466
Brachythecium
salebrosum var. *palustre* 466
velutinum 469
Breutelia
chrysocoma 388
Bryoerythrophyllum
ferruginascens 266
recurvirostrum 265
Bryum
affine 355
algovicum var. rutheanum 349
alpinum 369
alpinum var. *viride* 369
amblyodon 350
argenteum 360
argenteum var. *lanatum* 360
argenteum var. *majus* 360
atropurpureum 361
atropurpureum var. *gracilentum* 361
bicolor 361
bimum 357
bornholmense 367
caespiticium 359
caespiticium var. *caespiticium* 359
calophyllum 347
capillare var. capillare 352
capillare var. *elegans* 354
capillare var. *macrocarpum* 352
capillare var. *obconicum* 355
capillare var. rufifolium 354
cernuum 347
concinnatum 346
creberrimum 355
donianum 351
donii 351
dunense 362
duvalii 349
elegans 354
erythrocarpum 368
fallax 348
filiforme 346
flaccidum 355
gemmiferum 361
imbricatum 350
inclinatum 350
intermedium 351
klinggraeffii 365
laevifilum 355
marratii 347
microerythrocarpum 366
mildeanum 369
mildei 369
murale 362
neodamense 358
obconicum 355

Bryum
pallens 348
pallens var. *fallax* 348
pallescens 355
pendulum 349
proliferum 370
pseudotriquetrum var. bimum 357
pseudotriquetrum var. pseudotriquetrum 356
radiculosum 362
riparium 369
roseum 370
rubens 367
ruderale 363
rufifolium 354
salinum 350
sauteri 365
stenotrichum 350
subapiculatum 366
subelegans 355
tenuisetum 366
torquescens 355
turbinatum 349
uliginosum 347
ventricosum 356
violaceum 364
warneum 347
weigelii 349
Buxbaumia
aphylla 202
Calliergon
cordifolium 456
cuspidatum 458
giganteum 457
sarmentosum 458
stramineum 455
trifarium 456
Calliergonella
cuspidata 458
Calomnion
complanatum 382
Calypogeia
arguta 30
azurea 27
fissa 25
integristipula 29
muellerana 27
muelleriana 27
neesiana 28
neesiana var. *meylanii* 29
sphagnicola 29
suecica 30
trichomanis 27
Camptothecium
lutescens 464
nitens 451
Camptothecium
sericeum 463
Campyliadelphus
chrysophyllus 435
elodes 436
Campylium
calcareum 436
chrysophyllum 435
elodes 436
hispidulum var. *sommerfeltii* 436
polygamum 444
protensum 434
stellatum var. protensum 434
stellatum var. stellatum 432
Campylophyllum
calcareum 436
Campylopus
atrovirens var. atrovirens 233
atrovirens var. falcatus 234
atrovirens var. gracilis 234
atrovirens var. *muticus* 233
brevipilus 236
brevipilus var. *auriculatus* 236
flexuosus 231
flexuosus var. *paludosus* 231
flexuosus var. *zonatus* 231
fragilis 228
gracilis 228
introflexus 234
introflexus 235
paradoxus 231
pilifer 234
polytrichoides 234
pyriformis var. azoricus 231
pyriformis var. *fallaciosus* 231
pyriformis var. pyriformis 230
schimperi 228
schwarzii 228
setifolius 232
shawii 233
shawii var. *hamatus* 233
subulatus 228
symplectus 228
Campylostelium
saxicola 321
Catharinea
angustata 200
angustata var. *rhystophylla* 200
undulata 199
Catoscopium
nigritum 383
Cephalozia
bicuspidata 31
bicuspidata subsp. *lammersiana* 31
bicuspidata var. *lammersiana* 31

Cephalozia
catenulata 32
connivens 36
curvifolia 37
fluitans 37
francisci 38
hibernica 36
leucantha 34
loitlesbergeri 35
lunulaefolia 34
lunulifolia 34
macrostachya var. macrostachya 33
macrostachya var. spiniflora 33
media 34
pallida 34
pleniceps 35
Cephaloziella
byssacea 42
divaricata 42
elachista 41
hampeana 41
integerrima 44
massalongi 44
massalongoi 44
pearsonii 56
rubella 41
spinigera 41
starkei 42
starkei var. *scabra* 42
starkii 42
stellulifera 43
subdentata 41
turneri 44
Ceratodon
conicus 209
purpureus 208
purpureus subsp. *purpureus* 208
Chiloscyphus
pallescens 87
polyanthos 86
polyanthos var. *polyanthos* 86
polyanthos var. *pallescens* 87
polyanthos var. *rivularis* 86
Cinclidium
stygium 373
Cinclidotus
fontinaloides 300
riparius 302
Cirriphyllum
crassinervium 484
piliferum 474
Cladopodiella
fluitans 37
francisci 38
Clasmatocolea
cuneifolia 82
Climacium
dendroides 411
Cololejeunea
calcarea 115
microscopica 117
minutissima 116
rossettiana 115
Colura
calyptrifolia 114
Colurolejeunea
calyptrifolia 114
Conardia
compacta 442
Conocephalum
conicum 137
Cratoneuron
commutatum var. *commutatum* 429
commutatum var. *falcatum* 430
commutatum var. *virescens* 431
filicinum 431
filicinum var. *fallax* 431
Cryphaea
arborea 412
heteromalla 412
Cryptothallus
mirabilis 127
Ctenidium
molluscum var. condensatum 505
molluscum var. *croceum* 506
molluscum var. fastigiatum 505
molluscum var. molluscum 504
molluscum var. robustum 506
Cyclodictyon
laetevirens 421
Cylindrothecium
concinnum 487
Cynodontium
bruntonii 211
jenneri 211
Daltonia
splachnoides 421
Desmatodon
convolutus 289
Dichodontium
flavescens 213
pellucidum 211
pellucidum var. *compactum* 211
pellucidum var. *fagimontanum* 211
pellucidum var. *flavescens* 213
Dicranella
cerviculata 219
crispa 216
curvata 216

Dicranella
grevilleana 216
heteromalla 220
heteromalla var. *sericea* 220
heteromalla var. *stricta* 220
palustris 214
rufescens 217
schreberana 214
schreberi var. *elata* 214
schreberiana 214
secunda 216
squarrosa 214
staphylina 217
subulata 216
subulata var. *curvata* 216
varia 216
Dicranodontium
asperulum 227
denudatum 227
denudatum var. *alpinum* 227
uncinatum 227
Dicranoweisia
cirrata 221
crispula 222
Dicranum
affine 225
asperulum 227
bergeri 225
bonjeanii 222
bonjeanii var. *rugifolium* 222
flagellare 226
flexicaule 226
fulvellum 222
fuscescens 225
fuscescens var. *congestum* 226
fuscescens var. *falcifolium* 225
majus 224
montanum 226
scoparium 223
scoparium var. *alpestre* 223
scoparium var. *orthophyllum* 223
scoparium var. *spadiceum* 223
scoparium var. *turfosum* 223
scottianum 226
scottii 226
uncinatum 227
undulatum 225
Didymodon
acutus var. acutus 275
acutus var. icmadophilus 275
australasiae var. umbrosus 277
denudatus 227
denudatus var. *alpinus* 227
fallax 282
ferrugineus 283
Didymodon
giganteus 284
icmadophilus 275
insulanus 277
luridus 278
maximus 284
nicholsonii 276
rigidulus 275
sinuosus 279
spadiceus 281
tomaculosus 283
tophaceus 280
umbrosus 277
vinealis 277
Diphyscium
foliosum 201
Diplophyllum
albicans 72
obtusifolium 73
ovatum 71
Discelium
nudum 324
Distichium
capillaceum 208
inclinatum 208
Ditrichum
crispatissimum 206
cylindricum 204
flexicaule 206
flexicaule s.s. 206
gracile 206
heteromallum 205
homomallum 205
lineare 205
pusillum 205
tenuifolium 204
tortile 205
zonatum var. scabrifolium 206
zonatum var. zonatum 206
Douinia
ovata 71
Drepanocladus
aduncus 445
cossonii 449
exannulatus var. *exannulatus* 443
exannulatus var. *rotae* 443
falcatus 442
fluitans var. *falcatus* 442
fluitans var. *fluitans* 442
lycopodioides 447
polycarpos 445
polygamus 444
revolvens agg. 448
revolvens s.s. 447
revolvens var. *intermedius* 449

Drepanocladus
sendtneri 446
sendtneri var. *wilsonii* 446
uncinatus 451
vernicosus 450
Drepanolejeunea
hamatifolia 107
Dryptodon
patens 311
Dumortiera
hirsuta 137
Encalypta
alpina 251
ciliata 252
commutata 251
rhaptocarpa 251
streptocarpa 250
vulgaris 251
Entodon
concinnus 487
orthocarpus 487
Entosthodon
attenuatus 326
fascicularis 327
obtusus 327
Ephemerum
cohaerens 330
minutissimum 330, 331
serratum 330
serratum var. *minutissimum* 331
serratum var. *serratum* 330
sessile 329
spinulosum 332
stellatum 330
Epipterygium
tozeri 345
Eremonotus
myriocarpus 55
Eucalyx
hyalinus 63
obovatus 65
paroicus 64
Eucladium
verticillatum 252
Eurhynchium
alopecuroides 476
alopecurum 476
confertum 477
crassinervium 484
curvisetum 486
hians 482
megapolitanum 478
murale 476
murale var. *julaceum* 476
myosuroides 459
Eurhynchium
myosuroides var. *brachythecioides* 460
myurum 461
piliferum 474
praelongum 481
praelongum var. *stokesii* 481
pulchellum var. diversifolium 480
pumilum 480
riparioides 475
riparioides var. *alopecuroides* 476
schleicheri 483
speciosum 484
striatulum 479
striatum 478
swartzii var. *rigidum* 482
swartzii var. *swartzii* 482
teesdalei 486
tenellum 485
Fissidens
adianthoides 248
algarvicus 245
bambergeri 239
bryoides 242
celticus 245
crassipes 244
cristatus 247
cristatus var. *brevifolius* 247
curnovii 243
curvatus 245
decipiens 247
dubius 247
exiguus 238
exilis 244
fontanus 250
gracilifolius 241
herzogii 240
incurvus 242
incurvus var. *tamarindifolius* 242
limbatus 240
minutulus 240
minutulus var. *tenuifolius* 241
monguillonii 243
osmundoides 245
polyphyllus 249
pusillus 240
pusillus var. *tenuifolius* 241
rivularis 243
rufulus 244
serrulatus 249
taxifolius subsp. *pallidicaulis* 247
taxifolius subsp. *taxifolius* 246
taxifolius var. pallidicaulis 247
taxifolius var. taxifolius 246
viridulus 240
viridulus agg. 238

Fissidens
viridulus s.s. 239
viridulus var. *bambergeri* 239
viridulus var. *tenuifolius* 241
viridulus var. *viridulus* 239
Fontinalis
antipyretica var. antipyretica 408
antipyretica var. cymbifolia 410
antipyretica var. gigantea 410
antipyretica var. gracilis 410
gracilis 410
squamosa var. dixonii 411
squamosa var. squamosa 410
Fossombronia
angulosa 118
caespitiformis 118
dumortieri 117
fimbriata 121
foveolata 117
husnotii 118
husnotii var. *anglica* 118
incurva 120
maritima 120
pusilla 118
pusilla var. *maritima* 120
pusilla var. *pusilla* 118
wondraczekii 120
Frullania
dilatata 105
fragilifolia 104
germana 103
microphylla var. microphylla 104
tamarisci 102
tamarisci var. *atrovirens* 102
tamarisci var. *cornubica* 102
tamarisci var. *robusta* 102
teneriffae 103
Funaria
attenuata 326
calcarea 326
ericetorum 327
fascicularis 327
hibernica 326
hygrometrica 325
hygrometrica var. *calvescens* 325
muhlenbergii 326
obtusa 327
templetonii 326
Geocalyx
graveolens 88
Georgia
brownii 201
pellucida 200
Glyphomitrium
daviesii 321
Glyphomitrium
polyphyllum 320
saxicola 321
Grimmia
robusta 311
acicularis 312
acicularis var. *denticulata* 312
affinis 307
alpicola var. *rivularis* 302
apocarpa 304
apocarpa var. *rivularis* 302
aquatica 313
atrata 307
austrofunalis 311
britannica 311
campestris 306
conferta 305
conferta var. *pruinosa* 305
crinita 306
curvata 311
decipiens 311
decipiens var. *robusta* 311
doniana 307
donii 307
donii var. *sudetica* 307
donniana 307
donniana var. *donniana* 307
elliptica 312
fascicularis 314
funalis 308
hartmanii 310
hypnoides 317
laevigata 306
lisae 310
longirostris 307
maritima 302
nuda 324
orbicularis 308
ovalis 307
patens 311
pulvinata var. pulvinata 307
ramondii 311
retracta 310
stirtonii 309
stricta 305
subsquarrosa 309
torquata 308
trichophylla 309
trichophylla var. *robusta* 311
trichophylla var. *stirtonii* 309
trichophylla var. *subsquarrosa* 309
trichophylla var. *trichophylla* 309
Gymnocolea
inflata 55
inflata var. *heterostipa* 55

Gymnocybe
palustris 380
Gymnomitrion
concinnatum 70
corallioides 71
crenulatum 71
obtusum 71
Gymnostomum
aeruginosum 271
calcareum 270
insigne 268
recurvirostrum 267
viridulum 270
Gyroweisia
tenuis 269
Hamatocaulis
vernicosus 450
Haplomitrium
hookeri 18
Harpalejeunea
molleri 107
ovata 107
Harpanthus
scutatus 88
Hedwigia
albicans 407
ciliata var. ciliata 407
imberbis 408
integrifolia 408
stellata 407
Hennediella
heimii 295
stanfordensis 295
Herberta
hutchinsiae 18
Herbertus
aduncus subsp. hutchinsiae 18
Heterocladium
heteropterum 425
heteropterum var. *fallax* 424
heteropterum var. flaccidum 424
heteropterum var. heteropterum 423
macounii 423
wulfsbergii 425
Heteroscyphus
fissistipus 88
Homalia
trichomanoides 417
Homalothecium
lutescens 464
nitens 451
sericeum 463
Homomallium
incurvatum 496
Hookeria
lucens 420
Hygroamblystegium
fluviatile 438
tenax 439
Hygrobiella
laxifolia 38
Hygrohypnum
dilatatum 454
duriusculum 454
eugyrium 453
luridum var. luridum 452
luridum var. subsphaericarpon 453
ochraceum 452
Hylocomium
brevirostre 510
loreum 509
parietinum 487
proliferum 511
proliferum var. *lambayensis* 511
splendens 511
splendens var. *gracilius* 511
squarrosum 508
triquetrum 507
umbratum 511
Hymenostylium
insigne 268
recurvirostrum 267
Hyocomium
armoricum 506
flagellare 506
Hyophila
stanfordensis 295
Hypnum
aduncum 445
aduncum var. *gracilescens* 445
aduncum var. *polycarpon* 445
aduncum var. *polycarpum* 445
albicans 465
algirianum 485
andoi 500
brevirostre 510
callichroum 503
chrysophyllum 435
chrysophyllum var. *erectum* 435
circinatum 462
commutatum 429
confertum 477
cordifolium 456
crassinerve 484
crassinervium 484
cupressiforme s.s. 496
cupressiforme var. *cupressiforme* 496
cupressiforme var. *elatum* 497
cupressiforme var. *ericetorum* 501

Hypnum
cupressiforme var. *filiforme* 500
cupressiforme var. *lacunosum* 497
cupressiforme var. *mammillatum* 500
cupressiforme var. *resupinatum* 499
cupressiforme var. *tectorum* 498
curvisetum 486
cuspidatum 458
cuspidatum var. *pungens* 458
elodes 436
eugyrium 453
eugyrium var. *mackayi* 453
exannulatum 443
exannulatum var. *brachydictyon* 443
falcatum 430
falcatum var. *gracilescens* 430
fluitans 442
fluitans var. *atlanticum* 442
giganteum 457
glareosum 465
hians 482
illecebrum 474
imponens 502
intermedium 449
jutlandicum 501
lacunosum var. lacunosum 497
lacunosum var. tectorum 498
lindbergii 502
luridum 452
lutescens 464
lycopodioides 447
mammillatum 500
megapolitanum 478
molluscum 504
molluscum var. *condensatum* 505
molluscum var. *fastigiatum* 505
murale 476
pallidirostre 480
palustre 452
patientiae 502
piliferum 474
plumosum 471
praelongum 481
praelongum var. *stokesii* 481
pseudoplumosum 471
pseudoplumosum var. *homomallum* 471
purum 472
resupinatum 499
riparium 440
riparium var. *longifolium* 440
rivulare 468
rivulare var. *tenue* 468
rugosum 495
rusciforme 475
rusciforme var. *alopecuroides* 476

Hypnum
rusciforme var. *atlanticum* 475
rutabulum 467
rutabulum var. *robustum* 467
scorpioides 454
sericeum 463
speciosum 484
stellatum 432
stellatum var. *protensum* 434
stramineum 455
striatulum 479
striatum 478
swartzii 482
sylvaticum 492
teesdalii 486
uncinatum 451
uncinulatum 501
velutinum 469
velutinum var. *praelongum* 469
viride 470
viride var. *majus* 470
wilsonii 446
Hypopterygium
immigrans 421
Isopterygiopsis
muelleriana 494
pulchella 494
Isopterygium
depressum 495
elegans 494
muellerianum 494
pulchellum 494
Isothecium
alopecuroides 461
holtii 462
myosuroides var. brachythecioides 460
myosuroides var. myosuroides 459
myosuroides var. *rivulare* 462
myosuroides var. *tenuinerve* 459
myurum 461
striatulum 479
viviparum 461
Jubula
hutchinsiae 106
hutchinsiae var. *integrifolia* 106
Jungermannia
atrovirens 60
exsertifolia subsp. cordifolia 62
gracillima 63
hyalina 63
obovata 65
paroica 64
pumila 61
sphaerocarpa 62
sphaerocarpa var. *lurida* 62

Jungermannia
subelliptica 65
Kantia
arguta 30
sprengelii 26
trichomanis 25
Kiaeria
blyttii 222
starkei 222
Kurzia
pauciflora 20
sylvatica 21
trichoclados 21
Leersia
contorta 250
extinctoria 251
laciniata 252
rhabdocarpa 251
Leiocolea
alpestris 53
badensis 53
bantriensis 52
collaris 53
fitzgeraldiae 52
gillmanii 52
heterocolpos 53
muelleri 53
rutheana var. rutheana 52
turbinata 54
Lejeunea
cavifolia 109
cavifolia var. *heterophylla* 110
cavifolia var. *planiuscula* 109
diversiloba 113
eckloniana 114
flava subsp. moorei 113
heterophylla 110
hibernica 113
holtii 114
lamacerina 110
lamacerina var. *azorica* 110
mandonii 114
patens 112
planiuscula 110
ulicina 108
Lepidozia
cupressina 24
pearsonii 23
pinnata 24
reptans 22
setacea 20
setacea var. *sertularioides* 20
sylvatica 21
trichoclados 21
Leptobarbula
berica 286
Leptobryum
pyriforme 334
Leptodictyum
riparium 440
Leptodon
smithii 414
Leptodontium
flexifolium 267
recurvifolium 263
Leptoscyphus
anomalus 59
cuneifolius 82
taylorii 58
Leptotheca
gaudichaudii 382
Leskea
polycarpa 421
Leucobryum
glaucum 236
juniperoideum 238
Leucodon
sciuroides var. sciuroides 413
Lophocolea
bidentata 82
bidentata var. *rivularis* 82
bispinosa 84
cuspidata 82
fragrans 85
heterophylla 84
semiteres 85
spicata 85
Lophozia
alpestris 49, 53
attenuata 46
badensis 53
bantriensis 52
bantryensis 52
bicrenata 51
capitata 50
excisa 50
floerkei 45
gracilis 46
guttulata 49
incisa 50
inflata 55
inflata var. *compacta* 55
inflata var. *heterostipa* 55
inflata var. *laxa* 55
kunzeana 45
longiflora 49
muelleri 52
muelleri var. *bantriensis* 52
opacifolia 51

Lophozia
porphyroleuca 49
quinquedentata 58
silvicola 47
sudetica 49
turbinata 54
ventricosa 47
ventricosa var. *confertifolia* 47
ventricosa var. *longiflora* 47
ventricosa var. *silvicola* 47
Lunularia
cruciata 136
Madotheca
cordaeana 100
laevigata 100
platyphylla 99
porella 101
rivularis 100
thuja 101
Marchantia
alpestris 142
polymorpha subsp. montivagans 142
polymorpha subsp. polymorpha 140
polymorpha subsp. ruderalis 141
polymorpha var. *aquatica* 140
Marchesinia
mackaii 106
Marsupella
adusta 70
aquatica 68
aquatica var. *pearsonii* 69
emarginata var. aquatica 68
emarginata var. emarginata 67
emarginata var. *minor* 67
emarginata var. pearsonii 69
erythrorhiza 69
funckii 69
pearsonii 69
sphacelata 69
sphacelata var. *media* 69
sprucei 70
sullivantii 69
ustulata 70
Mastigophora
woodsii 18
Meesia
longiseta 382
triquetra 382
tristicha 382
uliginosa 382
Metzgeria
conjugata 135
fruticulosa 131, 133
fruticulosa 133
furcata 134
Metzgeria
furcata var. *aeruginosa* 131
furcata var. *fruticulosa* 131
furcata var. *ulvula* 134
hamata 136
leptoneura 136
pubescens 136
temperata 133
Microbryum
curvicolle 295
davallianum 294
rectum 295
starckeanum 293
Microlejeunea
ulicina 108
Mnium
affine 376
affine var. *elatum* 377
cuspidatum 375, 376
cuspidatum var. *elatum* 377
hornum 371
longirostrum 379
marginatum var. dioicum 373
marginatum var. marginatum 372
orthorhynchum 372
pseudopunctatum 374
punctatum 373
riparium 372
rostratum 379
rugicum 377
seligeri 377
serratum 372
silvaticum 375
stellare 373
sylvaticum 375
thomsonii 372
undulatum 378
Moerckia
flotoviana 125
flotowiana 125
hibernica 125
Molendoa
warburgii 272
Mollia
aeruginosa 271
aeruginosa var. *ramosissima* 271
brachydontia 260
brachydontia var. *cophocarpa* 260
calcarea 270
calcarea var. *mutica* 270
crispa 256
crispata 254
crispula 261
crispula var. *elata* 261
crispula var. *nigro-viride* 261

Mollia
flavovirens 259
fragilis 258
hibernica 262
inclinata 259
littoralis 260
littoralis var. *angustifolia* 260
lutescens 260
microstoma 255
nitida 258
rostellata 256
rutilans 255
tenuirostris 262
tenuirostris var. *holtii* 262
tenuis 269
tortilis 255
tortuosa 256
tortuosa var. *angustifolia* 256
verticillata 252
viridula 253
viridula var. *amblyodon* 253
Mylia
anomala 59
cuneifolia 82
taylorii 58
Myurella
julacea var. julacea 488
julacea var. scabrifolia 488
Myurium
hebridarum 414
hochstetteri 414
Nardia
compressa 65
geoscyphus 67
scalaris 66
Neckera
complanata 416
crispa 414
crispa var. *falcata* 414
fontinaloides 415
fontinaloides var. *philippei* 415
pennata 414
pumila 415
pumila var. *philippeana* 415
Nowellia
curvifolia 37
Octodiceras
fontanum 250
Odontoschisma
denudatum 40
elongatum 40
sphagni 39
Oedipodium
griffithianum 332
Oligotrichum
hercynicum 198
hercynicum var. *laxum* 198
incurvum 198
Omalia
trichomanoides 417
Oncophorus
bruntonii 211
crenulatus 210
crispatus 210
striatus 210
Orthodontium
gracile 334
gracile var. *heterocarpum* 334
lineare 334
Orthopyxis
androgyna 381
Orthothecium
intricatum 489
rufescens 489
Orthotrichum
affine 395
affine var. *fastigiatum* 395
affine var. *rivale* 395
anomalum 396
anomalum var. *cylindricum* 396
anomalum var. *saxatile* 396
cupulatum var. cupulatum 397
cupulatum var. *nudum* 398
cupulatum var. riparium 398
diaphanum 400
diaphanum var. *aquaticum* 400
leiocarpum 394
lyellii 393
pallens 400
pulchellum 401
pumilum 400
rivulare 398
rupestre 396
rupestre var. *rupincola* 396
rupestre var. *sturmii* 396
schimperi 400
shawii 394
sprucei 399
stramineum 399
striatum 394
tenellum 399
Oxystegus
hibernicus 262
sinuosus 279
tenuirostris var. *holtii* 262
tenuirostris var. *tenuirostris* 262
Pallavicinia
lyellii 124

Paludella
squarrosa 382
Palustriella
commutata var. commutata 429
commutata var. falcata 430
commutata var. virescens 431
Paraleptodontium
recurvifolium 263
Pedinophyllum
interruptum 89
Pellia
borealis 121
endiviifolia 123
epiphylla 121
fabbroniana 123
fabbroniana var. *lorea* 123
neesiana 122
Petalophyllum
ralfsii 121
Phaeoceros
laevis 150
laevis subsp. *laevis* 150
Phascum
acaulon var. *piliferum* 293
crispum 256
curvicolle 295
cuspidatum subsp. *papillosum* 293
cuspidatum var. *cuspidatum* 292
cuspidatum var. *piliferum* 293
Philonotis
adpressa 385
arnellii 385
caespitosa 385
calcarea 387
capillaris 385
cernua 388
fontana 385
fontana var. *adpressa* 385
fontana var. *compacta* 385
fontana var. *falcata* 385
rigida 384
seriata 387
tomentella 387
wilsonii 388
Physcomitrella
patens 329
Physcomitrium
pyriforme 328
sphaericum 329
Plagiobryum
zieri 346
Plagiochila
ambagiosa 93
asplenioides 90
asplenioides 91
Plagiochila
asplenioides var. *humilis* 90
asplenioides var. *major* 91
asplenioides var. *minor* 90
atlantica 93
bifaria 94
britannica 92
carringtonii 90
dillenii 90
exigua 95
killarniensis 94
owenii 95
porelloides 90
punctata 95
spinulosa 93, 94
tridenticulata 95
Plagiomnium
affine 376
cuspidatum 375
elatum 377
ellipticum 377
rostratum 379
undulatum 378
Plagiopus
oederi 383
oederianus 383
Plagiothecium
cavifolium 491
curvifolium 490
denticulatum var. denticulatum 490
denticulatum var. obtusifolium 490
depressum 495
elegans 494
laetum 491
latebricola 490
nemorale 492
platyphyllum 491
pulchellum 494
roeseanum 491
silvaticum 492
succulentum 491
sylvaticum 492
undulatum 493
Platydictya
confervoides 440
jungermannioides 489
Plectocolea
hyalina 63
obovata 65
paroica 64
subelliptica 65
Pleuridium
acuminatum 202
alternifolium 203
axillare 203

Pleuridium
subulatum 202
subulatum 203
Pleurochaete
squarrosa 263
Pleurozia
purpurea 96
Pleurozium
schreberi 487
Pleurozygodon
aestivus 268
Pogonatum
aloides 190
aloides var. *minimum* 190
nanum 190
urnigerum 191
Pohlia
acuminata 336
albicans 344
andalusica 338
annotina 340
bulbifera 339
camptotrachela 342
carnea 343
cruda 336
delicatula 343
drummondii 338
elongata subsp. elongata var. acuminata 336
elongata subsp. elongata var. elongata 335
elongata subsp. polymorpha 336
filum 338
flexuosa 342
gracilis 338
lescuriana 343
lutescens 343
melanodon 343
muyldermansii 342
muyldermansii var. *pseudomuyldermansii* 342
nutans 336
nutans var. *alpina* 336
nutans var. *longiseta* 336
polymorpha 336
proligera 340
proligera 342
pulchella 343
rothii 338
wahlenbergii var. calcarea 345
wahlenbergii var. glacialis 345
wahlenbergii var. wahlenbergii 344
Polytrichum
aloides 190
aloides var. *dicksonii* 190
alpestre 197
alpinum 192
alpinum var. *septentrionale* 192
Polytrichum
attenuatum 193
aurantiacum 193
commune var. commune 194
commune var. humile 195
commune var. *minus* 195
formosum 193
gracile 193
juniperinum 196
longisetum 193
nanum 190
piliferum 195
strictum 197
subrotundum 190
subrotundum var. *longisetum* 190
urnigerum 191
Porella
arboris-vitae 100
arboris-vitae var. *killarniensis* 100
arboris-vitae var. *obscura* 100
cordaeana 100
cordaeana var. *faroensis* 100
cordaeana var. *simplicior* 100
laevigata 100
obtusata 101
pinnata 101
platyphylla 99
thuja 101
Porotrichum
alopecurum 418
alopecurum var. *acutum* 418
angustifolium 419
Pottia
asperula 290
bryoides 292
commutata 294
crinita 290
davalliana 294
heimii 295
intermedia 290
lanceolata 290
minutula 294
recta 295
starckeana subsp. *conica* 294
starckeana subsp. *minutula* 294
starckeana subsp. *starckeana* 293
starckeana var. *brachyodus* 293
starckeana var. *starckeana* 293
starckei 293
starckei var. *affinis* 293
starckei var. *davallii* 294
truncata 291
truncatula 291
viridifolia 290
wilsonii 290

Preissia
  quadrata 139
Prionolobus
  turneri 44
Pseudephemerum
  nitidum 203
Pseudocrossidium
  hornschuchianum 263
  revolutum 264
Pseudoscleropodium
  purum 472
Pseudotaxiphyllum
  elegans 494
Pterigynandrum
  filiforme var. filiforme 420
  filiforme var. majus 420
Pterogonium
  gracile 414
  ornithopodioides 414
Pterygoneurum
  lamellatum 284
  ovatum 284
Pterygophyllum
  lucens 420
Ptilidium
  ciliare 98
  pulcherrimum 99
Ptilium
  crista-castrensis 504
Ptychomitrium
  polyphyllum 320
Pylaisia
  polyantha 496
Racomitrium
  aciculare 312
  affine 316
  affine 316
  aquaticum 313
  canescens 318
  canescens 320
  canescens var. *canescens* 320
  canescens var. *ericoides* 318
  ellipticum 312
  elongatum 320
  ericoides 318
  fasciculare 314
  heterostichum 316
  heterostichum agg. 315
  heterostichum var. *gracilescens* 316
  lanuginosum 317
  macounii subsp. alpinum 315
  obtusum 316
  sudeticum 316
Radula
  aquilegia 98
  carringtonii 98
  complanata 96
  holtii 98
  lindbergiana 97
  lindenbergiana 97
  voluta 98
Reboulia
  hemisphaerica 138
Rhabdoweisia
  crenulata 210
  crispata 210
  denticulata 210
  fugax 210
Rhacomitrium
  aciculare 312
  affine 316
  aquaticum 313
  canescens 320
  ellipticum 312
  elongatum 320
  ericoides 318
  fasciculare 314
  heterostichum 316
  lanuginosum 317
  sudeticum 316
Rhizomnium
  pseudopunctatum 374
  punctatum 373
Rhodobryum
  roseum 370
Rhynchostegiella
  curviseta 486
  pallidirostra 480
  pumila 480
  teesdalei 486
  tenella 485
  tenella var. *tenella* 485
  teneriffae 486
Rhynchostegium
  alopecuroides 476
  confertum 477
  lusitanicum 476
  megapolitanum 478
  murale 476
  riparioides 475
Rhytidiadelphus
  loreus 509
  squarrosus 508
  squarrosus var. *calvescens* 509
  subpinnatus 509
  triquetrus 507
Rhytidium
  rugosum 495

Riccardia
chamedryfolia 128
incurvata 129
latifrons 130
major 128
multifida 127
palmata 129
pinguis 126
sinuata 128
sinuata var. *major* 128
Riccia
beyrichiana 147
bifurca 147
cavernosa 143
crozalsii 146
crystallina 143
fluitans 143
glauca 145
glaucescens 147
huebeneriana 143
lescuriana 147
sorocarpa 144
subbifurca 146
warnstorfii 146
Ricciocarpos
natans 142
Saccogyna
viticulosa 89
Sanionia
uncinata 451
Scapania
aequiloba 79
aspera 80
calcicola 73
compacta 73
curta 74
cuspiduligera 74
dentata 77
dentata var. *ambigua* 77
gracilis 81
gracilis var. *integrifolia* 81
gracilis var. *laxifolia* 81
gymnostomophila 73
intermedia 77
irrigua 76
lingulata 74
nemorea 75
nemorosa 75
nimbosa 82
ornithopodioides 82
paludosa 79
purpurascens 77
purpurascens var. *speciosa* 77
scandica 74
subalpina 78
Scapania
subalpina var. *undulifolia* 78
uliginosa 78
umbrosa 74
undulata 77
Schistidium
agassizii 303
alpicola var. *alpicola* 303
alpicola var. *rivulare* 302
apocarpum agg. 303
apocarpum s.s. 304
apocarpum var. *confertum* 305
confertum 305
crassipilum 306
elegantulum subsp. elegantulum 306
elegantulum subsp. wilsonii 306
maritimum 302
platyphyllum 303
pruinosum 305
rivulare 302
rivulare subsp. *latifolium* 303
strictum 305
Scleropodium
caespitosum 473
cespitans 473
illecebrum 474
purum 472
tourettii 474
tourretii 474
Scorpidium
scorpioides 454
Scorpiurium
circinatum 462
Seligeria
acutifolia 322
acutifolia var. *longiseta* 322
calcarea 323
calycina 323
doniana 323
donniana 323
donnii 323
oelandica 324
patula 324
paucifolia 323
pusilla 322
recurvata 323
setacea 323
trifaria 324
trifaria agg. 324
tristicha 324
Sematophyllum
demissum 496
micans 496
novae-caesareae 496

Solenostoma
atrovirens var. *sphaerocarpoidea* 60
cordifolium 62
crenulatum 63
pumilum 61
sphaerocarpoideum 60
sphaerocarpum 62
triste 60
Southbya
tophacea 95
Sphaerocarpos
michelii 136
Sphagnum
of uncertain identity 180-182
acutifolium 163
acutifolium var. *deflexum* 163
acutifolium var. *elegans* 163
acutifolium var. *fuscum* 164
acutifolium var. *luridum* 165
acutifolium var. *purpureum* 163
acutifolium var. *quinquefarium* 162
acutifolium var. *rubellum* 163
acutifolium var. *subnitens* 165
affine 155
amblyphyllum 179
amblyphyllum var. *macrophyllum* 179
amblyphyllum var. *mesophyllum* 179
angustifolium 180
auriculatum 171
auriculatum var. *auriculatum* 171
auriculatum var. *canovirescens* 171
auriculatum var. *inundatum* 169
auriculatum var. *laxifolium* 171
auriculatum var. *ovatum* 171
auriculatum var. *racemosum* 171
auriculatum var. *submersum* 171
auriculatum var. *tenellum* 171
austinii 154
austinii var. *imbricatum* 154
capillaceum 163
capillifolium subsp. rubellum 163
capillifolium var. *rubellum* 163
compactum 167
compactum var. *imbricatum* 167
compactum var. *subsquarrosum* 167
contortum 174
crassicladum 171
crassicladum var. *diversifolium* 171
crassicladum var. *intermedium* 171
crassicladum var. *magnifolium* 171
cuspidatum 176
cuspidatum var. *falcatum* 176
cuspidatum var. *plumosum* 176
cuspidatum var. *serrratum* 176
cuspidatum var. *submersum* 176
Sphagnum
cymbifolium 156
cymbifolium var. *congestum* 156
cymbifolium var. *flavescens* 156
cymbifolium var. *squarrosulum* 156
denticulatum 171
denticulatum var. *inundatum* 169
fallax subsp. fallax 178
fallax subsp. isoviitae 179
fimbriatum 160
fimbriatum var. *intermedium* 160
fimbriatum var. *laxifolium* 160
fimbriatum var. *robustum* 160
fimbriatum var. *validus* 160
flexuosum 179
fuscum 164
girgensohnii 161
hakkodense 155
imbricatum subsp. *affine* 155
imbricatum subsp. *austinii* 154
intermedium 178
inundatum 169
inundatum var. densum 169
inundatum var. *diversifolium* 169
inundatum var. *eurycladum* 169
inundatum var. *lancifolium* 169
inundatum var. *ovalifolium* 169
inundatum var. *robustum* 169
laricinum 174
magellanicum 157
medium 157
medium var. *obscurum* 157
medium var. *purpurascens* 157
medium var. *roseum* 157
molle 166
molluscum 175
nemoreum 163
obesum 171
obesum var. *canovirens* 171
obesum var. *hemi-isophyllum* 171
obesum var. *mastigocladum* 171
obesum var. *plumosum* 171
obesum var. *teretiramosum* 171
other names 180-182
palustre var. palustre 156
papillosum 155
papillosum var. *confertum* 155
papillosum var. *normale* 155
papillosum var. *sublaeve* 155
platyphyllum 175
plumulosum 165
plumulosum var. *flavofuscescens* 165
plumulosum var. *lilacinum* 165
plumulosum var. *viride* 165
pulchrum 177

Sphagnum
quinquefarium 162
recurvum var. *amblyphyllum* 179
recurvum var. *mucronatum* 178
recurvum var. *tenue* 180
rigidum 167
rigidum var. *compactum* 167
rigidum var. *squarrosum* 167
riparium 180
robustum 161
rubellum 163
rufescens 171
russowii 161
russowii var. *girgensohnioides* 161
squarrosum 158
squarrosum var. *imbricatum* 158
squarrosum var. *spectabile* 158
squarrosum var. *subsquarrosum* 158
squarrosum var. *teres* 159
strictum 167
subfulvum 166
subnitens subsp. *ferrugineum* 166
subnitens var. ferrugineum 166
subnitens var. subnitens 165
subsecundum 168
subsecundum subsp. *inundatum* 169
subsecundum subsp. *subsecundum* 168
subsecundum var. *auriculatum* 171
subsecundum var. *contortum* 171
subtile 163
tenellum 175
teres 159
viride 176
warnstorfianum 162
warnstorfii 162
Sphenolobopsis
pearsonii 56
Sphenolobus
exsectiformis 57
exsectus 57
hellerianus 57
minutus 56
pearsonii 56
Splachnum
ampullaceum 333
ovatum 332
pedunculatum 332
pedunculatum var. *sphaericum* 332
sphaericum 332
Stereodon
callichrous 503
canariensis 501
circinalis 501
cupressiformis 496
cupressiformis var. *elatus* 497
Stereodon
cupressiformis var. *ericetorum* 501
cupressiformis var. filiformis 500
cupressiformis var. *longirostris* 496
cupressiformis var. *mammillatus* 500
lindbergii 502
resupinatus 499
rufescens 489
subrufus 489
Swartzia
inclinata 208
montana 208
montana var. *compacta* 208
Syntrichia
intermedia 297
laevipila var. laevipila 298
laevipila var. laevipilaeformis 299
latifolia 300
papillosa 299
princeps 298
ruraliformis 297
ruralis 296
Targionia
hypophylla 136
Taxiphyllum
wissgrillii 495
Tayloria
longicollis 332
tenuis 332
Telaranea
nematodes 20
sejuncta 20
Tetraphis
browniana 201
pellucida 200
Tetraplodon
angustatus 332
bryoides 332
mnioides 332
Tetrodontium
brownianum 201
Thamnobryum
alopecurum 418
angustifolium 419
Thuidium
abietinum subsp. abietinum 426
abietinum subsp. hystricosum 426
assimile 428
delicatulum 427
erectum 427
hystricosum 426
philibertii 428
recognitum 429
tamariscifolium 426
tamariscinum 426

Timmia
austriaca 389
norvegica 389
Tomentypnum
nitens 451
Tortella
densa 258
flavovirens var. flavovirens 259
flavovirens var. glareicola 259
fragilis 258
inclinata 259
nitida 258
tortuosa 256
Tortula
caulon var. acaulon 292
acaulon var. papillosa 293
acaulon var. pilifera 293
aloides 285
atrovirens 289
calcicolens 296
cuneifolia 287
ericaefolia 286
intermedia 297
laevipila var. *laevipila* 298
laevipila var. *laevipilaeformis* 299
lamellata 284
lanceola 290
latifolia 300
marginata 288
modica 290
montana 297
muralis var. aestiva 289
muralis var. muralis 288
muralis var. *rupestris* 288
mutica 300
papillosa 299
princeps 298
potobryoides 292
pusilla 284
ruraliformis 297
ruralis subsp. *ruraliformis* 297
ruralis subsp. *ruralis* 296
ruralis var. *arenicola* 297
stanfordensis 295
stellata 284
subulata var. angustata 287
subulata var. graeffii 287
subulata var. subinermis 287
subulata var. subulata 286
truncata 291
vahliana 288
vahliana var. *subflaccida* 288
vahlii 288
viridifolia 290
wilsonii 290
Trichocolea
tomentella 19
Trichostomopsis
umbrosa 277
Trichostomum
bachydontium 260
cispulum 261
crispulum var. *brevifolium* 261
crispulum var. *elatum* 261
hibernicum 262
mutabile 260
mutabile var. *cophocarpum* 260
sinuosum 279
tenuirostre var. holtii 262
tenuirostre var. tenuirostre 262
tortuosum 256
tortuosum var. *fragilifolium* 256
Tritomaria
exsecta 57
exsectiformis 57
quinquedentata 58
Ulota
bruchii 404
calvescens 405
coarctata 402
crispa 403
crispa var. *crispa* 403
crispa var. *norvegica* 404
crispula 403
drummondii 402
hutchinsiae 405
nicholsonii 403
phyllantha 406
vittata 405
Warnstorfia
exannulata 443
fluitans 442
Webera
acuminata 336
albicans 344
annotina 340
calcarea 345
carnea 343
cruda 336
elongata 335
nutans 336
nutans var. *longiseta* 336
proligera 340
sessilis 201
sessilis var. *acutifolia* 201
calcarea 270
Weisia
curvirostris 267
curvirostris var. *insignis* 268
microstoma 255

Weisia
rupestris 271
verticillata 252
Weissia
americana 405
brachycarpa var. brachycarpa 255
brachycarpa var. obliqua 255
bruchii 404
calcarea 270
coarctata 402
condensa 255
controversa var. controversa 253
controversa var. crispata 254
controversa var. densifolia 254
crispa 256
crispata 254
curvirostris 267
curvirostris var. *commutata* 267
curvirostris var. *insignis* 268
drummondii 402
longifolia var. angustifolia 256
microstoma var. *brachycarpa* 255
microstoma var. *microstoma* 255
occidentalis 254
perssonii 254
rostellata 256
rupestris 271
rutilans 255
tortilis 255
ulophylla 403
ulophylla var. *crispula* 403
ulophylla var. *intermedia* 403
verticillata 252
vittata 405
Zygodon
baumgartneri 392
conoideus 392
gracilis 393
mougeotii 389
rupestris 392
stirtonii 391
viridissimus var. *occidentalis* 390
viridissimus var. *rupestris* 392
viridissimus var. stirtonii 391
viridissimus var. viridissimus 390
viridissimus var. *vulgaris* 392

THE CD-ROM

Instructions for use of CD ROM

To install this CD-ROM:

- If necessary, start Windows.
- Insert the CD-ROM in the CD drive.
- It should automatically run using the web browser installed on your PC computer.
- If this CD-ROM does not run automatically please open the file INDEX.HTM with your web browser (Internet Explorer or Netscape).

Once the CD-ROM has loaded, choose one of the categories (*Introduction, Species accounts, Vice County* etc.) displayed across the top of the main window. In the example shown below, the *Species accounts* category was selected. The vertical frame along the left displays the various taxonomic groups that can be chosen. At the top of this list is *Liverworts Marchantiopsida,* and, by default, all the Liverwort species are listed in the middle vertical frame. Use the mouse to click on one of the other taxonomic groups to change the species list in the middle vertical frame. The large frame on the right hand side is used to display the Irish records for the species. In this example, *Anastrophyllum minutum* (Schreb.) R.M.Schust. was chosen by clicking on its name in the list shown in the middle vertical frame.

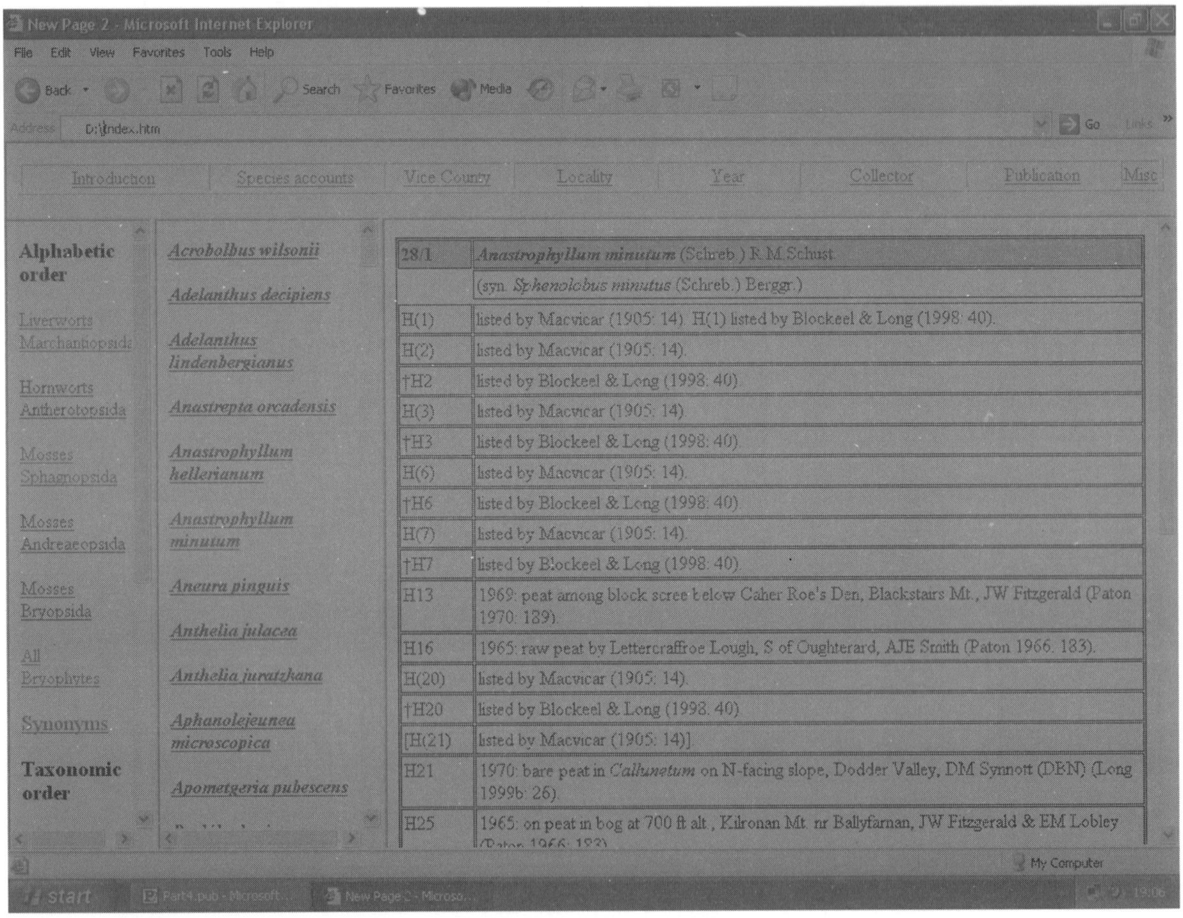

The categories *Locality*, *Collector* and *Misc* were generated as follows. The words (for example, the place names in the *Locality* category) were cut and pasted from the text of the book to make a list. A computer program then searched through the text of the book for every occurrence of each word in the list, and then generated the appropriate web pages. It should be stressed that this process cannot be guaranteed 100% accurate, because any unforseen variations in spelling or punctuation may not be picked up by the program.

This CD-ROM includes all the text in the book and this has been re-formatted as if it were a website. As a result the contents of the CD-ROM are displayed using web browser software. It has been tested with Microsoft Internet Explorer 5.0 and 6.0 on a variety of PC computers (Windows ME, XP and 2000). It has not been tested on an Apple Mac. For best results, the computer display should be set at 1024 x 768 pixels. This CD-ROM uses 'frames' and will not work with early versions of Microsoft Internet Explorer.